SCHEMATIC SYMBOLS USED IN CIRCUIT DIAGRAMS

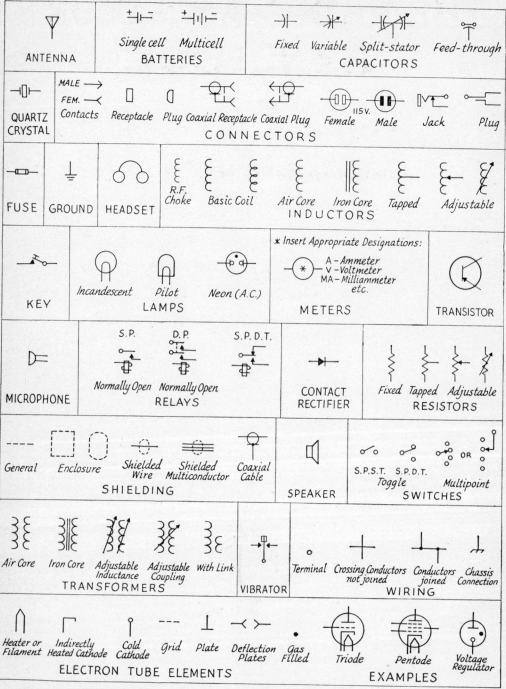

Where it is necessary or desirable to identify the electrodes or capacitors, the curved element represents the *outside* electrode (marked "outside foil," "ground," etc.) in fixed paper- and ceramic-dielectric capacitors, and the *negative* electrode in electrolytic capacitors.

In the modern symbol, the curved line indicates the moving element (rotor plates) in variable and adjustable air- or mica-dielectric capacitors.

In the case of switches, jacks, etc., only the basic combinations are shown. Any combination of these symbols may be assembled as required, following the elementary forms shown.

THE RADIO AMATEUR'S HANDBOOK

By the HEADQUARTERS STAFF
of the
AMERICAN RADIO RELAY LEAGUE
WEST HARTFORD, CONN., U.S.A.

1960

Thirty-seventh Edition

THE RUMFORD PRESS
Concord, New Hampshire, U. S. A.

Foreword

In over thirty years of continuous publication *The Radio Amateur's Handbook* has become as much of an institution as amateur radio itself. Produced by the amateur's own organization, the American Radio Relay League, and written with the needs of the practical amateur constantly in mind, it has earned universal acceptance not only by amateurs but by all segments of the technical radio world. This wide dependence on the *Handbook* is founded on its practical utility, its treatment of radio communication problems in terms of how-to-do-it rather than by abstract discussion.

Virtually continuous modification is a feature of the *Handbook* — always with the objective of presenting the soundest and best aspects of current practice rather than the merely new and novel. Its annual revision, a major task of the headquarters group of the League, is participated in by skilled and experienced amateurs well acquainted with the practical problems in the art.

The *Handbook* is printed in the format of the League's monthly magazine, *QST*. This, together with extensive and useful catalog advertising by manufacturers producing equipment for the radio amateur and industry, makes it possible to distribute for a very modest charge a work which in volume of subject matter and profusion of illustration surpasses most available radio texts selling for several times its price.

The *Handbook* has long been considered an indispensable part of the amateur's equipment. We earnestly hope that the present edition will succeed in bringing as much assistance and inspiration to amateurs and would-be amateurs as have its predecessors.

A. L. BUDLONG
General Manager, A.R.R.L.

West Hartford, Conn.

CONTENTS

THE AMATEUR'S CODE

• ONE •

The Amateur is Gentlemanly . . . He never knowingly uses the air for his own amusement in such a way as to lessen the pleasure of others. He abides by the pledges given by the ARRL in his behalf to the public and the Government.

• TWO •

The Amateur is Loyal . . . He owes his amateur radio to the American Radio Relay League, and he offers it his unswerving loyalty.

• THREE •

The Amateur is Progressive . . . He keeps his station abreast of science. It is built well and efficiently. His operating practice is clean and regular.

• FOUR •

The Amateur is Friendly . . . Slow and patient sending when requested, friendly advice and counsel to the beginner, kindly assistance and cooperation for the broadcast listener; these are marks of the amateur spirit.

• FIVE •

The Amateur is Balanced . . . Radio is his hobby. He never allows it to interfere with any of the duties he owes to his home, his job, his school, or his community.

• SIX •

The Amateur is Patriotic . . . His knowledge and his station are always ready for the service of his country and his community.

— *Paul M. Segal*

CHAPTER 1

Amateur Radio

Amateur radio is a scientific hobby, a means of gaining personal skill in the fascinating art of electronics and an opportunity to communicate with fellow citizens by private short-wave radio. Scattered over the globe are over 250,000 amateur radio operators who perform a service defined in international law as one of "self-training, intercommunication and technical investigations carried on by . . . duly authorized persons interested in radio technique solely with a personal aim and without pecuniary interest."

From a humble beginning at the turn of the century, amateur radio has grown to become an established institution. Today the American followers of amateur radio number over 200,000, trained communicators from whose ranks will come the professional communications specialists and executives of tomorrow — just as many of today's radio leaders were first attracted to radio by their early interest in amateur radio communication. A powerful and prosperous organization now provides a bond between amateurs and protects their interests; an internationally respected magazine is published solely for their benefit. The military services seek the cooperation of the amateur in developing communications reserves. Amateur radio supports a manufacturing industry which, by the very demands of amateurs for the latest and best equipment, is always up-to-date in its designs and production techniques — in itself a national asset. Amateurs have won the gratitude of the nation for their heroic performances in times of natural disaster; traditional amateur skills in emergency communication are also the stand-by system for the nation's civil defense. Amateur radio is, indeed, a magnificently useful institution.

Although as old as the art of radio itself, amateur radio did not always enjoy such prestige. Its first enthusiasts were private citizens of an experimental turn of mind whose imaginations went wild when Marconi first proved that messages actually could be sent by wireless. They set about learning enough about the new scientific marvel to build home-made spark transmitters. By 1912 there were numerous Government and commercial stations, and hundreds of amateurs; regulation was needed, so laws, licenses and wavelength specifications appeared. There was then no amateur organization nor spokesman. The official viewpoint toward amateurs was something like this:

"Amateurs? . . . Oh, yes. . . . Well, stick 'em on 200 meters and below; they'll never get out of their backyards with that."

But as the years rolled on, amateurs found out how, and DX (distance) jumped from local to 500-mile and even occasional 1000-mile two-way contacts. Because all long-distance messages had to be relayed, relaying developed into a fine art — an ability that was to prove invaluable when the Government suddenly called hundreds of skilled amateurs into war service in 1917. Meanwhile U. S. amateurs began to wonder if there were amateurs in other countries across the seas and if, some day, we might not span the Atlantic on 200 meters.

Most important of all, this period witnessed the birth of the American Radio Relay League, the amateur radio organization whose name was to be virtually synonymous with subsequent amateur progress and short-wave development. Conceived and formed by the famous inventor, the late Hiram Percy Maxim, ARRL was formally launched in early 1914. It had just begun to exert its full force in amateur activities when the United States declared war in 1917, and by that act sounded the knell for amateur radio for the next two and a half years. There were then over 6000 amateurs. Over 4000 of them served in the armed forces during that war.

Today, few amateurs realize that World War I not only marked the close of the first phase of amateur development but came very

HIRAM PERCY MAXIM
President ARRL, 1914–1936

9

near marking its end for all time. The fate of amateur radio was in the balance in the days immediately following the signing of the Armistice. The Government, having had a taste of supreme authority over communications in wartime, was more than half inclined to keep it. The war had not been ended a month before Congress was considering legislation that would have made it impossible for the amateur radio of old ever to be resumed. ARRL's President Maxim rushed to Washington, pleaded, argued, and the bill was defeated. But there was still no amateur radio; the war ban continued. Repeated representations to Washington met only with silence. The League's offices had been closed for a year and a half, its records stored away. Most of the former amateurs had gone into service; many of them would never come back. Would those returning be interested in such things as amateur radio? Mr. Maxim, determined to find out, called a meeting of the old Board of Directors. The situation was discouraging: amateur radio still banned by law, former members scattered, no organization, no membership, no funds. But those few determined men financed the publication of a notice to all the former amateurs that could be located, hired Kenneth B. Warner as the League's first paid secretary, floated a bond issue among old League members to obtain money for immediate running expenses, bought the magazine *QST* to be the League's official organ, started activities, and dunned officialdom until the wartime ban was lifted and amateur radio resumed again, on October 1, 1919. There was a headlong rush by amateurs to get back on the air. Gangway for King Spark! Manufacturers were hard put to supply radio apparatus fast enough. Each night saw additional dozens of stations crashing out over the air. Interference? It was bedlam!

But it was an era of progress. Wartime needs had stimulated technical development. Vacuum tubes were being used both for receiving and transmitting. Amateurs immediately adapted the new gear to 200-meter work. Ranges promptly increased and it became possible to bridge the continent with but one intermediate relay.

● TRANSATLANTICS

As DX became 1000, then 1500 and then 2000 miles, amateurs began to dream of transatlantic work. Could they get across? In December, 1921, ARRL sent abroad an expert amateur, Paul F. Godley, 2ZE, with the best receiving equipment available. Tests were run, and *thirty* American stations were heard in Europe. In 1922 another transatlantic test was carried out and 315 American calls were logged by European amateurs and one French and two British stations were heard on this side.

Everything now was centered on one objective: two-way amateur communication across

the Atlantic! It must be possible — but somehow it couldn't quite be done. More power? Many already were using the legal maximum. Better receivers? They had superheterodynes. Another wavelength? What about those undisturbed wavelengths *below* 200 meters? The engineering world thought they were worthless — but they had said that about 200 meters. So, in 1922, tests between Hartford and Boston were made on 130 meters with encouraging results. Early in 1923, ARRL-sponsored tests on wavelengths down to 90 meters were successful. Reports indicated that *as the wavelength dropped the results were better*. Excitement began to spread through amateur ranks.

Finally, in November, 1923, after some months of careful preparation, two-way amateur transatlantic communication was accomplished, when Schnell, 1MO, and Reinartz, 1XAM (now W4CF and K6BJ, respectively) worked for several hours with Deloy, 8AB, in France, with all three stations on 110 meters! Additional stations dropped down to 100 meters and found that they, too, could easily work two-way across the Atlantic. The exodus from the 200-meter region had started. The "short-wave" era had begun!

By 1924 dozens of commercial companies had rushed stations into the 100-meter region. Chaos threatened, until the first of a series of national and international radio conferences partitioned off various bands of frequencies for the different services. Although thought still centered around 100 meters, League officials at the first of these frequency-determining conferences, in 1924, wisely obtained amateur bands not only at 80 meters but at 40, 20, and even 5 meters.

Eighty meters proved so successful that "forty" was given a try, and QSOs with Australia, New Zealand and South Africa soon became commonplace. Then how about 20 meters? This new band revealed entirely unexpected possibilities when 1XAM worked 6TS on the West Coast, direct, at high noon. The dream of amateur radio — daylight DX! — was finally true.

● PUBLIC SERVICE

Amateur radio is a grand and glorious hobby but this fact alone would hardly merit such wholehearted support as is given it by our Government at international conferences. There are other reasons. One of these is a thorough appreciation by the military and civil defense authorities of the value of the amateur as a source of skilled radio personnel in time of war. Another asset is best described as "public service."

About 4000 amateurs had contributed their skill and ability in '17–'18. After the war it was only natural that cordial relations should prevail between the Army and Navy and the amateur. These relations strengthened in the next few years and, in gradual steps, grew into cooperative activities which resulted, in 1925, in

Public Service

the establishment of the Naval Communications Reserve and the Army-Amateur Radio System (now the Military Affiliate Radio System). In World War II thousands of amateurs in the Naval Reserve were called to active duty, where they served with distinction, while many other thousands served in the Army, Air Forces, Coast Guard and Marine Corps. Altogether, more than 25,000 radio amateurs served in the armed forces of the United States. Other thousands were engaged in vital civilian electronic research, development and manufacturing. They also organized and manned the War Emergency Radio Service, the communications section of OCD.

The "public-service" record of the amateur is a brilliant tribute to his work. These activities can be roughly divided into two classes, expeditions and emergencies. Amateur cooperation with expeditions began in 1923 when a League member, Don Mix, 1TS, of Bristol, Conn. (now assistant technical editor of *QST*), accompanied MacMillan to the Arctic on the schooner *Bowdoin* with an amateur station. Amateurs in Canada and the U.S. provided the home contacts. The success of this venture was so outstanding that other explorers followed suit. During subsequent years a total of perhaps two hundred voyages and expeditions were assisted by amateur radio, the several explorations of the Antarctic being perhaps the best known.

Since 1913 amateur radio has been the principal, and in many cases the only, means of outside communication in several hundred storm, flood and earthquake emergencies in this country. The 1936 and 1937 eastern states floods, the Southern California flood and Long Island-New England hurricane disaster in 1938, the Florida-Gulf Coast hurricanes of 1947, and the 1955 flood disasters called for the amateur's greatest emergency effort. In these disasters and many others — tornadoes, sleet storms, forest fires, blizzards — amateurs played a major rôle in the relief work and earned wide commendation for their resourcefulness in effecting communication where all other means had failed. During 1938 ARRL inaugurated a new emergency-preparedness program, registering personnel and equipment in its Emergency Corps and putting into effect a comprehensive program of cooperation with the Red Cross, and in 1947 a National Emergency Coordinator was appointed to full-time duty at League headquarters.

The amateur's outstanding record of organized preparation for emergency communications and performance under fire has been largely responsible for the decision of the Federal Government to set up special regulations and set aside special frequencies for use by amateurs in providing auxiliary communications for civil defense purposes in the event of war. Under the banner, "Radio Amateur Civil Emergency Service," amateurs are setting up and manning community and area networks integrated with civil defense functions of the municipal governments. Should a war cause the shut-down of routine amateur activi-

ties, the RACES will be immediately available in the national defense, manned by amateurs highly skilled in emergency communication.

● TECHNICAL DEVELOPMENTS

Throughout these many years the amateur was careful not to slight experimental development in the enthusiasm incident to international DX. The experimenter was constantly at work on ever-higher frequencies, devising improved apparatus, and learning how to cram several stations where previously there was room for only one! In particular, the amateur pressed on to the development of the very high frequencies and his experience with five meters is especially representative of his initiative and resourcefulness and his ability to make the most of what is at hand. In 1924, first amateur experiments in the vicinity of 56 Mc. indicated that band to be practically worthless for DX. Nonetheless, great "short-haul" activity eventually came about in the band and new gear was developed to meet its special problems. Beginning in 1934 a series of investigations by the brilliant experimenter, Ross Hull (later *QST*'s editor), developed the theory of v.h.f. wave-bending in the lower atmosphere and led amateurs to the attainment of better distances; while occasional manifestations of ionospheric propagation, with still greater distances, gave the band uniquely erratic performance. By Pearl Harbor thousands of amateurs were spending much of their time on this and the next higher band, many having worked hundreds of stations at distances up to several thousand miles. Transcontinental 6-meter DX is not uncommon; during solar peaks, even the oceans have been bridged! It is a tribute to these indefatigable amateurs that today's concept of v.h.f. propagation was developed largely through amateur research.

The amateur is constantly in the forefront of technical progress. His incessant curiosity, his eagerness to try anything new, are two reasons. Another is that ever-growing amateur radio continually overcrowds its frequency assignments, spurring amateurs to the development and adoption of new techniques to permit the

A corner of the ARRL laboratory.

accommodation of more stations. For examples, amateurs turned from spark to c.w., designed more selective receivers, adopted crystal control and pure d.c. power supplies. From the ARRL's own laboratory in 1932 came James Lamb's "single-signal" superheterodyne — the world's most advanced high-frequency radiotelegraph receiver — and, in 1936, the "noise-silencer" circuit. Amateurs are now turning to speech "clippers" to reduce bandwidths of phone transmissions and "single-sideband suppressed-carrier" systems as well as even more selectivity in receiving equipment for greater efficiency in spectrum use.

During World War II, thousands of skilled amateurs contributed their knowledge to the development of secret radio devices, both in Government and private laboratories. Equally as important, the prewar technical progress by amateurs provided the keystone for the development of modern military communications equipment. Perhaps more important today than individual contributions to the art is the mass cooperation of the amateur body in Government projects such as propagation studies; each participating station is in reality a separate field laboratory from which reports are made for correlation and analysis. An outstanding example was varied amateur participation in several activities of the International Geophysical Year program. ARRL, with Air Force sponsorship, conducted an intensive study of v.h.f. propagation phenomena — DX transmissions via little-understood methods such as meteor and auroral reflections, and transequatorial scatter. ARRL-affiliated clubs and groups have operated precision receiving antennas and apparatus to help track earth satellites via radio. For volunteer astronomers searching visually for the satellites, other amateurs have manned networks to provide instant radio reports of sightings to a central agency so that an orbit might be computed.

Emergency relief, expedition contact, experimental work and countless instances of other forms of public service — rendered, as they always have been and always will be, without hope or expectation of material reward — made amateur radio an integral part of our peacetime national life. The importance of amateur participation in the armed forces and in other aspects of national defense have emphasized more strongly than ever that amateur radio is vital to our national existence.

● **THE AMERICAN RADIO RELAY LEAGUE**

The ARRL is today not only the spokesman for amateur radio in this country but it is the largest amateur organization in the world. It is strictly of, by and for amateurs, is noncommercial and has no stockholders. The members of the League are the owners of the ARRL and *QST*.

The League is pledged to promote interest in two-way amateur communication and experimentation. It is interested in the relaying of

The operating room at W1AW.

messages by amateur radio. It is concerned with the advancement of the radio art. It stands for the maintenance of fraternalism and a high standard of conduct. It represents the amateur in legislative matters.

One of the League's principal purposes is to keep amateur activities so well conducted that the amateur will continue to justify his existence. Amateur radio offers its followers countless pleasures and unending satisfaction. It also calls for the shouldering of responsibilities — the maintenance of high standards, a cooperative loyalty to the traditions of amateur radio, a dedication to its ideals and principles, so that the institution of amateur radio may continue to operate "in the public interest, convenience and necessity."

The operating territory of ARRL is divided into one Canadian and fifteen U. S. divisions. The affairs of the League are managed by a Board of Directors. One director is elected every two years by the membership of each U. S. division, and one by the Canadian membership. These directors then choose the president and vice-president, who are also members of the Board. The secretary and treasurer are also appointed by the Board. The directors, as representatives of the amateurs in their divisions, meet annually to examine current amateur problems and formulate ARRL policies thereon. The directors appoint a general manager to supervise the operations of the League and its headquarters, and to carry out the policies and instructions of the Board.

ARRL owns and publishes the monthly magazine, *QST*. Acting as a bulletin of the League's organized activities, *QST* also serves as a medium for the exchange of ideas and fosters amateur spirit. Its technical articles are renowned. It has grown to be the "amateur's bible," as well as one of the foremost radio magazines in the world. Membership dues include a subscription to *QST*.

ARRL maintains a model headquarters amateur station, known as the Hiram Percy Maxim Memorial Station, in Newington, Conn. Its call is W1AW, the call held by Mr. Maxim until his death and later transferred to the League station by a special FCC action. Separate transmitters of maximum legal power on each amateur band have permitted the station to be heard regularly all over the world. More important, W1AW transmits on regular schedules bulletins of general interest to amateurs, conducts code practice as a training feature, and engages in two-way work on all popular bands with as many amateurs as time permits.

At the headquarters of the League in West Hartford, Conn., is a well-equipped laboratory to assist staff members in preparation of technical material for *QST* and the *Radio Amateur's Handbook*. Among its other activities, the League maintains a Communications Department concerned with the operating activities of League members. A large field organization is headed by a Section Communications Manager in each of the League's seventy-three sections. There are appointments for qualified members in various fields, as outlined in Chapter 24. Special activities and contests promote operating skill. A special section is reserved each month in *QST* for amateur news from every section of the country.

● AMATEUR LICENSING IN THE UNITED STATES

Pursuant to the law, FCC has issued detailed regulations for the amateur service.

A radio amateur is a duly authorized person interested in radio technique solely with a personal aim and without pecuniary interest. Amateur operator licenses are given to U. S. citizens who pass an examination on operation and apparatus and on the provisions of law and regulations affecting amateurs, and who demonstrate ability to send and receive code. There are four available classes of amateur license — Novice, Technician, General (called "Conditional" if exam taken by mail), and Amateur Extra Class. Each has different requirements, the first two being the simplest and consequently conveying limited privileges as to frequencies available. Exams for Novice, Technician and Conditional classes are taken by mail under the supervision of a volunteer examiner. Station licenses are granted only to licensed operators and permit communication between such stations for amateur purposes, i.e., for personal noncommercial aims flowing from an interest in radio technique. An amateur station may not be used for material compensation of any sort nor for broadcasting. Narrow bands of frequencies are allocated exclusively for use by amateur stations. Transmissions may be on any frequency within the assigned bands. All the frequencies may be used for c.w. telegraphy; some are available for radiotelephone, others for special forms of transmission such as teletype, facsimile, amateur television or radio control. The input to the final stage of amateur stations is limited to 1000 watts and on frequencies below 144 Mc. must be adequately filtered direct current. Emissions must be free from spurious radiations. The licensee must provide for measurement of the transmitter frequency and establish a procedure for checking it regularly. A complete log of station operation must be maintained, with specified data. The station license also authorizes the holder to operate portable and mobile stations subject to further regulations. All radio licensees are subject to penalties for violation of regulations.

Amateur licenses are issued entirely free of charge. They can be issued only to citizens but that is the only limitation, and they are given without regard to age or physical condition to anyone who successfully completes the examination. When you are able to copy code at the required speed, have studied basic transmitter theory and are familiar with the law and amateur regulations, you are ready to give serious thought to securing the Government amateur licenses which are issued you, after examination by an FCC engineer (or by a volunteer, depending on the license class), through FCC at Washington. A complete up-to-the-minute discussion of license requirements, and study guides for those preparing for the examinations, are to be found in an ARRL publication, *The Radio Amateur's License Manual*, available from the American Radio Relay League, West Hartford 7, Conn., for 50¢, postpaid.

● LEARNING THE CODE

In starting to learn the code, you should consider it simply another means of conveying

A	didah	N	dahdit
B	dahdididit	O	dahdahdah
C	dahdidahdit	P	didahdahdit
D	dahdidit	Q	dahdahdidah
E	dit	R	didahdit
F	dididahdit	S	dididit
G	dahdahdit	T	dah
H	dividit	U	dididah
I	didit	V	didididah
J	didahdahdah	W	didahdah
K	dahdidah	X	dahdididah
L	didahdidit	Y	dahdidahdah
M	dahdah	Z	dahdahdidit
1	didahdahdahdah	6	dahdidididit
2	dididahdahdah	7	dahdahdididit
3	dididahdah	8	dahdahdahdidit
4	didididah	9	dahdahdahdahdit
5	dididididit	0	dahdahdahdahdah

Period: didahdidahdidah. Comma: dahdahdididahdah. Question mark: dididahdahdidit. Error: dididididididididit. Double dash: dahdididah. Wait: didahdididit. End of message: didahdidahdit. Invitation to transmit: dahdidah. End of work: dididahdidah. Fraction bar: dahdididahdit.

Fig. 1-1—The Continental (International Morse) code.

information. The spoken word is one method, the printed page another, and typewriting and shorthand are additional examples. Learning the code is as easy — or as difficult — as learning to type.

The important thing in beginning to study code is to think of it as a language of *sound*, never as combinations of dots and dashes. It is easy to "speak" code equivalents by using "dit" and "*dah*," so that A would be "di*dah*" (the "t" is dropped in such combinations). The sound "di" should be staccato; a code character such as "5" should sound like a machine-gun burst: dididididit! Stress each "*dah*" equally; they are underlined or italicized in this text because they should be slightly accented and drawn out.

Take a few characters at a time. Learn them thoroughly in di*dah* language before going on to new ones. If someone who is familiar with code can be found to "send" to you, either by whistling or by means of a buzzer or code oscillator, enlist his coöperation. Learn the code by *listening* to it. Don't think about speed to start; the first requirement is to learn the characters to the point where you can recognize each of them without hesitation. Concentrate on any difficult letters. Learning the code is not at all hard; a simple booklet treating the subject in detail is another of the beginner publications available from the League, and is entitled, *Learning the Radiotelegraph Code*, 50¢ postpaid.

Code-practice transmissions are sent by W1AW every evening at 2130 EST (EDST May through October). See Chapter 24, "Code Proficiency."

● THE AMATEUR BANDS

Amateurs are assigned bands of frequencies at approximate harmonic intervals throughout the spectrum. Like assignments to all services, they are subject to modification to fit the changing picture of world communications needs. Modifications of rules to provide for domestic needs are also occasionally issued by FCC, and in that respect each amateur should keep himself informed by W1AW bulletins, *QST* reports, or by communication with ARRL Hq. concerning a specific point.

In the adjoining table is a summary of the U. S. amateur bands on which operation is permitted as of our press date. Figures are megacycles. AØ means an unmodulated carrier, A1 means c.w. telegraphy, A2 is tone-modulated c.w. telegraphy, A3 is amplitude-modulated phone, A4 is facsimile, A5 is television, n.f.m. designates narrow-band frequency- or phase-modulated radiotelephony, f.m. means frequency modulation, phone (including n.f.m.) or telegraphy, and F1 is frequency-shift keying.

80 meters	3.500–4.000	— A1
	3.500–3.800	— F1
	3.800–4.000	— A3 and n.f.m.
40 m.	7.000–7.300	— A1
	7.000–7.200	— F1
	7.200–7.300	— A3 and n.f.m.
20 m.	14.000–14.350	— A1
	14.000–14.200	— F1
	14.200–14.300	— A3 and n.f.m.
	14.300–14.350	— F1
15 m.	21.000–21.450	— A1
	21.000–21.250	— F1
	21.250–21.450	— A3 and n.f.m.
10 m.	28.000–29.700	— A1
	28.500–29.700	— A3 and n.f.m.
	29.000–29.700	— f.m.
6 m.	50–54	— A1, A2, A3, A4, n.f.m.
	51–54	— AØ
	52.5–54	— f.m.
2 m.	144–148 } 220–225 }	— A1, AØ, A1, A2, A3, A4. f.m.
	420–450[1] 1,215–1,300 }	AØ, A1, A2, A3, A4, A5, f.m.
	2,300– 2,450 } 3,500– 3,700 } 5,650– 5,925 } 10,000–10,500[2] } 21,000–22,000 } All above 30,000 }	AØ, A1, A2, A3, A4, A5, f.m., pulse

[1] Input power must not exceed 50 watts.
[2] No pulse permitted in this band.
NOTE: The bands 220 through 10,500 Mc. are shared with the Government Radio Positioning Service, which has priority.

In addition, A1 and A3 on portions of 1.800–2.000, as follows:

Area	Band ,kc.	Power (watts)	
		Day	Night
Minn., Iowa, Wis., Mich., Pa., Md., Del. and states to north	1800–1825	500	200
N.D., S.D., Nebr., Colo., N. Mex., and states west, including Hawaiian Ids.	1975–2000	500*	200*
Okla., Kans., Mo., Ark., Ill., Ind., Ky., Tenn., Ohio, W. Va., Va., N. C., S. C., and Texas (west of 99° W *or* north of 32° N)	1800–1825	200	50

No operation elsewhere.

* Except in state of Washington, 200 watts day, 50 watts night.

Novice licensees may use the following frequencies, transmitters to be crystal-controlled and have a maximum power input of 75 watts.

3.700–3.750	A1	21.100–21.250	A1
7.150–7.200	A1	145–147	A1, A2, A3, f.m.

Technician licensees are permitted all amateur privileges in 50–54 Mc., 145–147 Mc., and in the bands 220 Mc. and above.

CHAPTER 2

Electrical Laws and Circuits

● ELECTRIC AND MAGNETIC FIELDS

When something occurs at one point in space because something else happened at another point, with no visible means by which the "cause" can be related to the "effect," we say the two events are connected by a **field**. In radio work, the fields with which we are concerned are the **electric** and **magnetic**, and the combination of the two called the **electromagnetic** field.

A field has two important properties, intensity (magnitude) and direction. The field exerts a *force* on an object immersed in it; this force represents potential (ready-to-be-used) energy, so the **potential** of the field is a measure of the **field intensity**. The **direction** of the field is the direction in which the object on which the force is exerted will tend to move.

An electrically charged object in an electric field will be acted on by a force that will tend to move it in a direction determined by the direction of the field. Similarly, a magnet in a magnetic field will be subject to a force. Everyone has seen demonstrations of magnetic fields with pocket magnets, so intensity and direction are not hard to grasp.

A "static" field is one that neither moves nor changes in intensity. Such a field can be set up by a stationary electric charge (**electrostatic field**) or by a stationary magnet (**magnetostatic field**). But if either an electric or magnetic field is moving in space or changing in intensity, the motion or change sets up the other kind of field. That is, a changing electric field sets up a magnetic field, and a changing magnetic field generates an electric field. This interrelationship between magnetic and electric fields makes possible such things as the electromagnet and the electric motor. It also makes possible the **electromagnetic waves** by which radio communication is carried on, for such waves are simply traveling fields in which the energy is alternately handed back and forth between the electric and magnetic fields.

Lines of Force

Although no one knows what it is that composes the field itself, it is useful to invent a picture of it that will help in visualizing the forces and the way in which they act.

A field can be pictured as being made up of **lines of force**, or **flux lines**. These are purely imaginary threads that show, by the direction in which they lie, the direction the object on which the force is exerted will move. The *number* of lines in a chosen cross section of the field is a measure of the *intensity* of the force. The number of lines per unit of area (square inch or square centimeter) is called the **flux density**.

● ELECTRICITY AND THE ELECTRIC CURRENT

Everything physical is built up of atoms, particles so small that they cannot be seen even through the most powerful microscope. But the atom in turn consists of several different kinds of still smaller particles. One is the **electron**, essentially a small particle of electricity. The quantity or **charge** of electricity represented by the electron is, in fact, the smallest quantity of electricity that can exist. The kind of electricity associated with the electron is called **negative**.

An ordinary atom consists of a central core called the **nucleus**, around which one or more electrons circulate somewhat as the earth and other planets circulate around the sun. The nucleus has an electric charge of the kind of electricity called **positive**, the amount of its charge being just exactly equal to the sum of the negative charges on all the electrons associated with that nucleus.

The important fact about these two "opposite" kinds of electricity is that they are strongly attracted to each other. Also, there is a strong force of repulsion between two charges of the *same* kind. The positive nucleus and the negative electrons are attracted to each other, but two electrons will be repelled from each other and so will two nuclei.

In a normal atom the positive charge on the nucleus is exactly balanced by the negative charges on the electrons. However, it is possible for an atom to lose one of its electrons. When that happens the atom has a little less negative charge than it should — that is, it has a net positive charge. Such an atom is said to be **ionized**, and in this case the atom is a **positive ion**. If an atom picks up an extra electron, as it sometimes does, it has a net negative charge and is called a **negative ion**. A positive ion will attract any stray electron in the vicinity, including the extra one that may be attached to a nearby negative ion. In this way it is possible for electrons to travel from atom to atom. The movement of ions or electrons constitutes the **electric current**.

The **amplitude** of the current (its intensity or magnitude) is determined by the rate at which electric charge — an accumulation of electrons or ions of the same kind — moves past a point in a circuit. Since the charge on a single electron or ion is extremely small, the number that must move as a group to form even a tiny current is almost inconceivably large.

Conductors and Insulators

Atoms of some materials, notably metals and acids, will give up an electron readily, but atoms of other materials will not part with any of their electrons even when the electric force is extremely strong. Materials in which electrons or ions can be moved with relative ease are called **conductors**, while those that refuse to permit such movement are called **nonconductors** or **insulators**. The following list shows how some common materials divide between the conductor and insulator classifications:

Conductors	Insulators
Metals	Dry Air
Carbon	Wood
Acids	Porcelain
	Textiles
	Glass
	Rubber
	Resins

Electromotive Force

The electric force or potential (called **electromotive force**, and abbreviated **e.m.f.**) that causes current flow may be developed in several ways. The action of certain chemical solutions on dissimilar metals sets up an e.m.f.; such a combination is called a **cell**, and a group of cells forms an electric **battery**. The amount of current that such cells can carry is limited, and in the course of current flow one of the metals is eaten away. The amount of electrical energy that can be taken from a battery consequently is rather small. Where a large amount of energy is needed it is usually furnished by an electric **generator**, which develops its e.m.f. by a combination of magnetic and mechanical means.

In picturing current flow it is natural to think of a single, constant force causing the electrons to move. When this is so, the electrons always move in the same direction through a path or **circuit** made up of conductors connected together in a continuous chain. Such a current is called a **direct current**, abbreviated **d.c.** It is the type of current furnished by batteries and by certain types of generators. However, it is also possible to have an e.m.f. that periodically reverses. With this kind of e.m.f. the current flows first in one direction through the circuit and then in the other. Such an e.m.f. is called an **alternating e.m.f.**, and the current is called an **alternating current** (abbreviated **a.c.**). The reversals (**alternations**) may occur at any rate from a few per second up to several billion per second. Two reversals make a **cycle**; in one cycle the force acts first in one direction, then in the other, and then returns to the first direction to begin the next cycle. The number of cycles in one second is called the **frequency** of the alternating current.

Direct and Alternating Currents

The difference between direct current and alternating current is shown in Fig. 2-1. In these graphs the horizontal axis measures time, increasing toward the right away from the vertical axis. The vertical axis represents the amplitude or strength of the current, increasing in either the up or down direction away from the horizontal axis. If the graph is *above* the horizontal axis the current is flowing in one direction through the circuit (indicated by the + sign) and if it is *below* the horizontal axis the current is flowing in the reverse direction through the circuit (indicated by the − sign). Fig. 2-1A shows that, if we close the circuit — that is, make the path for the current complete — at the time indicated by X, the current instantly takes the amplitude indicated by the height A. After that, the current continues at the same amplitude as time goes on. This is an ordinary *direct* current.

In Fig. 2-1B, the current starts flowing with the amplitude A at time X, continues at that amplitude until time Y and then instantly ceases. After an interval YZ the current again begins to flow and the same sort of start-and-stop performance is repeated. This is an *intermittent* direct current. We could get it by alternately closing and opening a switch in the circuit. It is a *direct* current because the *direction* of current flow does not change; the graph is always on the + side of the horizontal axis.

In Fig. 2-1C the current starts at zero, increases in amplitude as time goes on until it reaches the amplitude A_1 while flowing in the + direction, then decreases until it drops to zero amplitude once more. At that time (X) the

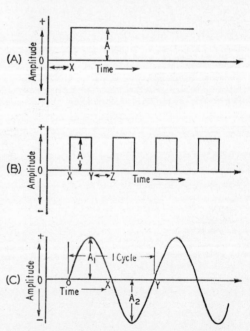

Fig. 2-1 — Three types of current flow. A—direct current; B—intermittent direct current; C—alternating current.

Frequency and Wavelength

direction of the current flow reverses; this is indicated by the fact that the next part of the graph is below the axis. As time goes on the amplitude increases, with the current now flowing in the — direction, until it reaches amplitude A_2. Then the amplitude decreases until finally it drops to zero (Y) and the direction reverses once more. This is an *alternating* current.

Waveforms

The type of alternating current shown in Fig. 2-1C is known as a **sine wave**. The variations in many a.c. waves are not so smooth, nor is one half-cycle necessarily just like the preceding one in shape. However, these **complex waves** can be shown to be the sum of two or more sine waves of frequencies that are exact integral (whole-number) multiples of some lower frequency. The lowest frequency is called the **fundamental** frequency, and the higher frequencies (2 times, 3 times the fundamental frequency, and so on) are called **harmonics**.

Fig. 2-2 shows how a fundamental and a second harmonic (twice the fundamental) might add to form a complex wave. Simply by changing the relative amplitudes of the two waves, as well as the times at which they pass through zero amplitude, an infinite number of waveshapes can be constructed from just a fundamental and second harmonic. Waves that are still more complex can be constructed if more harmonics are used.

Electrical Units

The unit of electromotive force is called the **volt**. An ordinary flashlight cell generates an e.m.f. of about 1.5 volts. The e.m.f. commonly supplied for domestic lighting and power is 115 volts, usually a.c. having a frequency of 60 cycles per second. The voltages used in radio receiving and transmitting circuits range from a few volts (usually a.c.) for filament heating to as high as a few thousand d.c. volts for the operation of power tubes.

The flow of electric current is measured in **amperes**. One ampere is equivalent to the movement of many billions of electrons past a point in the circuit in one second. Currents in the neighborhood of an ampere are required for heating the filaments of small power tubes. The *direct* currents used in amateur radio equipment usually are not so large, and it is customary to measure such currents in **milliamperes**. One milliampere is equal to one one-thousandth of an ampere, or 1000 milliamperes equal one ampere.

A "d.c. ampere" is a measure of a *steady* current, but the "a.c. ampere" must measure a current that is continually varying in amplitude and periodically reversing direction. To put the two on the same basis, an a.c. ampere is defined as the amount of current that will cause the same heating effect (see later section) as one ampere of steady direct current. For sine-wave a.c., this **effective** (or **r.m.s.**) value is equal to the *maximum* amplitude (A_1 or A_2 in Fig. 2-1C) multiplied by 0.707. The **instantaneous value** is the value

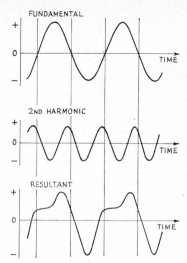

Fig. 2-2—A complex waveform. A fundamental (top) and second harmonic (center) added together, point by point at each instant, result in the waveform shown at the bottom. When the two components have the same polarity at a selected instant, the resultant is the simple sum of the two. When they have opposite polarities, the resultant is the *difference*; if the negative-polarity component is larger, the resultant is negative at that instant.

that the current (or voltage) has at any selected instant in the cycle.

If all the instantaneous values in a sine wave are averaged over a *half-cycle*, the resulting figure is the **average value**. It is equal to 0.636 times the maximum amplitude. The average value is useful in connection with rectifier systems, as described in a later chapter.

● FREQUENCY AND WAVELENGTH

Frequency Spectrum

Frequencies ranging from about 15 to 15,000 cycles per second are called **audio** frequencies, because the vibrations of air particles that our ears recognize as sounds occur at a similar rate. Audio frequencies (abbreviated **a.f.**) are used to actuate loudspeakers and thus create sound waves.

Frequencies above about 15,000 cycles are called **radio** frequencies (**r.f.**) because they are useful in radio transmission. Frequencies all the way up to and beyond 10,000,000,000 cycles have been used for radio purposes. At radio frequencies the numbers become so large that it becomes convenient to use a larger unit than the cycle. Two such units are the **kilocycle**, which is equal to 1000 cycles and is abbreviated **kc.**, and the **megacycle**, which is equal to 1,000,000 cycles or 1000 kilocycles and is abbreviated **Mc.**

The various radio frequencies are divided off into classifications for ready identification. These classifications, listed below, constitute the **frequency spectrum** so far as it extends for radio purposes at the present time.

Frequency	Classification	Abbreviation
10 to 30 kc.	Very-low frequencies	v.l.f.
30 to 300 kc.	Low frequencies	l.f.
300 to 3000 kc.	Medium frequencies	m.f.
3 to 30 Mc.	High frequencies	h.f.
30 to 300 Mc.	Very-high frequencies	v.h.f
300 to 3000 Mc.	Ultrahigh frequencies	u.h.f.
3000 to 30,000 Mc.	Superhigh frequencies	s.h.f.

Wavelength

Radio waves travel at the same speed as light — 300,000,000 meters or about 186,000 miles a second in space. They can be set up by a radio-frequency current flowing in a circuit, because the rapidly changing current sets up a magnetic field that changes in the same way, and the v‑ ying magnetic field in turn sets up a varying electric field. And whenever this happens, the two fields move outward at the speed of light.

Suppose an r.f. current has a frequency of 3,000,000 cycles per second. The fields will go through complete reversals (one cycle) in 1/3,000,000 second. In that same period of time the fields — that is, the wave — will move 300,000,000/3,000,000 meters, or 100 meters. By the time the wave has moved that distance the next cycle has begun and a new wave has started out. The first wave, in other words, covers a distance of 100 meters before the beginning of the next, and so on. This distance is the **wavelength**.

The longer the time of one cycle — that is, the lower the frequency — the greater the distance occupied by each wave and hence the longer the wavelength. The relationship between wavelength and frequency is shown by the formula

$$\lambda = \frac{300,000}{f}$$

where λ = Wavelength in meters
  f = Frequency in kilocycles

or

$$\lambda = \frac{300}{f}$$

where λ = Wavelength in meters
  f = Frequency in megacycles

Example: The wavelength corresponding to a frequency of 3650 kilocycles is

$$\lambda = \frac{300,000}{3650} = 82.2 \text{ meters}$$

Resistance

Given two conductors of the same size and shape, but of different materials, the amount of current that will flow when a given e.m.f. is applied will be found to vary with what is called the **resistance** of the material. The lower the resistance, the greater the current for a given value of e.m.f.

Resistance is measured in **ohms**. A circuit has a resistance of one ohm when an applied e.m.f. of one volt causes a current of one ampere to flow. The **resistivity** of a material is the resistance, in ohms, of a cube of the material measuring one centimeter on each edge. One of the best conductors is copper, and it is frequently convenient, in making resistance calculations, to compare the resistance of the material under consideration with that of a copper conductor of the same size and shape. Table 2-I gives the ratio of the resistivity of various conductors to that of copper.

The longer the path through which the current flows the higher the resistance of that conductor. For direct current and low-frequency alternating currents (up to a few thousand cycles per second) the resistance is *inversely* proportional to the cross-sectional area of the path the current must travel; that is, given two conductors of the same material and having the same length, but differing in cross-sectional area, the one with the larger area will have the lower resistance.

Resistance of Wires

The problem of determining the resistance of a round wire of given diameter and length — or its opposite, finding a suitable size and length of wire to supply a desired amount of resistance — can be easily solved with the help of the copper-wire table given in a later chapter. This table gives the resistance, in ohms per thousand feet, of each standard wire size.

Example: Suppose a resistance of 3.5 ohms is needed and some No. 28 wire is on hand. The wire table in Chapter 20 shows that No. 28 has a resistance of 66.17 ohms per thousand feet. Since the desired resistance is 3.5 ohms, the length of wire required will be

$$\frac{3.5}{66.17} \times 1000 = 52.89 \text{ feet.}$$

Or, suppose that the resistance of the wire in the circuit must not exceed 0.05 ohm and that the length of wire required for making the connections totals 14 feet. Then

$$\frac{14}{1000} \times R = 0.05 \text{ ohm}$$

where R is the maximum allowable resistance in ohms per thousand feet. Rearranging the formula gives

$$R = \frac{0.05 \times 1000}{14} = 3.57 \text{ ohms/1000 ft.}$$

Reference to the wire table shows that No. 15 is the smallest size having a resistance less than this value.

When the wire is not copper, the resistance values given in the wire table should be multi-

TABLE 2-I
Relative Resistivity of Metals

Material	Resistivity Compared to Copper
Aluminum (pure)	1.70
Brass	3.57
Cadmium	5.26
Chromium	1.82
Copper (hard-drawn)	1.12
Copper (annealed)	1.00
Iron (pure)	5.65
Lead	14.3
Nickel	6.25 to 8.33
Phosphor Bronze	2.78
Silver	0.94
Tin	7.70
Zinc	3.54

Resistance

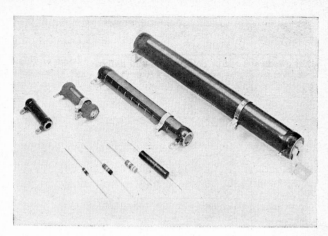

Types of resistors used in radio equipment. Those in the foreground with wire leads are carbon types, ranging in size from ½ watt at the left to 2 watts at the right. The larger resistors use resistance wire wound on ceramic tubes; sizes shown range from 5 watts to 100 watts. Three are of the adjustable type, having a sliding contact on an exposed section of the resistance winding.

plied by the ratios given in Table 2-I to obtain the resistance.

Example: If the wire in the first example were iron instead of copper the length required for 3.5 ohms would be

$$\frac{3.5}{66.17 \times 5.65} \times 1000 = 9.35 \text{ feet.}$$

Temperature Effects

The resistance of a conductor changes with its temperature. Although it is seldom necessary to consider temperature in making resistance calculations for amateur work, it is well to know that the resistance of practically all metallic conductors increases with increasing temperature. Carbon, however, acts in the opposite way; its resistance *decreases* when its temperature rises. The temperature effect is important when it is necessary to maintain a constant resistance under all conditions. Special materials that have little or no change in resistance over a wide temperature range are used in that case.

Resistors

A "package" of resistance made up into a single unit is called a **resistor**. Resistors having the same resistance value may be considerably different in size and construction. The flow of current through resistance causes the conductor to become heated; the higher the resistance and the larger the current, the greater the amount of heat developed. Resistors intended for carrying large currents must be physically large so the heat can be radiated quickly to the surrounding air. If the resistor does not get rid of the heat quickly it may reach a temperature that will cause it to melt or burn.

Skin Effect

The resistance of a conductor is not the same for alternating current as it is for direct current. When the current is alternating there are internal effects that tend to force the current to flow mostly in the outer parts of the conductor. This decreases the effective cross-sectional area of the conductor, with the result that the resistance increases.

For low audio frequencies the increase in resistance is unimportant, but at radio frequencies this **skin effect** is so great that practically all the current flow is confined within a few thousandths of an inch of the conductor surface. The r.f. resistance is consequently many times the d.c. resistance, and increases with increasing frequency. In the r.f. range a conductor of thin tubing will have just as low resistance as a solid conductor of the same diameter, because material not close to the surface carries practically no current.

Conductance

The reciprocal of resistance (that is, $1/R$) is called **conductance**. It is usually represented by the symbol G. A circuit having large conductance has low resistance, and vice versa. In radio work the term is used chiefly in connection with vacuum-tube characteristics. The unit of conductance is the **mho**. A resistance of one ohm has a conductance of one mho, a resistance of 1000 ohms has a conductance of 0.001 mho, and so on. A unit frequently used in connection with vacuum tubes is the **micromho**, or one-millionth of a mho. It is the conductance of a resistance of one megohm.

● OHM'S LAW

The simplest form of electric circuit is a battery with a resistance connected to its terminals, as shown by the symbols in Fig. 2-3. A complete circuit must have an unbroken path so current

Fig. 2-3—A simple circuit consisting of a battery and resistor.

can flow out of the battery, through the apparatus connected to it, and back into the battery. The circuit is **broken**, or open, if a connection is removed at any point. A **switch** is a device for making and breaking connections and thereby closing or opening the circuit, either allowing current to flow or preventing it from flowing.

19

TABLE 2-II Conversion Factors for Fractional and Multiple Units			
To change from	To	Divide by	Multiply by
Units	Micro-units		1,000,000
	Milli-units		1000
	Kilo-units	1000	
	Mega-units	1,000,000	
Micro-units	Milli-units	1000	
	Units	1,000,000	
Milli-units	Micro-units		1000
	Units	1000	
Kilo-units	Units		1000
	Mega-units	1000	
Mega-units	Units		1,000,000
	Kilo-units		1000

The values of current, voltage and resistance in a circuit are by no means independent of each other. The relationship between them is known as **Ohm's Law.** It can be stated as follows: The current flowing in a circuit is directly proportional to the applied e.m.f. and inversely proportional to the resistance. Expressed as an equation, it is

$$I \text{ (amperes)} = \frac{E \text{ (volts)}}{R \text{ (ohms)}}$$

The equation above gives the value of current when the voltage and resistance are known. It may be transposed so that each of the three quantities may be found when the other two are known:

$$E = IR$$

(that is, the voltage acting is equal to the current in amperes multiplied by the resistance in ohms) and

$$R = \frac{E}{I}$$

(or, the resistance of the circuit is equal to the applied voltage divided by the current).

All three forms of the equation are used almost constantly in radio work. It must be remembered that the quantities are in *volts, ohms* and *amperes;* other units cannot be used in the equations without first being converted. For example, if the current is in milliamperes it must be changed to the equivalent fraction of an ampere before the value can be substituted in the equations.

Table 2-II shows how to convert between the various units in common use. The prefixes attached to the basic-unit name indicate the nature of the unit. These prefixes are:

micro — one-millionth (abbreviated μ)
milli — one-thousandth (abbreviated m)
kilo — one thousand (abbreviated k)
mega — one million (abbreviated M)

For example, one microvolt is one-millionth of a volt, and one megohm is 1,000,000 ohms. There are therefore 1,000,000 microvolts in one volt, and 0.000001 megohm in one ohm.

The following examples illustrate the use of Ohm's Law:

The current flowing in a resistance of 20,000 ohms is 150 milliamperes. What is the voltage? Since the voltage is to be found, the equation to use is $E = IR$. The current must first be converted from milliamperes to amperes, and reference to the table shows that to do so it is necessary to divide by 1000. Therefore,

$$E = \frac{150}{1000} \times 20{,}000 = 3000 \text{ volts}$$

When a voltage of 150 is applied to a circuit the current is measured at 2.5 amperes. What is the resistance of the circuit? In this case R is the unknown, so

$$R = \frac{E}{I} = \frac{150}{2.5} = 60 \text{ ohms}$$

No conversion was necessary because the voltage and current were given in volts and amperes. How much current will flow if 250 volts is applied to a 5000-ohm resistor? Since I is unknown,

$$I = \frac{E}{R} = \frac{250}{5000} = 0.05 \text{ ampere}$$

Milliampere units would be more convenient for the current, and 0.05 amp. $\times$ 1000 = 50 milliamperes.

● SERIES AND PARALLEL RESISTANCES

Very few actual electric circuits are as simple as the illustration in the preceding section. Commonly, resistances are found connected in a

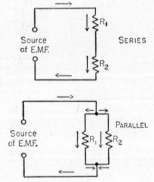

Fig. 2-4—Resistors connected in series and in parallel.

variety of ways. The two fundamental methods of connecting resistances are shown in Fig. 2-4. In the upper drawing, the current flows from the source of e.m.f. (in the direction shown by the arrow, let us say) down through the first resistance, R_1, then through the second, R_2, and then back to the source. These resistors are connected in **series.** The current everywhere in the circuit has the same value.

In the lower drawing the current flows to the common connection point at the top of the two resistors and then divides, one part of it flowing through R_1 and the other through R_2. At the lower connection point these two currents again combine; the total is the same as the current that flowed into the upper common connection. In this case the two resistors are connected in **parallel.**

Series and Parallel Resistance

Resistors in Series

When a circuit has a number of resistances connected in series, the total resistance of the circuit is the sum of the individual resistances. If these are numbered R_1, R_2, R_3, etc., then

$$R(\text{total}) = R_1 + R_2 + R_3 + R_4 + \ldots$$

where the dots indicate that as many resistors as necessary may be added.

Example: Suppose that three resistors are connected to a source of e.m.f. as shown in Fig. 2-5. The e.m.f. is 250 volts, R_1 is 5000 ohms, R_2 is 20,000 ohms, and R_3 is 8000 ohms. The total resistance is then

$$R = R_1 + R_2 + R_3 = 5000 + 20,000 + 8000$$
$$= 33,000 \text{ ohms}$$

The current flowing in the circuit is then

$$I = \frac{E}{R} = \frac{250}{33,000} = 0.00757 \text{ amp.} = 7.57 \text{ ma.}$$

(We need not carry calculations beyond three significant figures, and often two will suffice because the accuracy of measurements is seldom better than a few per cent.)

Voltage Drop

Ohm's Law applies to *any part* of a circuit as well as to the whole circuit. Although the current is the same in all three of the resistances in the example, the total voltage divides among them. The voltage appearing across each resistor (the **voltage drop**) can be found from Ohm's Law.

Example: If the voltage across R_1 (Fig. 2-5) is called E_1, that across R_2 is called E_2, and that across R_3 is called E_3, then

$$E_1 = IR_1 = 0.00757 \times 5000 = 37.9 \text{ volts}$$
$$E_2 = IR_2 = 0.00757 \times 20,000 = 151.4 \text{ volts}$$
$$E_3 = IR_3 = 0.00757 \times 8000 = 60.6 \text{ volts}$$

The applied voltage must equal the sum of the individual voltage drops:

$$E = E_1 + E_2 + E_3 = 37.9 + 151.4 + 60.6$$
$$= 249.9 \text{ volts}$$

The answer would have been more nearly exact if the current had been calculated to more decimal places, but as explained above a very high order of accuracy is not necessary.

In problems such as this considerable time and trouble can be saved, when the current is small enough to be expressed in milliamperes, if the

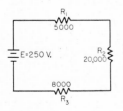

Fig. 2-5—An example of resistors in series. The solution of the circuit is worked out in the text.

resistance is expressed in kilohms rather than ohms. When resistance in kilohms is substituted directly in Ohm's Law the current will be in milliamperes if the e.m.f. is in volts.

Resistors in Parallel

In a circuit with resistances in parallel, the total resistance is *less* than that of the *lowest* value of resistance present. This is because the total current is always greater than the current in any individual resistor. The formula for finding the total resistance of resistances in parallel is

$$R = \cfrac{1}{\cfrac{1}{R_1} + \cfrac{1}{R_2} + \cfrac{1}{R_3} + \cfrac{1}{R_4} + \cdots}$$

where the dots again indicate that any number of resistors can be combined by the same method. For only two resistances in parallel (a very common case) the formula becomes

$$R = \frac{R_1 R_2}{R_1 + R_2}$$

Example: If a 500-ohm resistor is paralleled with one of 1200 ohms, the total resistance is

$$R = \frac{R_1 R_2}{R_1 + R_2} = \frac{500 \times 1200}{500 + 1200} = \frac{600,000}{1700}$$
$$= 353 \text{ ohms}$$

It is probably easier to solve practical problems by a different method than the "reciprocal of reciprocals" formula. Suppose the three re-

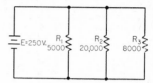

Fig. 2-6—An example of resistors in parallel. The solution is worked out in the text.

sistors of the previous example are connected in parallel as shown in Fig. 2-6. The same e.m.f., 250 volts, is applied to all three of the resistors. The current in each can be found from Ohm's Law as shown below, I_1 being the current through R_1, I_2 the current through R_2 and I_3 the current through R_3.

For convenience, the resistance will be expressed in kilohms so the current will be in milliamperes.

$$I_1 = \frac{E}{R_1} = \frac{250}{5} = 50 \text{ ma.}$$

$$I_2 = \frac{E}{R_2} = \frac{250}{20} = 12.5 \text{ ma.}$$

$$I_3 = \frac{E}{R_3} = \frac{250}{8} = 31.25 \text{ ma.}$$

The total current is

$$I = I_1 + I_2 + I_3 = 50 + 12.5 + 31.25$$
$$= 93.75 \text{ ma.}$$

The total resistance of the circuit is therefore

$$R = \frac{E}{I} = \frac{250}{93.75} = 2.66 \text{ kilohms } (= 2660 \text{ ohms})$$

Resistors in Series-Parallel

An actual circuit may have resistances both in parallel and in series. To illustrate, we use the same three resistances again, but now connected as in Fig. 2-7. The method of solving a circuit such as Fig. 2-7 is as follows: Consider R_2 and R_3 in parallel as though they formed a single resistor. Find their equivalent resistance. Then this resistance in series with R_1 forms a simple series circuit, as shown at the right in Fig. 2-7.

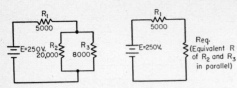

Fig. 2-7—An example of resistors in series-parallel. The equivalent circuit is at the right. The solution is worked out in the text.

Example: The first step is to find the equivalent resistance of R_2 and R_3. From the formula for two resistances in parallel,

$$R_{eq.} = \frac{R_2 R_3}{R_2 + R_3} = \frac{20 \times 8}{20 + 8} = \frac{160}{28}$$
$$= 5.71 \text{ kilohms}$$

The total resistance in the circuit is then

$$R = R_1 + R_{eq.} = 5 + 5.71 \text{ kilohms}$$
$$= 10.71 \text{ kilohms}$$

The current is

$$I = \frac{E}{R} = \frac{250}{10.71} = 23.3 \text{ ma.}$$

The voltage drops across R_1 and $R_{eq.}$ are

$$E_1 = IR_1 = 23.3 \times 5 = 117 \text{ volts}$$
$$E_2 = IR_{eq.} = 23.3 \times 5.71 = 133 \text{ volts}$$

with sufficient accuracy. These total 250 volts, thus checking the calculations so far, because the sum of the voltage drops must equal the applied voltage. Since E_2 appears across both R_2 and R_3.

$$I_2 = \frac{E_2}{R_2} = \frac{133}{20} = 6.65 \text{ ma.}$$

$$I_3 = \frac{E_2}{R_3} = \frac{133}{8} = 16.6 \text{ ma.}$$

where I_2 = Current through R_2
I_3 = Current through R_3

The total is 23.25 ma., which checks closely enough with 23.3 ma., the current through the whole circuit.

● POWER AND ENERGY

Power — the rate of doing work — is equal to voltage multiplied by current. The unit of electrical power, called the **watt**, is equal to one volt multiplied by one ampere. The equation for power therefore is

$$P = EI$$

where P = Power in watts
E = E.m.f. in volts
I = Current in amperes

Common fractional and multiple units for power are the **milliwatt**, one one-thousandth of a watt, and the **kilowatt**, or one thousand watts.

Example: The plate voltage on a transmitting vacuum tube is 2000 volts and the plate current is 350 milliamperes. (The current must be changed to amperes before substitution in the formula, and so is 0.35 amp.) Then

$$P = EI = 2000 \times 0.35 = 700 \text{ watts}$$

By substituting the Ohm's Law equivalents for E and I, the following formulas are obtained for power:

$$P = \frac{E^2}{R}$$

$$P = I^2 R$$

These formulas are useful in power calculations when the resistance and either the current or voltage (but not both) are known.

Example: How much power will be used up in a 4000-ohm resistor if the voltage applied to it is 200 volts? From the equation

$$P = \frac{E^2}{R} = \frac{(200)^2}{4000} = \frac{40,000}{4000} = 10 \text{ watts}$$

Or, suppose a current of 20 milliamperes flows through a 300-ohm resistor. Then

$$P = I^2 R = (0.02)^2 \times 300 = 0.0004 \times 300$$
$$= 0.12 \text{ watt}$$

Note that the current was changed from milliamperes to amperes before substitution in the formula.

Electrical power in a resistance is turned into heat. The greater the power the more rapidly the heat is generated. Resistors for radio work are made in many sizes, the smallest being rated to "dissipate" (or carry safely) about ¼ watt. The largest resistors used in amateur equipment will dissipate about 100 watts.

Generalized Definition of Resistance

Electrical power is not always turned into heat. The power used in running a motor, for example, is converted to mechanical motion. The power supplied to a radio transmitter is largely converted into radio waves. Power applied to a loudspeaker is changed into sound waves. But in every case of this kind the power is completely "used up" — it cannot be recovered. Also, for proper operation of the device the power must be supplied at a definite ratio of voltage to current. Both these features are characteristics of resistance, so it can be said that any device that dissipates power has a definite value of "resistance." This concept of resistance as something that absorbs power at a definite voltage/current ratio is very useful, since it permits substituting a simple resistance for the **load** or power-consuming part of the device receiving power, often with considerable simplification of calculations. Of course, every electrical device has some resistance of its own in the more narrow sense, so a part of the power supplied to it is dissipated in that resistance and hence appears as heat even though the major part of the power may be converted to another form.

Efficiency

In devices such as motors and vacuum tubes, the object is to obtain power in some other form than heat. Therefore power used in heating is considered to be a loss, because it is not the *useful* power. The **efficiency** of a device is the useful power output (in its converted form) divided by the power input to the device. In a vacuum-tube transmitter, for example, the object is to convert power from a d.c. source into a.c. power at some radio frequency. The ratio of the r.f. power output to the d.c. input is the efficiency of the tube. That is,

$$Eff. = \frac{P_o}{P_i}$$

Capacitance

Capacitance

where *Eff.* = Efficiency (as a decimal)
P_o = Power output (watts)
P_i = Power input (watts)

Example: If the d.c. input to the tube is 100 watts and the r.f. power output is 60 watts, the efficiency is

$$Eff. = \frac{P_o}{P_i} = \frac{60}{100} = 0.6$$

Efficiency is usually expressed as a percentage; that is, it tells what per cent of the input power will be available as useful output. The efficiency in the above example is 60 per cent.

Energy

In residences, the power company's bill is for electric **energy**, not for power. What you pay for is the *work* that electricity does for you, not the *rate* at which that work is done.

Electrical work is equal to power multiplied by time; the common unit is the **watt-hour,** which means that a power of one watt has been used for one hour. That is,

$$W = PT$$
where W = Energy in watt-hours
P = Power in watts
T = Time in hours

Other energy units are the **kilowatt-hour** and the **watt-second.** These units should be self-explanatory.

Energy units are seldom used in amateur practice, but it is obvious that a small amount of power used for a long time can eventually result in a "power" bill that is just as large as though a large amount of power had been used for a very short time.

Capacitance

Suppose two flat metal plates are placed close to each other (but not touching) and are connected to a battery through a switch, as shown in Fig. 2-8. At the instant the switch is closed, electrons will be attracted from the upper plate to the positive terminal of the battery, and the same number will be repelled into the lower plate from

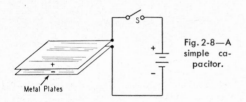

Fig. 2-8—A simple capacitor.

Metal Plates

the negative battery terminal. Enough electrons move into one plate and out of the other to make the e.m.f. between them the same as the e.m.f. of the battery.

If the switch is opened after the plates have been **charged** in this way, the top plate is left with a deficiency of electrons and the bottom plate with an excess. The plates remain charged despite the fact that the battery no longer is connected. However, if a wire is touched between the two plates (**short-circuiting** them) the excess electrons on the bottom plate will flow through the wire to the upper plate, thus restoring electrical neutrality. The plates have then been **discharged.**

The two plates constitute an electrical **capacitor,** and from the discussion above it should be clear that a capacitor possesses the property of storing electricity. (The energy actually is stored in the electric field between the plates.) It should also be clear that during the time the electrons are moving — that is, while the capacitor is being charged or discharged — a current is flowing in the circuit even though the circuit is "broken" by the gap between the capacitor plates. However, the current flows only during the time of charge and discharge, and this time is usually very short. There can be no continuous flow of direct current "through" a capacitor.

The **charge** or quantity of electricity that

can be placed on a capacitor is proportional to the applied voltage and to the **capacitance** of the capacitor. The larger the plate area and the smaller the spacing between the plate the greater the capacitance. The capacitance also depends upon the kind of insulating material between the plates; it is smallest with air insulation, but substitution of other insulating materials for air may increase the capacitance many times. The ratio of the capacitance with some material other than air between the plates, to the capacitance of the same capacitor with air insulation, is called the **specific inductive capacity** or **dielectric constant** of that particular insulating material. The material itself is called a **dielectric.** The dielectric constants of a number of materials commonly used as dielectrics in capacitors are given in Table 2-III. If a sheet of photographic glass is substituted for air between the plates of a capacitor, for example, the capacitance will be increased 7.5 times.

TABLE 2-III		
Dielectric Constants and Breakdown Voltages		
Material	*Dielectric Constant*	*Puncture Voltage**
Air	1.0	19.8–22.8
Alsimag A196	5.7	240
Bakelite (paper-base)	3.8–5.5	650–750
Bakelite (mica-filled)	5–6	475–600
Cellulose acetate	6–8	300–1000
Fiber	5–7.5	150–180
Formica	4.6–4.9	450
Glass (window)	7.6–8	200–250
Glass (photographic)	7.5	
Glass (Pyrex)	4.2–4.9	335
Lucite	2.5–3	480–500
Mica	2.5–8	
Mica (clear India)	6.4–7.5	600–1500
Mycalex	7.4	250
Paper	2.0–2.6	1250
Polyethylene	2.3–2.4	1000
Polystyrene	2.4–2.9	500–2500
Porcelain	6.2–7.5	40–100
Rubber (hard)	2–3.5	450
Steatite (low-loss)	4.4	150–315
Teflon	1.9–2.6	700–1100
Wood (dry oak)	2.5–6.8	

* In volts per mil (0.001 inch).

Unit

The fundamental unit of capacitance is the **farad**, but this unit is much too large for practical work. Capacitance is usually measured in **microfarads** (abbreviated µf.) or **micromicrofarads** (µµf.). The microfarad is one-millionth

Fig. 2-9—A multiple-plate capacitor. Alternate plates are connected together.

of a farad, and the micromicrofarad is one-millionth of a microfarad. Capacitors nearly always have more than two plates, the alternate plates being connected together to form two sets as shown in Fig. 2-9. This makes it possible to attain a fairly large capacitance in a small space, since several plates of smaller individual area can be stacked to form the equivalent of a single large plate of the same total area. Also, all plates, except the two on the ends, are exposed to plates of the other group on *both sides*, and so are twice as effective in increasing the capacitance.

The formula for calculating capacitance is:

$$C = 0.224 \frac{KA}{d} (n - 1)$$

where C = Capacitance in µµf.
   K = Dielectric constant of material between plates
   A = Area of one side of *one* plate in square inches
   d = Separation of plate surfaces in inches
   n = Number of plates

If the plates in one group do not have the same area as the plates in the other, use the area of the *smaller* plates.

The usefulness of a capacitor in electrical circuits lies in the fact that it can be charged with electrical energy at one time and then discharged at a later time. In other words, it is an "electrical reservoir."

Capacitors in Radio

The types of capacitors used in radio work differ considerably in physical size, construction, and capacitance. Some representative types are shown in the photograph. In **variable** capacitors (almost always constructed with air for the dielectric) one set of plates is made movable with respect to the other set so that the capacitance can be varied. **Fixed** capacitors — that is, assemblies having a single, non-adjustable value of capacitance — also can be made with metal plates and with air as the dielectric, but usually are constructed from plates of metal foil with a thin solid or liquid dielectric sandwiched in between, so that a relatively large capacitance can be secured in a small unit. The solid dielectrics commonly used are mica, paper and special ceramics. An example of a liquid dielectric is mineral oil. The **electrolytic** capacitor uses aluminum-foil plates with a semiliquid conducting chemical compound between them; the actual dielectric is a very thin film of insulating material that forms on one set of plates through electrochemical action when a d.c. voltage is applied to the capacitor. The capacitance obtained with a given plate area in an electrolytic capacitor is very large, compared with capacitors having other dielectrics, because the film is so extremely thin — much less than any thickness that is practicable with a solid dielectric.

Voltage Breakdown

When a high voltage is applied to the plates of a capacitor, a considerable force is exerted on the electrons and nuclei of the dielectric. Because the dielectric is an insulator the electrons do not become detached from atoms the way they do in conductors. However, if the force is great enough the dielectric will "break down"; usually it will puncture and may char (if it is solid) and permit current to flow. The **breakdown voltage** depends upon the kind and thickness of the dielectric, as shown in Table 2-III. It is not directly proportional to the thickness; that is, doubling the thickness does not quite double the breakdown voltage. If the dielectric is air or any other gas, breakdown is

Fixed and variable capacitors. The large unit at the left is a transmitting-type variable capacitor for r.f. tank circuits. To its right are other air-dielectric variables of different sizes ranging from the midget "air padder" to the medium-power tank capacitor at the top center. The cased capacitors in the top row are for power-supply filters, the cylindrical-can unit being an electrolytic and the rectangular one a paper-dielectric capacitor. Various types of mica, ceramic, and paper-dielectric capacitors are in the foreground.

Capacitors

evidenced by a spark or arc between the plates, but if the voltage is removed the arc ceases and the capacitor is ready for use again. Breakdown will occur at a lower voltage between pointed or sharp-edged surfaces than between rounded and polished surfaces; consequently, the breakdown voltage between metal plates of given spacing in air can be increased by buffing the edges of the plates.

Since the dielectric must be thick to withstand high voltages, and since the thicker the dielectric the smaller the capacitance for a given plate area, a high-voltage capacitor must have more plate area than a low-voltage one of the same capacitance. High-voltage high-capacitance capacitors are physically large.

● CAPACITORS IN SERIES AND PARALLEL

The terms "parallel" and "series" when used with reference to capacitors have the same circuit meaning as with resistances. When a number of capacitors are connected in parallel, as in Fig. 2-10, the total capacitance of the group is equal to the sum of the individual capacitances, so

$$C \text{ (total)} = C_1 + C_2 + C_3 + C_4 + \cdots\cdots\cdots$$

However, if two or more capacitors are connected in series, as in the second drawing, the total capacitance is less than that of the smallest capacitor in the group. The rule for finding the capacitance of a number of series-connected capacitors is the same as that for finding the resistance of a number of *parallel*-connected resistors. That is,

$$C \text{ (total)} = \cfrac{1}{\cfrac{1}{C_1} + \cfrac{1}{C_2} + \cfrac{1}{C_3} + \cfrac{1}{C_4} + \cdots\cdots\cdots}$$

and, for only two capacitors in series,

$$C \text{ (total)} = \frac{C_1 C_2}{C_1 + C_2}$$

The same units must be used throughout; that is, all capacitances must be expressed in either $\mu f.$ or $\mu\mu f.$; both kinds of units cannot be used in the same equation.

Capacitors are connected in parallel to obtain a larger total capacitance than is available in one unit. The largest voltage that can be applied safely to a group of capacitors in parallel is the voltage that can be applied safely to the one having the *lowest* voltage rating.

When capacitors are connected in series, the applied voltage is divided up among them; the situation is much the same as when resistors are in series and there is a voltage drop across each. However, the voltage that appears across each capacitor of a group connected in series is in *inverse* proportion to its capacitance, as

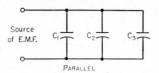

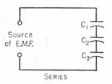

Fig. 2-10—Capacitors in series and parallel.

compared with the capacitance of the whole group.

Example: Three capacitors having capacitances of 1, 2 and 4 $\mu f.$, respectively, are connected in series as shown in Fig. 2-11. The total capacitance is

$$C = \cfrac{1}{\cfrac{1}{C_1} + \cfrac{1}{C_2} + \cfrac{1}{C_3}} = \cfrac{1}{\cfrac{1}{1} + \cfrac{1}{2} + \cfrac{1}{4}} = \cfrac{1}{\cfrac{7}{4}} = \frac{4}{7}$$
$$= 0.571 \ \mu f.$$

The voltage across each capacitor is proportional to the *total* capacitance divided by the capacitance of the capacitor in question, so the voltage across C_1 is

$$E_1 = \frac{0.571}{1} \times 2000 = 1142 \text{ volts}$$

Similarly, the voltages across C_2 and C_3 are

$$E_2 = \frac{0.571}{2} \times 2000 = 571 \text{ volts}$$

$$E_3 = \frac{0.571}{4} \times 2000 = 286 \text{ volts}$$

totaling approximately 2000 volts, the applied voltage.

Capacitors are frequently connected in series to enable the group to withstand a larger voltage (at the expense of decreased total capacitance) than any individual capacitor is rated to stand. However, as shown by the previous example, the applied voltage does not divide equally among the capacitors (except when all the capacitances are the same) so care must be taken to see that the voltage rating of no capacitor in the group is exceeded.

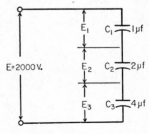

Fig. 2-11—An example of capacitors connected in series. The solution to this arrangement is worked out in the text.

2 – ELECTRICAL LAWS AND CIRCUITS

Inductance

It is possible to show that the flow of current through a conductor is accompanied by magnetic effects; a compass needle brought near the conductor, for example, will be deflected from its normal north-south position. The current, in other words, sets up a magnetic field.

The transfer of energy to the magnetic field represents work done by the source of e.m.f. Power is required for doing work, and since power is equal to current multiplied by voltage, there must be a voltage drop in the circuit during the time in which energy is being stored in the field. This voltage "drop" (which has nothing to do with the voltage drop in any resistance in the circuit) is the result of an opposing voltage "induced" in the circuit while the field is building up to its final value. When the field becomes constant the **induced e.m.f.** or **back e.m.f.** disappears, since no further energy is being stored.

Since the induced e.m.f. opposes the e.m.f. of the source, it tends to prevent the current from rising rapidly when the circuit is closed. The amplitude of the induced e.m.f. is proportional to the rate at which the current is changing and to a constant associated with the circuit itself, called the **inductance** of the circuit.

Inductance depends on the physical characteristics of the conductor. If the conductor is formed into a coil, for example, its inductance is increased. A coil of many turns will have more inductance than one of few turns, if both coils are otherwise physically similar. Also, if a coil is placed on an iron core its inductance will be greater than it was without the magnetic core.

The polarity of an induced e.m.f. is always such as to oppose any change in the current in the circuit. This means that when the current in the circuit is increasing, work is being done against the induced e.m.f. by storing energy in the magnetic field. If the current in the circuit tends to decrease, the stored energy of the field returns to the circuit, and thus adds to the energy being supplied by the source of e.m.f. This tends to keep the current flowing even though the applied e.m.f. may be decreasing or be removed entirely.

The values of inductance used in radio equipment vary over a wide range. Inductance of several henrys is required in power-supply circuits (see chapter on Power Supplies) and to obtain such values of inductance it is necessary to use coils of many turns wound on iron cores. In radio-frequency circuits, the inductance values used will be measured in **millihenrys** (a millihenry is one one-thousandth of a henry) at low frequencies, and in **microhenrys** (one one-millionth of a henry) at medium frequencies and higher. Although coils for radio frequencies may be wound on special iron cores (ordinary iron is not suitable) most r.f. coils made and used by amateurs are of the "air-core" type; that is, wound on an insulating support consisting of nonmagnetic material.

Every conductor has inductance, even though the conductor is not formed into a coil. The inductance of a short length of straight wire is small, but it may not be negligible because if the current through it changes its intensity rapidly enough the induced voltage may be appreciable. This will be the case in even a few inches of wire when an alternating current having a frequency of the order of 100 Mc. or higher is flowing. However, at much lower frequencies the inductance of the same wire could be left out of any calculations because the induced voltage would be negligibly small.

Calculating Inductance

The inductance of air-core coils may be calculated from the formula

$$L \ (\mu h.) = \frac{0.2 \ a^2 n^2}{3a + 9b + 10c}$$

where L = Inductance in microhenrys
a = Average diameter of coil in inches
b = Length of winding in inches

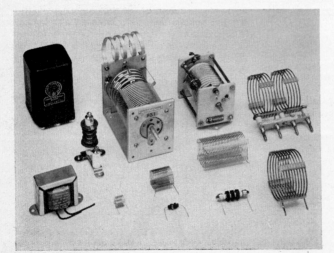

Inductors for power and radio frequencies. The two iron-core coils at the left are "chokes" for power-supply filters. The mounted air-core coils at the top center are adjustable inductors for transmitting tank circuits. The "pie-wound" coils at the left and in the foreground are radio-frequency choke coils. The remaining coils are typical of inductors used in r.f. tuned circuits, the larger sizes being used principally for transmitters.

Inductance

c = Radial depth of winding in inches
n = Number of turns

The notation is explained in Fig 2-12. The

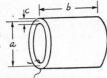

Fig. 2-12 — Coil dimensions used in the inductance formula.

quantity $10c$ may be neglected if the coil only has one layer of wire.

Example: Assume a coil having 35 turns of No. 30 d.s.c. wire on a form 1.5 inches in diameter. Consulting the wire table, 35 turns of No. 30 d.s.c. will occupy 0.5 inch. Therefore, $a = 1.5$, $b = 0.5$, $n = 35$, and

$$L = \frac{0.2 \times (1.5)^2 \times (35)^2}{(3 \times 1.5) + (9 \times 0.5)} = 61.25 \ \mu h.$$

To calculate the number of turns of a single-layer coil for a required value of inductance:

$$N = \sqrt{\frac{3a + 9b}{0.2a^2} \times L}$$

Example: Suppose an inductance of 10 microhenrys is required. The form on which the coil is to be wound has a diameter of one inch and is long enough to accommodate a coil length of $1\frac{1}{4}$ inches. Then $a = 1$, $b = 1.25$, and $L = 10$. Substituting,

$$N = \sqrt{\frac{(3 \times 1) + (9 \times 1.25)}{0.2 \times 1^2} \times 10}$$

$$= \sqrt{\frac{14.25}{0.2} \times 10} = \sqrt{712.5}$$

$$= 26.6 \text{ turns.}$$

A 27-turn coil would be close enough to the required value of inductance, in practical work. Since the coil will be 1.25 inches long, the number of turns per inch will be $27/1.25 = 21.6$. Consulting the wire table, we find that No. 18 enameled wire (or any smaller size) can be used. The proper inductance is obtained by winding the required number of turns on the form and then adjusting the spacing between the turns to make a uniformly-spaced coil 1.25 inches long.

Inductance Charts

Most inductance formulas lose accuracy when applied to small coils (such as are used in v.h.f. work and in low-pass filters built for reducing harmonic interference to television) because the conductor thickness is no longer negligible in comparison with the size of the coil. Fig. 2-13 shows the measured inductance of v.h.f. coils, and may be used as a basis for circuit design. Two curves are given: curve A is for coils wound to an inside diameter of $\frac{1}{2}$ inch; curve B is for coils of $\frac{3}{4}$-inch inside diameter. In both curves the wire size is No. 12, winding pitch 8 turns to the inch ($\frac{1}{8}$ inch center-to-center turn spacing). The inductance values given include leads $\frac{1}{2}$ inch long.

The charts of Figs. 2-14 and 2-15 are useful for rapid determination of the inductance of coils of the type commonly used in radio-frequency circuits in the range 3-30 Mc. They are based on the formula above, and are of sufficient accuracy for most practical work. Given the coil

length in inches, the curves show the multiplying factor to be applied to the inductance value given in the table below the curve for a coil of the same diameter and number of turns per inch.

Example: A coil 1 inch in diameter is $1\frac{1}{4}$ inches long and has 20 turns. Therefore it has 16 turns per inch, and from the table under Fig. 2-15 it is found that the reference inductance for a coil of this diameter and number of turns per inch is 16.8 μh. From curve B in the figure the multiplying factor is 0.35, so the inductance is

$$16.8 \times 0.35 = 5.9 \ \mu h.$$

The charts also can be used for finding suitable dimensions for a coil having a required value of inductance.

Example: A coil having an inductance of 12 μh. is required. It is to be wound on a form having a diameter of 1 inch, the length available for the winding being not more than $1\frac{1}{4}$ inches. From Fig. 2-15, the multiplying factor for a 1-inch diameter coil (curve B) having the maximum possible length of $1\frac{1}{4}$ inches is 0.35. Hence the number of turns per inch must be chosen for a reference inductance of at least $12/0.35$, or 34 μh. From the Table under Fig. 2-15 it is seen that 16 turns per inch (reference inductance 16.8 μh.) is too small. Using 32 turns per inch, the multiplying factor is $12/68$, or 0.177, and from curve B this corresponds to a coil length of $\frac{3}{4}$ inch. There will be 24 turns in this length, since the winding "pitch" is 32 turns per inch.

● IRON-CORE COILS

Permeability

Suppose that the coil in Fig. 2-16 is wound on an iron core having a cross-sectional area of 2 square inches. When a certain current is sent through the coil it is found that there are 80,000 lines of force in the core. Since the area is 2 square inches, the flux density is 40,000 lines per square inch. Now suppose that the iron core is removed and the same current is maintained in the coil, and that the flux density without the iron core is found to be 50 lines per square inch. The ratio of the flux density with the given core

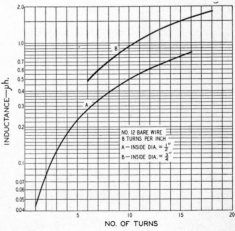

Fig. 2-13—Measured inductance of coils wound with No. 12 bare wire, 8 turns to the inch. The values include half-inch leads.

material to the flux density (with the same coil and same current) with an air core is called the **permeability** of the material. In this case the permeability of the iron is 40,000/50 = 800. The inductance of the coil is increased 800 times by inserting the iron core since, other things being equal, the inductance will be proportional to the magnetic flux through the coil.

The permeability of a magnetic material varies with the flux density. At low flux densities (or with an air core) increasing the current through the coil will cause a proportionate increase in flux, but at very high flux densities, increasing the current may cause no appreciable change in the flux. When this is so, the iron is said to be **saturated.** Saturation causes a rapid decrease in permeability, because it decreases the ratio of

flux lines to those obtainable with the same current and an air core. Obviously, the inductance of an iron-core inductor is highly dependent upon the current flowing in the coil. In an air-core coil, the inductance is independent of current because air does not saturate.

Iron core coils such as the one sketched in

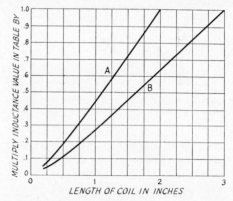

Fig. 2-15—Factor to be applied to the inductance of coils listed in the table below, as a function of coil length. Use curve A for coils marked A, curve B for coils marked B.

Coil diameter, Inches	No. of turns per inch	Inductance in μh.
½ (A)	4	0.18
	6	0.40
	8	0.72
	10	1.12
	16	2.9
	32	12
⅝ (A)	4	0.28
	6	0.62
	8	1.1
	10	1.7
	16	4.4
	32	18
¾ (B)	4	0.6
	6	1.35
	8	2.4
	10	3.8
	16	9.9
	32	40
1 (B)	4	1.0
	6	2.3
	8	4.2
	10	6.6
	16	16.8
	32	68

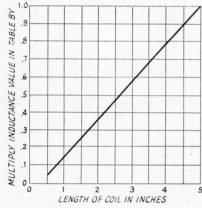

Fig. 2-14—Factor to be applied to the inductance of coils listed in the table below, for coil lengths up to 5 inches.

Coil diameter, Inches	No. of turns per inch	Inductance in μh.
1¼	4	2.75
	6	6.3
	8	11.2
	10	17.5
	16	42.5
1½	4	3.9
	6	8.8
	8	15.6
	10	24.5
	16	63
1¾	4	5.2
	6	11.8
	8	21
	10	33
	16	85
2	4	6.6
	6	15
	8	26.5
	10	42
	16	108
2½	4	10.2
	6	23
	8	41
	10	64
3	4	14
	6	31.5
	8	56
	10	89

Fig. 2-16 are used chiefly in power-supply equipment. They usually have direct current flowing through the winding, and the variation in inductance with current is usually undesirable. It may be overcome by keeping the flux density below

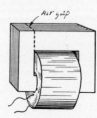

Air gap

Fig. 2-16—Typical construction of an iron-core inductor. The small air gap prevents magnetic saturation of the iron and thus maintains the inductance at high currents.

Inductance

the saturation point of the iron. This is done by opening the core so that there is a small "air gap," as indicated by the dashed lines. The magnetic "resistance" introduced by such a gap is so large — even though the gap is only a small fraction of an inch — compared with that of the iron that the gap, rather than the iron, controls the flux density. This reduces the inductance, but makes it practically constant regardless of the value of the current.

Eddy Currents and Hysteresis

When alternating current flows through a coil wound on an iron core an e.m.f. will be induced, as previously explained, and since iron is a conductor a current will flow in the core. Such currents (called **eddy currents**) represent a waste of power because they flow through the resistance of the iron and thus cause heating. Eddy-current losses can be reduced by **laminating** the core; that is, by cutting it into thin strips. These strips or **laminations** must be insulated from each other by painting them with some insulating material such as varnish or shellac.

There is also another type of energy loss: the iron tends to resist any change in its magnetic state, so a rapidly-changing current such as a.c. is forced continually to supply energy to the iron to overcome this "inertia." Losses of this sort are called **hysteresis** losses.

Eddy-current and hysteresis losses in iron increase rapidly as the frequency of the alternating current is increased. For this reason, ordinary iron cores can be used only at power and audio frequencies — up to, say, 15,000 cycles. Even so, a very good grade or iron or steel is necessary if the core is to perform well at the higher audio frequencies. Iron cores of this type are completely useless at radio frequencies.

For radio-frequency work, the losses in iron cores can be reduced to a satisfactory figure by grinding the iron into a powder and then mixing it with a "binder" of insulating material in such a way that the individual iron particles are insulated from each other. By this means cores can be made that will function satisfactorily even through the v.h.f. range — that is, at frequencies up to perhaps 100 Mc. Because a large part of the magnetic path is through a nonmagnetic material, the permeability of the iron is low compared with the values obtained at power-supply frequencies. The core is usually in the form of a "slug" or cylinder which fits inside the insulating form on which the coil is wound. Despite the fact that, with this construction, the major portion of the magnetic path for the flux is in air, the slug is quite effective in increasing the coil inductance. By pushing the slug in and out of the coil the inductance can be varied over a considerable range.

● INDUCTANCES IN SERIES AND PARALLEL

When two or more inductors are connected in series (Fig. 2-17, left) the total inductance is

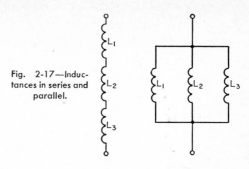

Fig. 2-17—Inductances in series and parallel.

equal to the sum of the individual inductances, *provided the coils are sufficiently separated so that no coil is in the magnetic field of another.* That is,

$$L_{total} = L_1 + L_2 + L_3 + L_4 + \ldots\ldots$$

If inductors are connected in parallel (Fig. 2-17, right), the total inductance is

$$L_{total} = \frac{1}{\dfrac{1}{L_1} + \dfrac{1}{L_2} + \dfrac{1}{L_3} + \dfrac{1}{L_4} + \ldots\ldots}$$

and for two inductances in parallel,

$$L = \frac{L_1 L_2}{L_1 + L_2}$$

Thus the rules for combining inductances in series and parallel are the same as for resistances, *if the coils are far enough apart so that each is unaffected by another's magnetic field.* When this is not so the formulas given above cannot be used.

● MUTUAL INDUCTANCE

If two coils are arranged with their axes on the same line, as shown in Fig. 2-18, a current sent through Coil 1 will cause a magnetic field which "cuts" Coil 2. Consequently, an e.m.f. will be induced in Coil 2 whenever the field strength is changing. This induced e.m.f. is similar to the e.m.f. of self-induction, but since it appears in the *second* coil because of current flowing in the *first*, it is a "mutual" effect and results from the **mutual inductance** between the two coils.

If all the flux set up by one coil cuts all the turns of the other coil the mutual inductance has its maximum possible value. If only a small part of the flux set up by one coil cuts the turns of the other the mutual inductance is relatively small. Two coils having mutual inductance are said to be **coupled**.

The ratio of actual mutual inductance to the maximum possible value that could theoretically be obtained with two given coils is called the **coefficient of coupling** between the coils. It is frequently expressed as a percentage. Coils that have nearly the maximum possible (coefficient = 1 or 100%) mutual inductance are said to be **closely**, or **tightly**, coupled, but if the mutual inductance is relatively small the coils are said to be **loosely** coupled. The degree of coupling

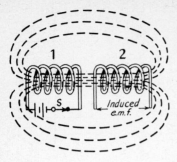

Fig. 2-18—Mutual inductance. When the switch, S, is closed current flows through coil No. 1, setting up a magnetic field that induces an e.m.f. in the turns of coil No. 2.

depends upon the physical spacing between the coils and how they are placed with respect to each other. Maximum coupling exists when they have a common axis and are as close together as possible (one wound over the other). The coupling is least when the coils are far apart or are placed so their axes are at right angles.

The maximum possible coefficient of coupling is closely approached only when the two coils are wound on a closed iron core. The coefficient with air-core coils may run as high as 0.6 or 0.7 if one coil is wound over the other, but will be much less if the two coils are separated.

Time Constant

Capacitance and Resistance

Connecting a source of e.m.f. to a capacitor causes the capacitor to become charged to the full e.m.f. practically instantaneously, if there is no resistance in the circuit. However, if the circuit contains resistance, as in Fig. 2-19A, the resistance limits the current flow and an appreciable length of time is required for the e.m.f. between the capacitor plates to build up to the same value as the e.m.f. of the source. During this "building-up" period the current gradually decreases from its initial value, because the increasing e.m.f. stored on the capacitor offers increasing opposition to the steady e.m.f. of the source.

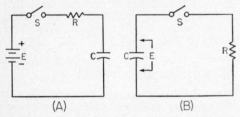

(A)   (B)

Fig. 2-19—Illustrating the time constant of an RC circuit.

Theoretically, the charging process is never really finished, but eventually the charging current drops to a value that is smaller than anything that can be measured. The **time constant** of such a circuit is the length of time, in seconds, required for the voltage across the capacitor to reach 63 per cent of the applied e.m.f. (this figure is chosen for mathematical reasons). The voltage across the capacitor rises with time as shown by Fig. 2-20.

The formula for time constant is

$$T = CR$$

where T = Time constant in seconds
C = Capacitance in farads
R = Resistance in ohms

If C is in microfarads and R in megohms, the time constant also is in seconds. These units usually are more convenient.

Example: The time constant of a 2-μf. capacitor and a 250,000-ohm (0.25 megohm) resistor is

$$T = CR = 2 \times 0.25 = 0.5 \text{ second}$$

If the applied e.m.f. is 1000 volts, the voltage between the capacitor plates will be 630 volts at the end of $\frac{1}{2}$ second.

If a charged capacitor is *discharged* through a resistor, as indicated in Fig. 2-19B, the same time constant applies. If there were no resistance, the capacitor would discharge instantly when S was closed. However, since R limits the current flow the capacitor voltage cannot instantly go to zero, but it will decrease just as rapidly as the capacitor can rid itself of its charge through R. When the capacitor is discharging through a resistance, the time constant (calculated in the same way as above) is the time, in seconds, that it takes for the capacitor to *lose* 63 per cent of its voltage; that is, for the voltage to drop to 37 per cent of its initial value.

Example: If the capacitor of the example above is charged to 1000 volts, it will discharge to 370 volts in $\frac{1}{2}$ second through the 250,000-ohm resistor.

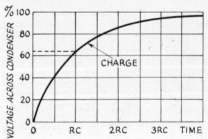

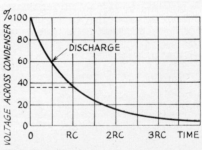

Fig. 2-20—How the voltage across a capacitor rises, with time, when charged through a resistor. The lower curve shows the way in which the voltage decreases across the capacitor terminals on discharging through the same resistor.

Time Constant

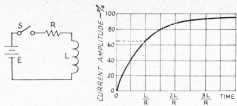

Fig. 2-21—Time constant of an *LR* circuit.

Inductance and Resistance

A comparable situation exists when resistance and inductance are in series. In Fig. 2-21, first consider *L* to have no resistance and also assume that *R* is zero. Then closing *S* would tend to send a current through the circuit. However, the instantaneous transition from no current to a finite value, however small, represents a very rapid *change* in current, and a *back e.m.f.* is developed by the self-inductance of *L* that is practically equal and opposite to the applied e.m.f. The result is that the initial current is very small.

The back e.m.f. depends upon the *change* in current and would cease to offer opposition if the current did not continue to increase. With no resistance in the circuit (which would lead to an infinitely large current, by Ohm's Law) the current would increase forever, always growing just fast enough to keep the e.m.f. of self-induction equal to the applied e.m.f.

When resistance is in series, Ohm's Law sets a limit to the value that the current can reach. The back e.m.f. generated in *L* has only to equal the *difference* between *E* and the drop across *R*, because that difference is the voltage actually applied to *L*. This difference becomes smaller as the current approaches the final Ohm's Law value. Theoretically, the back e.m.f. never quite disappears and so the current never quite reaches the Ohm's Law value, but practically the difference becomes unmeasurable after a time. The time constant of an inductive circuit is the time

in seconds required for the current to reach 63 per cent of its final value. The formula is

$$T = \frac{L}{R}$$

where T = Time constant in seconds
L = Inductance in henrys
R = Resistance in ohms

The resistance of the wire in a coil acts as though it were in series with the inductance.

Example: A coil having an inductance of 20 henrys and a resistance of 100 ohms has a time constant of

$$T = \frac{L}{R} = \frac{20}{100} = 0.2 \text{ second}$$

if there is no other resistance in the circuit. If a d.c. e.m.f. of 10 volts is applied to such a coil, the final current, by Ohm's Law, is

$$I = \frac{E}{R} = \frac{10}{100} = 0.1 \text{ amp. or 100 ma.}$$

The current would rise from zero to 63 milliamperes in 0.2 second after closing the switch.

An inductor cannot be "discharged" in the same way as a capacitor, because the magnetic field disappears as soon as current flow ceases. Opening *S* does not leave the inductor "charged." The energy stored in the magnetic field instantly returns to the circuit when *S* is opened. The rapid disappearance of the field causes a very large voltage to be induced in the coil — ordinarily many times larger than the voltage applied, because the induced voltage is proportional to the *speed* with which the field changes. The common result of opening the switch in a circuit such as the one shown is that a spark or arc forms at the switch contacts at the instant of opening. If the inductance is large and the current in the circuit is high, a great deal of energy is released in a very short period of time. It is not at all unusual for the switch contacts to burn or melt under such circumstances.

Time constants play an important part in numerous devices, such as electronic keys, timing and control circuits, and shaping of keying characteristics by vacuum tubes. The time constants of circuits are also important in such applications as automatic gain control and noise limiters. In nearly all such applications a capacitance-resistance (*CR*) time constant is involved, and it is usually necessary to know the voltage across the capacitor at some time interval larger or smaller than the actual time constant of the circuit as given by the formula above. Fig. 2-22 can be used for the solution of such problems, since the curve gives the voltage across the capacitor, in terms of percentage of the initial charge, for percentages between 5 and 100, at any time after discharge begins.

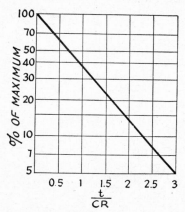

Fig. 2-22—Voltage across capacitor terminals in a discharging *CR* circuit, in terms of the initial charged voltage. To obtain time in seconds, multiply the factor *t*/*CR* by the time constant of the circuit.

Example: A 0.01-μf. capacitor is charged to 150 volts and then allowed to discharge through a 0.1-megohm resistor. How long will it take the voltage to fall to 10 volts? In percentage, 10/150 = 6.7%. From the chart, the factor corresponding to 6.7% is 2.7. The time constant of the circuit is equal to $CR = 0.01 \times 0.1 = 0.001$. The time is therefore $2.7 \times 0.001 = 0.0027$ second, or 2.7 milliseconds.

Alternating Currents

● **PHASE**

The term **phase** essentially means "time," or the *time interval* between the instant when one thing occurs and the instant when a second related thing takes place. The later event is said to **lag** the earlier, while the one that occurs first is said to **lead**. In a.c. circuits the current amplitude changes continuously, so the concept of phase or time becomes important. Phase can be measured in the ordinary time units, such as the second, but there is a more convenient method: Since each a.c. cycle occupies exactly the same amount of time as every other cycle of the same frequency, we can use the cycle itself as the time unit. Using the cycle as the time unit makes the specification or measurement of phase independent of the frequency of the current, so long as only one frequency is under consideration at a time. When two or more frequencies are to be considered, as in the case where harmonics are present, the phase measurements are made with respect to the lowest, or fundamental, frequency.

The time interval or "phase difference" under consideration usually will be less than one cycle. Phase difference could be measured in decimal parts of a cycle, but it is more convenient to divide the cycle into 360 parts or **degrees**. A phase degree is therefore 1/360 of a cycle. The reason for this choice is that with sine-wave alternating current the value of the current at any instant is proportional to the sine of the angle that corresponds to the number of degrees — that is, length of time — from the instant the cycle began. There is no actual "angle" associated with an alternating current. Fig. 2-23 should help make this method of measurement clear.

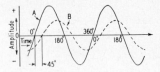

Fig. 2-24—When two waves of the same frequency start their cycles at slightly different times, the time difference or phase difference is measured in degrees. In this drawing wave B starts 45 degrees (one-eighth cycle) later than wave A, and so lags 45 degrees behind A.

Two important special cases are shown in Fig. 2-25. In the upper drawing *B* lags 90 degrees behind *A*; that is, its cycle begins just one-quarter cycle later than that of *A*. When one wave is passing through zero, the other is just at its maximum point.

In the lower drawing *A* and *B* are 180 degrees out of phase. In this case it does not matter which one is considered to lead or lag. *B* is always positive while *A* is negative, and vice versa. The two waves are thus *completely* out of phase.

The waves shown in Figs. 2-24 and 2-25 could represent current, voltage, or both. *A* and *B* might be two currents in separate circuits, or *A* might represent voltage and *B* current in the same circuit. If *A* and *B* represent two currents in the *same* circuit (or two voltages in the same circuit) the total or **resultant** current (or voltage) also is a sine wave, because adding any number of sine waves of the same frequency always gives a sine wave also of the same frequency.

Phase in Resistive Circuits

When an alternating voltage is applied to a resistance, the current flows exactly in step with the voltage. In other words, the voltage and current are **in phase**. This is true at any frequency if the resistance is "pure" — that is, is free from the reactive effects discussed in the next section. Practically, it is often difficult to obtain a purely

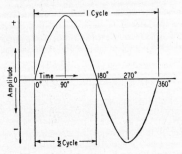

Fig. 2-23—An a.c. cycle is divided off into 360 degrees that are used as a measure of time or phase.

Measuring Phase

The phase difference between two currents of the same frequency is the time or angle difference between corresponding parts of cycles of the two currents. This is shown in Fig. 2-24. The current labeled *A* leads the one marked *B* by 45 degrees, since *A*'s cycles begin 45 degrees earlier in time. It is equally correct to say that *B lags A* by 45 degrees.

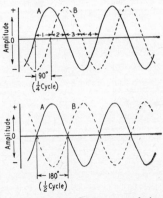

Fig. 2-25—Two important special cases of phase difference. In the upper drawing, the phase difference between *A* and *B* is 90 degrees; in the lower drawing the phase difference is 180 degrees.

Alternating Currents

resistive circuit at radio frequencies, because the reactive effects become more pronounced as the frequency is increased.

In a purely resistive circuit, or for purely resistive parts of circuits, Ohm's Law is just as valid for a.c. of any frequency as it is for d.c.

⬤ REACTANCE

Alternating Current in Capacitance

In Fig. 2-26 a sine-wave a.c. voltage having a maximum value of 100 volts is applied to a capacitor. In the period OA, the applied voltage increases from zero to 38 volts; at the end of this period the capacitor is charged to that voltage. In interval AB the voltage increases to 71 volts; that is, 33 volts additional. In this interval a *smaller* quantity of charge has been added than in OA, because the voltage rise during interval AB is smaller. Consequently the average current during AB is smaller than during OA. In the third interval, BC, the voltage rises from 71 to 92 volts, an increase of 21 volts. This is less than the voltage increase during AB, so the quantity of electricity added is less; in other words, the average current during interval BC is still smaller. In the fourth interval, CD, the voltage increases only 8 volts; the charge added is smaller than in any preceding interval and therefore the current also is smaller.

By dividing the first quarter cycle into a very large number of intervals it could be shown that the current charging the capacitor has the shape of a sine wave, just as the applied voltage does. The current is largest at the beginning of the cycle and becomes zero at the maximum value of the voltage, so there is a phase difference of 90 degrees between the voltage and current. During the first quarter cycle the current is flowing in the

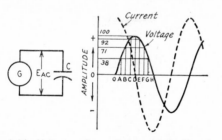

Fig. 2-26—Voltage and current phase relationships when an alternating voltage is applied to a capacitor.

normal direction through the circuit, since the capacitor is being charged. Hence the current is positive, as indicated by the dashed line in Fig. 2-26.

In the second quarter cycle — that is, in the time from D to H, the voltage applied to the capacitor decreases. During this time the capacitor *loses* its charge. Applying the same reasoning, it is plain that the current is small in interval DE and continues to increase during each succeeding interval. However, the current is flowing *against* the applied voltage because the capacitor is discharging into the circuit. Hence the current is

negative during this quarter cycle.

The third and fourth quarter cycles repeat the events of the first and second, respectively, with this difference — the polarity of the applied voltage has reversed, and the current changes to correspond. In other words, an alternateng current flows in the circuit because of the alternate charging and discharging of the capacitance. As shown by Fig. 2-26, the current starts its cy le 90 degrees before the voltage, so the current in a capacitor leads the applied voltage by 90 degrees.

Capacitive Reactance

The quantity of electric charge that can be placed on a capacitor is proportional to the applied e.m.f. and the capacitance. This amount of charge moves back and forth in the circuit once each cycle, and so the *rate* of movement of charge — that is, the current — is proportional to voltage, capacitance and frequency. If the effects of capacitance and frequency are lumped together, they form a quantity that plays a part similar to that of resistance in Ohm's Law. This quantity is called **reactance**, and the unit for it is the ohm, just as in the case of resistance. The formula for it is

$$X_C = \frac{1}{2\pi f C}$$

where X_C = Capacitive reactance in ohms
f = Frequency in cycles per second
C = Capacitance in farads
π = 3.14

Although the unit of reactance is the ohm, there is no power dissipation in reactance. The energy stored in the capacitor in one quarter of the cycle is simply returned to the circuit in the next.

The fundamental units (cycles per second, farads) are too large for practical use in radio circuits. However, if the capacitance is in microfarads and the frequency is in megacycles, the reactance will come out in ohms in the formula.

Example: The reactance of a capacitor of 470 μμf. (0.00047 μf.) at a frequency of 7150 kc. (7.15 Mc.) is

$$X = \frac{1}{2\pi f C} = \frac{1}{6.28 \times 7.15 \times 0.00047} = 47.4 \text{ ohms}$$

Inductive Reactance

When an alternating voltage is applied to a *pure* inductance (one with no resistance — all *practical* inductors have resistance) the current is again 90 degrees out of phase with the applied voltage. However, in this case the current *lags* 90 degrees behind the voltage — the opposite of the capacitor current-voltage relationship.

The primary cause for this is the *back e.m.f.* generated in the inductance, and since the amplitude of the back e.m.f. is proportional to the rate at which the current changes, and this in turn is proportional to the frequency, the amplitude of the current is inversely proportional to the applied frequency. Also, since the back e.m.f. is proportional to inductance for a given rate of current change, the current flow is inversely proportional to inductance for a given applied voltage and frequency. (Another way of saying this is that just enough current flows to generate an induced e.m.f. that equals and opposes the applied voltage.)

The combined effect of inductance and frequency is called **inductive reactance,** also expressed in ohms, and the formula for it is

$$X_L = 2\pi f L$$

where X_L = Inductive reactance in ohms
f = Frequency in cycles per second
L = Inductance in henrys
π = 3.14

Example: The reactance of a coil having an inductance of 8 henrys, at a frequency of 120 cycles, is
$X_L = 2\pi f L = 6.28 \times 120 \times 8 = 6029$ ohms

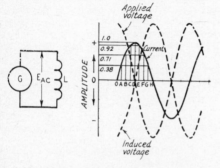

Fig. 2-27 — Phase relationships between voltage and current when an alternating voltage is applied to an inductance.

In radio-frequency circuits the inductance values usually are small and the frequencies are large. If the inductance is expressed in millihenrys and the frequency in kilocycles, the conversion factors for the two units cancel, and the formula for reactance may be used without first converting to fundamental units. Similarly, no conversion is necessary if the inductance is in microhenrys and the frequency is in megacycles.

Example: The reactance of a 15-microhenry coil at a frequency of 14 Mc. is
$X_L = 2\pi f L = 6.28 \times 14 \times 15 = 1319$ ohms

The resistance of the wire of which the coil is wound has no effect on the reactance, but simply acts as though it were a separate resistor connected in series with the coil.

Ohm's Law for Reactance

Ohm's Law for an a.c. circuit containing *only* reactance is

$$I = \frac{E}{X}$$

$$E = IX$$

$$X = \frac{E}{I}$$

where E = E.m.f. in volts

I = Current in amperes
X = Reactance in ohms

The reactance may be either inductive or capacitive.

Example: If a current of 2 amperes is flowing through the capacitor of the previous example (reactance = 47.4 ohms) at 7150 kc., the voltage drop across the capacitor is
$E = IX = 2 \times 47.4 = 94.8$ volts

If 400 volts at 120 cycles is applied to the 8-henry inductor of the previous example, the current through the coil will be
$I = \dfrac{E}{X} = \dfrac{400}{6029} = 0.0663$ amp. (66.3 ma.)

Reactance Chart

The accompanying chart, Fig. 2-28, shows the reactance of capacitances from 1 $\mu\mu f$. to 100 μf., and the reactance of inductances from 0.1 μh. to 10 henrys, for frequencies between 100 cycles and 100 megacycles per second. The approximate value of reactance can be read from the chart or, where more exact values are needed, the chart will serve as a check on the order of magnitude of reactances calculated from the formulas given above, and thus avoid "decimal-point errors".

Reactances in Series and Parallel

When reactances of the same kind are connected in series or parallel the resultant reactance is that of the resultant inductance or capacitance. This leads to the same rules that are used when determining the resultant resistance when resistors are combined. That is, for series reactances of the same kind the resultant reactance is

$$X = X_1 + X_2 + X_3 + X_4$$

and for reactances of the same kind in parallel the resultant is

$$X = \cfrac{1}{\dfrac{1}{X_1} + \dfrac{1}{X_2} + \dfrac{1}{X_3} + \dfrac{1}{X_4}}$$

or for two in parallel,

$$X = \frac{X_1 X_2}{X_1 + X_2}$$

The situation is different when reactances of opposite kinds are combined. Since the current in a capacitance leads the applied voltage by 90 degrees and the current in an inductance lags the applied voltage by 90 degrees, the voltages at the terminals of opposite types of reactance are 180 degrees out of phase in a series circuit (in which the current has to be the same through all elements), and the currents in reactances of opposite types are 180 degrees out of phase in a parallel circuit (in which the same voltage is applied to all elements). The 180-degree phase relationship means that the currents or voltages are of opposite polarity, so in the series circuit of Fig. 2-29A the voltage E_L across the inductive reactance X_L is of opposite polarity to the voltage E_C across the capacitive reactance X_C. Thus if we call X_L "positive" and X_C "negative" (a common convention) the applied voltage E_{AC} is $E_L - E_C$. In

Reactance

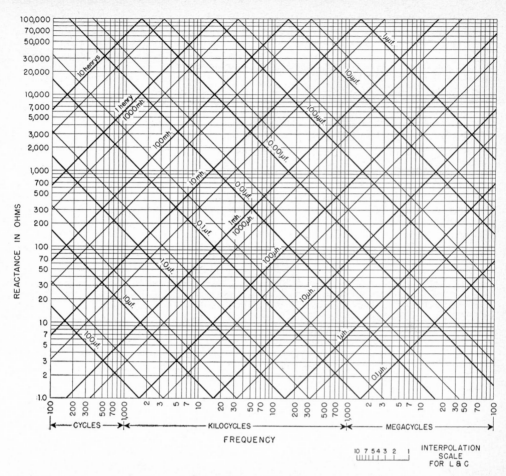

Fig. 2-28—Inductive and capacitive reactance *vs.* frequency. Heavy lines represent multiples of 10, intermediate light lines multiples of 5; e.g., the light line between 10 μh. and 100 μh. represents 50 μh., the light line between 0.1 μf. and 1 μf. represents 0.5 μf., etc. Intermediate values can be estimated with the help of the interpolation scale shown. Reactances outside the range of the chart may be found by applying appropiate factors to values within the chart range. For example, the reactance of 10 henrys at 60 cycles can be found by taking the reactance of 10 henrys at 600 cycles and dividing by 10 for the 10-times decrease in frequency.

the parallel circuit at B the total current, I, is equal to $I_L - I_C$, since the currents are 180 degrees out of phase.

In the series case, therefore, the resultant reactance of X_L and X_C is

$$X = X_L - X_C$$

and in the parallel case

$$X = \frac{-X_L X_C}{X_L - X_C}$$

Note that in the series circuit the total reactance is negative if X_C is larger than X; this indicates that the total reactance is capacitive in such a case. The resultant reactance in a series circuit is always smaller than the smaller of the two individual reactances.

In the parallel circuit, the resultant reactance is negative (i.e., capacitive) if X_L is larger than X_C, and positive (inductive) if X_L is smaller than X_C, but in every case is always larger than

the larger of the two individual reactances.

In the special case where $X_L = X_C$ the total reactance is zero in the series circuit and infinitely large in the parallel circuit.

Reactive Power

In Fig. 2-29A the voltage drop across the inductor is larger than the voltage applied to the circuit. This might seem to be an impossible condition, but it is not; the explanation is that while energy is being stored in the inductor's

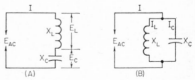

Fig. 2-29—Series and parallel circuits containing opposite kinds of reactance.

35

magnetic field, energy is being returned to the circuit from the capacitor's electric field, and vice versa. This stored energy is responsible for the fact that the voltages across reactances in series can be larger than the voltage applied to them.

In a resistance the flow of current causes heating and a power loss equal to I^2R. The power in a reactance is equal to I^2X, but is not a "loss"; it is simply power that is transferred back and forth between the field and the circuit but not used up in heating anything. To distinguish this "nondissipated" power from the power which is actually consumed, the unit of reactive power is called the **volt-ampere-reactive**, or **var**, instead of the watt. Reactive power is sometimes called "wattless" power.

● IMPEDANCE

When a circuit contains both resistance and reactance the combined effect of the two is called **impedance**, symbolized by the letter Z. (Impedance is thus a more general term than either resistance or reactance, and is frequently used even for circuits that have only resistance or reactance, although usually with a qualification — such as "resistive impedance" to indicate that the circuit has only resistance, for example.)

The reactance and resistance comprising an impedance may be connected either in series or in parallel, as shown in Fig. 2-30. In these circuits the reactance is shown as a box to indicate that it may be either inductive or capacitive. In the series circuit the current is the same in both elements, with (generally) different voltages appearing across the resistance and reactance. In the parallel circuit the same voltage is applied to both elements, but different currents flow in the two branches.

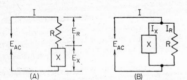

Fig. 2-30—Series and parallel circuits containing resistance and reactance.

Since in a resistance the current is in phase with the applied voltage while in a reactance it is 90 degrees out of phase with the voltage, the phase relationship between current and voltage in the circuit as a whole may be anything between zero and 90 degrees, depending on the relative amounts of resistance and reactance.

Series Circuits

When resistance and reactance are in series, the impedance of the circuit is

$$Z = \sqrt{R^2 + X^2}$$

where Z = impedance in ohms
R = resistance in ohms
X = reactance in ohms.

The reactance may be either capacitive or inductive. If there are two or more reactances in the circuit they may be combined into a resultant by the rules previously given, before substitution into the formula above; similarly for resistances.

The "square root of the sum of the squares" rule for finding impedance in a series circuit arises from the fact that the voltage drops across the resistance and reactance are 90 degrees out of phase, and so combine by the same rule that applies in finding the hypothenuse of a right-angled triangle when the base and altitude are known.

Parallel Circuits

With resistance and reactance in parallel, as in Fig. 2-30B, the impedance is

$$Z = \frac{RX}{\sqrt{R^2 + X^2}}$$

where the symbols have the same meaning as for series circuits.

Just as in the case of series circuits, a number of reactances in parallel should be combined to find the resultant reactance before substitution into the formula above; similarly for a number of resistances in parallel.

Equivalent Series and Parallel Circuits

The two circuits shown in Fig. 2-30 are equivalent if the same current flows when a given voltage of the same frequency is applied, and if the phase angle between voltage and current is the same in both cases. It is in fact possible to "transform" any given series circuit into an equivalent parallel circuit, and vice versa.

Transformations of this type often lead to simplification in the solution of complicated circuits. However, from the standpoint of practical work the usefulness of such transformations lies in the fact that the impedance of a circuit may be modified by the addition of *either* series or parallel elements, depending on which happens to be most convenient in the particular case. Typical applications are considered later in connection with tuned circuits and transmission lines.

Ohm's Law for Impedance

Ohm's Law can be applied to circuits containing impedance just as readily as to circuits having resistance or reactance only. The formulas are

$$I = \frac{E}{Z}$$
$$E = IZ$$
$$Z = \frac{E}{I}$$

where E = E.m.f. in volts
I = Current in amperes
Z = Impedance in ohms

Fig. 2-31 shows a simple circuit consisting of a resistance of 75 ohms and a reactance of 100 ohms in series. From the formula previously given, the impedance is

Impedance

$Z = \sqrt{R^2 + X_L^2} = \sqrt{(75)^2 + (100)^2} = 125$ ohms.

If the applied voltage is 250 volts, then

$$I = \frac{E}{Z} = \frac{250}{125} = 2 \text{ amperes}.$$

This current flows through both the resistance and reactance, so the voltage drops are

$$E_R = IR = 2 \times 75 = 150 \text{ volts}$$
$$E_{XL} = IX_L = 2 \times 100 = 200 \text{ volts}$$

The simple arithmetical sum of these two drops, 350 volts, is greater than the applied voltage because the two voltages are 90 degrees out of phase. Their actual resultant, when phase is taken into account, is $\sqrt{(150)^2 + (200)^2} = 250$ volts.

Power Factor

In the circuit of Fig. 2-31 an applied e.m.f. of 250 volts results in a current of 2 amperes, giving an apparent power of $250 \times 2 = 500$ watts. However, only the resistance actually consumes power. The power in the resistance is

$$P = I^2R = (2)^2 \times 75 = 300 \text{ watts}$$

The ratio of the power consumed to the apparent power is called the **power factor** of the circuit, and in this example the power factor would be $300/500 = 0.6$. Power factor is frequently expressed as a percentage; in this case, it would be 60 per cent.

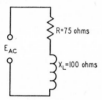

Fig. 2-31—Circuit used as an example for impedance calculations.

"Real" or dissipated power is measured in watts; apparent power, to distinguish it from real power, is measured in volt-amperes (just like the "wattless" power in a reactance). It is simply the product of volts and amperes and has no direct relationship to the power actually used up or dissipated unless the power factor of the circuit is known. The power factor of a purely resistive circuit is 100 per cent or 1, while the power factor of a pure reactance is zero. In this illustration, the reactive power is

$$VA \text{ (volt-amperes)} = I^2X = (2)^2 \times 100$$
$$= 400 \text{ volt-amperes}.$$

Reactance and Complex Waves

It was pointed out earlier in this chapter that a complex wave (a "nonsinusoidal" wave) can be resolved into a fundamental frequency and a series of harmonic frequencies. When such a complex voltage wave is applied to a circuit containing reactance, the current through the circuit will not have the same wave shape as the applied voltage. This is because the reactance of an inductor and capacitor depend upon the applied frequency. For the second-harmonic component of a complex wave, the reactance of the inductor is twice and the reactance of the capacitor one-half their respective values at the fundamental frequency; for the third harmonic the inductor reactance is three times and the capacitor reactance one-third, and so on. Thus the circuit impedance is different for each harmonic component.

Just what happens to the current wave shape depends upon the values of resistance and reactance involved and how the circuit is arranged. In a simple circuit with resistance and inductive reactance in series, the amplitudes of the harmonic currents will be reduced because the inductive reactance increases in proportion to frequency. When capacitance and resistance are in series, the harmonic current is likely to be accentuated because the capacitive reactance becomes lower as the frequency is raised. When both inductive and capacitive reactance are present the shape of the current wave can be altered in a variety of ways, depending upon the circuit and the "constants," or the relative values of L, C, and R, selected.

This property of nonuniform behavior with respect to fundamental and harmonics is an extremely useful one. It is the basis of "filtering," or the suppression of undesired frequencies in favor of a single desired frequency or group of such frequencies.

Transformers

Two coils having mutual inductance constitute a **transformer**. The coil connected to the source of energy is called the **primary** coil, and the other is called the **secondary** coil.

The usefulness of the transformer lies in the fact that electrical energy can be transferred from one circuit to another without direct connection, and in the process can be readily changed from one voltage level to another. Thus, if a device to be operated requires, for example, 115 volts a.c. and only a 440-volt source is available, a transformer can be used to change the source voltage to that required. A transformer can be used only with a.c., since no voltage will be in-

duced in the secondary if the magnetic field is not changing. If d.c. is applied to the primary of a transformer, a voltage will be induced in the secondary only at the instant of closing or opening the primary circuit, since it is only at these times that the field is changing.

● **THE IRON-CORE TRANSFORMER**

As shown in Fig. 2-32, the primary and secondary coils of a transformer may be wound on a core of magnetic material. This increases the inductance of the coils so that a relatively small number of turns may be used to induce a given value of voltage with a small current. A **closed core** (one

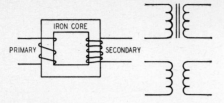

Fig. 2-32—The transformer. Power is transferred from the primary coil to the secondary by means of the magnetic field. The upper symbol at right indicates an iron-core transformer, the lower one an air-core transformer.

having a continuous magnetic path) such as that shown in Fig. 2-32 also tends to insure that practically all of the field set up by the current in the primary coil will cut the turns of the secondary coil. However, the core introduces a power loss because of hysteresis and eddy currents so this type of construction is practicable only at power and audio frequencies. The discussion in this section is confined to transformers operating at such frequencies.

Voltage and Turns Ratio

For a given varying magnetic field, the voltage induced in a coil in the field will be proportional to the number of turns in the coil. If the two coils of a transformer are in the same field (which is the case when both are wound on the same closed core) it follows that the induced voltages will be proportional to the number of turns in each coil. In the primary the induced voltage is practically equal to, and opposes, the applied voltage, as described earlier. Hence,

$$E_s = \frac{n_s}{n_p} E_p$$

where E_s = Secondary voltage
E_p = Primary applied voltage
n_s = Number of turns on secondary
n_p = Number of turns on primary

The ratio n_s/n_p is called the secondary-to-primary **turns ratio** of the transformer.

Example: A transformer has a primary of 400 turns and a secondary of 2800 turns, and an e.m.f. of 115 volts is applied to the primary. The secondary voltage will be

$$E_s = \frac{n_s}{n_p} E_p = \frac{2800}{400} \times 115 = 7 \times 115$$
$$= 805 \text{ volts}$$

Also, if an e.m.f. of 805 volts is applied to the 2800-turn winding (which then becomes the primary) the output voltage from the 400-turn winding will be 115 volts.
Either winding of a transformer can be used as the primary, providing the winding has enough turns (enough inductance) to induce a voltage equal to the applied voltage without requiring an excessive current flow.

Effect of Secondary Current

The current that flows in the primary when no current is taken from the secondary is called the **magnetizing current** of the transformer. In any properly-designed transformer the primary inductance will be so large that the magnetizing

current will be quite small. The power consumed by the transformer when the secondary is "open" — that is, not delivering power — is only the amount necessary to supply the losses in the iron core and in the resistance of the wire with which the primary is wound.

When power is taken from the secondary winding, the secondary current sets up a magnetic field that opposes the field set up by the primary current. But if the induced voltage in the primary is to equal the applied voltage, the original field must be maintained. Consequently, the primary must draw enough additional current to set up a field exactly equal and opposite to the field set up by the secondary current.

In practical calculations on transformers it may be assumed that the entire primary current is caused by the secondary "load." This is justifiable because the magnetizing current should be very small in comparison with the primary "load" current at rated power output.

If the magnetic fields set up by the primary and secondary currents are to be equal, the primary current multiplied by the primary turns must equal the secondary current multiplied by the secondary turns. From this it follows that

$$I_p = \frac{n_s}{n_p} I_s$$

where I_p = Primary current
I_s = Secondary current
n_p = Number of turns on primary
n_s = Number of turns on secondary

Example: Suppose that the secondary of the transformer in the previous example is delivering a current of 0.2 ampere to a load. Then the primary current will be

$$I_p = \frac{n_s}{n_p} I_s = \frac{2800}{400} \times 0.2 = 7 \times 0.2 = 1.4 \text{ amp.}$$

Although the secondary voltage is higher than the primary voltage, the secondary *current* is *lower* than the primary current, and by the same ratio.

Power Relationships; Efficiency

A transformer cannot create power; it can only transfer it and change the e.m.f. Hence, the power taken from the secondary cannot exceed that taken by the primary from the source of applied e.m.f. There is always some power loss in the resistance of the coils and in the iron core, so in all practical cases the power taken from the source will exceed that taken from the secondary. Thus,

$$P_o = nP_i$$

where P_o = Power output from secondary
P_i = Power input to primary
n = Efficiency factor

The efficiency, n, always is less than 1. It is usually expressed as a percentage; if n is 0.65, for instance, the efficiency is 65 per cent.

Example: A transformer has an efficiency of 85% at its full-load output of 150 watts. The power input to the primary at full secondary load will be

$$P_i = \frac{P_o}{n} = \frac{150}{0.85} = 176.5 \text{ watts}$$

Transformers

A transformer is usually designed to have its highest efficiency at the power output for which it is rated. The efficiency decreases with either lower or higher outputs. On the other hand, the *losses* in the transformer are relatively small at low output but increase as more power is taken. The amount of power that the transformer can handle is determined by its own losses, because these heat the wire and core. There is a limit to the temperature rise that can be tolerated, because too-high temperature either will melt the wire or cause the insulation to break down. A transformer always can be operated at reduced output, even though the efficiency is low, because the actual loss also will be low under such conditions.

The full-load efficiency of small power transformers such as are used in radio receivers and transmitters usually lies between about 60 per cent and 90 per cent, depending upon the size and design.

Leakage Reactance

In a practical transformer not all of the magnetic flux is common to both windings, although in well-designed transformers the amount of flux that "cuts" one coil and not the other is only a small percentage of the total flux. This **leakage flux** causes an e.m.f. of self-induction; consequently, there are small amounts of **leakage inductance** associated with both windings of the transformer. Leakage inductance acts in exactly the same way as an equivalent amount of ordinary inductance inserted in series with the circuit.

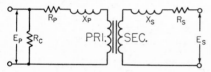

Fig. 2-33—The equivalent circuit of a transformer includes the effects of leakage inductance and resistance of both primary and secondary windings. The resistance R_C is an equivalent resistance representing the core losses, which are essentially constant for any given applied voltage and frequency. Since these are comparatively small, their effect may be neglected in many approximate calculations.

It has, therefore, a certain reactance, depending upon the amount of leakage inductance and the frequency. This reactance is called **leakage reactance**.

Current flowing through the leakage reactance causes a voltage drop. This voltage drop increases with increasing current, hence it increases as more power is taken from the secondary. Thus, the greater the secondary current, the smaller the secondary terminal voltage becomes. The resistances of the transformer windings also cause voltage drops when current is flowing; although these voltage drops are not in phase with those caused by leakage reactance, together they result in a lower secondary voltage under load than is indicated by the turns ratio of the transformer.

At power frequencies (60 cycles) the voltage at the secondary, with a reasonably well-designed transformer, should not drop more than about 10 per cent from open-circuit conditions to full load. The drop in voltage may be considerably more than this in a transformer operating at audio frequencies because the leakage reactance increases directly with the frequency.

Impedance Ratio

In an ideal transformer — one without losses or leakage reactance — the following relationship is true:

$$Z_p = Z_s N^2$$

where Z_p = Impedance looking into primary terminals from source of power

Z_s = Impedance of load connected to secondary

N = Turns ratio, primary to secondary

That is, a load of any given impedance connected to the secondary of the transformer will be transformed to a different value "looking into" the primary from the source of power. The impedance transformation is proportional to the square of the primary-to-secondary turns ratio.

Example: A transformer has a primary-to-secondary turns ratio of 0.6 (primary has 6/10 as many turns as the secondary) and a load of 3000 ohms is connected to the secondary. The impedance looking into the primary then will be

$$Z_p = Z_s N^2 = 3000 \times (0.6)^2 = 3000 \times 0.36 = 1080 \text{ ohms}$$

By choosing the proper turns ratio, the impedance of a fixed load can be transformed to any desired value, within practical limits. The transformed or "reflected" impedance has the same phase angle as the actual load impedance; thus if the load is a pure resistance the load presented by the primary to the source of power also will be a pure resistance.

The above relationship may be used in practical work even though it is based on an "ideal" transformer. Aside from the normal design requirements of reasonably low internal losses and low leakage reactance, the only requirement is that the primary have enough inductance to operate with low magnetizing current at the voltage applied to the primary.

The primary impedance of a transformer — *as it appears to the source of power* — is determined wholly by the load connected to the secondary and by the turns ratio. If the characteristics of the transformer have an appreciable effect on the impedance presented to the power source, the transformer is either poorly designed or is not suited to the voltage and frequency at which it is being used. Most transformers will operate quite well at voltages from slightly above to well below the design figure.

Impedance Matching

Many devices require a specific value of load resistance (or impedance) for optimum operation. The impedance of the actual load that is to dissipate the power may differ widely from this value, so a transformer is used to change the actual load into an impedance of the desired value. This is called **impedance matching**. From the preceding,

$$N = \sqrt{\frac{Z_p}{Z_s}}$$

where N = Required turns ratio, primary to secondary

Z_p = Primary impedance required

Z_s = Impedance of load connected to secondary

Example: A vacuum-tube a.f. amplifier requires a load of 5000 ohms for optimum performance, and is to be connected to a loudspeaker having an impedance of 10 ohms. The turns ratio, primary to secondary, required in the coupling transformer is

$$N = \sqrt{\frac{Z_p}{Z_s}} = \sqrt{\frac{5000}{10}} = \sqrt{500} = 22.4$$

The primary therefore must have 22.4 times as many turns as the secondary.

Impedance matching means, in general, adjusting the load impedance — by means of a transformer or otherwise — to a desired value. However, there is also another meaning. It is possible to show that any source of power will deliver its maximum possible output when the impedance of the load is equal to the internal impedance of the source. The impedance of the source is said to be "matched" under this condition. The efficiency is only 50 per cent in such a case; just as much power is used up in the source as is delivered to the load. Because of the poor efficiency, this type of impedance matching is limited to cases where only a small amount of power is available and heating from power loss in the source is not important.

Transformer Construction

Transformers usually are designed so that the magnetic path around the core is as short as possible. A short magnetic path means that the transformer will operate with fewer turns, for a given applied voltage, than if the path were long.

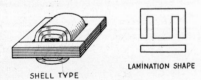

SHELL TYPE   LAMINATION SHAPE

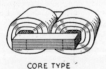

CORE TYPE

Fig. 2-34—Two common types of transformer construction. Core pieces are interleaved to provide a continuous magnetic path.

A short path also helps to reduce flux leakage and therefore minimizes leakage reactance.

Two core shapes are in common use, as shown in Fig. 2-34. In the shell type both windings are placed on the inner leg, while in the core type the primary and secondary windings may be placed on separate legs, if desired. This is sometimes done when it is necessary to minimize capacitive effects between the primary and secondary, or when one of the windings must operate at very high voltage.

Core material for small transformers is usually silicon steel, called "transformer iron." The core is built up of laminations, insulated from each other (by a thin coating of shellac, for example) to prevent the flow of eddy currents. The laminations are interleaved at the ends to make the magnetic path as continuous as possible and thus reduce flux leakage.

The number of turns required in the primary for a given applied e.m.f. is determined by the size, shape and type of core material used, and the frequency. The number of turns required is inversely proportional to the cross-sectional area of the core. As a rough indication, windings of small power transformers frequently have about six to eight turns per volt on a core of 1-square-inch cross section and have a magnetic path 10 or 12 inches in length. A longer path or smaller cross section requires more turns per volt, and vice versa.

In most transformers the coils are wound in layers, with a thin sheet of treated-paper insulation between each layer. Thicker insulation is used between coils and between coils and core.

Autotransformers

The transformer principle can be utilized with only one winding instead of two, as shown in Fig. 2-35; the principles just discussed apply

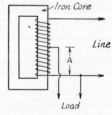

Fig. 2-35—The autotransformer is based on the transformer principle, but uses only one winding. The line and load currents in the common winding (A) flow in opposite directions, so that the resultant current is the difference between them. The voltage across A is proportional to the turns ratio.

equally well. A one-winding transformer is called an **autotransformer**. The current in the common section (A) of the winding is the difference between the line (primary) and the load (secondary) currents, since these currents are out of phase. Hence if the line and load currents are nearly equal the common section of the winding may be wound with comparatively small wire. This will be the case only when the primary (line) and secondary (load) voltages are not very different. The autotransformer is used chiefly for boosting or reducing the power-line voltage by relatively small amounts.

The Decibel

In most radio communication the received signal is converted into sound. This being the case, it is useful to appraise signal strengths in terms of relative loudness as registered by the ear. A peculiarity of the ear is that an increase or decrease in loudness is responsive to the *ratio* of the amounts of power involved, and is practically independent of absolute value of the power. For example, if a person estimates that the signal is "twice as loud" when the transmitter power is increased from 10 watts to 40 watts, he will also estimate that a 400-watt signal is twice as loud as a 100-watt signal. In other words, the human ear has a *logarithmic* response.

This fact is the basis for the use of the relative-power unit called the **decibel** (abbreviated **db.**) A change of one decibel in the power level is just detectable as a change in loudness under ideal conditions. The number of decibels corresponding to a given power ratio is given by the following formula:

$$Db. = 10 \log \frac{P_2}{P_1}$$

Common logarithms (base 10) are used.

Voltage and Current Ratios

Note that the decibel is based on *power* ratios. Voltage or current ratios can be used, but only when the impedance is the same for both values of voltage, or current. The gain of an amplifier cannot be expressed correctly in db. if it is based on the ratio of the output voltage to the input voltage unless both voltages are measured across the same value of impedance. When the impedance at both points of measurement is the same, the following formula may be used for voltage or current ratios:

$$Db. = 20 \log \frac{V_2}{V_1}$$

$$\text{or } 20 \log \frac{I_2}{I_1}$$

Decibel Chart

The two formulas are shown graphically in Fig. 2-36 for ratios from 1 to 10. Gains (increases) expressed in decibels may be added arithmetically; losses (decreases) may be subtracted. A power decrease is indicated by prefixing the decibel figure with a minus sign. Thus +6 db. means that the power has been multiplied by 4, while −6 db. means that the power has been divided by 4.

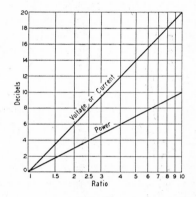

Fig. 2-36—Decibel chart for power, voltage and current ratios for power ratios of 1:1 to 10:1. In determining decibels for current or voltage ratios the currents (or voltages) being compared must be referred to the same value of impedance.

The chart may be used for other ratios by adding (or subtracting, if a loss) 10 db. each time the ratio scale is multiplied by 10, for power ratios; or by adding (or subtracting) 20 db. each time the scale is multiplied by 10 for voltage or current ratios. For example, a power ratio of 2.5 is 4 db. (from the chart). A power ratio of 10 times 2.5, or 25, is 14 db. (10 + 4), and a power ratio of 100 times 2.5, or 250, is 24 db. (20 + 4). A voltage or current ratio of 4 is 12 db., a voltage or current ratio of 40 is 32 db. (20 + 12), and a voltage or current ratio of 400 is 52 db. (40 + 12).

Radio-Frequency Circuits

● RESONANCE IN SERIES CIRCUITS

Fig. 2-37 shows a resistor, capacitor and inductor connected in series with a source of alternating current, the frequency of which can be varied over a wide range. At some *low* frequency the capacitive reactance will be much larger than the resistance of R, and the inductive reactance will be small compared with either the reactance of C or the resistance of R. (R is assumed to be the same at all frequencies.) On the other hand, at some very *high* frequency the reactance of C will be very small and the reactance of L will be very large. In either of these cases the current will be small, because the reactance is large at either low or high frequencies.

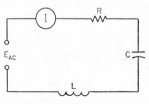

Fig. 2-37—A series circuit containing L, C and R is "resonant" at the applied frequency when the reactance of C is equal to the reactance of L.

41

At some intermediate frequency, the reactances of C and L will be equal and the voltage drops across the coil and capacitor will be equal and 180 degrees out of phase. Therefore they cancel each other completely and the current flow is determined wholly by the resistance, R. At that frequency the current has its largest possible value, assuming the source voltage to be constant regardless of frequency. A series circuit in which the inductive and capacitive reactances are equal is said to be **resonant**.

Although resonance is possible at any frequency, it finds its most extensive application in radio-frequency circuits. The reactive effects associated with even small inductances and capacitances would place drastic limitations on r.f. circuit operation if it were not possible to "cancel them out" by supplying the right amount of reactance of the opposite kind — in other words, "tuning the circuit to resonance."

Resonant Frequency

The frequency at which a series circuit is resonant is that for which $X_L = X_C$. Substituting the formulas for inductive and capacitive reactance gives

$$f = \frac{1}{2\pi\sqrt{LC}}$$

where f = Frequency in cycles per second
L = Inductance in henrys
C = Capacitance in farads
π = 3.14

These units are inconveniently large for radio-frequency circuits. A formula using more appropriate units is

$$f = \frac{10^6}{2\pi\sqrt{LC}}$$

where f = Frequency in kilocycles (kc.)
L = Inductance in microhenrys (μh.)
C = Capacitance in micromicrofarads ($\mu\mu$f.)
π = 3.14

Example: The resonant frequency of a series circuit containing a 5-μh. inductor and a 35-$\mu\mu$f. capacitor is

$$= \frac{10^6}{2\pi\sqrt{LC}} = \frac{10^6}{6.28 \times \sqrt{5 \times 35}}$$
$$= \frac{10^6}{6.28 \times 13.2} = \frac{10^6}{83} = 12{,}050 \text{ kc.}$$

The formula for resonant frequency is **not** affected by the resistance in the circuit.

Resonance Curves

If a plot is drawn of the current flowing in the circuit of Fig. 2-37 as the frequency is varied (the applied voltage being constant) it would look like one of the curves in Fig. 2-38. The shape of the **resonance curve** at frequencies near resonance is determined by the ratio of reactance to resistance.

If the reactance of either the coil or capacitor is of the same order of magnitude as the resistance,

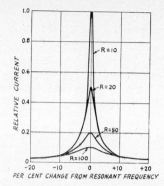

Fig. 2-38—Current in a series-resonant circuit with various values of series resistance. The values are arbitrary and would not apply to all circuits, but represent a typical case. It is assumed that the reactances (at the resonant frequency) are 1000 ohms. Note that at frequencies more than plus or minus ten per cent away from the resonant frequency the current is substantially unaffected by the resistance in the circuit.

the current decreases rather slowly as the frequency is moved in either direction away from resonance. Such a curve is said to be **broad**. On the other hand, if the reactance is considerably larger than the resistance the current decreases rapidly as the frequency moves away from resonance and the circuit is said to be **sharp**. A sharp circuit will respond a great deal more readily to the resonant frequency than to frequencies quite close to resonance; a broad circuit will respond almost equally well to a group or band of frequencies centering around the resonant frequency.

Both types of resonance curves are useful. A sharp circuit gives good **selectivity** — the ability to respond strongly (in terms of current amplitude) at one desired frequency and discriminate against others. A broad circuit is used when the apparatus must give about the same response over a band of frequencies rather than to a single frequency alone.

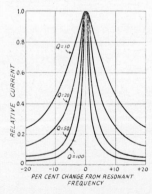

Fig. 2-39—Current in series-resonant circuits having different Qs. In this graph the current at resonance is assumed to be the same in all cases. The lower the Q, the more slowly the current decreases as the applied frequency is moved away from resonance.

Radio-Frequency Circuits

Q

Most diagrams of resonant circuits show only inductance and capacitance; no resistance is indicated. Nevertheless, resistance is always present. At frequencies up to perhaps 30 Mc. this resistance is mostly in the wire of the coil. Above this frequency energy loss in the capacitor (principally in the solid dielectric which must be used to form an insulating support for the capacitor plates) becomes appreciable. This energy loss is equivalent to resistance. When maximum sharpness or selectivity is needed the object of design is to reduce the inherent resistance to the lowest possible value.

The value of the reactance of either the inductor or capacitor at the resonant frequency of a series-resonant circuit, divided by the resistance in the circuit, is called the Q (quality factor) of the circuit, or

$$Q = \frac{X}{R}$$

where Q = Quality factor
X = Reactance of either coil or condenser, in ohms
R = Series resistance in ohms

Example: The inductor and capacitor in a series circuit each have a reactance of 350 ohms at the resonant frequency. The resistance is 5 ohms. Then the Q is

$$Q = \frac{X}{R} = \frac{350}{5} = 70$$

The effect of Q on the sharpness of resonance of a circuit is shown by the curves of Fig. 2-39. In these curves the frequency change is shown in percentage above and below the resonant frequency. Qs of 10, 20, 50 and 100 are shown; these values cover much of the range commonly used in radio work.

Voltage Rise

When a voltage of the resonant frequency is inserted in series in a resonant circuit, the voltage that appears across either the inductor or capacitor is considerably higher than the applied voltage. The current in the circuit is limited only by the resistance and may have a relatively high value; however, the same current flows through the high reactances of the inductor and capacitor and causes large voltage drops. The ratio of the reactive voltage to the applied voltage is equal to the ratio of reactance to resistance. This ratio is also the Q of the circuit. Therefore, the voltage across either the inductor or capacitor is equal to Q times the voltage inserted in series with the circuit.

Example: The inductive reactance of a circuit is 200 ohms, the capacitive reactance is 200 ohms, the resistance 5 ohms, and the applied voltage is 50. The two reactances cancel and there will be but 5 ohms of pure resistance to limit the current flow. Thus the current will be 50/5, or 10 amperes. The voltage developed across either the inductor or the capacitor will be equal to its reactance times the current, or 200 × 10 = 2000 volts. An alternate method: The Q of the circuit is $X/R = 200/5 = 40$. The reactive voltage is equal to Q times the applied voltage, or 40 × 50 = 2000 volts.

● RESONANCE IN PARALLEL CIRCUITS

When a variable-frequency source of constant voltage is applied to a parallel circuit of the type shown in Fig. 2-40 there is a resonance effect similar to that in a series circuit. However, in this case the "line" current (measured at the point indicated) is *smallest* at the frequency for which the inductive and capacitive reactances are equal. At that frequency the current through L is exactly canceled by the out-of-phase current through C, so that only the current taken by R flows in the line. At frequencies *below* resonance the current through L is larger than that through C, because the reactance of L is smaller and that of C higher at low frequencies; there is only partial cancellation of the two reactive currents and the line current therefore is larger than the current taken by R alone. At frequencies *above* resonance the situation is reversed and more current flows through C than through L, so the line current again increases. The current at resonance, being determined wholly by R, will be small if R is large and large if R is small.

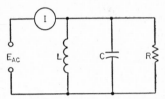

Fig. 2-40—Circuit illustrating parallel resonance.

The resistance R shown in Fig. 2-40 is not necessarily an actual resistor. In most cases it will be an "equivalent" resistance that represents the energy loss in the circuit. This loss can be inherent in the coil or capacitor, or may represent energy transferred to a load by means of the resonant circuit. (For example, the resonant circuit may be used for transferring power from a vacuum-tube amplifier to an antenna system.)

Parallel and series resonant circuits are quite alike in some respects. For instance, the circuits given at A and B in Fig. 2-41 will behave identically, when an external voltage is applied, if (1) L and C are the same in both cases; and (2) R_p multiplied by R_s equals the square of the reactance (at resonance) of either L or C. When these conditions are met the two circuits will have the

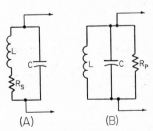

(A)   (B)

Fig. 2-41—Series and parallel equivalents when the two circuits are resonant. The series resistor, R_s, in A can be replaced by an equivalent parallel resistor, R_p, in B, and vice versa.

same Qs. (These statements are approximate, but are quite accurate if the Q is 10 or more.) The circuit at A is a *series* circuit if it is viewed from the "inside" — that is, going around the loop formed by L, C and R — so its Q can be found from the ratio of X to R_s.

Thus a circuit like that of Fig. 2-41A has an equivalent **parallel impedance** (at resonance) equal to R_p, the relationship between R_s and R_p being as explained above. Although R_p is not an actual resistor, to the source of voltage the parallel-resonant circuit "looks like" a pure resistance of that value. It is "pure" resistance because the inductive and capacitive currents are 180 degrees out of phase and are equal; thus there is no reactive current in the line. In a practical circuit with a high-Q capacitor, at the resonant frequency the parallel impedance is

$$Z_r = QX$$

where Z_r = Resistive impedance at resonance
  Q = Quality factor of inductor
  X = Reactance (in ohms) of either the inductor or capacitor

Example: The parallel impedance of a circuit with a coil Q of 50 and having inductive and capacitive reactances of 300 ohms will be
  $Z_r = QX = 50 \times 300 = 15{,}000$ ohms.

At frequencies off resonance the impedance is no longer purely resistive because the inductive and capacitive currents are not equal. The off-resonant impedance therefore is complex, and is lower than the resonant impedance for the reasons previously outlined.

The higher the Q of the circuit, the higher the parallel impedance. Curves showing the variation of impedance (with frequency) of a parallel circuit have just the same shape as the curves showing the variation of current with frequency in a series circuit. Fig. 2-42 is a set of such curves.

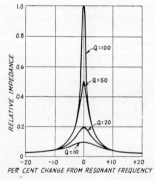

Fig. 2-42—Relative impedance of parallel-resonant circuits with different Qs. These curves are similar to those in Fig. 2-42 for current in a series-resonant circuit. The effect of Q on impedance is most marked near the resonant frequency.

Parallel Resonance in Low-Q Circuits

The preceding discussion is accurate only for Qs of 10 or more. When the Q is below 10, resonance in a parallel circuit having resistance in series with the coil, as in Fig. 2-41A, is not so easily defined. There is a set of values for L and C that will make the parallel impedance a pure resistance, but with these values the impedance does not have its maximum possible value. Another set of values for L and C will make the parallel impedance a maximum, but this maximum value is not a pure resistance. Either condition could be called "resonance," so with low-Q circuits it is necessary to distinguish between **maximum impedance** and **resistive impedance** parallel resonance. The difference between these L and C values and the equal reactances of a series-resonant circuit is appreciable when the Q is in the vicinity of 5, and becomes more marked with still lower Q values.

Q of Loaded Circuits

In many applications of resonant circuits the only power lost is that dissipated in the resistance of the circuit itself. At frequencies below 30 Mc. most of this resistance is in the coil. Within limits, increasing the number of turns in the coil increases the reactance faster than it raises the resistance, so coils for circuits in which the Q must be high may have reactances of 1000 ohms or more at the frequency under consideration.

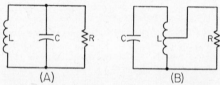

Fig. 2-43—The equivalent circuit of a resonant circuit delivering power to a load. The resistor R represents the load resistance. At B the load is tapped across part of L, which by transformer action is equivalent to using a higher load resistance across the whole circuit.

However, when the circuit delivers energy to a load (as in the case of the resonant circuits used in transmitters) the energy consumed in the circuit itself is usually negligible compared with that consumed by the load. The equivalent of such a circuit is shown in Fig. 2-43A, where the parallel resistor represents the load to which power is delivered. If the power dissipated in the load is at least ten times as great as the power lost in the inductor and capacitor, the parallel impedance of the resonant circuit itself will be so high compared with the resistance of the load that for all practical purposes the impedance of the combined circuit is equal to the load resistance. Under these conditions the Q of a parallel-resonant circuit loaded by a resistive impedance is

$$Q = \frac{R}{X}$$

where Q = Quality factor
  R = Parallel load resistance (ohms)
  X = Reactance (ohms) of either the inductor or capacitor

Example: A resistive load of 3000 ohms is connected across a resonant circuit in which the inductive and capacitive reactances are each 250 ohms. The circuit Q is then

$$Q = \frac{R}{X} = \frac{3000}{250} = 12$$

The "effective" Q of a circuit loaded by a parallel resistance becomes higher when the reactances are decreased. A circuit loaded with a relatively low resistance (a few thousand ohms) must have low-reactance elements (large capacitance and small inductance) to have reasonably high Q.

Impedance Transformation

An important application of the parallel-resonant circuit is as an impedance-matching device in the output circuit of a vacuum-tube r.f. power amplifier. As described in the section on vacuum tubes, there is an optimum value of load resistance for each type of tube and set of operating conditions. However, the resistance of the load to which the tube is to deliver power usually is considerably lower than the value required for proper tube operation. To transform the actual load resistance to the desired value the load may be tapped across part of the coil, as shown in Fig. 2-43B. This is equivalent to connecting a higher value of load resistance across the whole circuit, and is similar in principle to impedance transformation with an iron-core transformer. In high-frequency resonant circuits the impedance ratio does not vary exactly as the square of the turns ratio, because all the magnetic flux lines do not cut every turn of the coil. A desired reflected impedance usually must be obtained by experimental adjustment.

When the load resistance has a very low value (say below 100 ohms) it may be connected in series in the resonant circuit (as in Fig. 2-31A, for example), in which case it is transformed to an equivalent parallel impedance as previously described. If the Q is at least 10, the equivalent parallel impedance is

$$Z_r = \frac{X^2}{R}$$

where Z_r = Resistive parallel impedance at resonance

X = Reactance (in ohms) of either the coil or capacitor

R = Load resistance inserted in series

If the Q is lower than 10 the reactance will have to be adjusted somewhat, for the reasons given in the discussion of low-Q circuits, to obtain a resistive impedance of the desired value.

Reactance Values

The charts of Figs. 2-44 and 2-45 show reactance values of inductances and capacitances in the range commonly used in r.f. tuned circuits for the amateur bands. With the exception of the 3.5-4 Mc. band, limiting values for which are shown on the charts, the change in reactance over a band, for either inductors or capacitors, is small enough so that a single curve gives the reactance with sufficient accuracy for most practical purposes.

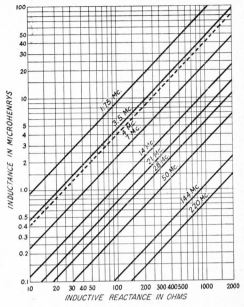

Fig. 2-44—Reactance chart for inductance values commonly used in amateur bands from 1.75 to 220 Mc.

L/C Ratio

The formula for resonant frequency of a circuit shows that the same frequency always will be obtained so long as the *product* of L and C is constant. Within this limitation, it is evident that L can be large and C small, L small and C large, etc. The relation between the two for a fixed frequency is called the **L/C ratio**. A high-C circuit

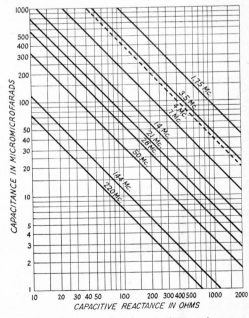

Fig. 2-45—Reactance chart for capacitance values commonly used in amateur bands from 1.75 to 220 Mc.

is one that has more capacitance than "normal" for the frequency; a **low-C** circuit one that has less than normal capacitance. These terms depend to a considerable extent upon the particular application considered, and have no exact numerical meaning.

LC Constants

It is frequently convenient to use the numerical value of the **LC constant** when a number of calculations have to be made involving different L/C ratios for the same frequency. The constant for any frequency is given by the following equation:

$$LC = \frac{25,330}{f^2}$$

where L = Inductance in microhenrys (μh.)

C = Capacitance in micromicrofarads ($\mu\mu$f.)

f = Frequency in megacycles

Example: Find the inductance required to resonate at 3650 kc. (3.65 Mc.) with capacitances of 25, 50, 100, and 500 $\mu\mu$f. The LC constant is

$$LC = \frac{25,330}{(3.65)^2} = \frac{25,330}{13.35} = 1900$$

With   25 $\mu\mu$f. $L = 1900/C = 1900/25$
     = 76 μh.
     50 $\mu\mu$f. $L = 1900/C = 1900/50$
     = 38 μh.
    100 $\mu\mu$f. $L = 1900/C = 1900/100$
     = 19 μh.
    500 $\mu\mu$f. $L = 1900/C = 1900/500$
     = 3.8 μh.

● COUPLED CIRCUITS

Energy Transfer and Loading

Two circuits are **coupled** when energy can be transferred from one to the other. The circuit delivering power is called the **primary** circuit; the one receiving power is called the **secondary** circuit. The power may be practically all dissipated in the secondary circuit itself (this is usually the case in receiver circuits) or the secondary may simply act as a medium through which the power is transferred to a load. In the latter case, the coupled circuits may act as a radio-frequency impedance-matching device. The matching can be accomplished by adjusting the loading on the secondary and by varying the amount of coupling between the primary and secondary.

Coupling by a Common Circuit Element

One method of coupling between two resonant circuits is through a circuit element common to both. The three common variations of this type of coupling are shown in Fig. 2-46; the circuit element common to both circuits carries the subscript M. At A and B current circulating in L_1C_1 flows through the common element, and the voltage developed across this element causes current to flow in L_2C_2. At C, C_M and C_2 form a capacitive voltage divider across L_1C_1, and some of the voltage developed across L_1C_1 is applied across L_2C_2.

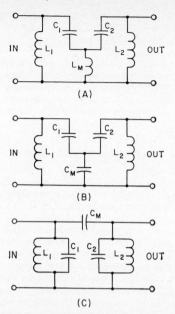

Fig. 2-46—Three methods of circuit coupling.

If both circuits are resonant to the same frequency, as is usually the case, the value of coupling reactance required for maximum energy transfer can be approximated by the following, based on $L_1 = L_2$, $C_1 = C_2$ and $Q_1 = Q_2$: (A) $L_M \approx L_1/Q_1$; (B) $C_M \approx Q_1C_1$; (C) $C_M \approx C_1/Q_1$.

The coupling can be increased by increasing the above coupling elements in A and C and decreasing the value in B. When the coupling is increased, the resultant bandwidth of the combination is increased, and this principle is sometimes applied to "broad-band" the circuits in a transmitter or receiver. When the coupling elements in A and C are decreased, or when the coupling element in B is increased, the coupling between the circuits is decreased below the *critical coupling* value on which the above approximations are based. Less than critical coupling will decrease the bandwidth and the energy transfer; the principle is often used in receivers to improve the selectivity.

Inductive Coupling

Figs. 2-47 and 2-48 show inductive coupling, or coupling by means of the mutual inductance between two coils. Circuits of this type resemble the iron-core transformer, but because only a part of

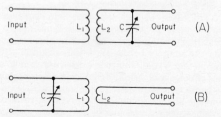

Fig. 2-47—Single-tuned inductively coupled circuits.

Coupled Circuits

the magnetic flux lines set up by one coil cut the turns of the other coil, the simple relationships between turns ratio, voltage ratio and impedance ratio in the iron-core transformer do not hold.

Two types of inductively-coupled circuits are shown in Fig. 2-47. Only one circuit is resonant. The circuit at A is frequently used in receivers for coupling between amplifier tubes when the tuning of the circuit must be varied to respond to signals of different frequencies. Circuit B is used principally in transmitters, for coupling a radio-frequency amplifier to a resistive load.

In these circuits the coupling between the primary and secondary coils usually is "tight" — that is, the coefficient of coupling between the coils is large. With very tight coupling either circuit operates nearly as though the device to which the untuned coil is connected were simply tapped across a corresponding number of turns on the tuned-circuit coil, thus either circuit is approximately equivalent to Fig. 2-43B.

By proper choice of the number of turns on the untuned coil, and by adjustment of the coupling, the parallel impedance of the tuned circuit may be adjusted to the value required for the proper operation of the device to which it is connected. In any case, the maximum energy transfer possible for a given coefficient of coupling is obtained when the reactance of the untuned coil is equal to the resistance of its load.

The Q and parallel impedance of the tuned circuit are reduced by coupling through an untuned coil in much the same way as by the tapping arrangement shown in Fig. 2-43B.

Coupled Resonant Circuits

When the primary and secondary circuits are both tuned, as in Fig. 2-48, the resonance effects

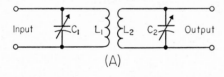

(A)

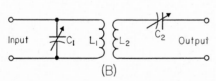

(B)

Fig. 2-48—Inductively-coupled resonant circuits. Circuit A is used for high-resistance loads (load resistance much higher than the reactance of either L_2 or C_2 at the resonant frequency). Circuit B is suitable for low resistance loads (load resistance much lower than the reactance of either L_2 or C_2 at the resonant frequency).

in both circuits make the operation somewhat more complicated than in the simpler circuits just considered. Imagine first that the two circuits are not coupled and that each is independently tuned to the resonant frequency. The impedance of each will be purely resistive. If the primary circuit is connected to a source of r.f. energy of the resonant

frequency and the secondary is then loosely coupled to the primary, a current will flow in the secondary circuit. In flowing through the resistance of the secondary circuit and any load that may be connected to it, the current causes a power loss. This power must come from the energy source through the primary circuit, and manifests itself in the primary as an increase in the equivalent resistance in series with the primary coil. Hence the Q and parallel impedance of the primary circuit are decreased by the coupled secondary. As the coupling is made greater (without changing the tuning of either circuit) the coupled resistance becomes larger and the parallel impedance of the primary continues to decrease. Also, as the coupling is made tighter the amount of power transferred from the primary to the secondary will increase to a maximum at one value of coupling, called **critical coupling**, but then decreases if the coupling is tightened still more (still without changing the tuning).

Critical coupling is a function of the Qs of the two circuits. A higher coefficient of coupling is required to reach critical coupling when the Qs are low; if the Qs are high, as in receiving applications, a coupling coefficient of a few per cent may give critical coupling.

With loaded circuits such as are used in transmitters the Q may be too low to give the desired power transfer even when the coils are coupled as tightly as the physical construction permits. In such case, increasing the Q of either circuit will be helpful, although it is generally better to increase the Q of the lower-Q circuit rather than the reverse. The Q of the parallel-tuned primary (input) circuit can be increased by decreasing the L/C ratio because, as shown in connection with Fig. 2-43, this circuit is in effect loaded by a parallel resistance (effect of coupled-in resistance). In the parallel-tuned secondary circuit, Fig. 2-48A, the Q can be increased, for a fixed value of load resistance, either by decreasing the L/C ratio or by tapping the load down (see Fig. 2-43). In the series-tuned secondary circuit, Fig. 2-48B, the Q may be increased by *increasing* the L/C ratio. There will generally be no difficulty in securing sufficient coupling, with practicable coils, if the product of the Qs of the two tuned circuits is 10 or more. A smaller product will suffice if the coil construction permits tight coupling.

Selectivity

In Fig. 2-47 only one circuit is tuned and the selectivity curve will be essentially that of a single resonant circuit. As stated, the effective Q depends upon the resistance connected to the untuned coil.

In Fig. 2-48, the selectivity is the same as that of a single tuned circuit having a Q equal to the *product* of the Qs of the individual circuits — *if* the coupling is well below critical (this is not the condition for optimum power transfer discussed immediately above) and both circuits are tuned to resonance. The Qs of the individual circuits

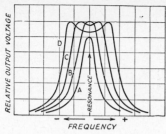

Fig. 2-49—Showing the effect on the output voltage from the secondary circuit of changing the coefficient of coupling between two resonant circuits independently tuned to the same frequency. The voltage applied to the primary is held constant in amplitude while the frequency is varied, and the output voltage is measured across the secondary.

are affected by the degree of coupling, because each couples resistance into the other; the tighter the coupling, the lower the individual Qs and therefore the lower the over-all selectivity.

If both circuits are independently tuned to resonance, the over-all selectivity will vary about as shown in Fig. 2-49 as the coupling is varied. With loose coupling, A, the output voltage (across the secondary circuit) is small and the selectivity is high. As the coupling is increased the secondary voltage also increases until critical coupling, B, is reached. At this point the output voltage at the resonant frequency is maximum but the selectivity is lower than with looser coupling. At still tighter coupling, C, the output voltage at the resonant frequency decreases, but as the frequency is varied either side of resonance it is found that there are two "humps" to the curve, one on either side of resonance. With very tight coupling, D, there is a further decrease in the output voltage at resonance and the "humps" are farther away from the resonant frequency. Curves such as those at C and D are called **flat-topped** because the output voltage does not change much over an appreciable band of frequencies.

Note that the off-resonance humps have the same maximum value as the resonant output voltage at critical coupling. These humps are caused by the fact that at frequencies off resonance the secondary circuit is reactive and couples reactance as well as resistance into the primary. The coupled resistance decreases off resonance, and each hump represents a new condition of critical coupling at a frequency to which the primary is tuned by the additional coupled-in reactance from the secondary.

Band-Pass Coupling

Over-coupled resonant circuits are useful where substantially uniform output is desired over a continuous band of frequencies, without readjustment of tuning. The width of the flat top of the resonance curve depends on the Qs of the two circuits as well as the tightness of coupling; the frequency separation between the humps will increase, and the curve become more flat-topped, as the Qs are lowered.

Band-pass operation also is secured by tuning

the two circuits to slightly different frequencies, which gives a double-humped resonance curve even with loose coupling. This is called **stagger tuning**. However, to secure adequate power transfer over the frequency band it is usually necessary to use tight coupling and experimentally adjust the circuits for the desired performance.

Link Coupling

A modification of inductive coupling, called **link coupling,** is shown in Fig. 2-50. This gives the effect of inductive coupling between two coils that have no mutual inductance; the link is simply a means for providing the mutual inductance. The total mutual inductance between two coils coupled by a link cannot be made as great as if the coils themselves were coupled. This is because the coefficient of coupling between air-core coils is considerably less than 1, and since there are two coupling points the over-all coupling

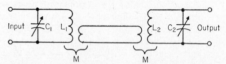

Fig. 2-50—Link coupling. The mutual inductances at both ends of the link are equivalent to mutual inductance between the tuned circuits, and serve the same purpose.

coefficient is less than for any *pair* of coils. In practice this need not be disadvantageous because the power transfer can be made great enough by making the tuned circuits sufficiently high-Q. Link coupling is convenient when ordinary inductive coupling would be impracticable for constructional reasons.

The link coils usually have a small number of turns compared with the resonant-circuit coils. The number of turns is not greatly important, because the coefficient of coupling is relatively independent of the number of turns on either coil; it is more important that both link coils should have about the *same* inductance. The length of the link between the coils is not critical if it is very small compared with the wavelength, but if the length is more than about one-twentieth of a wavelength the link operates more as a transmission line than as a means for providing mutual inductance. In such case it should be treated by the methods described in the chapter on Transmission Lines.

● IMPEDANCE-MATCHING CIRCUITS

The coupling circuits discussed in the preceding section have been based either on inductive coupling or on coupling through a common circuit element between two resonant circuits. These are not the only circuits that may be used for transferring power from one device to another. There is, in fact, a wide variety of such circuits available, all of them being classified generally as **impedance-matching networks.** Several networks frequently used in amateur equipment are shown in Fig. 2-51.

Filters

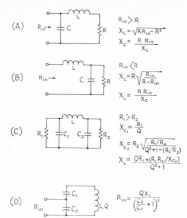

Fig. 2-51—Impedance-matching networks adaptable to amateur work. (A) L network for transforming to a higher value of resistance. (B) L network for transforming to a lower resistance value. (C) Pi network. R_1 is the larger of the two resistors; Q is defined as R_1/X_{C1}. (D) Tapped tuned circuit used in some receiver applications. The impedance of the tuned circuit is transformed to a lower value, R_{in}, by the capacitive divider.

The L Network

The L network is the simplest possible impedance-matching circuit. It closely resembles an ordinary resonant circuit with the load resistance, R, Fig. 2-51, either in series or parallel. The arrangement shown in Fig. 2-51A is used when the desired impedance, R_{IN}, is larger than the actual load resistance, R, while Fig. 2-51B is used in the opposite case. The design equations for each case are given in the figure, in terms of the circuit reactances. The reactances may be converted to inductance and capacitance by means of the formulas previously given or taken directly from the charts of Figs. 2-44 and 2-45.

When the impedance transformation ratio is large — that is, one of the two impedances is of the order of 100 times (or more) larger than the other — the operation of the circuit is exactly the same as previously discussed in connection with impedance transformation with a simple LC resonant circuit.

The Q of an L network is found in the same way as for simple resonant circuits. That is, it is equal to X_L/R or R_{IN}/X_C in Fig. 2-51A, and to X_L/R_{IN} or R/X_C in Fig. 2-51B. The value of Q is determined by the ratio of the impedances to be matched, and cannot be selected independently. In the equations of Fig. 2-51 it is assumed that both R and R_{IN} are pure resistances.

The Pi Network

The pi network, shown in Fig. 2-51C, offers more flexibility than the L since the operating Q may be chosen practically at will. The only limitation on the circuit values that may be used is that the reactance of the series arm, the inductor L in the figure, must not be greater than the square root of the product of the two values of resistive impedance to be matched. As the circuit is applied in amateur equipment, this limiting value

of reactance would represent a network with an undesirably low operating Q, and the circuit values ordinarily used are well on the safe side of the limiting values.

In its principal application as a "tank" circuit matching a transmission line to a power amplifier tube, the load R_2 will generally have a fairly low value of resistance (up to a few hundred ohms) while R_1, the required load for the tube, will be of the order of a few thousand ohms. In such a case the Q of the circuit is defined as R_1/X_{C1}, so the choice of a value for the operating Q immediately sets the value of X_{C1} and hence of C_1. The values of X_{C2} and X_L are then found from the equations given in the figure.

Graphical solutions of these equations for the most important practical cases are given in the chapter on transmitter design in the discussion of plate tank circuits. The L and C values may be calculated from the reactances or read from the charts of Figs. 2-44 and 2-45.

Tapped Tuned Circuit

The tapped tuned circuit of Fig. 2-51D is useful in some receiver applications, where it is desirable to use a high-impedance tuned circuit as a lower-impedance load. When the Q of the inductor has been determined, the capacitors can be selected to give the desired impedance transformation and the necessary resultant capacitance to tune the circuit to resonance.

● FILTERS

A **filter** is an electrical circuit configuration **(network)** designed to have specific characteristics with respect to the transmission or attenuation of various frequencies that may be applied to it. There are three general types of filters: **low-pass, high-pass,** and **band-pass.**

A low-pass filter is one that will permit all frequencies below a specified one called the **cut-off frequency** to be transmitted with little or no loss, but that will attenuate all frequencies above the cut-off frequency.

A high-pass filter similarly has a cut-off frequency, above which there is little or no loss in transmission, but below which there is considerable attenuation. Its behavior is the opposite of that of the low-pass filter.

A band-pass filter is one that will transmit a selected band of frequencies with substantially no loss, but that will attenuate all frequencies either higher or lower than the desired band.

The **pass band** of a filter is the frequency spectrum that is transmitted with little or no loss. The transmission characteristic is not necessarily perfectly uniform in the pass band, but the variations usually are small.

The **stop band** is the frequency region in which attenuation is desired. The attenuation may vary in the stop band, and in a simple filter usually is least near the cut-off frequency, rising to high values at frequencies considerably removed from the cut-off frequency.

Filters are designed for a specific value of purely resistive impedance (the **terminating im-**

2—ELECTRICAL LAWS AND CIRCUITS

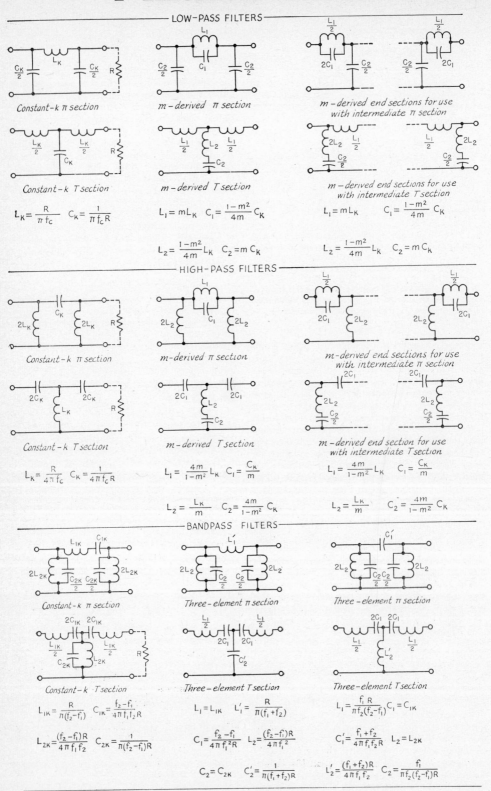

LOW-PASS FILTERS

Constant-k π section

m-derived π section

m-derived end sections for use with intermediate π section

Constant-k T section

m-derived T section

m-derived end sections for use with intermediate T section

$$L_K = \frac{R}{\pi f_c} \quad C_K = \frac{1}{\pi f_c R}$$

$$L_1 = m L_K \quad C_1 = \frac{1-m^2}{4m} C_K$$

$$L_1 = m L_K \quad C_1 = \frac{1-m^2}{4m} C_K$$

$$L_2 = \frac{1-m^2}{4m} L_K \quad C_2 = m C_K$$

$$L_2 = \frac{1-m^2}{4m} L_K \quad C_2 = m C_K$$

HIGH-PASS FILTERS

Constant-k π section

m-derived π section

m-derived end sections for use with intermediate π section

Constant-k T section

m-derived T section

m-derived end section for use with intermediate T section

$$L_K = \frac{R}{4\pi f_c} \quad C_K = \frac{1}{4\pi f_c R}$$

$$L_1 = \frac{4m}{1-m^2} L_K \quad C_1 = \frac{C_K}{m}$$

$$L_1 = \frac{4m}{1-m^2} L_K \quad C_1 = \frac{C_K}{m}$$

$$L_2 = \frac{L_K}{m} \quad C_2 = \frac{4m}{1-m^2} C_K$$

$$L_2 = \frac{L_K}{m} \quad C_2 = \frac{4m}{1-m^2} C_K$$

BANDPASS FILTERS

Constant-k π section

Three-element π section

Three-element π section

Constant-k T section

Three-element T section

Three-element T section

$$L_{1K} = \frac{R}{\pi(f_2-f_1)} \quad C_{1K} = \frac{f_2-f_1}{4\pi f_1 f_2 R}$$

$$L_1 = L_{1K} \quad L_1' = \frac{R}{\pi(f_1+f_2)}$$

$$L_1 = \frac{f_1 R}{\pi f_2(f_2-f_1)} \quad C_1 = C_{1K}$$

$$L_{2K} = \frac{(f_2-f_1)R}{4\pi f_1 f_2} \quad C_{2K} = \frac{1}{\pi(f_2-f_1)R}$$

$$C_1 = \frac{f_2-f_1}{4\pi f_1^2 R} \quad L_2 = \frac{(f_2-f_1)R}{4\pi f_1^2}$$

$$C_1' = \frac{f_1+f_2}{4\pi f_1 f_2 R} \quad L_2 = L_{2K}$$

$$C_2 = C_{2K} \quad C_2' = \frac{1}{\pi(f_1+f_2)R}$$

$$L_2' = \frac{(f_1+f_2)R}{4\pi f_1 f_2} \quad C_2 = \frac{f_1}{\pi f_2(f_2-f_1)R}$$

Fig. 2-52—Basic filter sections and design formulas. In the above formulas R is in ohms, C in farads, L in henrys, and f in cycles per second.

pedance of the filter). When such an impedance is connected to the output terminals of the filter, the impedance looking into the input terminals has essentially the same value, throughout most of the pass band. Simple filters do not give perfectly uniform performance in this respect, but the input impedance of a properly-terminated filter can be made fairly constant, as well as closer to the design value, over the pass band by using **m-derived** filter sections.

A discussion of filter design principles is beyond the scope of this *Handbook*, but it is not difficult to build satisfactory filters from the circuits and formulas given in Fig. 2-52. Filter circuits are built up from elementary sections as shown in the figure. These sections can be used alone or, if greater attenuation and sharper cut-off (that is, a more rapid rate of rise of attenuation with frequency beyond the cut-off frequency) are required, several sections can be connected in series. In the low- and high-pass filters, f_c represents the cut-off frequency, the highest (for the low-pass) or the lowest (for the high-pass) frequency transmitted without attenuation. In the band-pass filter designs, f_1 is the low-frequency cut-off and f_2 the high-frequency cut-off. The units for L, C, R and f are henrys, farads, ohms and cycles per second, respectively.

All of the types shown are "unbalanced" (one side grounded). For use in balanced circuits (e.g., 300-ohm transmission line, or push-pull audio circuits), the series reactances should be equally divided between the two legs. Thus the balanced constant-k π-section low-pass filter would use two inductors of a value equal to $L_k/2$, while the balanced constant-k π-section high-pass filter would use two capacitors each equal to $2C_k$.

If several low- (or high-) pass sections are to be used, it is advisable to use m-derived end sections on either side of a constant-k center section, although an m-derived center section can be used. The factor m determines the ratio of the cut-off frequency, f_c, to a frequency of high attenuation, f_∞. Where only one m-derived section is used, a value of 0.6 is generally used for m, although a deviation of 10 or 15 per cent from this value is not too serious in amateur work. For a value of $m = 0.6$, f_∞ will be $1.25f_c$ for the low-pass filter and $0.8f_c$ for the high-pass filter. Other values can be found from

$$m = \sqrt{1 - \left(\frac{f_c}{f_\infty}\right)^2} \text{ for the low-pass filter and}$$

$$m = \sqrt{1 - \left(\frac{f_\infty}{f_c}\right)^2} \text{ for the high-pass filter.}$$

The output sides of the filters shown should be terminated in a resistance equal to R, and there should be little or no reactive component in the termination.

Simple audio filters can be made with powdered-iron-core inductors and paper capacitors. Sharper cut-off characteristics will be obtained with more sections. The values of the components can vary by ±5% with little or no

reduction in performance. The more sections there are to a filter the greater is the need for accuracy in the values of the components. High-performance audio filters can be built with only two sections by winding the inductors on toroidial powdered-iron forms; three sections are generally needed for obtaining equivalent results when using other types of inductors.

Band-pass filters for single sideband work (see later chapter) are often designed to operate in the range 10 to 20 kc. Their attenuation requirements are such that usually at least a five-section filter is required. The coils should be as high-Q as possible, and mica is the most suitable capacitor dielectric.

Low-pass and high-pass filters for harmonic suppression and receiver-overload prevention in the television frequencies range are usually made with self-supporting coils and mica or ceramic capacitors, depending upon the power requirements.

In any filter, there should be no magnetic or capacitive coupling between sections of the filter unless the design specifically calls for it. This requirement makes it necessary to shield the coils from each other in some applications, or to mount them at right angles to each other.

● PIEZOELECTRIC CRYSTALS

A number of crystalline substances found in nature have the ability to transform mechanical strain into an electrical charge, and *vice versa*. This property is known as the **piezoelectric effect**. A small plate or bar cut in the proper way from a quartz crystal and placed between two conducting electrodes will be mechanically strained when the electrodes are connected to a source of voltage. Conversely, if the crystal is squeezed between two electrodes a voltage will be developed between the electrodes.

Piezoelectric crystals can be used to transform mechanical energy into electrical energy, and vice versa. They are used in microphones and phonograph pick-ups, where mechanical vibrations are transformed into alternating voltages of corresponding frequency. They are also used in headsets and loudspeakers, transforming electrical energy into mechanical vibration. Crystals of Rochelle salts are used for these purposes.

Crystal Resonators

Crystalline plates also are mechanical resonators that have natural frequencies of vibration ranging from a few thousand cycles to tens of megacycles per second. The vibration frequency depends on the kind of crystal, the way the plate is cut from the natural crystal, and on the dimensions of the plate. The thing that makes the **crystal resonator** valuable is that it has extremely high Q, ranging from 5 to 10 times the Qs obtainable with good LC resonant circuits.

Analogies can be drawn between various mechanical properties of the crystal and the electrical characteristics of a tuned circuit. This leads to an "equivalent circuit" for the crystal.

The electrical coupling to the crystal is through the holder plates between which it is sandwiched; these plates form, with the crystal as the dielectric, a small capacitor like any other capacitor constructed of two plates with a dielectric between. The crystal itself is equivalent to a series-resonant circuit, and together with the capacitance of the holder forms the equivalent circuit shown in Fig. 2-53. At frequencies of the order of 450 kc., where crystals are widely used as resonators, the equivalent L may be several henrys and

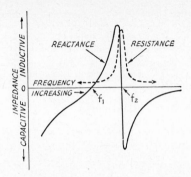

Fig. 2-54—Reactance and resistance vs. frequency of a circuit of the type shown in Fig. 2-53. Actual values of reactance, resistance and the separation between the series- and parallel-resonant frequencies, f_1, and f_2, respectively, depend on the circuit constants.

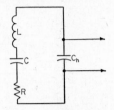

Fig. 2-53—Equivalent circuit of a crystal resonator. L, C and R are the electrical equivalents of mechanical properties of the crystal; C_h is the capacitance of the holder plates with the crystal plate between them.

the equivalent C only a few hundredths of a micromicrofarad. Although the equivalent R is of the order of a few thousand ohms, the reactance at resonance is so high that the Q of the crystal likewise is high.

A circuit of the type shown in Fig. 2-53 has a series-resonant frequency, when viewed from the circuit terminals indicated by the arrowheads, determined by L and C only. At this frequency the circuit impedance is simply equal to R, providing the reactance of C_h is large compared with R (this is generally the case). The circuit also has a parallel-resonant frequency determined by L and the equivalent capacitance of C and C_h in series. Since this equivalent capacitance is smaller than C alone, the parallel-resonant frequency is higher than the series-resonant frequency. The separation between the two resonant

frequencies depends on the ratio of C_h to C, and when this ratio is large (as in the case of a crystal resonator, where C_h will be a few $\mu\mu f$. in the average case) the two frequencies will be quite close together. A separation of a kilocycle or less at 455 kc. is typical of a quartz crystal.

Fig. 2-54 shows how the resistance and reactance of such a circuit vary as the applied frequency is varied. The reactance passes through zero at both resonant frequencies, but the resistance rises to a large value at parallel resonance, just as in any tuned circuit.

Quartz crystals may be used either as simple resonators for their selective properties or as the frequency-controlling elements in oscillators as described in later chapters. The series-resonant frequency is the one principally used in the former case, while the more common forms of oscillator circuit use the parallel-resonant frequency.

Practical Circuit Details

● COMBINED A.C. AND D.C.

Most radio circuits are built around vacuum tubes, and it is the nature of these tubes to require direct current (usually at a fairly high voltage) for their operation. They convert the direct current into an alternating current (and sometimes the reverse) at frequencies varying from well down in the audio range to well up in the super-high range. The conversion process almost invariably requires that the direct and alternating currents meet somewhere in the circuit.

In this meeting, the a.c. and d.c. are actually combined into a single current that "pulsates" (at the a.c. frequency) about an average value equal to the direct current. This is shown in Fig. 2-55. It is convenient to consider that the alternating current is **superimposed** on the direct current, so we may look upon the actual current as having two components, one d.c. and the other a.c.

In an alternating current the positive and negative alternations have the same average ampli-

tude, so when the wave is superimposed on a direct current the latter is alternately increased and decreased by the same amount. There is thus no *average* change in the direct current. If a d.c. instrument is being used to read the current, the reading will be exactly the same whether or not the a.c. is superimposed.

However, there is actually more power in such a combination current than there is in the direct current alone. This is because power varies as the square of the instantaneous value of the current, and when all the instantaneous squared values are averaged over a cycle the total power is greater than the d.c. power alone. If the a.c. is a

Fig. 2-55—Pulsating d.c., composed of an alternating current or voltage superimposed on a steady direct current or voltage.

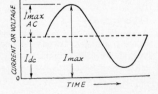

Practical Circuit Details

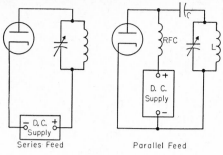

Fig. 2-56—Illustrating series and parallel feed.

sine wave having a peak value just equal to the d.c., the power in the circuit is 1.5 times the d.c. power. An instrument whose readings are proportional to power will show such an increase.

Series and Parallel Feed

Fig. 2-56 shows in simplified form how d.c. and a.c. may be combined in a vacuum-tube circuit. In this case, it is assumed that the a.c. is at radio frequency, as suggested by the coil-and-capacitor tuned circuit. It is also assumed that r.f. current can easily flow through the d.c. supply; that is, the impedance of the supply at radio frequencies is so small as to be negligible.

In the circuit at the left, the tube, tuned circuit, and d.c. supply all are connected in series. The direct current flows through the r.f. coil to get to the tube; the r.f. current generated by the tube flows through the d.c. supply to get to the tuned circuit. This is **series feed**. It works because the impedance of the d.c. supply at radio frequencies is so low that it does not affect the flow of *r.f.* current, and because the d.c. resistance of the coil is so low that it does not affect the flow of *direct* current.

In the circuit at the right the direct current does not flow through the r.f. tuned circuit, but instead goes to the tube through a second coil, *RFC* **(radio-frequency choke)**. Direct current cannot flow through *L* because a **blocking capacitance**, *C*, is placed in the circuit to prevent it. (Without *C*, the d.c. supply would be short-circuited by the low resistance of *L*.) On the other hand, the r.f. current generated by the tube can easily flow through *C* to the tuned circuit because the capacitance of *C* is intentionally chosen to have low reactance (compared with the impedance of the tuned circuit) at the radio frequency. The r.f. current cannot flow through the d.c. supply because the inductance of *RFC* is intentionally made so large that it has a very high reactance at the radio frequency. The resistance of *RFC*, however, is too low to have an appreciable effect on the flow of direct current. The two currents are thus in *parallel*, hence the name **parallel feed.**

Either type of feed may be used for both a.f. and r.f. circuits. In parallel feed there is no d.c. voltage on the a.c. circuit, a desirable feature from the viewpoint of safety to the operator, because the voltages applied to tubes — particu-

larly transmitting tubes — are dangerous. On the other hand, it is somewhat difficult to make an r.f. choke work well over a wide range of frequencies. Series feed is often preferred, therefore, because it is relatively easy to keep the impedance between the a.c. circuit and the tube low.

Bypassing

In the series-feed circuit just discussed, it was assumed that the d.c. supply had very low impedance at radio frequencies. This is not likely to be true in a practical power supply, partly because the normal physical separation between the supply and the r.f. circuit would make it necessary to use rather long connecting wires or leads. At radio frequencies, even a few feet of wire can have fairly large reactance — too large to be considered a really "low-impedance" connection.

An actual circuit would be provided with a **bypass capacitor**, as shown in Fig. 2-57. Capacitor *C* is chosen to have low reactance at the operating frequency, and is installed right in the circuit where it can be wired to the other parts with quite short connecting wires. Hence the r.f. current will tend to flow through it rather than through the d.c. supply.

To be effective, the reactance of the bypass capacitor should not be more than one-tenth of the impedance of the bypassed part of the circuit. Very often the latter impedance is not known, in which case it is desirable to use the largest capacitance in the bypass that circumstances permit. To make doubly sure that r.f. current will not flow through a non-r.f. circuit such as a power supply, an r.f. choke may be connected in the lead to the latter, as shown in Fig. 2-57.

The same type of bypassing is used when audio frequencies are present in addition to r.f. Because the reactance of a capacitor changes with frequency, it is readily possible to choose a capacitance that will represent a very low reactance at

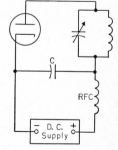

Fig. 2-57—Typical use of a bypass capacitor in a series-feed circuit.

radio frequencies but that will have such high reactance at audio frequencies that it is practically an open circuit. A capacitance of 0.001 μf. is practically a short circuit for r.f., for example, but is almost an open circuit at audio frequencies. (The actual value of capacitance that is usable will be modified by the impedances concerned.) Bypass capacitors also are used in audio circuits to carry the audio frequencies around a d.c. supply.

Distributed Capacitance and Inductance

In the discussions earlier in this chapter it was assumed that a capacitor has only capacitance and that an inductor has only inductance. Unfortunately, this is not strictly true. There is always a certain amount of inductance in a conductor of any length, and a capacitor is bound to have a little inductance in addition to its intended capacitance. Also, there is always capacitance between two conductors or between parts of the same conductor, and thus there is appreciable capacitance between the turns of an inductance coil.

This **distributed inductance** in a capacitor and the **distributed capacitance** in an inductor have important practical effects. Actually, every capacitor is a tuned circuit, resonant at the frequency where its capacitance and distributed inductance have the same reactance. The same thing is true of a coil and its distributed capacitance. At frequencies well below these **natural resonances**, the capacitor will act like a normal capacitance and the coil will act like a normal inductance. Near the natural resonant points, the coil and capacitor act like self-tuned circuits. Above resonance, the capacitor acts like an inductor and the inductor acts like a capacitor. Thus there is a limit to the amount of capacitance that can be used at a given frequency. There is a similar limit to the inductance that can be used. At audio frequencies, capacitances measured in microfarads and inductances measured in henrys are practicable. At low and medium radio frequencies, inductances of a few millihenrys and capacitances of a few thousand micromicrofarads are the largest practicable. At high radio frequencies, usable inductance values drop to a few microhenrys and capacitances to a few hundred micromicrofarads.

Distributed capacitance and inductance are important not only in r.f. tuned circuits, but in bypassing and choking as well. It will be appreciated that a bypass capacitor that actually acts like an inductance, or an r.f. choke that acts like a low-reactance capacitor, cannot work as it is intended they should.

Grounds

Throughout this book there are frequent references to **ground** and **ground potential**. When a connection is said to be "grounded" it does not necessarily mean that it actually goes to earth. What it means is that an actual earth connection to that point in the circuit should not disturb the operation of the circuit in any way. The term also is used to indicate a "common" point in the circuit where power supplies and metallic supports (such as a metal chassis) are electrically tied together. It is general practice, for example, to "ground" the negative terminal of a d.c. power supply, and to "ground" the filament or heater power supplies for vacuum tubes. Since the cathode of a vacuum tube is a junction point for grid and plate voltage supplies, and since the various circuits connected to the tube elements have at least one point connected to cathode,

these points also are "returned to ground." Ground is therefore a common reference point in the radio circuit. "Ground potential" means that there is no "difference of potential" — that is, no voltage — between the circuit point and the earth.

Single-Ended and Balanced Circuits

With reference to ground, a circuit may be either **single-ended** (unbalanced) or **balanced**. In a single-ended circuit, one side of the circuit is connected to ground. In a balanced circuit, the electrical midpoint is connected to ground, so that the circuit has two ends each at the same voltage "above" ground.

Typical single-ended and balanced circuits are shown in Fig. 2-58. R.f. circuits are shown in the upper row, while iron-core transformers (such

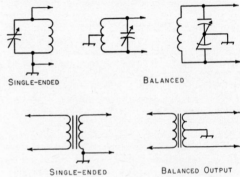

SINGLE-ENDED   BALANCED

SINGLE-ENDED   BALANCED OUTPUT

Fig. 2-58—Single-ended and balanced circuits.

as are used in power-supply and audio circuits) are shown in the lower row. The r.f. circuits may be balanced either by connecting the center of the coil to ground or by using a "balanced" or "split-stator" capacitor and connecting its rotor to ground. In the iron-core transformer, one or both windings may be tapped at the center of the winding to provide the ground connection.

Shielding

Two circuits that are physically near each other usually will be coupled to each other in some degree even though no coupling is intended. The metallic parts of the two circuits form a small capacitance through which energy can be transferred by means of the electric field. Also, the magnetic field about the coil or wiring of one circuit can couple that circuit to a second through the latter's coil and wiring. In many cases these unwanted couplings must be prevented if the circuits are to work properly.

Capacitive coupling may readily be prevented by enclosing one or both of the circuits in grounded low-resistance metallic containers, called **shields**. The electric field from the circuit components does not penetrate the shield. A metallic plate, called a **baffle shield**, inserted between two components also may suffice to prevent electrostatic coupling between them. It should be large enough to make the components invisible to each other.

U.H.F. Circuits

Similar metallic shielding is used at radio frequencies to prevent magnetic coupling. The shielding effect for magnetic fields increases with frequency and with the conductivity and thickness of the shielding material.

A closed shield is required for good magnetic shielding; in some cases separate shields, one about each coil, may be required. The baffle shield is rather ineffective for magnetic shielding, although it will give partial shielding if placed at right angles to the axes of, and between, the coils to be shielded from each other.

Shielding a coil reduces its inductance, because part of its field is canceled by the shield. Also, there is always a small amount of resistance in the shield, and there is therefore an energy loss.

This loss raises the effective resistance of the coil. The decrease in inductance and increase in resistance lower the Q of the coil, but the reduction in inductance and Q will be small if the spacing between the sides of the coil and the shield is at least half the coil diameter, and if the spacing at the ends of the coil is at least equal to the coil diameter. The higher the conductivity of the shield material, the less the effect on the inductance and Q. Copper is the best material, but aluminum is quite satisfactory.

For good magnetic shielding at audio frequencies it is necessary to enclose the coil in a container of high-permeability iron or steel. In this case the shield can be quite close to the coil without harming its performance.

U.H.F. Circuits

● RESONANT LINES

In resonant circuits as employed at the lower frequencies it is possible to consider each of the reactance components as a separate entity. The fact that an inductor has a certain amount of self-capacitance, as well as some resistance, while a capacitor also possesses a small self-inductance, can usually be disregarded.

At the very-high and ultrahigh frequencies it is not readily possible to separate these components. Also, the connecting leads, which at lower frequencies would serve merely to join the capacitor and coil, now may have more inductance than the coil itself. The required inductance coil may be no more than a single turn of wire, yet even this single turn may have dimensions comparable to a wavelength at the operating frequency. Thus the energy in the field surrounding the "coil" may in part be radiated. At a sufficiently high frequency the loss by radiation may represent a major portion of the total energy in the circuit.

For these reasons it is common practice to utilize resonant sections of transmission line as tuned circuits at frequencies above 100 Mc. or so. A quarter-wavelength line, or any odd multiple thereof, shorted at one end and open at the other exhibits large standing waves, as described in the section on transmission lines. When a voltage of the frequency at which such a line is resonant is applied to the open end, the response is very similar to that of a parallel resonant circuit The equivalent relationships are shown in Fig. 2-59. At frequencies off resonance the line displays qualities comparable with the inductive and capacitive reactances of a conventional tuned circuit, so sections of transmission line can be used in much the same manner as inductors and capacitors.

To minimize radiation loss the two conductors of a parallel-conductor line should not be more than about one-tenth wavelength apart, the spacing being measured between the conductor axes. On the other hand, the spacing should not be less than about twice the conductor diameter

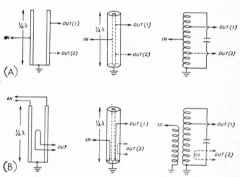

Fig. 2-59—Equivalent coupling circuits for parallel-line, coaxial-line and conventional resonant circuits.

because of "proximity effect," which causes eddy currents and an increase in loss. Above 300 Mc. it is difficult to satisfy both these requirements simultaneously, and the radiation from an open line tends to become excessive, reducing the Q. In such case the coaxial type of line is to be preferred, since it is inherently shielded.

Representative methods for adjusting coaxial lines to resonance are shown in Fig. 2-60. At the left, a sliding shorting disk is used to reduce the effective length of the line by altering the position of the short-circuit. In the center, the same effect is accomplished by using a telescoping tube in the end of the inner conductor to vary its length and thereby the effective length of the line. At the right, two possible methods of using parallel-plate capacitors are illustrated. The arrangement with the loading capacitor at the open

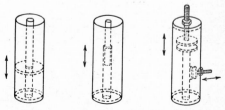

Fig. 2-60—Methods of tuning coaxial resonant lines.

end of the line has the greatest tuning effect per unit of capacitance; the alternative method, which is equivalent to tapping the capacitor down on the line, has less effect on the Q of the circuit. Lines with capacitive "loading" of the sort illustrated will be shorter, physically, than unloaded lines resonant at the same frequency.

Two methods of tuning a parallel-conductor lines are shown in Fig. 2-61. The sliding short-

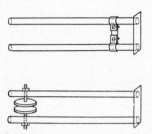

Fig. 2-61—Methods of tuning parallel-type resonant lines.

circuiting strap can be tightened by means of screws and nuts to make good electrical contact. The parallel-plate capacitor in the second drawing may be placed anywhere along the line, the tuning effect becoming less as the capacitor is located nearer the shorted end of the line. Although a low-capacitance variable capacitor of ordinary construction can be used, the circular-plate type shown is symmetrical and thus does not unbalance the line. It also has the further advantage that no insulating material is required.

● WAVEGUIDES

A waveguide is a conducting tube through which energy is transmitted in the form of electromagnetic waves. The tube is not considered as carrying a current in the same sense that the wires of a two-conductor line do, but rather as a *boundary* which confines the waves to the enclosed space. Skin effect prevents any electromagnetic effects from being evident outside the guide. The energy is injected at one end, either through capacitive or inductive coupling or by radiation, and is received at the other end. The waveguide then merely confines the energy of the fields, which are propagated through it to the receiving end by means of reflections against its inner walls.

Analysis of waveguide operation is based on the assumption that the guide material is a perfect conductor of electricity. Typical distributions of electric and magnetic fields in a rectangular guide are shown in Fig. 2-62. It will be observed that the intensity of the electric field is greatest (as indicated by closer spacing of the lines of force) at the center along the x dimension, Fig. 2-62B, diminishing to zero at the end walls. The latter is a necessary condition, since the existence of any electric field parallel to the walls at the surface would cause an infinite current to flow in a perfect conductor. This represents an impossible situation.

Modes of Propagation

Fig. 2-62 represents a relatively simple distribution of the electric and magnetic fields. There is in general an infinite number of ways in which the fields can arrange themselves in a guide so long as there is no upper limit to the frequency to be transmitted. Each field configuration is called a **mode**. All modes may be separated into two general groups. One group, designated *TM* (**transverse magnetic**), has the magnetic field entirely transverse to the direction of propagation, but has a component of electric field in that direction. The other type, designated *TE* (**transverse electric**) has the electric field entirely transverse, but has a component of magnetic field in the direction of propagation. *TM* waves are sometimes called *E* waves, and *TE* waves are sometimes called *H* waves, but the *TM* and *TE* designations are preferred.

The particular mode of transmission is identified by the group letters followed by two subscript numerals; for example, $TE_{1,0}$, $TM_{1,1}$, etc. The number of possible modes increases with frequency for a given size of guide. There is only one possible mode (called the **dominant mode**) for the lowest frequency that can be transmitted. The dominant mode is the one generally used in practical work.

Waveguide Dimensions

In the rectangular guide the critical dimension is x in Fig. 2-62; this dimension must be more than one-half wavelength at the lowest frequency to be transmitted. In practice, the y dimension usually is made about equal to $\frac{1}{2}x$

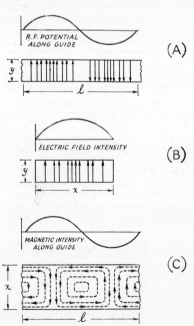

Fig. 2-62—Field distribution in a rectangular waveguide. The $TE_{1,0}$ mode of propagation is depicted

Waveguides

to avoid the possibility of operation at other than the dominant mode.

Other cross-sectional shapes than the rectangle can be used, the most important being the circular pipe. Much the same considerations apply as in the rectangular case.

Wavelength formulas for rectangular and circular guides are given in the following table, where x is the width of a rectangular guide and r is the radius of a circular guide. All figures are in terms of the dominant mode.

	Rectangular	Circular
Cut-off wavelength	$2x$	$3.41r$
Longest wavelength transmitted with little attenuation.	$1.6x$	$3.2r$
Shortest wavelength before next mode becomes possible.	$1.1x$	$2.8r$

Cavity Resonators

Another kind of circuit particularly applicable at wavelengths of the order of centimeters is the **cavity resonator,** which may be looked upon as a section of a waveguide with the dimensions chosen so that waves of a given length can be maintained inside.

Typical shapes used for resonators are the cylinder, the rectangular box and the sphere, as shown in Fig. 2-63. The resonant frequency depends upon the dimensions of the cavity and the mode of oscillation of the waves (comparable to the transmission modes in a waveguide).

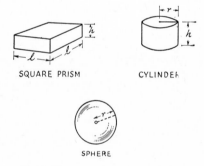

SQUARE PRISM   CYLINDER

SPHERE

Fig. 2-63—Forms of cavity resonators.

For the lowest modes the resonant wavelengths are as follows:

Cylinder.	$2.61r$
Square box.	$1.41l$
Sphere.	$2.28r$

The resonant wavelengths of the cylinder and square box are independent of the height when the height is less than a half wavelength. In other modes of oscillation the height must be a multiple of a half wavelength as measured inside the cavity. A cylindrical cavity can be tuned by a sliding shorting disk when operating in such a mode. Other tuning methods include placing adjustable tuning paddles or "slugs"

inside the cavity so that the standing-wave pattern of the electric and magnetic fields can be varied.

A form of cavity resonator in practical use is the re-entrant cylindrical type shown in Fig. 2-64. In construction it resembles a concentric line closed at both ends with capacitive loading at the top, but the actual mode of oscillation may differ considerably from that occurring in

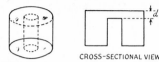

CROSS-SECTIONAL VIEW

Fig. 2-64—Re-entrant cylindrical cavity resonator.

coaxial lines. The resonant frequency of such a cavity depends upon the diameters of the two cylinders and the distance d between the ends of the inner and outer cylinders.

Compared with ordinary resonant circuits, cavity resonators have extremely high Q. A value of Q of the order of 1000 or more is readily obtainable, and Q values of several thousand can be secured with good design and construction.

Coupling to Waveguides and Cavity Resonators

Energy may be introduced into or abstracted from a waveguide or resonator by means of either the electric or magnetic field. The energy transfer frequently is through a coaxial line, two methods for coupling to which are shown in Fig. 2-65. The probe shown at A is simply a short extension of the inner conductor of the coaxial line, so oriented that it is parallel to the electric lines of force. The loop shown at B is arranged so that it encloses some of the magnetic lines of force. The point at which maximum coupling will be secured depends upon the particular mode of propagation in the guide or cavity; the coupling will be maximum when the coupling device is in the most intense field.

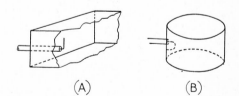

(A)   (B)

Fig. 2-65—Coupling to waveguides and resonators.

Coupling can be varied by turning either the probe or loop through a 90-degree angle. When the probe is perpendicular to the electric lines the coupling will be minimum; similarly, when the plane of the loop is parallel to the magnetic lines the coupling will have its least possible value.

Modulation, Heterodyning and Beats

Since one of the most widespread uses of radio frequencies is the transmission of speech and music, it would be very convenient if the audio spectrum to be transmitted could simply be shifted up to some radio frequency, transmitted as radio waves, and shifted back down to the audio spectrum at the receiving point. Suppose the audio signal to be transmitted by radio is a pure 1000-cycle tone, and we wish to transmit it at 1 Mc. (1,000,000 cycles). One possible way might be to add 1,000,000 cycles and 1,000 cycles together, thereby obtaining a radio frequency of 1,001,000 cycles. No simple method for doing such a thing directly has ever been devised, although the *effect* is obtained and used in advanced communications techniques.

Actually, when two different frequencies are present simultaneously in an ordinary circuit (specifically, one in which Ohm's Law holds) each behaves as though the other were not there. It is true that the total or resultant voltage (or current) in the circuit will be the sum of the instantaneous values of the two at every instant. This is because there can be only one value of current or voltage at any single point in a circuit at any instant. Figs. 2-66A and B show two such frequencies, and C shows the resultant. The amplitude of the 1,000,000-cycle current is not affected by the presence of the 1000-cycle current, but merely has its axis shifted back and forth at the 1000-cycle rate. An attempt to transmit such a combination as a radio wave would result simply in the transmission of the 1,000,000-cycle frequency, since the 1000-cycle frequency retains its identity as an audio frequency and hence will not be radiated.

There are devices, however, which make it possible for one frequency to control the amplitude of the other. If, for example, a 1000-cycle tone is used to control a 1-Mc. signal, the maximum r.f. output will be obtained when the 1000-cycle signal is at the peak of one alternation and the minimum will occur at the peak of the next alternation. The process is called **amplitude modulation,** and the effect is shown in Fig. 2-66D. The resultant signal is now entirely at radio frequency, but with its amplitude varying at the modulation rate (1000 cycles). Receiving equipment adjusted to receive the 1,000,000-cycle r.f. signal can reproduce these changes in amplitude, and thus tell what the audio signal is, through a process called **detection** or **demodulation.**

It might be assumed that the only radio frequency present in such a signal is the original 1,000,000 cycles, but such is not the case. It will be found that two new frequencies have appeared. These are the sum (1,000,000 + 1000) and difference (1,000,000 − 1000) of the two, and hence the radio frequencies appearing in the circuit after modulation are 999,000, 1,000,000 and 1,001,000 cycles.

When an audio frequency is used to control the amplitude of a radio frequency, the process

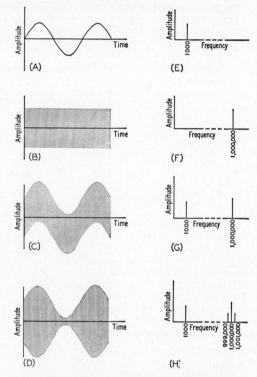

Fig. 2-66—Amplitude-vs.-time and amplitude-vs.-frequency plots of various signals. (A) 1½ cycles of an audio signal, assumed to be 1000 c.p.s. in this example. (B) A radio-frequency signal, assumed to be 1 Mc. (1,000,000 c.p.s.); 1500 cycles are completed during the same time as the 1½ cycles in A, so they cannot be shown accurately. (C) The signals of A and B in the same circuit; each maintains its own identity. (D) The signals of A and B in a circuit where the amplitude of A can control the amplitude of B. The 1-Mc. signal is *modulated* by the 1000-cycle signal.

E, F, G, and H show amplitude-vs.-frequency plots of the signals in A, B, C and D, respectively. Note the new frequencies in H, resulting from the modulation process.

is generally called "amplitude modulation," as mentioned, but when a radio frequency modulates another radio frequency it is called **heterodyning.** However, the processes are identical. A general term for the sum and difference frequencies generated during heterodyning or amplitude modulation is "beat frequencies," and a more specific one is **upper side frequency,** for the sum frequency, and **lower side frequency** for the difference frequency.

In the simple example, the modulating signal was assumed to be a pure tone, but the modulating signal can just as well be a *band* of frequencies making up speech or music. In this case, the side frequencies are grouped into what are called the **upper sideband** and the **lower sideband.** In any case, the frequency that is modulated is called the **carrier** frequency.

Modulation, Heterodyning and Beats

In A, B, C and D of Fig. 2-66, the sketches are obtained by plotting amplitude against time. However, it is equally helpful to be able to visualize the spectrum, or what a plot of amplitude *vs.* frequency looks like, at any given instant of time. E, F, G and H of Fig. 2-66 show the signals of Fig. 2-66A, B, C and D on an amplitude-*vs.*-frequency basis. Any one frequency is, of course, represented by a vertical line. Fig. 2-66H shows the side frequencies appearing as a result of the modulation process.

Amplitude modulation (a.m.) is not the only possible type nor is it the only one in use. Any signal property can be modulated. These properties include frequency and phase as well as amplitude, and methods are available for modulating all three. However, in every case the modulation process leads to the generation of a new set of radio frequencies symmetrically disposed about the original radio frequency (carrier frequency). The various types of modulation are treated in detail in later chapters.

CHAPTER 3

Vacuum-Tube Principles

● CURRENT IN A VACUUM

The outstanding difference between the vacuum tube and most other electrical devices is that the electric current does not flow through a conductor but through empty space — a vacuum. This is only possible when "free" electrons — that is, electrons that are not attached to atoms — are somehow introduced into the vacuum. Free electrons in an evacuated space will be attracted to a positively charged object within the same space, or will be repelled by a negatively charged object. The movement of the electrons under the attraction or repulsion of such charged objects constitutes the current in the vacuum.

The most practical way to introduce a sufficiently large number of electrons into the evacuated space is by thermionic emission.

Thermionic Emission

If a thin wire or filament is heated to incandescence in a vacuum, electrons near the surface are given enough energy of motion to fly off into the surrounding space. The higher the temperature, the greater the number of electrons emitted. A more general name for the filament is cathode.

If the cathode is the only thing in the vacuum, most of the emitted electrons stay in its immediate vicinity, forming a "cloud" about the cathode. The reason for this is that the electrons in the space, being negative electricity, form a negative charge (space charge) in the region of the cathode. The space charge repels

Representative tube types. Transmitting tubes having up to 500-watt capability are shown in the back row. The tube with the top cap in the middle row is a low-power transmitting type. Others are receiving tubes, with the exception of the one in the center foreground which is a v.h.f. transmitting type.

those electrons nearest the cathode, tending to make them fall back on it.

Now suppose a second conductor is introduced into the vacuum, but not connected to anything else inside the tube. If this second conductor is given a positive charge by connecting a source of e.m.f. between it and the

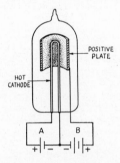

Fig. 3-1—Conduction by thermionic emission in a vacuum tube. The A battery is used to heat the filament to a temperature that will cause it to emit electrons. The B battery makes the plate positive with respect to the filament, thereby causing the emitted electrons to be attracted to the plate. Electrons captured by the plate flow back through the B battery to the filament.

cathode, as indicated in Fig. 3-1, electrons emitted by the cathode are attracted to the positively charged conductor. An electric current then flows through the circuit formed by the cathode, the charged conductor, and the source of e.m.f. In Fig. 3-1 this e.m.f. is supplied by a battery ("B" battery); a second battery ("A" battery) is also indicated for heating the cathode or filament to the proper operating temperature.

The positively charged conductor is usually a metal plate or cylinder (surrounding the cathode) and is called an anode or plate. Like the other working parts of a tube, it is a tube element or electrode. The tube shown in Fig. 3-1 is a two-element or two-electrode tube, one element being the cathode or filament and the other the anode or plate.

Since electrons are negative electricity, they will be attracted to the plate *only* when the plate is positive with respect to the cathode. If the plate is given a negative charge, the electrons will be repelled back to the cathode and no current will flow. The vacuum tube therefore can conduct *only in one direction*.

Cathodes

Before electron emission can occur, the cathode must be heated to a high temperature. However, it is not essential that the heating cur-

Rectification

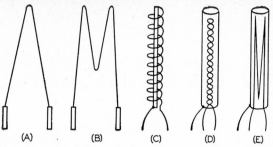

Fig. 3-2—Types of cathode construction. Directly heated cathodes or filaments are shown at A, B, and C. The inverted V filament is used in small receiving tubes, the M in both receiving and transmitting tubes. The spiral filament is a transmitting-tube type. The indirectly-heated cathodes at D and E show two types of heater construction, one a twisted loop and the other bunched heater wires. Both types tend to cancel the magnetic fields set up by the current through the heater.

rent flow through the actual material that does the emitting; the filament or heater can be electrically separate from the emitting cathode. Such a cathode is called **indirectly heated,** while an emitting filament is called **directly heated.** Fig. 3-2 shows both types in the forms in which they are commonly used.

Much greater electron emission can be obtained, at relatively low temperatures, by using special cathode materials rather than pure metals. One of these is **thoriated tungsten,** or tungsten in which thorium is dissolved. Still greater efficiency is achieved in the **oxide-coated** cathode, a cathode in which rare-earth oxides form a coating over a metal base.

Although the oxide-coated cathode has much the highest efficiency, it can be used successfully only in tubes that operate at rather low plate voltages. Its use is therefore confined to receiving-type tubes and to the smaller varieties of transmitting tubes. The thoriated filament, on the other hand, will operate well in high-voltage tubes.

Plate Current

If there is only a small positive voltage on the plate, the number of electrons reaching it will be small because the space charge (which is negative) prevents those electrons nearest the cathode from being attracted to the plate. As the plate voltage is increased, the effect of the space charge is increasingly overcome and the number of electrons attracted to the plate becomes larger. That is, the **plate current** increases with increasing plate voltage.

Fig. 3-3 shows a typical plot of plate current *vs.* plate voltage for a two-element tube or **diode.** A curve of this type can be obtained with the circuit shown, if the plate voltage is increased in small steps and a current reading taken (by means of the current-indicating instrument — a milliammeter) at each voltage. The plate current is zero with no plate voltage and the curve rises until a **saturation point** is reached. This is where the positive charge on the plate has substantially overcome the space charge and

almost all the electrons are going to the plate. At higher voltages the plate current stays at practically the same value.

The plate voltage multiplied by the plate current is the **power input** to the tube. In a circuit like that of Fig. 3-3 this power is all used in heating the plate. If the power input is large, the plate temperature may rise to a very high value (the plate may become red or even white hot). The heat developed in the plate is radiated to the bulb of the tube, and in turn radiated by the bulb to the surrounding air.

● RECTIFICATION

Since current can flow through a tube in only one direction, a diode can be used to change alternating current into direct current. It does this by permitting current to flow when the plate is positive with respect to the cathode, but by shutting off current flow when the plate is negative.

Fig. 3-4 shows a representative circuit. Alternating voltage from the secondary of the transformer, *T,* is applied to the diode tube in series with a **load resistor,** *R.* The voltage varies as is usual with a.c., but current flows through the tube and *R* only when the plate is positive with respect to the cathode — that is, during the half-cycle when the upper end of the transformer winding is positive. During the negative half-cycle there is simply a gap in the current flow. This **rectified** alternating current therefore is an *intermittent* direct current.

The load resistor, *R,* represents the actual circuit in which the rectified alternating current does work. All tubes work with a load of one type or another. In this respect a tube is much like a generator or transformer. A circuit that did not provide a load for the tube would be like a short-circuit across a transformer; no useful purpose would be accomplished and the only result would be the generation of heat in the transformer. So it is with vacuum tubes; they must cause power to be developed in a load in order to serve a useful purpose. Also, to be *efficient* most of the power must do useful work in the load and not be used in heating the plate of the tube. This means that most of the voltage should appear as a drop across the load rather than as a drop between the plate and cathode.

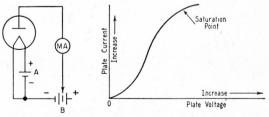

Fig. 3-3—The diode, or two-element tube, and a typical curve showing how the plate current depends upon the voltage applied to the plate.

With the diode connected as shown in Fig. 3-4, the polarity of the voltage drop across the load is such that the end of the load nearest the cathode is positive. If the connections to the diode elements are reversed, the direction of rectified current flow also will be reversed through the load.

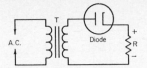
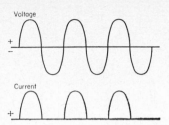

Fig. 3-4—Rectification in a diode. Current flows only when the plate is positive with respect to the cathode, so that only half-cycles of current flow through the load resistor, R.

Vacuum-Tube Amplifiers

● TRIODES

Grid Control

If a third element — called the **control grid,** or simply **grid** — is inserted between the cathode and plate as in Fig. 3-5, it can be used to control the effect of the space charge. If the grid is given a positive voltage with respect to the cathode, the positive charge will tend to neutralize the negative space charge. The

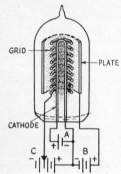

Fig. 3-5—Construction of an elementary triode vacuum tube, showing the filament, grid (with an end view of the grid wires) and plate. The relative density of the space charge is indicated roughly by the dot density.

result is that, at any selected plate voltage, more electrons will flow to the plate than if the grid were not present. On the other hand, if the grid is made negative with respect to the cathode the negative charge on the grid will add to the space charge. This will reduce the number of electrons that can reach the plate at any selected plate voltage.

The grid is inserted in the tube to control the space charge and not to attract electrons to itself, so it is made in the form of a wire mesh or spiral. Electrons then can go through the open spaces in the grid to reach the plate.

Characteristic Curves

For any particular tube, the effect of the grid voltage on the plate current can be shown by a set of **characteristic curves.** A typical set of curves is shown in Fig. 3-6, together with the circuit that is used for getting them. For each value of plate voltage, there is a value of negative grid voltage that will reduce the plate current to zero; that is, there is

a value of negative grid voltage that will **cut off** the plate current.

The curves could be extended by making the grid voltage positive as well as negative. When the grid is negative, it repels electrons and therefore none of them reaches it; in other words, no current flows in the grid circuit. However, when the grid is positive, it attracts electrons and a current **(grid current)** flows, just as current flows to the positive plate. Whenever there is grid current there is an accompanying power loss in the grid circuit, but so long as the grid is negative no power is used.

It is obvious that the grid can act as a valve to control the flow of plate current. Actually, the grid has a much greater effect on plate current flow than does the plate voltage. A small change in grid voltage is just as effective in bringing about a given change in plate current as is a large change in plate voltage.

The fact that a small voltage acting on the grid is equivalent to a large voltage acting on the plate indicates the possibility of **amplification** with the triode tube. The many uses of the electronic tube nearly all are based upon this amplifying feature. The amplified output is not obtained from the tube itself, but from the source of e.m.f. connected between its plate and cathode. The tube simply controls the power from this source, changing it to the desired form.

To utilize the controlled power, a load must be connected in the plate or "output" circuit, just as in the diode case. The load may be

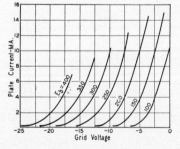
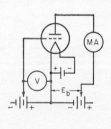

Fig. 3-6—Grid-voltage-vs.-plate-current curves at various fixed values of plate voltage (E_b) for a typical small triode. Characteristic curves of this type can be taken by varying the battery voltages in the circuit at the right.

Vacuum-Tube Amplifiers

either a resistance or an impedance. The term "impedance" is frequently used even when the load is purely resistive.

Tube Characteristics

The physical construction of a triode determines the relative effectiveness of the grid and plate in controlling the plate current. If a very small change in the grid voltage has just as much effect on the plate current as a very large change in plate voltage, the tube is said to have a high **amplification factor**. Amplification factor is commonly designated by the Greek letter μ. An amplification factor of 20, for example, means that if the grid voltage is changed by 1 volt, the effect on the plate current will be the same as when the plate voltage is changed by 20 volts. The amplification factors of triode tubes range from 3 to 100 or so. A high-μ tube is one with an amplification factor of perhaps 30 or more; **medium-μ** tubes have amplification factors in the approximate range 8 to 30, and low-μ tubes in the range below 7 or 8.

It would be natural to think that a tube that has a large μ would be the best amplifier, but to obtain a high μ it is necessary to construct the grid with many turns of wire per inch, or in the form of a fine mesh. This leaves a relatively small open area for electrons to go through to reach the plate, so it is difficult for the plate to attract large numbers of electrons. Quite a large change in the plate voltage must be made to effect a given change in plate current. This means that the resistance of the plate-cathode path — that is, the **plate resistance** — of the tube is high. Since this resistance acts in series with the load, the amount of current that can be made to flow through the load is relatively small. On the other hand, the plate resistance of a low-μ tube is relatively low.

The best all-around indication of the effectiveness of the tube as an amplifier is its **grid-plate transconductance** — also called **mutual conductance**. This characteristic takes account of both amplification factor and plate resistance, and therefore is a figure of merit for the tube. Transconductance is the change in plate current divided by the change in grid voltage that causes the plate-current change (the plate voltage being fixed at a desired value). Since current divided by voltage is conductance, transconductance is measured in the unit of conductance, the mho. Practical values of transconductance are very small, so the micromho (one-millionth of a mho) is the commonly-used unit. Different types of tubes have transconductances ranging from a few hundred to several thousand. The higher the transconductance the greater the possible amplification.

● AMPLIFICATION

The way in which a tube amplifies is best shown by a type of graph called the **dynamic characteristic**. Such a graph, together with the

circuit used for obtaining it, is shown in Fig. 3-7. The curves are taken with the plate-supply voltage fixed at the desired operating value. The difference between this circuit and the one shown in Fig. 3-6 is that in Fig. 3-7 a load resistance is connected in series with the plate of the tube. Fig. 3-7 thus shows how the plate current will vary, with different grid voltages, when the plate current is made to flow through a load and thus do useful work.

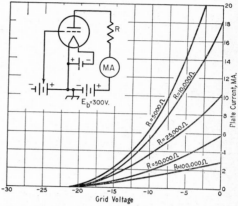

Fig. 3-7—Dynamic characteristics of a small triode with various load resistances from 5000 to 100,000 ohms.

The several curves in Fig. 3-7 are for various values of load resistance. When the resistance is small (as in the case of the 5000-ohm load) the plate current changes rather rapidly with a given change in grid voltage. If the load resistance is high (as in the 100,000-ohm curve), the change in plate current for the same grid-voltage change is relatively small; also, the curve tends to be straighter.

Fig. 3-8 is the same type of curve, but with the circuit arranged so that a source of alternating voltage (signal) is inserted between the grid and the grid battery ("C" battery). The voltage of the grid battery is fixed at −5 volts, and from the curve it is seen that the plate current at this grid voltage is 2 milliamperes. This current flows when the load resistance is 50,000 ohms, as indicated in the circuit diagram. If there is no a.c. signal in the grid circuit, the voltage drop in the load resistor is 50,000 × 0.002 = 100 volts, leaving 200 volts between the plate and cathode.

When a sine-wave signal having a peak value of 2 volts is applied in series with the bias voltage in the grid circuit, the instantaneous voltage at the grid will swing to −3 volts at the instant the signal reaches its positive peak, and to −7 volts at the instant the signal reaches its negative peak. The maximum plate current will occur at the instant the grid voltage is −3 volts. As shown by the graph, it will have a value of 2.65 milliamperes. The minimum plate current occurs at the instant the grid voltage is −7 volts, and has a value of 1.35 ma. At intermediate values of grid voltage, intermediate plate-current values will occur.

The instantaneous voltage between the plate

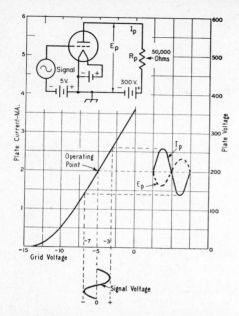

Fig. 3-8—Amplifier operation. When the plate current varies in response to the signal applied to the grid, a varying voltage drop appears across the load, R_p, as shown by the dashed curve, E_p. I_p is the plate current.

Bias

The fixed negative grid voltage (called **grid bias**) in Fig. 3-8 serves a very useful purpose. One object of the type of amplification shown in this drawing is to obtain, from the plate circuit, an alternating voltage that has the same wave-shape as the signal voltage applied to the grid. To do so, an **operating point** on the straight part of the curve must be selected. The curve must be straight in both directions from the operating point at least far enough to accommodate the maximum value of the signal applied to the grid. If the grid signal swings the plate current back and forth over a part of the curve that is not straight, as in Fig. 3-9, the shape of the a.c. wave in the plate circuit will not be the same as the shape of the grid-signal wave. In such a case the output wave shape will be **distorted**.

A second reason for using negative grid bias is that any signal whose peak positive voltage does not exceed the fixed negative voltage on the grid cannot cause grid current to flow. With no current flow there is no power consumption, so the tube will amplify without taking any power from the signal source. (However, if the positive peak of the signal does exceed the negative bias, current will flow in the grid circuit during the time the grid is positive.)

Distortion of the output wave shape that results from working over a part of the curve that is not straight (that is, a **nonlinear** part of the curve) has the effect of transforming a sine-wave grid signal into a more complex waveform. As explained in an earlier chapter, a complex wave can be resolved into a fundamental and a series of harmonics. In other words, distortion from nonlinearity causes the generation of harmonic frequencies — frequencies that are not present in the signal applied to the grid. Harmonic distortion is undesirable in most amplifiers, although

and cathode of the tube also is shown on the graph. When the plate current is maximum, the instantaneous voltage drop in R_p is 50,000 $\times$ 0.00265 = 132.5 volts; when the plate current is minimum the instantaneous voltage drop in R_p is 50,000 $\times$ 0.00135 = 67.5 volts. The actual voltage between plate and cathode is the difference between the plate-supply potential, 300 volts, and the voltage drop in the load resistance. The plate-to-cathode voltage is therefore 167.5 volts at maximum plate current and 232.5 volts at minimum plate current.

This varying plate voltage is an a.c. voltage superimposed on the steady plate-cathode potential of 200 volts (as previously determined for no-signal conditions). The peak value of this a.c. **output voltage** is the difference between either the maximum or minimum plate-cathode voltage and the no-signal value of 200 volts. In the illustration this difference is 232.5 − 200 or 200 − 167.5; that is, 32.5 volts in either case. Since the grid signal voltage has a peak value of 2 volts, the **voltage-amplification ratio** of the amplifier is 32.5/2 or 16.25. That is, approximately 16 times as much voltage is obtained from the plate circuit as is applied to the grid circuit.

As shown by the drawings in Fig. 3-8, the alternating component of the plate voltage swings in the *negative* direction (with reference to the no-signal value of plate-cathode voltage) when the grid voltage swings in the *positive* direction, and vice versa. This means that the alternating component of plate voltage (that is, the amplified signal) is 180 degrees out of phase with the signal voltage on the grid.

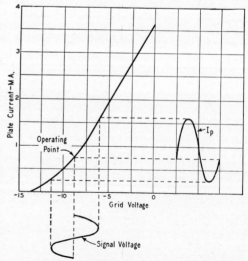

Fig. 3-9—Harmonic distortion resulting from choice of an operating point on the curved part of the tube characteristic. The lower half-cycle of plate current does not have the same shape as the upper half-cycle.

there are occasions when harmonics are deliberately generated and used.

Amplifier Output Circuits

The useful output of a vacuum-tube amplifier is the *alternating* component of plate current or plate voltage. The d.c. voltage on the plate of the tube is essential for the tube's operation, but it almost invariably would cause difficulties if it were applied, along with the a.c. output voltage, to the load. The output circuits of vacuum tubes are therefore arranged so that the a.c. is transferred to the load but the d.c. is not.

Three types of coupling are in common use at audio frequencies. These are **resistance coupling**, **impedance coupling**, and **transformer coupling**. They are shown in Fig. 3-10. In all three cases the output is shown coupled to the grid circuit of a subsequent amplifier tube, but the same types of circuits can be used to couple to other devices than tubes.

In the resistance-coupled circuit, the a.c. voltage developed across the **plate resistor** R_p (that is, the a.c. voltage between the plate and cathode of the tube) is applied to a second resistor, R_g, through a **coupling capacitor**, C_c. The capacitor "blocks off" the d.c. voltage on the plate of the first tube and prevents it from being applied to the grid of tube B. The latter tube has negative grid bias supplied by the battery shown. No current flows in the grid circuit of tube B and there is therefore no d.c. voltage drop in R_g; in other words, the full voltage of the bias battery is applied to the grid of tube B.

The **grid resistor**, R_g, usually has a rather high value (0.5 to 2 megohms). The reactance of the coupling capacitor, C_c, must be low enough compared with the resistance of R_g so that the a.c. voltage drop in C_c is negligible at the lowest frequency to be amplified. If R_g is at least 0.5 megohm, a 0.1-μf. capacitor will be amply large for the usual range of audio frequencies.

So far as the alternating component of plate voltage is concerned, it will be realized that if the voltage drop in C_c is negligible then R_p and R_g are effectively in parallel (although they are quite separate so far as d.c. is concerned). The resultant parallel resistance of the two is therefore the actual load resistance for the tube. That is why R_g is made as high in resistance as possible; then it will have the least effect on the load represented by R_p.

The impedance-coupled circuit differs from that using resistance coupling only in the substitution of a high-inductance coil (usually several hundred henrys for audio frequencies) for the plate resistor. The advantage of using an inductance rather than a resistor is that its impedance is high for alternating currents, but its resistance is relatively low for d.c. It thus permits obtaining a high value of load impedance for a.c. without an excessive d.c. voltage drop that would use up a good deal of the voltage from the plate supply.

The transformer-coupled amplifier uses a transformer with its primary connected in the plate

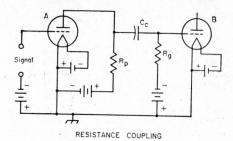

RESISTANCE COUPLING

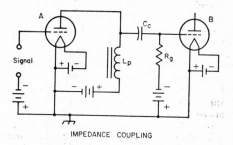

IMPEDANCE COUPLING

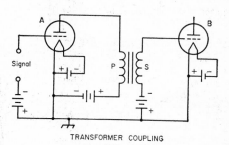

TRANSFORMER COUPLING

Fig. 3-10—Three basic forms of coupling between vacuum-tube amplifiers.

circuit of the tube and its secondary connected to the load (in the circuit shown, a following amplifier). There is no direct connection between the two windings, so the plate voltage on tube A is isolated from the grid of tube B. The transformer-coupled amplifier has the same advantage as the impedance-coupled circuit with respect to loss of d.c. voltage from the plate supply. Also, if the secondary has more turns than the primary, the output voltage will be "stepped up" in proportion to the turns ratio.

Resistance coupling is simple, inexpensive, and will give the same amount of amplification — or **voltage gain** — over a wide range of frequencies; it will give substantially the same amplification at any frequency in the audio range, for example. Impedance coupling will give somewhat more gain, with the same tube and same plate-supply voltage, than resistance coupling. However, it is not quite so good over a wide frequency range; it tends to "peak," or give maximum gain, over a comparatively narrow band of frequencies. With a good transformer the gain of a transformer-coupled amplifier can be kept fairly constant over the audio-frequency range. On the other hand, transformer coupling in voltage amplifiers (see below) is best suited to triodes having amplification factors of about 20 or less, for the reason that the primary inductance of a practicable transformer cannot be made large enough to work well with a tube having high plate resistance.

An amplifier in which voltage gain is the primary consideration is called a **voltage amplifier**. Maximum voltage gain is secured when the load resistance or impedance is made as high as possible in comparison with the plate resistance of the tube. In such a case, the major portion of the voltage generated will appear across the load and only a relatively small part will be "lost" in the plate resistance.

Voltage amplifiers belong to a group called **Class A amplifiers**. A Class A amplifier is one operated so that the wave shape of the output voltage is the same as that of the signal voltage applied to the grid. If a Class A amplifier is biased so that the grid is always negative, even with the largest signal to be handled by the grid, it is called a **Class A$_1$ amplifier**. Voltage amplifiers are always Class A$_1$ amplifiers, and their primary use is in driving a following Class A$_1$ amplifier.

Power Amplifiers

The end result of any amplification is that the amplified signal does some work. For example, an audio-frequency amplifier usually drives a loudspeaker that in turn produces sound waves. The greater the amount of a.f. power supplied to the speaker, the louder the sound it will produce.

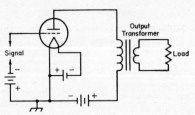

Fig. 3-11—An elementary power-amplifier circuit in which the power-consuming load is coupled to the plate circuit through an impedance-matching transformer.

Fig. 3-11 shows an elementary **power-amplifier** circuit. It is simply a transformer-coupled amplifier with the load connected to the secondary. Although the load is shown as a resistor, it actually would be some device, such as a loudspeaker, that employs the power usefully. Every power tube requires a specific value of load resistance from plate to cathode, usually some thousands of ohms, for optimum operation. The resistance of the actual load is rarely the right value for "matching" this optimum load resistance, so the transformer turns ratio is chosen to reflect the proper value of resistance into the primary. The turns ratio may be either step-up or step-down, depending on whether the actual load resistance is higher or lower than the load the tube wants.

The **power-amplification ratio** of an amplifier is the ratio of the power output obtained from the plate circuit to the power required from the a.c. signal in the grid circuit. There is no power lost in the grid circuit of a Class A$_1$ amplifier, so such an amplifier has an infinitely large power-amplification ratio. However, it is quite possible to operate a Class A amplifier in such a way that current flows in its grid circuit during at least part of the cycle. In such a case power is used up in the grid circuit and the power amplification ratio is not infinite. A tube operated in this fashion is known as a **Class A$_2$ amplifier**. It is necessary to use a power amplifier to drive a Class A$_2$ amplifier, because a voltage amplifier cannot deliver power without serious distortion of the wave shape.

Another term used in connection with power amplifiers is **power sensitivity**. In the case of a Class A$_1$ amplifier, it means the ratio of power output to the grid signal voltage that causes it. If grid current flows, the term usually means the ratio of plate power output to grid power input.

The a.c. power that is delivered to a load by an amplifier tube has to be paid for in power taken from the source of plate voltage and current. In fact, there is always more power going into the plate circuit of the tube than is coming out as useful output. The difference between the input and output power is used up in heating the plate of the tube, as explained previously. The ratio of useful power output to d.c. plate input is called the **plate efficiency**. The higher the plate efficiency, the greater the amount of power that can be taken from a tube having a given plate-dissipation rating.

Parallel and Push-Pull

When it is necessary to obtain more power output than one tube is capable of giving, two or more similar tubes may be connected in **parallel**. In this case the similar elements in all tubes are connected together. This method is shown in Fig. 3-12 for a transformer-coupled amplifier. The power output is in proportion to the number of tubes used; the grid signal or **exciting voltage** required, however, is the same as for one tube.

If the amplifier operates in such a way as to consume power in the grid circuit, the grid power required is in proportion to the number of tubes used.

An increase in power output also can be secured by connecting two tubes in **push-pull**. In this case the grids and plates of the two tubes are connected to opposite ends of a balanced circuit as shown in Fig. 3-12. At any instant the ends of the secondary winding of the input transformer, T_1, will be at opposite polarity with respect to the cathode connection, so the grid of one tube is swung positive at the same instant that the grid of the other is swung negative. Hence, in any push-pull-connected amplifier the voltages and currents of one tube are out of phase with those of the other tube.

Class B Amplifiers

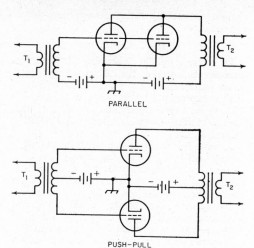

PARALLEL

PUSH-PULL

Fig. 3-12—Parallel and push-pull a.f. amplifier circuits.

In push-pull operation the even-harmonic (second, fourth, etc.) distortion is balanced out in the plate circuit. This means that for the same power output the distortion will be less than with parallel operation.

The exciting voltage measured between the two grids must be twice that required for one tube. If the grids consume power, the driving power for the push-pull amplifier is twice that taken by either tube alone.

Cascade Amplifiers

It is readily possible to take the output of one amplifier and apply it as a signal on the grid of a second amplifier, then take the second amplifier's output and apply it to a third, and so on. Each amplifier is called a **stage**, and stages used successively are said to be in **cascade**.

Class B Amplifiers

Fig. 3-13 shows two tubes connected in a push-pull circuit. If the grid bias is set at the point where (when no signal is applied) the plate current is just cut off, then a signal can cause plate current to flow in either tube only when the signal voltage applied to that particular tube is positive with respect to the cathode. Since in the balanced grid circuit the signal voltages on the grids of the two tubes always have opposite polarities, plate current flows only in one tube at a time.

The graphs show the operation of such an amplifier. The plate current of tube B is drawn inverted to show that it flows in the opposite direction, through the primary of the output transformer, to the plate current of tube A. Thus each half of the output-transformer primary works alternately to induce a half-cycle of voltage in the secondary. In the secondary of T_2, the original waveform is restored. This type of operation is called **Class B amplification**.

The Class B amplifier has considerably higher plate efficiency than the Class A amplifier. Furthermore, the d.c. plate current of a Class B amplifier is proportional to the signal voltage on the grids, so the power input is small with small signals. The d.c. plate power input to a Class A amplifier is the same whether the signal is large, small, or absent altogether; therefore the maximum d.c. plate input that can be applied to a Class A amplifier is equal to the rated plate dissipation of the tube or tubes. Two tubes in a Class B amplifier can deliver approximately twelve times as much audio power as the same two tubes in a Class A amplifier.

A Class B amplifier usually is operated in such a way as to secure the maximum possible power output. This requires rather large values of plate current, and to obtain them the signal voltage must completely overcome the grid bias during at least part of the cycle, so grid current flows and the grid circuit consumes power. While the power requirements are fairly low (as compared with the power output), the fact that the grids are positive during only part of the cycle means that the load on the preceding amplifier or **driver stage** varies in magnitude during the cycle; the effective load resistance is high when the grids are not drawing current and relatively low when they do take current. This must be allowed for when designing the driver.

Certain types of tubes have been designed specifically for Class B service and can be operated without fixed or other form of grid bias (**zero-bias tubes**). The amplification factor is so high that the plate current is small without signal. Because there is no fixed bias, the grids start drawing current immediately whenever a signal is applied, so the grid-current flow is continuous throughout the cycle. This makes the load on the driver much more constant than is the case with tubes of lower μ biased to plate-current cut-off.

Class B amplifiers used at radio frequencies are known as **linear amplifiers** because they are

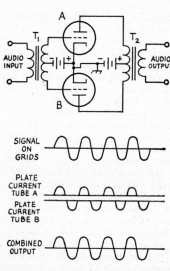

Fig. 3-13—Class B amplifier operation.

adjusted to operate in such a way that the power output is proportional to the square of the r.f. exciting voltage. This permits amplification of a modulated r.f. signal without distortion. Push-pull is not required in this type of operation; a single tube can be used equally well.

Class AB Amplifiers

A **Class AB amplifier** is a push-pull amplifier with higher bias than would be normal for pure Class A operation, but less than the cut-off bias required for Class B. At low signal levels the tubes operate practically as Class A amplifiers, and the plate current is the same with or without signal. At higher signal levels, the plate current of one tube is cut off during part of the negative cycle of the signal applied to its grid, and the plate current of the other tube rises with the signal. The plate current for the whole amplifier also rises above the no-signal level when a large signal is applied.

In a properly designed Class AB amplifier the distortion is as low as with a Class A stage, but the efficiency and power output are considerably higher than with pure Class A operation. A Class AB amplifier can be operated either with or without driving the grids into the positive region. A **Class AB₁ amplifier** is one in which the grids are never positive with respect to the cathode; therefore, no driving power is required — only voltage. A **Class AB₂ amplifier** is one that has grid-current flow during part of the cycle if the applied signal is large; it takes a small amount of driving power. The Class AB₂ amplifier will deliver somewhat more power (using the same tubes) but the Class AB₁ amplifier avoids the problem of designing a driver that will deliver power, without distortion, into a load of highly variable resistance.

Operating Angle

Inspection of Fig. 3-13 shows that either of the two tubes actually is working for only half the a.c. cycle and idling during the other half. It is convenient to describe the amount of time during which plate current flows in terms of electrical degrees. In Fig. 3-13 each tube has "180-degree" excitation, a half-cycle being equal to 180 degrees. The number of degrees during which plate current flows is called the **operating angle** of the amplifier. From the descriptions given above, it should be clear that a Class A amplifier has 360-degree excitation, because plate current flows during the whole cycle. In a Class AB amplifier the operating angle is between 180 and 360 degrees (in each tube) depending on the particular operating conditions chosen. The greater the amount of negative grid bias, the smaller the operating angle becomes.

An operating angle of less than 180 degrees leads to a considerable amount of distortion, because there is no way for the tube to reproduce even a half-cycle of the signal on its grid. Using two tubes in push-pull, as in Fig. 3-13, would merely put together two distorted half-cycles. An operating angle of less than 180 degrees

therefore cannot be used if distortionless output is wanted.

Class C Amplifiers

In power amplifiers operating at radio frequencies distortion of the r.f. wave form is relatively unimportant. For reasons described later in this chapter, an r.f. amplifier must be operated with tuned circuits, and the selectivity of such circuits "filters out" the r.f. harmonics resulting from distortion.

A radio-frequency power amplifier therefore can be used with an operating angle of less than 180 degrees. This is called **Class C** operation. The advantage is that the plate efficiency is increased, because the loss in the plate is proportional, among other things, to the amount of time during which the plate current flows, and this time is reduced by decreasing the operating angle.

Depending on the type of tube, the optimum load resistance for a Class C amplifier ranges from about 1500 to 5000 ohms. It is usually secured by using tuned-circuit arrangements, of the type described in the chapter on circuit fundamentals, to transform the resistance of the actual load to the value required by the tube. The grid is driven well into the positive region, so that grid current flows and power is consumed in the grid circuit. The smaller the operating angle, the greater the driving voltage and the larger the grid driving power required to develop full output in the load resistance. The best compromise between driving power, plate efficiency, and power output usually results when the minimum plate voltage (at the peak of the driving cycle, when the plate current reaches its highest value) is just equal to the peak positive grid voltage. Under these conditions the operating angle is usually between 150 and 180 degrees and the plate efficiency lies in the range of 70 to 80 percent. While higher plate efficiencies are possible, attaining them requires excessive driving power and grid bias, together with higher plate voltage than is "normal" for the particular tube type.

With proper design and adjustment, a Class C amplifier can be made to operate in such a way that the power input and output are proportional to the square of the applied plate voltage. This is an important consideration when the amplifier is to be plate-modulated for radiotelephony, as described in the chapter on amplitude modulation.

● FEEDBACK

It is possible to take a part of the amplified energy in the plate circuit of an amplifier and insert it into the grid circuit. When this is done the amplifier is said to have **feedback**.

If the voltage that is inserted in the grid circuit is 180 degrees out of phase with the signal voltage acting on the grid, the feedback is called **negative, or degenerative**. On the other hand, if the voltage is fed back in phase with the grid signal, the feedback is called **positive, or regenerative**.

Feedback

Negative Feedback

With negative feedback the voltage that is fed back opposes the signal voltage. This decreases the amplitude of the voltage acting between the grid and cathode and thus has the effect of reducing the voltage amplification. That is, a larger exciting voltage is required for obtaining the same output voltage from the plate circuit.

The greater the amount of negative feedback (when properly applied) the more independent the amplification becomes of tube characteristics and circuit conditions. This tends to make the frequency-response characteristic of the amplifier flat — that is, the amplification tends to be the same at all frequencies within the range for which the amplifier is designed. Also, any distortion generated in the plate circuit of the tube tends to "buck itself out." Amplifiers with negative feedback are therefore comparatively free from harmonic distortion. These advantages are worth while if the amplifier otherwise has enough voltage gain for its intended use.

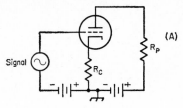

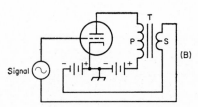

Fig. 3-14—Simple circuits for producing feedback.

In the circuit shown at A in Fig. 3-14 resistor R_c is in series with the regular plate resistor, R_p, and thus is a part of the load for the tube. Therefore, part of the output voltage will appear across R_c. However, R_c also is connected in series with the grid circuit, and so the output voltage that appears across R_c is in series with the signal voltage. The output voltage across R_c opposes the signal voltage, so the actual a.c. voltage between the grid and cathode is equal to the *difference* between the two voltages.

The circuit shown at B in Fig. 3-14 can be used to give either negative or positive feedback. The secondary of a transformer is connected back into the grid circuit to insert a desired amount of feedback voltage. Reversing the terminals of either transformer winding (but not both simultaneously) will reverse the phase.

Positive Feedback

Positive feedback increases the amplification because the feedback voltage adds to the original signal voltage and the resulting larger voltage on the grid causes a larger output voltage. The amplification tends to be greatest at one frequency (which depends upon the particular circuit arrangement) and harmonic distortion is increased. If enough energy is fed back, a self-sustaining **oscillation** — in which energy at essentially one frequency is generated by the tube itself — will be set up. In such case all the signal voltage on the grid can be supplied from the plate circuit; no external signal is needed because any small irregularity in the plate current — and there are always some such irregularities — will be amplified and thus give the oscillation an opportunity to build up. Positive feedback finds a major application in such "oscillators," and in addition is used for selective amplification at both audio and radio frequencies, the feedback being kept below the value that causes self-oscillation.

● INTERELECTRODE CAPACITANCES

Each pair of elements in a tube forms a small capacitor, with each element acting as a capacitor "plate." There are three such capacitances in a triode — that between the grid and cathode, that between the grid and plate, and that between the plate and cathode. The capacitances are very small — only a few micromicrofarads at most — but they frequently have a very pronounced effect on the operation of an amplifier circuit.

Input Capacitance

It was explained previously that the a.c. grid voltage and a.c. plate voltage of an amplifier having a resistive load are 180 degrees out of phase, using the cathode of the tube as a reference point. However, these two voltages are *in* phase going around the circuit from plate to grid as shown in Fig. 3-15. This means that their sum is acting between the grid and plate; that is, across the grid-plate capacitance of the tube.

As a result, a capacitive current flows around the circuit, its amplitude being directly proportional to the sum of the a.c. grid and plate voltages and to the grid-plate capacitance. The source of grid signal must furnish this amount of current, in addition to the capacitive current that flows in the grid-cathode capacitance. Hence the signal source "sees" an effective capacitance that is larger than the grid-cathode capacitance. This is known as the **Miller Effect**.

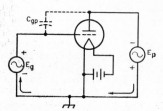

Fig. 3-15—The a.c. voltage appearing between the grid and plate of the amplifier is the sum of the signal voltage and the output voltage, as shown by this simplified circuit. Instantaneous polarities are indicated.

The greater the voltage amplification the greater the effective input capacitance. The input capacitance of a resistance-coupled amplifier is given by the formula

$$C_{\text{input}} = C_{gk} + C_{gp}(A + 1)$$

where C_{gk} is the grid-to-cathode capacitance, C_{gp} is the grid-to-plate capacitance, and A is the voltage amplification. The input capacitance may be as much as several hundred micromicrofarads when the voltage amplification is large, even though the interelectrode capacitances are quite small.

Output Capacitance

The principal component of the output capacitance of an amplifier is the actual plate-to-cathode capacitance of the tube. The output capacitance usually need not be considered in audio amplifiers, but becomes of importance at radio frequencies.

Tube Capacitance at R.F.

At radio frequencies the reactances of even very small interelectrode capacitances drop to very low values. A resistance-coupled amplifier gives very little amplification at r.f., for example, because the reactances of the interelectrode "capacitors" are so low that they practically short-circuit the input and output circuits and thus the tube is unable to amplify. This is overcome at radio frequencies by using tuned circuits for the grid and plate, making the tube capacitances part of the tuning capacitances. In this way the circuits can have the high resistive impedances necessary for satisfactory amplification.

The grid-plate capacitance is important at radio frequencies because its reactance, relatively low at r.f., offers a path over which energy can be fed back from the plate to the grid. In practically every case the feedback is in the right phase and of sufficient amplitude to cause self-oscillation, so the circuit becomes useless as an amplifier.

Special "neutralizing" circuits can be used to prevent feedback but they are, in general, not too satisfactory when used in radio receivers. They are, however, used in transmitters.

● SCREEN-GRID TUBES

The grid-plate capacitance can be reduced to a negligible value by inserting a second grid between the control grid and the plate, as indicated in Fig. 3-16. The second grid, called the **screen grid**, acts as an electrostatic shield to prevent capacitive coupling between the control grid and plate. It is made in the form of a grid or coarse screen so that electrons can pass through it.

Because of the shielding action of the screen grid, the positively charged plate cannot attract electrons from the cathode as it does in a triode. In order to get electrons to the plate, it is necessary to apply a positive voltage (with respect to the cathode) to the screen. The screen then attracts electrons much as does the plate in a triode tube. In traveling toward the screen the electrons acquire such velocity that most of them

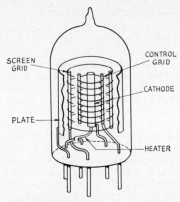

Fig. 3-16—Representative arrangement of elements in a screen-grid tetrode, with part of plate and screen cut away. This is "single-ended" construction with a button base, typical of miniature receiving tubes. To reduce capacitance between control grid and plate the leads from these elements are brought out at opposite sides; actual tubes probably would have additional shielding between these leads.

shoot between the screen wires and then are attracted to the plate. A certain proportion do strike the screen, however, with the result that some current also flows in the screen-grid circuit.

To be a good shield, the screen grid must be connected to the cathode through a circuit that has low impedance at the frequency being amplified. A bypass capacitor from screen grid to cathode, having a reactance of not more than a few hundred ohms, is generally used.

A tube having a cathode, control grid, screen grid and plate (four elements) is called a **tetrode**.

Pentodes

When an electron traveling at appreciable velocity through a tube strikes the plate it dislodges other electrons which "splash" from the plate into the interelement space. This is called **secondary emission**. In a triode the negative grid repels the secondary electrons back into the plate and they cause no disturbance. In the screen-grid tube, however, the positively charged screen attracts the secondary electrons, causing a reverse current to flow between screen and plate.

To overcome the effects of secondary emission, a third grid, called the **suppressor grid**, may be inserted between the screen and plate. This grid acts as a shield between the screen grid and plate so the secondary electrons cannot be attracted by the screen grid. They are hence attracted back to the plate without appreciably obstructing the regular plate-current flow. A five-element tube of this type is called a **pentode**.

Although the screen grid in either the tetrode or pentode greatly reduces the influence of the plate upon plate-current flow, the control grid still can control the plate current in essentially the same way that it does in a triode. Consequently, the grid-plate transconductance (or mutual conductance) of a tetrode or pentode will be of the same order of value as in a triode of corresponding structure. On the other hand, since a change in plate voltage has very little effect on the plate-current flow, both the amplification factor and plate resistance of a pentode or tetrode are very high. In small receiving pentodes the amplification factor is of the order of 1000 or higher, while the plate resistance may be from 0.5 to 1 or more megohms. Because of the high plate resistance, the actual voltage amplification possible with a pentode is very much less than the large amplification factor might indicate. A voltage gain in the vicinity of 50 to 200 is typical of a pentode stage.

In practical screen-grid tubes the grid-plate capacitance is only a small fraction of a micro-microfarad. This capacitance is too small to cause an appreciable increase in input capacitance as described in the preceding section, so the input capacitance of a screen-grid tube is simply the sum of its grid-cathode capacitance and control-grid-to-screen capacitance. The output capacitance of a screen-grid tube is equal to the capacitance between the plate and screen.

In addition to their applications as radio-frequency amplifiers, pentodes or tetrodes also are used for audio-frequency power amplification. In tubes designed for this purpose the chief function of the screen is to serve as an accelerator of the electrons, so that large values of plate current can be drawn at relatively low plate voltages. Such tubes have quite high power sensitivity compared with triodes of the same power output, although harmonic distortion is somewhat greater.

Beam Tubes

A **beam tetrode** is a four-element screen-grid tube constructed in such a way that the electrons are formed into concentrated beams on their way to the plate. Additional design features overcome the effects of secondary emission so that a suppressor grid is not needed. The "beam" construction makes it possible to draw large plate currents at relatively low plate voltages, and increases the power sensitivity.

For power amplification at both audio and radio frequencies beam tetrodes have largely supplanted the non-beam types because large power outputs can be secured with very small amounts of grid driving power.

Variable-μ Tubes

The mutual conductance of a vacuum tube decreases when its grid bias is made more negative, assuming that the other electrode voltages are held constant. Since the mutual conductance controls the amount of amplification, it is possible to adjust the gain of the amplifier by adjusting the grid bias. This method of gain control is universally used in radio-frequency amplifiers designed for receivers.

The ordinary type of tube has what is known as a **sharp-cutoff** characteristic. The mutual conductance decreases at a uniform rate as the negative bias is increased. The amount of signal voltage that such a tube can handle without causing distortion is not sufficient to take care of very strong signals. To overcome this, some tubes are made with a **variable-μ** characteristic — that is, the amplification factor decreases with increasing grid bias. The variable-μ tube can handle a much larger signal than the sharp-cutoff type before the signal swings either beyond the zero grid-bias point or the plate-current cutoff point.

● INPUT AND OUTPUT IMPEDANCES

The **input impedance** of a vacuum-tube amplifier is the impedance "seen" by the signal source when connected to the input terminals of the amplifier. In the types of amplifiers previously discussed, the input impedance is the impedance measured between the grid and cathode of the tube with operating voltages applied. At audio frequencies the input impedance of a Class A_1 amplifier is for all practical purposes the input capacitance of the stage. If the tube is driven into the grid-current region there is in addition a resistance component in the input impedance, the resistance having an average value equal to E^2/P, where E is the r.m.s. driving voltage and P is the power in watts consumed in the grid. The resistance usually will vary during the a.c. cycle because grid current may flow only during part of the cycle; also, the grid-voltage/grid-current characteristic is seldom linear.

The **output impedance** of amplifiers of this type consists of the plate resistance of the tube shunted by the output capacitance.

At radio frequencies, when tuned circuits are employed, the input and output impedances are usually pure resistances; any reactive components are "tuned out" in the process of adjusting the circuits to resonance at the operating frequency.

● OTHER TYPES OF AMPLIFIERS

In the amplifier circuits so far discussed, the signal has been applied between the grid and cathode and the amplified output has been taken from the plate-to-cathode circuit. That is, the cathode has been the meeting point for the input and output circuits. However, it is possible to use any one of the three principal elements as the common point. This leads to two additional kinds of amplifiers, commonly called the **grounded-grid amplifier** (or **grid-separation** circuit) and the **cathode follower**.

These two circuits are shown in simplified form in Fig. 3-17. In both circuits the resistor R represents the load into which the amplifier works; the actual load may be resistance-capacitance-coupled, transformer-coupled, may be a tuned circuit if the amplifier operates at radio frequencies, and so on. Also, in both circuits the batteries that supply grid bias and plate power are assumed to have such negligible impedance that they do not enter into the operation of the circuits.

Grounded-Grid Amplifier

In the grounded-grid amplifier the input signal is applied between the cathode and grid, and the output is taken between the plate and grid. The

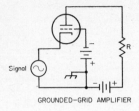

GROUNDED-GRID AMPLIFIER

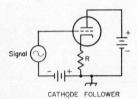

CATHODE FOLLOWER

Fig. 3-17—In the upper circuit, the grid is the junction point between the input and output circuits. In the lower drawing, the plate is the junction. In either case the output is developed in the load resistor, R, and may be coupled to a following amplifier by the usual methods.

An important feature of the cathode follower is its low output impedance, which is given by the formula (neglecting interelectrode capacitances)

$$Z_{out} = \frac{r_p}{1 + \mu}$$

where r_p is the tube plate resistance and μ is the amplification factor. Low output impedance is a valuable characteristic in an amplifier designed to cover a wide band of frequencies. In addition, the input capacitance is only a fraction of the grid-to-cathode capacitance of the tube, a feature of further benefit in a wide-band amplifier. The cathode follower is useful as a step-down impedance transformer, since the input impedance is high and the output impedance is low.

● CATHODE CIRCUITS AND GRID BIAS

Most of the equipment used by amateurs is powered by the a.c. line. This includes the filaments or heaters of vacuum tubes. Although supplies for the plate (and sometimes the grid) are usually rectified and filtered to give **pure d.c.** — that is, direct current that is constant and without a superimposed a.c. component — the relatively large currents required by filaments and heaters usually make a rectifier-type d.c. supply impracticable.

Filament Hum

Alternating current is just as good as direct current from the heating standpoint, but some of the a.c. voltage is likely to get on the grid and cause a low-pitched "a.c. hum" to be superimposed on the output.

Hum troubles are worst with directly-heated cathodes or filaments, because with such cathodes there has to be a direct connection between the source of heating power and the rest of the circuit. The hum can be minimized by either of the connections shown in Fig. 3-18. In both cases the grid- and plate-return circuits are connected to the electrical midpoint **(center tap)** of the filament supply. Thus, so far as the grid and plate are concerned, the voltage and current on one side of the filament are balanced by an equal and opposite voltage and current on the other side. The balance is never quite perfect, however, so filament-type tubes are never completely hum-

grid is thus the common element. The a.c. component of the plate current has to flow through the signal source to reach the cathode. The source of signal is in series with the load through the plate-to-cathode resistance of the tube, so some of the power in the load is supplied by the signal source. In transmitting applications this fed-through power is of the order of 10 per cent of the total power output, using tubes suitable for grounded-grid service.

The input impedance of the grounded-grid amplifier consists of a capacitance in parallel with an equivalent resistance representing the power furnished by the driving source to the grid and to the load. This resistance is of the order of a few hundred ohms. The output impedance, neglecting the interelectrode capacitances, is equal to the plate resistance of the tube. This is the same as in the case of the grounded-cathode amplifier.

The grounded-grid amplifier is widely used at v.h.f. and u.h.f., where the more conventional amplifier circuit fails to work properly. With a triode tube designed for this type of operation, an r.f. amplifier can be built that is free from the type of feedback that causes oscillation. This requires that the grid act as a shield between the cathode and plate, reducing the plate-cathode capacitance to a very low value.

Cathode Follower

The cathode follower uses the plate of the tube as the common element. The input signal is applied between the grid and plate (assuming negligible impedance in the batteries) and the output is taken between cathode and plate. This circuit is degenerative; in fact, all of the output voltage is fed back into the input circuit out of phase with the grid signal. The input signal therefore has to be larger than the output voltage; that is, the cathode follower gives a loss in voltage, although it gives the same power gain as other circuits under equivalent operating conditions.

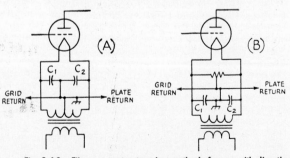

Fig. 3-18—Filament center-tapping methods for use with directly heated tubes.

Cathode Circuits and Grid Bias

free. For this reason directly-heated filaments are employed for the most part in power tubes, where the amount of hum introduced is extremely small in comparison with the power-output level.

With indirectly heated cathodes the chief problem is the magnetic field set up by the heater. Occasionally, also, there is leakage between the heater and cathode, allowing a small a.c. voltage to get to the grid. If hum appears, grounding one side of the heater supply usually will help to reduce it, although sometimes better results are obtained if the heater supply is center-tapped and the center-tap grounded, as in Fig. 3-18.

Cathode Bias

In the simplified amplifier circuits discussed in this chapter, grid bias has been supplied by a battery. However, in equipment that operates from the power line **cathode bias** is very frequently used.

The cathode-bias method uses a resistor (**cathode resistor**) connected in series with the cathode, as shown at R in Fig. 3-19. The direction of plate-current flow is such that the end of the resistor nearest the cathode is positive. The voltage drop

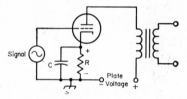

Fig. 3-19—Cathode biasing. R is the cathode resistor and C is the cathode bypass capacitor.

across R therefore places a *negative* voltage on the grid. This negative bias is obtained from the steady d.c. plate current.

If the alternating component of plate current flows through R when the tube is amplifying, the voltage drop caused by the a.c. will be degenerative (note the similarity between this circuit and that of Fig. 3-14A). To prevent this the resistor is bypassed by a capacitor, C, that has very low reactance compared with the resistance of R. Depending on the type of tube and the particular kind of operation, R may be between about 100 and 3000 ohms. For good bypassing at the low audio frequencies, C should be 10 to 50 microfarads (electrolytic capacitors are used for this purpose). At radio frequencies, capacitances of about 100 $\mu\mu$f. to 0.1 μf. are used; the small values are sufficient at very high frequencies and the largest at low and medium frequencies. In the range 3 to 30 megacycles a capacitance of 0.01 μf. is satisfactory.

The value of cathode resistor for an amplifier having negligible d.c. resistance in its plate circuit (transformer or impedance coupled) can easily be calculated from the known operating conditions of the tube. The proper grid bias and plate current always are specified by the manufacturer. Knowing these, the required resistance can be found by applying Ohm's Law.

Example: It is found from tube tables that the tube to be used should have a negative grid bias of 8 volts and that at this bias the plate current will be 12 milliamperes (0.012 amp.). The required cathode resistance is then

$$R = \frac{E}{I} = \frac{8}{0.012} = 667 \text{ ohms.}$$

The nearest standard value, 680 ohms, would be close enough. The power used in the resistor is

$$P = EI = 8 \times 0.012 = 0.096 \text{ watt.}$$

A ¼-watt or ½-watt resistor would have ample rating.

The current that flows through R is the total cathode current. In an ordinary triode amplifier this is the same as the plate current, but in a screen-grid tube the cathode current is the sum of the plate and screen currents. Hence these two currents must be added when calculating the value of cathode resistor required for a screen-grid tube.

Example: A receiving pentode requires 3 volts negative bias. At this bias and the recommended plate and screen voltages, its plate current is 9 ma. and its screen current is 2 ma. The cathode current is therefore 11 ma. (0.011 amp.). The required resistance is

$$R = \frac{E}{I} = \frac{3}{0.011} = 272 \text{ ohms.}$$

A 270-ohm resistor would be satisfactory. The power in the resistor is

$$P = EI = 3 \times 0.011 = 0.033 \text{ watt.}$$

The cathode-resistor method of biasing is self-regulating, because if the tube characteristics vary slightly from the published values (as they do in practice) the bias will increase if the plate current is slightly high, or decrease if it is slightly low. This tends to hold the plate current at the proper value.

Calculation of the cathode resistor for a resistance-coupled amplifier is ordinarily not practicable by the method described above, because the plate current in such an amplifier is usually much smaller than the rated value given in the tube tables. However, representative data for the tubes commonly used as resistance-coupled amplifiers are given in the chapter on audio amplifiers, including cathode-resistor values.

"Contact Potential" Bias

In the absence of any negative bias voltage on the grid of a tube, some of the electrons in the space charge will have enough velocity to reach the grid. This causes a small current (of the order of microamperes) to flow in the external circuit between the grid and cathode. If the current is made to flow through a high resistance — a megohm or so — the resulting voltage drop in the resistor will give the grid a negative bias of the order of one volt. The bias so obtained is called contact-potential bias.

Contact-potential bias can be used to advantage in circuits operating at low signal levels (less than one volt peak) since it eliminates the cathode-bias resistor and bypass capacitor. It is principally used in low-level resistance-coupled audio amplifiers. The bias resistor is connected directly between grid and cathode, and must be isolated from the signal source by a blocking capacitor.

Screen Supply

In practical circuits using tetrodes and pentodes the voltage for the screen frequently is taken from the plate supply through a resistor. A typical circuit for an r.f. amplifier is shown in Fig. 3-20. Resistor R is the **screen dropping resistor**, and C is the **screen bypass capacitor**. In flowing through R, the screen current causes a voltage drop in R that reduces the plate-supply voltage to the proper value for the screen. When the plate-supply voltage and the screen current are known, the value of R can be calculated from Ohm's Law.

Example: An r.f. receiving pentode has a rated screen current of 2 milliamperes (0.002 amp.) at normal operating conditions. The rated screen voltage is 100 volts, and the plate supply gives 250 volts. To put 100 volts on the screen, the drop across R must be equal to the difference between the plate-supply voltage and the screen voltage; that is, $250 - 100 = 150$ volts. Then

$$R = \frac{E}{I} = \frac{150}{0.002} = 75{,}000 \text{ ohms.}$$

The power to be dissipated in the resistor is

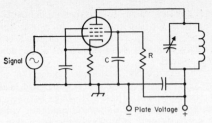

Fig. 3-20—Screen-voltage supply for a pentode tube through a dropping resistor, R. The screen bypass capacitor, C, must have low enough reactance to bring the screen to ground potential for the frequency or frequencies being amplified.

$$P = EI = 150 \times 0.002 = 0.3 \text{ watt.}$$

A ½- or 1-watt resistor would be satisfactory.

The reactance of the screen bypass capacitor, C, should be low compared with the screen-to-cathode impedance. For radio-frequency applications a capacitance in the vicinity of 0.01 µf. is amply large.

In some vacuum-tube circuits the screen voltage is obtained from a voltage divider connected across the plate supply. The design of voltage dividers is discussed at length in Chapter 7 on Power Supplies.

Oscillators

It was mentioned earlier that if there is enough positive feedback in an amplifier circuit, self-sustaining oscillations will be set up. When an amplifier is arranged so that this condition exists it is called an **oscillator**.

Oscillations normally take place at only one frequency, and a desired frequency of oscillation can be obtained by using a resonant circuit tuned to that frequency. For example, in Fig. 3-21A the circuit LC is tuned to the desired frequency of oscillation. The cathode of the tube is connected to a tap on coil L and the grid and plate are connected to opposite ends of the tuned circuit. When an r.f. current flows in the tuned circuit there is a voltage drop across L that increases progressively along the turns. Thus the point at which the tap is connected will be at an intermediate potential with respect to the two ends of the coil. The amplified current in the plate circuit, which flows through the bottom section of L, is in phase with the current already flowing in the circuit and thus in the proper relationship for positive feedback.

The amount of feedback depends on the position of the tap. If the tap is too near the grid end the voltage drop between grid and cathode is too small to give enough feedback to sustain oscillation, and if it is too near the plate end the impedance between the cathode and plate is too small to permit good amplification. Maximum feedback usually is obtained when the tap is somewhere near the center of the coil.

The circuit of Fig. 3-21A is parallel-fed, C_b being the blocking capacitor. The value of C_b is not critical so long as its reactance is low (not more than a few hundred ohms) at the operating frequency.

Capacitor C_g is the **grid capacitor**. It and R_g (the **grid leak**) are used for the purpose of ob-

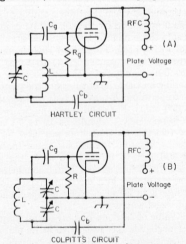

Fig. 3-21—Basic oscillator circuits. Feedback voltage is obtained by tapping the grid and cathode across a portion of the tuned circuit. In the Hartley circuit the tap is on the coil, but in the Colpitts circuit the voltage is obtained from the drop across a capacitor.

Oscillators

taining grid bias for the tube. In most oscillator circuits the tube generates its own bias. During the part of the cycle when the grid is positive with respect to the cathode, it attracts electrons. These electrons cannot flow through L back to the cathode because C_g "blocks" direct current. They therefore have to flow or "leak" through R_g to cathode, and in doing so cause a voltage drop in R_g that places a negative bias on the grid. The amount of bias so developed is equal to the grid current multiplied by the resistance of R_g (Ohm's Law). The value of grid-leak resistance required depends upon the kind of tube used and the purpose for which the oscillator is intended. Values range all the way from a few thousand to several hundred thousand ohms. The capacitance of C_g should be large enough to have low reactance (a few hundred ohms) at the operating frequency.

The circuit shown at B in Fig. 3-21 uses the voltage drops across two capacitors in series in the tuned circuit to supply the feedback. Other than this, the operation is the same as just described. The feedback can be varied by varying the ratio of the reactances of C_1 and C_2 (that is, by varying the ratio of their capacitances).

Another type of oscillator, called the **tuned-plate tuned-grid** circuit, is shown in Fig. 3-22.

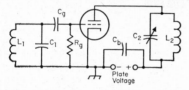

Fig. 3-22—The tuned-plate tuned-grid oscillator.

Resonant circuits tuned approximately to the same frequency are connected between grid and cathode and between plate and cathode. The two coils, L_1 and L_2, are not magnetically coupled. The feedback is through the grid-plate capacitance of the tube, and will be in the right phase to be positive when the plate circuit, C_2L_2, is tuned to a slightly higher frequency than the grid circuit, L_1C_1. The amount of feedback can be adjusted by varying the tuning of either circuit. The frequency of oscillation is determined by the tuned circuit that has the higher Q. The grid leak and grid capacitor have the same functions as in the other circuits. In this case it is convenient to use series feed for the plate circuit, so C_b is a bypass capacitor to guide the r.f. current around the plate supply.

There are many oscillator circuits (examples of others will be found in later chapters) but the basic feature of all of them is that there is positive feedback in the proper amplitude and phase to sustain oscillation.

Oscillator Operating Characteristics

When an oscillator is delivering power to a load, the adjustment for proper feedback will depend on how heavily the oscillator is loaded — that is, how much power is being taken from

the circuit. If the feedback is not large enough — grid excitation too small — a small increase in load may tend to throw the circuit out of oscillation. On the other hand, too much feedback will make the grid current excessively high, with the result that the power loss in the grid circuit becomes larger than necessary. Since the oscillator itself supplies this grid power, excessive feedback lowers the over-all efficiency because whatever power is used in the grid circuit is not available as useful output.

One of the most important considerations in oscillator design is **frequency stability**. The principal factors that cause a change in frequency are (1) temperature, (2) plate voltage, (3) loading, (4) mechanical variations of circuit elements. Temperature changes will cause vacuum-tube elements to expand or contract slightly, thus causing variations in the interelectrode capacitances. Since these are unavoidably part of the tuned circuit, the frequency will change correspondingly. Temperature changes in the coil or the tuning capacitor will alter the inductance or capacitance slightly, again causing a shift in the resonant frequency. These effects are relatively slow in operation, and the frequency change caused by them is called **drift**.

A change in plate voltage usually will cause the frequency to change a small amount, an effect called **dynamic instability**. Dynamic instability can be reduced by using a tuned circuit of high effective Q. The energy taken from the circuit to supply grid losses, as well as energy supplied to a load, represent an increase in the effective resistance of the tuned circuit and thus lower its Q. For highest stability, therefore, the coupling between the tuned circuit and the tube and load must be kept as loose as possible. Preferably, the oscillator should not be required to deliver power to an external circuit, and a high value of grid leak resistance should be used since this helps to raise the tube grid and plate resistances as seen by the tuned circuit. Loose coupling can be effected in a variety of ways — one, for example, is by "tapping down" on the tank for the connections to the grid and plate. This is done in the "series-tuned" Colpitts circuit widely used in variable-frequency oscillators for amateur transmitters and described in a later chapter. Alternatively, the L/C ratio may be made as small as possible while sustaining stable oscillation (**high C**) with the grid and plate connected to the ends of the circuit as shown in Figs. 3-21 and 3-22. Using relatively high plate voltage and low plate current also is desirable.

In general, dynamic stability will be at maximum when the feedback is adjusted to the least value that permits reliable oscillation. The use of a tube having a high value of transconductance is desirable, since the higher the transconductance the looser the permissible coupling to the tuned circuit and the smaller the feedback required.

Load variations act in much the same way as plate-voltage variations. A temperature change in the load may also result in drift.

Mechanical variations, usually caused by

vibration, cause changes in inductance and/ or capacitance that in turn cause the frequency to "wobble" in step with the vibration.

Methods of minimizing frequency variations in oscillators are taken up in detail in later chapters.

Ground Point

In the oscillator circuits shown in Figs. 3-21 and 3-22 the cathode is connected to ground. It is not actually essential that the radio-frequency circuit should be grounded at the cathode; in fact, there are many times when an *r.f.* ground on some other point in the circuit is desirable. The r.f. ground can be placed at any point so long as proper provisions are made for feeding the supply voltages to the tube elements.

Fig. 3-23 shows the Hartley circuit with the plate end of the circuit grounded. No r.f. choke is needed in the plate circuit because the plate already is at ground potential and there is no r.f. to choke off All that is necessary is a by pass capacitor, C_b, across the plate supply. Direct

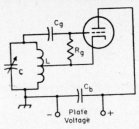

Fig. 3-23—Showing how the plate may be grounded for r.f. in a typical oscillator circuit (Hartley).

current flows to the cathode through the lower part of the tuned-circuit coil, L. An advantage of such a circuit is that the frame of the tuning capacitor can be grounded.

Tubes having indirectly heated cathodes are more easily adaptable to circuits grounded at other points than the cathode than are tubes having directly heated filaments. With the latter tubes special precautions have to be taken to prevent the filament from being by-passed to ground by the capacitance of the filament-heating transformer.

Clipping Circuits

Vacuum tubes are readily adaptable to other types of operation than ordinary (without substantial distortion) amplification and the genera-

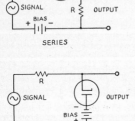

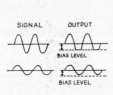

Fig. 3-24—Series and shunt diode clippers. Typical operation is shown at the right.

tion of single-frequency oscillations. Of particular interest is the clipper or limiter circuit, because of its several applications in receiving and other equipment.

Diode Clipper Circuits

Basic diode clipper circuits are shown in Fig. 3-24. In the series type a positive d.c. bias voltage is applied to the plate of the diode so it is normally conducting. When a signal is applied the current through the diode will change proportionately during the time the signal voltage is positive at the diode plate and for that part of the negative half of the signal during which the instantaneous voltage does not exceed the bias. When the negative signal voltage exceeds the positive bias the resultant voltage at the diode

plate is negative and there is no conduction. Thus part of the negative half cycle is clipped as shown in the drawing at the right. The level at which clipping occurs depends on the bias voltage, and the proportion of signal clipping depends on the signal strength in relation to the bias voltage. If the peak signal voltage is below the bias level there is no clipping and the output wave shape is the same as the input wave shape, as shown in the lower sketch. The output voltage results from the current flow through the load resistor R.

In the shunt-type diode clipper negative bias is applied to the plate so the diode is normally nonconducting. In this case the signal voltage is fed through the series resistor R to the output circuit (which must have high impedance compared with the resistance of R). When the negative half of the signal voltage exceeds the bias voltage the diode conducts, and because of the voltage drop in R when current flows the output voltage is reduced. By proper choice of R in relationship to the load on the output circuit the clipping can be made equivalent to that given by the series circuit. There is no clipping when the peak signal voltage is below the bias level.

Two diode circuits can be combined so that both the negative and positive peaks of the signal are clipped.

Triode Clippers

The circuit shown at A in Fig. 3-25 is capable of clipping both negative and positive signal peaks. On positive peaks its operation is similar to the shunt diode clipper, the clipping taking place when the positive peak of the signal voltage

Clipping Circuits

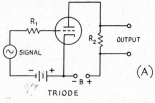

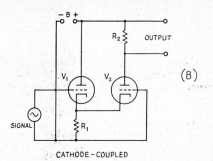

Fig. 3-25—Triode clippers. A—Single triode, using shunt-type diode clipping in the grid circuit for the positive peak and plate-current cut-off clipping for the negative peak. B—Cathode-coupled clipper, using plate-current cut-off clipping for both positive and negative peaks.

is large enough to drive the grid positive. The positive-clipped signal is amplified by the tube as a resistance-coupled amplifier. Negative peak clipping occurs when the negative peak of the signal voltage exceeds the fixed grid bias and thus cuts off the plate current in the output circuit.

In the cathode-coupled clipper shown at B in Fig. 3-25 V_1 is a cathode follower with its output circuit directly connected to the cathode of V_2, which is a grounded-grid amplifier. The tubes are biased by the voltage drop across R_1, which carries the d.c. plate currents of both tubes. When the negative peak of the signal voltage ex-

ceeds the d.c. voltage across R_1 clipping occurs in V_1, and when the positive peak exceeds the same value of voltage V_2's plate current is cut off. (The bias developed in R_1 tends to be constant because the plate current of one tube increases when the plate current of the other decreases.) Thus the circuit clips both positive and negative peaks. The clipping is symmetrical, providing the d.c. voltage drop in R_2 is small enough so that the operating conditions of the two tubes are substantially the same. For signal voltages below the clipping level the circuit operates as a normal amplifier with low distortion.

U.H.F. and Microwave Tubes

At ultrahigh frequencies, interelectrode capacitances and the inductance of internal leads determine the highest possible frequency to which a vacuum tube can be tuned. The tube usually will not oscillate up to this limit, however, because of dielectric losses, **transit time** and other effects. In low-frequency operation, the actual time of flight of electrons between the cathode and the anode is negligible in relation to the duration of the cycle. At 1000 kc., for example, transit time of 0.001 microsecond, which is typical of conventional tubes, is only 1/1000 cycle. But at 100 Mc., this same transit time represents $\frac{1}{10}$ of a cycle, and a full cycle at 1000 Mc. These limiting factors establish about 3000 Mc. as the upper frequency limit for negative-grid tubes.

With most tubes of conventional design, the upper limit of useful operation is around 150 Mc. For higher frequencies tubes of special construction are required. About the only means available for reducing interelectrode capacitances is to reduce the physical size of the elements, which is practical only in tubes which do not have to handle appreciable power. However, it is possible to reduce the internal lead inductance very materially by minimizing the lead length and by using two or more leads in parallel from an electrode.

In some types the electrodes are provided with up to five separate leads which may be connected in parallel externally. In double-lead types the plate and grid elements are supported by heavy single wires which run entirely through the envelope, providing terminals at either end of the

bulb. With linear tank circuits the leads become a part of the line and have distributed rather than lumped constants.

In "lighthouse" tubes or disk-seal tubes, the plate, grid and cathode are assembled in parallel

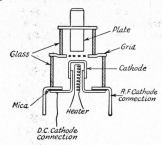

Fig. 3-26—Sectional view of the "lighthouse" tube's construction. Close electrode spacing reduces transit time while the disk electrode connections reduce lead inductance.

planes, as shown in Fig. 3-26, instead of coaxially. The disk-seal terminals practically eliminate lead inductance.

Velocity Modulation

In conventional tube operation the potential on the grid tends to reduce the electron velocity during the more negative half of the cycle, while on the other half cycle the positive potential on the grid serves to accelerate the electrons. Thus the electrons tend to separate into groups, those leaving the cathode during the negative half-cycle being collectively slowed down, while those leaving on the positive half are accelerated. After passing into the grid-plate space only a part of the electron stream follows the original form of the oscillation cycle, the remainder traveling to the plate at differing velocities. Since these contribute nothing to the power output at the operating frequency, the efficiency is reduced in direct proportion to the variation in velocity, the output reaching a value of zero when the transit time approaches a half-cycle.

This effect is turned to advantage in **velocity-modulated tubes** in that the input signal voltage on the grid is used to change the velocity of the electrons in a constant-current electron beam, rather than to vary the intensity of a constant-velocity current flow as is the method in ordinary tubes.

The velocity modulation principle may be used in a number of ways, leading to several tube designs. The major tube of this type is the "klystron."

The Klystron

In the **klystron** tube the electrons emitted by the cathode pass through an electric field established by two grids in a cavity resonator called the **buncher.** The high-frequency electric field between the grids is parallel to the electron stream. This field accelerates the electrons at one moment and retards them at another, in accordance with the variations of the r.f. voltage applied. The resulting velocity-modulated beam travels through a field-free "drift space," where the slower-moving electrons are gradually overtaken by the faster ones. The electrons emerging from the pair of grids therefore are separated into groups or "bunched" along the direction of motion. The velocity-modulated electron stream then goes to a **catcher** cavity where it again passes through two parallel grids, and the r.f. current created by the bunching of the electron beam induces an r.f. voltage between the grids. The catcher cavity is made resonant at the frequency of the velocity-modulated electron beam, so that an oscillating field is set up within it by the passage of the electron bunches through the grid aperture.

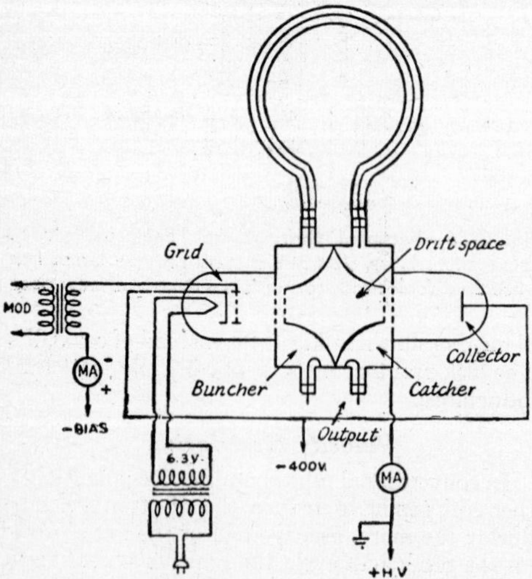

If a feed back loop is provided between the two cavities, as shown in Fig. 3-27, oscillations will occur. The resonant frequency depends on the electrode voltages and on the shape of the cavities, and may be adjusted by varying the supply voltage and altering the dimensions of the cavities. Although the bunched beam current is rich in harmonics the output wave form is remarkably pure because the high Q of the catcher cavity suppresses the unwanted harmonics.

Magnetrons

A **magnetron** is fundamentally a diode with cylindrical electrodes placed in a uniform magnetic field, with the lines of magnetic force parallel to the axes of the elements. The simple cylindrical magnetron consists of a cathode surrounded by a concentric cylindrical anode. In the more effi-

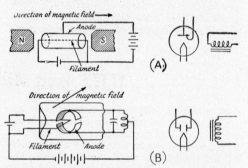

Fig. 3-28—Conventional magnetrons, with equivalent schematic symbols at the right. A, simple cylindrical magnetron. B, split-anode negative-resistance magnetron.

cient split-anode magnetron the cylinder is divided lengthwise.

Magnetron oscillators are operated in two different ways. Electrically the circuits are similar, the difference being in the relation between eletron transit time and the frequency of oscillation.

In the negative-resistance or dynatron type of magnetron oscillator, the element dimensions and anode voltage are such that the transit time is short compared with the period of the oscillation frequency. Electrons emitted from the cathode are driven toward both halves of the anode. If the potentials of the two halves are unequal, the effect of the magnetic field is such that the majority of the electrons travel to the half of the anode that is at the lower potential. That is, a decrease in the potential of either half of the anode results in an increase in the electron current flowing to that half. The magnetron consequently exhibits negative-resistance characteristics. Negative-resistance magnetron oscillators are useful between 100 and 1000 Mc. Under the best operating conditions efficiencies of 20 to 25 per cent may be obtained.

Fig. 3-27—Circuit diagram of the klystron oscillator, showing the feed-back loop coupling the frequency-controlling cavities.

U.H.F. and Microwave Tubes

In the transit-time magnetron the frequency is determined primarily by the tube dimensions and by the electric and magnetic field intensities rather than by the tuning of the tank circuits. The intensity of the magnetic field is adjusted so that, under static conditions, electrons leaving the cathode move in curved paths which just fail to reach the anode. All electrons are therefore deflected back to the cathode, and the anode current is zero. An alternating voltage applied between the two halves of the anode will cause the

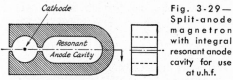

Fig. 3-29— Split-anode magnetron with integral resonant anode cavity for use at u.h.f.

potentials of these halves to vary about their average positive values. If the period (time required for one cycle) of the alternating voltage is made equal to the time required for an electron to make one complete rotation in the magnetic field, the a.c. component of the anode voltage reverses direction twice with each electron rotation. Some electrons will lose energy to the electric field, with the result that they are unable to reach the cathode and continue to rotate about it. Meanwhile other electrons gain energy from the field and are

assembly is a solid block of copper which assists in heat dissipation. At extremely high frequencies operation is improved by subdividing the anode structure into 4 to 16 or more segments, the resonant cavities for each anode being coupled to the common cathode region by slots of critical dimensions.

The efficiency of multisegment magnetrons reaches 65 or 70 per cent. Slotted-anode magnetrons with four segments function up to 30,000 Mc. (1 cm.), delivering up to 100 watts at efficiencies greater than 50 per cent. Using larger multiples of anodes and higher-order modes, performance can be attained at 0.2 cm.

Traveling-Wave Tubes

Gains as high as 23 db. over a bandwidth of 800 Mc. at a center frequency of 3600 Mc. have been obtained through the use of a **traveling-wave** amplifier tube shown schematically in Fig. 3-30. An electromagnetic wave travels down the helix, and an electron beam is shot through the helix parallel to its axis, and in the direction of propagation of the wave. When the electron velocity is about the same as the wave velocity in the absence of the electrons, turning on the electron beam causes a power gain for wave propagation in the direction of the electron motion.

The portions of Fig. 3-30 marked "input" and

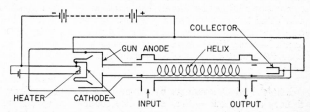

Fig. 3-30—Schematic drawing of a traveling-wave amplifier tube.

returned to the cathode. Since those electrons that lose energy remain in the interelectrode space longer than those that gain energy, the net effect is a transfer of energy from the electrons to the electric field. This energy can be used to sustain oscillations in a resonant transmission line connected between the two halves of the anode.

Split-anode magnetrons for u.h.f. are constructed with a cavity resonator built into the tube structure, as illustrated in Fig. 3-29. The

"output" are waveguide sections to which the ends of the helix are coupled. In practice two electromagnetic focusing coils are used, one forming a lens at the electron gun end, and the other a solenoid running the length of the helix.

The outstanding features of the traveling-wave amplifier tube are its great bandwidth and large power gain. However, the efficiency is rather low. Typical power output is of the order of 200 milliwatts.

CHAPTER 4

Semiconductor Devices

Certain materials whose resistivity is not high enough to classify them as good insulators, but is still high compared with the resistivity of common metals, are known as **semiconductors.** These materials, of which germanium and silicon are examples, have an atomic structure that normally is associated with insulators. However, when small amounts of impurities are introduced during the manufacture of germanium or silicon crystals, it is possible for free electrons to exist and to move through the crystals under the influence of an electric field. It is also possible for some of the atoms to be deficient in an electron, and these electron deficiencies or **holes** can move from atom to atom when urged to do so by an applied electric force. (The movement of a hole is actually the movement of an electron, the electron becoming detached from one atom, making a hole in that atom, in order to move into an existing hole in another atom.) The holes can be considered to be equivalent to particles carrying a positive electric charge, while the electrons of course have negative charges. Holes and electrons are called charge **carriers** in semiconductors.

Electron and Hole Conduction

Material which conducts by virtue of a deficiency in electrons — that is, by **hole conduction** — is called **p-type** material. In **n-type** material, which has an excess of electrons, the conduction is termed "electronic." If a piece of p-type material is joined to a piece of n-type material as at A in Fig. 4-1 and a voltage is applied to the pair as at B, current will flow across the boundary or junction between the two (and also in the external circuit) when the battery has the polarity indicated. Electrons, indicated by the minus symbol, are attracted across the junction from the n material through the p material to the positive terminal of the battery, and holes, indicated by the plus symbol, are attracted in the opposite direction across the junction by the negative potential of the battery. Thus current flows through the circuit by means of

electrons moving one way and holes the other.

If the battery polarity is reversed, as at C, the excess electrons in the n material are attracted away from the junction and the holes in the p material are attracted by the negative potential of the battery away from the junction. This leaves the junction region without any current carriers, consequently there is no conduction.

In other words, a junction of p- and n-type materials constitutes a rectifier. It differs from the tube diode rectifier in that there is a measurable, although comparatively very small, reverse current. The reverse current results from the presence of some carriers of the type opposite to those which principally characterize the material. The principal ones are called **majority carriers,** while the lesser ones are **minority carriers.**

The process by which the carriers cross the junction is essentially diffusion, and takes place comparatively slowly. This, together with the fact that the junction forms a capacitor with the two plates separated by practically zero spacing and hence has relatively high capacitance, places a limit on the upper frequency at which semiconductor devices of this construction will operate, as compared with vacuum tubes. Also, the number of excess electrons and holes in the material depends upon temperature, and since the conductivity in turn depends on the number of excess holes and electrons, the device is more temperature sensitive than is a vacuum tube.

Capacitance may be reduced by making the contact area very small. This is done by means of a **point contact,** a tiny p-type region being formed under the contact point during manufacture when n-type material is used for the main body of the device.

● SEMICONDUCTOR DIODES

Diodes of the point-contact type are used for many of the same purposes for which tube diodes are used. The construction of such a diode is

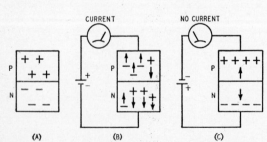

Fig. 4-1—A p-n junction (A) and its behavior when conducting (B) and non-conducting (C).

Semiconductor Diodes

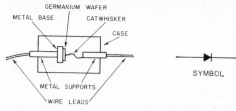

Fig. 4-2—Construction of a germanium-point-contact diode. In the circuit symbol for a contact rectifier the arrow points in the direction of minimum resistance measured by the conventional method—that is, going from the positive terminal of the voltage source through the rectifier to the negative terminal of the source. The arrow thus corresponds to the plate and the bar to the cathode of a tube diode.

shown in Fig. 4-2. Germanium and silicon are the most widely used materials, the latter principally in the u.h.f. region.

As compared with the tube diode for r.f. applications, the crystal diode has the advantages of very small size, very low interelectrode capacitance (of the order of 1 $\mu\mu$f. or less) and requires no heater or filament power.

Characteristic Curves

The germanium crystal diode is characterized by relatively large current flow with small applied voltages in the "forward" direction, and small, although finite, current flow in the reverse or "back" direction for much larger applied voltages. A typical characteristic curve is shown in Fig. 4-3. The dynamic resistance in either the forward or back direction is determined by the change in current that occurs, at any given point on the curve, when the applied voltage is changed by a small amount. The forward resistance shows some variation in the region of very small applied voltages, but the curve is for the most part quite straight, indicating fairly constant dynamic resistance. For small applied voltages, the forward resistance is of the order of 200 ohms in most such diodes. The back resistance shows considerable variation, depending on the particular voltage chosen for the measurement. It may run from a few hundred thousand ohms to over a megohm. In applications such as meter rectifiers for r.f. indicating instruments (r.f. voltmeters, wavemeter indicators, and so on) where the load resistance may be small and the applied voltage of the order of several volts, the resistances vary with the value of the applied voltage and are considerably lower.

Junction Diodes

Junction-type diodes made of germanium or silicon are employed principally as power rectifiers, in applications similar to those where selenium rectifiers are used. Depending on the design of the particular diode, they are capable of rectifying currents up to several hundred milliamperes. The safe inverse peak voltage of a junction is relatively low, so an appropriate number of rectifiers must be connected in series to operate safely on a given a.c. input voltage.

Ratings

Crystal diodes are rated primarily in terms of **maximum safe inverse voltage** and **maximum average rectified current**. Inverse voltage is a voltage applied in the direction opposite to that which causes maximum current flow. The average current is that which would be read by a d.c. meter connected in the current path.

It is also customary to specify standards of performance with respect to forward and back current. A minimum value of forward current is usually specified for one volt applied. The voltage at which the maximum tolerable back current is specified varies with the type of diode.

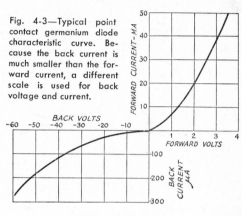

Fig. 4-3—Typical point contact germanium diode characteristic curve. Because the back current is much smaller than the forward current, a different scale is used for back voltage and current.

Zener Diodes

The "zener diode" is a special type of silicon junction diode that has a characteristic similar to that shown in Fig. 4-4. The sharp break from non-conductance to conductance is called the Zener Knee; at applied voltages greater than this breakdown point, the voltage drop across the diode is essentially constant over a wide range of currents. The substantially constant voltage

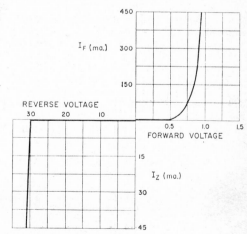

Fig. 4-4—Typical characteristic of a zener diode. In this example, the voltage drop is substantially constant at 30 volts in the (normally) reverse direction. Compare with Fig. 4-3. A diode with this characteristic would be called a "30-volt zener diode."

drop over a wide range of currents allows this semiconductor device to be used as a constant voltage reference or control element, in a manner somewhat similar to the gaseous voltage-regulator tube. Voltages for zener diode action range from a few volts to several hundred and power ratings run from a fraction of a watt to 50 watts.

Zener diodes can be connected in series to advantage; the temperature coefficient is improved over that of a single diode of equivalent rating and the power-handling capability is increased.

Two zener diodes connected in opposition, Fig. 4-5, form a simple and highly effective clipper.

Voltage-Variable Capacitors

Voltage-variable capacitors are p-n junction diodes that behave as capacitors of reasonable Q (35 or more) up to 50 Mc. and higher. They are useful in many applications because the actual capacitance value is dependent upon the d.c. bias voltage that is applied. In a typical capacitor

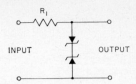

Fig. 4-5—Full-wave clipping action with two zener diodes in opposition. The output level would be at a peak-to-peak voltage of twice the zener rating of a single diode. R_1 should have a resistance value sufficient to limit the current to the zener diode rating.

the capacitance can be varied over a 10-to-1 range with a bias change from 0 to -100 volts. The current demand on the bias supply is on the order of a few microamperes.

Typical applications include remote control of tuned circuits, automatic frequency control of receiver local oscillators, and simple frequency modulators for communications and for sweep-tuning applications.

Transistors

Fig. 4-6 shows a "sandwich" made from two layers of p-type semiconductor material with a thin layer of n-type between. There are in effect two p-n junction diodes back to back. If a positive bias is applied to the p-type material at the left, current will flow through the left-hand junction, the holes moving to the right and the electrons from the n-type material moving to the left. Some of the holes moving into the n-type material will combine with the electrons there and be neutralized, but some of them also will travel to the region of the right-hand junction.

If the p-n combination at the right is biased negatively, as shown, there would normally be no current flow in this circuit (see Fig. 4-1C). However, there are now additional holes available at the junction to travel to point B and electrons can travel toward point A, so a current can flow even though this section of the sandwich considered alone is biased to prevent conduction. Most of the current is between A and B and does not flow out through the common connection to the n-type material in the sandwich.

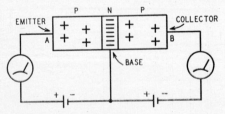

Fig. 4-6—The basic arrangement of a transistor. This represents a junction-type p-n-p unit.

A semiconductor combination of this type is called a **transistor**, and the three sections are known as the **emitter, base** and **collector**, re-

spectively. The amplitude of the collector current depends principally upon the amplitude of the emitter current; that is, the collector current is controlled by the emitter current.

Power Amplification

Because the collector is biased in the back direction the collector-to-base resistance is high. On the other hand, the emitter and collector currents are substantially equal, so the power in the collector circuit is larger than the power in the emitter circuit ($P = I^2 R$, so the powers are proportional to the respective resistances, if the current is the same). In practical transistors emitter resistance is of the order of a few hundred ohms while the collector resistance is hundreds or thousands of times higher, so power gains of 20 to 40 db. or even more are possible.

Types

The transistor may be either of the **point-contact** or **junction** type, as shown in Fig. 4-7. Also, the assembly of p- and n-type materials may be reversed; that is, n-type material may be used instead of p-type for the emitter and collector, and p-type instead of n-type for the base. The type shown in Fig. 4-6 is a **p-n-p** transistor, while the opposite is the **n-p-n**.

Point-Contact Transistors

The point-contact transistor shown at the left in Fig. 4-7, has two "cat whiskers" placed very close together on the surface of a germanium wafer, usually n-type material. Small p-type areas are formed under each point during manufacture. This type of construction results in quite low interelectrode capacitances, with the result that some point-contact transistors have been used at frequencies up to the v.h.f. region.

Transistor Characteristics

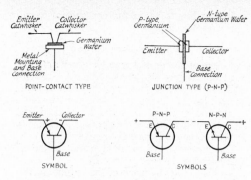

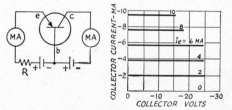

Fig. 4-7—Point-contact, junction-type and surface-barrier types of transistors with their circuit symbols. The plus and minus signs associated with the symbols indicate polarities of voltages, with respect to the base, to be applied to the elements.

The point-contact transistor is principally of historical interest, since it is now superseded by the junction type. It is difficult to manufacture, since the two contact points must be extremely close together if good characteristics are to be secured, particularly for high-frequency work.

Junction Transistors

The junction transistor, the essential construction of which is shown at the center in Fig. 4-7, has higher capacitances and higher power-handling capacity than the point-contact type. The "electrode" areas and thickness of the intermediate layer have an important effect on the upper frequency limit. Ordinary junction transistors may have cut-off frequencies (see next section) up to 20 Mc. or so. The types used for audio and low radio frequencies usually have cut-off frequencies ranging from 500 to 1000 kc.

The upper frequency limit is extended considerably in the **drift transistor**. This type has a particular form of distribution of impurities in the base material resulting in the creation of an internal electric field that accelerates the carriers across the junction. Typical drift transistors have cut-off frequencies of the order of 100 Mc.

Another type of transistor useful in high-frequency work is the **surface barrier transistor**, using plated emitter and collector electrodes on a wafer of n-type material, as shown at the right in Fig. 4-7 above. Surface barrier transistors will operate at frequencies up to 60 or 75 Mc. as amplifiers and oscillators.

● TRANSISTOR CHARACTERISTICS

An important characteristic of a transistor is its **current amplification factor**, usually designated by the symbol α. This is the ratio of the change in collector current to a small change in emitter current, measured in the common-base circuit described later, and is comparable with the voltage amplification factor (μ) of a vacuum tube. The current amplification factor is almost, but not quite, 1 in a junction transistor. It is larger than 1 in the point-contact type, values in the neighborhood of 2 being typical.

The α **cut-off frequency** is the frequency at which the current amplification drops 3 db. below its low-frequency value. Cut-off frequencies range from 500 kc. to frequencies in the v.h.f.

region. The cut-off frequency indicates in a general way the frequency spread over which the transistor is useful.

Each of the three elements in the transistor has a resistance associated with it. The emitter and collector resistances were discussed earlier. There is also a certain amount of resistance associated with the base, a value of a few hundred to 1000 ohms being typical of the base resistance.

The values of all three resistances vary with the type of transistor and the operating voltages. The collector resistance, in particular, is sensitive to operating conditions.

Characteristic Curves

The operating characteristics of transistors can be shown by a series of characteristic curves. One such set of curves is shown in Fig. 4-8. It

Fig. 4-8—A typical collector-current vs. collector-voltage characteristic of a junction-type transistor, for various emitter-current values. The circuit shows the setup for taking such measurements. Since the emitter resistance is low, a current-limiting resistor, R, is connected in series with the source of current. The emitter current can be set at a desired value by adjustment of this resistance.

shows the collector current *vs.* collector voltage for a number of fixed values of emitter current. Practically, the collector current depends almost entirely on the emitter current and is independent of the collector voltage. The separation between curves representing equal steps of emitter current is quite uniform, indicating that almost distortionless output can be obtained over the useful operating range of the transistor.

Another type of curve is shown in Fig. 4-9, together with the circuit used for obtaining it. This also shows collector current *vs.* collector voltage, but for a number of different values of base current. In this case the emitter element is used as the common point in the circuit. The collector current is not independent of collector voltage with this type of connection, indicating that the output resistance of the device is fairly low. The base current also is quite low, which

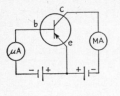 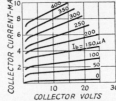

Fig. 4-9—Collector current vs. collector voltage for various values of base current, for a junction-type transistor. The values are determined by means of the circuit shown.

means that the resistance of the base-emitter circuit is moderately high with this method of connection. This may be contrasted with the high values of emitter current shown in Fig. 4-8.

Ratings

The principal ratings applied to transistors are maximum collector dissipation, maximum collector voltage, maximum collector current, and maximum emitter current. The voltage and current ratings are self-explanatory.

The collector dissipation is the power, usually expressed in milliwatts, that can safely be dissipated by the transistor as heat. With some types of transistors provision is made for transferring heat rapidly through the container, and such units usually require installation on a heat "sink," or mounting that can absorb heat.

The amount of undistorted output power that can be obtained depends on the collector voltage, the collector current being practically independent of the voltage in a given transistor. Increasing the collector voltage extends the range of linear operation, but must not be carried beyond the point where either the voltage or dissipation ratings are exceeded.

● TRANSISTOR AMPLIFIERS

Amplifier circuits used with transistors fall into one of three types, known as the **grounded-base**, **grounded-emitter**, and **grounded-collector** circuits. These are shown in Fig. 4-10 in elementary form. The three circuits correspond approximately to the grounded-grid, grounded-cathode and cathode-follower circuits, respectively, used with vacuum tubes.

The important transistor **parameters** in these circuits are the **short-circuit current transfer ratio**, the **cut-off frequency**, and the **input** and **output impedances**. The short-circuit current transfer ratio is the ratio of a small change in output current to the change in input current that causes it, the output circuit being short-circuited. The cut-off frequency is the frequency at which the amplification decreases by 3 db. from its value at some frequency well below that at which frequency effects begin to assume importance. The input and output impedances are, respectively, the impedance which a signal source working into the transistor would see, and the internal output impedance of the transistor

(corresponding to the plate resistance of a vacuum tube, for example).

Grounded-Base Circuit

The input circuit of a grounded-base amplifier must be designed for low impedance, since the emitter-to-base resistance is of the order of $25/I_e$ ohms, where I_e is the emitter current in milli-amperes. The optimum output load impedance, R_L, may range from a few thousand ohms to 100,000, depending upon the requirements.

The current transfer ratio is α and the cut-off frequency is as defined previously.

In this circuit the phase of the output (collector) current is the same as that of the input (emitter) current. The parts of these currents that flow through the base resistance are likewise in phase, so the circuit tends to be regenerative and will oscillate if the current amplification factor is greater than 1. A junction transistor is stable in this circuit since α is less than 1, but a point-contact transistor will oscillate.

Grounded-Emitter Circuit

The grounded-emitter circuit shown in Fig. 4-10 corresponds to the ordinary grounded-cathode vacuum-tube amplifier. As indicated by the curves of Fig. 4-9, the base current is small and the input impedance is therefore fairly high — several thousand ohms in the average case. The collector resistance is some tens of thousands of ohms, depending on the signal source impedance. The current transfer ratio in the common-emitter circuit is equal to

$$\frac{\alpha}{1 - \alpha}$$

Since α is close to 1 (0.98 or higher being representative), the short-circuit current gain in the grounded-emitter circuit may be 50 or more. The cut-off frequency is equal to the α cut-off frequency multiplied by $(1 - \alpha)$, and therefore is relatively low. (For example, a transistor with an α cut-off of 1000 kc. and $\alpha = 0.98$ would have a cut-off frequency of $1000 \times 0.02 = 20$ kc. in the grounded-emitter circuit.)

Within its frequency limitations, the grounded-emitter circuit gives the highest power gain of the three.

In this circuit the phase of the output (collector) current is opposite to that of the input (base) current so such feedback as occurs through the small emitter resistance is negative and the amplifier is stable with either junction or point-contact transistors.

Grounded-Collector Circuit

Like the vacuum-tube cathode follower, the grounded-collector transistor amplifier has high input impedance and low output impedance. The latter is approximately equal to the impedance of the signal input source multiplied by $(1 - \alpha)$. The input resistance depends on the load resistance, being approximately equal to the load resistance divided by $(1 - \alpha)$. The fact that input resistance is directly related to the load

Transistor Circuits

resistance is a disadvantage of this type of amplifier if the load is one whose resistance or impedance varies with frequency.

The current transfer ratio with this circuit is

$$\frac{1}{1 - \alpha}$$

and the cut-off frequency is the same as in the grounded-emitter circuit. The output and input currents are in phase.

Practical Circuit Details

The transistor is essentially a low-voltage device, so the use of a battery power supply rather than a rectified-a.c. supply is quite common. Usually, it is more convenient to employ a single battery as a power source in preference to the two-battery arrangements shown in Fig. 4-10, so most circuits are designed for single-battery operation. Provision must be included, therefore, for obtaining proper biasing voltage for the emitter-base circuit from the battery that supplies the power in the collector circuit.

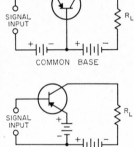

Fig. 4-10—Basic transistor amplifier circuits. R_L, the load resistance, may be an actual resistor or the primary of a transformer. The input signal may be supplied from a transformer secondary or by resistance-capacitance coupling. In any case it is to be understood that a d.c. path must exist between the base and emitter.

P-n-p transistors are shown in these circuits. If n-p-n types are used the battery polarities must be reversed.

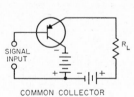

Coupling arrangements for introducing the input signal into the circuit and for taking out the amplified signal are similar to those used with vacuum tubes. However, the actual component values will in general be quite different from those used with tubes. This is because the impedances associated with the input and output circuits of transistors may differ widely from the comparable impedances in tube circuits. Also, d.c. voltage drops in resistances may require more careful attention with transistors because of the much lower voltage available from the ordinary battery power source. Battery economy becomes an important factor in circuit design, both with respect to voltage required and to overall current drain. A bias voltage divider, for example, easily may use more power than the transistor with which it is associated.

Typical single-battery grounded-emitter cir-

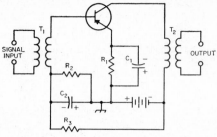

TRANSFORMER COUPLING

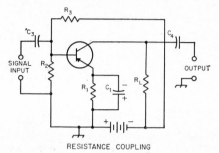

RESISTANCE COUPLING

Fig. 4-11—Practical grounded-emitter circuits using transformer and resistance coupling. A combination of either also can be used—e.g., resistance-coupled input and transformer-coupled output. Tuned transformers may be used for r.f. and i.f. circuits.

With small transistors used for low-level amplification the input impedance will be of the order of 1000 ohms and the input circuit should be designed for an impedance step-down, if necessary. This can be done by appropriate choice of turns ratio for T_1 or, in the case of tuned circuits, by tapping the base down on the tuned secondary circuit. In the resistance-coupled circuit R_2 should be large compared with the input impedance, values of the order of 10,000 ohms being used.

In low-level circuits R_1 will be of the order of 1000 ohms. R_3 should be chosen to bias the transistor to the desired no-signal collector current; its value depends on R_1 and R_2 (see text).

cuits are shown in Fig. 4-11. R_1, in series with the emitter, is for the purpose of "swamping out" the resistance of the emitter-base diode; this swamping helps to stabilize the emitter current. The resistance of R_1 should be large compared with that of the emitter-base diode, which, as stated earlier, is approximately equal to 25 divided by the emitter current in ma.

Since the current in R_1 flows in such a direction as to bias the emitter negatively with respect to the base (a p-n-p transistor is assumed), a base-emitter bias slightly greater than the drop in R_1 must be supplied. The proper operating point is achieved through adjustment of voltage divider R_2R_3, the constants of which are chosen to give the desired value of collector current at the no-signal operating point.

In the transformer-coupled circuit, input signal currents flow through R_1 and R_2, and there would be a loss of signal power at the base-emitter diode if these resistors were not bypassed by C_1 and C_2. The capacitors should have low reactance compared with the resistances across which they are connected. In the resistance-coupled circuit R_2

has the dual function of acting as part of the bias voltage divider and as part of the load resistance for the signal-input source. Also, as seen by the signal source, R_3 is in parallel with R_2 and thus becomes part of the input load resistance. C_3 must therefore have low reactance compared with the net resistance of the parallel combination of R_2, R_3 and the base-to-emitter resistance of the transistor. The reactance of C_4 will depend on the impedance of the load into which the circuit delivers output.

The output load resistance in the transformer-coupled case will be the actual load as reflected at the primary of the transformer, and its proper value will be determined by the transistor characteristics and the type of operation (Class A, B, etc.). The value of R_L in the resistance-coupled case is usually such as to permit the maximum a.c. voltage swing in the collector circuit without undue distortion, since Class A operation is usual with this type of amplifier.

Bias Stabilization

Transistor currents are rather sensitive to temperature variations, and so the operating point tends to shift as the transistor heats. The shift in operating point unfortunately is in such a direction as to increase the heating, leading to "thermal runaway" and possible destruction of the transistor. The heat developed depends on the amount of power dissipated in the transistor, so it is obviously advantageous in this respect to operate with as little internal dissipation as possible: i.e., the d.c. input should be kept to the lowest value that will permit the type of operation desired, and in any event should never exceed the rated value for the particular transistor used.

A contributing factor to the shift in operating point is the collector-to-base leakage current (usually designated I_{co}) — that is, the current that flows from collector to base with the emitter connection open. This current, which is highly temperature sensitive, has the effect of increasing the emitter current by an amount much larger than I_{co} itself, thus shifting the operating point in such a way as to increase the collector current. This effect is reduced to the extent that I_{co} can be made to flow out of the base terminal rather than through the base-emitter diode. In the circuits of Fig. 4-11, bias stabilization is improved by making the resistance of R_1 as large as possible and both R_2 and R_3 as small as possible, consistent with other considerations such as gain and battery economy.

● TRANSISTOR OSCILLATORS

Since more power is available from the output circuit than is necessary for its generation in the input circuit, it is possible to use some of the output power to supply the input circuit and thus sustain self-oscillation. Representative oscillator circuits are shown in Fig. 4-12. Their resemblance to the similarly-named vacuum-tube circuits is evident.

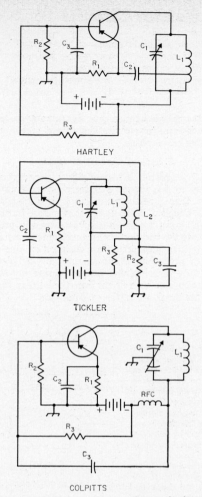

HARTLEY

TICKLER

COLPITTS

Fig. 4-12—Typical transistor oscillator circuits. Component values are discussed in the text.

The upper frequency limit for oscillation is principally a function of the cut-off frequency of the transistor used, and oscillation will cease at the frequency at which there is insufficient amplification to supply the energy required to overcome circuit losses. Transistor oscillators usually will operate up to, and sometimes well beyond, the α cut-off frequency of the particular transistor used.

The approximate oscillation frequency is that of the tuned circuit, L_1C_1. R_1, R_2 and R_3 have the same functions as in the amplifier circuits given in Fig. 4-11. Capacitors C_2 and C_3 are bypass or blocking capacitors and should have low reactance compared with the resistances with which they are associated.

Feedback in these circuits is adjusted in the same way as with tube oscillators. In the Hartley circuit it is dependent on the position of the tap on the tank coil; in the tickler circuit, on the number of turns in L_2 and degree of coupling between L_1 and L_2; and in the Colpitts circuit, on the ratio of the tank capacitance between base and emitter to the tank capacitance between collector and emitter.

CHAPTER 5

High-Frequency Receivers

A good receiver in the amateur station makes the difference between mediocre contacts and solid QSOs, and its importance cannot be over-emphasized. In the less crowded v.h.f. bands, **sensitivity** (the ability to bring in weak signals) is the most important factor in a receiver. In the more crowded amateur bands, good sensitivity must be combined with **selectivity** (the ability to distinguish between signals separated by only a small frequency difference). To receive weak signals, the receiver must furnish enough **amplification** to amplify the minute signal power delivered by the antenna up to a useful amount of power that will operate a loudspeaker or set of headphones. Before the amplified signal can operate the speaker or phones, it must be converted to audio-frequency power by the process of **detection.** The sequence of amplification is not too important — some of the amplification can take place (and usually does) before detection, and some can be used after detection.

There are major differences between receivers for phone reception and for code reception. An a.m. phone signal has side bands that make the signal take up about 6 or 8 kc. in the band, and the audio quality of the received signal is impaired if the bandwidth is less than half of this. A code signal occupies only a few hundred cycles at the most, and consequently the bandwidth of a code receiver can be small. A single-sideband phone signal takes up 3 to 4 kc., and the audio quality can be impaired if the bandwidth is much less than 3 kc. although the intelligibility will hold up down to around 2 kc. In any case, if the bandwidth of the receiver is more than nec-essary, signals adjacent to the desired one can be heard, and the selectivity of the receiver is less than maximum. The detection process delivers directly the audio frequencies present as modulation on an a.m. phone signal. There is no modulation on a code signal, and it is necessary to introduce a second radio frequency, differing from the signal frequency by a suitable audio frequency, into the detector circuit to produce an audible beat. The frequency difference, and hence the **beat note,** is generally made on the order of 500 to 1000 cycles, since these tones are within the range of optimum response of both the ear and the headset. There is no carrier frequency present in an s.s.b. signal, and this frequency must be furnished at the receiver before the audio can be recovered. The same source that is used in code reception can be utilized for the purpose. If the source of the locally generated radio frequency is a separate oscillator, the system is known as **heterodyne** reception; if the detector is made to oscillate and produce the frequency, it is known as an **autodyne** detector. Modern superheterodyne receivers generally use a separate oscillator **(beat oscillator)** to supply the locally generated frequency. Summing up the differences, phone receivers can't use as much selectivity as code receivers, and code and s.s.b. receivers require some kind of locally generated frequency to give a readable signal. Broadcast receivers can receive only a.m. phone signals because no beat oscillator is included. **Communications receivers** include beat oscillators and often some means for varying the selectivity. With high selectivity they often have a slow tuning rate.

Receiver Characteristics

Sensitivity

In commercial circles "sensitivity" is defined as the strength of the signal (in microvolts) at the input of the receiver that is required to produce a specified audio power output at the speaker or headphones. This is a satisfactory definition for broadcast and communications receivers operating below about 20 Mc., where atmospheric and man-made electrical noises normally mask any noise generated by the receiver itself.

Another commercial measure of sensitivity defines it as the signal at the input of the receiver required to give a signal-plus-noise output some stated ratio (generally 10 db.) above the noise output of the receiver. This is a more useful sensitivity measure for the amateur, since it indicates how well a weak signal will be heard and is not merely a measure of the over-all amplification of the receiver. However, it is not an absolute method, because the bandwidth of the receiver plays a large part in the result.

The random motion of the molecules in the antenna and receiver circuits generates small voltages called **thermal-agitation noise** voltages. Thermal-agitation noise is independent of frequency and is proportional to the (absolute) temperature, the resistance component of the impedance across which the thermal agitation is produced, and the bandwidth. Noise is generated in vacuum tubes by random irregularities in the current flow within them; it is convenient to express this **shot-effect noise** as an equivalent resistance in the grid circuit of a noise-free tube. This **equivalent noise resistance** is the resistance (at room temperature) that placed in the grid circuit of a noise-free tube will produce plate-circuit noise equal to that of the actual tube. The equivalent noise resistance of a vacuum tube increases with frequency.

An ideal receiver would generate no noise in its tubes and circuits, and the minimum detectable signal would be limited only by the thermal noise in the antenna. In a practical receiver, the limit is determined by how well the amplified antenna noise overrides the other noise in the plate circuit of the input stage. (It is assumed that the first stage in any good receiver will be the determining factor; the noise contributions of subsequent stages should be insignificant by comparison.) At frequencies below 20 or 30 Mc. the site noise (atmospheric and man-made noise) is generally the limiting factor.

The degree to which a practical receiver approaches the quiet ideal receiver of the same bandwidth is given by the **noise figure** of the receiver. Noise figure is defined as the ratio of the signal-to-noise power ratio of the ideal receiver to the signal-to-noise power ratio of the actual receiver output. Since the noise figure is a ratio, it is usually given in decibels; it runs around 5 to 10 db. for a good communications receiver below 30 Mc. Although noise figures of 2 to 4 db. can be obtained, they are of little or no use below 30 Mc. except in extremely quiet locations or when a very small antenna is used. The noise figure of a receiver is not modified by changes in bandwidth.

Selectivity

Selectivity is the ability of a receiver to discriminate against signals of frequencies differing from that of the desired signal. The over-all selectivity will depend upon the selectivity of the individual tuned circuits and the number of such circuits.

The selectivity of a receiver is shown graphically by drawing a curve that gives the ratio of signal strength required at various frequencies off resonance to the signal strength at resonance, to give constant output. A **resonance curve** of this type is shown in Fig. 5-1. The **bandwidth** is the width of the resonance curve (in cycles or kilocycles) of a receiver at a specified ratio; in Fig. 5-1, the bandwidths are indicated for ratios of response of 2 and 10 ("6 db. down" and "20 db. down").

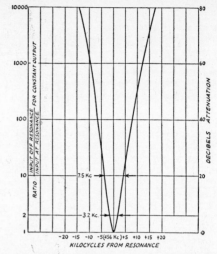

Fig. 5-1—Typical selectivity curve of a modern superheterodyne receiver. Relative response is plotted against deviations above and below the resonance frequency. The scale at the left is in terms of voltage ratios, the corresponding decibel steps are shown at the right.

The bandwidth at 6 db. down must be sufficient to pass the signal and its sidebands if faithful reproduction of the signal is desired. However, in the crowded amateur bands, it is generally advisable to sacrifice fidelity for intelligibility. The ability to reject adjacent-channel signals depends upon the **skirt selectivity** of the receiver, which is determined by the bandwidth at high attenuation. In a receiver with good skirt selectivity, the ratio of the 6-db. bandwidth to the 60-db. bandwidth will be about 0.25 for code and 0.5 for phone. The minimum usable bandwidth at 6 db. down is about 150 cycles for code reception and about 2000 cycles for phone.

Stability

The stability of a receiver is its ability to "stay put" on a signal under varying conditions of gain-control setting, temperature, supply-voltage changes and mechanical shock and distortion. The term "unstable" is also applied to a receiver that breaks into oscillation or a regenerative condition with some settings of its controls that are not specifically intended to control such a condition.

Detection and Detectors

Detection is the process of recovering the modulation from a signal (see "Modulation, Heterodyning and Beats"). Any device that is "nonlinear" (i.e., whose output is not *exactly* proportional to its input) will act as a detector. It can be used as a detector if an impedance for the desired modulation frequency is connected in the output circuit.

Detector sensitivity is the ratio of desired detector output to the input. Detector linearity is a measure of the ability of the detector to reproduce the exact form of the modulation on the incoming signal. The resistance or impedance of the detector is the resistance or impedance it presents to the circuits it is connected to. The input resistance is important in receiver design, since if it is relatively low it means that the detector will consume power, and this power must be furnished by the preceding stage. The signal-handling capability means the ability to accept signals of a specified amplitude without overloading or distortion.

Detection and Detectors

Diode Detectors

The simplest detector for a.m. is the diode. A galena, silicon or germanium **crystal** is an imperfect form of diode (a small current can pass in the reverse direction), and the principle of detection in a crystal is similar to that in a vacuum-tube diode.

Circuits for both half-wave and full-wave diodes are given in Fig. 5-2. The simplified half-wave circuit at 5-2A includes the r.f. tuned circuit, L_2C_1, a coupling coil, L_1, from which the r.f. energy is fed to L_2C_1, and the diode, D, with its load resistance, R_1, and by-pass capacitor, C_2. The flow of rectified r.f. current causes a d.c. voltage to develop across the terminals of R_1. The $-$ and $+$ signs show the polarity of the voltage. The variation in amplitude of the r.f. signal with modulation causes corresponding variations in the value of the d.c. voltage across R_1. In audio work the load resistor, R_1, is usually 0.1 megohm or

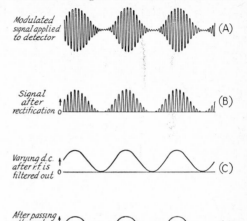

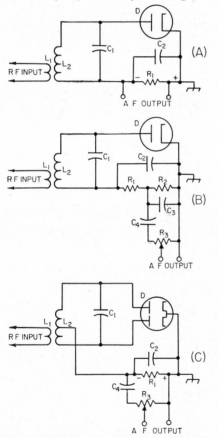

Fig. 5-2—Simplified and practical diode detector circuits. A, the elementary half-wave diode detector; B, a practical circuit, with r.f. filtering and audio output coupling; C, full-wave diode detector, with output coupling indicated. The circuit, L_2C_1, is tuned to the signal frequency; typical values for C_2 and R_1 in A and C are 250 $\mu\mu f$. and 250,000 ohms, respectively; in B, C_2 and C_3 are 100 $\mu\mu f$. each; R_1, 50,000 ohms; and R_2, 250,000 ohms. C_4 is 0.1 μf. and R_3 may be 0.5 to 1 megohm.

higher, so that a fairly large voltage will develop from a small rectified-current flow.

The progress of the signal through the detector or rectifier is shown in Fig. 5-3. A typical modulated signal as it exists in the tuned

Fig. 5-3—Diagrams showing the detection process.

circuit is shown at A. When this signal is applied to the rectifier tube, current will flow only during the part of the r.f. cycle when the plate is positive with respect to the cathode, so that the output of the rectifier consists of half-cycles of r.f. These current pulses flow in the load circuit comprised of R_1 and C_2, the resistance of R_1 and the capacity of C_2 being so proportioned that C_2 charges to the peak value of the rectified voltage on each pulse and retains enough charge between pulses so that the voltage across R_1 is smoothed out, as shown in C. C_2 thus acts as a filter for the radio-frequency component of the output of the rectifier, leaving a d.c. component that varies in the same way as the modulation on the original signal. When this varying d.c. voltage is applied to a following amplifier through a coupling capacitor (C_4 in Fig. 5-2), only the *variations* in voltage are transferred, so that the final output signal is a.c., as shown in D.

In the circuit at 5-2B, R_1 and C_2 have been divided for the purpose of providing a more effective filter for r.f. It is important to prevent the appearance of any r.f. voltage in the output of the detector, because it may cause overloading of a succeeding amplifier tube. The audio-frequency variations can be transferred to another circuit through a coupling capacitor, C_4, to a load resistor, R_3, which usually is a "potentiometer" so that the audio volume can be adjusted to a desired level.

Coupling to the potentiometer (volume control) through a capacitor also avoids any flow of d.c. through the control. The flow of d.c. through a high-resistance volume control often tends to make the control noisy (scratchy) after a short while.

The full-wave diode circuit at 5-2C differs

5 — HIGH-FREQUENCY RECEIVERS

in operation from the half-wave circuit only in that both halves of the r.f. cycle are utilized. The full-wave circuit has the advantage that r.f. filtering is easier than in the half-wave circuit. As a result, less attenuation of the higher audio frequencies will be obtained for any given degree of r.f. filtering.

The reactance of C_2 must be small compared to the resistance of R_1 at the radio frequency being rectified, but at audio frequencies must be relatively large compared to R_1. If the capacity of C_2 is too large, response at the higher audio frequencies will be lowered.

Compared with other detectors, the sensitivity of the diode is low, normally running around 0.8 in audio work. Since the diode consumes power, the Q of the tuned circuit is reduced, bringing about a reduction in selectivity. The loading effect of the diode is close to one-half the load resistance. The detector linearity is good, and the signal-handling capability is high.

Plate Detectors

The plate detector is arranged so that rectification of the r.f. signal takes place in the plate circuit of the tube. Sufficient negative bias is ap-

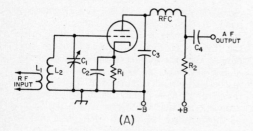

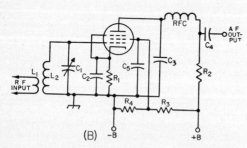

Fig. 5-4—Circuits for plate detection. A, triode; B, pentode. The input circuit, L_2C_1, is tuned to the signal frequency. Typical values for the other components are:

Component	Circuit A	Circuit B
C_2	0.5 μf. or larger.	0.5 μf. or larger.
C_3	0.001 to 0.002 μf.	250 to 500 μμf.
C_4	0.1 μf.	0.1 μf.
C_5		0.5 μf. or larger.
R_1	25,000 to 150,000 ohms.	10,000 to 20,000 ohms.
R_2	50,000 to 100,000 ohms.	100,000 to 250,000 ohms.
R_3		50,000 ohms.
R_4		20,000 ohms.
RFC	2.5 mh.	2.5 mh.

Plate voltages from 100 to 250 volts may be used. Effective screen voltage in B should be about 30 volts.

plied to the grid to bring the plate current nearly to the cut-off point, so that application of a signal to the grid circuit causes an increase in average plate current. The average plate current follows the changes in signal in a fashion similar to the rectified current in a diode detector.

Circuits for triodes and pentodes are given in Fig. 5-4. C_3 is the plate bypass capacitor, and, with RFC, prevents r.f. from appearing in the output. The cathode resistor, R_1, provides the operating grid bias, and C_2 is a bypass for both radio and audio frequencies. R_2 is the plate load resistance and C_4 is the output coupling capacitor. In the pentode circuit at B, R_3 and R_4 form a voltage divider to supply the proper screen potential (about 30 volts), and C_5 is a bypass capacitor. C_2 and C_5 must have low reactance for both radio and audio frequencies.

In general, transformer coupling from the plate circuit of a plate detector is not satisfactory, because the plate impedance of any tube is very high when the bias is near the plate-current cut-off point. Impedance coupling may be used in place of the resistance coupling shown in Fig. 5-4. Usually 100 henrys or more inductance is required.

The plate detector is more sensitive than the diode because there is some amplifying action in the tube. It will handle large signals, but is not so tolerant in this respect as the diode. Linearity, with the self-biased circuits shown, is good. Up to the overload point the detector takes no power from the tuned circuit, and so does not affect its Q and selectivity.

Infinite-Impedance Detector

The circuit of Fig. 5-5 combines the high signal-handling capabilities of the diode detector with low distortion and, like the plate detector, does not load the tuned circuit it connects to. The circuit resembles that of the plate detector, except that the load resistance, R_1, is connected between cathode and ground and thus is common to both grid and plate circuits, giving negative feedback for the audio frequencies. The cathode resistor is bypassed for r.f. but not for audio, while the plate circuit is bypassed to

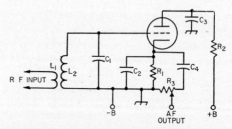

Fig. 5-5—The infinite-impedance detector. The input circuit, L_2C_1, is tuned to the signal frequency. Typical values for the other components are:

C_2—250 μμf. R_1—0.15 megohm.
C_3—0.5 μf. R_2—25,000 ohms.
C_4—0.1 μf. R_3—0.25-megohm volume control.

A tube having a medium amplification factor (about 20) should be used. Plate voltage should be 250 volts.

Detectors

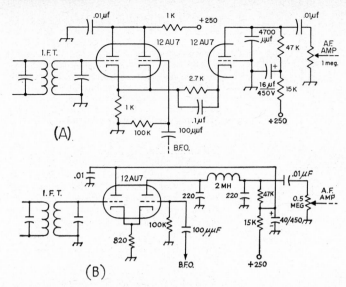

Fig. 5-6—Two versions of the "product detector" circuit. In the circuit at A separate tubes are used for the signal circuit cathode follower, the b.f.o. cathode follower and the mixer tube. In B the mixer and b.f.o. follower are combined in one tube, and a low-pass filter is used in the output.

ground for both audio and radio frequencies. An r.f. filter can be connected between the cathode and C_4 to eliminate any r.f. that might otherwise appear in the output.

The plate current is very low at no signal, increasing with signal as in the case of the plate detector. The voltage drop across R_1 consequently increases with signal. Because of this and the large initial drop across R_1, the grid usually cannot be driven positive by the signal, and no grid current can be drawn.

Product Detector

The **product detector** circuits of Fig. 5-6 are useful in s.s.b. and code reception because they minimize intermodulation at the detector. In Fig. 5-6A, two triodes are used as cathode followers, for the signal and for the b.f.o., working into a common cathode resistor (1000 ohms). The third triode also shares this cathode resistor and consequently the same signals, but it has an audio load in its plate circuit and it operates at a higher grid bias (by virtue of the 2700-ohm resistor in its cathode circuit). The signals and the b.f.o. mix in this third triode. If the b.f.o. is turned off, a modulated signal running through the signal cathode follower should yield little or no audio output from the detector, up to the overload point of the signal cathode follower. Turning on the b.f.o. brings in modulation, because now the detector output is the product of the two signals. The plates of the cathode followers are grounded and filtered for the i.f., and the 4700-$\mu\mu$f. capacitor from plate to ground in the output triode furnishes a bypass at the i.f. The b.f.o. voltage should be about 2 r.m.s., and the signal should not exceed about 0.3 volts r.m.s.

The circuit in Fig. 5-6B is a simplification requiring one less triode. Its principle of operation is substantially the same except that the additional bias for the output tube is derived from rectified b.f.o. voltage across the 100,000-ohm

resistor. More elaborate r.f. filtering is shown in the plate of the output tube (2-mh. choke and the 220-$\mu\mu$f. capacitors), and the degree of plate filtering in either circuit will depend upon the frequencies involved. At low intermediate frequencies, more elaborate filtering is required.

● REGENERATIVE DETECTORS

By providing controllable r.f. feedback (regeneration) in a triode or pentode detector circuit, the incoming signal can be amplified many times, thereby greatly increasing the sensitivity of the detector. Regeneration also increases the effective Q of the circuit and thus the selectivity. The grid-leak type of detector is most suitable for the purpose.

The grid-leak detector is a combination diode rectifier and audio-frequency amplifier. In the circuit of Fig. 5-7A, the grid corresponds to the diode plate and the rectifying action is exactly the same as in a diode. The d.c. voltage from rectified-current flow through the grid leak, R_1, biases the grid negatively, and the audio-frequency variations in voltage across R_1 are amplified through the tube as in a normal a.f. amplifier. In the plate circuit, R_2 is the plate load resistance and C_3 and RFC a filter to eliminate r.f. in the output circuit.

A grid-leak detector has considerably greater sensitivity than a diode. The sensitivity is further increased by using a screen-grid tube instead of a triode. The operation is equivalent to that of the triode circuit. The screen bypass capacitor should have low reactance for both radio and audio frequencies.

The circuit in Fig. 5-7B is regenerative, the feedback being obtained by feeding some signal from the plate circuit back to the grid by inductive coupling. The amount of regeneration must be controllable, because maximum regenerative amplification is secured at the critical point where the circuit is just about to oscillate. The critical

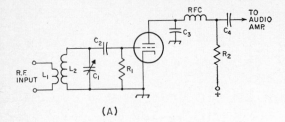

(A)

Fig. 5-7—(A) Triode grid-leak detector combines diode detection with triode amplification. Although shown here with resistive plate load, R_2, an audio choke coil or transformer could be used.

(B) Feeding some signal from the plate circuit back to the grid makes the circuit regenerative. When feedback is sufficient, the circuit will oscillate. Feedback is controlled here by varying reactance at C_5; with fixed capacitor at that point regeneration could be controlled by varying plate voltage or coupling between L_2 and L_3.

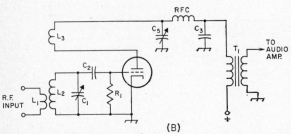

(B)

point in turn depends upon circuit conditions, which may vary with the frequency to which the detector is tuned. An oscillating detector can be detuned slightly from an incoming c.w. signal to give *autodyne* reception.

The circuit of Fig. 5-7B uses a variable by-pass capacitor, C_5, in the plate circuit to control regeneration. When the capacitance is small the tube does not regenerate, but as it increases toward maximum its reactance becomes smaller until there is sufficient feedback to cause oscillation. If L_2 and L_3 are wound end-to-end in the same direction, the plate connection is to the outside of the plate or "tickler" coil, L_3, when the grid connection is to the outside end of L_2.

Although the regenerative grid-leak detector is more sensitive than any other type, its many disadvantages commend it for use only in the simplest receivers. The linearity is rather poor, and the signal-handling capability is limited. The signal-handling capability can be improved by reducing R_1 to 0.1 megohm, but the sensitivity will be decreased. The degree of antenna coupling is often critical.

Tuning

For c.w. reception, the regeneration control is advanced until the detector breaks into a "hiss," which indicates that the detector is oscillating. Further advancing the regeneration control will result in a slight decrease in the hiss.

The proper adjustment of the regeneration control for best reception of code signals is where the detector just starts to oscillate. Then code signals can be tuned in and will give a tone with each signal depending on the setting of the tuning control. As the receiver is tuned through a signal the tone first will be heard as a very high pitch, then will go down through "zero beat" and rise again on the other side, finally disappearing at a very high pitch. This behavior

is shown in Fig. 5-8. A low-pitched beat-note cannot be obtained from a strong signal because the detector "pulls in" or "blocks"; that is, the signal forces the detector to oscillate at the signal frequency, even though the circuit may not be tuned exactly to the signal. It usually can be corrected by advancing the regeneration control until the beat-note is heard again, or by reducing the input signal.

The point just after the detector starts oscillating is the most sensitive condition for code reception. Further advancing the regeneration control makes the receiver less prone to blocking, but also less sensitive to weak signals.

If the detector is in the oscillating condition and a phone signal is tuned in, a steady audible beat-note will result. While it is possible to listen to phone if the receiver can be tuned to exact zero beat, it is more satisfactory to reduce the regeneration to the point just before the receiver goes into oscillation. This is also the most sensitive operating point.

Single-sideband phone signals can be received with a regenerative detector by advancing the regeneration control to the point used for code reception and tuning carefully across the s.s.b. signal. The tuning will be very critical, however, and the operator must be prepared to just "creep" across the signal. A strong signal will pull the detector and make reception impossible, so either the regeneration must be advanced far enough to prevent this condition, or the signal must be reduced by using loose antenna coupling.

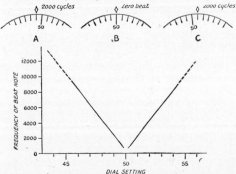

Fig. 5-8—As the tuning dial of a receiver is turned past a code signal, the beat-note varies from a high tone down through "zero beat" (no audible frequency difference) and back up to a high tone, as shown at A, B and C. The curve is a graphical representation of the action. The beat exists past 8000 or 10,000 cycles but usually is not heard because of the limitations of the audio system.

Band Spreading

Tuning and Band-Changing Methods

Band-Changing

The resonant circuits that are tuned to the frequency of the incoming signal constitute a special problem in the design of amateur receivers, since the amateur frequency assignments consist of groups or bands of frequencies at widely-spaced intervals. The same coil and tuning capacitor cannot be used for, say, 14 Mc. to 3.5 Mc., because of the impracticable maximum-to-minimum capacity ratio required, and also because the tuning would be excessively critical with such a large frequency range. It is necessary, therefore, to provide a means for changing the circuit constants for various frequency bands. As a matter of convenience the same tuning capacitor usually is retained, but new coils are inserted in the circuit for each band.

One method of changing inductances is to use a switch having an appropriate number of contacts, which connects the desired coil and disconnects the others. The unused coils are sometimes short-circuited by the switch, to avoid the possibility of undesirable self-resonances in the unused coils. This is not necessary if the coils are separated from each other by several coil diameters, or are mounted at right angles to each other.

Another method is to use coils wound on forms with contacts (usually pins) that can be plugged in and removed from a socket. These plug-in coils are advantageous when space in a multiband receiver is at a premium. They are also very useful when considerable experimental work is involved, because they are easier to work on than coils clustered around a switch.

Bandspreading

The tuning range of a given coil and variable capacitor will depend upon the inductance of the coil and the change in tuning capacity. For ease of tuning, it is desirable to adjust the tuning range so that practically the whole dial scale is occupied by the band in use. This is called **bandspreading**. Because of the varying widths of the bands, special tuning methods must be devised to give the correct maximum-minimum capacity ratio on each band. Several of these methods are shown in Fig. 5-9.

(A)

(B)

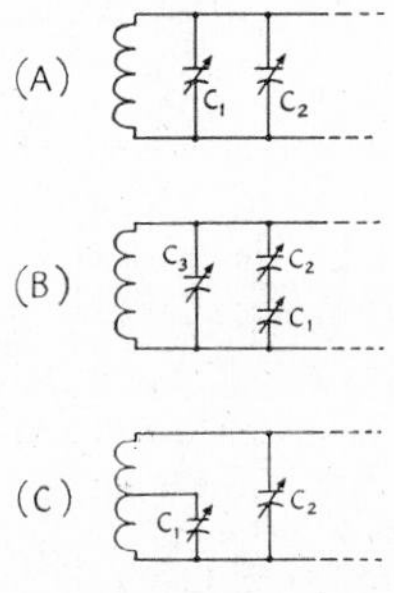

Fig. 5-9—Essentials of the three basic band-spread tuning systems.

(C)

In A, a small **bandspread capacitor**, C_1 (15- to 25-$\mu\mu$f. maximum capacity), is used in parallel with a capacitor, C_2, which is usually large enough (100 to 140 $\mu\mu$f.) to cover a 2-to-1 frequency range. The setting of C_2 will determine the minimum capacitance of the circuit, and the maximum capacity for bandspread tuning will be the maximum capacity of C_1 plus the setting of C_2. The inductance of the coil can be adjusted so that the maximum-minimum ratio will give adequate bandspread. It is almost impossible, because of the non-harmonic relation of the various band limits, to get full bandspread on all bands with the same pair of capacitors. C_2 is variously called the **band-setting** or **main-tuning** capacitor. It must be reset each time the band is changed.

The method shown at B makes use of capacitors in series. The tuning capacitor, C_1, may have a maximum capacitance of 100 $\mu\mu$f. or more. The minimum capacitance is determined principally by the setting of C_3, which usually has low capacitance, and the maximum capacitance by the setting of C_2, which is of the order of 25 to 50 $\mu\mu$f. This method is capable of close adjustment to practically any desired degree of bandspread. Either C_2 and C_3 must be adjusted for each band or separate preadjusted capacitors must be switched in.

The circuit at C also gives complete spread on each band. C_1, the bandspread capacitor, may have any convenient value; 50 $\mu\mu$f. is satisfactory. C_2 may be used for continuous frequency coverage ("general coverage") and as a band-setting capacitor. The effective maximum-minimum capacitance ratio depends upon C_2 and the point at which C_1 is tapped on the coil. The nearer the tap to the bottom of the coil, the greater the bandspread, and vice versa. For a given coil and tap, the bandspread will be greater if C_2 is set at higher capacitance. C_2 may be connected permanently across the individual inductor and preset, if desired. This requires a separate capacitor for each band, but eliminates the necessity for resetting C_2 each time.

Ganged Tuning

The tuning capacitors of the several r.f. circuits may be coupled together mechanically and operated by a single control. However, this operating convenience involves more complicated construction, both electrically and mechanically. It becomes necessary to make the various circuits **track** — that is, tune to the same frequency at each setting of the tuning control.

True tracking can be obtained only when the inductance, tuning capacitors, and circuit inductances and minimum and maximum capacities are identical in all "ganged" stages. A small **trimmer** or **padding** capacitor may be connected across the coil, so that variations in minimum capacity can be compensated. The fundamental circuit is shown in Fig. 5-10, where C_1 is the trimmer and C_2 the tuning capacitor. The use of the trimmer necessarily increases the minimum circuit capacity, but it is a necessity for satisfactory tracking. Midget capacitors having maximum capacities of 15 to 30 $\mu\mu f.$ are commonly used.

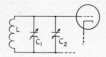

Fig. 5-10—Showing the use of a trimmer capacitor to set the minimum circuit capacity in order to obtain true tracking for gang-tuning.

The same methods are applied to band-spread circuits that must be tracked. The circuits are identical with those of Fig. 5-9. If both general-coverage and bandspread tuning are to be available, an additional trimmer capacitor must be connected across the coil in each circuit shown. If only amateur-band tuning is desired, however, then C_3 in Fig. 5-9B, and C_2 in Fig. 5-9C, serve as trimmers.

The coil inductance can be adjusted by starting with a larger number of turns than necessary and removing a turn or fraction of a turn at a time until the circuits track satisfactorily. An alternative method, provided the inductance is reasonably close to the correct value initially, is to make the coil so that the last turn is variable with respect to the whole coil.

Another method for trimming the inductance is to use an adjustable brass (or copper) or powdered-iron core. The brass core acts like a single shorted turn, and the inductance of the coil is decreased as the brass core, or "slug," is moved into the coil. The powdered-iron core has the opposite effect, and *increases* the inductance as it is moved into the coil. The Q of the coil is not affected materially by the use of the brass slug, provided the brass slug has a clean surface or is silverplated. The use of the powdered-iron core will raise the Q of a coil, provided the iron is suitable for the frequency in use. Good powdered-iron cores can be obtained for use up to about 50 Mc.

The Superheterodyne

For many years (until about 1932) practically the only type of receiver to be found in amateur stations consisted of a regenerative detector and one or more stages of audio amplification. Receivers of this type can be made quite sensitive but strong signals block them easily and, in our present crowded bands, they are seldom used except in emergencies. They have been replaced by **superheterodyne** receivers, generally called "superhets."

The Superheterodyne Principle

In a superheterodyne receiver, the frequency of the incoming signal is heterodyned to a new radio frequency, the **intermediate frequency** (abbreviated "i.f."), then amplified, and finally detected. The frequency is changed by modulating the output of a tunable oscillator (the **high-frequency**, or local, **oscillator**) by the incoming signal in a **mixer** or **converter** stage (**first detector**) to produce a side frequency equal to the intermediate frequency. The other side frequency is rejected by selective circuits. The audio-frequency signal is obtained at the **second detector**. Code signals are made audible by autodyne or heterodyne reception at the second detector.

As a numerical example, assume that an intermediate frequency of 455 kc. is chosen and that the incoming signal is at 7000 kc. Then the high-frequency oscillator frequency may be set to 7455 kc., in order that one side frequency (7455 minus 7000) will be 455 kc. The high-frequency oscillator could also be set to 6545 kc. and give the same difference frequency. To produce an audible code signal at the second detector of, say, 1000 cycles, the autodyning or heterodyning oscillator would be set to either 454 or 456 kc.

The frequency-conversion process permits r.f. amplification at a relatively low frequency, the i.f. High selectivity and gain can be obtained at this frequency, and this selectivity and gain are constant. The separate oscillators can be designed for good stability and, since they are working at frequencies considerably removed from the signal frequencies (percentage-wise), they are not normally "pulled" by the incoming signal.

Images

Each h.f. oscillator frequency will cause i.f. response at two signal frequencies, one higher and one lower than the oscillator frequency. If the oscillator is set to 7455 kc. to tune to a 7000-kc. signal, for example, the receiver can respond also to a signal on 7910 kc., which likewise gives a 455-kc. beat. The undesired signal is called the **image**. It can cause unnecessary interference if it isn't eliminated.

The radio-frequency circuits of the receiver (those used before the signal is heterodyned to the i.f.) normally are tuned to the desired signal, so that the selectivity of the circuits reduces or eliminates the response to the image signal. The ratio of the receiver voltage output from the desired signal to that from the image is called the **signal-to-image ratio,** or **image ratio.**

The image ratio depends upon the selectivity of the r.f. tuned circuits preceding the mixer tube. Also, the higher the intermediate frequency, the higher the image ratio, since raising the i.f. increases the frequency separation between the signal and the image and places the latter further away from the resonance peak of the signal-frequency input circuits. Most receiver designs represent a compromise between economy (few r.f. stages) and image rejection (large number of r.f. stages).

Frequency Converters

Other Spurious Responses

In addition to images, other signals to which the receiver is not ostensibly tuned may be heard. Harmonics of the high-frequency oscillator may beat with signals far removed from the desired frequency to produce output at the intermediate frequency; such spurious responses can be reduced by adequate selectivity before the mixer stage, and by using sufficient shielding to prevent signal pick-up by any means other than the antenna. When a strong signal is received, the harmonics generated by rectification in the second detector may, by stray coupling, be introduced into the r.f. or mixer circuit and converted to the intermediate frequency, to go through the receiver in the same way as an ordinary signal. These "birdies" appear as a heterodyne beat on the desired signal, and are principally bothersome when the frequency of the incoming signal is not greatly different from the intermediate frequency. The cure is proper circuit isolation and shielding.

Harmonics of the beat oscillator also may be converted in similar fashion and amplified through the receiver; these responses can be reduced by shielding the beat oscillator and operating it at a low power level.

The Double Superheterodyne

At high and very-high frequencies it is difficult to secure an adequate image ratio when the intermediate frequency is of the order of 455 kc. To reduce image response the signal frequently is converted first to a rather high (1500, 5000, or even 10,000 kc.) intermediate frequency, and then — sometimes after further amplification — reconverted to a lower i.f. where higher adjacent-channel selectivity can be obtained. Such a receiver is called a **double superheterodyne.**

● FREQUENCY CONVERTERS

A circuit tuned to the intermediate frequency is placed in the plate circuit of the mixer, to offer a high impedance load for the i.f. voltage that is developed. The signal- and oscillator-frequency voltages appearing in the plate circuit are rejected by the selectivity of this circuit. The i.f. tuned circuit should have low impedance for these frequencies, a condition easily met if they do not approach the intermediate frequency.

The **conversion efficiency** of the mixer is the ratio of i.f. output voltage from the plate circuit to r.f. signal voltage applied to the grid. High conversion efficiency is desirable. The mixer tube noise also should be low if a good signal-to-noise ratio is wanted, particularly if the mixer is the first tube in the receiver.

A change in oscillator frequency caused by tuning of the mixer grid circuit is called **pulling.** Pulling should be minimized, because the stability of the whole receiver depends critically upon the stability of the h.f. oscillator. Pulling decreases with separation of the signal and h.f.-oscillator frequencies, being less with high intermediate frequencies. Another type of pulling is caused by regulation in the power supply. Strong signals cause the voltage to change, which in turn shifts the oscillator frequency.

Circuits

If the first detector and high-frequency oscillator are separate tubes, the first detector is called a "mixer." If the two are combined in one envelope (as is often done for reasons of economy or efficiency), the first detector is called a "converter." In either case the function is the same.

Typical mixer circuits are shown in Fig. 5-11. The variations are chiefly in the way in which the oscillator voltage is introduced. In 5-11A, a pentode functions as a plate detector; the oscillator voltage is capacity-coupled to the grid of the tube through C_2. Inductive coupling may be used instead. The conversion gain and

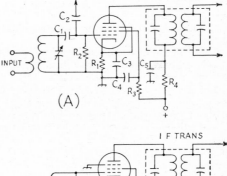

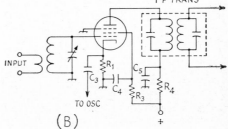

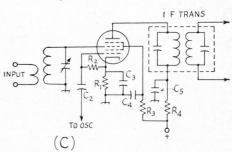

Fig. 5-11—Typical circuits for separately excited mixers. Grid injection of a pentode mixer is shown at A, cathode injection at B, and separate excitation of a pentagrid converter is given in C. Typical values for C will be found in Table 5-I—the values below are for the pentode mixer of A and B.

C_1—10 to 50 $\mu\mu$f.	R_2—1.0 megohm.
C_2—5 to 10 $\mu\mu$f.	R_3—0.47 megohm.
C_3, C_4, C_5—0.001 μf.	R_4—1500 ohms.
R_1—6800 ohms.	

Positive supply voltage can be 250 volts with a 6AC7 or 6AH6, 150 with a 6AK5.

input selectivity generally are good, so long as the sum of the two voltages (signal and oscillator) impressed on the mixer grid does not exceed the grid bias. It is desirable to make the oscillator voltage as high as possible without exceeding this limitation. The oscillator power required is negligible. If the signal frequency is only 5 or 10 times the i.f., it may be difficult to develop enough oscillator voltage at the grid (because of the selectivity of the tuned input circuit). However, the circuit is a sensitive one and makes a good mixer, particularly with high-transconductance tubes like the 6AC7, 6AK5 or 6U8 (pentode section). Triode tubes can be used as mixers in grid-injection circuits, but they are commonly used only at 50 Mc. and higher, where mixer noise may become a significant factor. The triode mixer has the lowest inherent noise, the pentode is next, and the multigrid converter tubes are the noisiest.

The circuit in Fig. 5-11B shows cathode injection at the mixer. Operation is similar to the grid-injection case, and the same considerations apply.

It is difficult to avoid "pulling" in a triode or pentode mixer, and a pentagrid mixer tube provides much better isolation. A typical circuit is shown in Fig. 5-11C, and tubes like the 6SA7, 6BA7 or 6BE6 are commonly used. The oscillator voltage is introduced through an "injection" grid. Measurement of the rectified current flowing in R_2 is used as a check for proper oscillator-voltage amplitude. Tuning of the signal-grid circuit can have little effect on the oscillator frequency because the injection grid is isolated from the signal grid by a screen grid that is at r.f. ground potential. The pentagrid mixer is much noisier than a triode or pentode mixer, but its isolating characteristics make it a very useful device.

Many receivers use pentagrid converters, and two typical circuits are shown in Fig. 5-12. The circuit shown in Fig. 5-12A, which is suitable for the 6K8, is for a "triode-hexode" converter. A triode oscillator tube is mounted in the same envelope with a hexode, and the control grid of the oscillator portion is connected internally to an injection grid in the hexode. The isolation between oscillator and converter tube is reasonably good, and very little pulling results, except on signal frequencies that are quite large compared with the i.f.

The pentagrid-converter circuit shown in Fig.

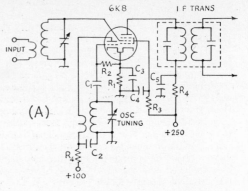

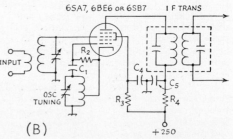

Fig. 5-12—Typical circuits for triode-hexode (A) and pentagrid (B) converters. Values for R_1, R_2 and R_3 can be found in Table 5-I; others are given below.

C_1—47 $\mu\mu f$. C_3—0.01 μf.
C_2, C_4, C_5—0.001 μf. R_4—1000 ohms.

5-12B can be used with a tube like the 6SA7, 6SB7Y, 6BA7 or 6BE6. Generally the only care necessary is to adjust the feedback of the oscillator circuit to give the proper oscillator r.f. voltage. This condition is checked by measuring the d.c. current flowing in grid resistor R_2.

A more stable receiver generally results, particularly at the higher frequencies, when separate tubes are used for the mixer and oscillator. Practically the same number of circuit components is required whether or not a combination tube is used, so that there is very little difference to be realized from the cost standpoint.

Typical circuit constants for converter tubes are given in Table 5-I. The grid leak referred to is the oscillator grid leak or injection-grid return, R_2 of Figs. 5-11C and 5-12.

The effectiveness of converter tubes of the type just described becomes less as the signal frequency is increased. Some oscillator voltage will

TABLE 5-I

Circuit and Operating Values for Converter Tubes

Plate voltage=250   Screen voltage=100, or through specified resistor from 250 volts

| | | SELF-EXCITED | | | | SEPARATE EXCITATION | | | |
Tube	Cathode Resistor	Screen Resistor	Grid Leak	Grid Current	Cathode Resistor	Screen Resistor	Grid Leak	Grid Current
6BA7[1]	0	12,000	22,000	0.35 ma.	68	15,000	22,000	0.35 ma.
6BE6[1]	0	22,000	22,000	0.5	150	22,000	22,000	0.5
6K8[2]	240	27,000	47,000	0.15-0.2	—	—	—	—
6SA7[2]	0	18,000	22,000	0.5	150	18,000	22,000	0.5
6SB7Y[2]	0	15,000	22,000	0.35	68	15,000	22,000	0.35

[1] Miniature tube [2] Octal base, metal.

High-frequency Oscillator

be coupled to the signal grid through "space-charge" coupling, an effect that increases with frequency. If there is relatively little frequency difference between oscillator and signal, as for example a 14- or 28-Mc. signal and an i.f. of 455 kc., this voltage can become considerable because the selectivity of the signal circuit will be unable to reject it. If the signal grid is not returned directly to ground, but instead is returned through a resistor or part of an a.v.c. system, considerable bias can be developed which will cut down the gain. For this reason, and to reduce image response, the i.f. following the first converter of a receiver should be not less than 5 or 10 per cent of the signal frequency, for best results.

Transistors in Mixers

Typical transistor circuitry for a mixer operating at frequencies below 20 Mc. is shown in Fig. 5-13. The local oscillator current is injected in the emitter circuit by inductive coupling to L_1; L_1 should have low reactance at the oscillator frequency. The input from the r.f. amplifier should be at low impedance, obtained by inductive coupling or tapping down on the tuned circuit. The output transformer T_1 has the collector connection tapped down on the inductance to maintain a high Q in the tuned circuit.

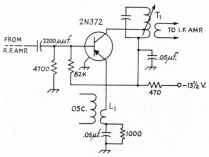

Fig. 5-13—Typical transistor mixer circuit.
L_1—Low-impedance inductive coupling to oscillator.
T_1—Transistor i.f. transformer. Primary impedance of 100,000 ohms, secondary impedance of 1700 ohms, unloaded $Q = 100$, loaded $Q = 35$.

Audio Converters

Converter circuits of the type shown in Fig. 5-12 can be used to advantage in the reception of code and single-sideband suppressed-carrier signals, by introducing the local oscillator on the No. 1 grid, the signal on the No. 3 grid, and working the tube into an audio load. Its operation can be visualized as heterodyning the incoming signal into the audio range. The use of such circuits for audio conversion has been limited to selective i.f. amplifiers operating below 500 kc. and usually below 100 kc. An ordinary a.m. signal cannot be received on such a detector unless the tuning is adjusted to make the local oscillator zero-beat with the incoming carrier.

Since the beat oscillator modulates the electron stream completely, a large beat-oscillator component exists in the plate circuit. To prevent overload of the following audio amplifier stages, an adequate i.f. filter must be used in the output of the converter.

The "product detector" of Fig. 5-6 is also a converter circuit, and the statements above for audio converters apply to the product detector.

⬤ THE HIGH-FREQUENCY OSCILLATOR

Stability of the receiver is dependent chiefly upon the stability of the h.f. oscillator, and particular care should be given this part of the receiver. The frequency of oscillation should be insensitive to mechanical shock and changes in voltage and loading. Thermal effects (slow change in frequency because of tube or circuit heating) should be minimized. They can be reduced by using ceramic instead of bakelite insulation in the r.f. circuits, a large cabinet relative to the chassis (to provide for good radiation of developed heat), minimizing the number of high-wattage resistors in the receiver and putting them in the separate power supply, and not mounting the oscillator coils and tuning capacitor too close to a tube. Propping up the lid of a receiver will often reduce drift by lowering the terminal temperature of the unit.

Sensitivity to vibration and shock can be minimized by using good mechanical support for coils and tuning capacitors, a heavy chassis, and by not hanging any of the oscillator-circuit components on long leads. Tie-points should be used to avoid long leads. Stiff *short* leads are excellent because they can't be made to vibrate.

Smooth tuning is a great convenience to the operator, and can be obtained by taking pains with the mounting of the dial and tuning capacitors. They should have good alignment and no back-lash. If the capacitors are mounted off the chassis on posts instead of brackets, it is almost impossible to avoid some back-lash unless the posts have extra-wide bases. The capacitors should be selected with good wiping contacts to the rotor, since with age the rotor contacts can be a source of erratic tuning. All joints in the oscillator tuning circuit should be carefully soldered, because a loose connection or "rosin joint" can develop trouble that is sometimes hard to locate. The chassis and panel materials should be heavy and rigid enough so that pressure on the tuning dial will not cause torsion and a shift in the frequency.

In addition, the oscillator must be capable of furnishing sufficient r.f. voltage and power for the particular mixer circuit chosen, at all frequencies within the range of the receiver, and its harmonic output should be as low as possible to reduce the possibility of spurious responses.

The oscillator plate power should be as low as is consistent with adequate output. Low plate power will reduce tube heating and thereby lower the frequency drift. The oscillator and mixer circuits should be well isolated, pref-

Fig. 5-14—High-frequency oscillator circuits. A, pentode grounded-plate oscillator; B, triode grounded-plate oscillator; C, triode oscillator with tickler circuit. Coupling to the mixer may be taken from points X and Y. In A and B, coupling from Y will reduce pulling effects, but gives less voltage than from X; this type is best adapted to mixer circuits with small oscillator-voltage requirements. Typical values for components are as follows:

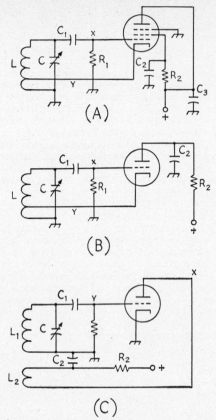

Circuit A	Circuit B	Circuit C
C_1—100 $\mu\mu$f.	100 $\mu\mu$f.	100 $\mu\mu$f.
C_2—0.01 μf.	0.01 μf.	0.01 μf.
C_3—0.01 μf.		
R_1—47,000 ohms.	47,000 ohms.	47,000 ohms.
R_2—47,000 ohms.	10,000 to	10,000 to
	25,000 ohms.	25,000 ohms.

The plate-supply voltage should be 250 volts. In circuits B and C, R_2 is used to drop the supply voltage to 100–150 volts; it may be omitted if voltage is obtained from a voltage divider in the power supply.

erably by shielding, since coupling other than by the intended means may result in pulling.

If the h.f.-oscillator frequency is affected by changes in plate voltage, a voltage-regulated plate supply (VR tube) can be used.

Circuits

Several oscillator circuits are shown in Fig. 5-14. Circuits A and B will give about the same results, and require only one coil. However, in these two circuits the cathode is above ground potential for r.f., which often is a cause of hum modulation of the oscillator output at 14 Mc. and higher frequencies when a.c.-heated-cathode tubes are used. The circuit of Fig. 5-14C reduces hum because the cathode is grounded. It is simple to adjust, and it is also the best circuit to use with filament-type tubes. With filament-type tubes, the other two circuits would require r.f. chokes to keep the filament above r.f. ground.

Besides the use of a fairly high C/L ratio in the tuned circuit, it is necessary to adjust the feedback to obtain optimum results. Too much feedback may cause "squegging" of the oscillator and the generation of several frequencies simultaneously; too little feedback will cause the output to be low. In the tapped-coil circuits (A, B), the feedback is increased by moving the tap toward the grid end of the coil. In C, more feedback is obtained by increasing the number of turns on L_2 or moving L_2 closer to L_1.

The Intermediate-Frequency Amplifier

One major advantage of the superhet is that high gain and selectivity can be obtained by using a good i.f. amplifier. This can be a one-stage affair in simple receivers, or two or three stages in the more elaborate sets.

Choice of Frequency

The selection of an intermediate frequency is a compromise between conflicting factors. The lower the i.f. the higher the selectivity and gain, but a low i.f. brings the image nearer the desired signal and hence decreases the image ratio. A low i.f. also increases pulling of the oscillator frequency. On the other hand, a high i.f. is beneficial to both image ratio and pulling, but the gain is lowered and selectivity is harder to obtain by simple means.

An i.f. of the order of 455 kc. gives good selectivity and is satisfactory from the standpoint of image ratio and oscillator pulling at frequencies up to 7 Mc. The image ratio is poor at 14 Mc. when the mixer is connected to the antenna, but adequate when there is a tuned r.f. amplifier between antenna and mixer. At 28 Mc. and on the very high frequencies, the image ratio is very poor unless several r.f. stages are used. Above 14 Mc., pulling is likely to be bad without very loose coupling between mixer and oscillator.

With an i.f. of about 1600 kc., satisfactory image ratios can be secured on 14, 21 and 28 Mc. with one r.f. stage of good design. For frequencies of 28 Mc. and higher, a common solution is to use a double superheterodyne, choosing one high i.f. for image reduction (5 and 10 Mc. are frequently used) and a lower one for gain

I.F. Amplifiers

and selectivity.

In choosing an i.f. it is wise to avoid frequencies on which there is considerable activity by the various radio services, since such signals may be picked up directly on the i.f. wiring. Shifting the i.f. or better shielding are the solutions to this interference problem.

Fidelity; Sideband Cutting

Modulation of a carrier causes the generation of sideband frequencies numerically equal to the carrier frequency plus and minus the highest modulation frequency present. If the receiver is to give a faithful reproduction of modulation that contains, for instance, audio frequencies up to 5000 cycles, it must at least be capable of amplifying equally all frequencies contained in a band extending from 5000 cycles above or below the carrier frequency. In a superheterodyne, where all carrier frequencies are changed to the fixed intermediate frequency, the i.f. amplification must be uniform over a band 5 kc. wide, when the carrier is set at one edge. If the carrier is set in the center, a 10-kc. band is required. The signal-frequency circuits usually do not have enough over-all selectivity to affect materially the "adjacent-channel" selectivity, so that only the i.f.-amplifier selectivity need be considered.

If the selectivity is too great to permit uniform amplification over the band of frequencies occupied by the modulated signal, some of the sidebands are "cut." While sideband cutting reduces fidelity, it is frequently preferable to sacrifice naturalness of reproduction in favor of communications effectiveness.

The selectivity of an i.f. amplifier, and hence the tendency to cut sidebands, increases with the number of amplifier stages and also is greater the lower the intermediate frequency. From the standpoint of communication, sideband cutting is never serious with two-stage amplifiers at frequencies as low as 455 kc. A two-stage i.f. amplifier at 85 or 100 kc. will be sharp enough to cut some of the higher-frequency sidebands, if good transformers are used. However, the cutting is not at all serious, and the gain in selectivity is worthwhile in crowded amateur bands.

Circuits

I.f. amplifiers usually consist of one or two stages. At 455 kc. two stages generally give all the gain usable, and also give suitable selectivity

for phone reception.

A typical circuit arrangement is shown in Fig. 5-15. A second stage would simply duplicate the circuit of the first. The i.f. amplifier practically always uses a remote cut-off pentode-type tube operated as a Class A amplifier. For maximum selectivity, double-tuned transformers are used for interstage coupling, although single-tuned circuits or transformers with untuned primaries can be used for coupling, with a consequent loss in selectivity. All other things being equal, the selectivity of an i.f. amplifier is proportional to the number of tuned circuits in it.

In Fig. 5-15, the gain of the stage is reduced by introducing a negative voltage to the lead marked "AGC" or a positive voltage to R_1 at the point marked "manual gain control." In either case, the voltage increases the bias on the tube and reduces the mutual conductance and hence the gain. When two or more stages are used, these voltages are generally obtained from common sources. The decoupling resistor, R_3, helps to prevent unwanted interstage coupling. C_2 and R_4 are part of the automatic gain-control circuit (described later); if no a.g.c. is used, the lower end of the i.f.-transformer secondary is connected to chassis.

Tubes for I.F. Amplifiers

Variable-μ (remote cut-off) pentodes are almost invariably used in i.f. amplifier stages, since grid-bias gain control is practically always applied to the i.f. amplifier. Tubes with high plate resistance will have least effect on the selectivity of the amplifier, and those with high mutual conductance will give greatest gain. The choice of i.f. tubes normally has no effect on the signal-to-noise ratio, since this is determined by the preceding mixer and r.f. amplifier.

Typical values of cathode and screen resistors for common tubes are given in Table 5-II. The 6K7, 6SK7 and 6BJ6 are recommended for i.f. work because they have desirable remote cut-off characteristics. The indicated screen resistors drop the plate voltage to the correct screen voltage, as R_2 in Fig. 5-15.

When two or more stages are used the high gain may tend to cause instability and oscillation, so that good shielding, bypassing, and careful circuit arrangement to prevent stray coupling between input and output circuits are necessary.

When single-ended tubes are used, the plate and grid leads should be well separated. With these tubes it is advisable to mount the screen

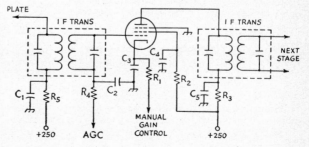

Fig. 5-15—Typical intermediate-frequency amplifier circuit for a superheterodyne receiver. Representative values for components are as follows:

C_1, C_3, C_4, C_5—0.02 µf. at 455 kc.; 0.01 µf. at 1600 kc. and higher.

C_2—0.01 µf.

R_1, R_2—See Table 5-II.

R_3, R_5—1500 ohms.

R_4—0.1 megohm.

TABLE 5-II
Cathode and Screen-Dropping Resistors for R.F. or I.F. Amplifiers

Tube	Plate Volts	Screen Volts	Cathode Resistor R1	Screen Resistor R2
6AC7[1]	300		160	62,000
6AH6[2]	300	150	160	62,000
6AK5[2]	180	120	200	27,000
6AU6[2]	250	150	68	33,000
6BA6[2]*	250	100	68	33,000
6BH6[2]	250	150	100	33,000
6BJ6[2]*	250	100	82	47,000
6BZ6[2]*	200	150	180	20,000
6CB6	200	150	180	56,000
6SG7[1]*	250	125	68	27,000
6SH7[1]	250	150	68	39,000
6SJ7[1]	250	100	820	180,000
6SK7[1]*	250	100	270	56,000

[1] Octal base, metal.   [2] Miniature tube.
* Remote cut-off type.

bypass capacitor directly on the bottom of the socket, crosswise between the plate and grid pins, to provide additional shielding. If a paper capacitor is used, the outside foil should be grounded to the chassis.

I.F. Transformers

The tuned circuits of i.f. amplifiers are built up as transformer units consisting of a metal shield container in which the coils and tuning capacitors are mounted. Both air-core and powdered iron-core universal-wound coils are used, the latter having somewhat higher Qs and hence greater selectivity and gain. In universal windings the coil is wound in layers with each turn traversing the length of the coil, back and forth, rather than being wound perpendicular to the axis as in ordinary single-layer coils. In a straight multilayer winding, a fairly large capacitance can exist between layers. Universal winding, with its "criss-crossed" turns, tends to reduce distributed-capacity effects.

For tuning, air-dielectric tuning capacitors are preferable to mica compression types because their capacity is practically unaffected by changes in temperature and humidity. Iron-core transformers may be tuned by varying the inductance (permeability tuning), in which case stability comparable to that of variable air-capacitor tuning can be obtained by use of high-stability fixed mica or ceramic capacitors. Such stability is of great importance, since a circuit whose frequency "drifts" with time eventually will be tuned to a different frequency than the other circuits, thereby reducing the gain and selectivity of the amplifier. Typical i.f.-transformer construction is shown in Fig. 5-16.

The normal **interstage** i.f. transformer is loosely coupled, to give good selectivity consistent with adequate gain. A so-called **diode transformer** is similar, but the coupling is tighter, to give sufficient transfer when working into the finite load presented by a diode detector. Using a diode transformer in place of an interstage transformer would result in loss of selectivity; using an interstage transformer to couple to the diode would result in loss of gain.

Besides the type of i.f. transformer shown in Fig. 5-16, special units to give desired selectivity characteristics are available. For higher-than-ordinary adjacent-channel selectivity **triple-tuned** transformers, with a third tuned circuit inserted between the input and output windings, are sometimes used. The energy is transferred from the input to the output windings via this **tertiary winding**, thus adding its selectivity to the over-all selectivity of the transformer.

A method of varying the selectivity is to vary the coupling between primary and secondary, overcoupling being used to broaden the selectivity curve. Special circuits using single tuned circuits, coupled in any of several different ways, are used in some advanced receivers.

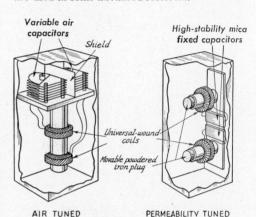

Variable air capacitors · Shield · High-stability mica fixed capacitors · Universal-wound coils · Movable powdered iron plug

AIR TUNED   PERMEABILITY TUNED

Fig. 5-16—Representative i.f.-transformer construction. Coils are supported on insulating tubing or (in the air-tuned type) on wax-impregnated wooden dowels. The shield in the air-tuned transformer prevents capacity coupling between the tuning capacitors. In the permeability-tuned transformer the cores consist of finely-divided iron particles supported in an insulating binder, formed into cylindrical "plugs." The tuning capacitance is fixed, and the inductances of the coils are varied by moving the iron plugs in and out.

Selectivity

The over-all selectivity of the r.f. amplifier will depend on the frequency and the number of stages. The following figures are indicative of the bandwidths to be expected with good-quality transformers in amplifiers so constructed as to keep regeneration at a minimum:

| | Bandwidth in Kilocycles | | |
| | 6 db. | 20 db. | 40 db. |
Intermediate Frequency	down	down	down
One stage, 50 kc. (iron core) . . .	2.0	3.0	4.2
One stage, 455 kc. (air core) . .	8.7	17.8	32.3
One stage, 455 kc. (iron core) . .	4.3	10.3	20.4
Two stages, 455 kc. (iron core) .	2.9	6.4	10.8
Two stages, 1600 kc.	11.0	16.6	27.4

Transistor I. F. Amplifier

A typical circuit for a two-stage transistor i.f. amplifier is shown in Fig. 5-17. Constants are given for a 455-kc. amplifier, but the same gen-

Second Detectors

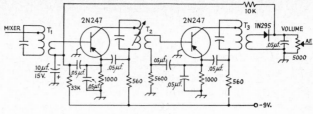

T_1—Transistor input i.f. transformer. Primary impedance = 100,000 ohms, secondary impedance = 1700 ohms, unloaded Q = 100, loaded Q = 35.

T_2—Transistor interstage i.f. transformer. Primary impedance = 4600 ohms, secondary impedance

= 1700 ohms, unloaded Q = 39, loaded Q = 35.

T_3—Transistor output i.f. transformer. Primary impedance = 30,000 ohms, secondary impedance = 1000 ohms, unloaded Q = 100, loaded Q = 35.

eral circuitry applies to an amplifier at any frequency within the operating range of the transistors. When higher frequencies are used, it may be necessary to neutralize the amplifier to avoid overall oscillation; this is done by connecting a small variable capacitor of a few μμf. from base to base of the transistors.

Automatic gain control is obtained by using the developed d.c. at the 1N295 diode detector to modify the emitter bias current on the first stage. As the bias current changes, the input and output impedances change, and the resultant impedance mismatches causes a reduction in gain. Such a.g.c. assumes, of course, that the amplifier is set up initially in a matched condition.

THE SECOND DETECTOR AND BEAT OSCILLATOR

Detector Circuits

The second detector of a superheterodyne receiver performs the same function as the detector in the simple receiver, but usually operates at a higher input level because of the relatively great amplification ahead of it. Therefore, the ability to handle large signals without distortion is preferable to high sensitivity. Plate detection is used to some extent, but the diode detector is most popular. It is especially adapted to furnishing automatic gain or volume control. The basic circuits have been described, although in many

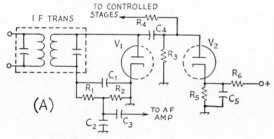

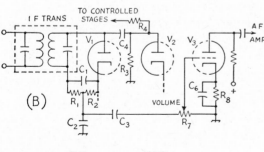

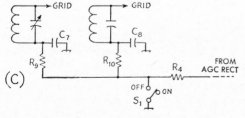

Fig. 5-18—Delayed automatic gain-control circuits using a twin diode (A) and a dual-diode triode. The circuits are essentially the same and differ only in the method of biasing the a.g.c. rectifier. The a.g.c. control voltage is applied to the controlled stages as in (C). For these circuits typical values are:

C_1, C_3, C_4—100 μμf.
C_2, C_5, C_7, C_8—0.01 μf.
C_6—5-μf. electrolytic.
R_1, R_9, R_{10}—0.1 megohm.
R_2—0.47 megohm.
R_3—2 megohms.
R_4—0.47 megohm.
R_5, R_6—Voltage divider to give 2 to 10 volts bias at 1 to 2 ma. drain.
R_7—0.5-megohm volume control.
R_8—Correct bias resistor for triode section of dual-diode triode.

cases the diode elements are incorporated in a multipurpose tube that contains an amplifier section in addition to the diode.

Audio-converter circuits and product detectors are often used for code or s.s.b. detectors.

The Beat Oscillator

Any standard oscillator circuit may be used for the beat oscillator required for heterodyne reception. Special beat-oscillator transformers are available, usually consisting of a tapped coil with adjustable tuning; these are most conveniently used with the circuits shown in Fig. 5-14A and B, with the output taken from Y. A variable capacitor of about 25-$\mu\mu$f. capacitance can be connected between cathode and ground to provide fine adjustment of the frequency. The beat oscillator usually is coupled to the second-detector tuned circuit through a fixed capacitor of a few $\mu\mu$f.

The beat oscillator should be well shielded, to prevent coupling to any part of the receiver except the second detector and to prevent its harmonics from getting into the front end and being amplified along with desired signals. The b.f.o. power should be as low as is consistent with sufficient audio-frequency output on the strongest signals. However, if the beat-oscillator output is too low, strong signals will not give a proportionately strong audio signal. Contrary to some opinion, a weak b.f.o. is never an advantage.

● AUTOMATIC GAIN CONTROL

Automatic regulation of the gain of the receiver in inverse proportion to the signal strength is an operating convenience in phone reception, since it tends to keep the output level of the receiver constant regardless of input-signal strength. The average rectified d.c. voltage, developed by the received signal across a resistance in a detector circuit, is used to vary the bias on the r.f. and i.f. amplifier tubes. Since this voltage is proportional to the average amplitude of the signal, the gain is reduced as the signal strength becomes greater. The control will be more complete and the output more constant as the number of stages to which the a.g.c. bias is applied is increased. Control of at least two stages is advisable.

Circuits

Although some receivers derive the a.g.c. voltage from the diode detector, the usual practice is to use a separate a.g.c. rectifier. Typical circuits are shown in Figs. 5-18A and 5-18B. The two rectifiers can be combined in one tube, as in the 6H6 and 6AL5. In Fig. 5-18A V_1 is the diode detector; the signal is developed across R_1R_2 and coupled to the audio stages through C_3. C_1, R_1 and C_2 are included for r.f. filtering, to prevent a large r.f. component being coupled to the audio circuits. The a.g.c. rectifier, V_2, is coupled to the last i.f. transformer through C_4, and most of the rectified voltage is developed across R_3. V_2 does not rectify on weak signals, however; the fixed

bias at R_5 must be exceeded before rectification can take place. The developed negative a.g.c. bias is fed to the controlled stages through R_4.

The circuit of Fig. 5-18B is similar, except that a dual-diode triode tube is used. Since this has only one common cathode, the circuitry is slightly different but the principle is the same. The triode stage serves as the first audio stage, and its bias is developed in the cathode circuit across R_8. This same bias is applied to the a.g.c. rectifier by returning its load resistor, R_3, to ground. To avoid placing this bias on the detector, V_1, its load resistor R_1R_2 is returned to cathode, thus avoiding any bias on the detector and permitting it to respond to weak signals.

The developed negative a.g.c. bias is applied to the controlled stages through their grid circuits, as shown in Fig. 5-18C. C_7R_9 and C_8R_{10} serve as filters to avoid common coupling and possible feedback and oscillator. The a.g.c. is disabled by closing switch S_1.

The a.g.c. rectifier bias in Fig. 5-18B is set by the bias required for proper operation of V_3. If less bias for the a.g.c. rectifier is required, R_3 can be tapped up on R_8 instead of being returned to chassis ground. In Fig. 5-18A, proper choice of bias at R_5 depends upon the over-all gain of the receiver and the number of controlled stages. In general, the bias at R_5 will be made higher for receivers with more gain and more stages.

Time Constant

The time constant of the resistor-capacitor combinations in the a.g.c. circuit is an important part of the system. It must be long enough so that the modulation on the signal is completely filtered from the d.c. output, leaving only an average d.c. component which follows the relatively slow carrier variations with fading. Audio-frequency variations in the a.g.c. voltage applied to the amplifier grids would reduce the percentage of modulation on the incoming signal. But the time constant must not be too long or the a.g.c. will be unable to follow rapid fading. The capacitance and resistance values indicated in Fig. 5-18 will give a time constant that is satisfactory for average reception.

C.W. and S.S.B.

A.g.c. can be used for c.w. and s.s.b. reception but the circuit is usually more complicated. The a.g.c. voltage must be derived from a rectifier that is isolated from the beat-frequency oscillator (otherwise the rectified b.f.o. voltage will reduce the receiver gain even with no signal coming through). This is done by using a separate a.g.c. channel connected to an i.f. amplifier stage ahead of the second detector (and b.f.o.) or by rectifying the audio output of the detector. If the selectivity ahead of the a.v.c. rectifier isn't good, strong adjacent-channel signals may develop a.g.c. voltages that will reduce the receiver gain while listening to weak signals. When clear channels are available, however, c.w. and s.s.b. a.g.c. will hold the receiver output constant over

Noise Reduction

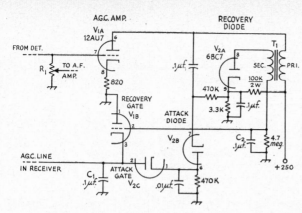

Fig. 5-19—Audio "hang" a.g.c. system. Resistors are ½-watt unless specified otherwise.

R₁—Normal audio volume control in receiver.

T₁—1:3 step-up audio transformer (Stancor A-53 or equiv.)

The hang time can be adjusted by changing the value of the recovery diode load resistor (4.7 megohms shown here). The a.g.c. line in the receiver must have no d.c. return to ground and the receiver should have good skirt selectivity for maximum effectiveness at the system.

a wide range of signal inputs. A.g.c. systems designed to work on these signals should have fast-attack and slow-decay characteristics to work satisfactorily, and often a selection of time constants is made available.

The a.g.c. circuit shown in Fig. 5-19 is applicable to many receivers without too much modification. Audio from the receiver is amplified in V_{1A} and rectified in V_{2B}. The resultant voltage is applied to the a.g.c. line through V_{2C}. The capacitor C_1 charges quickly and will remain charged until discharged by V_{1B}. This will occur some time after the signal has disappeared, because the audio was stepped up through T_1 and rectified in V_{2A}, and the resultant used to charge C_2. This voltage holds V_{1B} cut off for an

appreciable time, until C_2 discharges through the 4.7-megohm resistor. The threshold of compression is set by adjusting the bias on the diodes (changing the value of the 3.3K or 100K resistors). There can be no d.c. return to ground from the a.g.c. line, because C_1 must be discharged only by V_{1B}. Even a v.t.v.m. across the a.g.c. line will be too low a resistance, and the operation of the system must be observed by the action of the S meter.

Occasionally a strong noise pulse may cause the a.g.c. to hang until C_2 discharges, but most of the time the gain should return very rapidly to that set by the signal. A.g.c. of this type is very helpful in handling netted s.s.b. signals of widely varying strengths.

Noise Reduction

Types of Noise

In addition to tube and circuit noise, much of the noise interference experienced in reception of high-frequency signals is caused by domestic or industrial electrical equipment and by automobile ignition systems. The interference is of two types in its effects. The first is the "hiss" type, consisting of overlapping pulses similar in nature to the receiver noise. It is largely reduced by high selectivity in the receiver, especially for code reception. The second is the "pistol-shot" or "machine-gun" type, consisting of separated impulses of high amplitude. The "hiss" type of interference usually is caused by commutator sparking in d.c. and series-wound a.c. motors, while the "shot" type results from separated spark discharges (a.c. power leaks, switch and key clicks, ignition sparks, and the like).

The only known approach to reducing tube and circuit noise is through better "front-end" design and through more over-all selectivity.

Impulse Noise

Impulse noise, because of the short duration of the pulses compared with the time between them, must have high amplitude to contain much average energy. Hence, noise of this type strong enough to cause much interfer-

ence generally has an instantaneous amplitude much higher than that of the signal being received. The general principles of devices intended to reduce such noise is to allow the desired signal to pass through the receiver unaffected, but to make the receiver inoperative for amplitudes greater than that of the signal. The greater the amplitude of the pulse compared with its time of duration, the more successful the noise reduction.

Another approach is to "silence" (render inoperative) the receiver during the short duration time of any individual pulse. The listener will not hear the "hole" because of its short duration, and very effective noise reduction is obtained. Such devices are called "silencers" rather than "limiters."

In passing through selective receiver circuits, the time duration of the impulses is increased, because of the Q of the circuits. Thus the more selectivity ahead of the noise-reducing device, the more difficult it becomes to secure good pulse-type noise suppression.

Audio Limiting

A considerable degree of noise reduction in code reception can be accomplished by amplitude-limiting arrangements applied to the audio-output circuit of a receiver. Such limiters

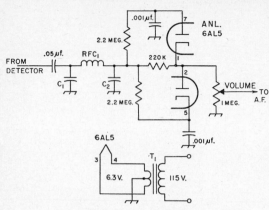

Fig. 5-20—Full-wave shunt limiter using contact-potential-biased diodes. A low-level limiter (½ volt), this circuit finds greatest usefulness following a product detector.

C_1, C_2—Part of low-pass filter with cutoff below i.f.
RFC_1—Part of low-pass filter; see C_1.
T_1—Center-tapped heater transformer.

also maintain the signal output nearly constant during fading. These output-limiter systems are simple, and adaptable to most receivers. However, they cannot prevent noise peaks from overloading previous stages.

● SECOND-DETECTOR NOISE LIMITER CIRCUITS

Most audio limiting circuits are based on one of two principles. In a series limiting circuit, a normally conducting element (or elements) is connected in the circuit in series and operated in such a manner that it becomes non-conductive above a given signal level. In a shunt limiting circuit, a non-conducting element is connected in shunt across the circuit and operated so that it becomes conductive above a given signal level, thus short-circuiting the signal and preventing its being transmitted to the remainder of the amplifier. The usual conducting element will be a forward-biased diode, and the usual non-conducting element will be a back-biased diode. In many applications the value of bias is set manually by the operator; usually the clipping level will be set at about 5 to 10 volts.

A full-wave clipping circuit that operates at a low level (approximately ½ volt) is shown in Fig. 5-20. Each diode is biased by its own contact potential, developed across the 2.2-megohm resistors. The .001-μf. capacitors become charged to close to this value of contact potential. A negative-going signal in excess of the bias will

be shorted to ground by the upper diode; a positive-going signal will be conducted by the lower diode. The conducting resistance of the diodes is small by comparison with the 220,000 ohms in series with the circuit, and little if any of the excessive signal will appear across the 1-megohm volume control. In order that the clipping does not become excessive and cause distortion, the input signal must be held down by a gain control ahead of the detector. This circuit finds good application following a low-level detector.

To minimize hum in the receiver output, it is desirable to ground the center tap of the heater transformer, as shown, instead of the more common practice of returning one side of the heater circuit to chassis.

Second-detector noise-limiting circuits that automatically adjust themselves to the received carrier level are shown in Fig. 5-21. In either circuit, V_1 is the usual diode second detector, R_1R_2 is the diode load resistor, and C_1 is an r.f. bypass. A negative voltage proportional to the carrier level is developed across C_2, and this voltage cannot change rapidly because R_3 and C_2 are both large. In the circuit at A, diode V_2 acts as a conductor for the audio signal up to the point where its anode is negative with respect to the cathode. Noise peaks that exceed the maximum carrier-modulation level will drive the anode negative instantaneously, and during this time the diode does not conduct. The long time constant of C_2R_3 prevents any rapid change of the reference voltage. In the circuit at B, the diode V_2 is inactive until its cathode voltage exceeds its anode voltage. This condition will obtain under noise peaks, and when it does, the diode V_2 short-circuits the signal and no voltage is passed on to the audio amplifier. Diode rectifiers such as the 6H6 and 6AL5 can be used for these types of noise limiters. Neither circuit is useful for c.w. or s.s.b. reception, but they are both quite effective

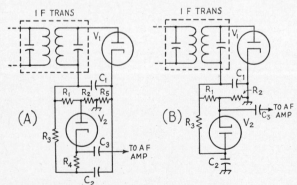

Fig. 5-21—Self-adjusting series (A) and shunt (B) noise limiters. The functions of V_1 and V_2 can be combined in one tube like the 6H6 or 6AL5.

C_1—100 μμf.
C_2, C_3—0.05 μf.
R_1—0.27 meg. in A; 47,000 ohms in B.
R_2—0.27 meg. in A; 0.15 meg. in B.
R_3—1.0 megohm.
R_4—0.82 megohm.
R_5—6800 ohms.

Noise Silencer

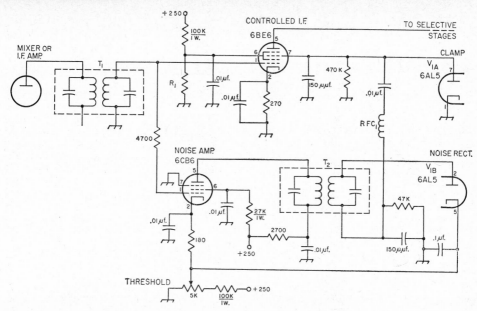

Fig. 5-22—Practical circuit diagram of an i.f. noise silencer. For best results the silencer should be used ahead of the high-selectivity portion of the receiver.
T₁—Interstage i.f. transformer

T₂—Diode i.f. transformer.
R₁—33,000 to 68,000 ohms, depending upon gain up to this stage.
RFC₁—R.f. choke, preferably self-resonant at i.f.

for a.m. phone work. The series circuit (A) is slightly better than the shunt circuit.

● I.F. NOISE SILENCER

The i.f. noise silencer circuit shown in Fig. 5-22 is designed to be used in a receiver as far along from the antenna stage as possible but ahead of the high-selectivity section of the receiver. Noise pulses are amplified and rectified, and the resulting negative-going d.c. pulses are used to cut off an amplifier stage during the pulse. A manual "threshold" control is set by the operator to a level that only permits rectification of the noise pulses that rise above the peak amplitude of the desired signal. The clamp diode, V_{1A}, short circuits the positive-going pulse "overshoots." Running the 6BE6 controlled i.f. amplifier at low screen voltage makes it possible for the No. 3 grid (pin 7) to cut off the stage at a lower voltage than if the screen were operated at the more-normal 100 volts, but it also reduces the available gain through the stage.

It is necessary to avoid i.f. feedback around the 6BE6 stage, and the closer RFC_1 can be to self-resonant at the i.f. the better will be the filtering. The filtering cannot be improved by increasing the values of the 150-$\mu\mu$f. capacitors because this will tend to "stretch" the pulses and reduce the signal strength when the silencer is operative.

● SIGNAL-STRENGTH AND TUNING INDICATORS

The simplest tuning indicator is a milliammeter

connected in the d.c. plate lead of an a.g.c.-controlled r.f. or i.f. stage. Since the plate current is reduced as the a.g.c. voltage becomes higher with a stronger signal, the plate current is a measure of the signal strength. The meter can have a 0-1, 0-2 or 0-5 ma. movement, and it should be shunted by a 25-ohm rheostat which is used to set the no-signal reading to full scale on the meter. If a "forward-reading" meter is desired, the meter can be mounted upside down.

Two other S-meter circuits are shown in Fig. 5-23. The system at A uses a milliammeter in a bridge circuit, arranged so that the meter readings increase with the a.v.c. voltage and signal strength. The meter reads approximately in a linear decibel scale and will not be "crowded."

To adjust the system in Fig. 5-23A, pull the tube out of its socket or otherwise break the cathode circuit so that no plate current flows, and adjust the value of resistor R_1 across the meter until the scale reading is maximum. The value of resistance required will depend on the internal resistance of the meter, and must be determined by trial and error (the current is approximately 2.5 ma.). Then replace the tube, allow it to warm up, turn the a.g.c. switch to "off" so the grid is shorted to ground, and adjust the 3000-ohm variable resistor for zero meter current. When the a.g.c. is "on," the meter will follow the signal variations up to the point where the voltage is high enough to cut off the meter tube's plate current. With a 6J5 or 6SN7GT this will occur in the neighborhood of 15 volts, a high-amplitude signal.

The circuit of Fig. 5-23B requires no additional tubes. The resistor R_2 is the normal cathode

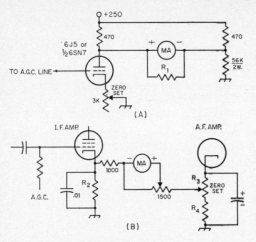

Fig. 5-23—Tuning indicator or S-meter circuits for super-heterodyne receivers.

MA—0-1 or 0-2 milliammeter. R_1–R_4—See text.

resistor of an a.g.c.-controlled i.f. stage; its cathode resistor should be returned to chassis and not to the manual gain control. The sum of R_3 plus R_4 should equal the normal cathode resistor for the audio amplifier, and they should be proportioned so that the arm of R_3 can pick off a voltage equal to the normal cathode voltage for the i.f. stage. In some cases it may be necessary to interchange the positions of R_3 and R_4 in the circuit.

The zero-set control R_3 should be set for no reading of the meter with no incoming signal, and the 1500-ohm sensitivity control should be set for a full meter reading with the i.f. tube removed from its socket.

Neither of these S-meter circuits can be "pinned", and only severe misadjustment of the zero-set control can injure the meter.

⬤ HEADPHONES AND LOUDSPEAKERS

There are two basic types of headphones in common use, the magnetic and the crystal. A magnetic headphone uses a small electromagnet that attracts and releases a steel diaphragm in accordance with the electrical output of the radio receiver; this is similar to the "receiver" portion of the household telephone. A crystal headphone uses the piezoelectric properties of a pair of Rochelle-salt or other crystals to vibrate a diaphragm in accordance with the electrical output of the radio receiver. Magnetic headphones can be used in circuits where d.c. is flowing, such as the plate circuit of a vacuum tube, provided the current is not too heavy to be carried by the wire in the coils; the limit is usually a few milliamperes. Crystal headphones can be used only on a.c. (a steady d.c. voltage will damage the crystal unit), and consequently must be coupled to a tube through a device, such as a capacitor or transformer, that isolates the d.c. but passes the a.c. Most modern receivers have a.c. coupling to the headphones and hence either type of headphone can be used, but it is wise to look first at the circuit diagram in the instruction book and make sure that the headphone jack is connected to the secondary of the output transformer, as is usually the case.

In general, crystal headphones will have considerably wider and "flatter" audio response than will magnetic headphones (except those of the "hi-fi" type that sell at premium prices). The lack of wide response in the magnetic headphones is sometimes an advantage in code reception, since the desired signal can be set on the peak and be given a boost in volume over the undesired signals at slightly different frequencies.

Crystal headphones are available only in high-impedance values around 50,000 ohms or so, while magnetic headphones run around 10,000 to 20,000 ohms, although they can be obtained in values as low as 15 ohms. Usually the impedance of a headphone set is unimportant because there is more than enough power available from the radio receiver, but in marginal cases it is possible to improve the acoustic output through a better match of headphone to output impedance. When headphone sets are connected in series or in parallel they must be of similar impedance levels or one set will "hog" most of the power.

Loud speakers are practically always of the low-impedance permanent-field dynamic variety, and the loudspeaker output connections of a receiver can connect directly to the voice coil of the loudspeaker. Some receivers also provide a "500-ohm output" for connection to a long line to a remote loudspeaker. A loudspeaker requires mounting in a suitable enclosure if full low-frequency response is to be obtained.

Improving Receiver Selectivity

⬤ INTERMEDIATE-FREQUENCY AMPLIFIERS

As mentioned earlier in this chapter, one of the big advantages of the superheterodyne receiver is the improved selectivity that is possible. This selectivity is obtained in the i.f. amplifier, where the lower frequency allows more selectivity per stage than at the higher signal frequency. For phone reception, the limit to useful selectivity in the i.f. amplifier is the point where so many of the sidebands are cut that intelligibility is lost, although it is possible to remove completely one full set of side bands without impairing the quality at all. Maximum receiver selectivity in phone reception requires good stability in both transmitter and receiver, so that they will both remain "in tune" during the transmission. The limit to useful selectivity in code work is around 100 or 200 *cycles* for hand-key speeds, but this much selectivity requires good stability in both transmitter and

Selectivity

receiver, and a slow receiver tuning rate for ease of operation.

Single-Signal Effect

In heterodyne c.w. reception with a super-heterodyne receiver, the beat oscillator is set to give a suitable audio-frequency beat note when the incoming signal is converted to the intermediate frequency. For example, the beat oscillator may be set to 456 kc. (the i.f. being 455 kc.) to give a 1000-cycle beat note. Now, if an interfering signal appears at 457 kc., or if the receiver is tuned to heterodyne the incoming signal to 457 kc., it will also be heterodyned by the beat oscillator to produce a 1000-cycle beat. Hence every signal can be tuned in at two places that will give a 1000-cycle beat (or any other low audio frequency). This **audio-frequency image** effect can be reduced if the i.f. selectivity is such that the incoming signal, when heterodyned to 457 kc., is attenuated to a very low level.

When this is done, tuning through a given signal will show a strong response at the desired beat note on one side of zero beat only, instead of the two beat notes on either side of zero beat characteristic of less-selective reception, hence the name: **single-signal reception**.

The necessary selectivity is not obtained with nonregenerative amplifiers using ordinary tuned circuits unless a low i.f. or a large number of circuits is used.

Regeneration

Regeneration can be used to give a single-signal effect, particularly when the i.f. is 455 kc. or lower. The resonance curve of an i.f. stage at critical regeneration (just below the oscillating point) is extremely sharp, a bandwidth of 1 kc. at 10 times down and 5 kc. at 100 times down being obtainable in one stage. The audio-frequency image of a given signal thus can be reduced by a factor of nearly 100 for a 1000-cycle beat note (image 2000 cycles from resonance).

Regeneration is easily introduced into an i.f. amplifier by providing a small amount of capacity coupling between grid and plate. Bringing a short length of wire, connected to the grid, into the vicinity of the plate lead usually will suffice. The feedback may be controlled by the regular cathode-resistor gain control. When the i.f. is regenerative, it is preferable to operate the tube at reduced gain (high bias) and depend on regeneration to bring up the signal strength. This prevents overloading and increases selectivity.

The higher selectivity with regeneration reduces the over-all response to noise generated in the earlier stages of the receiver, just as does high selectivity produced by other means, and therefore improves the signal-to-noise ratio. However, the regenerative gain varies with signal strength, being less on strong signals.

Crystal-Filters; Phasing

Probably the simplest means for obtaining high selectivity is by the use of a piezoelectric

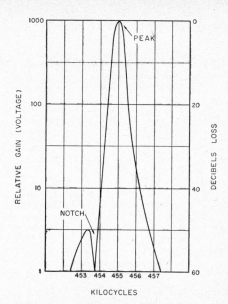

Fig. 5-24—Typical response curve of a crystal filter. The notch can be moved to the other side of the response peak by adjustment of the "phasing" control. With the above curve, setting the b.f.o. at 454 kc. would give good single-signal c.w. reception.

quartz crystal as a selective filter in the i.f. amplifier. Compared to a good tuned circuit, the Q of such a crystal is extremely high. The crystal is ground resonant at the i.f. and used as a selective coupler between i.f. stages.

Fig. 5-24 gives a typical crystal-filter resonance curve. For single-signal reception, the audio-frequency image can be reduced by 50 db. or more. Besides practically eliminating the a.f. image, the high selectivity of the crystal filter provides good discrimination against adjacent signals and also reduces the noise.

Two crystal-filter circuits are shown in Fig. 5-25. The circuit at A (or a variation) is found in many of the current communications receivers. The crystal is connected in one side of a bridge circuit, and a *phasing* capacitor, C_1, is connected in the other. When C_1 is set to balance the crystal-holder capacitance, the resonance curve of the filter is practically symmetrical; the crystal acts as a series-resonant circuit of very high Q and allows signals over a narrow band of frequencies to pass through to the following tube. More or less capacitance at C_1 introduces the "rejection notch" of Fig. 5-24 (at 453.7 kc. as drawn). The Q of the load circuit for the filter is adjusted by the setting of R_1, which in turn varies the bandwidth of the filter from "sharp" to a bandwidth suitable for phone reception. Some of the components of this filter are special and not generally available to amateurs.

The "band-pass" crystal filter at B uses two crystals separated slightly in frequency to give a band-pass characteristic to the filter. If the frequencies are only a few hundred cycles apart, the characteristic is an excellent one for c.w.

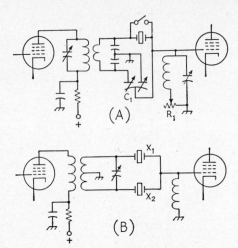

Fig. 5-25—A variable-selectivity crystal filter (A) and a band-pass crystal filter (B).

reception. With crystals about 2 kc. apart, a good phone characteristic is obtained.

Additional I.F. Selectivity

Many commercial communications receivers do not have sufficient selectivity for amateur use, and their performance can be improved by additional i.f. selectivity. One method is to loosely couple a BC-453 aircraft receiver (war surplus, tuning range 190 to 550 kc.) to the tail end of the 455-kc. i.f. amplifier in the communications receiver and use the resultant output of the BC-453. The aircraft receiver uses an 85-kc. i.f. amplifier that is sharp for voice work — 6.5 kc. wide at −60 db. — and it helps considerably in separating phone signals and in backing up crystals filters for improved c.w. reception.

If a BC-453 is not available, one can still enjoy the benefits of improved selectivity. It is only necessary to heterodyne to a lower frequency the 455-kc. signal existing in the receiver i.f. amplifier and then rectify it after passing it through the sharp low-frequency amplifier. The J. W. Miller Company offers 50-kc. transformers for this application.

● RADIO-FREQUENCY AMPLIFIERS

While selectivity to reduce audio-frequency images can be built into the i.f. amplifier, discrimination against radio-frequency images can only be obtained in circuits ahead of the first detector. These tuned circuits and their associated vacuum tubes are called **radio-frequency amplifiers**. For top performance of a communications receiver on frequencies above 7 Mc., it is mandatory that it have a stage of r.f. amplification, for image rejection and a good noise figure (mixers are noisier than amplifiers).

Receivers with an i.f. of 455 kc. can be expected to have some r.f. image response at a signal frequency of 14 Mc. and higher if only one stage of r.f. amplification is used. (Regen-

eration in the r.f. amplifier will reduce image response, but regeneration usually requires frequent readjustment when tuning across a band.) With two stages of r.f. amplification and an i.f. of 455 kc., no images should be apparent at 14 Mc., but they will show up on 28 Mc. and higher. Three stages or more of r.f. amplification, with an i.f. of 455 kc., will reduce the images at 28 Mc., but it really takes four or more stages to do a good job. A common solution at 28 Mc. is to use a "double-conversion" superheterodyne, with one stage of r.f. amplification and a first i.f. of 1600 kc. or higher. A normal receiver with an i.f. of 455 kc. can be converted to a double conversion by connecting a "converter" ahead of the receiver.

For best selectivity, r.f. amplifiers should use high-Q circuits and tubes with high input and output resistance. Variable-μ pentodes are practically always used, although triodes (neutralized or otherwise connected so that they won't oscillate) are often used on the higher frequencies because they introduce less noise. Pentodes are better where maximum image rejection is desired, because they have less loading effect on the tuned circuits.

Transistor R. F. Amplifier

A typical r.f. amplifier circuit using a 2N370 transistor is shown in Fig. 5-26. Since it is desirable to maintain a reasonable Q in the tuned circuits, to reduce r.f. image response, the base and collector are both tapped down on their tuned circuits. An alternative method, using low-impedance inductive coupling, is shown in Fig. 5-26B; this method is sometimes easier to adjust than the taps illustrated in Fig. 5-26A. The tuned

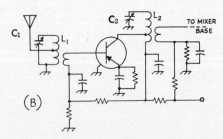

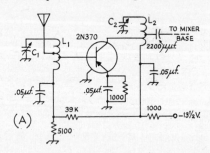

Fig. 5-26—Transistor r.f. amplifier circuit. The low-impedance connections to the base and collector can be (A) taps on the inductors or (B) low-impedance coupling links. L_1C_1, L_2C_2—Resonant at signal frequency.

Feedback

circuits, L_1C_1 and L_2C_2, should resonate at the operating frequency, and they should be mounted or shielded to eliminate inductive coupling between each other.

● FEEDBACK

Feedback giving rise to regeneration and oscillation can occur in a single stage or it may appear as an over-all feedback through several stages that are on the same frequency. To avoid feedback in a single stage, the output must be isolated from the input in every way possible, with the vacuum tube furnishing the only coupling between the two circuits. An oscillation can be obtained in an r.f. or i.f. stage if there is any undue capacitive or inductive coupling between output and input circuits, if there is too high an impedance between cathode and ground or screen and ground, or if there is any appreciable impedance through which the grid and plate currents can flow in common. This means good shielding of coils and tuning capacitors in r.f. and i.f. circuits, the use of good bypass capacitors (mica or ceramic at r.f., paper or ceramic at i.f.), and returning all bypass capacitors (grid, cathode, plate and screen) for a given stage with short leads to one spot on the chassis. If single-ended tubes are used, the screen or cathode bypass capacitor should be mounted across the socket, to serve as a shield between grid and plate pins. Less care is required as the frequency is lowered, but in high-impedance circuits, it is sometimes necessary to shield grid and plate leads and to be careful not to run them close together.

To avoid over-all feedback in a multistage amplifier, attention must be paid to avoid running any part of the output circuit back near the input circuit without first filtering it carefully. Since the signal-carrying parts of the circuit (the "hot" grid and plate leads) can't be filtered, the best design for any multistage amplifier is a straight line, to keep the output as far away from the input as possible. For example, an r.f. amplifier might run along a chassis in a straight line, run into a mixer where the frequency is changed, and then the i.f. amplifier could be run back parallel to the r.f. amplifier, provided there was a very large frequency difference between the r.f. and the i.f. amplifiers. However, to avoid any possible coupling, it would be better to run the i.f. amplifier off at right angles to the r.f.-amplifier line, just to be on the safe side. Good shielding is important in preventing over-all oscillation in high-gain-per-stage amplifiers, but it becomes less important when the stage gain drops to a low value. In a high-gain amplifier, the power leads (including the heater circuit) are common to all stages, and they can provide the over-all coupling if they aren't properly filtered. Good bypassing and the use of series isolating resistors will generally eliminate any possibility of coupling through the power leads. R.f. chokes, instead of resistors, are used in the heater leads where necessary.

● CROSS-MODULATION

Since a one- or two-stage r.f. amplifier will have a bandwidth measured in hundreds of kc. at 14 Mc. or higher, strong signals will be amplified through the r.f. amplifier even though it is not tuned exactly to them. If these signals are strong enough, their amplified magnitude may be measurable in volts after passing through several r.f. stages. If an undesired signal is strong enough after amplification in the r.f. stages to shift the operating point of a tube (by driving the grid into the positive region), the undesired signal will modulate the desired signal. This effect is called **cross-modulation,** and is often encountered in receivers with several r.f. stages working at high gain. It shows up as a superimposed modulation on the signal being listened to, and often the effect is that a signal can be tuned in at several points. It can be reduced or eliminated by greater selectivity in the antenna and r.f. stages (difficult to obtain), the use of variable-μ tubes in the r.f. amplifier, reduced gain in the r.f. amplifier, or reduced antenna input to the receiver. The 6BJ6, 6BA6 and 6DC6 are recommended for r.f. amplifiers where cross-modulation may be a problem.

A receiver designed for minimum cross-modulation will use as little gain as possible ahead of the high-selectivity stages, to hold strong unwanted signals below the overload point.

Gain Control

To avoid cross-modulation and other overload effects in the mixer and r.f. stages, the gain of the r.f. stages is usually made adjustable. This is accomplished by using variable-μ tubes and varying the d.c. grid bias, either in the grid or cathode circuit. If the gain control is automatic, as in the case of a.g.c., the bias is controlled in the grid circuit. Manual control of r.f. gain is generally done in the cathode circuit. A typical r.f. amplifier stage with the two types of gain control is shown in schematic form in Fig. 5-27.

Tracking

In a receiver with no r.f. stage, it is no incon-

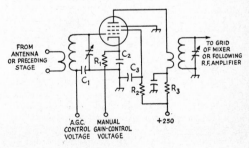

Fig. 5-27—Typical radio-frequency amplifier circuit for a superheterodyne receiver. Representative values for components are as follows:

C_1 to C_4—0.01 μf. below 15 Mc., 0.001 μf. at 30 Mc.
R_1, R_2—See Table 5-II.
R_3—1800 ohms.

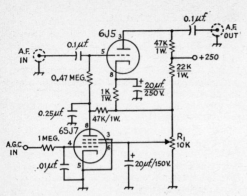

Fig. 5-28 — A practical squelch circuit for cutting off the receiver output when no signal is present.

venience to adjust the high-frequency oscillator and the mixer circuit independently, because the mixer tuning is broad and requires little attention over an amateur band. However, when r.f. stages are added ahead of the mixer, the r.f. stages and mixer will require retuning over an entire amateur band. Hence most receivers with one or more r.f. stages gang all of the tuning controls to give a single-tuning-control receiver. Obviously there must exist a constant difference in frequency (the i.f.) between the oscillator and the mixer/r.f. circuits, and when this condition is achieved the circuits are said to **track.**

In amateur-band receivers, tracking is simplified by choosing a bandspread circuit that gives practically straight-line-frequency tuning (equal frequency change for each dial division), and then adjusting the oscillator and mixer tuned circuits so that both cover the same total number of kilocycles. For example, if the i.f. is 455 kc. and the mixer circuit tunes from 7000 to 7300 kc. between two given points on the dial, then the oscillator must tune from 7455 to 7755 kc. between the same two dial readings. With the bandspread arrangement of Fig. 5-9A, the tuning will be practically straight-line-frequency if C_2 (bandset) is 4 times or more the maximum capacity of C_1 (bandspread), as is usually the case for strictly amateur-band coverage. C_1 should be of the straight-line-capacity type (semicircular plates).

Squelch Circuits

An audio squelch circuit is one that cuts off the receiver output when no signal is coming through the receiver. It is useful in mobile or net work where the no-signal receiver noise may be as loud as the signal, causing undue operator fatigue during no-signal periods.

A practical squelch circuit is shown in Fig. 5-28, When the a.g.c. voltage is low or zero, the 6SJ7 draws plate current. Voltage drop across the 47,000-ohm resistor in its plate circuit cuts off the 6J5 and no receiver signal or noise is passed. When the a.g.c. voltage rises to the cut-off value of the 6SJ7, the pentode no longer draws current and the bias on the 6J5 is now only the operating bias, furnished by the 1000-ohm cathode resistor. The triode now functions as an ordinary amplifier and passes signals. By varying the screen voltage on the 6SJ7 through R_1, the pentode's cut-off bias can be varied, so that the relation between a.g.c. voltage and signal cut-off point of the amplifier is adjustable.

Connections to the receiver consist of two a.f. lines (shielded), the a.g.c. lead, and chassis ground. The squelch circuit is normally inserted between detector output and the audio volume control of the receiver. Since the circuit is used in the low-level audio point, its plate supply must be free from a.c. or objectionable hum will be introduced.

Improving Receiver Sensitivity

The sensitivity (signal-to-noise ratio) of a receiver on the higher frequencies above 20 Mc. is dependent upon the band width of the receiver and the noise contributed by the "front end" of the receiver. Neglecting the fact that image rejection may be poor, a receiver with no r.f. stage is generally satisfactory, from a sensitivity point, in the 3.5- and 7-Mc. bands. However, as the frequency is increased and the atmospheric noise becomes less, the advantage of a good "front end" becomes apparent. Hence at 14 Mc. and higher it is worth while to use at least one stage of r.f. amplification ahead of the first detector for best sensitivity as well as image rejection. The multigrid converter tubes have very poor noise figures, and even the best pentodes and triodes are three or four times noisier when used as mixers than they are when used as amplifiers.

If the purpose of an r.f. amplifier is to improve the receiver noise figure at 14 Mc. and higher, a high-g_m pentode or triode should be used. Among the pentodes, the best tubes are the 6AC7, 6AK5 and the 6SG7, in the order named. The 6AK5 takes the lead around 30 Mc. The 6J4, 6J6, and triode-connected 6AK5 are the best of the triodes. For best noise figure, the antenna circuit should be coupled a little heavier than optimum. This cannot give best selectivity in the antenna circuit, so it is futile to try to maximize sensitivity *and* selectivity in this circuit.

When a receiver is satisfactory in every respect (stability and selectivity) except sensitivity on 14 through 30 Mc., the best solution for the amateur is to add a **preamplifier,** a stage of r.f. amplification designed expressly to improve the sensitivity. If image rejection is lacking in the receiver, some selectivity should be built into the preamplifier (it is then called a preselector). If, however, the receiver operation is poor on the higher frequencies but is satisfactory on the lower ones, a "converter" is the best solution.

Some commercial receivers that appear to lack sensitivity on the higher frequencies can be improved simply by tighter coupling to the antenna. This can be accomplished by changing the antenna feed line to the right value (as determined from the receiver instruction book) or by using a simple matching device as described later in this chapter. Overcoupling the input circuit will often improve sensitivity but it will, of course, always reduce the image-rejection contribution of the antenna circuit.

Regeneration

Regeneration in the r.f. stage of a receiver (where only one stage exists) will often improve the sensitivity because the greater gain it provides serves to mask more completely the first-detector noise, and it also provides a measure of automatic matching to the antenna through tighter coupling. However, accurate ganging becomes a problem, because of the increased selectivity of the regenerative r.f. stage, and the receiver almost invariably becomes a two-handed-

tuning device. Regeneration should not be overlooked as an expedient, however, and amateurs have used it with considerable success. High-g_m tubes are the best as regenerative amplifiers, and the feedback should not be controlled by changing the operating voltages (which should be the same as for the tube used in a high-gain amplifier) but by changing the loading or the feedback coupling. This is a tricky process and another reason why regeneration is not too widely used.

Gain Control

In a receiver front end designed for best signal-to-noise ratio, it is advantageous in the reception of weak signals to eliminate the gain control from the first r.f. stage and allow it to run "wide open" all of the time. If the first stage is controlled along with the i.f. (and other r.f. stages, if any), the signal-to-noise ratio of the receiver will suffer. As the gain is reduced, the g_m of the first tube is reduced, and its noise figure becomes higher. A good receiver might well have two gain controls, one for the first radio-frequency stage and another for the i.f. and other r.f. stages.

Tuning a Receiver

C.W. Reception

For making code signals audible, the beat oscillator should be set to a frequency slightly different from the intermediate frequency. To adjust the beat-oscillator frequency, first tune in a moderately weak but steady carrier with the beat oscillator turned off. Adjust the receiver tuning for maximum signal strength, as indicated by maximum hiss. Then turn on the beat oscillator and adjust its frequency (leaving the receiver tuning unchanged) to give a suitable beat note. The beat oscillator need not subsequently be touched, except for occasional checking to make certain the frequency has not drifted from the initial setting. The b.f.o. may be set on either the high- or low-frequency side of zero beat.

The best receiver condition for the reception of code signals will have the first r.f. stage running at maximum gain, the following r.f., mixer and i.f. stages operating with just enough gain to maintain the signal-to-noise ratio, and the audio gain set to give comfortable headphone or speaker volume. The audio volume should be controlled by the audio gain control, not the i.f. gain control. Under the above conditions, the selectivity of the receiver is being used to best advantage, and cross-modulation is minimized. It precludes the use of a receiver in which the gains of the r.f. and i.f. stages are controlled simultaneously.

Tuning with the Crystal Filter

If the receiver is equipped with a crystal filter the tuning instructions in the preceding paragraph still apply, but more care must be used

both in the initial adjustment of the beat oscillator and in tuning. The beat oscillator is set as described above, but with the crystal filter set at its sharpest position, if variable selectivity is available. The initial adjustment should be made with the phasing control in an intermediate position. Once adjusted, the beat oscillator should be left set and the receiver tuned to the other side of zero beat (audio-frequency image) on the same signal to give a beat note of the same tone. This beat will be considerably weaker than the first, and may be "phased out" almost completely by careful adjustment of the phasing control. This is the adjustment for normal operation; it will be found that one side of zero beat has practically disappeared, leaving maximum response on the other.

An interfering signal having a beat note differing from that of the a.f. image can be similarly phased out, provided its frequency is not too near the desired signal.

Depending upon the filter design, maximum selectivity may cause the dots and dashes to lengthen out so that they seem to "run together." It must be emphasized that, to realize the benefits of the crystal filter in reducing interference, it is necessary to do *all* tuning with it in the circuit. Its high selectivity often makes it difficult to find the desired station quickly, if the filter is switched in only when interference is present.

A.M. Phone Reception

In reception of a.m. phone signals, the normal procedure is to set the r.f. and i.f. gain at maximum, switch on the a.g.c., and use the audio gain control for setting the volume. This insures maximum effectiveness of the a.g.c. system in compensating for fading and maintaining constant audio output on either strong or weak signals. On occasion a strong signal close to the frequency of a weaker desired station may take control of the a.g.c., in which case the weaker station may disappear because of the reduced gain. In this case better reception may result if the a.g.c. is switched off, using the manual r.f. gain control to set the gain at a point that prevents "blocking" by the stronger signal.

When receiving an a.m. signal on a frequency within 5 to 20 kc. from a single-sideband signal it may also be necessary to switch off the a.g.c. and resort to the use of manual gain control, unless the receiver has excellent skirt selectivity. No ordinary a.g.c. circuit can handle the syllabic bursts of energy from the sideband station, but there are special circuits that will.

A crystal filter will help reduce interference in phone reception. Although the high selectivity cuts sidebands and reduces the audio output at the higher audio frequencies, it is possible to use quite high selectivity without destroying intelligibility. As in code reception, it is advisable to do all tuning with the filter in the circuit. Variable-selectivity filters permit a choice of selectivity to suit interference conditions.

An undesired carrier close in frequency to a desired carrier will heterodyne with it to produce a beat note equal to the frequency difference. Such a heterodyne can be reduced by adjustment of the phasing control in the crystal filter.

A tone control often will be of help in reducing the effects of high-pitched heterodynes, sideband splatter and noise, by cutting off the higher audio frequencies. This, like sideband cutting with high selectivity circuits, reduces naturalness.

Spurious Responses

Spurious responses can be recognized without a great deal of difficulty. Often it is possible to identify an image by the nature of the transmitting station, if the frequency assignments applying to the frequency to which the receiver is tuned are known. However, an image also can be recognized by its behavior with tuning. If the signal causes a heterodyne beat note with the desired signal and is actually on the same frequency, the beat note will not change as the receiver is tuned through the signal; but if the interfering signal is an image, the beat will vary in pitch as the receiver is tuned. The beat oscillator in the receiver must be turned off for this test. Using a crystal filter with the beat oscillator on, an image will peak on the side of zero beat opposite that on which desired signals peak.

Harmonic response can be recognized by the "tuning rate," or movement of the tuning dial required to give a specified change in beat note. Signals getting into the i.f. via high-frequency oscillator harmonics tune more rapidly (less dial movement) through a given change in beat note than do signals received by normal means.

Harmonics of the beat oscillator can be recognized by the tuning rate of the beat-oscillator pitch control. A smaller movement of the control will suffice for a given change in beat note than that necessary with legitimate signals. In poorly-shielded receivers it is often possible to find b.f.o. harmonics below 2 Mc., but they should be very weak at higher frequencies.

Alignment and Servicing of Superheterodyne Receivers

I.F. Alignment

A calibrated signal generator or test oscillator is a useful device for alignment of an i.f. amplifier. Some means for measuring the output of the receiver is required. If the receiver has a tuning meter, its indications will serve. Lacking an S meter, a high-resistance voltmeter or a vacuum-tube voltmeter can be connected across the second-detector load resistor, if the second detector is a diode. Alternatively, if the signal generator is a modulated type, an a.c. voltmeter can be connected across the primary of the transformer feeding the speaker, or from the plate of the last audio amplifier through a 0.1-μf. blocking capacitor to the receiver chassis. Lacking an a.c. voltmeter, the audio output can be judged by ear, although this method is not as accurate as the others. If the tuning meter is used as an indication, the a.g.c. of the receiver should be turned on, but any other indication requires that it be turned off. Lacking a test oscillator, a steady signal tuned through the input of the receiver (if the job is one of just touching up the i.f.

amplifier) will be suitable. However, with no oscillator and tuning an amplifier for the first time, one's only recourse is to try to peak the i.f. transformers on "noise," a difficult task if the transformers are badly off resonance, as they are apt to be. It would be much better to haywire together a simple oscillator for test purposes.

Initial alignment of a new i.f. amplifier is as follows: The test oscillator is set to the correct frequency, and its output is coupled through a capacitor to the grid of the last i.f. amplifier tube. The trimmer capacitors of the transformer feeding the second detector are then adjusted for maximum output, as shown by the indicating device being used. The oscillator output lead is then clipped on to the grid of the next-to-the-last i.f. amplifier tube, and the second-from-the-last transformer trimmer adjustments are peaked for maximum output. This process is continued, working back from the second detector, until all of the i.f. transformers have been aligned. It will be necessary to reduce the output of the test oscillator as more of the i.f. amplifier is brought

Alignment and Servicing

into use. It is desirable in all cases to use the minimum signal that will give useful output readings. The i.f. transformer in the plate circuit of the mixer is aligned with the signal introduced to the grid of the mixer. Since the tuned circuit feeding the mixer grid may have a very low impedance at the i.f., it may be necessary to boost the test generator output or to disconnect the tuned circuit temporarily from the mixer grid.

If the i.f. amplifier has a crystal filter, the filter should first be switched out and the alignment carried out as above, setting the test oscillator as closely as possible to the crystal frequency. When this is completed, the crystal should be switched in and the oscillator frequency varied back and forth over a small range either side of the crystal frequency to find the exact frequency, as indicated by a sharp rise in output. Leaving the test oscillator set on the crystal peak, the i.f. trimmers should be realigned for maximum output. The necessary readjustment should be small. The oscillator frequency should be checked frequently to make sure it has not drifted from the crystal peak.

A modulated signal is not of much value for aligning a crystal-filter i.f. amplifier, since the high selectivity cuts sidebands and the results may be inaccurate if the audio output is used as the tuning indication. Lacking the a.v.c. tuning meter, the transformers may be conveniently aligned by ear, using a weak unmodulated signal adjusted to the crystal peak. Switch on the beat oscillator, adjust to a suitable tone, and align the i.f. transformers for maximum audio output.

An amplifier that is only slightly out of alignment, as a result of normal drift or aging, can be realigned by using any steady signal, such as a local broadcast station, instead of the test oscillator. One's 100-kc. standard makes an excellent signal source for "touching up" an i.f. amplifier. Allow the receiver to warm up thoroughly, tune in the signal, and trim the i.f. for maximum output.

If you bought your receiver instead of making it, be sure to read the instruction book carefully before attempting to realign the receiver. Most instruction books include alignment details, and any little special tricks that are peculiar to the receiver will also be described in detail.

R.F. Alignment

The objective in aligning the r.f. circuits of a gang-tuned receiver is to secure adequate tracking over each tuning range. The adjustment may be carried out with a test oscillator of suitable frequency range, with harmonics from your 100-kc. standard or other known oscillator, or even on noise or such signals as may be heard. First set the tuning dial at the high-frequency end of the range in use. Then set the test oscillator to the frequency indicated by the receiver dial. The test-oscillator output may be connected to the antenna terminals of the receiver for this test. Adjust the oscillator trimmer capacitor

in the receiver to give maximum response on the test-oscillator signal, then reset the receiver dial to the low-frequency end of the range. Set the test-oscillator frequency near the frequency indicated by the receiver dial and tune the test oscillator until its signal is heard in the receiver. If the frequency of the signal as indicated by the test-oscillator calibration is higher than that indicated by the receiver dial, more inductance (or more capacity in the tracking capacitor) is needed in the receiver oscillator circuit; if the frequency is lower, less inductance (less tracking capacity) is required in the receiver oscillator. Most commercial receivers provide some means for varying the inductance of the coils or the capacity of the tracking capacitor, to permit aligning the receiver tuning with the dial calibration. Set the test oscillator to the frequency indicated by the receiver dial, and then adjust the tracking capacity or inductance of the receiver oscillator coil to obtain maximum response. After making this adjustment, recheck the high-frequency end of the scale as previously described. It may be necessary to go back and forth between the ends of the range several times before the proper combination of inductance and capacity is secured. In many cases, better over-all tracking will result if frequencies near but not actually at the ends of the tuning range are selected, instead of taking the extreme dial settings.

After the oscillator range is properly adjusted, set the receiver and test oscillator to the high-frequency end of the range. Adjust the mixer trimmer capacitor for maximum hiss or signal, then the r.f. trimmers. Reset the tuning dial and test oscillator to the low-frequency end of the range, and repeat; if the circuits are properly designed, no change in trimmer settings should be necessary. If it is necessary to increase the trimmer capacity in any circuit, more inductance is needed; conversely, if less capacity resonates the circuit, less inductance is required.

Tracking seldom is perfect throughout a tuning range, so that a check of alignment at intermediate points in the range may show it to be slightly off. Normally the gain variation will be small, however, and it will suffice to bring the circuits into line at both ends of the range. If most reception is in a particular part of the range, such as an amateur band, the circuits may be aligned for maximum performance in that region, even though the ends of the frequency range as a whole may be slightly out of alignment.

Oscillation in R.F. or I.F. Amplifiers

Oscillation in high-frequency amplifier and mixer circuits shows up as squeals or "birdies" as the tuning is varied, or by complete lack of audible output if the oscillation is strong enough to cause the a.g.c. system to reduce the receiver gain drastically. Oscillation can be caused by poor connections in the common ground circuits. Inadequate or defective bypass capacitors in cathode, plate and screen-grid circuits also can cause such oscillation. A metal tube with an ungrounded shell may cause trouble. Improper screen-grid voltage, resulting from a shorted or too-low screen-grid series resistor, also may be responsible for such instability.

Oscillation in the i.f. circuits is independent of high-frequency tuning, and is indicated by a continuous squeal that appears when the gain is advanced with the c.w. beat oscillator on. It can result from defects in i.f.-amplifier circuits. Inadequate screen or plate bypass capacitance is a common cause of such oscillation.

Improving the Performance of Receivers

Frequently amateurs unjustly criticize a receiver's performance when actually part of the trouble lies with the operator, in his lack of knowledge about the receiver's operation or in his inability to recognize a readily curable fault. The best example of this is a complaint about "lack of selectivity" when the receiver contains an i.f. crystal filter and the operator hasn't bothered to learn how to use it properly. "Lack of sensitivity" may be nothing more than poor alignment of the r.f. and mixer tuning. The cures for these two complaints are obvious, and the details are treated both in this chapter and in the receiver instruction book.

However, many complaints about selectivity, sensitivity, and other points are justified. Inexpensive, and most second-hand, receivers cannot be expected to measure up to the performance standards of some of the current and top-priced receivers. Nevertheless, many amateurs overlook the possibility of improving the performance of these "bargains" (they may or may not be bargains) by a few simple additions or modifications. From time to time articles in *QST* describe improvements for specific receivers, and it may repay the owner of a newly-acquired second-hand receiver to examine past issues and see if an applicable article was published. The annual index in each December issue is a help in this respect.

Where no applicable article can be found, a few general principles can be laid down. If the complaint is the inability to separate stations, better i.f. (and occasionally audio) selectivity is indicated. The answer is not to be found in better bandspread tuning of the dial as is sometimes erroneously concluded. For code reception the addition of a "Q Multiplier" to the i.f. amplifier is a simple and effective attack; a Q Multiplier is at its best in the region 100 to 900 kc., and higher than this its effectiveness drops off. The Selectoject is a selective audio device based on similar principles. For phone reception the addition of a Q Multiplier will help to reject an interfering carrier, and the use of a BC-453 as a "Q5-er" will add adjacent-channel selectivity.

With the addition of more i.f. selectivity, it may be found that the receiver's tuning rate (number of kc. tuned per dial revolution) is too high, and consequently the tuning with good i.f. selectivity becomes too critical. If this is the case, a 5-to-1 reduction planetary dial drive mechanism may be added to make the tuning rate more favorable. These drives are sold by the larger supply houses and can usually be added to the receiver if a suitable mounting bracket is made from sheet metal. If there is already some backlash in the dial mechanism, the addition of the planetary drive will magnify its effect, so it is necessary to minimize the backlash before attempting to improve the tuning rate. While this is not possible in all cases, it should be investigated from every angle before giving up. Replacing a small tuning knob with a larger one will add to ease of tuning; in many cases after doing so it will then be desirable or necessary to raise the receiver higher above the table.

If the receiver appears to lack the ability to bring in the weak signals, particularly on the higher-frequency bands, the performance can often be improved by the addition of an antenna coupler (described elsewhere in this chapter); it will always be improved by the addition of a preselector (also described elsewhere in this chapter).

If the receiver shortcoming is inadequate r.f. selectivity, as indicated by r.f. "images" on the higher-frequency bands, a simple antenna coupler will often add sufficient selectivity to cure the trouble. However, if the images are severe, it is likely that a preselector will be required, preferably of the regenerative type. The preselector will also add to the ability of the receiver to detect weak signals at 14 Mc. and higher.

In many of the inexpensive receivers the frequency calibration of the dial is not very accurate. The receiver's usefulness for determining band limits will be greatly improved by the addition of a 100-kc. crystal-controlled frequency standard. These units can be built or purchased complete at very reasonable prices, and no amateur station worthy of the name should be without one.

Some receivers that show a considerable frequency drift as they are warming up can be improved by the simple expedient of furnishing more ventilation, by propping up the lid or by drilling extra ventilation holes. In many cases the warm-up drift can be cut in half.

Receivers that show frequency changes with line-voltage or gain-control variations can be greatly improved by the addition of regulated voltage on the oscillators (high-frequency and b.f.o.) and the screen of the mixer tube. There is usually room in any receiver for the addition of a VR tube of the right rating.

SimpleX Super

The "SimpleX Super" Three-Tube Receiver

The name of this receiver derives from "simple", "X" for crystal (filter), and "super" for superheterodyne; hence a "simple crystal-filter superheterodyne." For about fifty dollars and a few nights at the workbench this little receiver will allow you to copy practically any c.w. or s.s.b. signal in the 40- or 80-meter band that a much more expensive receiver might drag in. By the flip of a switch you can tune to 5 Mc. for WWV.

This 3-tube receiver will permit the single-signal reception of code signals. Single-sideband phone can be handled with no difficulty at all. With the b.f.o. turned off for the reception of a.m. signals, a threshold effect shows up that prevents digging all the way down for the weak ones, but one can still copy plenty of a.m. signals. Since the receiver uses only three tubes, it doesn't have the more-than-enough gain of a big receiver, and its performance won't be very impressive on a poor (short or low) antenna. However, if the transmitting antenna is also used for receiving, you will find yourself backing down on the volume control to save your ears.

Referring to the circuit diagram in Fig. 5-30, the receiver is a superheterodyne with an intermediate frequency of 1700 kc. With the h.f. oscillator tuning 5.2 to 5.7 Mc., the 3.5- or the 7-Mc. amateur bands can be tuned merely by retuning the input circuit, L_1C_1. Since C_1 is large enough to hit the two bands without a coil change, the band-changing process consists of turning C_1 to the low- or high-capacitance end of its range. To copy WWV at 5 Mc., the oscillator must be tuned to 3.3 Mc., and this is done by switching in an additional capacitor across the oscillator circuit.

If you are disappointed because the receiver doesn't tune the 21-Mc. band, remember that the "under-$100" receivers don't either. Sure, the dials show 21 Mc., but try to use the receivers to hold a signal for any length of time! The SimpleX Super, with a crystal-controlled converter between it and the antenna, will handle 15 meters like 80.

Selectivity at the i.f. is obtained through the use of a single crystal. Although not as sharp as the usual 455-kc. crystal filter, it is sharp enough to provide a fair degree of single-signal c.w. reception and yet broad enough for good copy of an s.s.b. phone signal.

In the detector stage, the pentode section of a 6U8A is used as a grid-leak detector, and the triode section serves as the b.f.o. Stray coupling at the socket and in the tube provides adequate injection. Audio amplification is obtained from the two triode sections of a 6CG7. The primary of a small output transformer, T_1, serves as the coupling for high-impedance headphone output, and a small loudspeaker or low-impedance headphones can be connected at the output winding of the transformer. Although the audio power output is less than a watt, it is sufficient to drive a loudspeaker adequately in a small quiet room.

The power supply uses a large choke and two 40-μf. capacitors, and the very slight hum that can be detected in the headphones with the volume full on is stray a.c. picked up by the detector grid; it doesn't come from inadequate filtering of the power supply. (The hum can only be heard with no antenna on; under normal operation the incoming noise will mask the slight hum.)

A switch at the input of the receiver is included so that the receiver can be used to listen to one's own transmitter without too severe blocking. Using the b.f.o. switch to cut in the WWV padder was done (instead of by the more logical S_1) to keep the input short-circuiting leads short.

An 8 × 12 × 3-inch aluminum chassis takes all of the parts without crowding, and the location of the components can be seen in the photographs. The 7¼ × 13-inch aluminum panel (1/16-inch thick) is held to the chassis by the b.f.o. capacitor mounting screws, the phone jack, the dial drive and the two rotary switches. The tuning capacitor C_2 is mounted on a small aluminum bracket made from an extra strip of the panel material; before the bracket is finally fastened to the chassis the capacitor and bracket should be used to locate the dial hole on the panel. When

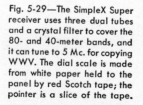

Fig. 5-29—The SimpleX Super receiver uses three dual tubes and a crystal filter to cover the 80- and 40-meter bands, and it can tune to 5 Mc. for copying WWV. The dial scale is made from white paper held to the panel by red Scotch tape; the pointer is a slice of the tape.

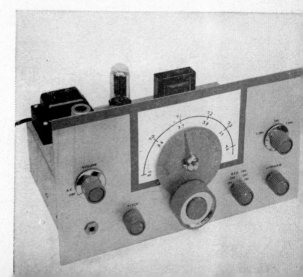

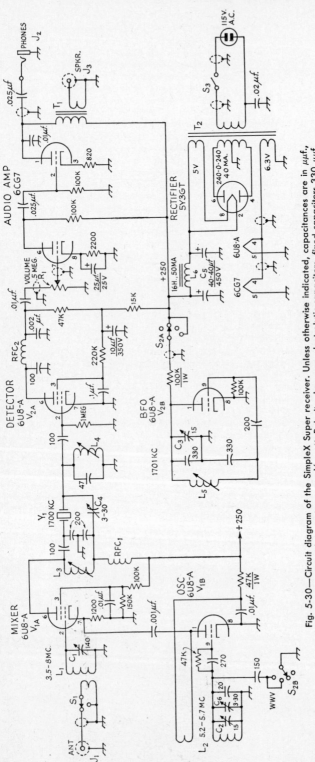

Fig. 5-30—Circuit diagram of the SimpleX Super receiver. Unless otherwise indicated, capacitances are in μμf., resistances are in ohms, resistors are ½ watt. Polarity shown on electrolytic capacitors; fixed capacitors 330 μμf. or less are silver mica or NP0 ceramic. Nonelectrolytic fixed capacitors over 0.025 μf. are 400-volt molded tubulars. Fixed capacitors 0.001 through 0.025 are ceramic.

C_1—140-μμf. midget variable (Hammarlund APC-140-B).
C_2—15-μμf. midget variable (Hammarlund HF-15).
C_3—15-μμf. trimmer (Hammarlund MAPC-15-B).
C_4, C_6—3-30-μμf. mica compression trimmer.
C_5—Dual 40-μf. 450-volt electrolytic (Mallory TCD-78 or equiv.).

J_1, J_3—Phono jack.
J_2—Open-circuit headphone jack.
L_1, L_2—See Fig. 5-35.
L_3, L_4—105-200-μh. slug-tuned (North Hills S-120 shield can).

L_5—36-64-μh. slug-tuned (North Hills 120-F coil mounted in North Hills S-120 shield can).
L_6—16-hy. 50-ma. filter choke (Knight 62-G-137 or equiv.).
R_1—½ megohm volume control, audio taper, with switch.
RFC_1, RFC_2—2.5-mh. r.f. choke (Waters C1155).
S_1—1-pole 12-position (2 used) rotary ceramic switch (Centralab PA-2001).
S_2—2-pole 6-position (4 used) rotary ceramic switch (Centralab PA-2003).
S_3—S.p.s.t. switch, part of R_1.

T_1—10,000-ohms-to-voice-coil output transformer (Stancor A-3822 or equiv.).
T_2—480 v. c.t. at 40 ma., 5 v. at 2 amp., 6.3 v. at 2 amp. (Knight 62-G-034 or equiv.).
Y_1—1700-kc. crystal in FT-243 holder (E. B. Lewis or equiv.).

(All radio stores do not handle the above components. For prices and names of dealers write to North Hills Electric Co., 402 Sagamore Ave., Mineola, N. Y.; Knight is handled by Allied Radio, 100 N. Western Ave., Chicago 80, Ill.; Waters Mfg. Inc., Boston Post Rd., Wayland, Mass.; E. B. Lewis, 11 Bragg St., E. Hartford, Conn.)

SimpleX Super

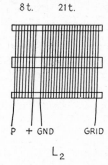

6 t.   26 t.   8 t.   21 t.

ANT GND   GRID   P + GND   GRID

L_1 L_2

Fig. 5-31—Details of the coil construction. Each one is made from B & W 3016 Miniductor stock, which is wound 32 t.p.i. and 1-inch diameter. The separation between coils in L_1 is 7 turns; the separation between coils L_2 is 1 turn. It is important that the coils be connected as indicated. The Miniductor stock can be cut into the required lengths by pushing in a turn, cutting it inside the coil and then pushing the newly cut ends through to outside the coil. Once outside, it is easy to peel away the wire with the help of long-nose pliers. When sufficient turns have been removed, the support bars can be cut with a fine saw.

drilling the hole for the dial drive, measure the dimension instead of using the template provided with the National K dial. It pays to take care in mounting the tuning capacitor and the dial, since a smooth tuning drive is an essential in any receiver. To facilitate tuning, a National HRT knob was used instead of the puny knob furnished with the K dial. The other knobs are gray National HR and HR-4.

Tie points are used liberally throughout the receiver, as junctions for components and interconnecting wires. The coils L_1 and L_2 are mounted on tie points, using short leads. If the leads from L_2 are too long, the coil will be "floppy" and the receiver may be unstable. Fig. 5-35 shows how coils L_1 and L_2 are constructed and connected. The leads from C_1 and C_2 are brought through the chassis in insulating grommets. The 3- to 30-$\mu\mu$f. mica compression trimmer across L_2 is soldered to the tie points that support the coil.

The receiver is wired with shielded wire for many of the leads, in an effort to minimize hum in the audio and feedthrough around the crystal filter. The shielded leads are marked in Fig. 5-30 where feasible; the simple rule to follow is to shield all B+ leads along with those shown shielded in Fig. 5-30. For easy of wiring, these shielded leads should be installed first or at least early in the construction. As the wiring progresses, a neat-looking unit can be obtained by dressing the leads and components in parallel lines or at right angles. D.c. and a.c. leads can be tucked out of the way along the edges of the chassis, while r.f. leads should be as direct as is reasonable.

If this is your first receiver or construction job, there are several pitfalls to be avoided. When installing a tube socket, first give a little thought to where the grid and plate leads will run, and orient the socket so that these leads will be direct and not cross over the socket.

Another thing to look out for is the well-meaning store clerk who sells you stranded wire for making the connections throughout the receiver. The only stranded wire in this receiver is in the leads from the transformers, filter capacitor and filter choke, and in the shielded wire, and all this only because there was no choice. Where stranded wire is used, be very careful to avoid wild strands that stray over to an adjacent socket terminal and short-circuit a part of the circuit without your knowing it. No. 20 or 22 insulated

solid tinned copper wire should be used for connections wherever no shielding is used. Long bare leads from resistors or capacitors should be covered with insulating tubing unless they go to chassis grounds.

The final bugaboo is, of course, a poorly-soldered connection. If this is your first venture, by all means practice soldering before you start to wire this receiver. Read an article or two on how to solder, or get a friend to show you how and to criticize your first attempts. A good soldering iron is an essential; there have been instances of a first venture having been "soldered" with an iron that would just barely melt the solder; the iron was incapable of heating the solder and work to the point where the solder would flow properly.

There is no need to worry about the dial scale when the receiver is first built, because the receiver has to be checked. The scale is a sheet of white paper held in place by red or black Scotch tape. The dial pointer is a slice of the same tape.

When the wiring has been completed and checked once more against the circuit diagram, plug in the tubes and the line cord and turn on the receiver through S_3. The tube heaters and rectifier filament should light up and nothing should start to smoke or get hot. If you have a voltmeter you should measure about 250 volts on the B+ line.

With headphones plugged in the receiver, you should be able to hear a little hum when the volume control is advanced all the way. If you can't hear any hum, touching a screwdriver to Pin 2 should produce hum and a loud click. This shows that the detector and audio amplifier are working.

The next step is to tune L_3, L_4 and L_5 to 1700 kc., the crystal frequency. If you have or can borrow a signal generator, put 1700-kc. r.f. in at the grid of the 6U8A mixer and peak L_3 and L_4. Lacking a signal generator, you may be lucky enough to find a strong signal by tuning around with C_2, but it isn't likely. Your best bet is to tune a broadcast receiver to around 1245 kc.; if the receiver has a 455-kc. i.f. the oscillator will then be on 1700 kc. Don't depend upon the calibration of the broadcast receiver; make your own by checking known stations. The oscillator of the broadcast receiver will furnish a steady (possibly hum-modulated) carrier that can be picked up by running a wire temporarily from the grid of the 6U8A mixer to a point near the chassis of the

Fig. 5-32—Top view of the SimpleX Super. The tube between the two variable capacitors is the mixer-oscillator 6U8A; the 6CG7 audio amplifier is at the far right. The flexible insulated coupling between main tuning dial and the tuning capacitor is a Millen 39016.

b.c. receiver. Adjust L_5 until you get a beat with the 1700-kc. signal, and then peak L_3 and L_4. If the signal gets too loud, reduce the signal by moving the wire away from the b.c. receiver. Now slowly swing the signal frequency back and forth with the b.f.o. turned off; you should find a spot where the noise rushes up quickly and then drops off. This is the crystal frequency, and L_3 and L_4 should be peaked again on this frequency if you were a little off the first time.

An antenna connected to the receiver should now permit the reception of signals. With C_1 nearly unmeshed, you will be in the region of the 7-Mc. band, and with C_1 almost completely meshed, you will be near 3.5 Mc. Do your tuning with the compression trimmer in the oscillator circuit, until you find a known frequency (it can be your own transmitter). Let's say your transmitter has a crystal at 3725 kc. Set C_2 at half capacitance and tune with C_6 until you hear your transmitter. You shouldn't need any antenna on the receiver for this test. Once you have the setting for the trimmer, put the antenna on the receiver and look around for other known signals.

(CHU, the Canadian standard-frequency station at 7335 kc., is a good marker.) With luck you should just be able to cover the 80-meter band; if you can get one end but not the other, a minor readjustment of the trimmer is indicated.

Once you have acquainted yourself with the 80- and 40-meter bands, and appreciate that you have to peak up the input circuit (C_1) fairly often as you tune across the bands, you are ready to trim up the crystal filter. Run the volume fairly high, so that you can hear noise from the properly peaked input circuit, and turn C_3 until the noise takes on a higher-pitched characteristic. (The b.f.o. stage is originally set up with C_3 at midcapacitance and L_5 adjusted for lowest-pitched noise.) Now tune in a code signal with C_2 and swing back and forth through it. "One side" of the signal should be louder than the other. Tune to the weak side with a beat note of around 800 cycles and then adjust C_4 for minimum signal. After a few attempts, juggling C_3, C_4, L_3 and L_4, you should get a condition where the single-signal c.w. effect is quite apparent.

All that remains is to install the dial scale and calibrate it. A 100-kc. oscillator is ideal for this job; lacking one or the ability to borrow one, you will have to rely on other signals. If your crystal filter is 1700 kc. exactly, the 80- and 40-meter calibrations will coincide as they do on the scale shown in Fig. 5-33; if not, the calibration marks will be offset on the two bands.

If you find that you can't get WWV at 5 Mc. with the 150-$\mu\mu$f. capacitor switched in, substitute a 130-$\mu\mu$f. mica in parallel with a 30-$\mu\mu$f. trimmer, and adjust so that WWV falls on scale.

As you acquaint yourself with the operation of the receiver, you will notice that tuning C_1 will have a slight effect on the tuning of the signal. In other words, tuning C_1 "pulls" the oscillator slightly. To remedy this would have made the receiver more complicated, and the simple solution is merely to first peak C_1 on noise and then tune with C_2.

You will find this to be a practical receiver in every way for the c.w. (or s.s.b.) operator. The tuning rate is always the same on 80 or 40, or 15 with a converter, and 21-Mc. s.s.b. signals tune as easily as those on 3.9 Mc. The warm-up drift is negligible, and the oscillator is surprisingly insensitive to voltage changes. Whether or not the oscillator is insensitive to shock and vibration will depend upon the care with which the components are anchored to their respective tie points.

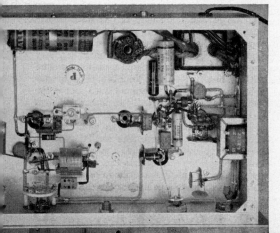

Fig. 5-33—Shielded wire, used for most of the d.c. and 60-cycle leads, lends to the clean appearance underneath the chassis. The switch at the left shorts the input of the receiver, and the adjacent switch handles the b.f.o. and the padding capacitor for WWV.

The phono jack at the top left is for the antenna; the other phono jack is for low-impedance audio output. The headphone jack (lower right) is for high-impedance audio output.

The 2X4+1 Superheterodyne

The receiver shown in Figs. 5-34, 5-37 and 5-38 is a two-band four-tube (2X4) receiver with a transistor (+1) 100-kc. frequency standard. Other features include the ability to tune to 5 Mc., for the reception of WWV, and a dual-crystal filter for single-sideband and single-signal c.w. reception. Tuning the 40- and 80-meter amateur bands with good stability and selectivity, the receiver can be used on other bands by the addition of crystal-controlled converters ahead of it.

Referring to the circuit in Fig. 5-35, the pentode section of a 6U8-A is used as a mixer, with the triode portion of the same tube serving as the oscillator. The i.f. is 1700 kc. and the oscillator tunes 5.2 to 5.7 Mc.; tuning the input circuit to the 80-meter band brings in 80-meter signals, and all that is required to hear 40-meter signals is to swing the input tuning, C_1, to the low-capacitance end of its range. Although, e.g., a 7.05-Mc. (5.35 + 1.7) and a 3.65-Mc. (5.35 − 1.7) signal will appear at the same setting of the tuning dial, the two signals cannot be received simultaneously because the double-tuned circuit, $C_{1A} L_2$ and $C_{1B} L_3$, between antenna and mixer grid provides the necessary rejection. To provide optimum coupling in both ranges, the coupling capacitance is changed by a switch, S_1, actuated by the shaft of C_1. Thus the coupling change takes place automatically as the capacitor is tuned to the desired band. To make the two cir-

cuits track over the entire range, a 3- to 30-$\mu\mu f$ trimmer is provided to compensate for the input capacitance of the mixer. For WWV reception, capacitance C_6 is added to the oscillator circuit to bring its frequency to 3.3 Mc.

The mixer is followed by the dual crystal filter at 1700 kc. and a stage of i.f. amplification. I.f. gain is manually controlled by a variable bias control in the cathode circuit of the 6BA6 i.f. amplifier stage. A triode section of a 6CG7, V_{2A}, serves as a grid-leak detector, and the other section is used as the b.f.o. A two-stage audio amplifier follows, providing high-impedance output for headphones or low-impedance output for a loudspeaker. The audio power is sufficient to give more than enough high-impedance headphone volume and quite adequate loudspeaker volume in a quiet room.

The power supply includes a 0C3 to supply regulated 105 volts for the two oscillators and the screen of the mixer.

The transistor 100-kc. calibration oscillator uses for its power source the 8 volts developed across the cathode resistor of V_{3B}. Switch S_3 turns the oscillator on and off and also adds the capacitance to the oscillator circuit that permits WWV reception. The four positions of S_3 are OFF — WWV (only) — CAL (oscillator only) — BOTH. Although the 100-kc. standard is not essential to the operation of the receiver, its inclusion will be found to be quite valuable.

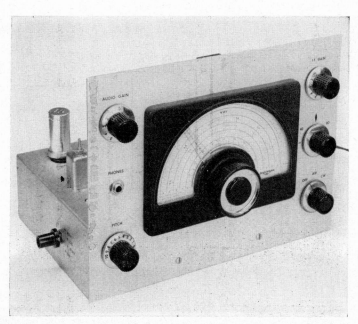

Fig. 5-34—The 2X4 + 1 superheterodyne is a four-tube receiver with 7-tube performance. It tunes the 80- and 40-meter amateur bands, and provision is included for receiving WWV on 5 Mc. A built-in crystal oscillator provides 100-kc. frequency markers throughout the bands. Black knob on the left-hand side controls the calibration oscillator and the WWV reception.

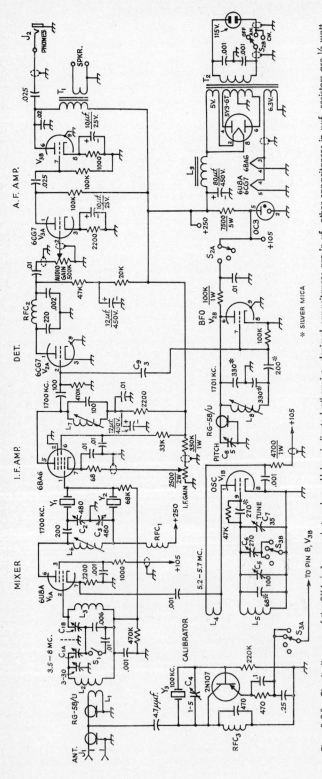

Fig. 5-35—Circuit diagram of the 2X4 + 1 super-heterodyne. Unless indicated otherwise, decimal capacitances are in μf., other capacitances in μμf., resistors are ½ watt.

C₁—Dual variable, 140 μμf. per section (Hammarlund MCD-140-M).

C₂, C₃—480-μμf. mica compression trimmer (Arco-Elmenco 466).

C₄—5-μμf. variable (Hammarlund MAC-5).

C₅—100-μμf. midget variable (Hammarlund HF-100).

C₆—240 μμf. ± 5% mica in parallel with 30-μμf. mica compression trimmer.

C₇—35-μμf. midget variable (Hammarlund HF-35).

C₈—5-μμf. midget variable (Hammarlund HF-15 with 3 plates removed).

C₉—3 μμf. approx. Insulated wires twisted together for 3 turns.

J₁—Phono jack.

L₁—19 turns No. 24, part of L₂ stock, ⅛ inch from L₂.

L₂, L₃—43 turns No. 24, ¾-inch diam, 32 t.p.i. (B&W 3012 or Illumitronic 632).

L₄—7 turns No. 24, part of L₅ stock, ½ inch from L₅.

L₅—17 turns No. 24, ¾-inch diam, 32 t.p.i. (B&W 3012 or Illumitronic 632).

L₆, L₇—64 to 105 μh., adjustable (North Hills 120-G in North Hills S-120 shield can).

L₈—36 to 64 μh., adjustable (North Hills 120-F in North Hills S-120 shield can).

L₉—15-henry, 75-ma. filter choke (Stancor C-1002).

RFC₁, RFC₂—2.2 mh., self resonant at 1.6 Mc. (Waters

RFC₃—10 mh. (National R-50-I).

S₁—Homemade cam switch mounted on C₁. See text.

S₂—2-pole 3-position rotary switch (Centralab 1472).

S₃—2-pole 6-position (4 used) miniature ceramic switch (Centralab PA-3 with Centralab PA-301 index, 2½ inches used).

T₁—3-watt, 8000 to 3.2 ohms, output transformer (Stancor A-3329).

T₂—650 v.c.t. at 55 ma., 5 v., 6.3 v. at 2 amp. (Stancor PC-8407).

Y₁, Y₂—1700-kc. crystals, FT-243 holders, surplus.

2X4+1 Superhet

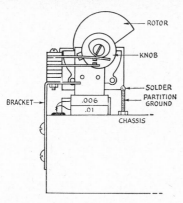

Fig. 5-36—The cam-operated switch, S_1, is made from the contacts and insulators taken from an open-circuit phone jack (Mallory 703) and mounted on an aluminum bracket. The cam, mounted on the shaft of C_1, is made by grinding one side of a small insulated knob (Johnson 116-214-1). Switch is open during minimum-capacitance half of capacitor range. Bracket is made from a $1\frac{1}{4} \times 3\frac{1}{2}$-inch strip of aluminum; the shelf is $\frac{3}{4}$-inch deep.

Construction

The receiver is built on an $8 \times 12 \times 3$-inch aluminum chassis. A panel can be made from $\frac{1}{16}$-inch thick sheet aluminum or from a standard $8\frac{3}{4}$-inch rack panel. While the rack panel will be more substantial, it really isn't necessary, and the $\frac{1}{16}$-inch stock will be adequate. The panel is held to the chassis by the b.f.o. capacitor, C_8, the line/b.f.o. switch, S_2, the dial, and an extra pair of 6-32 screws.

It is worth while to mount the tuning capacitor, C_7, as accurately as possible with respect to the National ICN dial. For minimum backlash and maximum strength, C_7 is mounted on a three-sided aluminum housing that is securely fastened to the chassis on three sides by $\frac{3}{8}$-inch lips. A good flexible insulated coupling should be used between dial and capacitor shaft — a Millen 39006 is shown in the photograph.

The location of most of the major components can be determined by reference to the photographs. The inductors L_1L_2, L_3 and L_4L_5 are supported by suitable tie strips, as are the two 480-$\mu\mu$f. mica compression trimmers, C_2 and C_3, in the crystal filter circuit and the pair of 330-$\mu\mu$f. capacitors in the b.f.o. L_1L_2 should be wired so that the outside ends go to antenna and grid, and L_4L_5 should be wired with outside ends to plate and grid.

Details of the only unusual construction, the cam-operated switch S_1, are shown in Fig. 5-36. Note that the associated .006- and .01-μf. coupling capacitors are mounted above the chassis; a clearance hole with a rubber grommet is provided in the chassis for the common lead back to L_2 and L_3.

Since the rotor of C_1 must not make contact with the panel, a large clearance hole must be provided for the shaft bushing, and a pair of extruded fiber washers used to insulate the bushing from the panel. A brass screw or bayonet lug should be set into the chassis at the shield partition between the two stators of C_1, and the shield soldered to this chassis connection. The 3- to 30-$\mu\mu$f. compression trimmer across C_{1A} can be soldered between rotor and shield partition.

Many of the connections are made with shielded leads, to minimize hum and chances for feedback or feedthrough. The shielded leads are indicated in Fig. 5-35. The lead from the antenna jack is run in RG-58/U coaxial cable, as is the short lead from C_8 to a 330-$\mu\mu$f. capacitor. Heater leads to the tubes are made of shielded wire.

Alignment

The alignment procedure can be simplified if a short-wave receiver or a signal generator can be borrowed. Lacking these, a grid-dip meter can be used to provide a signal source and to check the resonances of the tuned circuits. If the 100-kc. oscillator can be checked on another receiver, it can be used to align the receiver. A broadcast receiver will tell if the 100-kc. oscillator is functioning — it should be possible to identify several of the oscillator's harmonics at 100-kc. intervals in the broadcast band, by the reduction in noise at those points.

The audio amplifier of the receiver can be checked by turning on the receiver and listening to the headphones as the audio gain control is advanced. When it is full clockwise a low-pitched hum should be just audible in the headphones. A further check can be made by bringing a finger near the arm of the audio gain control — the hum should increase.

If a means is available for checking the frequency of the b.f.o., it should be turned on at S_2 and set on or about 1700 kc. by means of the slug in L_8. Do this with C_8 set at half scale. If a broadcast receiver is the only measuring equipment you have, a 1700-kc. signal can be derived from it by tuning the receiver to 1245 kc., which puts its oscillator on 1700 kc. if the standard 455-kc. i.f. is used. A wire from around the receiver to the 2X4+1 should provide sufficient signal. Feeding a 1700-kc. signal into the detector by laying the source wire near the grid of the 6BA6 (i.f. gain arm at ground), it should be possible to peak L_7 for maximum signal and, as the signal frequency is changed slightly, a change in pitch of the whistle should be heard. With no incoming signal, a slight rushing noise should be heard in the head-phones when the b.f.o. is switched on by S_2. If this rushing noise is just barely discernible increase the capacitance at C_9 by adding a few more twists.

If the oscillator V_{1B} is operating, a voltmeter connected across the 4700-ohm 1-watt resistor in its plate lead should show an increase in voltage when the stator of C_5 or C_7 is shorted to ground momentarily with a screwdriver or other conductor. Connect the + lead of the voltmeter to the side of the resistor running to + 105 and the − connection to the .001-μf. side. If the oscillator doesn't work, it may be because the outside turns of L_4 and L_5 are not connected to plate and grid respectively. With the b.f.o. on and C_1 almost fully meshed, set the tuning capacitor C_7 at about 90 per cent full capacitance. Run C_5 to full capacitance and slowly reduce capacitance. At one point you should hear a loud signal, the second harmonic of the b.f.o. at 3400 kc. If the b.f.o. is reasonably close to frequency, turning on the calibration oscillator should give a weaker signal nearby (on the main tuning dial). Tune C_7 to a higher frequency (less capacitance) and you should hear another weaker signal, the 35th harmonic of the oscillator (3500 kc.). Peak C_1 for maximum signal and leave it. Run C_7 back to about 90 per cent full capacitance and then slowly reduce capacitance at C_5 until the 35th harmonic of the oscillator is again heard. If a 3500-kc. signal is available the adjustment can be made in a more straightforward manner.

Once the oscillator trimmer C_5 has been set to give the proper tuning range of the oscillator circuit (5.2 to 5.7 Mc.), the next problem is that of adjusting the crystal filter circuit. With a capacitance bridge, or a grid-dip meter and an inductance, are set the two capacitors C_2 and C_3 at the same capacitance (near maximum compression)

before soldering them in the receiver. The actual value of capacitance isn't important. Lacking these instruments, tighten the capacitors to full compression and then loosen their screws by ¾ turn. Tune in a signal — it can be from the 100-kc. oscillator or any other steady source — and peak L_6 for maximum response. Tune off the signal until it disappears and set the pitch control, C_8, to a point where the background noise is reasonably high-pitched. This is easy to determine because at the lowest-pitched point there will be an increase in hum; make the lowest-pitched point the center of the knob scale by adjustment of L_8, and then set the pitch control to one end of its range. Tune back to the signal and "rock" the tuning, C_7, as you change the adjustment of L_6. Look for a condition that gives considerably more response on one side of zero beat than on the other. It is a good idea to buy several extra 1700-kc. crystals and try them in different combinations. Small changes in the setting of C_2 or C_3 will have an effect on the selectivity characteristic, but bear in mind that a change in C_2 or C_3 must be compensated for by a readjustment of L_6. With a little patience it should be possible to obtain a marked difference in the output strength on the two sides of zero beat. This will

Fig. 5-37—Top view of the 2X4 + 1 receiver. The dual capacitor at the left tunes the receiver input; a homemake cam switch on its shaft changes the coupling between the two bands. The main tuning capacitor, rear center, is mounted on a three-sided aluminum bracket for maximum stability. The tube to the left of the bracket is the 6U8-A mixer-oscillator stage, and the 6BA6 i.f. stage is in front of the main tuning capacitor. The remaining tubes in shields are the 6CG7 detector/b.f.o. and the audio 6CG7 (near panel). Metal can plugged in socket above antenna jack houses 100-kc. calibrating crystal.

"flip over" to the other side if the pitch control is set at the other end of its range.

The remaining alignment job consists of bringing the input circuits into resonance on both bands. With a signal tuned in at 40 meters, "rock" C_1 back and forth to see if there are two (close-together) points where the signal peaks. If there are, adjust the 3-30-$\mu\mu$f. trimmer across L_2 until only one peak is found. Check on 80 meters in a similar fashion. If for any reason it is found that the two-peak condition can be eliminated on only one band at a time, it indicates an abnormal amount of antenna reactance, and a compromise adjustment will have to be made.

In operation, the receiver input control, C_1, should be set for maximum volume on the incoming signal or noise. The i.f. gain should be run at close to maximum on all but the loudest signals, and the audio gain control should be set for comfortable headphone or speaker volume. If an antenna changeover relay is used, it may be possible to monitor your own transmitter by detuning the input circuit to another band; this ability will depend upon the transmitter power and field in the vicinity of the receiver.

Frequency Standard

No trouble should be encountered with the 100-kc. oscillator if care is exercised in handling the transistor. When soldering its leads in place, hold the lead with a pair of pliers; the metal of the pliers will absorb heat and prevent injury to the transistor.

To tune the receiver to WWV, set C_7 to mid scale, set S_3 at the WWV position, peak C_1 on noise and slowly tune with C_6. On a busy day a wide variety of signals will be heard in this region; look for one with steady tone modulation and time ticks. If it can't be found within the range of C_6, set C_7 near one end of its range and try again. An alternate method is to disconnect the antenna, establish the position on the tuning dial (C_7) of several 100-kc. harmonics, connect the antenna and investigate each one of these frequencies. Depending upon one's geographical location, there will be times when WWV cannot be heard on 5 Mc., so don't be discouraged by failure on the first try. Once WWV has been located with good strength, the 50th harmonic of the 100-kc. crystal can be brought to zero beat with WWV by adjustment of C_4.

Fig. 5-38—The input inductors L_1L_2 are supported by a terminal strip on the side of the chassis (upper right), and L_3 is supported nearby by a terminal strip mounted on the chassis. The coils are at right angles to minimize inductive coupling. The oscillator inductors, L_4L_5, are also supported by a terminal strip (top center). A mica compression trimmer to the left of the oscillator inductors is used to center WWV on the tuning dial; the pair of compression trimmers below L_3 are in the crystal filter circuit.

A Selective Converter for 80 and 40 Meters

Many inexpensive "communications" receivers are lacking in selectivity and bandspread. The 80- and 40-meter performance of such a receiver can be improved considerably by using ahead of it the converter shown in Figs. 5-39 and 5-41. This converter is not intended to be used ahead of a broadcast receiver except for phone reception, because the BC set has no b.f.o. or manual gain control, and both of these features are necessary for good c.w. reception. The converter can be built for less than $20, and that cost can be cut

Fig. 5-39—Used ahead of a small receiver that tunes to 1700 kc., this converter will add tuning ease and selectivity on the 80- and 40-meter bands. The input capacitor is the dual section unit at the upper left-hand corner. The crystal and the tuning slug for L_6 are near the center at the foreground edge.

appreciably if the power can be "borrowed" from another source.

The converter uses the tuning principle employed in the two-band superheterodynes described earlier in this section. A double-tuned input circuit with large capacitors covers both 80 and 40 meters without switching, and the oscillator tunes from 5.2 to 5.7 Mc. Consequently with an i.f. of 1700 kc. the tuning range of the converter is 3.5 to 4.0 Mc. and 6.9 to 7.4 Mc. Which band is being heard will depend upon the setting of the input circuit tuning (C_1 in Fig. 5-40). The converter output is amplified in the receiver, which must of course be set to 1700 kc. To add selectivity, a 1700-kc. quartz crystal is used in series with the output connection. A small power supply is shown with the converter, and some expense can be eliminated if 300 volts d.c. at 15 ma. and 6.3 volts a.c. at 0.45 ampere is available from an existing supply.

Construction

The unit is built on a 7 × 11 × 2-inch aluminum chassis. The front panel is made from a 6 × 7-inch piece of aluminum. The power supply is mounted to the rear of the chassis and the converter components are in the center and front. The layout shown in the bottom view should be followed, at least for the placement of L_1, L_2, L_3 and L_4.

The input and oscillator coils are made from a single length of B & W Miniductor stock, No.

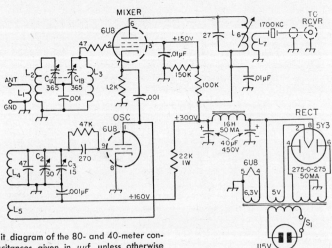

Fig. 5-40—Circuit diagram of the 80- and 40-meter converter. All capacitances given in $\mu\mu$f. unless otherwise noted.

C_1—365-$\mu\mu$f. dual variable, t.r.f. type.
C_2—3-30-$\mu\mu$f. trimmer.
C_3—15-$\mu\mu$f. variable (Bud 1850, Cardwell ZR-15AS, Millen 20015).
L_1, L_2, L_3, L_4, L_5—B & W No. 3016 Miniductor, 1-inch diameter, 32 turns per inch, No. 22 wire, cut as below.
L_1—8 turns separated from L_2 by one turn (see text).

L_2, L_3—19 turns.
L_4—21 turns separated from L_5 by one turn.
L_5—8 turns.
L_6—105-200-μh. slug-tuned coil (North Hills Electric 120H).
L_7—See text.
Crystal—1700 kc. (E. B. Lewis Co. Type EL-3).

A Selective Converter

3016. Count off 31 turns of the coil stock and bend the 32nd turn in toward the axis of the coil. Cut the wire at this point and then unwind the 32nd turn from the support bars. Using a hacksaw blade, carefully cut the polystyrene support bars and separate the 31-turn coil from the original stock. Next, count off 9 turns from the 31-turn coil and cut the wire at the 9th turn. At the cut unwind a half turn from each coil, and also unwind a half turn at the outside ends. This will leave two coils on the same support bars, with half-turn leads at their ends. One coil has 21 turns and the other has 8 turns, and they are separated by the space of one turn. These coils are L_4 and L_5.

The input coils L_1 and L_2 are made up in the same manner. Standard bakelite tie points are used to mount the coils. Two 4-terminal tie points are needed for L_1L_2 and L_4L_5, and a one-terminal unit is required for L_3. The plate load inductance L_6 is a 105–200 μh. variable-inductance coil (North Hills 120H). The coupling coil L_7 is 45 turns of No. 32 enam. scramble-wound adjacent to L_6. If the constructor should have difficulty in obtaining No. 32 wire, any size small enough to allow 45 turns on the coil form can be substituted.

The input capacitor, C_1, is a 2-gang t.r.f. variable, 365 $\mu\mu$f. per section. As both the stators and rotor must be insulated from the chassis, extruded fiber washers should be used with the screws that hold the unit to the chassis. The panel shaft hole should be made large enough to clear the rotor shaft.

A National type O dial assembly is used to tune C_3. One word of advice when drilling the holes for the dial assembly: the template furnished with the unit is in error on the 2-inch dimension (it is slightly short) so use a ruler to measure the hole spacing.

In wiring the unit, it is important that the output lead from the crystal socket be run in shielded wire. A phono jack is mounted on the back of the chassis, and a piece of shielded lead connects from the jack to the crystal socket terminal. The leads from the stators of C_1 and C_3 are insulated from the chassis by means of rubber grommets.

Testing and Adjustment

A length of shielded wire is used to connect the converter to the receiver: the inner conductor of the wire is connected to one antenna terminal; the shield is connected to the other terminal and grounded to the receiver chassis. The use of shielded wire helps to prevent pickup of unwanted 1700-kc. signals. Turn on the converter and receiver and allow them to warm up. Tune the receiver to the 5.2-Mc. region and listen for the oscillator of the converter. The b.f.o. in the receiver should be turned on. Tune around until the oscillator is heard. Once you spot it, tune C_3 to maximum capacitance and the receiver to as close to 5.2 Mc. as you can. Adjust the oscillator trimmer capacitor, C_2, until you hear the oscillator signal. Put your receiving antenna on the converter, set the receiver to 1700 kc., and tune the input capacitor, C_1, to near maximum capacitance. At one point you'll hear the background noise come up. This is the 80-meter tuning. The point near minimum capacitance — where the noise is loudest — is the 40-meter tuning.

With the input tuning set to 80 meters, turn on your transmitter and tune in the signal. By spotting your crystal-controlled frequency you'll have one sure calibration point for the dial. By listening in the evening when the band is crowded you should be able to find the band edges.

You'll find by experimenting that there is one point at or near 1700 kc. on your receiver where the background noise is the loudest. Set the receiver to this point and adjust the slug on L_6 for maximum noise or signal. When you have the receiver tuned *exactly* to the frequency of the crystal in the converter, you'll find that you have quite a bit of selectivity. Tune in a c.w. signal and tune slowly through zero beat. You should notice that on one side of zero beat the signal is strong, and on the other side you won't hear the signal or it will be very weak (if it isn't, off-set the b.f.o. a bit). This is single-signal c.w. reception.

When listening to phone signals, it may be found that the use of the quartz crystal destroys some of the naturalness of the voice signal. If this is the case, the crystal should be unplugged and replaced by a 10- or 20-$\mu\mu$f. capacitor.

Fig. 5-41—Bottom view of the converter showing placement of parts. The coil at the lower left is L_3, and the input coil, L_1L_2, is just to the right of L_3. The oscillator coil L_4L_5, is at the left near the center. The output coil, L_6, is near the top center.

The "Bonus" 21-Mc. Converter

The cure for most of the high-frequency ills of many receivers is the installation of a good crystal-controlled converter between the antenna and the receiver. The converter shown in Figs. 5-42 and 5-43, while intended primarily for 21-Mc. operation, gives a bonus of 28-Mc. reception without any additional parts or switching. This is accomplished by using signal circuits that tune more than the 21- to 30-Mc. range and using a crystal-controlled oscillator at 25 Mc. Using the converter ahead of a receiver, the 15-meter band, 21.0 to 21.45 Mc., will be found from 4.0 to 3.55 on the receiver. The receiver tunes "backwards." The 10-meter band tunes 3.0 to 4.7 Mc. on the receiver.

Referring to Fig. 5-44, the converter consists of three stages, but it uses only two tubes. An r.f. stage amplifies the incoming signals, and an oscillator provides a steady signal that, in a mixer stage, heterodynes the incoming signal to the *difference* frequency mentioned above. If the input and output circuits of the r.f. stage aren't tuned to 21 Mc. the 21-Mc. signals can't be amplified to the full capability of the stage. However, the 21-Mc. tuned circuits aren't too sharp, so a single-setting will usually suffice for most of the 21-Mc. band, and all of the tuning will normally be done at the receiver alone. The 47,000-ohm resistor across C_2 was used to make the associated circuit a bit broader.

The selenium-rectifier power supply is quite adequate for the job and makes the converter a self-sufficient unit, although the power may be "borrowed" from the receiver if it is felt that the selenium supply is an unnecessary expense.

In the crystal-controlled oscillator portion, a capacitive divider (C_3 and C_4) provides a tap on the tank circuit so that the oscillator is loaded very lightly. If you didn't tap down on the tuned circuit the overtone crystal, Y_1, might show lower-frequency energy as well, or it might not oscillate at all.

The size of the chassis shown in Figs. 5-42 and 5-43 is $2 \times 5 \times 7$ inches. However, any chassis large enough to accommodate the parts can be used. Most of the construction is simple but there are a few places where certain precautions should be taken, and these will be treated in detail.

Study the photographs, particularly the bottom view, to see how the coils and tube socket are mounted. Notice the shield that cuts across the 6AK5 socket. The purpose of the shield is to minimize the coupling between the grid and plate circuits of the r.f. stage, to avoid oscillation. A scrap of roofing copper was cut to $3\frac{1}{2}$ by 2 inches for the shield. Brass, or any other metal that can be soldered, could be substituted. The shield and socket should be mounted so that the shield bisects the socket between Pins 4 and 5. There is a $\frac{1}{4}$-inch lip on the shield which is used to mount it to the chassis top. The metal tube in the center of the tube socket should be soldered to the shield; the shield is held to the chassis by two 6-32 screws. Soldering lugs should be mounted under

21 Mc. Converter

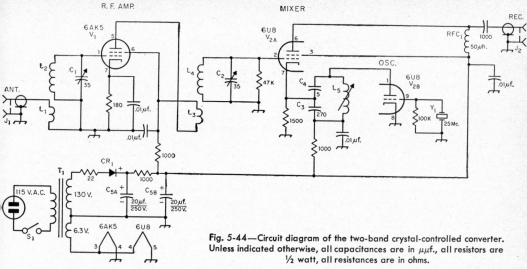

Fig. 5-44—Circuit diagram of the two-band crystal-controlled converter. Unless indicated otherwise, all capacitances are in μμf., all resistors are ½ watt, all resistances are in ohms.

C₁, C₂—35-μμf. midget variable (Hammarlund MAPC-35-B).
C₃—270-μμf. silver mica or NPO ceramic.
C₄—5-μμf. silver mica or NPO ceramic.
C₅—Dual electrolytic, 20-20 μf. at 250 volts.
CR₁—100-ma. 150-volt selenium rectifier (International Rectifier RS-100-E or equiv.).
J₁, J₂—Phono jack, RCA style.
L₁, L₂, L₃, L₄—Made of No. 20 bare, ⅝-inch diam., 16

t.p.i. stock. See text. (B & W Miniductor No. 3007).
L₅—2- to 3-μh. slug-tuned inductor (North Hills 120-A).
RFC₁—50-μh. r.f. choke (National R-33, Millen 34300-50).
S₁—S.p.s.t. toggle.
T₁—125 volts at 50 ma., 6.3 volts at 2 amperes (Stancor PA8422) or 135 volts at 50 ma., 6.3 volts at 1.5 amperes (Triad R-30-X).
Y₁—25.00-Mc. crystal (International Crystal Co., type FA-9).

the nuts that hold the 6AK5 socket, and all the chassis ground connections of the 6AK5 grid and plate circuit should be made to these lugs.

The coils are made from B & W 3007 Miniductor stock. To make the coils, first cut off a coil of 21 turns from the stock. Next, unwind one turn from each end of the 21-turn coil. Now count off 5½ turns from one end and cut the wire at this point. If you bend the 4th and 6th turns in toward the center of the coil you should be able to reach the 5th turn with your wire cutters. Unwind the half turn from each side leaving two coils on the same support bars, one 5 turns and the other 13 turns. Two of these dual coils are needed, one for the r.f. stage and the other for the mixer. They can be mounted on a standard terminal tie point or supported by their own leads. Tie points provide a more rigid support.

The power supply is a simple half-wave rectifier, using a transformer, selenium rectifier, and an *RC* filter circuit. Incidentally, when connecting the rectifier, the + side is connected to the *output* side of the supply. Again, a standard terminal tie point is used for most of the connections of the supply.

The preliminary checks are simple and should present no problems to the builder. First, turn on S₁ and see if the tubes light up. If they don't, turn off the switch and carefully check the wiring. Once the tubes light, allow a minute or two for the unit to warm up. The first thing to check is the crystal-controlled oscillator. If your receiver tunes to 25 Mc., listen in that region for the oscillator signal, which should come in loud and clear.

If it doesn't, adjust the slug of L₅ until the oscillator starts. Should you find that it doesn't oscillate you'll need to make some voltage checks to make sure there is plate voltage on the oscillator. The voltage should be approximately 110, give or take 10 volts. If no voltage is indicated, check the wiring for errors.

Connect the converter to your receiver, using a piece of coax as the connecting line. Coax is used for the lead between the two units to minimize any pickup of unwanted signals near or in the 80-meter band. Set your receiver to tune the right range, 4000 to 3550 kc., and turn both units on.

Adjust C₁ and C₂ for maximum background noise. You'll find two values of capacitance (four points) on each capacitor that will give an increase in noise, one near minimum capacitance (plates unmeshed) and the other with more capacitance. The setting at the greater capacitance point is 21 Mc. while the lesser is 28 Mc. Adjust the converter for maximum noise at 21 Mc. and tune your receiver across the band. If the band is open — and don't forget that sometimes it's as dead as the famous doornail — you should hear signals. Tune in one and peak it up by tuning C₁ and C₂ of the converter. Each control should give a definite peak. Pretty nice to know that your receiving front end is lined up, isn't it? And it is, you know; you align it when you peak the two controls. Your receiver is now working as a tunable i.f. and the only adjustment required is to peak the antenna trimmer (if you have one) for maximum signal.

The "Selectoject"

The Selectoject is a receiver adjunct that can be used as a sharp amplifier or as a single-frequency rejection filter. The frequency of operation may be set to any point in the audio range by turning a single knob. The degree of selectivity (or depth of the null) is continuously adjustable and is independent of tuning. In phone work, the rejection notch can be used to reduce or eliminate a heterodyne. In c.w. reception, interfering signals may be rejected or, alternatively, the desired signal may be picked out and amplified. The Selectoject may also be operated as a low-distortion variable-frequency audio oscillator suitable for amplifier frequency-response measurements, modulation tests, and the like, by advancing the "selectivity" control far enough in the selective-amplifier condition. The Selectoject is connected in a receiver between the detector and the first audio stage. Its power requirements are 4 ma. at 150 volts and 6.3 volts at 0.6 ampere. For proper operation, the 150 volts should be obtained from across a VR-150 or from a supply with an output capacity of at least 20 μf.

The wiring diagram of the Selectoject is shown in Fig. 5-45. Resistors R_2 and R_3, and R_4 and R_5, can be within 10 per cent of the nominal value but

they should be as close to each other as possible. An ohmmeter is quite satisfactory for doing the matching. One-watt resistors are used because the larger ratings are usually more stable over a long period of time.

If the station receiver has an "accessory socket" on it, the cable of the Selectoject can be made up to match the connections to the socket, and the numbers will not necessarily match those shown in Fig. 5-45. The lead between the second detector and the receiver gain control should be broken and run in shielded leads to the two pins of the socket corresponding to those on the plug marked "A.F. Input" and "A.F. Output." If the receiver has a VR-150 included in it for voltage stabilization there will be no problem in getting the plate voltage — otherwise a suitable voltage divider should be incorporated in the receiver, with a 20- to 40-μf. electrolytic capacitor connected from the +150-volt tap to ground.

In operation, overload of the receiver or the Selectoject should be avoided, or all of the possible selectivity may not be realized.

The Selectoject is useful as a means for obtaining much of the performance of a crystal filter from a receiver lacking a filter.

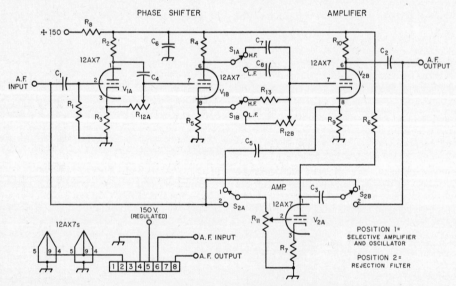

Fig. 5-45—Complete schematic of Selectoject using 12AX7 tubes.

C_1—0.01-μf. mica, 400 volts.
C_2, C_3—0.1-μf. paper, 200 volts.
C_4, C_8—0.002-μf. paper, 400 volts.
C_5—0.05-μf. paper, 400 volts.
C_6—16-μf. 150-volt electrolytic.
C_7—0.0002-μf. mica.
R_1—1 megohm, ½ watt.
R_2, R_3—1000 ohms, 1 watt, matched as closely as possible (see text).
R_4, R_5—2000 ohms, 1 watt, matched as closely as possible (see text).

R_6—20,000 ohms, ½ watt.
R_7—2000 ohms, ½ watt.
R_8—10,000 ohms, 1 watt.
R_9—6000 ohms, ½ watt.
R_{10}—20,000 ohms, ½ watt.
R_{11}—0.5-megohm ½-watt potentiometer (selectivity).
R_{12}—Ganged 5-megohm potentiometers (tuning control) (IRC PQ11-141 with IRC M11-141.)
R_{13}—0.12 megohm, ½ watt.
S_1, S_2—D.p.d.t. toggle (can be ganged).

Antenna Coupler for Receiving

In many instances reception can be improved by the addition of an antenna coupler between the antenna feedline and the receiver, and in all cases the r.f. image rejection will be increased. The unit shown on this page consists of one series-tuned circuit and one parallel-tuned circuit; usually its best performance is obtained with the parallel-tuned circuit connected to the receiver input, as indicated in Fig. 5-46. However, the coupler should also be tried with the connections reversed, to see which gives the better results. The desired connection is the one that gives the sharper peak or louder signals when the circuits are resonated.

The coupler is built on one section of a 5 × 4 × 3-inch Minibox (Bud CU-2105A). Tuning capacitors C_1 and C_2 are mounted directly on the Minibox face, since there is no need to insulate the rotors. The arrangement of the components can be seen in Fig. 5-47.

The coils L_1 and L_2 are made from a single length of B & W 3011 Miniductor. The wire is snipped at the center of the coil and unwound in both directions until there are three empty spaces on three support bars and two empty spaces on the bar from which the snipped ends project. These inner ends run to the connectors J_1 and J_2. (Fig. 5-46). Unwind turns at the ends of the coils until each coil has a total of 22 turns. When soldering the leads to the 3rd, 6th, 8th and 12th turns from the inside ends of the coils, protect the adjacent turns from solder and flux by placing strips of aluminum cooking foil between the turns. An iron with a sharp point will be required for the soldering.

The "panel" side of the box can be finished off with decals indicating the knob functions and switch positions.

The antenna coupler should be mounted within a few feet of the receiver, to minimize the length of RG-59/U between coupler and receiver. In crowded quarters, the use of M-359A right-angle

Fig. 5-47—Receiver antenna coupler, with cover removed from case. Unit tunes 6 to 30 Mc. The coil is supported by the leads to the capacitors and switches.

adapters (Amphenol 83–58) and J_1 and J_2 will make it possible to bring out the cables in better lines.

Normally the coupler will be adjusted for optimum coupling or maximum image rejection, but by detuning the coupler it can be used as an auxiliary gain control to reduce the overloading effects of strong local signals. The coupler circuits do not resonate below 6 Mc., but a coupler of this type is seldom if ever used in the 80-meter band; its major usefulness will be found at the higher frequencies.

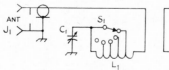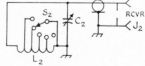

Fig. 5-46—Circuit diagram of the receiver antenna coupler.

C_1, C_2—100-$\mu\mu$f. midget variable (Hammarlund HF-100).
J_1, J_2—Coaxial cable connector, SO-239.
L_1, L_2—22 turns No. 20, ¾-inch diameter, 16 t.p.i. Tapped 3, 6, 8 and 12 turns from inside end. See text on spacing and tapping.
S_1, S_2—Single-pole 11-position switch (5 used) rotary switch (Centralab PA-1000).

A Regenerative Preselector for 7 to 30 Mc.

The performance of many receivers begins to drop off at 14 Mc. and higher. The signal-to-noise ratio is reduced, and unless double conversion is used in the receiver there is likely to be increased trouble with r.f. images at the higher frequencies. The preselector shown in Figs. 5-48 and 5-49 can be added ahead of any receiver without making any changes within the receiver, and a self-contained power supply eliminates the problem of furnishing heater and plate power. The poorer the receiver is at the higher frequencies, the more it will benefit by the addition of the preselector.

A truly good receiver at 28 Mc. will show little or no improvement when the preselector is added, but a mediocre receiver or one without an r.f. stage will be improved greatly through the use of the preselector.

A 6CG7 dual triode is used in the preselector, one triode as a band switched regenerative r.f. stage and the other as a cathode follower. A conventional neutralizing circuit is used in the amplifier; by upsetting this circuit enough the stage can be made to oscillate. Smooth control of regeneration up to this point is obtained by varying one of the capacitances in the neutralizing circuit.

If and when it becomes necessary to reduce gain (to avoid overloading the receiver), the regeneration control can be retarded. One position of the bandswitch permits straight-through operation, so the preselector unit can be left connected to the receiver even during low-frequency reception.

The preselector is built on a 5 × 10 × 3-inch chassis (Bud AC-404). A 5 × 6½-inch aluminum panel is held to the chassis by the extension-shaft bushing for the regeneration-control capacitor, C_3, and the bushing for the rotary switch. The coils, L_1 and L_2, are supported on a small staging

Fig. 5-48—The regenerative preselector covers the range 7 to 30 Mc.; it can be used ahead of any receiver to improve gain, image rejection and, in many cases, sensitivity. A dual triode 6CG7 is used as r.f. amplifier and cathode follower.

of 1¼ × 3-inch clear plastic. (It can be made from the lid of the box that the Sprague 5GA-S1 .01-μf. disk ceramic capacitors come in.) All coils can be made from a single length of B&W 3011 Miniductor. They are cemented to the plastic staging with Duco cement.

The rotor of C_1 can be insulated from the chassis by mounting the capacitor bracket on insulating bushings (National XS-6 or Millen 37201); its shaft is extended through the use of an insulated extender shaft (Allied Radio No. 60 H 355). The bandswitch S_1 is made from the specified sections (see Fig. 5-50).

The first section is spaced ¾ inch from the indexing head, there is 1-inch separation be-

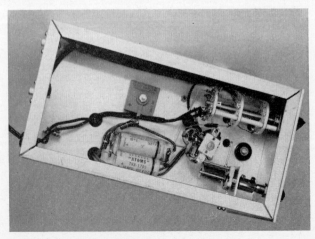

Fig. 5-49—The r.f. components are bunched around the 9-pin miniature tube socket. Power supply components are supported by screws and tie points.

Regenerative Preselector

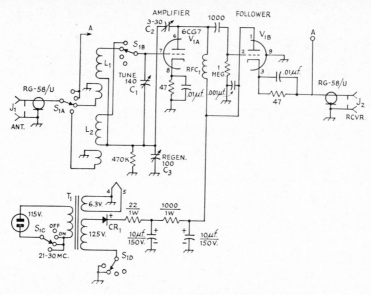

Fig. 5-50—Circuit diagram of the regenerative preselector. Unless otherwise specified, resistors are ½ watt, capacitors are in μμf., capacitors marked in polarity are electrolytic.

C_1—140-μμf. midget variable (Hammarlund HF-140).
C_2—3- to 30-μμf. mica compression trimmer.
C_3—100-μμf. midget variable (Hammarlund MAPC-100-B).
CR_1—50-ma. selenium rectifier (International Rectifier RSO50).
J_1, J_2—Phono jack.
L_1—19 turns, 7-turn primary.
L_2—5 turns, 2-turn primary. Coils are ¾-inch diameter, 16 t.p.i., No. 20 wire (B & W 3011 Miniductor).

One-turn spacing between coils and primaries.
S_1—Three-wafer switch. S_{1A} and S_{1B} are 1-pole 12-position (4 used) miniature ceramic switch sections (Centralab PA-1); S_{1C} and S_{1D} are 2-pole 6-position (4 used) miniature switch (Centralab PA-3). Sections mounted on Centralab PA-301 index assembly.
T_1—125 v. at 15 ma., 6.3 v. at 0.6 amp. (Stancor PS-8415).
RFC_1—100-μh. r.f. choke (National R-33).

tween this and the next section (S_{1B}), and the next section (S_{1C}, S_{1D}) is spaced 2½ inches from S_{1B}.

The regeneration control, C_3, is mounted on a small aluminum bracket. Its shaft does not have to be insulated from the chassis, so either an insulated or a solid shaft connector can be used. The small neutralizing capacitor, C_2, is supported by soldering one lead of it to a stator bar of C_3 and running a wire from the other lead to pin 6 of the tube socket. The rotor and stator connections from C_1 are brought through the chassis deck through small rubber grommets.

Power supply components, resistors and capacitors are supported by suitable lugs and tie points. Phono jacks are used for the input and output connectors.

Adjustment

Assuming that the wiring is correct and that the coils have been constructed properly and cover the required ranges, the only preliminary adjustment is the proper setting of C_2. Connect an antenna to the input jack and connect the receiver to the output jack through a suitable length of RG-58/U. Turn on the receiver b.f.o. and tune to 28 Mc. with S_1 in the ON position. Now turn S_1 to the 21- to 30-Mc. range. Swing

the TUNING capacitor, C_1, and listen for a loud rough signal which indicates that the preselector is oscillating. If nothing is heard, advance the regeneration control toward the minimum capacitance end and repeat. If no oscillation is heard, it may be necessary to change the setting of C_2. Once the oscillating condition has been found, set the regeneration control at minimum capacitance and slowly adjust C_2 until the preselector oscillates only when the regeneration control is set at minimum capacitance. You can now swing the receiver to 21 Mc. and peak the preselector tuning capacitor. It will be found that the regeneration capacitance will have to be increased to avoid oscillation.

Check the performance on the lower range by tuning in signals at 14 and 7 Mc. and peaking the preselector. It should be possible to set the regeneration control in these two ranges to give both an oscillating and a non-oscillating condition of the preselector.

A little experience will be required before you can get the best performance out of the preselector. Learn to set the regeneration control so that the preselector is selective, but not so selective that it must be retuned every 10 kc. or so. Changing antenna loads will modify the correct regeneration control setting.

A Clipper/Filter for C.W. or Phone

The clipper/filter shown in Fig. 5-51 is plugged into the receiver headphone jack and the head-phones are plugged into the limiter, with no work required on the receiver. The limiter will cut down serious noise on phone or c.w. signals and it will keep the strength of c.w. signals at a constant level, and while the filter will add selectivity to your receiver for c.w. reception, the unit will do much to relieve the operating fatigue caused by long hours of listening to static crashes, key clicks encountered on the air and with break-in operation, and the like.

There are times when only the selective audio circuits will be wanted, while on other occasions only clipping will be needed. Since it is a simple matter to provide a switching arrangement so that either function, or both, can be used at will, this has been done in the unit described here.

The frequency response of the selective circuits reaches a peak at about 700 cycles and has a null at about 2000 cycles. The peak frequency is determined by the combined values of L_1, C_1, and C_2 (or L_2, C_3 and C_4), while the notch frequency is that of the parallel-resonant circuit L_1C_1 (or L_2C_3). If different peak and null frequencies are desired the values of C_1 and C_2 (and C_3 and C_4) can be changed; for raising the notch frequency the capacitance of C_1 and C_3 should be made

smaller; to raise the peak frequency reduce the capacitance at C_2 and C_4.

The rotary switch S_2 (Fig. 5-51) is used to provide different combinations of the clipper and filter. To simplify the wiring diagram the switching circuit is shown separately in the diagram.

The filter-clipper can be built on an aluminum chassis, but a steel cabinet should be used to house the unit. Steel is preferable to aluminum because L_1 and L_2 are sensitive to stray magnetic fields (which would show up as hum at the output) and the steel cabinet aids in shielding. One layout precaution should be observed: Place the filter inductors L_1 and L_2 as far as possible from the power transformer, and mount them with their cores at right angles to the core of the transformer. This will minimize hum pickup by the inductors.

Before mounting L_1 and L_2, it will be necessary to remove the mounting frames and insulate the "I" laminations, as shown in Fig. 5-52. The frame is removed easily by prying out its two legs and then lifting it from the core. The "I" laminations are in the form of a bar lying across the top of the "E" core.

By mounting the chokes with nonmetallic straps the Q will remain high. If aluminum or other nonmagnetic materials are used the Q will

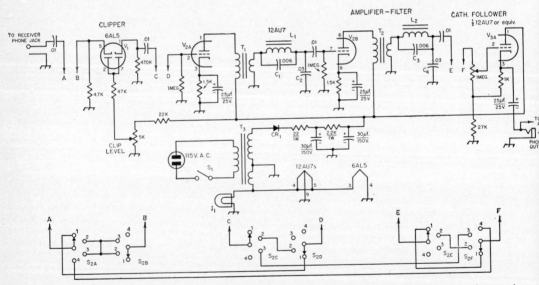

Fig. 5-51—Circuit of the two-stage clipper-filter. All capacitances are in μf. All 0.01 μf. capacitors may be ceramic; capacitors marked with polarity are electrolytic. Others should be tubular plastic or mica. Resistors are $\frac{1}{2}$ watt unless otherwise specified. Switch functions are as follows: Position 1, dual filter alone; Position 2, clipper and dual filter; Position 3, clipper alone; Position 4, straight through with cathode-follower output.

CR_1—50-ma. selenium rectifier.

I_1—6.3-volt pilot lamp.

J_1—Open-circuit phone jack.

L_1, L_2—5-h. 65-ma. filter choke; frame removed and choke remounted as described in the text.

S_1—S.p.s.t. toggle switch

S_2—3-section 6-pole 4-position rotary switch, shorting type preferable. (Centralab PA-1020).

T_1, T_2—Output transformer: 7000–10,000-ohm primary to 3.2-ohm voice coil (Thordarson24S52).

T_3—Power transformer: 125 volts, 50 ma.; 6.3 volts, 2 amps. (Stancor PA-8421).

A Clipper/Filter

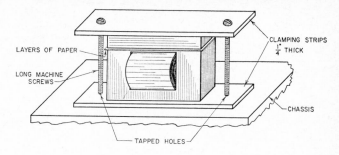

Fig. 5-52—Sketch showing the method of clamping and tuning the filter inductors. Clamping strips must be of bakelite, phenol, plastic or other suitable *insulating* material. Metal should not be used.

be adversely affected and the selectivity of the filter will suffer.

The switch wiring shown at the bottom of the schematic diagram can be done before mounting S_2 in place. After the switch is mounted the wiring between it and the other components can be completed.

Apply power by closing S_1, insert the plug in the receiver phone jack and turn switch S_2 to the "out" or straight-through position. Tune the receiver until a c.w. signal is found and adjust the receiver controls for comfortable copying.

Now turn S_2 to the "clipper" position. In order to become familiar with the action of the clipper these steps should be followed: Adjust the "clipping" control so no clipping occurs (maximum positive bias on the diode plates). Set the "clip level" control on the unit so that there will be no apparent change in the strength of the c.w. signal when switching from "clipper" to "out" and back to "clipper." Then turn the "clipping" control until the positive bias is low enough to cause limiting to start; the point at which limiting begins can be recognized by the fact that the signal strength begins to decrease. Back off slightly with the "clipping" control so that the signal strength in the phones is just at the original level.

Tuning the receiver without the use of the limiter shows signals of all strengths, some so loud

as to be ear-breaking; but switching to "clipper" will make these big ones drop down to the "comfortable" preset level.

The filter can be aligned with the help of an audio signal generator and a scope. The procedure is to set the two tuned circuits individually to within 10 to 15 cycles of the chosen peak frequency, but on opposite sides of that frequency. This adjustment can be made by tightening or loosening the clamping screws on each choke until each circuit is tuned to the desired frequency. Altering the number of layers of paper placed between the "I" and "E" laminations of either or both chokes will allow any two similar chokes which, due to manufacturing tolerances, may be of slightly different inductances, to be tuned to the same frequency. The filter is then ready to go. If the response is too sharp, slightly greater separation of the two frequencies can be achieved by readjusting the clamp on one of the chokes.

In order to peak a desired signal the receiver b.f.o. or tuning control should be adjusted so the pitch of the signal is 700 cycles. Since the selectivity curve is rather sharp, any adjacent undesired signals will fall short of the peak and be attenuated. If the receiver b.f.o. has sufficient range to tune 700 cycles or more on both sides of zero beat, the undesired signal can always be placed on the notch side of the peak.

A Simple Audio Limiter

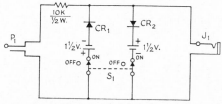

Fig. 5-53—Circuit diagram of a simple audio limiter.
CR$_1$, CR$_2$—1N34A or similar germanium diode.
J$_1$—Open-circuit headphone jack.
P$_1$—Headphone plug.
S$_1$—D.p.s.t. toggle or rotary switch.
A Keystone battery holder No. 155 (Allied Radio) will hold two Burgess N, Eveready W468 or Ray-o-Vac 716 flashlight cells.

A simple audio limiter to hold down static crashes and key clicks can be made from two flashlight cells, two germanium diodes and a few other parts. Its use requires no alteration of the receiver, since it is plugged in at the output jack of the receiver and the headphones are plugged into the limiter. A suitable circuit is shown in Fig. 5-53. No constructional details are given because there is nothing critical. If desired, the parts can be housed in a small utility cabinet or "Minibox." Leads can be soldered directly to the flashlight cells or, if desired, a suitable battery holder can be obtained from a radio or model airplane store. Hold the germanium diode leads with pliers when soldering, to prevent heat from reaching and injuring the crystals.

DCS-500 Double-Conversion Superheterodyne

The receiver shown in Fig. 5-54 was designed to meet a need for a better-than-average ham receiver requiring a minimum of mechanical work and using standard and easily obtainable parts. It incorporates such features as a 100-kc. calibrator, provision for reception on all ham bands from 80 through 10 meters, adequate selectivity for today's crowded bands, and stability high enough for copying s.s.b. signals. Dubbed the DCS-500 because of its 500-cycle selectivity in the sharpest i.f. position, it is a double-conversion superheterodyne receiver capable of giving good results on either a.m., c.w. or s.s.b.

The Circuit

Referring to the circuit diagram, Figs. 5-55 and 5-56, a 6BA6 r.f., stage is followed by a 6U8A mixer-oscillator. The 4.5-Mc. mixer output is amplified by a 6BA6 and filtered by a two-stage crystal filter, after which a 6U8A second mixer-oscillator, crystal-controlled, heterodynes the signal to 50 kc.

The combination of i.f. amplifiers may appear rather unusual at first glance, since one might expect that a cascade crystal filter in the high-frequency i.f. would make further selectivity unnecessary. This would be true with highly developed filters, but two filters are needed if the best possible job is to be done on both phone and c.w., and such filters are expensive. With inexpensive surplus crystals such as are used in this receiver it would be difficult, if not impossible, to match the performance of the high-class filters; in addition, special test equipment and extreme care in adjustment would be necessary. The approach used here is to use the surplus crystals without such special adjustment, thereby achieving a good, if not quite optimum, degree of selectivity against strong signals near the desired one, and then to back up the filter by a low-frequency i.f. amplifier that will give the "close-in" straight-sided selectivity needed in present-day operation. The overall result is a high order of protection against strong interfering signals at considerably less cost, for the entire double-i.f. system, than that of two high-performance filters alone. The choice of 4.5 Mc., approximately, for the first i.f. was based on the availability of surplus crystals around this frequency, with due consideration for minimizing spurious responses. A second i.f. of 50 kc. was chosen because it lent itself nicely to the utilization of low-cost TV horizontal-oscillator coils as i.f. transformers.

The two i.f. amplifiers at 50 kc. contribute the necessary adjacent-channel selectivity. Three degrees of selectivity are available, depending on the degree of capacitive coupling between the two windings of each i.f. transformer. The greater the number of capacitors switched in parallel — that is, the larger the coupling capacitance — the lower the coupling between the windings and thus the greater the selectivity.

A standard diode detector develops the audio output for all reception modes. The output of the detector is simultaneously applied to both the first audio amplifier and the audio a.g.c. circuit. A series-type noise limiter can be used on a.m. to reduce impulse-noise interference, but this type is ineffective on c.w. or s.s.b. because of the large amplitude of the b.f.o. injection voltage.

The b.f.o., a Hartley-type oscillator, can be tuned from 3 kc. above to 3 kc. below its 50-kc. center frequency by the tuning capacitor.

The first audio stage is a normal Class A voltage amplifier with its output either coupled to the grid circuit of the audio output tube or to a phone jack. High-impedance head-phones (20,000 ohms a.c. impedance or higher) are required. Plugging in the phones automatically disconnects the speaker. If low-impedance headphones are used, they can be connected to the speaker terminals. Capacitances shunting the grid resistors restrict the audio response to an upper limit of about 4000 cycles.

The audio output transformer couples to a low-impedance (3.2-ohm) speaker. The 47-ohm resistor across the secondary protects the transformer in the absence of a speaker load.

The audio output of the detector is also amplified separately in the audio a.g.c. circuit and then rectified to develop a negative voltage that can be used for a.g.c. on c.w. and s.s.b. Two different time constants are used in the rectifier filter circuit, for either fast- or slow-decay a.g.c.

The 100-kc. calibrator employs two 2N107 p-n-p transistors, one as the oscillator and the second as a 100-kc. amplifier. Its transistors obtain the necessary operating potential from the cathode resistor of the audio output tube. Output from the 100-kc. unit is capacity-coupled to the antenna winding of the r.f. coil. Calibrating signals at 100-kc. intervals are available on all frequencies covered by the receiver.

The calibrator unit is constructed in a separate

Fig. 5-54—The DCS-500 double-conversion superheterodyne. Left bottom, antenna trimmer, 100-kc. calibrator switch; center, left, top to bottom, noise-limiter switch, volume control, sensitivity control; center, right, b.f.o. switch, a.g.c. speed, selectivity; right, headphone jack, b.f.o. pitch control. The dial is a National ICN. Front panel is 8¾ inches high; the receiver is mounted in a Bud CR-1741 rack cabinet.

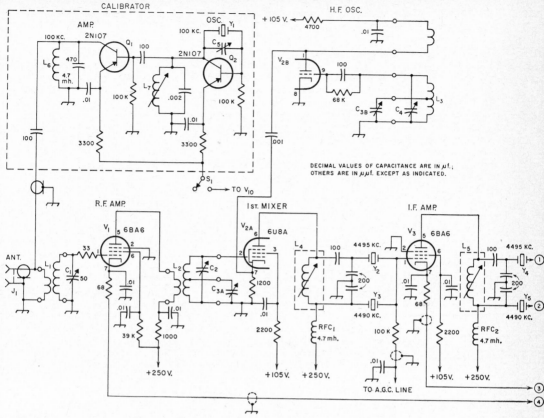

Fig. 5-55—Front-end circuit of the receiver. Unless otherwise specified, resistors are ½ watt; 0.01 and 0.02-μf. capacitors are disk ceramic, 600 volts; 0.5 capacitors are tubular paper; capacitors below 0.01 μf. are mica; capacitors marked with polarities are electrolytic.

C₁—50-μμf. variable (Hammarlund HF-50).
C₂, C₄—See coil table.
C₃—2-section variable, 5—28.5 μμf. per section, double spaced (Hammarlund HFD-30-X).
C₅—3-30-μμf. ceramic trimmer.
J₁—Coaxial receptacle, chassis mounting (SO-239).
L₁, L₂, L₃—See coil table.
L₄, L₅—18-36-μh. slug-tuned (North Hills 120E coil

mounted in North Hills S-120 shield can).
L₆—4.7 mh. (Waters C1061).
L₇—1-2-mh. slug-tuned (North Hills 120K).
RFC₁, RFC₂—4.7 mh. (Waters C1061).
S₁—Single-pole rotary.
Y₁—100 kc. (James Knights H-93).
Y₂, Y₄—4495 kc. (surplus).
Y₃, Y₅—4490 kc. (surplus).

Minibox so that it can be plugged into the accessory socket of the receiver or used as an individual unit powered by penlite cells.

The power supply, Fig. 5-57, is a full-wave rectifier with a choke-input filter. It provides approximately 250 volts d.c. under load. A 0.25-μf. capacitor is shunted across the 10-henry filter choke to form a parallel-resonant circuit at 120 cycles; this provides an increased impedance to the ripple component and thus reduces hum in the output of the supply.

The power-supply requirements are 250 volts at 110 milliamperes, and 6.3 volts at approximately 5 amperes. Any transformer-choke combination fulfilling the requirements can be used.

Front End

The use of plug-in coils for the front end eliminated the mechanical problems of a band-

switching tuner, and also offered the possibility of realizing higher-Q tuned circuits. Ganged tuning of the r.f. amplifier along with the h.f. oscillator and mixer circuits was decided against because of the complexities it would cause in coil construction and the problem of keeping three stages tracking with each other. The r.f. amplifier has to be peaked separately by the antenna trimmer, but separate peaking insures maximum performance at all frequencies.

Construction

The receiver is constructed on a 12 × 17 × 2-inch aluminum chassis with an 8¾ × 19-inch aluminum front panel, which permits it to be installed in a table-type rack cabinet. The general layout of components can be seen in Figs. 5-58 and 5-60. A good procedure to follow when

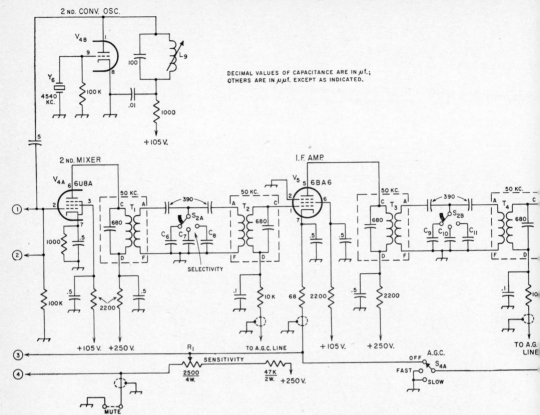

DECIMAL VALUES OF CAPACITANCE ARE IN µf.;
OTHERS ARE IN µµf. EXCEPT AS INDICATED.

Fig. 5-56—I.f. amplifier, detector, a.g.c. and audio circuits. Unless otherwise specified, resistors are ½ watt; 0.01- and 0.02-µf. capacitors are disk ceramic, 600 volts; 0.5-µf. capacitors are tubular paper; capacitors below 0.01 µf. are mica; capacitors marked with polarities are electrolytic.

$C_6, C_7, C_8, C_9, C_{10}, C_{11}$—0.01 mica (Aerovox CM-30B-103).
C_{12}—9-180-µµf. mica compression trimmer.
C_{13}—50-µµf. variable (Hammarlund HF-50).
C_{14}—0.1-µf. paper (Sprague 2TM-P1).
J_2—Phono jack.
J_3—Closed-circuit phone jack.
L_8—125 mh. (Meissner 19-6848).
L_9—9-18 µh., slug-tuned (North Hills 120D).
M_1—0-1 d.c. milliammeter (Triplett 227-PL).
R_1—2500-ohm, 4-watt control, wire-wound.
R_2—0.5-megohm control, audio taper with push-pull type switch (S_6) (Mallory No. PP55DT1683).
R_3—1000-ohm, 1-watt control, wire-wound.
RFC_3—10 mh. (National R-50-1).
S_1, S_3—Rotary, 1 section, 1 pole, 2 position.

S_2—Rotary, 2 section, 1 pole per section, progressively shorting. Switch section Centralab PA-12, index Centralab PA-302.
S_4—Rotary, 1 section, 5 poles per section (4 poles used), 3 positions used, Centralab PA-2015.
S_5—Rotary, 1 section, 2 poles per section, 2 positions used. Centralab PA-2003.
T_1-T_5, inc.—50-kc. i.f. transformers made from TV components (Miller 6183); see text.
T_6—B.f.o. transformer (Miller 6183); see text.
T_7—Audio interstage transformer, 1:2 ratio (Thordarson 20A16).
T_8—Audio output transformer, 5000 to 4 ohms (Stancor 3856).
Y_6—4540 Kc. (surplus).

starting to wire the receiver is first to complete the power supply and heater wiring, and then start wiring from the antenna toward the speaker. This allows proceeding in a logical order so that the work can be picked up readily at any time after an intermission.

The use of good quality ceramic tube and coil sockets, particularly in the front end, is highly recommended. When mounting the sockets orient them so that the leads to the various points in the circuit will be as short as possible.

Millen coil shields (80008) are used around the plug-in coils in the front end — i.e., the r.f., mixer and oscillator — and the shield bases are mounted with the same screws that hold the

ceramic coil sockets. All plug-in coils are wound with No. 26 enameled wire on Amphenol polystyrene forms, and Hammarlund APC-type airpadder capacitors are mounted in the recesses at the tops of the coil forms. After finishing a coil it is a good idea to fasten the winding and the trimmer capacitor in place with Duco cement. Decal each set of coils for a particular band and mount them on small wooden bases that have holes to take the pins Then paint or stain each of the coil-set bases. The final result will be a neat and convenient arrangement for holding the coils for each band (Fig. 5-59). Plug-in coil data for each band are given in the coil table.

The tuning capacitor, C_3, is mounted on the

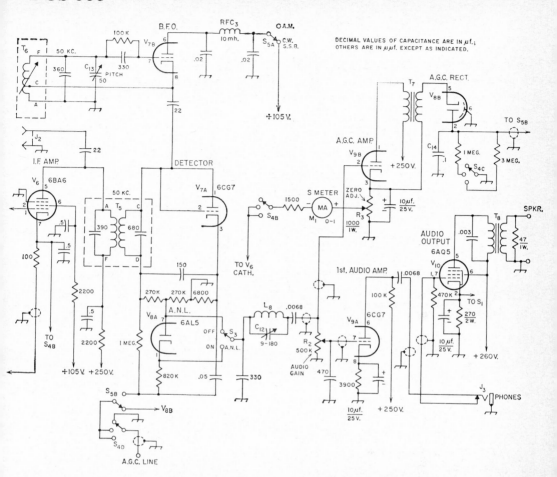

chassis and reinforced by a bracket to minimize any rocking movement. This bracket is triangular in shape with a right-angle flange at the bottom. It is drilled to take the front bearing sleeve of the tuning capacitor and held firmly to it by the capacitor mounting nut and a lock washer, as shown in Fig. 5-58. Flexing of the chassis can be minimized by the use of lengths of angle stock bolted to the chassis at strategic points throughout the receiver. Exact alignment of the tuning capacitor with the dial shaft is not always possible, so a flexible coupling (Millen 39016) is used.

When wiring the crystal filter keep leads as short and direct as possible, as this will minimize stray coupling between the input and output ends, which would deteriorate the performance of the crystal-filter circuits.

The 50-kc. i.f. circuits used Miller 6183 TV horizontal-oscillator replacement coils as i.f. transformers. These coils must be altered before they can be used. As they are supplied, the terminal lugs are brought out at the top of the can; these lugs must be reversed before the can is mounted. By applying slight pressure to the phenolic coil form the assembly will slide out of the aluminum shield can and then can be re-

versed. However, before reassembling the unit a few slight changes must be made. There are actually two separate windings; each one will be tuned and used either as a primary or secondary for the 50-kc. i.f. transformer. The tap on the large winding must be lifted off the soldering lug C, taped, and tucked away, being careful not to break it; this leaves just the lead from the small winding on terminal C. Terminals A and F represent the large winding. The small coil is tuned by connecting a 680-μμf. mica capacitor between terminals C and D; these capacitors should be fastened on the soldering lugs inside the shield can. The can is then slipped back over the coil and capacitor, keeping in mind that the lugs must come out the bottom, and the assembly is ready for mounting on the chassis.

The b.f.o. coil is also a Miller 6183, and the procedure for reversing the assembly before mounting is identical to that followed with the 50-kc. transformers. However, it is not necessary to alter any of the wiring in the b.f.o. transformer, since only the large winding (A — F) and its tap (C) is used.

Point-to-point wiring is recommended, along with generous use of both insulated tie points and

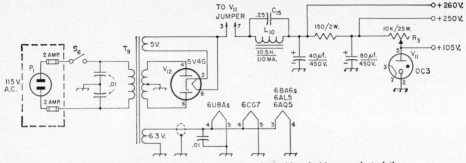

Fig. 5-57—Power-supply circuit. Capacitors marked with polarities are electrolytic.

C_{15}—0.25-μf. paper, 600 volts.
L_{10}—Filter choke, 10.5 henry, 110 ma. (Knight 62 G 139).
P_1—Fuse plug.

S_6—See R_2, Fig. 5-56.
T_9—Power transformer, 700 v. c.t., 120 ma.; 5 v., 3 amp.;
6.3 v., 4.7 amp. (Knight 62 G 044).

ground lugs. Use of shielded wire facilitates routing wires throughout the receiver as the shields can be spot-soldered to ground lugs and to each other in bundles. When wiring, mount components at right angles to the chassis sides wherever possible; this helps give the finished unit a neat appearance. In critical circuits, however, do not sacrifice short and direct leads for the sake of making the unit look pretty.

Placing the receiver in a rack cabinet and marking all controls on the front panel with decals also helps in giving the finished receiver a neat and "commercial" appearance.

The Calibrator

The 100-kc. calibrator is built in a separate 4 × 4 × 2-inch aluminum box and plugs into the accessory socket at the left rear of the receiver chassis. Fig. 5-61 shows the internal construction. The accessory socket provides the necessary operating voltage for the transistors and offers a convenient means for coupling the 100-kc. harmonics out of the calibrator into the receiver. If the calibrator is to be used as a self-contained unit it must be supplied with approximately 7–10 volts. A series arrangement of penlite cells, or a mercury battery, can be used. A battery clip

mounted on the side of the box is a convenient way to hold the internal batteries. If the unit is to be self-contained, a separate output jack for the calibrator must be provided. A phono jack may be used.

I.F. Alignment

Before starting alignment of the receiver, first determine whether the audio stages are functioning correctly. An audio signal should be coupled to the top end of the volume control, and varying the control should change the output level of the audio signal. If an audio signal is not available, the 60-cycle heater voltage will provide a convenient audio signal for checking.

There are various ways to approach the alignment problem. A 50-kc. signal generator can be used; however, these are hard to come by. Some of the better audio oscillators go as high as 50 kc. and can be used for alignment purposes. A second, and possibly superior, method is to use any of the numerous signal generators which will deliver 4.5-Mc. output; fed into the first i.f. amplifier grid, the 4.5-Mc. signal will beat against the second conversion oscillator to produce a 50-kc. i.f. signal which then can be used for alignment. This method also insures that the first i.f. signal

Fig. 5-58—The power supply is built along the back of the chassis; filter capacitor and VR tube are just in back of the filter choke in this view. The crystal calibrator unit at right is cushioned by rubber bumpers mounted on the receiver chassis. C_5 is on top of the calibrator unit. Front-end coil shields are at the top right in this photograph, along with the tuning capacitor bracket and flexible coupling. The on-off switch, S_6, on rear of the audio gain control, is a new push-pull type. Filter crystals are grouped behind the volume control, and the second conversion oscillator crystal is slightly to their left. The 4.5-Mc. i.f. transformers (in the small shield cans) are close to the filter crystals. The b.f.o. coil is at the extreme left in this view; all other large cans contain the 50-kc. i.f. transformers. Connections on the back chassis wall, left to right, are the muting terminals, B-plus output for auxiliary use, speaker terminals, i.f. output (phono jack), and antenna input connector.

DCS-500

Fig. 5-59—Each set of coils is provided with a wooden base for storage. C₂ and C₄ are mounted in the recesses at the tops of the oscillator and mixer coil forms.

DCS-500 Coil Table

All coils wound with No. 26 enameled wire on $1\frac{1}{4}$-inch diameter polystyrene forms. R.f. coil forms are four-prong (Amphenol 24-4P); mixer and oscillator coils are five-prong (Amphenol 24-5P). C_2 and C_4 are Hammarlund APC-50 except on 3.5 Mc., which takes APC-75. Taps are counted from ground end. Primaries and ticklers are close-wound in the same direction as the main coil at bottom of coil form; grid and plate (or antenna) connections at outside ends.

Band	Secondary	Primary or Tickler
	L_1, $45\frac{1}{4}$ turns close-wound.	
3.5 Mc.	L_2, $36\frac{3}{4}$ turns close-wound, tapped at $26\frac{3}{4}$ turns.	$10\frac{3}{4}$ turns, $\frac{3}{8}$-inch spacing from secondary.
	L_3, $28\frac{3}{4}$ turns close-wound, tapped at 19 turns.	$11\frac{3}{4}$ turns, $\frac{1}{4}$-inch spacing from secondary.
	L_1, $26\frac{1}{4}$ turns, close-wound.	$7\frac{3}{4}$ turns, $\frac{1}{4}$-inch spacing from secondary.
7 Mc.	L_2, $18\frac{3}{4}$ turns spaced to 1 inch. Tapped at $9\frac{3}{4}$ turns.	$6\frac{3}{4}$ turns, $\frac{3}{8}$-inch spacing from secondary.
	L_3, $17\frac{3}{4}$ turns spaced to $\frac{7}{8}$ inch. Tapped at $4\frac{3}{4}$ turns.	$7\frac{3}{4}$ turns, $\frac{1}{4}$-inch spacing from secondary.
	L_1, $13\frac{1}{4}$ turns spaced to $\frac{5}{8}$ inch.	$6\frac{3}{4}$ turns, $\frac{5}{16}$-inch spacing from secondary.
14 Mc.	L_2, $10\frac{3}{4}$ turns spaced to 1 inch. Tapped at 3 turns.	$5\frac{3}{4}$ turns, $\frac{5}{8}$-inch spacing from secondary.
	L_3, $5\frac{3}{4}$ turns spaced to $\frac{15}{16}$ inch. Tapped at $1\frac{7}{8}$ turns.	$3\frac{3}{4}$ turns, $\frac{3}{8}$-inch spacing from secondary.
	L_1, $9\frac{1}{4}$ turns spaced to $\frac{1}{2}$ inch.	$6\frac{3}{4}$ turns, $\frac{5}{16}$-inch spacing from secondary.
21 Mc.	L_2, $7\frac{3}{4}$ turns spaced to $1\frac{1}{8}$ inches. Tapped at 2 turns.	$5\frac{3}{4}$ turns, $\frac{5}{8}$-inch spacing from secondary.
	L_3, $6\frac{3}{4}$ turns spaced to $\frac{15}{16}$ inch. Tapped at 2 turns.	$3\frac{3}{4}$ turns, $\frac{3}{8}$-inch spacing from secondary.
	L_1, $6\frac{1}{4}$ turns spaced to $\frac{7}{16}$-inch.	$5\frac{3}{4}$ turns, $\frac{1}{4}$-inch spacing from secondary.
28 Mc.	L_2, $5\frac{3}{4}$ turns spaced to $1\frac{1}{4}$ inches. Tapped at 2 turns.	$4\frac{3}{4}$ turns, $\frac{1}{4}$-inch spacing from secondary.
	L_3, $4\frac{3}{4}$ turns spaced to $\frac{3}{4}$ inch. Tapped at $1\frac{1}{2}$ turns.	$2\frac{3}{4}$ turns, $\frac{1}{4}$-inch spacing from secondary.

will fall within the crystal filter bandpass in case the crystal frequencies are not exact. When aligning, connect a d.c. voltmeter (preferably a v.t.v.m.) across the detector load resistor (point D of T_5 and chassis), turn the i.f. gain control about three-quarters open, and tune both the plate circuit of the second conversion oscillator and the 50-kc. i.f. transformers for maximum output, as indicated on the meter. The output of the signal generator should not be modulated, and at the start will most likely be "wide open." However, as alignment progresses the output of the generator will have to be progressively decreased. When aligning the i.f. transformers there should

Fig. 5-60—The potentiometer for S-meter adjustment and the audio output transformer are on the right chassis wall in this view. The 50-kc. i.f. trap is located just above the power transformer in the lower right-hand corner. The antenna trimmer is located at extreme left center. The crystal filter sockets are at top center, and to their left on the front wall is the calibrator switch S_1. To the right of the calibrator switch is the sensitivity control, followed to the right by the selectivity switch S_2 and the b.f.o. pitch-control capacitor. The octal accessory socket for the calibrator is at the lower left. As shown, shielded wire spot-soldered together in bundles can be routed conveniently to various points in the receiver. Ceramic sockets are used throughout the front end (center left). Mounting components parallel with the chassis sides helps give the finished unit a neat appearance.

be a definite peak in output as each circuit is brought through resonance. If a particular coil does not peak, that coil and its associated circuits should be checked. After peaking one winding of a transformer, recheck the other; it may need touching up. After alignment of all the 50-kc. coils is completed, go back and "rock" each coil slug to be sure it is peaked for maximum output. This completes the 50-kc. alignment.

Leave the signal generator on, set the b.f.o. pitch control at half capacitance, turn the b.f.o. on, and adjust its coil slug for zero beat with the 50-kc. i.f. signal. Varying the pitch control over its range should produce a tone with a maximum frequency of 3 kc. either side of zero beat.

Next, the 50-kc. trap on the output of the detector should be adjusted. Connect the vertical input terminals of an oscilloscope between the plate of the first audio amplifier and chassis, turn on the b.f.o., and adjust C_{12} for minimum 50-kc. signal on the scope. This trap, made up of C_{12} and L_8, attenuates any 50-kc. feed-through.

The first-i.f. coils at 4.5-Mc. should next be adjusted. Couple the signal generator to the grid of the first mixer and peak L_4 and L_5 for maximum deflection of the v.t.v.m. at the detector. The i.f. system is then completely aligned.

Front-End Alignment

To adjust the front end, plug in a set of coils and check the oscillator frequency range either with a calibrated g.d.o. or on a calibrated general-coverage receiver, the latter being preferable. Keep in mind that the oscillator works 4.5 Mc. above the signal on 80, 40 and 20 meters, and 4.5 Mc. below the signal frequency on the 15- and 10-meter bands. This means that on 15 and 10 meters the oscillator trimmer capacitor, C_4, must be at the larger-capacitance setting of the two that bring in signals. After establishing the correct frequency range of the oscillator, inject a signal at the low end of the band into the antenna terminals and peak the mixer capacitor, C_2, and the antenna trimmer, C_1, for maximum signal. Then move the test signal to the high end of the band and recheck the mixer trimmer capacitor (the antenna trimmer also will have to be repeaked) for correct tracking. If C_2 has to be readjusted, spread the mixer coil turns apart or compress them together until the signal strength is uniform at both ends of the band, without readjustment of C_2. If the mixer trimmer capacitance had to be increased at the high-frequency end of the band to maintain tracking, the coil tap is too

far up the coil and the turns below the tap must be spread apart or the tap itself must be moved down. If the trimmer capacitance has to be decreased the tap is too low. Coil specifications might possibly have to be altered slightly from those given in the table, particularly on the higher frequencies, because of variations in strays from one receiver to another.

General

Adjustment of the calibrator is relatively straightforward, and should present no problems. Turn on the calibrator and you should hear the 100-kc. harmonics on whatever band you happen to be using. Once it is determined that the unit is working correctly, the only adjustment necessary is to set the frequency of the calibrator exactly. The usual reference is WWV or any broadcast station that is on a frequency which is a whole-number multiple of 100 kc. The frequency tolerance for standard broadcast stations is 20 cycles, thus b.c. stations represent a source for accurate frequency determination.

Using a general-coverage or b.c. receiver, tune in either WWV or a known broadcast station and adjust the calibrator trimmer C_5 for zero beat. The calibrator will then provide accurate 100-kc. signals that can be used for frequency determination and band-edge marking.

The first intermediate frequency can be altered slightly to facilitate the use of particular sets of crystals available. However, if the deviation is more than 20 kc. or so, slight changes may be needed in the h.f. oscillator coil specifications to maintain the proper bandspread.

If the receiver is to be worked in a rack cabinet as shown in Fig. 5-54, or if a cover plate is attached to the bottom of the receiver chassis, minor alignment touch-up may be necessary.

Spraying the receiver chassis with a light coat of clear plastic lacquer before mounting any of the components will prevent fingerprints and oxidation of the chassis.

The audio output stage has adequate power to drive a 5- or 6-inch speaker, which may be mounted in a small open-back metal utility box.

The i.f. output jack at the rear provides a convenient way of attaching accessory devices such as an oscilloscope for modulation checking.

A side-by-side comparison of the finished receiver with some of the better-quality commercial units will show that this receiver can hold its own in sensitivity, selectivity and stability. Needless to say, the more care taken in construction, wiring and alignment the better the results.

Fig. 5-61—Inside view of the calibrator unit. The 100-kc. oscillator coil, L_{15}, is at the right, the oscillator transistor, Q_2, is in the foreground mounted to the crystal socket, and the amplifier transistor, Q_1, is mounted at the right on a terminal strip. The 100-kc. crystal is mounted horizontally between the plate and the octal plug. The plug can be mounted on 2-inch screws as shown in the photograph, or on the bottom plate of the Minibox, with flexible leads to the circuit. If the calibrator is to be used as a self-contained unit (see text) the octal plug is not necessary.

Q Multiplier

A Transistorized Q Multiplier

A "*Q* multiplier" is an electronic device that boosts the *Q* of a tuned circuit many times beyond its normal value. In this condition the single tuned circuit has much greater selectivity than normal, and it can be utilized to reject or amplify a narrow band of frequencies. There are vacuum-tube versions of the *Q*-multiplier circuit, but the transistorized *Q* multiplier to be described has the advantage that it eliminates a power-supply problem and is very compact.

Circuit and Theory

Parallel-tuned circuits have been used for years as "suck-out" trap circuits. Properly coupling a parallel-tuned circuit loosely to a vacuum-tube amplifier stage, it will be found that the amplifier stage has no gain at the frequency to which the trap circuit is tuned. The additional tuned circuit puts a "notch" in the response of the amplifier. The principle is used in TV and other amplifiers to minimize response to a narrow band of frequencies. Increasing the *Q* of the trap circuit reduces the width of the rejection notch.

The transistorized *Q* multiplier makes use of the above effect for its operation. A tuned circuit is made regenerative to increase its *Q* and is coupled into the i.f. stage of a receiver. By changing the frequency of the regenerative circuit, the sharp notch can be moved about across the passband of the receiver. The width of the notch is changed by controlling the amount of regeneration.

Although it seems paradoxical, the transistorized *Q* multiplier with no change in circuitry will also permit "peaking" an incoming signal the way a vacuum-tube *Q* multiplier does. The mode of operation is selected by adjustment of the regeneration control, and this then usually requires a slight readjustment of the frequency control. The peaking effect is not quite as pronounced as the notch, but it is still adequate to give fairly good single-signal c.w. reception with a receiver of otherwise inadequate selectivity.

The regenerative circuit builds up the signal and feeds it back to the amplifier at a higher level

and in the proper phase to add to the original signal. The notch effect described earlier works in a similar manner except that the tuning of the regenerative circuit is such that it feeds back the signal out of phase.

The schematic diagram of the *Q* multiplier is shown in Fig. 5-62. The inductor L_1 furnishes coupling from the receiver to the *Q* multiplier, and C_4 is required to prevent short-circuiting the receiver's plate supply. The multiplier proper consists of the tunable circuit $C_1 C_3 L_2$ connected to a transistor in the collector-tuned common-base oscillator circuit using capacitive feedback via C_2. Regeneration is controlled by varying the d.c. operating voltage through dropping resistor R_1.

Layout

The unit and power supply are built in a small aluminum "Minibox" measuring $5 \times 2\frac{1}{4} \times 2\frac{1}{4}$ inches (Bud CU-3004) and the operating controls are mounted on a lucite or aluminum subpanel. All parts of the unit are built on one half of the box. This feature not only simplifies construction but makes a battery change a simple job, even if this is required only a couple of times a year.

All major components, such as the two slug-tuned coils, tie point, battery holder, regeneration and tuning controls, are mounted directly on the box and subpanel. The remaining resistors, capacitors and the single transistor are supported by their connections to the above parts.

The two slug-tuned coils, L_1 and L_2, are centered on the box and spaced one inch apart on centers. Operating controls C_1 and R_1 are placed $1\frac{1}{4}$ inches from the ends of the subpanel and centered. The tie point mounts directly behind tuning control C_1.

Power for the unit is supplied by four penlight cells (type 912) which are mounted in the battery holder (Lafayette Radio Co. Stock No. MS-170) directly behind regeneration control R_1. Total drain on the battery never exceeds 0.2 ma.

Connection to the receiver is made with a three-foot length of RG-58/U cable brought through the rear wall of the Minibox. A rubber grommet

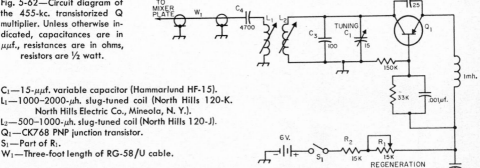

Fig. 5-62—Circuit diagram of the 455-kc. transistorized Q multiplier. Unless otherwise indicated, capacitances are in μμf., resistances are in ohms, resistors are ½ watt.

C_1—15-μμf. variable capacitor (Hammarlund HF-15).
L_1—1000–2000-μh. slug-tuned coil (North Hills 120-K. North Hills Electric Co., Mineola, N. Y.).
L_2—500–1000-μh. slug-tuned coil (North Hills 120-J).
Q_1—CK768 PNP junction transistor.
S_1—Part of R_1.
W_1—Three-foot length of RG-58/U cable.

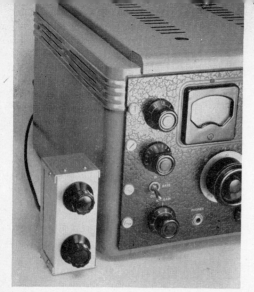

Fig. 5-63—View of the Q multiplier showing its single connecting cable to the receiver. The box can be placed in any convenient spot on or around the receiver.

should be placed in the hole to prevent chafing of the cable insulation.

When soldering the transistor in place, be sure to take the usual precautions against heat damage.

Alignment

After completing the wiring (and double-checking it) connect the open end of the three-foot cable to the plate circuit of the receiver mixer tube. This can be done in a permanent fashion by soldering the inner conductor of the cable to the plate pin on the tube socket or any point that is connected directly to this pin, and by soldering the shield to any convenient nearby ground point. If you are one of those people who is afraid to take the bottom plate off his receiver, and you have a receiver with octal tubes, a "chicken connection" can be made by removing the mixer tube and wrapping a short piece of small wire around the plate pin. Reinsert the tube in its socket and solder the center conductor of the coax to the small wire coming from the plate pin. Now ground the coax shield to the receiver chassis.

Fig. 5-64—The Q multiplier and its battery supply are combined in one small Minibox. The single transistor is visible near the top right corner.

It is important to keep the lead from the tube pin to the coax as short as possible, to prevent stray pickup.

Check the schematic diagram of the receiver for help in locating the above receiver connections.

Turn on the receiver and tune in a signal strong enough to give an S-meter reading. Any decent signal on the broadcast band will do. Next, tune the slug on L_1 until the signal peaks up. You are tuning out the reactance of the connecting cable, and effectively peaking up the i.f. If the receiver has no S meter, use an a.c. voltmeter across the audio output. When this step has been successfully completed the Q multiplier is properly connected to the receiver and when switched to "off" (S_1 opened) will not affect normal receiver operation.

The next step is to bring the multiplier into oscillation, and to adjust its frequency to a useful range. Set the tuning control to half capacity and advance the regeneration control to about half open. This latter movement also turns the power on. Tune the receiver to a clear spot and set the receiver b.f.o. to the center of the pass-band. Now adjust the slug of L_2. The multiplier should be oscillating, and somewhere in the adjustment of L_2 a beat note will be heard from the receiver. This indicates the frequency of oscillation is somewhere on or near the i.f. Swing this into zero beat with the b.f.o.

Final Adjustment

One of the best ways to make final alignment is to simulate an unwanted heterodyne in the receiver and adjust the Q multiplier for maximum attenuation of the unwanted signal. To do this, tune in a moderately weak signal with the b.f.o. on. A broadcast station received with the antenna disconnected will do. The b.f.o. will beat with the incoming signal, producing an audio tone. Adjust the b.f.o. for a tone of about 1 kc. or so.

Back off on control R_1 until the oscillator becomes regenerative. By alternately adjusting the tuning control, C_1, and the regeneration control, R_1, a point can be found where the audio tone disappears, or at least is attenuated. Some slight retouching of L_2 may have to be done in the above alignment, since the movement of any one control tends to "pull" the others. The optimum situation is to have the tuning control C_1 set at about half capacity when the notch is in the center of the passband.

If you happen to get a super active transistor and the regeneration control does not have the range to stop oscillator action, increase the value of the series resistor R_2. Conversely, if the unit fails to oscillate, reduce the value of R_2.

When making the above adjustments, you should notice that the audio tone can be peaked as well as nulled. If it can not be peaked, a little more practice with the controls should produce this condition. In the unit shown here, the best null was produced with the regeneration control turned only a few degrees. Optimum peak position was obtained with the regeneration control almost at the point of oscillation.

Conelrad

Effective January 2, 1957, the "Conelrad" rules became part of the amateur regulations. Essentially, compliance with the rules consists of monitoring a broadcast station — standard band, f.m. or TV — either continuously or at intervals not exceeding ten minutes, during periods in which the amateur transmitter is in use. On receipt of a Conelrad Alert all transmitting must cease, except as authorized in 12.193 and 12.194 of the FCC regulations.

The existence of an Alert may be determined

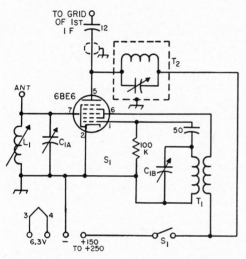

Fig. 5-65—Converter circuit for monitoring broadcast stations in connection with a communications receiver. Capacitances are in $\mu\mu$f.

C_{1A}, C_{1B}—Two-gang broadcast capacitor, oscillator section according to intermediate frequency to be used.

L_1—Loop stick.

T_1—B.c. oscillator transformer (for i.f. to be used).

T_2—I.f. coil and trimmer. This can be taken from an i.f. transformer, or the transformer can be used intact, the output being taken from the secondary.

Note: If only one broadcast station is to be monitored C_{1A} and C_{1B} can be padder-type capacitors (or a combination of padding and fixed capacitance as required) adjusted for the desired station and intermediate frequencies. Other types of converter tubes may be substituted if desired.

Power for the unit can be taken from the receiver's "accessory" socket.

as outlined in 12.192(b)(3). Operation during hours when local broadcast stations are not on the air will require tuning through the standard broadcast band to determine if operation appears to be normal. The presence of any U. S. broadcast stations on frequencies other than 640 and 1240 kc. indicates normal operation.

Perhaps the simplest form of compliance is by means of a simple converter working into the i.f. amplifier of the regular station receiver. A typical circuit is shown in Fig. 5-65. The converter can be built in a small metal case and mounted at a

convenient spot on the receiver so that S_1 can be closed at regular intervals for checking the broadcast station. As an alternative, the converter can be mounted out of the way at the rear of the receiver and the switch leads brought out to a convenient spot.

● A "FAIL-PROOF" CONELRAD ALARM

The conelrad alarm shown in Fig. 5-65 uses a small BC receiver to furnish both audible and visible indications of a Conelrad Alert (the receiver may still be used for normal broadcast reception).

With the receiver tuned to a broadcast carrier and the alarm circuit in operation, a green "safe" light indicates that all is well on the broadcast band. When the broadcast carrier goes off, as it will in a Conelrad Radio Alert, the green light goes out, a red "danger" light comes on, a buzzer sounds, and the 115-volt a.c. line to the transmitter is opened up. In other words, the device *puts* you off the air! The audible and visible warnings also are given in the event of a component failure in either the control receiver or the alarm. Even the disappearance of the 115-volt supply will not go unnoticed, since in that case the green "safe" light will go out, indicating that the alarm is inoperative.

The alarm requires a minimum of 0.7 volts (negative) from the receiver's a.v.c. (automatic volume control) circuit for dependable operation. Receivers having one stage of i.f. amplification will develop at least this much a.v.c. voltage when tuned to a signal of reasonable strength. But watch out for the "superhets" that do not have an i.f. stage; they are of little value as a source of control voltage for the alarm. You can usually find out if the receiver has an i.f. stage by looking at the tube list pasted on either the chassis or the inside of the cabinet.

The circuit of the alarm is shown in section B, Fig. 5-66. Section A is a typical a.v.c.-detector-first audio stage of an a.c.-d.c. receiver, and shows how the alarm circuit is tied into a receiver.

Although a 12AV6 is shown as the detector, other tubes may be used in some receivers. However, the basic circuit will be the same or very similar.

Finding the a.v.c. line in the jumble beneath the chassis of the ordinary a.c.-d.c. receiver is not always easy. Here are a few hints:

Using section A, Fig. 5-66, as a guide, locate the detector tube socket. Trace out the leads going to the secondary of the last i.f. transformer, T_1. This transformer usually will be adjacent to the detector tube. The lower end of the secondary winding will be connected to several different resistors, one of these being the diode-load filter resistor (approximately 50K in most circuits) and another the a.v.c. filter resistor, R_1. The value of the latter resistor is ordinarily above one megohm. Trace through R_1 in the direction of the arrow (Fig. 5-66), until you locate the fairly high

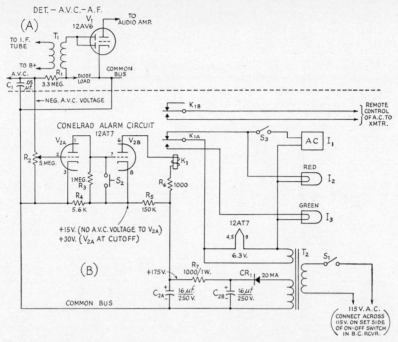

Fig. 5-66—Circuit of the Conelrad alarm (B) connected to the a.v.c. circuit (A) of a typical a.c.-d.c. broadcast receiver Resistors are ½ watt unless otherwise specified. C_1, R_1 and T_1 in section A are components in the broadcast receiver

I_1—6-volt a.c. buzzer (Edwards 725).
I_2, I_3—6-volt pilot lamp, No. 47.
K_1—D.p.d.t. sensitive relay, 5000-ohm coil, 5-amp. contacts (Potter & Brumfield GB11D).
R_2—5-megohm potentiometer.

S_1, S_2—S.p.s.t. rotary canopy switch (ICA 1257).
S_2—Momentary-contact switch (Switchcraft 101).
T_2—Replacement-type power transformer, 150 volts, 25 ma.; 6.3 volts, 0.5 amp. (Merit P-3046 or equivalent).

value (0.05 μf. or so) a.v.c. filter capacitor, C_1. Now you have the a.v.c. line clearly identified and the tap for the alarm circuit may be made.

Notice that the cathode of V_1 and the cold side of C_1 are both returned to a common bus or −B line, not directly to the chassis. Also observe that the return for the alarm circuit is made to the common bus in the receiver, not to the chassis of the set. *Do not ground this lead to the chassis or connect it to any exposed metal parts.* If there is any difficulty in locating the common bus in the vicinity of the detector stage, check back from the negative side of the power-supply filter capacitors, as this point is always attached to the common bus.

The monitor should be built in an insulated box of some kind and not in a metal case. The box can be made of plywood, or a bakelite instrument case (e.g., ICA type 8202). The bakelite case is ideal for the application, but it must be handled with care during construction, to avoid scratching, chipping, or breakage. Be especially careful when drilling large holes such as those used in mounting the pilot-lamp assemblies and switches, because a large drill tends to bind and crack the case.

Testing and Operating

The chances are pretty good that right after the receiver and the monitor have been turned on the red lamp will light and and — if you haven't had the foresight to open S_3 to prevent the noise — the buzzer will sound. Tune the receiver to a broadcast station and see if the red light goes out and the green light comes on. If this happens, close S_3 and you're all set for conelrad compliance. If the "safe" light does not come on, tune around for a signal strong enough to actuate the alarm. Should the signal of greatest apparent strength fail to trigger the monitor, leave the receiver tuned to this signal and then momentarily press S_2. The alarm should now lock on "safe," provided the a.v.c. circuit delivers 0.7 volt or more to V_{2A}.

The only d.c. measurements of any consequence that need be made in checking through the alarm circuit are the output voltage of the power supply and the voltage at the cathode of V_{2B}. The proper voltages at these two points are given on the circuit diagram. If the alarm fails to respond properly, it may be advisable to check the a.v.c. voltage with a v.t.v.m.

CHAPTER 6

High-Frequency Transmitters

The principal requirements to be met in c.w. transmitters for the amateur bands between 1.8 and 30 Mc. are that the frequency must be as stable as good practice permits, the output signal must be free from modulation and that harmonics and other spurious emissions must be eliminated or reduced to the point where they do not cause interference to other stations.

The over-all design depends primarily upon the bands in which operation is desired, and the power output. A simple oscillator with satisfactory frequency stability may be used as a transmitter at the lower frequencies, as indicated in Fig. 6-1A, but the power output obtainable is small. As a general rule, the output of the oscillator is fed into one or more amplifiers to bring the power fed to the antenna up to the desired level, as shown in B.

An amplifier whose output frequency is the same as the input frequency is called a **straight amplifier**. A **buffer amplifier** is the term sometimes applied to an amplifier stage to indicate that its primary purpose is one of isolation, rather than power gain.

Because it becomes increasingly difficult to maintain oscillator frequency stability as the frequency is increased, it is most usual practice in working at the higher frequencies to operate the oscillator at a low frequency and follow it with one or more **frequency multipliers** as required to arrive at the desired output frequency. A frequency multiplier is an amplifier that delivers output at a multiple of the exciting frequency. A **doubler** is a multiplier that gives output at twice the exciting frequency; a **tripler** multiplies the exciting frequency by three, etc. From the viewpoint of any particular stage in a transmitter, the preceding stage is its **driver**.

As a general rule, frequency multipliers should not be used to feed the antenna system directly, but should feed a straight amplifier which, in turn, feeds the antenna system, as shown in Fig. 1-C, D and E. As the diagrams indicate, it is often possible to operate more than one stage from a single power supply.

Good frequency stability is most easily obtained through the use of a **crystal-controlled oscillator**, although a different crystal is needed for each frequency desired (or multiples of that frequency). A **self-controlled oscillator** or **v.f.o.** (variable-frequency oscillator) may be tuned to any frequency with a dial in the manner of a

receiver, but requires great care in design and construction if its stability is to compare with that of a crystal oscillator.

In all types of transmitter stages, screen-grid tubes have the advantage over triodes that they require less driving power. With a lower-power exciter, the problem of harmonic reduction is made easier. Most satisfactory oscillator circuits use a screen-grid tube.

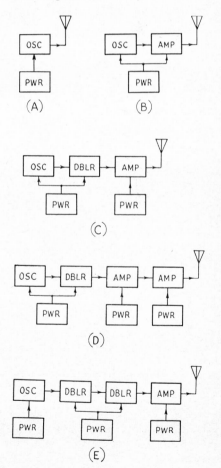

Fig. 6-1—Block diagrams showing typical combinations of oscillator and amplifiers and power-supply arrangements for transmitters. A wide selection is possible, depending upon the number of bands in which operation is desired and the power output.

Oscillators

● **CRYSTAL OSCILLATORS**

The frequency of a crystal-controlled oscillator is held constant to a high degree of accuracy by the use of a quartz crystal. The frequency depends almost entirely on the dimensions of the crystal (essentially its thickness); other circuit values have comparatively negligible effect. However, the power obtainable is limited by the heat the crystal will stand without fracturing. The amount of heating is dependent upon the r.f. crystal current which, in turn, is a function of the amount of feedback required to provide proper excitation. Crystal heating short of the danger point results in frequency drift to an extent depending upon the way the crystal is cut. Excitation should always be adjusted to the minimum necessary for proper operation.

Crystal-Oscillator Circuits

The simplest crystal-oscillator circuit is shown in Fig. 6-2A. An equivalent is shown at B. It is a Colpitts circuit (see chapter on vacuum-tube principles) with the tube tapped across part of the tuned circuit. The crystal has been replaced by its equivalent — a series-tuned circuit L_1C_4. (See chapter on electrical laws and circuits.) C_5 and C_6 are the tube grid-cathode and plate-circuit in the actual plate circuit. Although the oscillator itself is not entirely independent of adjustments made in the plate tank circuit when the latter is tuned near the fundamental frequency of the crystal, the effects can be satisfactorily minimized by proper choice of the oscillator tube.

The circuit of Fig. 6-3A is known as the Tritet. The oscillator circuit is that of Fig. 6-2C. Excitation is controlled by adjustment of the tank L_1C_1, which should have a low L/C ratio, and be tuned considerably to the high-frequency side of the crystal frequency (approximately 5 Mc. for a 3.5-Mc. crystal) to prevent over-excitation and high crystal current. Once the proper adjustment for average crystals has been found, C_1 may be replaced with a fixed capacitor of equal value.

The oscillator circuit of Fig. 3-B is that of Fig. 6-2A. Excitation is controlled by C_9.

The oscillator of the grid-plate circuit of Fig. 6-3C is the same as that of Fig. 6-3B, except that the ground point has been moved from the cathode to the plate of the oscillator (in other words, to the screen of the tube). Excitation is adjusted by proper proportioning of C_6 and C_7.

When most types of tubes are used in the circuits of Fig. 6-3, oscillation will stop when the output plate circuit is tuned to the crystal fre-

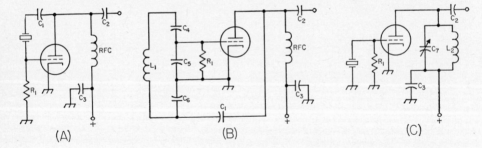

Fig. 6-2—Simple crystal-oscillator circuits. A—Pierce. B—Equivalent of circuit A. C—Simple triode oscillator. C_1 is a plate blocking capacitor, C_2 an output coupling capacitor, and C_3 a plate bypass. L_1, C_4, C_5 and C_6 are discussed in the text. C_7 and L_2 should tune to the crystal fundamental frequency. R_1 is the grid leak.

cathode capacitances, respectively. In best practical form, C_5 or C_6, or both, would be augmented by external capacitors from grid to cathode and plate to cathode so that feedback could be adjusted properly.

The circuit shown in Fig. 6-2C is the equivalent of the tuned-grid tuned-plate circuit discussed in the chapter on vacuum-tube principles, the crystal replacing the tuned grid circuit

The most commonly used crystal-oscillator circuits are based on one or the other of these two simple types, and are shown in Fig. 6-3. Although these circuits are somewhat more complicated, they combine the functions of oscillator and amplifier or frequency multiplier in a single tube. In all of these circuits, the screen of a tetrode or pentode is used as the plate in a triode oscillator. Power output is taken from a separate tuned tank

quency, and it is necessary to operate with the plate tank circuit critically detuned for maximum output with stability. However, when the 6AG7, 5763, or the lower-power 6AH6 is used with proper adjustment of excitation, it is possible to tune to the crystal frequency without stopping oscillation. The plate tuning characteristic should then be similar to Fig. 6-4. These tubes also operate with less crystal current than most other types for a given power output, and less frequency change occurs when the plate circuit is tuned through the crystal frequency (less than 25 cycles at 3.5 Mc.).

Crystal current may be estimated by observing the relative brilliance of a 60-ma. dial lamp connected in series with the crystal. Current should be held to the minimum for satisfactory output by careful adjustment of excitation. With the

Oscillators

operating voltages shown, satisfactory output should be obtained with crystal currents of 40 ma. or less.

In these circuits, output may be obtained at multiples of the crystal frequency by tuning the plate tank circuit to the desired harmonic, the

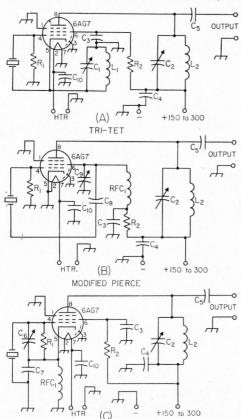

TRI-TET (A)

MODIFIED PIERCE (B)

GRID-PLATE (C)

Fig. 6-3—Commonly used crystal-controlled oscillator circuits. Values are those recommended for a 6AG7 or 5763 tube. (See reference in text for other tubes.)

C_1—Feedback-control capacitor—3.5-Mc. crystals—approx. 220-$\mu\mu$f. mica—7-Mc. crystals—approx. 150-$\mu\mu$f. mica.

C_2—Output tank capacitor—100-$\mu\mu$f. variable for single-band tank; 250-$\mu\mu$f. variable for two-band tank.

C_3—Screen bypass—0.001-μf. disk ceramic.

C_4—Plate bypass—0.001-μf. disk ceramic.

C_5—Output coupling capacitor—50 to 100 $\mu\mu$f.

C_6—Excitation-control capacitor—30-$\mu\mu$f. trimmer.

C_7—Excitation capacitor—220-$\mu\mu$f. mica for 6AG7; 100-$\mu\mu$f. for 5763.

C_8—D.c. blocking capacitor—0.001-μf. mica.

C_9—Excitation-control capacitor—220-$\mu\mu$f. mica.

C_{10}—Heater bypass—0.001-μf. disk ceramic.

R_1—Grid leak—0.1 megohm, ½ watt.

R_2—Screen resistor—47,000 ohms, 1 watt.

L_1—Excitation-control inductance—3.5-Mc. crystals—approx. 4 μh.; 7-Mc. crystals—approx. 2 μh.

L_2—Output-circuit coil—single band:—3.5 Mc.—17 μh.; 7 Mc.—8 μh.; 14 Mc.—2.5 μh.; 28 Mc.—1 μh. Two-band operation: 3.5 & 7 Mc.—7.5 μh.; 7 & 14 Mc.—2.5 μh.

RFC_1—2.5-mh. 50-ma. r.f. choke.

output dropping off, of course, at the higher harmonics. Especially for harmonic operation, a low-C plate tank circuit is desirable.

For best performance with a 6AG7 or 5763, the values given under Fig. 6-3 should be followed closely. (For a discussion of values for other tubes, see *QST* for March, 1950, page 28.)

● VARIABLE-FREQUENCY OSCILLATORS

The frequency of a v.f.o. depends entirely on the values of inductance and capacitance in the circuit. Therefore, it is necessary to take careful steps to minimize changes in these values not under the control of the operator. As examples, even the minute changes of dimensions with temperature, particularly those of the coil, may result in a slow but noticeable change in frequency called **drift**. The effective input capacitance of the oscillator tube, which must be connected across the circuit, changes with variations in electrode voltages. This, in turn, causes a change in the frequency of the oscillator. To make use of the power from the oscillator, a load, usually in the form of an amplifier, must be coupled to the oscillator, and variations in the load may reflect on the frequency. Very slight mechanical movement of components may result in a shift in frequency, and vibration can cause modulation.

V.F.O. Circuits

Fig. 6-5 shows the most commonly used circuits. They are all designed to minimize the effects mentioned above. All are similar to the crystal oscillators of Fig. 6-3 in that the screen of a tetrode or pentode is used as the oscillator plate. The oscillating circuits in Figs. 6-5A and B are the Hartley type; those in C and D are Colpitts circuits. (See chapter on vacuum-tube principles.) In the circuits of A and C, all of the above-mentioned effects, except changes in inductance, are minimized by the use of a high-Q tank circuit obtained through the use of large tank capacitances. Any uncontrolled changes in capacitance thus become a very small percentage of the total circuit capacitance.

In the series-tuned Colpitts circuit of Fig. 6-5D (sometimes called the Clapp circuit), a high-Q circuit is obtained in a different manner. The tube is tapped across only a small portion of the oscillating tank circuit, resulting in very loose coupling between tube and circuit. The taps are provided by a series of three capacitors across the coil. In addition, the tube capacitances are shunted by large capacitors, so the effects of the tube — changes in electrode voltages and loading — are still further reduced. In contrast

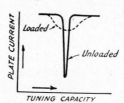

Fig. 6-4 — Plate tuning characteristic of circuits of Fig. 6-3 with preferred types (see text). The plate-current dip at resonance broadens and is less pronounced when the circuit is loaded.

to the preceding circuits, the resulting tank circuit has a high L/C ratio and therefore the tank current is much lower than in the circuits using high-C tanks. As a result, it will usually be found that, other things being equal, drift will be less with the low-C circuit.

For best stability, the ratio of C_{13} or C_{14} (which are usually equal) to $C_{11} + C_{12}$ should be as high as possible without stopping oscillation. The permissible ratio will be higher the higher the Q of the coil and the mutual conductance of the tube. If the circuit does not oscillate over the desired range, a coil of higher Q must be used or the capacitance of C_{13} and C_{14} reduced.

Load Isolation

In spite of the precautions already discussed, the tuning of the output plate circuit will cause a noticeable change in frequency, particularly in the region around resonance. This effect can be reduced considerably by designing the oscillator for half the desired frequency and doubling frequency in the output circuit.

It is desirable, although not a strict necessity if detuning is recognized and taken into account, to approach as closely as possible the condition where the adjustment of tuning controls in the transmitter, beyond the v.f.o. frequency control, will have negligible effect on the frequency. This can be done by substituting a fixed-tuned circuit in the output of the oscillator, and adding isolating stages whose tuning is fixed between the oscillator and the first tunable amplifier stage in the transmitter. Fig. 6-6 shows such an arrangement that gives good isolation. In the first stage, a 6C4 is connected as a cathode follower. This

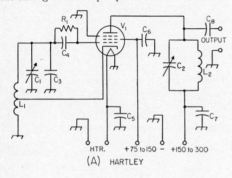

(A) HARTLEY

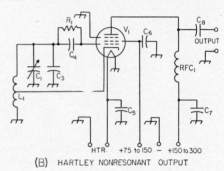

(B) HARTLEY NONRESONANT OUTPUT

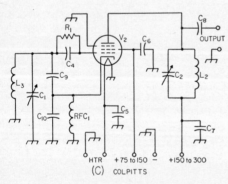

(C) COLPITTS

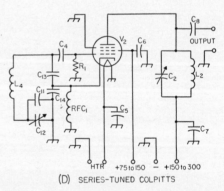

(D) SERIES-TUNED COLPITTS

Fig. 6-5—V.f.o. circuits. Approximate values for 3.5 Mc. are given below. For 1.75 Mc., all tank-circuit values of capacitance and inductance, all tuning capacitances and C_{13} and C_{14} should be doubled; for 7 Mc., they should be cut in half.

C_1—Oscillator bandspread tuning capacitor—150-$\mu\mu$f. variable.

C_2—Output-circuit tank capacitor—100-$\mu\mu$f.

C_3—Oscillator tank capacitor—500-$\mu\mu$f. zero-temperature-coefficient mica.

C_4—Grid coupling capacitor—100-$\mu\mu$f. zero-temperature-coefficient mica.

C_5—Heater bypass—0.001-μf. disk ceramic.

C_6—Screen bypass—0.001-μf. disk ceramic.

C_7—Plate bypass—0.001-μf. disk ceramic.

C_8—Output coupling capacitor—50 to 100-$\mu\mu$f. mica.

C_9—Oscillator tank capacitor—680-$\mu\mu$f. zero-temperature-coefficient mica.

C_{10}—Oscillator tank capacitor—0.0022-μf. zero-temperature-coefficient mica.

C_{11}—Oscillator bandspread padder—50-$\mu\mu$f. variable air.

C_{12}—Oscillator bandspread tuning capacitor—25-$\mu\mu$f. variable.

C_{13}, C_{14}—Tube-coupling capacitor—0.001-μf. zero-temperature-coefficient mica.

R_1—47,000 ohms, 1/2 watt.

L_1—Oscillator tank coil—4.3 μh., tapped about one-third-way from grounded end.

L_2—Output-circuit tank coil—22 μh.

L_3—Oscillator tank coil—4.3 μh.

L_4—Oscillator tank coil—33 μh. (B & W JEL-80).

RFC$_1$—2.5-mh. 50-ma. r.f. choke.

V_1—6AG7, 5763 or 6AH6 preferred; other types usable.

V_2—6AG7, 5763 or 6AH6 required for feedback capacitances shown.

Oscillators

drives a 5763 buffer amplifier whose input circuit is fixed-tuned to the approximate band of the v.f.o. output. For best isolation, it is important that the 6C4 does not draw grid current. The output of the v.f.o., or the cathode resistor of the 6C4 should be adjusted until the voltage across the cathode resistor of the 6C4 (as measured with a high-resistance d.c. voltmeter with an r.f. choke in the positive lead) is the same with or without excitation from the v.f.o. L_1 should be adjusted for most constant output from the 5763 over the band.

Chirp

In all of the circuits shown there will be some change of frequency with changes in screen and plate voltages, and the use of regulated voltages for both usually is necessary. One of the most serious results of voltage instability occurs if the oscillator is keyed, as it often is for break-in operation. Although voltage regulation will supply a steady voltage from the power supply and therefore is still desirable, it cannot alter the fact that the voltage on the tube must rise from zero when the key is open, to full voltage when the key is closed, and must fall back again to zero when the key is opened. The result is a chirp each time the key is opened or closed, unless the time constant in the keying circuit is reduced to the point where the chirp takes place so rapidly that the receiving operator's ear cannot detect it. Unfortunately, as explained in the chapter on keying, a certain minimum time constant is necessary if key clicks are to be minimized. Therefore it is evident that the measures necessary for the reduction of chirp and clicks are in opposition, and a compromise is necessary. For best keying characteristics, the oscillator should be allowed to run continuously while a subsequent amplifier is keyed. However, a keyed amplifier represents a widely variable load and unless sufficient isolation is provided between the oscillator and the keyed amplifier, the keying characteristics may be little better than when the oscillator itself is keyed. (See keying chapter for other methods of break-in keying.)

Frequency Drift

Frequency drift is further reduced most easily by limiting the power input as much as possible and by mounting the components of the tuned circuit in a separate shielded compartment, so that they will be isolated from the direct heat from tubes and resistors. The shielding also will eliminate changes in frequency caused by movement of nearby objects, such as the operator's hand when tuning the v.f.o. The circuit of Fig. 6-5D lends itself well to this arrangement, since relatively long leads between the tube and the tank circuit have negligible effect on frequency because of the large shunting capacitances. The grid, cathode and ground leads to the tube can be bunched in a cable up to several feet long.

Variable capacitors should have ceramic insulation, good bearing contacts and should preferably be of the double-bearing type, and fixed capacitors should have zero temperature coefficient. The tube socket also should have ceramic insulation and special attention should be paid to the selection of the coil in the oscillating section.

Oscillator Coils

The Q of the tank coil used in the oscillating portion of any of the circuits under discussion should be as high as circumstances (usually space) permit, since the losses, and therefore the heating, will be less. With recommended care in regard to other factors mentioned previously, most of the drift will originate in the coil. The coil should be well spaced from shielding and other large metal surfaces, and be of a type that radiates heat well, such as a commercial air-

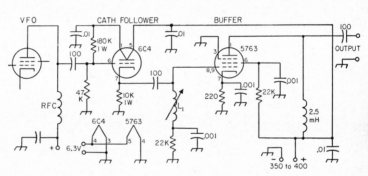

Fig. 6-6—Circuit of an isolating amplifier for use between v.f.o. and first tunable stage. All capacitances below 0.001 µf. are in µµf. All resistors are ½ watt. L_1, for the 3.5-Mc. band, consists of 93 turns No. 36 enam., 17/32 inch long, ½-inch diameter, close-wound on National XR-50 iron-slug form. Inductance 69 to 134 µh. All capacitors are disk ceramic.

wound type, or should be wound tightly on a threaded ceramic form so that the dimensions will not change readily with temperature. The wire with which the coil is wound should be as large as practicable, especially in the high-C circuits.

Mechanical Vibration

To eliminate mechanical vibration, components should be mounted securely. Particularly in the circuit of Fig. 6-5D, the capacitor should preferably have small, thick plates and the coil braced, if necessary, to prevent the slightest mechanical movement. Wire connections between tank-circuit components should be as short as possible and flexible wire will have less tendency to vibrate than solid wire. It is advisable to cushion the entire oscillator unit by mounting on sponge rubber or other shock mounting.

Tuning Characteristic

If the circuit is oscillating, touching the grid of the tube or any part of the circuit connected to it will show a change in plate current. In tuning the plate output circuit without load, the plate current will be relatively high until it is tuned near resonance where the plate current will dip to a low value, as illustrated in Fig. 6-4. When the output circuit is loaded, the dip should still be found, but broader and much less pronounced as indicated by the dashed line. The circuit should not be loaded beyond the point where the dip is still recognizable.

Checking V.F.O. Stability

A v.f.o. should be checked thoroughly before it is placed in regular operation on the air. Since succeeding amplifier stages may affect the signal characteristics, final tests should be made with the complete transmitter in operation. Almost any v.f.o. will show signals of good quality and stability when it is running free and not connected to a load. A well-isolated monitor is a necessity. Perhaps the most convenient, as well as one of the most satisfactory, well-shielded monitoring arrangements is a receiver combined with a crystal oscillator, as shown in Fig. 6-7. (See "Crystal Oscillators," this chapter.) The crystal frequency should lie in the band of the lowest frequency to be checked and in the frequency range where its harmonics will fall in the higher-frequency bands. The receiver b.f.o. is turned off and the v.f.o. signal is tuned to beat with the signal from the crystal oscillator instead. In this way any receiver instability caused by overloading of the input circuits, which may result in "pulling" of the h.f. oscillator in the receiver, or by a change in line voltage to the receiver when the transmitter is keyed, will not

affect the reliability of the check. Most crystals have a sufficiently low temperature coefficient to give a check on drift as well as on chirp and signal quality if they are not overloaded.

Harmonics of the crystal may be used to beat with the transmitter signal when monitoring at the higher frequencies. Since any chirp at the lower frequencies will be magnified at the higher frequencies, accurate checking can best be done by monitoring at a harmonic.

The distance between the crystal oscillator and receiver should be adjusted to give a good beat between the crystal oscillator and the transmitter signal. When using harmonics of the crystal oscillator, it may be necessary to attach a piece

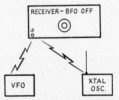

Fig. 6-7—Setup for checking v.f.o. stability. The receiver should be tuned preferably to a harmonic of the v.f.o. frequency. The crystal oscillator may operate somewhere in the band in which the v.f.o. is operating. The receiver b.f.o. should be turned off.

of wire to the oscillator as an antenna to give sufficient signal in the receiver. Checks may show that the stability is sufficiently good to permit oscillator keying at the lower frequencies, where break-in operation is of greater value, but that chirp becomes objectionable at the higher frequencies. If further improvement does not seem possible, it would be logical in this case to use oscillator keying at the lower frequencies and amplifier keying at the higher frequencies.

R.F. Power-Amplifier Tanks and Coupling

R.f. power amplifiers used in amateur transmitters usually are operated under Class C conditions (see chapter on vacuum-tube fundamentals). Fig. 6-10 shows a screen-grid tube with the required tuned tank in its plate circuit. Equivalent cathode connections for a filament-type tube are shown in Fig. 6-8 It is assumed that the tube is being properly driven and that the various electrode voltages are appropriate for Class C operation.

● PLATE TANK Q

The main objective, of course, is to deliver as much fundamental power as possible into a load, R, without exceeding the tube ratings. The load resistance R may be in the form of a transmission line to an antenna, or the grid circuit of another amplifier. A further objective is to minimize the harmonic energy (always generated by a Class C amplifier) fed into the load circuit. In attaining these objectives, the Q of the tank circuit is of importance. When a load is coupled inductively, as in Fig. 6-10, the Q of the tank circuit will have an effect on the coefficient of coupling nec-

essary for proper loading of the amplifier. In respect to all of these factors, a tank Q of 10 to 20 is usually considered optimum. A much lower Q will result in less efficient operation of the amplifier tube, greater harmonic output, and greater difficulty in coupling inductively to a load. A much higher Q will result in higher tank current with increased loss in the tank coil.

The Q is determined (see chapter on electrical laws and circuits) by the L/C ratio and the load resistance at which the tube is operated. The tube load resistance is related, in approximation, to

Fig. 6-8—Filament center-tap connections to be substituted in place of cathode connections shown in diagrams when filament-type tubes are substituted. T_1 is the filament transformer. Filament bypasses, C_1, should be 0.001-μf. disk ceramic capacitors. If a self-biasing (cathode) resistor is used, it should be placed between the center tap and ground.

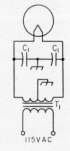

R.F. Amplifiers

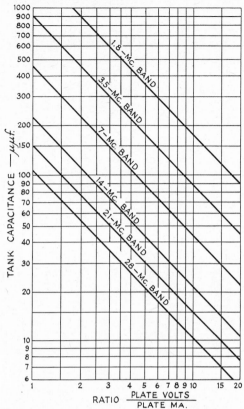

Fig. 6-9—Chart showing plate tank capacitance required for a Q of 10. Divide the tube plate voltage by the plate current in milliamperes. Select the vertical line corresponding to the answer obtained. Follow this vertical line to the diagonal line for the band in question, and thence horizontally to the left to read the capacitance. For a given ratio of plate-voltage/plate current, doubling the capacitance shown doubles the Q etc. When a split-stator capacitor is used in a balanced circuit, the capacitance of each section may be one half of the value given by the chart.

the ratio of the d.c. plate voltage to d.c. plate current at which the tube is operated.

The amount of C that will give a Q of 10 for various ratios is shown in Fig. 6-9. For a given plate-voltate/plate-current ratio, the Q will vary directly as the tank capacitance, twice the capacitance doubles the Q etc. For the same Q, the capacitance of *each section* of a split-stator capacitor in a balanced circuit should be half the value shown.

These values of capacitance include the output capacitance of the amplifier tube, the input capacitance of a following amplifier tube if it is coupled capacitively, and all other stray capacitances. At the higher plate-voltage/plate-current ratios, the chart may show values of capacitance, for the higher frequencies, smaller than those attainable in practice. In such a case, a tank Q higher than 10 is unavoidable.

In low-power exciter stages, where capacitive coupling is used, very low-Q circuits, tuned only by the tube and stray circuit capacitances are sometimes used for the purpose of "broadband-

ing" to avoid the necessity for retuning a stage across a band. Higher-order harmonics generated in such a stage can usually be attentuated in the tank circuit of the final amplifier.

● INDUCTIVE-LINK COUPLING

Coupling to Flat Coaxial Lines

When the load R in Fig. 6-10 is located for convenience at some distance from the amplifier, or when maximum harmonic reduction is desired, it is advisable to feed the power to the load through a low-impedance coaxial cable. The shielded construction of the cable prevents radiation and makes it possible to install the line in any convenient manner without danger of unwanted coupling to other circuits.

If the line is more than a small fraction of a wavelength long, the load resistance at its output end should be adjusted, by a matching circuit if necessary, to match the impedance of the cable. This reduces losses in the cable and makes the coupling adjustments at the transmitter independent of the cable length. Matching circuits for use between the cable and another transmission line are discussed in the chapter on transmission lines, while the matching adjustments when the load is the grid circuit of a following amplifier are described elsewhere in this chapter.

Assuming that the cable is properly terminated, proper loading of the amplifier will be assured, using the circuit of Fig. 6-11C, if

1) The plate tank circuit has reasonably high value of Q. A value of 10 is usually sufficient.

2) The inductance of the pick-up or link coil is close to the optimum value for the frequency and type of line used. The optimum coil is one whose self-inductance is such that its reactance at the operating frequency is equal to the charac-

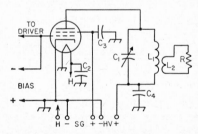

Fig. 6-10—Inductive-link output coupling circuits.

C_1—Plate tank capacitor—see text and Fig. 6-9 for capacitance, Fig. 6-33 for voltage rating.

C_2—Heater bypass—0.001-μf. disk ceramic.

C_3—Screen bypass—voltage rating depends on method of screen supply. See paragraphs on screen considerations. Voltage rating same as plate voltage will be safe under any condition.

C_4—Plate bypass—0.001-μf. disk ceramic or mica. Voltage rating same as C_1, plus safety factor.

L_1—To resonate at operating frequency with C_1. See LC chart and inductance formula in electrical-laws chapter, or use ARRL *Lightning Calculator*.

L_2—Reactance equal to line impedance. See reactance chart and inductance formula in electrical-laws section, or use ARRL *Lightning Calculator*.

R—Representing load.

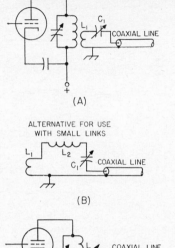

(A)

ALTERNATIVE FOR USE
WITH SMALL LINKS

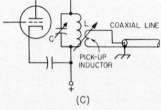

(B)

(C)

Fig. 6-11—With flat transmission lines power transfer is obtained with looser coupling if the line input is tuned to resonance. C_1 and L_1 should resonate at the operating frequency. See table for maximum usable value of C_1. If circuit does not resonate with maximum C_1 or less, inductance of L_1 must be increased, or added in series at L_2.

teristic impedance, Z_0, of the line.

3) It is possible to make the coupling between the tank and pick-up coils very tight.

The second in this list is often hard to meet. Few manufactured link coils have adequate inductance even for coupling to a 50-ohm line at low frequencies.

If the line is operating with a low s.w.r., the system shown in Fig. 6-11C will require tight coupling between the two coils. Since the secondary (pick-up coil) circuit is not resonant, the leakage reactance of the pick-up coil will cause some detuning of the amplifier tank circuit. This detuning effect increases with increasing coupling, but is usually not serious. However, the amplifier tuning must be adjusted to resonance, as indicated by the plate-current dip, each time the coupling is changed.

Tuned Coupling

The design difficulties of using "untuned" pick-up coils, mentioned above, can be avoided by using a coupling circuit tuned to the operating frequency. This contributes additional selectivity as well, and hence aids in the suppression of spurious radiations.

If the line is flat the input impedance will be essentially resistive and equal to the Z_0 of the line. With coaxial cable, a circuit of reasonable Q can be obtained with practicable values of inductance and capacitance connected in series with the line's input terminals. Suitable circuits are given in Fig. 6-11 at A and B. The Q of the coupling circuit often may be as low as 2, without running into difficulty in getting adequate coupling to a tank circuit of proper design. Larger values of Q can be used and will result in increased ease of coupling, but as the Q is increased the frequency range over which the circuit will operate without readjustment becomes smaller. It is usually good practice, therefore, to use a coupling-circuit Q just low enough to permit operation, over as much of a band as is normally used for a particular type of communication, without requiring retuning.

Capacitance values for a Q of 2 and line impedances of 52 and 75 ohms are given in the accompanying table. These are the *maximum* values that should be used. The inductance in the circuit should be adjusted to give resonance at the operating frequency. If the link coil used for a particular band does not have enough inductance to resonate, the additional inductance may be connected in series as shown in Fig. 6-11B.

Characteristics

In practice, the amount of inductance in the circuit should be chosen so that, with somewhat loose coupling between L_1 and the amplifier tank coil, the amplifier plate current will increase when the variable capacitor, C_1, is tuned through the value of capacitance given by the table. The coupling between the two coils should then be increased until the amplifier loads normally, without changing the setting of C_1. If the transmission line is flat over the entire frequency band under consideration, it should not be necessary to readjust C_1 when changing frequency, if the values given in the table are used. However, it is unlikely that the line actually will be flat over such a range, so some readjustment of C_1 may be needed to compensate for changes in the input impedance of the line. If the input impedance variations are not large, C_1 may be used as a loading control, no changes in the coupling between L_1 and the tank coil being necessary.

The degree of coupling between L_1 and the amplifier tank coil will depend on the coupling-circuit Q. With a Q of 2, the coupling should be tight — comparable with the coupling that is typical of "fixed-link" manufactured coils. With a swinging link it may be necessary to increase the Q of the coupling circuit in order to get sufficient power transfer. This can be done by increasing the L/C ratio.

Capacitance in $\mu\mu$f. Required for Coupling to Flat Coaxial Lines with Tuned Coupling Circuit		
Frequency Band Mc.	Characteristic Impedance of Line	
	52 ohms [1]	75 ohms [1]
1.8	900	600
3.5	450	300
7	230	150
14	115	75
28	60	40

[1] Capacitance values are maximum usable.

Note: Inductance in circuit must be adjusted to resonate at operating frequency.

Pi-Section Output Tanks

● PI-SECTION OUTPUT TANK

A pi-section tank circuit may also be used in coupling to an antenna or transmission line, as shown in Fig. 6-12. The values of capacitance for C_1 and C_2, and inductance for L_1 for any values of tube load resistance and output load resistance may be calculated from the formulas in the chapter on electrical laws.

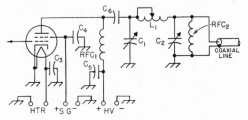

Fig. 6-12—Pi-section output tank circuit.

C_1—Input capacitor. See text or Fig. 6-13 for reactance. Voltage rating should be equal to d.c. plate voltage for c.w.; double this value for plate modulation.

C_2—Output capacitor. See text or Fig. 6-15 for reactance. See text for voltage rating.

C_3—Heater bypass—0.001-μf. disk ceramic.

C_4—Screen bypass. See Fig. 6-10.

C_5—Plate bypass. See Fig. 6-10.

C_6—Plate blocking capacitor—0.001-μf. disk ceramic or mica. Voltage rating same as C_1.

L_1—See text or Fig. 6-14 for reactance.

RFC_1—See later paragraph on r.f. chokes.

RFC_2—2.5-mh. receiving type (essential to reduce peak voltage across both input and output capacitors).

Values of reactance for C_1, L_1 and C_2 may be taken directly from the charts of Figs. 6-13, 6-14 and 6-15 if the output load resistance is 52 or 72 ohms. It should be borne in mind that these values apply only where the output load is resistive, i.e., where the antenna and line have been matched. The tube load resistance R_1 in ohms is determined by dividing the plate voltage by twice the d.c. plate current in decimal parts of an ampere.

Output-Capacitor Ratings

The voltage rating of the output capacitor will depend upon the s.w.r. If the load is resistive, receiving-type air capacitors should be adequate for amplifier input powers up to 1 kw. with plate modulation when feeding 52- or 72-ohm loads. In obtaining the larger capacitances required for the lower frequencies, it is common practice to switch fixed capacitors in parallel with the variable air capacitor. While the voltage rating of a mica or ceramic capacitor may not be exceeded in a particular case, capacitors of these types are limited in current-carrying capacity. Postage-stamp silver-mica capacitors should be adequate for amplifier inputs over the range from about 70 watts at 28 Mc. to 400 watts at 14 Mc. and lower. The larger mica capacitors (CM-45 case) having voltage ratings of 1200 and 2500 volts are usually satisfactory for inputs varying from about 350 watts at 28 Mc. to 1 kw. at 14 Mc. and lower. Because of these current limitations, particularly at the higher frequencies, it is ad-

PI-NETWORK DESIGN CHARTS FOR FEEDING 52- OR 72-OHM COAXIAL TRANSMISSION LINES

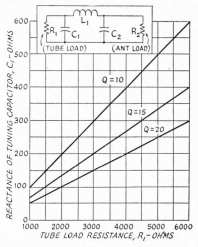

Fig. 6-13—Reactance of input capacitor, C_1, as a function of tube load resistance, R_1, for pi networks. R_1 equals plate voltage divided by twice plate current (amperes).

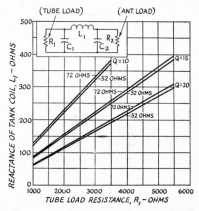

Fig. 6-14—Reactance of tank coil, L_1, as a function of load resistance. R_1, for pi networks.

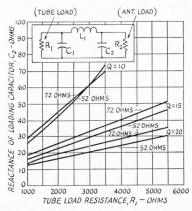

Fig. 6-15—Reactance of loading capacitor, C_2, as a function of tube load resistance, R_1, for pi networks.

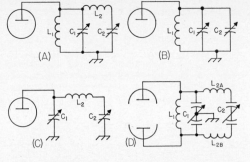

Fig. 6-16—Multiband tuner circuits. In the unbalanced circuit of A, C_1 and C_2 are sections of a single split-stator capacitor. In the balanced circuit of D, the two split-stator capacitors are ganged to a single control with an insulated shaft coupling between the two. In D, the two sections of L_2 are wound on the same form, with the inner ends connected to C_2. In A, each section of the capacitor should have a voltage rating the same as Fig. 6-33A. In D, C_1 should have a rating the same as Fig. 6-33H (or Fig. 6-33E if the feed system corresponds). C_2 may have the rating of Fig. 6-33E so long as the rotor is not grounded or bypassed to ground.

visable to use as large an air capacitor as practicable, using the micas only at the lower frequencies. Broadcast-receiver replacement-type capacitors can be obtained very reasonably. They are available in triple units totaling about 1100 $\mu\mu$f., or dual units totaling about 900 $\mu\mu$f. Their insulation should be sufficient for inputs of 500 watts or more. Air capacitors have the additional advantage that they are seldom permanently damaged by a voltage break-down.

Neutralizing with Pi Network

Screen-grid amplifiers using a pi-network output circuit may be neutralized by the system shown in Figs. 6-23B and C.

● MULTIBAND TANK CIRCUITS

Multiband tank circuits provide a convenient means of covering several bands without the need for changing coils. Tuners of this type consist essentially of two tank circuits, tuned simultaneously with a single control. In a tuner designed to cover 80 through 10 meters, each circuit has a sufficiently large capacitance variation to assure an approximately 2-to-1 frequency range. Thus, one circuit is designed so that it covers 3.5 through 7.3 Mc., while the other covers 14 through 29.7 Mc.

A single-ended, or unbalanced, circuit of this type is shown in Fig. 6-16A. In principle, the reactance of the high-frequency coil, L_2, is small enough at the lower frequencies so that it can be largely neglected, and C_1 and C_2 are in parallel across L_1. Then the circuit for low frequencies becomes that shown in Fig. 6-16B.

At the high frequencies, the reactance of L_1 is high, so that it may be considered simply as a choke shunting C_1. The high-frequency circuit is essentially that of Fig. 6-16C, L_2 being tuned by C_1 and C_2 in series.

In practice, the effect of one circuit on the other cannot be neglected entirely. L_2 tends to increase the effective capacitance of C_2, while L_1 tends to decrease the effective capacitance of C_1. This effect, however, is relatively small. Each circuit must cover somewhat more than a 2-to-1 frequency range to permit staggering the two ranges sufficiently to avoid simultaneous responses to a frequency in the low-frequency range, and one of its harmonics lying in the range of the high-frequency circuit.

In any circuit covering a frequency range as great as 2 to 1 by capacitance alone, the circuit Q must vary rather widely. If the circuit is designed for a Q of 12 at 80, the Q will be 6 at 40, 24 at 20, 18 at 15, and 12 at 10 meters. The increase in tank current as a result of the increase in Q toward the low-frequency end of the high-frequency range may make it necessary to design the high-frequency coil with care to minimize loss in this portion of the tuning range. It is generally found desirable to provide separate output coupling coils for each circuit.

Fig. 6-16D shows a similar tank for balanced circuits. The same principles apply.

Series or parallel feed may be used with either balanced or unbalanced circuits. In the balanced circuit of Fig. 6-16D, the series feed point would be at the center of L_1, with an r.f. choke in series.

(For further discussion see *QST*, July, 1954.)

R.F. Amplifier-Tube Operating Conditions

In addition to proper tank and output-coupling circuits discussed in the preceding sections, an r.f. amplifier must be provided with suitable electrode voltages and an r.f. driving or excitation voltage (see vacuum-tube chapter).

All r. f. amplifier tubes require a voltage to operate the filament or heater (a.c. is usually permissible), and a positive d.c. voltage between the plate and filament or cathode (plate voltage). Most tubes also require a negative d.c. voltage (biasing voltage) between control grid (Grid No. 1) and filament or cathode. Screen-grid

tubes require in addition a positive voltage (screen voltage or Grid No. 2 voltage) between screen and filament or cathode.

Biasing and plate voltages may be fed to the tube either in series with or in parallel with the associated r.f. tank circuit as discussed in the chapter on electrical laws and circuits.

It is important to remember that true plate, screen or biasing voltage is the voltage between the particular electrode and filament or cathode. Only when the cathode is directly grounded to the chassis may the electrode-to-chassis voltage be taken as the true voltage.

The required r.f. driving voltage is applied between grid and cathode.

Power Input and Plate Dissipation

Plate power input is the d.c. power input to the plate circuit (d.c. plate voltage × d.c. plate current. Screen power input likewise is the d.c. screen voltage × the d.c. screen current.

Plate dissipation is the difference between the r.f. power delivered by the tube to its loaded plate tank circuit and the d.c. plate power input. The screen, on the other hand, does not deliver any output power, and therefore its dissipation is the same as the screen power input.

● TRANSMITTING-TUBE RATINGS

Tube manufacturers specify the maximum values that should be applied to the tubes they produce. They also publish sets of typical operating values that should result in good efficiency and normal tube life.

Maximum values for all of the most popular transmitting tubes will be found in the tables of transmitting tubes in the last chapter. Also included are as many sets of typical operating values as space permits. However, it is recommended that the amateur secure a transmitting-tube manual from the manufacturer of the tube or tubes he plans to use.

CCS and ICAS Ratings

The same transmitting tube may have different ratings depending upon the manner in which the tube is to be operated, and the service in which it is to be used. These different ratings are based primarily upon the heat that the tube can safely dissipate. Some types of operation, such as with grid or screen modulation, are less efficient than others, meaning that the tube must dissipate more heat. Other types of operation, such as c.w. or single-sideband phone are intermittent in nature, resulting in less average heating than in other modes where there is a continuous power input to the tube during transmissions. There are also different ratings for tubes used in transmitters that are in almost constant use (CCS — Continuous Commercial Service), and for tubes that are to be used in transmitters that average only a few hours of daily operation (ICAS — Intermittent Commercial and Amateur Service). The latter are the ratings used by amateurs who wish to obtain maximum output with reasonable tube life.

Maximum Ratings

Maximum ratings, where they differ from the values given under typical operating values, are not normally of significance to the amateur except in special applications. No single maximum value should be used unless all other ratings can simultaneously be held within the maximum values. As an example, a tube may have a maximum plate-voltage rating of 2000, a maximum

plate-current rating of 300 ma., and a maximum plate-power-input rating of 400 watts. Therefore, if the maximum plate voltage of 2000 is used, the plate current should be limited to 200 ma. (instead of 300 ma.) to stay within the maximum power-input rating of 400 watts.

● SOURCES OF ELECTRODE VOLTAGES

Filament or Heater Voltage

The filament voltage for the indirectly heated cathode-type tubes found in low-power classifications may vary 10 per cent above or below rating without seriously reducing the life of the tube. But the voltage of the higher-power filament-type tubes should be held closely between the rated voltage as a minimum and 5 per cent above rating as a maximum. Make sure that the plate power drawn from the power line does not cause a drop in filament voltage below the proper value when plate power is applied.

Thoriated-type filaments lose emission when the tube is overloaded appreciably. If the overload has not been too prolonged, emission sometimes may be restored by operating the filament at rated voltage with all other voltages removed for a period of 10 minutes, or at 20 per cent above rated voltage for a few minutes.

Plate Voltage

D.c. plate voltage for the operation of r.f. amplifiers is most often obtained from a transformer-rectifier-filter system (see power-supply chapter) designed to deliver the required plate voltage at the required current. However, batteries or other d.c.-generating devices are sometimes used in certain types of operation (see portable-mobile chapter).

Bias and Tube Protection

Several methods of obtaining bias are shown in Fig. 6-17. In A, bias is obtained by the voltage drop across a resistor in the grid d.c. return circuit when rectified grid current flows. The proper value of resistance may be determined by dividing the required biasing voltage by the d.c. grid current at which the tube will be operated. Then, so long as the r.f. driving voltage is adjusted so that the d.c. grid current is the recommended value, the biasing voltage will be the proper value. The tube is biased only when excitation is applied, since the voltage drop across the resistor depends upon grid-current flow. When excitation is removed, the bias falls to zero. At zero bias most tubes draw power far in excess of the plate-dissipation rating. So it is advisable to make provision for protecting the tube when excitation fails by accident, or by intent as it does when a preceding stage in a c.w. transmitter is keyed.

If the maximum c.w. ratings shown in the tube tables are to be used, the input should be cut to zero when the key is open. Aside from this, it is not necessary that plate current be cut off completely but only to the point where the rated

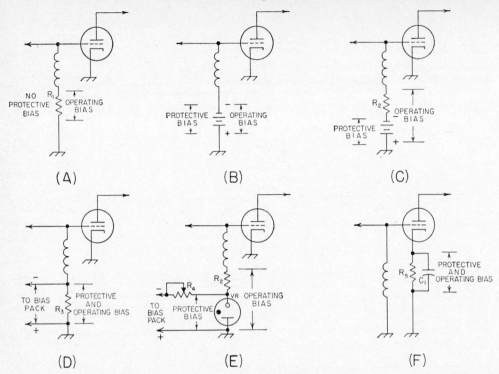

Fig. 6-17—Various systems for obtaining protective and operating bias for r.f. amplifiers. A—Grid-leak. B—Battery. C—Combination battery and grid leak. D—Grid leak and adjusted-voltage bias pack. E—Combination grid leak and voltage-regulated pack. F—Cathode bias.

dissipation is not exceeded. In this case plate-modulated phone ratings should be used for c.w. operation, however.

With triodes this protection can be supplied by obtaining all bias from a source of fixed voltage, as shown in Fig. 6-17B. It is preferable, however, to use only sufficient fixed bias to protect the tube and obtain the balance needed for operating bias from a grid leak, as in C. The grid-leak resistance is calculated as above, except that the fixed voltage is subtracted first.

Fixed bias may be obtained from dry batteries or from a power pack (see power-supply chapter). If dry batteries are used, they should be checked periodically, since even though they may show normal voltage, they eventually develop a high internal resistance. Grid-current flow through this battery resistance may increase the bias considerably above that anticipated. The life of batteries in bias service will be approximately the same as though they were subject to a drain equal to the grid current, despite the fact that the grid-current flow is in such a direction as to charge the battery, rather than to discharge it.

In Fig. 6-17F, bias is obtained from the voltage drop across a resistor in the cathode (or filament center-tap) lead. Protective bias is obtained by the voltage drop across R_5 as a result of plate (and screen) current flow. Since plate current must flow to obtain a voltage drop across the resistor, it is obvious that cut-off protective bias cannot be obtained. When excitation is ap-

plied, plate (and screen) current increases and the grid current also contributes to the drop across R_5, thereby increasing the bias to the operating value. Since the voltage between plate and cathode is reduced by the amount of the voltage drop across R_5, the over-all supply voltage must be the sum of the plate and operating-bias voltages. For this reason, the use of cathode bias usually is limited to low-voltage tubes when the extra voltage is not difficult to obtain.

The resistance of the cathode biasing resistor R_5 should be adjusted to the value which will give the correct operating bias voltage with rated grid, plate and screen currents flowing with the amplifier loaded to rated input. When excitation is removed, the input to most types of tubes will fall to a value that will prevent damage to the tube, at least for the period of time required to remove plate voltage. A disadvantage of this biasing system is that the cathode r.f. connection to ground depends upon a bypass capacitor. From the consideration of v.h.f. harmonics and stability with high-perveance tubes, it is preferable to make the cathode-to-ground impedance as close to zero as possible.

Screen Voltage

For c.w. operation, and under certain conditions of phone operation (see amplitude-modulation chapter), the screen may be operated from a power supply of the same type used for plate supply, except that voltage and current ratings

Bias and Tube Protection

should be appropriate for screen requirements. The screen may also be operated through a series resistor or voltage-divider from a source of higher voltage, such as the plate-voltage supply, thus making a separate supply for the screen unnecessary. Certain precautions are necessary, depending upon the method used.

It should be kept in mind that screen current varies widely with both excitation and loading. If the screen is operated from a fixed-voltage source, the tube should never be operated without plate voltage and load, otherwise the screen may be damaged within a short time. Supplying the screen through a series dropping resistor from a higher-voltage source, such as the plate supply, affords a measure of protection, since the resistor causes the screen voltage to drop as the current increases, thereby limiting the power drawn by the screen. However, with a resistor, the screen voltage may vary considerably with excitation, making it necessary to check the voltage at the screen terminal under actual operating conditions to make sure that the screen voltage is normal. Reducing excitation will cause the screen current to drop, increasing the voltage; increasing excitation will have the opposite effect. These changes are in addition to those caused by changes in bias and plate loading, so if a screen-grid tube is operated from a series resistor or a voltage divider, its voltage should be checked as one of the final adjustments after excitation and loading have been set.

An approximate value for the screen-voltage dropping resistor may be obtained by dividing the voltage *drop* required from the supply voltage (difference between the supply voltage and rated screen voltage) by the rated screen current in decimal parts of an ampere. Some further adjustment may be necessary, as mentioned above, so an adjustable resistor with a total resistance above that calculated should be provided.

Protecting Screen-Grid Tubes

Screen-grid tubes cannot be cut off with bias unless the screen is operated from a fixed-voltage supply. In this case the cut-off bias is approximately the screen voltage divided by the amplification factor of the screen. This figure is not always shown in tube-data sheets, but cut-off voltage may be determined from an inspection of tube curves, or by experiment.

When the screen is supplied from a series dropping resistor, the tube can be protected by the use of a clamper tube, as shown in Fig. 6-18. The grid-leak bias of the amplifier tube with excitation is supplied also to the grid of the clamper tube. This is usually sufficient to cut off the clamper tube. However, when excitation is removed, the clamper-tube bias falls to zero and it draws enough current through the screen dropping resistor usually to limit the input to the amplifier to a safe value. If complete screen-voltage cut-off is desired, a VR tube may be inserted in the screen lead as shown. The VR-tube voltage rating should be high enough so that it will extinguish when excitation is removed.

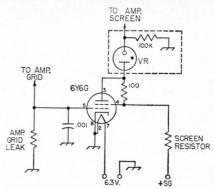

Fig. 6-18—Screen clamper circuit for protecting screen-grid power tubes. The VR tube is needed only for complete cut-off.

● FEEDING EXCITATION TO THE GRID

The required r.f. driving voltage is supplied by an oscillator generating a voltage at the desired frequency, either directly or through intermediate amplifiers or frequency multipliers.

As explained in the chapter on vacuum-tube fundamentals, the grid of an amplifier operating under Class C conditions must have an exciting voltage whose peak value exceeds the negative biasing voltage over a portion of the excitation cycle. During this portion of the cycle, current will flow in the grid-cathode circuit as it does in a diode circuit when the plate of the diode is positive in respect to the cathode. This requires that the r.f. driver supply power. The power required to develop the required peak driving voltage across the grid-cathode impedance of the amplifier is the r.f. driving power.

The tube tables give approximate figures for the grid driving power required for each tube under various operating conditions. These figures, however, do not include circuit losses. In general, the driver stage for any Class C amplifier should be capable of supplying at least three times the driving power shown for typical operating conditions at frequencies up to 30 Mc., and from three to ten times at higher frequencies.

Since the d.c. grid current relative to the biasing voltage is related to the peak driving voltage, the d.c. grid current is commonly used as a convenient indicator of driving conditions. A driver adjustment that results in rated d.c. grid current when the d.c. bias is at its rated value, indicates proper excitation to the amplifier when it is fully loaded.

In coupling the grid input circuit of an amplifier to the output circuit of a driving stage the objective is to load the driver plate circuit so that the desired amplifier grid excitation is obtained without exceeding the plate-input ratings of the driver tube.

Driving Impedance

The grid-current flow that results when the grid is driven positive in respect to the cathode

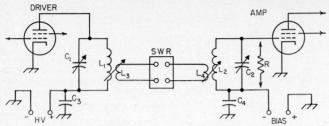

Fig. 6-19—Coupling excitation to the grid of an r.f. power amplifier by means of a low-impedance coaxial line.

C_1, C_3, L_1, L_3—See corresponding components in Fig. 6-10.

C_2—Amplifier grid tank capacitor—see text and Fig. 6-20 for capacitance, Fig. 6-34 for voltage rating.

C_4—0.-001-μf. disk ceramic.

L_2—To resonate at operating frequency with C_2. See LC chart inductance formula in electrical-laws chapter, or use ARRL *Lightning Calculator.*

L_4—Reactance equal to line impedance—see reactance chart and inductance formula in electrical-laws chapter, or use ARRL *Lightning Calculator.*

R is used to simulate grid impedance of the amplifier when a low-power s.w.r. indicator, such as a resistance bridge, is used. See formula in text for calculating value. Standing-wave indicator SWR is inserted only while line is made flat.

over a portion of the excitation cycle represents an average resistance across which the exciting voltage must be developed by the driver. In other words, this is the load resistance into which the driver plate circuit must be coupled. The approximate grid input resistance is given by:

$$Input\ impedance\ (ohms)$$
$$= \frac{driving\ power\ (watts)}{d.c.\ grid\ current\ (ma.)^2} \times 622 \times 10^3$$

For normal operation, the driving power and grid current may be taken from the tube tables.

Since the grid input resistance is a matter of a few thousand ohms, an impedance step-down is necessary if the grid is to be fed from a low-impedance transmission line. This can be done by the use of a tank as an impedance-transforming device in the grid circuit of the amplifier as shown in Fig. 6-19. This coupling system may be considered either as simply a means of obtaining mutual inductance between the two tank coils, or as a low-impedance transmission line. If the line is longer than a small fraction of a wave length, and if a s.w.r. bridge is available, the line is more easily handled by adjusting it as a matched transmission line.

Inductive Link Coupling with Flat Line

In adjusting this type of line, the object is to make the s.w.r. on the line as low as possible over as wide a band of frequencies as possible so that power can be transferred over this range without retuning. It is assumed that the output coupling considerations discussed earlier have been observed in connection with the driver plate circuit. So far as the amplifier grid circuit is concerned, the controlling factors are the Q of the tuned grid circuit, L_2C_2, (see Fig. 6-20) the inductance of the coupling coil, L_4, and the degree of coupling between L_2 and L_4. Variable coupling between the coils is convenient, but not strictly necessary if one or both of the other factors can be varied. An s.w.r. indicator (shown as "SWR" in the drawing) is essential. An indicator such as the "Micromatch" (a commercially available instrument) may be connected as shown and the adjustments made under actual operating

conditions; that is, with full power applied to the amplifier grid.

Assuming that the coupling is adjustable, start with a trial position of L_4 with respect to L_2, and adjust C_2 for the lowest s.w.r. Then change the coupling slightly and repeat. Continue until the s.w.r. is as low as possible; if the circuit constants are in the right region it should not be difficult to get the s.w.r. down to 1 to 1. The Q of the tuned grid circuit should be designed to be at least 10, and if it is not possible to get a very low s.w.r. with such a grid circuit the probable reason is that L_4 is too small. Maximum coupling, for a given degree of physi-

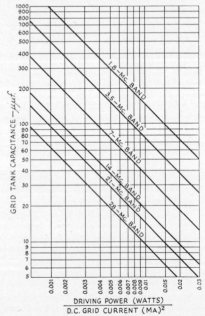

Fig. 6-20—Chart showing required grid tank capacitance for a Q of 12. To use, divide the driving power in watts by the square of the d.c. grid current in milliamperes and proceed as described under Fig. 6-9. Driving power and grid current may be taken from the tube tables. When a split-stator capacitor is used in a balanced grid circuit, the capacitance of *each* section may be half that shown.

Interstage Coupling

cal coupling, will occur when the inductance of L_4 is such that its reactance at the operating frequency is equal to the characteristic impedance of the link line. The reactance can be calculated as described in the chapter on electrical fundamentals if the inductance is known; the inductance can either be calculated from the formula in the same chapter or measured as described in the chapter on measurements.

Once the s.w.r. has been brought down to 1 to 1, the frequency should be shifted over the band so that the variation in s.w.r. can be observed, without changing C_2 or the coupling between L_2 and L_4. If the s.w.r. rises rapidly on either side of the original frequency the circuit can be made "flatter" by reducing the Q of the tuned grid circuit. This may be done by decreasing C_2 and correspondingly increasing L_2 to maintain resonance, and by tightening the coupling between L_2 and L_4, going through the same adjustment process again. It is possible to set up the system so that the s.w.r. will not exceed 1.5 to 1 over, for example, the entire 7-Mc. band and proportionately on other bands. Under these circumstances a single setting will serve for work anywhere in the band, with essentially constant power transfer from the line to the power-amplifier grids.

If the coupling between L_2 and L_4 is not adjustable the same result may be secured by varying the L/C ratio of the tuned grid circuit — that is, by varying its Q. If any difficulty is encountered it can be overcome by changing the number of turns in L_4 until a match is secured. The two coils should be tightly coupled.

When a resistance-bridge type s.w.r. indicator (see measuring-equipment section) is used it is not possible to put the full power through the line when making adjustments. In such case the operating conditions in the amplifier grid circuit can be simulated by using a *carbon resistor* ($\frac{1}{2}$ or 1 watt size) of the same value as the calculated amplifier grid impedance, connected as indicated by the arrows in Fig. 6-19. In this case the amplifier tube *must* be operated "cold" — without filament or heater power. The adjustment process is the same as described above, but with the driver power reduced to a value suitable for operating the s.w.r. bridge.

When the grid coupling system has been adjusted so that the s.w.r. is close to 1 to 1 over the desired frequency range, it is certain that the power put into the link line will be delivered to the grid circuit. Coupling will be facilitated if the line is tuned as described under the earlier section on output coupling systems.

Link Feed with Unmatched Line

When the system is to be treated without regard to transmission-line effects, the link line must not offer appreciable reactance at the operating frequency. Any appreciable reactance will in effect reduce the coupling, making it impossible to transfer sufficient power from the driver to the amplifier grid circuit. Coaxial cables especially have considerable capacitance for even short lengths and it may be more desirable to use a spaced line, such as Twin-Lead, if the radiation can be tolerated.

The reactance of the line can be nullified only by making the link resonant. This may require changing the number of turns in the link coils, the length of the line, or the insertion of a tuning capacitance. Since the s.w.r. on the link line may be quite high, the line losses increase because of the greater current, the voltage increase may be sufficient to cause a breakdown in the insulation of the cable and the added tuned circuit makes adjustment more critical with relatively small changes in frequency.

These troubles may not be encountered if the link line is kept very short for the highest frequency. A length of 5 feet or more may be tolerable at 3.5 Mc., but a length of a foot at 28 Mc. may be enough to cause serious effects on the functioning of the system.

Adjusting the coupling in such a system must necessarily be largely a matter of cut and try. If the line is short enough so as to have negligible reactance, the coupling between the two tank circuits will increase within limits by adding turns to the link coils, or by coupling the link coils more tightly, if possible, to the tank coils. If it is impossible to change either of these, a variable capacitor of 300 $\mu\mu$f. may be connected in series with or in parallel with the link coil at the driver end of the line, depending upon which connection is the most effective.

If coaxial line is used, the capacitor should be connected in series with the inner conductor. If the line is long enough to have appreciable reactance, the variable capacitor is used to resonate the entire link circuit.

As mentioned previously, the size of the link coils and the length of the line, as well as the size of the capacitor, will affect the resonant frequency and it may take an adjustment of all three before the capacitor will show a pronounced effect on the coupling.

When the system has been made resonant, coupling may be adjusted by varying the link capacitor.

Simple Capacitive Interstage Coupling

The capacitive system of Fig. 6-21A is the simplest of all coupling systems. (See Fig. 6-8 for filament-type tubes.) In this circuit, the plate tank circuit of the driver, C_1L_1, serves also as the grid tank of the amplifier. Although it is used more frequently than any other system, it is less flexible and has certain limitations that must be taken into consideration.

The two stages cannot be separated physically any appreciable distance without involving loss in transferred power, radiation from the coupling lead and the danger of feedback from this lead. Since both the output capacitance of the driver tube and the input capacitance of the amplifier are across the single circuit, it is sometimes difficult to obtain a tank circuit with a sufficiently low Q to provide an efficient circuit at the higher frequencies. The coupling can be varied by altering the capacitance of the coupling

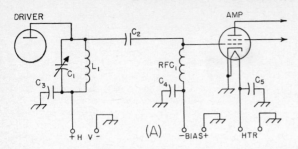

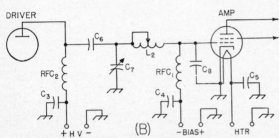

C_1—Driver plate tank capacitor—see text and Fig. 6-9 for capacitance, Fig. 6-33 for voltage rating.
C_2—Coupling capacitor—50 to 150 $\mu\mu$f. mica, as necessary for desired coupling. Voltage rating sum of driver plate and amplifier biasing voltages, plus safety factor.
C_3—Driver plate bypass capacitor—0.001-μf. disk ceramic or mica. Voltage rating same as plate voltage.
C_4—Grid bypass—0.001-μf. disk ceramic.
C_5—Heater bypass—0.001-μf. disk ceramic.
C_6—Driver plate blocking capacitor—0.001-μf. disk ceramic or mica. Voltage rating same as C_2.
C_7—Pi-section input capacitor—see text referring to Fig. 6-12 for capacitance. Voltage rating—see Fig. 6-33A.
C_8—Pi-section output capacitor—100-$\mu\mu$f. mica. Voltage rating same as driver plate voltage plus safety factor.
L_1—To resonate at operating frequency with C_1. See LC chart and inductance formula in electrical-laws chapter, or use ARRL *Lightning Calculator*.
L_2—Pi-section inductor—See Fig. 6-12. Approx. same as L_1.
RFC_1—Grid r.f. choke—2.5-mh.
RFC_2—Driver plate r.f. choke—2.5 mh.

capacitor, C_2. The driver load impedance is the sum of the amplifier grid resistance and the reactance of the coupling capacitor in series, the coupling capacitor serving simply as a series reactor. The driver load resistance increases with a decrease in the capacitance of the coupling capacitor.

When the amplifier grid impedance is lower than the optimum load resistance for the driver, a transforming action is possible by tapping the grid down on the tank coil, but this is not recommended because it invariably causes an increase in v.h.f. harmonics and sometimes sets up a parasitic circuit.

So far as coupling is concerned, the Q of the circuit is of little significance. However, the other considerations discussed earlier in connection with tank-circuit Q should be observed.

Pi-Network Interstage Coupling

A pi-section tank circuit, as shown in Fig. 6-21B, may be used as a coupling device between screen-grid amplifier stages. The circuit is actually a capacitive coupling arrangement with the grid of the amplifier tapped down on the circuit by means of a capacitive divider. In contrast to the tapped-coil method mentioned previously, this system will be very effective in reducing

v.h.f. harmonics, because the output capacitor, C_8, provides a direct capacitive shunt for harmonics across the amplifier grid circuit.

To be most effective in reducing v.h.f. harmonics, C_8 should be a mica capacitor connected directly across the tube-socket terminals. Tapping down on the circuit in this manner also helps to stabilize the amplifier at the operating frequency because of the grid-circuit loading provided by C_8. For the purposes both of stability and harmonic reduction, experience has shown that a value of 100 $\mu\mu$f for C_8 usually is sufficient. In general, C_7 and L_2 should have values approximating the capacitance and inductance used in a conventional tank circuit. A reduction in the inductance of L_2 results in an increase in coupling because C_7 must be increased to retune the circuit to resonance. This changes the ratio of C_7 to C_8 and has the effect of moving the grid tap up on the circuit. Since the coupling to the grid is comparatively loose under any condition, it may be found that it is impossible to utilize the full power capability of the driver stage. If sufficient excitation cannot be obtained, it may be necessary to raise the plate voltage of the driver, if this is permissible. Otherwise a larger driver tube may be required. As shown in Fig. 6-21B, parallel driver plate feed and amplifier grid feed are necessary.

Stabilizing Amplifiers

STABILIZING AMPLIFIERS

External Coupling

A straight amplifier operates with its input and output circuits tuned to the same frequency. Therefore, unless the coupling between these two circuits is brought to the necessary minimum, the amplifier will oscillate as a tuned-plate tuned-grid circuit. Care should be used in arranging components and wiring of the two circuits so that there will be negligible opportunity for coupling external to the tube itself. Complete shielding between input and output circuits usually is required. All r.f. leads should be kept as short as possible and particular attention should be paid to the r.f. return paths from plate and grid tank circuits to cathode. In general, the best arrangement is one in which the cathode (or filament center tap) connection to ground, and the plate tank circuit are on the same side of the chassis or other shielding. Then the "hot" lead from the grid tank (or driver plate tank) should be brought to the socket through a hole in the shielding. Then when the grid tank capacitor or bypass is grounded, a return path through the hole to cathode will be encouraged, since transmission-line characteristics are simulated.

A check on external coupling between input and output circuits can be made with a sensitive indicating device, such as the one diagrammed in Fig. 6-22. The amplifier tube is removed from its socket and if the plate terminal is

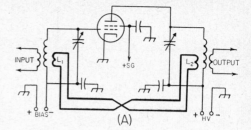

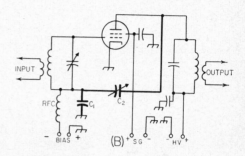

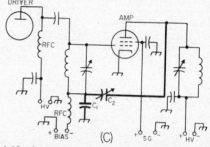

Fig. 6-23—Screen-grid neutralizing circuits. A—Inductive neutralizing. B–C—Capacitive neutralizing.

C_1—Grid bypass capacitor—approx. 0.001-μf. mica. Voltage rating same as biasing voltage in B, same as driver plate voltage in C.

C_2—Neutralizing capacitor—approx. 2 to 10 $\mu\mu$f.—see text. Voltage rating same as amplifier plate voltage for c.w., twice this value for plate modulation.

L_1, L_2—Neutralizing link—usually a turn or two will be sufficient.

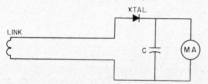

Fig. 6-22—Circuit of sensitive neutralizing indicator. *Xtal* is a 1N34 crystal detector, MA a 0–1 direct-current milliammeter and C a 0.001-μf. mica bypass capacitor.

at the socket, it should be disconnected. With the driver stage running and tuned to resonance, the indicator should be coupled to the output tank coil and the output tank capacitor tuned for any indication of r.f. feedthrough. Experiment with shielding and rearrangement of parts will show whether the isolation can be improved.

Screen-Grid Neutralizing Circuits

The plate-grid capacitance of screen-grid tubes is reduced to a fraction of a micromicrofarad by the interposed grounded screen. Nevertheless, the power sensitivity of these tubes is so great that only a very small amount of feedback is necessary to start oscillation. To assure a stable amplifier, it is usually necessary to load the grid circuit, or to use a neutralizing circuit. A neutralizing circuit is one external to the tube that balances the voltage fed back through the grid-plate capacitance, by another voltage of opposite phase.

Fig. 6-23A shows how a screen-grid amplifier may be neutralized by the use of an inductive link line coupling the input and output

tank circuits in proper phase. The two coils must be properly polarized. If the initial connection proves to be incorrect, connections to one of the link coils should be reversed. Neutralizing is adjusted by changing the distance between the link coils and the tank coils. In the case of capacitive coupling between stages, one of the link coils will be coupled to the plate tank coil of the driver stage.

A capacitive neutralizing system for screen-grid tubes is shown in Fig. 6-23B. C_2 is the neutralizing capacitor. The capacitance should be chosen so that at some adjustment of C_2,

$$\frac{C_2}{C_1} = \frac{Tube\ grid\text{-}plate\ capacitance\ (or\ C_{gp})}{Tube\ input\ capacitance\ (or\ C_{IN})}$$

The tube interelectrode capacitances C_{gp} and C_{IN} are given in the tube tables in the last chapter. The grid-cathode capacitance must include all strays directly across the tube capacitance, including the capacitance of the tuning-capacitor stator to ground. This may amount to 5 to 20 $\mu\mu$f. In the case of capacitance coupling, as shown in Fig. 6-23C, the output capacitance of the driver tube must be added to the grid-cathode capacitance of the amplifier in arriving at the value of C_2. If C_2 works out to an impractically large or small value, C_1 can be changed to compensate by using combinations of fixed mica capacitors in parallel.

Neutralizing Adjustment

The procedure in neutralizing is essentially the same for all types of tubes and circuits. The filament of the amplifier tube should be lighted and excitation from the preceding stage fed to the grid circuit. Both screen and plate voltages should be disconnected at the transmitter terminals.

The immediate objective of the neutralizing process is reducing to a minimum the r.f. driver voltage fed from the input of the amplifier to its output circuit through the grid-plate capacitance of the tube. This is done by adjusting carefully, bit by bit, the neutralizing capacitor or link coils until an r.f. indicator in the output circuit reads minimum.

The device shown in Fig. 6-22 makes a sensitive neutralizing indicator. The link should be coupled to the output tank coil at the low-potential or "ground" point. Care should be taken to make sure that the coupling is loose enough at all times to prevent burning out the meter or the rectifier. The plate tank capacitor should be readjusted for maximum reading after each change in neutralizing.

The grid-current meter may also be used as a neutralizing indicator. With plate and screen voltages removed as described above, there will be a change in grid current as the plate tank circuit is tuned through resonance. The neutralizing capacitor should be adjusted until this deflection is brought to a minimum. As a final adjustment, plate and screen voltages should be applied and the neutralizing capacitance adjusted to the point where minimum plate current, maximum grid current and maximum screen current occur simultaneously. An increase in grid current when the plate tank circuit is tuned slightly on the high-frequency side of resonance indicates that the neutralizing capacitance is too small. If the increase is on the low-frequency side, the neutralizing capacitance is too large. When neutralization is complete, there should be a slight decrease in grid current on either side of resonance.

Grid Loading

The use of a neutralizing circuit may often be avoided by loading the grid circuit if the driving stage has some power capability to spare. Loading by tapping the grid down on the grid tank coil (or the plate tank coil of the driver in the case of capacitive coupling), or by a resistor from grid to cathode is effective in stabilizing an amplifier, but either device may increase v.h.f.

harmonics. The best loading system is the use of a pi-section filter, as shown in Fig. 6-21B. This circuit places a capacitance directly between grid and cathode. This not only provides the desirable loading, but also a very effective capacitive short for v.h.f. harmonics. A 100-$\mu\mu$f. mica capacitor for C_8, wired directly between tube terminals will usually provide sufficient loading to stabilize the amplifier.

V.H.F. Parasitic Oscillation

Parasitic oscillation in the v.h.f. range will take place in almost every r.f. power amplifier. To test for v.h.f. parasitic oscillation, the grid tank coil (or driver tank coil in the case of capacitive coupling) should be short-circuited with a clip lead. This is to prevent any possible t.g.t.p. oscillation at the operating frequency which might lead to confusion in identifying the parasitic. Any fixed bias should be replaced with a grid leak of 10,000 to 20,000 ohms. All load on the output of the amplifier should be disconnected. Plate and screen voltages should be reduced to the point where the rated dissipation is not exceeded. If a Variac is not available, voltage may be reduced by a 115-volt lamp in series with the primary of the plate transformer.

With power applied only to the amplifier under test, a search should be made by adjusting input capacitor to several settings, including minimum and maximum, and turning the plate capacitor through its range for each of the grid-capacitor settings. Any grid current, or any dip or flicker in plate current at any point, indicates oscillation. This can be confirmed by an indicating absorption wavemeter tuned to the frequency of the parasitic and held close to the plate lead of the tube.

The heavy lines of Fig. 6-24A show the usual parasitic tank circuit, which resonates, in most cases, between 150 and 200 Mc. For each type of tetrode, there is a region, usually below the parasitic frequency, in which the tube will be self-neutralized. By adding the right amount of inductance to the parasitic circuit, its resonant frequency can be brought down to the frequency

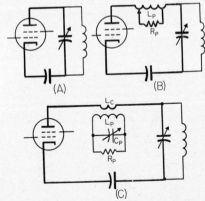

Fig. 6-24—A—Usual parasitic circuit. B—Resistive loading of parasitic circuit. C—Inductive coupling of loading resistance into parasitic circuit.

Parasitics

at which the tube is self-neutralized. However, the resonant frequency should not be brought down so low that it falls close to TV Channel 6 (88 Mc.). From the consideration of TVI, the circuit may be loaded down to a frequency not lower than 100 Mc. If the self-neutralizing frequency is below 100 Mc., the circuit should be loaded down to somewhere between 100 and 120 Mc. with inductance. Then the parasitic can be suppressed by loading with resistance, as shown in Fig. 6-24B. A coil of 4 or 5 turns, $\frac{1}{4}$ inch in diameter, is a good starting size. With the tank capacitor turned to maximum capacitance, the circuit should be checked with a g.d.o. to make sure the resonance is above 100 Mc. Then, with the shortest possible leads, a noninductive 100-ohm 1-watt resistor should be connected across the entire coil. The amplifier should be tuned up to its highest-frequency band and operated at low voltage. The tap should be moved a little at a time to find the minimum number of turns required to suppress the parasitic. Then voltage should be increased until the resistor begins to feel warm after several minutes of operation, and the power input noted. This input should be compared with the normal input and the *power* rating of the resistor increased by this proportion; i.e., if the power is half normal, the wattage rating should be doubled. This increase is best made by connecting 1-watt *carbon* resistors in parallel to give a resultant of about 100 ohms. As power input is increased, the parasitic may start up again, so power should be applied only momentarily until it is made certain that the parasitic is still suppressed. If the parasitic starts up again when voltage is raised, the tap must be moved to include more turns. So long as the parasitic is suppressed, the resistors will heat up only from the operating-frequency current.

Since the resistor can be placed across only that portion of the parasitic circuit represented by L_p, the latter should form as large a portion of the circuit as possible. Therefore, the tank and bypass capacitors should have the lowest possible inductance and the leads shown in heavy lines should be as short as possible and of the heaviest practical conductor. This will permit L_p to be of maximum size without tuning the circuit below the 100-Mc. limit.

Another arrangement that has been used successfully is shown in Fig. 6-24C. A small turn or two is inserted in place of L_p and this is coupled to a circuit tuned to the parasitic frequency and loaded with resistance. The heavy-line circuit should first be checked with a g.d.o. Then the loaded circuit should be tuned to the same frequency and coupled in to the point where the parasitic ceases. The two coils can be wound on the same form and the coupling varied by sliding one of them. Slight retuning of the loaded circuit may be required after coupling. Start out with low power as before, until the parasitic is suppressed. Since the loaded circuit in this case carries much less operating-frequency current, a single 100-ohm 1-watt resistor will often be sufficient and a 30-$\mu\mu$f. mica trimmer should serve as the tuning capacitor, C_p.

Low-Frequency Parasitic Oscillation

The screening of most transmitting screen-grid tubes is sufficient to prevent low-frequency parasitic oscillation caused by resonant circuits set up by r.f. chokes in grid and plate circuits. Should this type of oscillation (usually between 1200 and 200 kc.) occur, see paragraph under triode amplifiers.

● PARALLEL-TUBE AMPLIFIERS

The circuits for parallel-tube amplifiers are the same as for a single tube, similar terminals of the tubes being connected together. The grid impedance of two tubes in parallel is half that of a single tube. This means that twice the grid tank capacitance shown in Fig. 6-20 should be used for the same Q.

The plate load resistance is halved so that the plate tank capacitance for a single tube (Fig. 6-10) also should be doubled. The total grid current will be doubled, so to maintain the same grid bias, the grid-leak resistance should be half that used for a single tube. The required driving power is doubled. The capacitance of a neutralizing capacitor, if used, should be doubled and the value of the screen dropping resistor should be cut in half.

In treating parasitic oscillation, it may be necessary to use a choke in each plate lead, rather than one in the common lead. Input and output capacitances are doubled, which may be a factor in obtaining efficient operation at higher frequencies.

● PUSH-PULL AMPLIFIERS

Basic push-pull circuits are shown in Fig. 6-26C and D. Amplifiers using this circuit are cumbersome to bandswitch and consequently are not very popular below 30 Mc. However, since the push-pull configuration places tube input and output capacitances in series, the circuit is widely used at 50 Mc. and higher.

● TRIODE AMPLIFIERS

Circuits for triode amplifiers are shown in Fig. 6-26. Neglecting references to the screen, all of the foregoing information applies equally well to triodes. All triode straight amplifiers must be neutralized, as Fig. 6-26 indicates. From the tube tables, it will be seen that triodes require considerably more driving power than screen-grid tubes. However, they also have less power sensitivity, so that greater feedback can be tolerated without the danger of instability.

Low-Frequency Parasitic Oscillation

When r.f. chokes are used in both grid and plate circuits of a triode amplifier, the split-stator tank capacitors combine with the r.f. chokes to form a low-frequency parasitic circuit, unless the amplifier circuit is arranged to prevent it. In the circuit of Fig. 6-26B, the amplifier grid

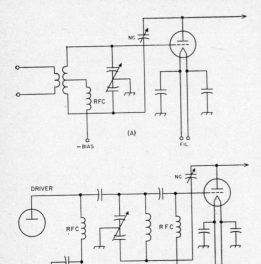

is series fed and the driver plate is parallel fed. For low frequencies, the r.f. choke in the driver plate circuit is shorted to ground through the tank coil. In Figs. 6-26C and D, a resistor is substituted for the grid r.f. choke. This resistance should be at least 100 ohms. If any grid-leak resistance is used for biasing, it should be substituted for the 100-ohm resistor.

Triode Amplifiers with Pi-Network Output

Pi-network output tanks, designed as described earlier for screen-grid tubes, may also be used with triodes. However, in this case, a balanced input circuit must be provided for neutralizing. Fig. 6-25A shows the circuit when inductive-link input coupling is used, while B shows the circuit to be used when the amplifier is coupled capacitively to the driver. Pi-network circuits cannot be used in *both* input and output circuits, since no means is provided for neutralizing.

Fig. 6-25—When a pi-network output circuit is used with a triode, a balanced grid circuit must be provided for neutralizing. A—Inductive-link input. B—Capacitive input coupling.

● GROUNDED-GRID AMPLIFIERS

Fig. 6-27A shows the input circuit of a grounded-grid triode amplifier. In configuration it is similar to the conventional grounded-cathode circuit except that the grid, instead of the cathode, is at ground potential. An amplifier of this type is characterized by a comparatively low input im-

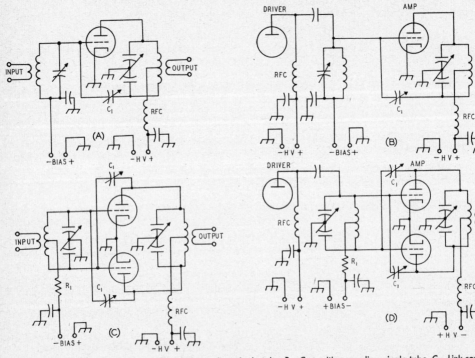

Fig. 6-26—Triode amplifier circuits. A—Link coupling, single tube. B—Capacitive coupling, single tube. C—Link coupling, push-pull. D—Capacitive coupling, push-pull. Aside from the neutralizing circuits, which are mandatory with triodes, the circuits are the same as for screen-grid tubes, and should have the same values throughout. The neutralizing capacitor, C_1, should have a capacitance somewhat greater than the grid-plate capacitance of the tube. Voltage rating should be twice the d.c. plate voltage for c.w., or four times for plate modulation, plus safety factor. The resistance R_1 should be at least 100 ohms and it may consist of part or preferably all of the grid leak. For other component values, see similar screen-grid diagrams.

Grounded-Grid Amplifiers

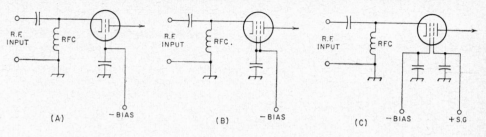

Fig. 6-27—A—Grounded-grid triode input circuit. B—Tetrode input circuit with grid and screen directly in parallel. C—Tetrode circuit with d.c. voltage applied to the screen. Plate circuits are conventional.

pedance and a relatively high driver-power requirement. The additional driver power is not consumed in the amplifier but is "fed through" to the plate circuit where it combines with the normal plate output power. The total r.f. power output is the sum of the driver and amplifier output powers less the power normally required to drive the tube in a grounded-cathode circuit.

Positive feedback is from plate to cathode through the plate-cathode, or plate-filament, capacitance of the tube. Since the grounded grid is interposed between the plate and cathode, this capacitance is very small, and neutralization usually is not necessary.

A disadvantage of the grounded-grid circuit is that the cathode must be isolated for r.f. from ground. This presents a practical difficulty, especially in the case of a filament-type tube whose filament current is large. Another disadvantage in plate-modulated phone operation is that the driver power fed through to the output is not modulated.

The chief application for grounded-grid amplifiers in amateur work at frequencies below 30 Mc. is in the case where the available driving power far exceeds the power that can be used in driving a conventional grounded-cathode amplifier.

D.c. electrode voltages and currents in grounded-grid triode-amplifier operation are the same as for grounded-cathode operation. Approximate values of driving power, driving impedance, and total power output in Class C operation can be calculated as follows, using information normally provided in tube data sheets. R.m.s. values are of the fundamental components:

E_p = r.m.s. value of r.f. plate voltage

$$= \frac{d.c.\ plate\ volts + d.c.\ bias\ volts - peak\ r.f.\ grid\ volts}{1.41}$$

I_p = r.m.s. value of r.f. plate current

$$= \frac{rated\ power\ output\ watts}{E_p}$$

E_g = r.m.s. value of grid driving voltage

$$= \frac{peak\ r.f.\ grid\ volts}{1.41}$$

I_g = r.m.s. value of r.f. grid current

$$= \frac{rated\ driving\ power\ watts}{E_g}$$

Then,

$$Driving\ power\ (watts) = E_g\ (I_p + I_g)$$

$$Driving\ impedance\ (ohms) = \frac{E_g}{I_g + I_p}$$

$$Power\ fed\ through\ from\ driver\ stage\ (watts) = E_g I_p$$

$$Total\ power\ output\ (watts) = I_p\ (E_g + E_p)$$

Screen-grid tubes are also used sometimes in grounded-grid amplifiers. In some cases, the screen is simply connected in parallel with the grid, as in Fig. 6-27B, and the tube operates as a high-μ triode. In other cases, the screen is by-passed to ground and operated at the usual d.c. potential, as shown at C. Since the screen is still in parallel with the grid for r.f., operation is very much like that of a triode except that the positive voltage on the screen reduces driver-power requirements. Since the information usually furnished in tube-data sheets does not apply to triode-type operation, operating conditions are usually determined experimentally. In general, the bias is adjusted to produce maximum output (within the tube's dissipation rating) with the driving power available.

Fig. 6-28 shows two methods of coupling a grounded-grid amplifier to the 50-ohm output of an existing transmitter. At A an L network is used, while a conventional link-coupled tank is shown at B. The values shown will be approximately correct for most triode amplifiers operating at 3.5 Mc. Values should be cut in half each time frequency is doubled, i.e., 250 μμf. and 7.5 μh. for 7 Mc., etc.

Filament Isolation

Since the filament or cathode of the grounded-grid amplifier tube operates at some r.f. potential above ground, it is necessary to isolate the filament from the power line. In the case of low-power tubes with indirectly heated cathodes, it is sometimes feasible to depend on the small capacitance existing between the heater and cathode, although it is preferable to provide additional isolation.

In Fig. 6-29, isolation is provided by a special low-capacitance filament transformer. RFC_1 carries only the cathode current. However, since transformers of this type are not generally avail-

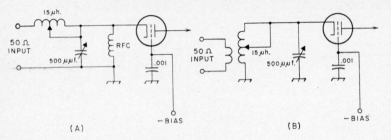

Fig. 6-28 — Two methods of coupling a low-impedance driver to a grounded-grid input. A—L network. B—Link-coupled tank circuit.

able, other means must usually be employed.

In Fig. 6-29B, chokes are used to isolate the filament from the filament transformer. The reactance of the chokes should be several times the input impedance of the amplifier and must be wound with conductor of sufficient size to carry the filament current. It is usually necessary to use a transformer delivering more than the rated filament voltage to compensate the voltage drop across the chokes. In Fig. 6-29C, r.f. chokes are placed in the primary side of the transformer. This reduces the current that the chokes must handle, but the filament transformer must be mounted so that it is spaced from the chassis and other grounded metal to minimize the capacitance of the transformer to ground. RFC_1 carries cathode current only.

In the case of the input circuit of Fig. 6-28B, it is sometimes feasible to wind the tank inductor with two conductors in parallel, and feed the filament voltage to the tube through the two conductors, as shown in Fig. 6-29D. This arrangement does not lend itself well to bandchanging, however.

● FREQUENCY MULTIPLIERS

Single-Tube Multiplier

Output at a multiple of the frequency at which it is being driven may be obtained from an amplifier stage if the output circuit is tuned to a harmonic of the exciting frequency instead of to the fundamental. Thus, when the frequency at the grid is 3.5 Mc., output at 7 Mc., 10.5 Mc., 14 Mc., etc., may be obtained by tuning the plate tank circuit to one of these frequencies. The circuit otherwise remains the same as that for a straight amplifier, although some of the values and operating conditions may require change for maximum multiplier efficiency.

Efficiency in a single- or parallel-tube multiplier comparable with the efficiency obtainable when operating the same tube as a straight amplifier involves decreasing the operating angle in proportion to the increase in the order of frequency multiplication. Obtaining output comparable with that possible from the same tube as a straight amplifier involves greatly increasing the plate voltage. A practical limit as to efficiency and output within normal tube

Fig. 6-29—Methods of isolating filament from ground. A—Special low-capacitance filament transformer. B—R.f. chokes in filament circuit. C—R.f. chokes in transformer primary. D—Filament fed through input tank inductor.

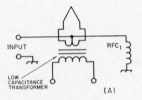

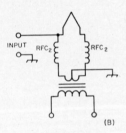

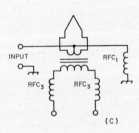

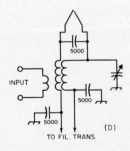

Frequency Multipliers

ratings is reached when the multiplier is operated at maximum permissible plate voltage and maximum permissible grid current. The plate current should be reduced as necessary to limit the dissipation to the rated value by increasing the bias. High efficiency in multipliers is not often required in practice, since the purpose is usually served if the frequency multiplication is obtained without an appreciable gain in power in the stage.

Multiplications of four or five sometimes are used to reach the bands above 28 Mc. from a lower-frequency crystal, but in the majority of lower-frequency transmitters, multiplication in a single stage is limited to a factor of two or three, because of the rapid decline in practicably obtainable efficiency as the multiplication factor is increased. Screen-grid tubes make the best frequency multipliers because their high power-sensitivity makes them easier to drive properly than triodes.

Since the input and output circuits are not tuned close to the same frequency, neutralization usually will not be required. Instances may be encountered with tubes of high transconductance, however, when a doubler will oscillate in t.g.t.p. fashion, requiring neutralization. The link neutralizing system of Fig. 6-23A is convenient in such a contingency.

Push-Push Multipliers

A two-tube circuit which works well at even harmonics, but not at the fundamental or odd harmonics, is shown in Fig. 6-30. It is known as

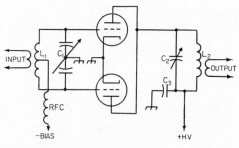

Fig. 6-30—Circuit of a push-push frequency multiplier for even harmonics.

C_1L_1 and C_2L_2—See text.

C_3—Plate bypass—0.001-μf. disk ceramic or mica. Voltage rating equal to plate voltage plus safety factor.

RFC—2.5-mh. r.f. choke.

the push-push circuit. The grids are connected in push-pull while the plates are connected in parallel. The efficiency of a doubler using this circuit may approach that of a straight amplifier, because there is a plate-current pulse for each cycle of the output frequency.

This arrangement has an advantage in some applications. If the heater of one tube is turned off, its grid-plate capacitance, being the same as that of the remaining tube, serves to neutralize the circuit. Thus provision is made for either straight amplification at the fundamental with a single tube, or doubling frequency with two tubes as desired.

The grid tank circuit is tuned to the frequency of the driving stage and should have the same constants as indicated in Fig. 6-20 for balanced grid circuits. The plate tank circuit is tuned to an even multiple of the exciting frequency, and should have the same values as a straight amplifier for the harmonic frequency (see Fig. 6-10), bearing in mind that the total plate current of both tubes determines the C to be used.

Push-Pull Multiplier

A single- or parallel-tube multiplier will deliver output at either even or odd multiples of the exciting frequency. A push-pull multiplier does not work satisfactorily at even multiples because even harmonics are largely canceled in the output. On the other hand, amplifiers of this type work well as triplers or at other odd harmonics. The operating requirements are similar to those for single-tube multipliers, the plate tank circuit being tuned, of course, to the desired odd harmonic frequency.

● METERING

Fig. 6-31 shows how a voltmeter and milliammeter should be connected to read various voltages and currents. Voltmeters are seldom installed permanently, since their principal use is in preliminary checking. Also, milliammeters are not normally installed permanently in all of the positions shown. Those most often used are the ones reading grid current and plate current, or grid current and cathode current.

Milliammeters come in various current ranges. Current values to be expected can be taken from the tube tables and the meter ranges selected accordingly. To take care of normal overloads and pointer swing, a meter having a current range of about twice the normal current to be expected should be selected.

Meter Installation

Grid-current meters connected as shown in Fig. 6-31 and meters connected in the cathode circuit need no special precautions in mounting on the transmitter panel so far as safety is concerned. However, milliammeters having zero-adjusting screws on the face of the meter should be recessed behind the panel so that accidental contact with the adjusting screw is not possible, if the meter is connected in any of the other positions shown in Fig. 6-31. The meter can be mounted on a small subpanel attached to the front panel with long screws and spacers. The meter opening should be covered with glass or celluloid. Illuminated meters make reading easier. Reference should also be made to the TVI chapter of this *Handbook* in regard to wiring and shielding of meters to suppress TVI.

Meter Switching

Milliammeters are expensive items and there-

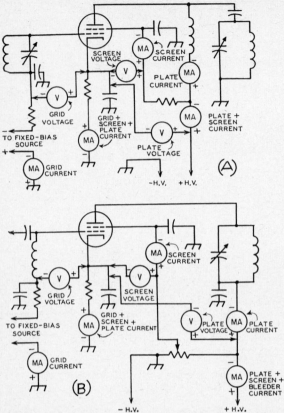

Fig. 6-31—Diagrams showing placement of voltmeter and milliammeter to obtain desired measurements. A—Series grid feed, parallel plate feed and series screen voltage-dropping resistor. B—Parallel grid feed, series plate feed and screen voltage divider.

● AMPLIFIER ADJUSTMENT

Earlier sections in this chapter have dealt with the design and adjustment of input (grid) and output (plate) coupling systems, the stabilitization of amplifiers, and the methods of obtaining the required electrode voltages. Reference to these sections should be made as necessary in following a procedure of amplifier adjustment.

The objective in the adjustment of an intermediate amplifier stage is to secure adequate excitation to the following stage. In the case of the output or final amplifier, the objective is to obtain maximum power output to the antenna. In both cases, the adjustment must be consistent with the tube ratings as to voltage, current and dissipating ratings.

Adequate drive to a following amplifier is normally indicated when rated grid current in the following stage is obtained with the stage operating at rated bias, the stage loaded to rated plate current, and the driver stage tuned to resonance. In a final amplifier, maximum output is normally indicated when the output coupling is adjusted so that the amplifier tube draws rated plate current when it is tuned to resonance.

Resonance in the plate circuit is normally indicated by the dip in plate-current reading as the plate tank capacitor is tuned through its range. When the stage is unloaded, or lightly

fore it is seldom feasible to provide even grid-current and plate-current meters for all stages. The exciter stages in a multistage transmitter often do not require metering after initial adjustments. It is common practice to provide a meter-switching system by which a single milliammeter may be switched to read currents in as many circuits as desired. Such a meter-switching circuit is shown in Fig. 6-32. The resistors, R, are connected in the various circuits in place of the milliammeters shown in Fig. 6-31. Since the resistance of R is several times the internal resistance of the milliammeter, it will have no practical effect upon the reading of the meter.

When the meter must read currents of widely differing values, a meter with a range sufficiently low to accommodate the lowest values of current to be measured may be selected. In the circuits in which the current will be above the scale of the meter, the resistance of R can be adjusted to a lower value which will give the meter reading a multiplying factor. (See chapter on Measurements.) Care should be taken to observe proper polarity in making the connections between the resistors and the switch.

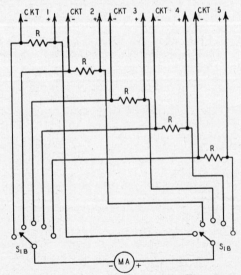

Fig. 6-32—Switching a single milliammeter. The resistors, R, should be 10 to 20 times the internal resistance of the meter; 47 ohms will usually be satisfactory. S_1 is a 2-section rotary switch. Its insulation should be ceramic for high voltages, and an insulating coupling should always be used between shaft and control.

Amplifier Adjustment

loaded, this dip in plate current will be quite pronounced. As the loading is increased, the dip will become less noticeable. See Fig. 6-4. However, in the case of a screen-grid tube whose screen is fed through a series resistor, maximum output may not be simultaneous with the dip in plate current. The reason for this is that the screen current varies widely as the plate circuit is tuned through resonance. This variation in screen current causes a corresponding variation in the voltage drop across the screen resistor. In this case, maximum output may occur at an adjustment that results in an optimum combination of screen voltage and nearness to resonance. This effect will seldom be observed when the screen is operated from a fixed-voltage source.

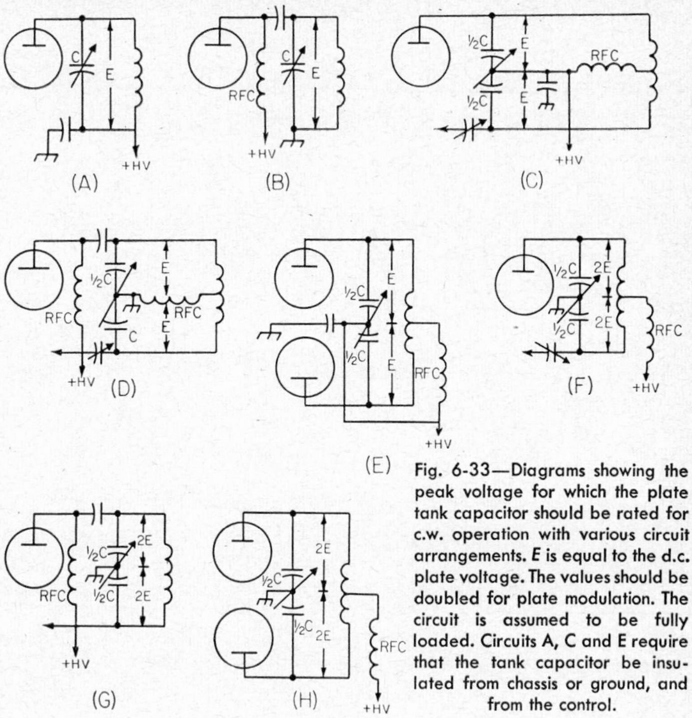

The first step in the adjustment of an amplifier is to stabilize it, both at the operating frequency by neutralizing it if necessary, and at parasitic frequencies by introducing suppression circuits.

If "flat" transmission-line coupling is used, the output end of the line should be matched, as described in this chapter for the case where the amplifier is to feed the grid of a following stage, or in the transmission-line section if the amplifier is to feed an antenna system. After proper match has been obtained, all adjustments in coupling should be made at the *input* end of the line.

Until preliminary adjustments of excitation have been made, the amplifier should be operated with filament voltage on and fixed bias, if it is required, but screen and plate voltages off. With the exciter coupled to the amplifier, the coupling to the driver should be adjusted until the amplifier draws rated grid current, or somewhat above the rated value. Then a load (the antenna grid of the following stage, or a dummy load) should be coupled to the amplifier.

With screen and plate voltages (preferably reduced) applied, the plate tank capacitor should be adjusted to resonance as indicated by a dip in plate current. Then, with full screen and plate voltages applied, the coupling to the load should be adjusted until the amplifier draws rated plate current. Changing the coupling to the load will usually detune the tank circuit, so that it will be necessary to readjust for resonance each time a change in coupling is made. An amplifier should not be operated with its plate circuit off resonance for any except the briefest necessary time, since the plate dissipation increases greatly when the plate circuit is not at resonance. Also, a screen-grid tube should not be operated without normal load for any appreciable length of time, since the screen dissipation increases.

It is normal for the grid current to decrease when plate voltage is applied, and to decrease again as the amplifier is loaded more heavily. As the grid current falls off, the coupling to the driver should be increased to maintain the grid current at its rated value.

Fig. 6-33—Diagrams showing the peak voltage for which the plate tank capacitor should be rated for c.w. operation with various circuit arrangements. E is equal to the d.c. plate voltage. The values should be doubled for plate modulation. The circuit is assumed to be fully loaded. Circuits A, C and E require that the tank capacitor be insulated from chassis or ground, and from the control.

● COMPONENT RATINGS AND INSTALLATION

Plate Tank-Capacitor Voltage

In selecting a tank capacitor with a spacing between plates sufficient to prevent voltage breakdown, the peak r.f. voltage across a tank circuit under load, but without modulation, may be taken conservatively as equal to the d.c. plate voltage. If the d.c. plate voltage also appears across the tank capacitor, this must be added to the peak r.f. voltage, making the total peak voltage twice the d.c. plate voltage. If the amplifier is to be plate-modulated, this last value must be doubled to make it four times the d.c. plate voltage, because both d.c. and r.f. voltages double with 100-per-cent plate modulation. At the higher plate voltages, it is desirable to choose a tank circuit in which the d.c. and modulation voltages do not appear across the tank capacitor, to permit the use of a smaller capacitor with less plate spacing. Fig. 6-33 shows the peak voltage, in terms of d.c. plate voltage, to be expected across the tank capacitor in various circuit arrangements. These peak-voltage values are given assuming that the amplifier is loaded to rated plate current. Without load, the peak r.f. voltage will run much higher.

The plate spacing to be used for a given peak voltage will depend upon the design of the variable capacitor, influencing factors being the mechanical construction of the unit, the insulation used and its placement in respect to intense fields, and the capacitor plate shape and degree of polish. Capacitor manufacturers usually rate their products in terms of the peak voltage between plates. Typical plate spacings are shown in the following table.

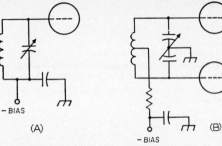

Fig. 6-34—The voltage rating of the grid tank capacitor in A should be equal to the biasing voltage plus about 20 per cent of the plate voltage.

Plate Tank Coils

The inductance of a manufactured coil usually is based upon the highest plate-voltage/plate-current ratio likely to be used at the maximum power level for which the coil is designed. Therefore in the majority of cases, the capacitance shown by Figs. 6-9 and 6-20 will be greater than that for which the coil is designed and turns must be removed if a Q of 10 or more is needed. At 28 Mc., and sometimes 14 Mc., the value of capacitance shown by the chart for a high plate-voltage/plate-current ratio may be lower than that attainable in practice with the components available. The design of manufactured coils usually takes this into consideration also and it may be found that values of capacitance greater than those shown (if stray capacitance is included) are required to tune these coils to the band.

Manufactured coils are rated according to the plate-power input to the tube or tubes when the stage is loaded. Since the circulating tank current is much greater when the amplifier is unloaded, care should be taken to operate the amplifier conservatively when unloaded to prevent damage to the coil as a result of excessive heating.

Tank coils should be mounted at least their diameter away from shielding to prevent a marked loss in Q. Except perhaps at 28 Mc., it is not important that the coil be mounted quite close to the tank capacitor. Leads up to 6 or 8 inches are permissible. It is more important to keep the tank capacitor as well as other components out of the immediate field of the coil. For this reason, it is preferable to mount the coil so that its axis is parallel to the capacitor shaft, either alongside the capacitor or above it.

There are many factors that must be taken into consideration in determining the size of wire that should be used in winding a tank coil. The considerations of form factor and wire size that will produce a coil of minimum loss are often of less importance in practice than the coil size that will fit into available space or that will handle the required power without excessive heating. This is particularly true in the case of screen-grid tubes where the relatively small driving power required can be easily obtained even if the losses in the driver are quite high. It may be considered preferable to take the power loss if the physical

Typical Tank-Capacitor Plate Spacings					
Spacing (In.)	Peak Voltage	Spacing (In.)	Peak Voltage	Spacing (In.)	Peak Voltage
0.015	1000	0.07	3000	0.175	7000
0.02	1200	0.08	3500	0.25	9000
0.03	1500	0.125	4500	0.35	11000
0.05	2000	0.15	6000	0.5	13000

Plate tank capacitors should be mounted as close to the tube as temperature considerations will permit to make possible the shortest capacitive path from plate to cathode. Especially at the higher frequencies where minimum circuit capacitance becomes important, the capacitor should be mounted with its stator plates well spaced from the chassis or other shielding. In circuits where the rotor must be insulated from ground, the capacitor should be mounted on ceramic insulators of size commensurate with the plate voltage involved and — most important of all, from the viewpoint of safety to the operator — a well-insulated coupling should be used between the capacitor shaft and the dial. *The section of the shaft attached to the dial should be well grounded.* This can be done conveniently through the use of panel shaft-bearing units.

Grid Tank Capacitors

In the circuit of Fig. 6-34, the grid tank capacitor should have a voltage rating approximately equal to the biasing voltage plus 20 per cent of the plate voltage. In the balanced circuit of B, the voltage rating of *each section* of the capacitor should be this same value.

The grid tank capacitor is preferably mounted with shielding between it and the tube socket for isolation purposes. It should, however, be mounted close to the socket so that a short lead can be passed through a hole to the socket. The rotor ground lead or bypass lead should be run directly to the nearest point on the chassis or other shielding. In the circuit of Fig. 6-34A, the same insulating precautions mentioned in connection with the plate tank capacitor should be used.

Component Ratings

size of the exciter can be kept down by making the coils small.

The accompanying table shows typical conductor sizes that are usually found to be adequate for various power levels. For powers under 25 watts, the minimum wire sizes shown are largely a matter of obtaining a coil of reasonable Q. So far as the power is concerned, smaller wire could be used.

Wire Sizes for Transmitting Coils		
Power Input (Watts)	Band (Mc.)	Wire Size
1000	28–21	6
	14–7	8
	3.5–1.8	10
500	28–21	8
	14–7	12
	3.5–1.8	14
150	28–21	12
	14–7	14
	3.5–1.8	18
75	28–21	14
	14–7	18
	3.5–1.8	22
25 or less*	28–21	18
	14–7	24
	3.5–1.8	28

* Wire size limited principally by consideration of Q.

Space-winding the turns invariably will result in a coil of higher Q, especially at frequencies above 7 Mc., and a form factor in which the turns spacing results in a coil length between 1 and 2 times the diameter is usually considered satisfactory. Space winding is especially desirable at the higher power levels because the heat developed is dissipated more readily. The power lost in a tank coil that develops appreciable heat at the higher-power levels does not usually represent a serious loss percentagewise. A more serious consequence, especially at the higher frequencies, is that coils of the popular "air-wound" type supported on plastic strips may deform. In this case, it may be necessary to use wire (or copper tubing) of sufficient size to make the coil self-supporting. Coils wound on tubular forms of ceramic or mica-filled bakelite will also stand higher temperatures.

Plate-Blocking and Bypass Capacitors

Plate-blocking capacitors should have low inductance; therefore capacitors of the mica or ceramic type are preferred. For frequencies between 3.5 and 30 Mc., a capacitance of 0.001 is commonly used. The voltage rating should be 25 to 50% above the plate-supply voltage (twice this rating for plate modulation).

Small disk ceramic capacitors (approximately ¼ inch in diameter) are to be preferred as bypass capacitors, since when they are applied correctly (see TVI chapter), they are series resonant in the TV range and therefore are an important measure in filtering power-supply leads. Capacitors of this type are rated at 600 to 1000 volts. At higher voltages, disk ceramics with higher-voltage ratings, or capacitors of the TV "doorknob" type are recommended. Voltage ratings of bypass capacitors should be similar to those for blocking capacitors.

R. F. Chokes

The characteristics of any r.f. choke will vary with frequency, from characteristics resembling those of a parallel-resonant circuit, of high impedance, to those of a series-resonant circuit, where the impedance is lowest. In between these extremes, the choke will show varying amounts of inductive or capacitive reactance.

In series-feed circuits, these characteristics are of relatively small importance because, in a correctly operating circuit, the r.f. voltage across the choke is negligible. In a parallel-feed circuit, however, the choke is shunted across the tank circuit, and is subject to the full tank r.f. voltage. If the choke does not present a sufficiently high impedance, enough power will be absorbed by the choke to cause it to burn out. With chokes of the usual type, wound with small wire for compactness, a relatively small amount of power loss in the choke will cause excessive heating.

To avoid this, the choke must have a sufficiently high reactance to be effective at the lowest frequency, and yet have no series resonances near the higher-frequency bands. The design of a choke that meets requirements over a range as wide as 3.5 to 30 Mc. at the higher voltages is quite critical.

Universal pie-wound chokes of the "receiver" type (2.5 mh., 125 ma.) are usually satisfactory if the plate voltage does not exceed 750. For higher voltages, a single-layer solenoid-type choke of correct design has been found satisfactory. The National type R-175A and Raypar RL-100, RL-101 and RL-102 are representative manufactured types. An example of a satisfactory homemade choke for voltages up to at least 3000 consists of 112 turns of No. 26 wire, spaced to a length of 3⅞ inches on a 1-inch ceramic form (Centralab stand-off insulator, type X3022H). A ceramic form is advisable from the consideration of temperature. This choke has only one series resonance (near 24 Mc.), and exhibits an equivalent parallel resistance of 0.25 megohm or more in all of the amateur bands from 80 through 10.

Since the characteristics of a choke will be affected by any metal in its field, it should be checked when mounted in the position in which it is to be used, or in a temporary set-up simulating the same conditions. The plate end of the choke should not be connected, but the power-supply end should be connected directly, or by-passed, to the chassis. The g.d.o. should be coupled as close to the ground end of the choke as possible. Series resonances, indicating the frequencies of greatest loss, should be checked with the choke short-circuited with a short piece of wire. Parallel resonances, indicating frequencies of least loss are checked with the short removed.

A Three-Band Oscillator Transmitter for the Novice

The novice transmitter shown in Figs. 6-35–6-38, inclusive, is easy to build and get working. It is a crystal-controlled, one-tube oscillator capable of running at 30 watts input on the 3.5-, 7, and 21 Mc. Novice bands. A special feature of the transmitter is a built-in keying monitor which permits the operator to listen to his own sending.

Regulated voltage is used on the screen of the oscillator. This minimizes frequency shift of the oscillator with keying, which is the cause of chirp. In addition, a small amount of cathode bias (R_4) is used on the oscillator. This also tends to improve the keying characteristics in a cathode-keyed simple-oscillator transmitter.

Circuit Details

The oscillator circuit used is the grid-plate type, and the tube is a 6DQ6A pentode. The power output is taken from the plate circuit of the tube. On 80 meters, an 80-meter crystal is needed. On 40, either 80- or 40-meter crystals can be used, although slightly more output will be obtained by using 40-meter crystals. To operate on 15 meters, a 40-meter crystal is used.

The tank circuit is a pi network. The plate tank capacitor is the variable C_6, and the tank inductance is L_2L_3. C_8 is a two-section variable, approximately 365 $\mu\mu f.$ per section, with the stators connected together to give a total capacitance of about 730 $\mu\mu f.$ This range of capacitance is adequate for coupling to 50 or 75 ohms on 7 and 21 Mc. When operating on 3.5 Mc., an additional 1000 $\mu\mu f.$ (C_7) is added to furnish the needed range of capacitance. L_1 and R_2 are essential for suppressing v.h.f. parasitic oscillations.

The keying-monitor circuit uses a neon bulb (type NE-2) audio-frequency oscillator connected to the cathode of the 6DQ6A at the key jack, J_1. The headphones are plugged into J_2, a jack mounted on the back of the transmitter chassis. Another jack, J_3, is used as a terminal for the leads that go to the headphone jack on the receiver.

Power Supply

The power supply uses a 5U4G in a full-wave circuit. A capacitor-input filter is used and the output voltage is approximately 370 volts with a cathode current of 90 milliamperes. A 0–150 milliammeter reads cathode current. The screen and grid currents are approximately 4 ma. when the oscillator is loaded.

Construction

All of the components, including the power supply, are mounted on a $2 \times 7 \times 13$-inch aluminum chassis that is in turn enclosed in a $7 \times 9 \times 15$-inch aluminum box. (Premier AC-1597). One of the removable covers of the box is used as the front panel, as shown in Fig. 6-35. The box has a $\frac{1}{2}$-inch lip around both openings, so the bottom edge of the chassis should be placed one inch from the bottom of the panel. The sides of the chassis are also one inch from the sides of the panel. The chassis is held to the panel by S_2, J_1, and the mounting screws for the crystal socket, so both the front edge of the chassis and the panel must be drilled alike for these components. S_1, at the left in the front view, is one inch from the edge of the chassis (that is, two inches from the edge of the panel) and centered vertically on the chassis edge. Thus it is one inch from the bottom of the chassis edge and two inches from the bottom edge of the panel. The hole for J_1 is centered on the chassis edge and the holes for the crystal socket are drilled at the right-hand end of the chassis to correspond with the position of S_1 at the left.

Fig. 6-35—This 30-watt three-band Novice transmitter is enclosed in a 7 × 9 × 15-inch aluminum box. A group of ¼-inch-diameter holes should be drilled in the top of the box over the oscillator tube, as shown, to provide ventilation. A similar set of holes should be drilled in the back cover behind the oscillator circuit.

Novice Transmitter

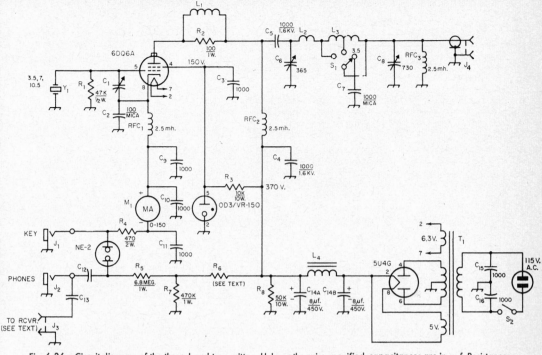

Fig. 6-36—Circuit diagram of the three-band transmitter. Unless otherwise specified, capacitances are in $\mu\mu$f. Resistances are in ohms (K = 1000).

C_1—3-30-$\mu\mu$f. trimmer.
C_2—100-$\mu\mu$f. mica.
C_3, C_9, C_{10}, C_{11}, C_{15}, C_{16}—0.001-μf. disk ceramic.
C_4, C_5—0.001-μf. 1600-volt disk ceramic.
C_6—365-$\mu\mu$f. variable capacitor, single section, broadcast-replacement type.
C_7—0.001-μf. 600-volt mica.
C_8—365-$\mu\mu$f. variable capacitor, dual section, broadcast-replacement type.
C_{12}—500-$\mu\mu$f. mica or ceramic.
C_{13}—0.01-μf. disk ceramic.
C_{14}—8/8-μf. 450-volt dual electrolytic capacitor.
J_1, J_2—Open-circuit phone jack.
J_3—Phono jack, RCA type.
J_4—Coaxial chassis connector, SO-239.
L_1—10 turns No. 18 wire space-wound on R_2.

L_2—6 turns No. 16 wire, 8 turns per inch, 1¼ inches diam. (B & W 3018).
L_3—23 turns No. 16 wire, 8 turns per inch, 1¼ inches diam. (B & W 3018). The 7-Mc. tap is 18 turns from the junction of L_2 and L_3.
L_4—8-h. 150-ma. filter choke (Thordarson 20C54).
M_1—0-150 ma. (Shurite 950).
R_1-R_8 inc.—As specified.
RFC$_1$, RFC$_2$, RFC$_3$—2.5-mh. r.f. choke (National R-50 or or similar).
S_1—Single-pole 3-position switch (Centralab 1461).
S_2—Single-pole single-throw toggle switch.
T_1—Power transformer: 360-0-360 volts, 120 ma.; 6.3 volts, 3.5 amp.; 5 volts, 3 amp (Stancor PM-8410).
Y_1—Crystal (see text).

There is nothing critical about the placement of the meter or the shafts for C_6, C_8 and S_1. As shown in Fig. 6-38, C_6 is mounted directly above J_1 and approximately two inches from the top of the panel. C_8 similarly is above the crystal socket and on the same horizontal line as C_6. S_1 is about at the middle of the square formed by these four components.

The holes on the rear edge of the chassis for the coaxial connector J_4, phone jack J_2, receiver connector J_3, and for the a.c. cord are drilled at the same height as those on the front edge. Access holes should be cut in the rear cover of the box at the corresponding positions; these holes may be large enough to clear the components, but not larger than is necessary for this purpose. The cover fits tightly against the rear edge of the chassis and thus maintains the shielding for preventing radiation of harmonics

in the television bands. However, it is advisable to fasten the cover to the chassis edge with a few sheet-metal screws, in order to insure good electrical contact.

There are several different types of broadcast-replacement variable capacitors on the market. Some of these have holes tapped in the front of the frame, and this type can be mounted directly on the panel using machine screws and spacers. Others have mounting holes only in the bottom. In this case, the capacitor can be mounted on a pair of L-shaped brackets made from strips of aluminum.

Both L_2 and L_3 are supported by their leads. One end of L_3 is connected to the stator of C_8 and the other end is connected to a junction on top of a one-inch-long steatite stand-off insulator. L_2 has one end connected to the stator of C_6 and the other end to one of the terminals on S_1.

Fig. 6-37—Rear view of the transmitter showing the placement of components above chassis. The loading capacitor, C_8, is at the left, L_3 is the vertical coil and L_2 the horizontal one. Rubber grommets are used to prevent chafing and to furnish additional insulation on the leads coming from below chassis.

The voltage-dividing network consisting of R_6 and R_7 provides the correct voltage for operating the keying monitor, R_6 is 1.65 megohms, a value obtained by using two 3.3-megohm 1-watt resistors in parallel. These resistors and other small components may be mounted on standard bakelite tie points.

Adjustment and Testing

When the unit is ready for testing, a 15- or 25-watt electric light will serve as a dummy load. One side of the lamp should be connected to the output lead and the other side to chassis ground. A crystal appropriate for the band to be used should be plugged into the crystal socket, and a key connected to the key jack. S_1 should be set to the proper band. S_2 may then be closed and the transmitter allowed to warm up.

Set C_8 at maximum capacitance (plates completely meshed) and close the key. Quickly tune C_6 to resonance, as indicated by a dip in the cathode-current reading. Gradually decrease the capacitance of C_8, while retouching the tuning of C_6 as the loading increases. Increased loading

will be indicated by increasing lamp brightness and by larger values of cathode current. Tune for maximum lamp brilliance. The cathode current should read between 90 and 100 milliamperes when the oscillator is fully loaded.

C_1 should be adjusted for the best keying characteristics consistent with reasonably good power output. It is not advisable to attempt to adjust C_1 with a lamp dummy load, since the lamp resistance will change during the heating and cooling that take place during keying, and this will affect the keying characteristic of the oscillator. Use a regular antenna, with or without an antenna coupler or matching network as the antenna system may require, and listen to the keying on the station receiver. Remove the antenna from the receiver to prevent overloading, and adjust the r.f. gain control for a signal level comparable with that at which signals on that band are normally heard. Further details on checking keying will be found in the chapter on keying and break-in.

(Originally described in *QST* December, 1957.)

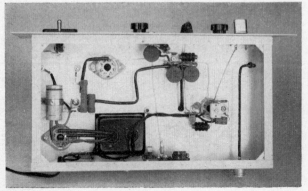

Fig. 6-38—Below-chassis view. Power-supply components are mounted in the left-hand side and the oscillator section is at the right-hand side. Mounted on the back wall of the chassis is the keying monitor. Although not visible in this view, the monitor components are mounted on a four-terminal tie point.

50-Watt Transmitter

A One-Tube 50-Watt Transmitter

The transmitter shown in Figs. 6-39 and 6-41 is similar in some respects to the one described previously. However, it demonstrates a different type of construction and will handle more power. For simplicity, operation is confined to two bands — 80 and 40 meters.

The circuit is shown in Fig. 6-40. The single 6146 is used in a Colpitts-type crystal-oscillator circuit. The dial lamp I_1 serves as an indicator of r.f. crystal current and will also act as a fuse in case the crystal current becomes sufficient to endanger the crystal. (A crystal will fracture if the current through the crystal is sufficient to cause excessive heating.)

The output circuit, consisting of C_2, L_1 and C_4, is a pi network designed to feed a low-impedance (50-75-ohm) load. The band switch S_1 shorts out a portion of the coil for 40-meter operation and adds C_3 in parallel with C_4 for 80-meter output.

One of the functions of the r.f. choke RFC_4 is that of a safety device. Should the 1000-$\mu\mu$f. 1200-volt blocking capacitor break down, high voltage would be fed to the antenna or transmission line — a dangerous situation for the operator. The choke provides a d.c. short to ground should this occur, although it has no effect on the normal operation of the transmitter. The choke also makes it possible to use capacitors with a lower break-down voltage rating at C_2 and C_4.

The meter M_1 and the key are in the cathode circuit. Screen voltage is obtained from a voltage divider consisting of R_1 and R_2. R_1 consists of three 33,000-ohm 1-watt resistors connected in parallel, and R_2 is two 100,000-ohm resistors in parallel. If desired, 10,000-ohm and 50,000-ohm 10-watt resistors can be used instead.

Power Supply

A power supply delivering approximately 400 volts is included. The supply uses a 5U4GA or 5R4GY rectifier and a capacitive-input filter. The 100,000-ohm bleeder resistance across the output of the supply (shown in Fig. 6-40 as 100K, 5 watts) is made up of three 33,000-ohm, 2-watt resistors in series.

Construction

The transmitter is built on a 7 × 11 × 3-inch aluminum chassis. The meter requires a 2-inch hole, and the two tube sockets (Amphenol type MIP) take 1⅛-inch holes. The power transformer is mounted in the left rear corner of the chassis with the rectifier tube alongside. The crystal socket and 6146 tube are placed close together in front of the transformer. The lamp I_1 is mounted in a ½-inch rubber grommet set in the chassis close to the crystal socket. Connections to the lamp are made by soldering directly to its terminals.

On the front wall of the chassis, the power switch and key jack are mounted at the left-hand end. On the other side of the meter are the plate tank capacitor C_2, the band switch and the output capacitor C_4.

On the under side of the chassis, the filter choke is fastened against one end wall, and the

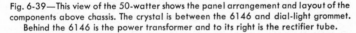

Fig. 6-39—This view of the 50-watter shows the panel arrangement and layout of the components above chassis. The crystal is between the 6146 and dial-light grommet. Behind the 6146 is the power transformer and to its right is the rectifier tube.

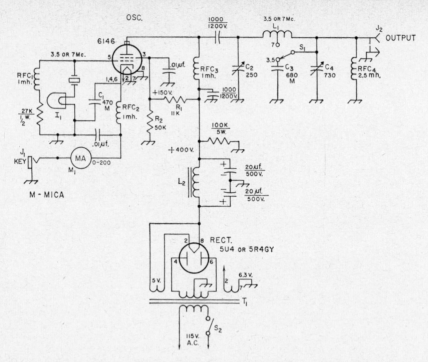

Fig. 6-40—Circuit diagram of the Novice-50 watter. Unless otherwise specified, capacitances are in $\mu\mu f$. Capacitors marked with polarity are electrolytic. Capacitors not otherwise identified are disk ceramic.

C_1—470-$\mu\mu f$. mica capacitor.
C_2—250-$\mu\mu f$. variable capacitor (Hammarlund MC-250M).
C_3—680-$\mu\mu f$. mica capacitor.
C_4—365-$\mu\mu f$.-per-section dual variable capacitor, broadcast-replacement type, sections connected in parallel (Allied Radio 60H725).
I_1—Dial lamp, 2 volts, 60 ma., No. 48 or 49.
J_1—Key jack, open-circuit.
J_2—RCA type phono jack.
L_1—35 turns No. 20, 1¼-inch diam., 16 t.p.i., tapped 15 turns from the C_4 end (B & W No. 3019).

L_2—9-hy. 125-ma. filter choke (Triad C-10X or equiv.).
M_1—2½-inch square (Shurite 850).
R_1—11,000 ohms 3 watts. (See text.)
R_2—50,000 ohms, 2 watts. (See text.)
RFC_1, RFC_2, RFC_3—1-mh. r.f. choke (National R-50, Millen 34300–1000).
RFC_4—2.5-mh. r.f. choke (National R-100S).
S_1—1-pole 2-position switch (Centralab No. 1460).
S_2—Single-pole single-throw toggle switch.
T_1—750 volts, c.t., 150 ma., 5 volts 3 amp., 6.3 volts, 4.5 amp. (Stancor PC-8411 or equiv.).

filter capacitors are against the rear wall, supported at the positive end by an insulated terminal strip, and at the negative end by soldering to the grounded terminal of the phono jack used as an output connector.

The coil L_1 is suspended by its leads between the stator terminals of the tank capacitor C_2 and the output or loading capacitor C_4.

On the 6146 socket, the three cathode prongs, Nos. 1, 4 and 6, should be connected together and the leads from C_1 and RFC_2 should be soldered to any of the three prongs.

On S_1, the center terminal connects to the stators of C_4. The 40-meter tap from L_1 goes to one outside terminal on S_1, and the mica capacitor C_3 goes to the other terminal.

Operation

After completing the wiring, check all connections to make sure you haven't made a mistake. When you feel you are ready to try the transmitter, plug in the key, an 80-meter crystal,

the line cord, and turn the power on. Leave the key open until the 6146 warms up. A 40-watt light bulb makes a good load for testing the transmitter, the threaded portion connecting to the chassis ground and the base pin to the output lead.

Switch S_1 to the 80-meter position and set C_4 at maximum capacitance (plates fully meshed). Close the key and tune C_2 for a "dip" in meter reading. Once you've resonated the tank circuit by tuning C_2 to a dip, you may or may not find that the lamp lights. Also, the meter reading at the dip will probably be only 20 or 30 ma. By decreasing the capacitance of C_4 and redipping with C_2 you'll find that the lamp will get brighter and the loading heavier, as indicated by an increasing meter reading at the dip point. Be careful not to hold the key down any longer than necessary with the 6146 out of resonance as the tube is easily damaged during such operation. Increase the loading until the meter reads 100 to 125 ma. at the dip. This will be an input

50-Watt Transmitter

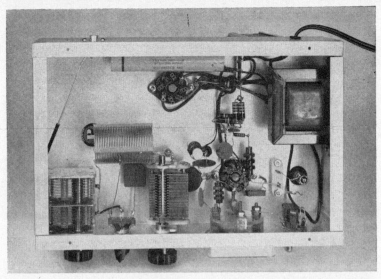

Fig. 6-41—This view shows the arrangement of the components below chassis. At the far right, mounted against the side of the chassis, is L_2, the power-supply choke. The filter capacitors are mounted along the back wall. At the lower left is C_4, the output capacitor. The other variable is C_2.

of approximately 50 watts, and the dummy load should be fairly bright. Under these conditions you should have approximately 400 volts on the plate of the 6146 and roughly 150 volts on the screen. Use an 80-meter crystal for 80-meter operation and a 40-meter one for 40. It is possible to use an 80-meter crystal for 40-meter work, but the oscillator will be operating as a frequency doubler and the output is less than when operating straight through at the crystal frequency.

Antennas

Antenna systems of any of the types discussed in the antenna chapter of this *Handbook* may be used with the transmitter, provided it is appropriate for the bands to be used. Two simple types of antenna are shown in the sketch of Fig. 6-42. Each will work on both of the two bands covered by the transmitter. The antenna shown in Fig.

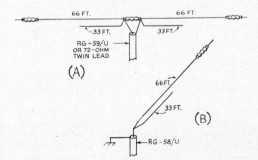

Fig. 6-42—Sketch of simple antennas described in the text. A shows a parallel-dipole system. The system of B requires a ground connection.

6-42A consists of two dipoles, one for 80 meters and one for 40 meters, connected in parallel at the center where the feed line is attached. The antenna can be made of 300-ohm television ribbon line. First measure off two sections of ribbon each 66 ft. long. Then at the center of each section cut *one* of the two wires in the ribbon. Peel off *one* of the two 33-ft. sections of wire. Then connect the remaining 33-ft. wire and the 66-ft. section of the other conductor together as shown in the sketch. Repeat the same operation with the other 66-ft. section of ribbon line and attach an insulator between the two sections. The feed line should be connected across the insulator as shown.

The antenna shown in Fig. 6-42B is similar in principle, except that the antennas are quarter-wave systems. This antenna is suitable if a good ground connection, such as a water pipe, is available within a few feet of the base of the antenna. The antenna is constructed in a manner similar to that described previously for the half-wave system. The antenna may be run vertically or run slanting to a tree or other support. If necessary, the first portion of it may be run vertically and the remainder horizontally.

The system of Fig. 6-42A should be fed with 72-ohm coax or ribbon line. The system of Fig. 6-42 should be fed with 52-ohm coaxial line.

To avoid possible second-harmonic radiation, particularly when operating in the 80-meter Novice band, an antenna tuner, such as the one described in *QST* for August, 1958, is recommended.

(Originally described in *QST* for December, 1958.)

6 – HIGH-FREQUENCY TRANSMITTERS

A 75-Watt 6DQ5 Transmitter

The transmitter shown in Fig. 6-43 is designed to satisfy the requirements of either a Novice or General class licensee. As described here it is capable of running the full 75 watts limit in the 80-, 40- and 15-meter Novice bands, with band-switching, crystal switching and other operating features. The General license holder can use the transmitter in any band 80 through 10 meters, and he can add v.f.o. control or amplitude modulation at any time without modifying the 6DQ5 transmitter. Crystal switching is a convenience for rapidly shifting frequency within a band to dodge QRM, and a SPOT position on the operate switch permits identifying one's frequency relative to others in a band. An accessory socket, X_3, furnishes a convenient point for borrowing power for a v.f.o. or for controlling the oscillator by an external switch.

Referring to Fig. 6-44, the circuit diagram of the transmitter, the crystal selector switch, S_1, is used to choose the desired crystal. For crystal-controlled operation crystals would be plugged in pins 1 and 3 and 5 and 7 of socket X_1. Similar sockets (not shown in the diagram) are used to hold the other crystals. When v.f.o. operation is desired, the v.f.o. output is connected to J_1, the plug P_1 is inserted in socket X_1, and the former 6AG7 crystal oscillator stage becomes an amplifier or multiplier stage when switch S_1 is turned to position 1.

Since the output of the 6AG7 stage will vary considerably with the bands in use, an excitation control, R_1, is included to allow for proper adjustment of the drive to the 6DQ5 amplifier. The 6DQ5, a highly sensitive tube, is neutralized to avoid oscillation; the small variable capacitor C_2 and the 390-$\mu\mu f$. mica capacitor form the neutralizing circuit. Screen or screen and plate modulation power can be introduced at socket X_2; for radiotelegraph operation these connections are

completed by P_2. Grid or plate current of the 6DQ5 can be read by proper positioning of S_5; the 0–15 milliammeter reads 0–15 ma. in the grid-current position and 0–300 ma. in the plate-current position.

The transmitter is keyed at J_3, and a key-click filter (100-ohm resistor and C_5) is included to give substantially click-free keying. The v.f.o. jack, J_4, allows a v.f.o. to be keyed along with the transmitter for full break-in operation.

Construction

A 10 × 17 × 3-inch aluminum chassis is used as the base of the transmitter, with a standard 8¾-inch aluminum relay rack panel held in place by the bushings of the pilot light, excitation control and other components common to the chassis and panel. The panel was cut down to 17 inches in length so that the unit would take a minimum of room on the operating table. A good idea of the relative location of the parts can be obtained from the photographs. The support for the r.f. portion housing is made by fastening strips of 1-inch aluminum angle stock (Reynolds aluminum, available in many hardware stores) to the panel and to a sheet of aluminum 9½ inches long that is held to the rear chassis apron by screws and the key jack, J_3. A piece of aluminum angle must also be cut to mount on the chassis and hold the cane-metal (Reynolds aluminum) housing. Fig. 6-45 shows the three clearance holes for the screws that hold this latter angle to the chassis after the cane metal is in place. Build the can-metal housing as though the holes weren't there and the box has to hold water; this will minimize electrical leakage and the chances for TVI. To insure good electrical contact between panel and angle stock, remove the paint where necessary by heavy applications of varnish remover, with the rest of the panel

Fig. 6-43 — This 75-watt crystal-controlled transmitter has provision for the addition of v.f.o. control. A 6AG7 oscillator drives a 6DQ5 amplifier on 80 through 15 meters.

As a precaution against electrical shock, the meter switch, to the immediate right of the meter, is protected by a cane-metal housing. The switch to the right of the meter switch handles the spot-operate function, and the switch at the far top right is the plate-circuit band switch.

Along the bottom, from left to right: pilot light, excitation control, crystal switch, grid circuit band switch, and grid circuit tuning.

A 75-Watt Transmitter

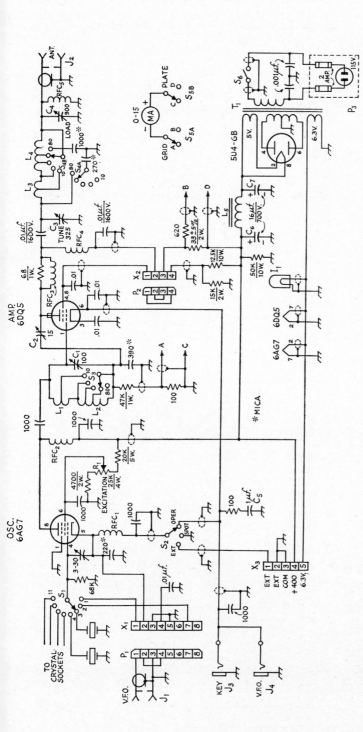

Fig. 6-44—Circuit diagram of the 75-watt 6DQ5 transmitter. Unless specified otherwise, capacitance is in μμf., resistance is in ohms, resistors are ½ watt.

C₁—100-μμf. midget variable (Hammarlund HF-100).

C₂—15-μμfd. midget variable, .025 inch spacing (Johnson 15J12).

C₃—325-μμf. variable (Hammarlund MC-325-M).

C₄—Dual 450-μμf. broadcast replacement variable, two sections connected in parallel.

C₅—1-μf. 400-volt tubular.

C₆, C₇—16-μf. 700-volt electrolytic (Aerovox PRS).

I₁—6-volt pilot lamp.

J₁—Phono jack.

J₂—Coaxial connector, chassis mounting, type SO-239.

J₃, J₄—Open-circuit phone jack.

L₁—7½ t. No. 18, ⅝ inch diam., 8 t.p.i., tapped 5½

turns from grid end (B&W 3006).

L₂—38 t. No. 32, 1 inch diam., 32 t.p.i., tapped 23 and 31 turns up (B&W 3016).

L₃—5 turns No. 14, 1-inch diam., 4 t.p.i., self-supporting, tapped 3½ turns from plate end.

L₄—15 turns No. 14, 1¾ inch diam., 4 t.p.i., tapped 6¼ and 10¼ from output end (B&W 3021).

L₅—10-henry 200-ma. filter choke (Triad C-16A).

P₁—Octal plug (Amphenol 86-PM8).

P₂—4-pin plug (Amphenol 86-PM4).

P₃—Fused line plug.

R₁—25,000-ohm 4-watt potentiometer (Mallory M25MPK).

RFC₁, RFC₂—750-μh. 100-ma. r.f. choke (National R-33).

RFC₃—3 turns No. 14 around 68-ohm 1-watt composition resistor.

RFC₄—1-mh. r.f. choke, 500 ma. (Johnson 102-752).

RFC₅—2.5-mh. r.f. choke (National R-100S).

S₁—1-pole 11-position rotary ceramic switch (Centralab Y section on P-121 index assembly).

S₂—Single-pole 11-position (3 used) non-shorting rotary switch (Centralab PA-1001).

S₃—Single-pole 12-position (5 used) rotary ceramic switch (Centralab PA-1 on PA-301 index assembly).

S₄—2-pole 5-position rotary ceramic switch (Centralab 2505).

S₅—S.p.s.t. toggle.

T₁—800 v.c.t. 200-ma. power transformer (Triad R-21A).

X₁—Octal tube socket.

X₂—4-pin tube socket.

X₃—5-pin tube socket.

179

masked off. The paint will blister and be easy to remove; wash the panel and then drill the holes for the components and screws. (If the holes are drilled first, the varnish remover may leak through and spoil the paint on the front of the panel.)

From a suitable piece of cane metal, make the four-sided $2\frac{1}{4} \times 2\frac{1}{4} \times 2\frac{1}{4}$-inch box that covers S_5, and fasten it to the utility-box cover with sheet-metal screws. Don't forget J_1 on the side of the box.

The self-supporting coil, L_4, can be wound on the envelope of the 6AG7 and then pulled apart to give the correct winding length.

Installation of the electrical components should present no problems. To insulate it from the chassis, capacitor C_1 is mounted on a small ceramic cone insulator (Johnson 135–500 or National GS-10). The socket for the 6DQ5 is mounted above the chassis on a pair of $\frac{3}{4}$-inch sleeves, with a large clearance hole under the socket for the several leads running from under the chassis. Cathode and screen bypass capacitors for the 6DQ5 connect to the chassis at soldering lugs under the sleeves.

Taps on L_2 are readily made by first pushing the wire on either side of the desired turn toward the center of the coil.

Note that shielded wire is used for many of the power leads; this is done to minimize the chances for stray radiation and it also contributes to the stability of the transmitter. Don't neglect it.

Adjustment

When the wiring is completed and checked, disable the amplifier stage by removing P_2, plug in P_3 and turn on S_5. The tube heaters and filaments should light up. If a voltmeter is available and connected across C_6, it should indicate over 500 volts. Later on, with full loading, the plate voltage will run around 400.

With S_1 switched to an 80-meter crystal, S_3 switched to 80 or 40 and S_5 switched to GRID, flip S_2 to SPOT and tune C_1 through its range. If the crystal is oscillating the meter should give an indication at some setting of C_1. The grid current reading should vary with the setting of C_1 (maximum at resonance) and with the setting of R_1 (maximum with arm at 20K end). If a key is plugged in at J_3 and S_2 is set to OPER, the grid current should appear only when the key is closed. Listen to the signal on a receiver (no antenna); if the signal is chirpy try adjusting the 3–30 $\mu\mu$f. compression trimmer between grid and cathode of the 6AG7.

With a 40-meter crystal switched in, check for grid current at 14 and 21 Mc., by switching S_3 to the desired band and tuning with C_1. These settings should be checked with an absorption-type wavemeter, since it is possible in some cases to find more than one harmonic in the range of C_1. The 28-Mc. range can also be checked, but the 4th harmonic of the 7-Mc. crystal will yield only about 1 ma. of grid current.

Next check the neutralization on the 15-meter

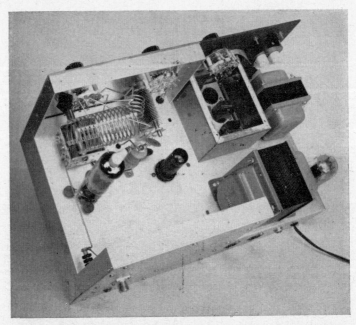

Fig. 6-45 — Top view of the 6DQ5 transmitter with cane-metal cover removed. A 3 X 4 X 5-inch utility box (upper right) serves as a shield for the crystals; the cane-metal protection for the meter switch is fastened to the box cover. Phono jack mounted on the meter-side of the box receives v.f.o. output; short length of Twin-Lead from this jack to octal plug brings v.f.o. output to crystal socket.

For protection against high voltage, meter terminals are covered by ceramic tube plate caps (Millen 36001).

A 75-Watt Transmitter

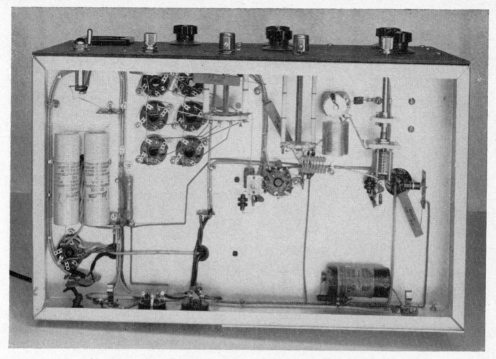

Fig. 6-46 — Group of six octal sockets (upper left) serves as crystal sockets. Socket at center of chassis holds 6AG7 oscillator tube; the 3–30-μμf. mica compression trimmer mounted alongside is excitation control for oscillator stage. Small midget capacitor above coil is neutralizing capacitor adjusted from above chassis; this capacitor and grid tuning capacitor to right must be insulated from chassis.

band. With 21-Mc. grid current indicating, switch S_4 to 15, set C_4 at half scale, and swing C_3 through its range. Watch closely for a flicker in grid current. If one is observed, try a different setting of C_2. Work carefully until the flicker is a minimum. A more sensitive indication of neutralization can be obtained by using a germanium diode and a 0–1 milliammeter in the output at J_2; adjust C_2 for minimum meter indication. If using this sensitive test, it is wise to start out with R_1 set at half range or less, until it has been determined that the meter will not swing off scale. Under no circumstances use this test with P_2 in place; the 6DQ5 output is quite likely to destroy the crystal diode.

When the amplifier has been neutralized, connect a dummy load (a 60-watt lamp will do) at J_2 and replace P_2. Set S_5 to PLATE and send a few dots as C_3 is tuned through its range. At resonance the lamp should light up and the plate current should dip. The plate current can be made to increase, along with the lamp brilliance, by decreasing the capacitance at C_4. The 6DQ5 plate current can be run up to 180 ma. (9 ma. on the meter) for Novice work; the grid current should be held at 2 to 4 ma. Crystals in the 3.5-

to 4.0-Mc. range should be used for 80- and 40-meter operation, and 7-Mc. crystals should be used on 40, 20 and 15 meters. For 10-meter operation, it is recommended that a v.f.o. with 20-meter output be used to drive the 6AG7; trying to drive the 6DQ5 with the 4th harmonic of a 7-Mc. crystal is too marginal for all but the most experienced operators. With v.f.o. control, always frequency multiply (double or triple) in the 6AG7 stage to the desired band.

Because the 6DQ5 is capable of drawing high values of plate current when not tuned properly, it will pay to take care in learning how to adjust the transmitter. Once the controls have been "calibrated" and the approximate settings for each band become known, it should no longer be necessary to tune up with the "series-of-dots" technique mentioned above. However, in the early stages of familiarization with the transmitter, the dots, or a fast hand on the key, may save a tube or power supply. The fact that the 6DQ5 can draw such heavy currents at low plate voltages makes it an excellent tube for an effective inexpensive transmitter, but the tube is not as tolerant of careless tuning habits as are some other tubes.

A 90-Watt All-Purpose Amplifier

The amplifier shown in Figs. 6-47 through 6-50 will serve as a Class-AB_1 linear amplifier or as a Class-C power amplifier with no changes other than the proper adjustment of excitation and loading. To accomplish this, a stabilized bias supply provides proper Class-AB_1 bias; the bias increases to the correct value for Class-C operation when the excitation is brought up to the point that yields normal grid current. A stabilized screen supply is included to insure good linear operation.

Referring to the amplifier circuit in Fig. 6-49, excitation on the desired band is introduced at J_1. The grid circuit is a commercial assembly, Z_1, that can be switched to the correct band by S_1 and tuned by C_1. A pi-network coupler is used in the output, switched by S_2 and tuned by C_3. Proper loading is obtained by adjustment of C_4; to provide sufficient output capacitance in the 80-meter band an additional 680 $\mu\mu f$. is added. A neutralizing circuit, C_2 and a 680-$\mu\mu f$. capacitor, adds to the fundamental stability at the higher frequencies. Parasitic suppressors were found to be necessary in the grid and plate circuits.

Overload protection is provided by a 250-ma. fuse in the cathode circuit. The grid, plate or screen current can be metered by a suitable setting of S_3; with the resistances shown the meter provides a full-scale reading of 5 ma. on grid current, 25 ma. on screen current, and 250 ma. on plate current.

If it is desired to plate- or screen-modulate the amplifier for a.m. operation, the necessary audio

Fig. 6-47—Front view of the 6146 all-purpose amplifier The upper panel is part of an 8 × 6 × 3½-inch Minibox (Bud CU-2109); the ventilated shielding of Reynolds Aluminum cane metal is fastened to the Minibox and base with sheet-metal screws.

Plate-circuit tuning controls and switch are mounted on the Minibox, and the grid-circuit controls, power switches and meter are mounted on the end of the 8 × 12 × 3-inch aluminum chassis that serves as a base.

power can be introduced at J_3.

The power-supply circuit is shown separately (Fig. 6-51) for convenience only, since the amplifier and power supply are all built on the same 8 × 12 × 3-inch chassis. High voltage for the plate of the 6146 is provided by a bridge rectifier using a 5U4-GB and two 6DE4 rectifiers; stabilized screen voltage is obtained from the same supply and two voltage-regulator tubes.

Fig. 6-48—Rear view of the 90-watt all-purpose amplifier with the cane-metal cover removed. One voltage-regulator tube has been removed from its socket (right edge of transformer) to allow the neutralizing capacitor and plate blocking capacitor to be seen. The plate r.f. choke (RFC_3 in Fig. 6-49) is mounted on one side wall, and the load capacitor and safety choke (C_4 and RFC_4 in Fig. 6-49) are mounted on the far side wall.

The rear apron of the chassis (foreground) carries the input and output coaxial-connector jacks, the 6146 cathode fuse, and the socket for the a.m. modulator connections. A shorting plug is shown in the socket.

A 90-Watt Amplifier

Construction

Most of the components can be identified in Figs. 6-47, 6-48 and 6-50, but a few construction notes are in order. The octal socket for the 6146 is mounted on two $\frac{1}{2}$-inch-long collars above the usual $1\frac{1}{8}$-inch diameter hole in the chassis. The three .001-μf. ceramic capacitors connected to the cathode pins (1, 4 and 6) ground to the chassis at lugs under the nuts holding the socket-mounting screws. The .001-μf. ceramic capacitors in the screen and heater circuits ground to their respective wire shields which in turn are connected to the same ground lugs as the cathode circuit. The grounded side of the 680-$\mu\mu f$. capacitor in the grid-circuit return should also be soldered to one of the ground lugs.

The neutralizing capacitor, C_2, has its rotor insulated from the chassis by mounting it in ex-truded fiber washers and a suitable hole in the chassis. Connection to the rotor should be made under the chassis by using a suitable soldering lug under the nut on the threaded sleeve bearing. (Old volume controls are a good source for this lug.)

The high-voltage lead from the base of RFC_3 is run in well-insulated wire to a feed-through bushing that runs through the chassis and to the meter switch terminal z_1. A high-voltage bypass capacitor is connected between the bushing and the chassis.

A simple clamp, Fig. 6–52, holds the length of RG-58/U from C_4 in place and at the same time insures that the r.f. leaves the compartment via the inside of the cable and not the outside.

Aluminum cane metal is available in many hardware stores, and it is an easy matter to bend

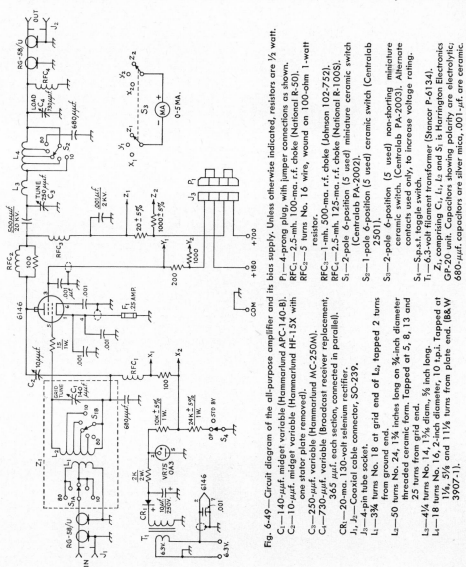

Fig. 6-49—Circuit diagram of the all-purpose amplifier and its power supply. Unless otherwise indicated, resistors are $\frac{1}{2}$ watt.

C_1—140-$\mu\mu f$. midget variable (Hammarlund APC-140-B).
C_2—10-$\mu\mu f$. midget variable (Hammarlund HF-15X with one stator plate removed).
C_3—250-$\mu\mu f$. variable (Hammarlund MC-250M).
C_4—730-$\mu\mu f$. variable (Broadcast receiver replacement; 365 $\mu\mu f$. each section, connected in parallel).
CR_1—20-ma. 130-volt selenium rectifier.
J_1, J_2—Coaxial cable connector, SO-239.
J_3—4-pin tube socket.
L_1—33$\frac{3}{4}$ turns No. 18 at grid end of L_2, tapped 2 turns from ground end.
L_2—50 turns No. 24, 1$\frac{3}{4}$ inches long on $\frac{3}{4}$-inch diameter threaded ceramic form. Tapped at 5, 8, 13 and 25 turns from grid end.
L_3—4$\frac{1}{4}$ turns No. 14, 1$\frac{3}{16}$ inch diam., $\frac{5}{8}$ inch long.
L_4—18 turns No. 16, 2-inch diameter, 10 t.p.i. Tapped at 1$\frac{1}{8}$, 5$\frac{1}{8}$ and 11$\frac{1}{8}$ turns from plate end. (B&W 3907-1).
P_1—4-prong plug, with jumper connections as shown.
RFC_1—2.5-mh. 100-ma. r.f. choke (National R-50).
RFC_2—5 turns No. 16 wire, wound on 100-ohm 1-watt resistor.
RFC_3—1-mh. 500-ma. r.f. choke (Johnson 102-752).
RFC_4—2.5-mh. 125-ma. r.f. choke (National R-100S).
S_1—2-pole 6-position (5 used) miniature ceramic switch (Centralab PA-2002).
S_2—1-pole 6-position (5 used) ceramic switch (Centralab 2501).
S_3—2-pole 6-position (5 used) non-shorting miniature ceramic switch. (Centralab PA-2003). Alternate contacts used only, to increase voltage rating.
S_4—S.p.s.t. toggle switch.
T_1—6.3-volt filament transformer (Stancor P-6134).
Z_1, comprising C_1, L_1, L_2 and S_1 is Harrington Electronics GP-20 unit. Capacitors showing polarity are electrolytic; 680-$\mu\mu f$. capacitors are silver mica, .001-μf. are ceramic.

a piece of it to form the cover. Make the cover with lips on the vertical portion that slip tightly over the sides of the Minibox, and with a bend at the bottom that can be fastened to the chassis. Another piece of cane metal should be cut to serve as a bottom cover; mounting the chassis on rubber feet lifts it above the table and permits good air circulation through the unit.

The self-supported inductor L_3 can be wound on the envelope of one of the 6DE4 rectifiers, removed and pulled apart slightly to give the specified winding length. The taps on L_4 are made by first bending inward the wire on either side of the turn to be tapped, then looping the tap wire around the turn and soldering it securely in place. Both L_3 and L_4 are supported only by their leads.

Testing and Adjustment

With all tubes in their sockets except the 6146, the line cord should be plugged in and the power switch turned on. The bias-supply 0A3 should glow immediately and the rectifier filament and heaters should light up. The screen-supply regu-

lators should glow. If a voltmeter is available, the high-voltage supply should show first around 400 volts, and then rise slowly to about 950 volts. Switch off the power; the plate supply voltage should decay to less than 100 in under 20 seconds, indicating that the 40,000-ohm resistors are "bleeding" the supply. Note also how long it takes for the voltage to reach a value of only a few volts: this will demonstrate forcefully how long it takes to discharge a high-capacitance filter.

When the power supply has discharged, plug in the 6146, connect the plate cap, and set S_4 to STAND BY. Set the neutralizing capacitor C_2 at half capacitance and the band switches on 80 meters. Turn on the power and set the meter switch, S_3, to read plate current. The 6146 heater should warm up. Now flip S_4 to operate; the meter should read 10–20 ma. (.2-.4 on the scale). Switching to read screen current, the meter should show under 1 ma. (2 divisions on the meter). There should be no grid current.

Turn off the power and remove the three rectifier tubes. Connect at J_1 the driver or excita-

Fig. 6-50—Bottom view of the all-purpose amplifier. The 150-ma. filter choke is mounted on the left-hand wall; the smaller filter choke, the small filament transformer (T_1 in Fig. 6-51) and the selenium rectifier are mounted on the right-hand wall. The strap of aluminum, visible below the meter at the top right, provides additional support for the length of RF-58/U cable that runs to the output coaxial connector. All power leads except the high voltage to the plate are run in shielded wire.

A 90-Watt Amplifier

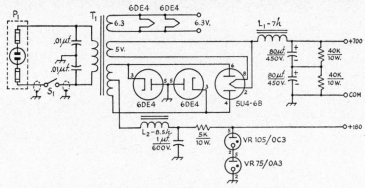

Fig. 6-51—Power supply section of the all-purpose amplifier.

L₁—7-henry 150-ma. choke (Stancor C-1710).
L₂—8½-henry 50-ma. choke (Stancor C-1279).
P₁—Fused line plug, 3-ampere fuses.
S₁—S.p.s.t. toggle.
T₁—800 v.c.t. at 200 ma., 6.3 v. at 5 amp., 5 v. at 3 amp. (Allied Radio Knight 62 G 033).

tion source to be used — less than a watt is required for linear operation, and only a shade more for Class C. Use the drive at a high frequency, such as 21 or 28 Mc. Turn on the amplifier and switch the band switches to the band corresponding to the excitation-source frequency. Adjust the grid tuning capacitor for a show of grid current; peak the tuning and (if necessary) adjust the excitation for a half-scale reading of grid current. With the loading capacitor C_4 set at half scale, swing the tuning capacitor C_3 through its range. Watch carefully for a slight flicker in grid current. If one is found, adjust the neutralizing capacitor C_2 until the flicker is minimized. The amplifier is now neutralized. Alternatively, a sensitive detector of r.f. can be coupled at the output connector, J_2, and used instead of the grid-current flicker. Adjust C_2 for minimum r.f. in the output when the plate circuit is tuned through resonance. Turn off the power switch and disconnect the excitation source.

Remove the sensitive detector, if used, and replace the rectifier tubes. Turn on the power and switch the meter to read plate current. With the grid and plate circuits switched to the same band (10, 15, 20 or 40) it should be possible to swing the grid and plate tuning to any combination of settings with no change in plate current reading. This indicates that the amplifier is stable and free from oscillation. (The amplifier can be made to oscillate on 80 meters with no grid or plate loading, but in loaded operation it will be stable.)

The antenna and excitation can now be connected and the amplifier used in normal fashion. Used as a linear amplifier, the excitation should be adjusted just below the level that would kick the grid-current indication on signal peaks. Proper loading will be obtained when a steady carrier just under the grid-current level is used for drive and the loading at resonance is set for about 100 ma. plate current. Under these conditions

of loading, a sideband signal will kick the plate current to about 40 or 50 ma. on peaks. Measured p.e.p. input before clipping should be 60 to 70 watts.

When used as a Class-C amplifier, the drive should be increased to where about 2 to 3 ma. grid current is drawn, and the loading to where the 6146 draws about 125 ma. If the amplifier is plate modulated, the plate current should be reduced to 95 ma., to stay within the tube ratings.

Since the amplifier uses a fixed and "stiff" screen supply, it is good practice always to bring up the excitation and loading together, while checking to see that the screen current never exceeds about 15 ma. In normal Class-C operation the screen current will run around 10 ma.

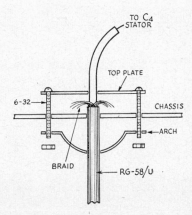

Fig. 6-52—Exploded view of the cable clamp used to hold the coaxial cable running to J_2. The top plate is a 1½-inch square of sheet aluminum with holes at the four corners for 6-32 screws. The arch is a ⁷⁄₁₆-inch wide strap that mounts diagonally under the chassis. When tightened, the top plate clamps the cable braid to the chassis; the arch lends support to the cable.

6 — HIGH-FREQUENCY TRANSMITTERS

A Self-Contained 500-Watt Transmitter

Figs. 6-53 through 6-58 show the details of a 500-watt c.w. transmitter, completely self-contained except for the external remote v.f.o. tuning box shown in Figs. 6-57 and 6-58. Provision is made for introducing s.s.b. input at the grid of the driver stage. While plate modulation can be applied to the final amplifier in the usual manner, ratings of the plate power supply limit the safe input to about 250 watts.

The circuit is shown in Fig. 6-54. Switch S_2 permits either v.f.o. or crystal-controlled operation using a 6AH6 oscillator. Either 80- or 40-meter crystals may be used. The v.f.o. circuit is in the 80-meter band and S_1 selects either of two frequency ranges — 3.5 to 4 Mc. for complete coverage of all bands, and 3.5 to 3.6 Mc. for greater bandspread over the low-frequency ends of the wider bands. The plate circuit of the oscillator is on 40 meters for all output bands except 80 meters where it is non-resonant.

A 6CL6 buffer separates the oscillator and the first keyed stage. This stage doubles to 20 meters for 20- and 10-meter output and triples to 15 meters. The driver is a 2E26 which doubles to 10 meters and works straight through on all other bands. This stage is neutralized and a potentiometer in its screen circuit serves as an excitation control.

The final is a 7094, also neutralized, with a pi-network output circuit using a B&W 851 band-switching inductor unit.

A differential break-in keying system using a 12AU7 is included. Both the final amplifier and driver are keyed by the grid-block method. The differential is adjusted by R_1. Clicks are prevented by envelope-shaping circuits which include C_7, C_{11} and the grid-leak resistances.

The 100-ohm meter shunts give a full-scale reading of 50 ma., the 51-ohm shunts a full-scale reading of 100 ma., and the 10-ohm resistor in the negative high-voltage lead provides a 500-ma. scale.

Power Supply

The plate transformer in the high-voltage supply uses a transformer designed for a conventional full-wave rectifier circuit with an ICAS d.c. output rating of 300 ma. at 750 volts. A bridge rectifier is used with this transformer so that an output voltage of 1500 is obtained. The short duty cycle of c.w. or s.s.b. operation makes it possible to draw up to the rated maximum of the 7094 (330 ma.) through a choke-input filter without a prohibitive rise in transformer temperature.

The low-voltage supply has two rectifiers. A full-wave rectifier with a capacitive-input filter provides 400 volts for the plate of the driver and the screen of the final amplifier. A tap on a voltage divider across 400 volts provides 300 volts for the plates of the oscillator, buffer and keyer tubes. A half-wave rectifier with a choke-input filter supplies 250 volts of bias for the keyer and fixed bias for the 2E26 and 7094 when they are operating as Class AB_1 linear amplifiers.

Control Circuits

S_7 is the main power switch. It turns on the low-voltage, filament and bias supplies. Until it has been closed, the high-voltage supply cannot be turned on. In addition to turning on the high-voltage supply, S_8 operates the relay K_1 which applies screen voltage to the final amplifier. Thus, to protect the screen, screen voltage cannot be applied without applying plate voltage simultaneously. J_8 is in parallel with S_8 so that the high-voltage supply can be controlled remotely from an external switch. Also, in parallel with the primary of the high-voltage transformer is another jack, J_7, which permits control of an antenna relay or other device by S_8 if desired.

The v.f.o.-set switch S_5 turns on the exciter and grounds the screen of the final amplifier.

S_2 has three positions. One is for crystal control, the second for v.f.o. operation, and the third position is for operating the last two stages of the transmitter as linear amplifiers with an external s.s.b. exciter. In addition to shifting the input of the driver stage from the buffer amplifier to an s.s.b. input connector, fixed bias is provided for AB_1 operation of both stages.

Construction

The transmitter is assembled on a 17 × 13 ×

Fig. 6-53—A 500-watt transmitter. Power supplies and a differential keyer are included. It operates with the external v.f.o. tuner shown in Fig. 6-57. Controls along the bottom, from left to right, are for low-voltage power, v.f.o./crystals/s.s.b. switch, driver tank switch, driver tank capacitor, final loading, v.f.o. set switch, and high-voltage. Above, from left to right, are controls for excitation, final tank switch, final tank capacitor and meter switch. The band-switch pointer is made by cutting down the metal skirt of a dial similar to the one to the right. All dials are Johnson.

500-Watt Transmitter

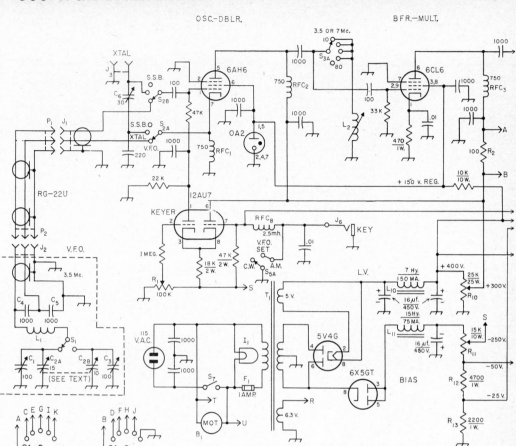

Fig. 6-54—Circuit of the 500-watt self-contained transmitter. Capacitance less than 0.001 μf. are in μμf. Fixed capacitors of capacitance greater than 100 μμf. should be disk ceramic, except as noted below. Fixed capacitors of 100 μμf. and 220 μμf. should be mica. Capacitors marked with polarity are electrolytic. Resistors not otherwise marked are ½ watt.

B₁—Blower (Allied 72P715).

C₁, C₃—100-μμf. air trimmer (Hammarlund APC-100-B).

C₂—Midget dual variable, 25 μμf. per section (Johnson 167-51 altered as described in the text).

C₄, C₅—0.001-μf. silver mica.

C₆—30-μμf. mica trimmer (National M-30).

C₇, C₁₁—0.1-μf. paper (keyer shaping).

C₈—30-μμf. miniature variable (Johnson 160-130).

C₉—100-μμf. midget variable (Johnson 167-11).

C₁₀—330-μμf. mica.

C₁₂—10-μμf. neutralizing capacitor (Johnson 159-125).

C₁₃—0.001-μf. 3000-volt disk ceramic.

C₁₄—0.001-μf. 5000-volt ceramic (CRL 858S).

C₁₅—250-μμf. 2000-volt variable (Johnson 154-1).

C₁₆—Triple-gang broadcast variable, 365 μμf. or more per section, sections connected in parallel.

I₁, I₂—One-inch 115-volt panel lamp.

J₁, J₂—Cable connector for RG-22/U (Amphenol 83-22R, UG-103/U).

J₃—Crystal socket (Millen 33102).

J₄, J₅—Coaxial receptacle (SO-239).

J₆—Key jack, open circuit.

J₇, J₈—Chassis-mounting a.c. receptacle (Amphenol 61-F).

K₁—S.p.s.t. 115-volt a.c. relay (Advance GHA/1C/ 115VA or similar).

L₁—35 μh.—32 turns No. 18, 2 inches diameter, 2 inches long (Airdux 1616).

L₂—Approx. 10 μh.—65 turns No. 26 enam., on ⅜-inch iron-slug form (Waters CSA-1011-3).

L₃—Approx. 2 μh.—16 turns No. 26 enam., close-wound at center of form similar to L₂.

L₄—Approx. 1 μh.—13 turns No. 26 enam., ½ inch long at center of form similar to L₂.

L₅—16 turns No. 20, ¾ inch diameter, 1 inch long, tapped at 10 turns and 13 turns from L₆ end (Airdux 616).

L₆—40 turns No. 16, 1¼ inches diameter, 2¾ inches long, tapped at mid point and at L₅ end (Airdux 1016).

L₇—3 turns No. 14, ½ inch diameter, ¾ inch long.

L₈—4 turns ³⁄₁₆ × ¹⁄₁₆-inch copper strip, 1⅜ inches diameter, 2½ inches long (part of B&W 851 coil unit).

L₉—4¾ turns No. 8, 2½ inches diameter, 1¾ inches long, tapped at 1¾ turns from L₈ end, plus 9½ turns No. 12, 2½ inches diameter, 1½ inches long, tapped at 6 turns from output end (part of B&W 851 coil unit).

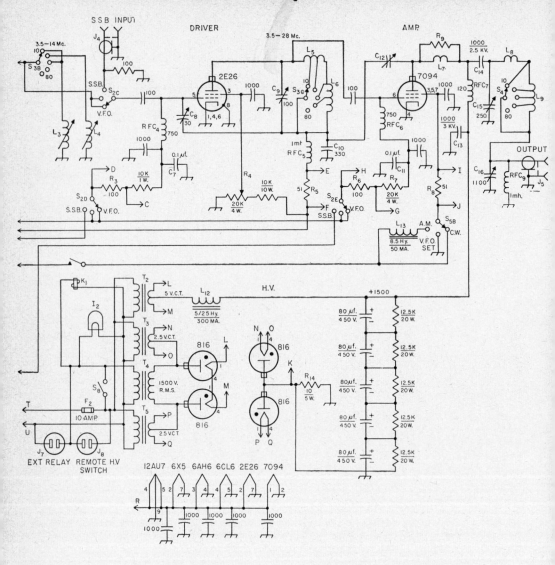

L10—7-hy. 150-ma. filter choke (Stancor C-1710).

L11—15-hy. 75-ma. filter choke (Stancor C-1002).

L12—5/25-hy. 300-ma. swinging filter choke (Triad C-33A).

M1—Shielded 0- 5-ma. d.c. milliammeter, 3½-inch rectangular (Phaostron).

P1, P2—Plug for RG-22/U cable (Amphenol 83-22SP).

R1—100,000-ohm potentiometer.

R2, R3, R6—100 ohms, 5%.

R4—20,000-ohm 4-watt potentiometer (Mallory M20-MPK)

R5, R8—51 ohms, 1 watt, 5%.

R7—Two 10,000-ohm 2-watt resistors in series.

R9—Three 100-ohm 1-watt noninductive resistors in parallel.

R10—25,000 ohms, 25 watts with slider.

R11—15,000 ohms, 20 watts, with slider.

R12—4700 ohms, 1 watt.

R13—2200 ohms, 1 watt.

R14—10 ohms (Five 51-ohm 1-watt 5% resistors in parallel.)

R15—1000 ohms ½ watt 5%.

S1—Single-pole ceramic rotary switch (Centralab 2000, 2 of 12 positions used).

S2—Two-wafer ceramic rotary switch (Centralab PA-300 index, PA-4 wafers. S2A and S2B are on one wafer, S2C, S2D and S2E on second wafer).

S3—Three-wafer ceramic rotary switch (Centralab PA-301 index, wafers PA-0, 5 positions used).

S4—Part of B&W 851 coil unit.

S5—2-pole 3-position ceramic rotary switch (Centralab 2003, two positions used).

S6—Double-pole ceramic rotary switch (Centralab 2003).

S7, S8—S.p.s.t. toggle switch.

T1—Power transformer: 750 v.a.c., c.t., 150 ma.; 5 volts 3 amps.; 6.3 volts, 4.7 amps. (Thordarson 22R06).

T2, T3—Filament transformer: 2.5 volts, c.t., 3 amps. (Triad F-1X).

T4—Plate transformer: 1780 volts, c.t., 310 ma., center tap not used (Triad P-14A).

T5—Filament transformer: 5 volts, c.t., 3 amps. (Triad F-7X).

Fig. 6-55—The only shielding required on top of the chassis is the amplifier enclosure shown. A perforated cover for the enclosure is not shown.

4-inch aluminum chassis with a 19 × 12¼-inch panel. The amplifier enclosure measures 8½ inches wide, 8¼ inches deep and 7½ inches high. The three permanent sides shown in Fig. 6-55 can be bent up from a single sheet of solid aluminum stock. The top and back (not shown) are made from a single piece of Reynolds perforated sheet aluminum.

The tube socket is mounted on ¾-inch ceramic cones over a large hole cut in the chassis and covered with a patch of perforated sheet. The tank capacitor C_{15} is mounted on metal spacers to bring its shaft level up to that of the switch on the B&W inductor which is mounted directly on the chassis. The two shafts are spaced 4 inches.

Exciter

A 4 × 5 × 6-inch aluminum box is used as the foundation for the exciter. The driver tank capacitor is centered on the chassis with its center approximately 3 inches back from the front edge of the chassis. The capacitor specified has an insulated mounting. If an uninsulated capacitor is substituted, an insulating mounting must be provided. The shafts of S_2 and S_3 are spaced 2½ inches and centered on the front end of the box. On the side of the box toward the tuning capacitor, the oscillator tube, the buffer tube, the low-frequency section (L_6) of the driver tank coil, and the 2E26 are lined up so as to clear the tank capacitor and its shaft. The latter is fitted with an insulated coupling and a panel-bearing unit. The slug-tuned coils are mounted in holes near the bottom edge of the box. Neutralizing capacitor C_8 is mounted at the rear end of the box, close to the 2E26 socket. The high-frequency section (L_5) of the tank coil is suspended between the outer end of

the low-frequency section and the plate cap of the 2E26. Coil-tap leads run through small feed-through points or grommeted clearance holes in the side of the box.

The loading capacitor C_{16} is placed so that its shaft is symmetrical with the shaft of S_3, and S_5 is spaced from it to balance S_2 at the other end.

The V.F.O. Tuner

The v.f.o. tuner is assembled in a 5 × 6 × 9-inch aluminum box (Premier AC-596). The dual tuning capacitor C_2 has 7 plates, 4 rotor and 3 stationary, in each section. In the front section, which is used to cover the entire 80-meter band, the two rotor plates nearest the front should be removed. This leaves two rotor plates and two active stator plates, the front stator plate being inactive. In the rear section, the front rotor plate and the last two rotor plates are removed. This leaves one rotor plate riding between two stators.

The capacitor is mounted on a bracket fastened against the bottom of the box, although it could be mounted from the front cover with spacers to clear the hub of the Millen 10035 dial. The shaft of the capacitor should be central on the front cover. The coil is suspended between a pair of

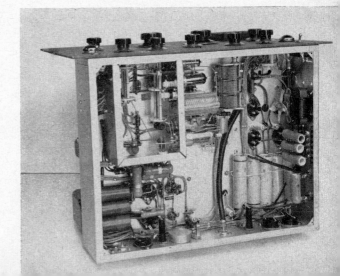

Fig. 6-56—The exciter is assembled using a standard aluminum box as the foundation. The perforated cover has been removed. The bottom of the chassis should also have a perforated metal cover.

$2\frac{1}{2}$-inch ceramic pillars (Millen 31002). It is placed immediately to the rear of the tuning capacitor. The two air trimmers, C_1 and C_3, are mounted on the top side of the box with their shafts protruding so that they can be adjusted from the top. The bandspread switch is mounted in one end of the box and the cable connector at the other end.

The unit is housed in a standard cabinet (Bud C-1781) having an 8×10-inch panel. The dial should be fastened to the panel, making sure that the hub of the dial lines up accurately with the shaft of the tuning capacitor. Then the box is inserted in the cabinet through the front opening. The switch shaft goes out through a hole drilled in the side of the cabinet, and the cable goes

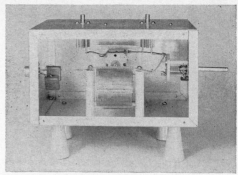

Fig. 6-58—Interior of the v.f.o. tuning box showing the mounting of the coil and other components.

Fig. 6-57—The remote v.f.o. tuning unit is housed in a standard metal cabinet. The cable at the right plugs into the main chassis.

through a hole in the opposite end to the cable connector. The dial should be set to read zero at maximum capacitance of the tuning capacitor. The box should be supported on spacers.

Adjustment

With all tubes except the rectifiers out of their sockets, the power supplies should be checked first to be sure that they are functioning properly. The voltage output of the low-voltage supply should be in excess of 400 volts, the biasing voltage 300 or more and the high voltage above 1500. The slider on the low-voltage bleeder should be set at approximately three quarters of the way from ground. The slider on the bias-supply bleeder should be set for a reading of -250 volts to ground.

Plug in the oscillator and buffer tubes and an 80-meter crystal if one is available; otherwise connect the v.f.o. tuner. With the low-voltage supply turned on, the 0A2 should glow. When the key is closed, the 0A2 should dim but stay ignited. If it does not, the value of the 10K VR resistor should be reduced.

The v.f.o. can now be adjusted to frequency. Set C_2 at maximum capacitance. Set S_1 to the 80-meter position. Adjust the 80-meter trimmer until a signal is heard at 3500 kc. on a calibrated receiver. Then set the receiver to 4000 kc. and tune the v.f.o. until the signal is heard. If the signal is not close to 100 on the dial, carefully

bend the rear rotor plate of the 80-meter section of C_2 outward a little at a time to get the desired bandspread. Each time this adjustment is made, the trimmer should be reset to bring 3500 kc. at zero on the dial.

The same procedure should be followed in adjusting for the other v.f.o. range, aiming for 3600 kc. (or above if desired) at 100 on the dial.

The 2E26 should now be plugged in and the excitation control R_4 set at the ground end (zero screen voltage). S_2 should be set in the v.f.o. position. With low voltage on and the key closed, a 5763 grid-current reading should be obtained with the band switch in the 80-meter position. With the switch in the 40-meter position, the slug of L_2 should be adjusted for maximum grid current to the 2E26. With the band switch in the 20-meter position, L_3 should be adjusted for maximum grid current, and then the slug of L_4 should be adjusted for maximum grid current with the band switch in the 15-meter position.

Now insert the 7094 in its socket and neutralize the 2E26 as described earlier in this chapter.

Testing of the final amplifier requires a load applied to the output connector. Two 150-watt lamps connected in parallel should serve the purpose. Turning on the high voltage will also apply screen voltage through the relay K_1. With both band switches set to 10 meters, and C_{16} set at about half capacitance, quickly tune the output circuit to resonance as indicated by the plate-current dip. The load lamp should show an indication of output. Switch the meter to read grid current and neutralize as described earlier in this chapter. After neutralization the amplifier can be loaded to rated plate current. If it is above the rated maximum value, increase C_{16} and retune to resonance, or decrease C_{16} if the plate current is below the rated value.

With the final adjusted and the entire transmitter operating, make a final check on the voltage at the tap on the low-voltage supply, adjusting the slider if necessary to bring the voltage to 300 with the key closed. Be sure to turn off all voltages each time an adjustment is made.

The last adjustment is in the keyer. Adjust the potentiometer R_1 to the point where the oscillator cannot be heard between dots and dashes at normal keying speed.

813 Amplifier

An All-Purpose 813 Amplifier

Figs. 6-59 through 6-62 show the circuit and photographs of an 813 amplifier designed for c.w., a.m., or s.s.b. operation. Provision has been made for convenient changing from one mode to another as well as to any of the bands from 80 through 10 meters.

The circuit is shown in 6-60. A turret-type grid circuit is used and the output circuit is a pi network designed to work into coax cable. The inductor is the rotary-type variable. Provision for neutralizing is included. R_1 is a parasitic suppressor.

For Class C c.w. or phone operation, S_4 is open. The 90 volts of fixed bias, furnished by a small bias supply and regulated by the VR90, is augmented by a drop of about 50 volts across the grid-leak resistor R_2 at a normal grid current of 15 ma. This brings the total bias to 140 volts. With S_4 closed, the grid leak is short-circuited and the 90 volts of fixed bias alone remains for AB_2 s.s.b. operation. (An advantage in AB_2 for c.w. operation is that it preserves the keying characteristics of the exciter better than with Class C operation.) R_3 should be adjusted so that the VR90 just ignites with no excitation.

Screen voltage is regulated at 750 volts by a string of five 0A2s for s.s.b. operation. When the grid drive is increased for Class C operation, the screen current increases, increasing the drop across the screen resistor R_5, and the screen voltage falls to 400. The regulators then lose control and the amplifier is ready for plate-screen modulation.

The screen is protected against excessive input, should the load or plate voltage be removed, by the overload relay K_1. The tripping point is set at 40 ma. by the variable shunt resistor R_4. If the relay trips, current through R_6 will hold the screen circuit open until plate voltage is removed. One meter, M_1, measures cathode current, while the other meter, M_2, may be switched to read either grid current or screen current.

Forced-air ventilation is always advisable for a medium- or high-power amplifier if it is buttoned up tight to suppress TVI. A surplus 100 c.f.m. blower does the job more than adequately.

Construction

The amplifier is built on a $13 \times 17 \times 4$-inch aluminum chassis fastened to a standard $12\frac{3}{4} \times 19$-inch rack panel. The r.f. output portion is enclosed in a $12\frac{1}{2} \times 13 \times 8\frac{1}{2}$-inch box made of aluminum angle and sheet. The VR tubes, relay, blower and meters are mounted external to the box.

The grid tank-circuit components are mounted underneath the chassis and are shielded with a $5 \times 7 \times 3$-inch aluminum box. A standard chassis of these dimensions might be substituted. The bias and filament transformers are in a second box measuring 6 by 3 by 3 inches. This type of construction, together with the use of shielded wire for all power circuits, was followed to reduce TVI to a minimum. Each wire was bypassed at both ends with 0.001-μf. ceramic disk capacitors. L_4 can be adjusted to series resonate with the 600-$\mu\mu$f. capacitor at the frequency of the most troublesome channel. A Bud low-pass filter completes the TVI treatment. As a result, the amplifier is completely free of TVI on all channels even in most fringe areas.

Adjustment

In the pi network, the output capacitors are fixed. However, the adjustment of the network is similar to that of the more conventional arrangement using a variable portion of the output capacitance. The only difference is that the "fine" loading adjustment is done with the variable inductor.

The inductor is fitted with a Groth turns counter, making it easy to return to the proper

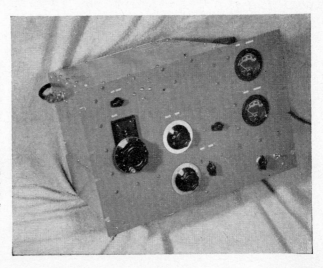

Fig. 6-59—W4SUD's all-purpose 813 amplifier. The output-capacitor switch (coarse loading) is above the turns counter for the variable inductor. Dials near the center are for the plate tank capacitor C_4 (above) and the grid tank capacitor C_1 (below). To the right of the dials are the controls for the plate padder switch S_3 (above) and the grid band switch S_1 (below). The toggle switch below the meters is the mode switch S_4 with the meter switch S_5 to the left. Ventilating holes are drilled in the cover in the area above the tube. The output connector is on the left-hand wall of the shielding box

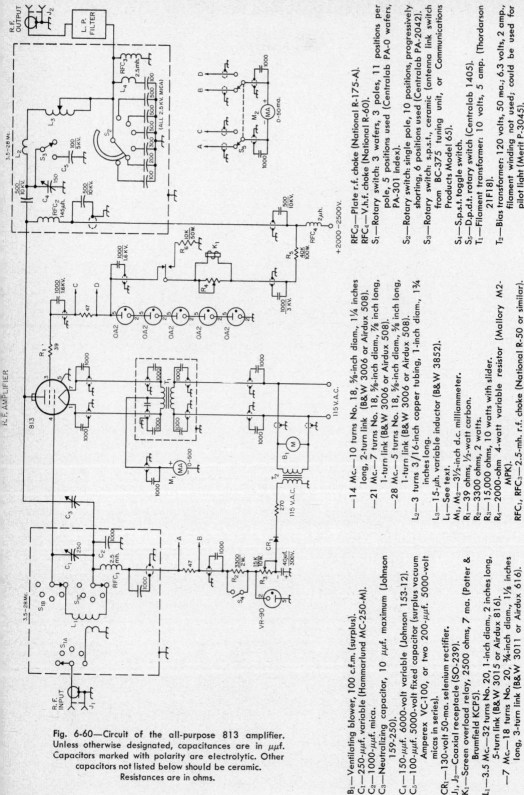

Fig. 6-60—Circuit of the all-purpose 813 amplifier. Unless otherwise designated, capacitances are in μμf. Capacitors marked with polarity are electrolytic. Other capacitors not listed below should be ceramic. Resistances are in ohms.

B₁—Ventilating blower, 100 c.f.m. (surplus).
C₁—250-μμf. variable (Hammarlund MC-250-M).
C₂—1000-μμf. mica.
C₃—Neutralizing capacitor, 10 μμf. maximum (Johnson 159-250).
C₄—150-μμf. 6000-volt variable (Johnson 153-12).
C₅—100-μμf. 5000-volt fixed capacitor (surplus vacuum Amperex VC-100, or two 200-μμf. 5000-volt micas in series).
CR₁—130-volt 50-ma. selenium rectifier.
J₁, J₂—Coaxial receptacle (SO-239).
K₁—Screen overload relay, 2500 ohms, 7 ma. (Potter & Brumfield KCP5).
L₁—3.5 Mc.—32 turns No. 20, 1-inch diam., 2 inches long, 5-turn link (B&W 3015 or Airdux 816).
—7 Mc.—18 turns No. 20, ¾-inch diam., 1⅛ inches long, 3-turn link (B&W 3011 or Airdux 616).

—14 Mc.—10 turns No. 18, ⅝-inch diam., 1¼ inches long, 2-turn link (B&W 3006 or Airdux 508).
—21 Mc.—7 turns No. 18, ⅝-inch diam., ⅞ inch long, 1-turn link (B&W 3006 or Airdux 508).
—28 Mc.—5 turns No. 18, ⅝-inch diam., ⅝ inch long, 1-turn link (B&W 3006 or Airdux 508).
L₂—3 turns 3/16-inch copper tubing, 1-inch diam., 1¾ inches long.
L₃—15-μh. variable inductor (B&W 3852).
L₄—See text.
M₁, M₂—3½-inch d.c. milliammeter.
R₁—39 ohms, ½-watt carbon.
R₂—3300 ohms, 2 watts.
R₃—15,000 ohms, 10 watts with slider.
R₄—2000-ohm 4-watt variable resistor (Mallory M2-MPK).
RFC₁, RFC₃—2.5-mh. r.f. choke (National R-50 or similar).

RFC₂—Plate r.f. choke (National R-175-A).
RFC₄—V.h.f. choke (National R-60).
S₁—Rotary switch: 3 wafers, 3 poles, 11 positions per pole, 5 positions used (Centralab PA-0 wafers, PA-301 index).
S₂—Rotary switch: single pole, 10 positions, progressively shorting, 6 positions used (Centralab PA-2042).
S₃—Rotary switch: s.p.s.t., ceramic (antenna link switch from BC-375 tuning unit, or Communications Products Model 65).
S₄—S.p.s.t. toggle switch.
S₅—D.p.d.t. rotary switch (Centralab 1405).
T₁—Filament transformer: 10 volts, 5 amp. (Thordarson 21F18).
T₂—Bias transformer: 120 volts, 50 ma.; 6.3 volts, 2 amp., filament winding not used; could be used for pilot light (Merit P-3045).

813 Amplifier

Fig. 6-61—This view shows the placement of components on the chassis. The 813 socket is mounted on spacers over a large clearance hole in the chassis. The several mica output capacitors are assembled in a stack on a threaded rod fastened to the left-hand wall of the shielding box. The neutralizing capacitor and the 80-meter plate padder are to the right of the tank capacitor. To the right of the box are the five 0A2s (the front one hidden), the screen overload relay and the VR90, the blower and meters.

setting for each band. Until the settings for each band have been found, S_3 should be turned so that all of the output capacitance is in circuit. The inductor should be set near maximum for 80, and approximately half maximum for 40. On the higher-frequency bands, the inductor should be set so that the circuit resonates with the tank capacitor near minimum capacitance. Loading should increase as the output capacitance is de-

creased. A change in output capacitance requires a readjustment of C_4 for resonance. When the loading is near the desired point, final adjustment can be made by altering the inductance slightly.

A 20-A or similar exciter is well suited as a driver for this amplifier on all modes. The 813 runs cool at 500 watts input on a.m. and c.w. and at 1000 watts p.e.p. on s.s.b. (Originally described in *QST* for August, 1958.)

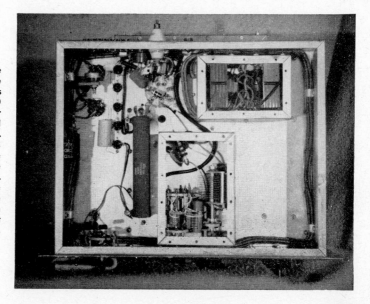

Fig. 6-62—Bottom view of the all-purpose 813 amplifier. The grid tank-circuit components within dashed lines in Fig. 6-70 are enclosed in the box at lower center. Input links are wound over ground ends of grid coils. Filament and bias transformers are in the second box. The large resistor to the left of the grid box is the screen resistor. The variable resistor in the upper left-hand corner is the relay shunt R_4. The selenium bias rectifier is fastened against the left-hand wall of the chassis.

A Medium-Power Tetrode Amplifier

Fig. 6-63—This medium-power tetrode amplifier is assembled on a 17 × 12 × 3-inch aluminum chassis with a 19 × 12¼-inch rack panel. Controls along the bottom of the panel are for the grid band switch, grid tuning capacitor, meter switch, a.c. power, and pi-network loading capacitor. Above are the controls for the plate tank capacitor and plate band switch. The sides and back of the shielding enclosure are a single piece of Reynolds perforated aluminum sheet "wrapped" around the chassis. A 1-inch lip is bent along the three top edges so that the top cover can be fastened on with sheet-metal screws.

Figs. 6-63 through 6-66 show photographs and circuit diagram of an amplifier using an RCA 7094 tetrode that will handle up to 500 watts input on c.w. or 330 watts with plate-screen modulation. Construction has been simplified by the use of manufactured subassemblies — a Harrington Electronics GP-50 multiband grid tank and a B & W type 851 bandswitching pi-network inductor. The amplifier is neutralized by the capacitive-bridge method. R_1 and L_5 are adjusted to suppress v.h.f. parasitic oscillation. The single milliammeter M_1 may be switched to read either grid or plate current. The shunt R_2 multiplies the original 50-ma. scale by 10, giving readings up to 500 ma. when the meter switch S_3 is in the plate-current position. Forced-air ventilation is provided by a small blower B_1.

Shielded wire is used in all power circuits and terminal leads are bypassed for v.h.f. as they enter the chassis.

Construction

The plate blocking capacitor is threaded onto one of the plate tank-capacitor stator rods. Plate-circuit leads are made of ½-inch copper strip. Screen and filament bypasses are connected directly between the tube-socket terminals and the perforated sheet. Each of the three screen terminals is bypassed with a 1000-$\mu\mu$f. 1600-volt disk ceramic capacitor. The grid-tank unit is spaced from the front wall of the chassis on 1-inch pillar insulators to provide space for an insulating shaft coupling.

Along the rear wall of the chassis are the coax

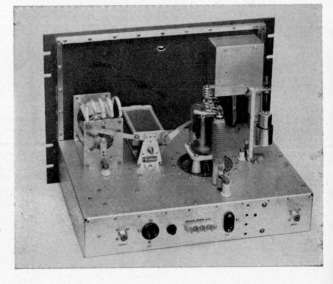

Fig. 6-64—Rear view of the medium-power amplifier. The shafts of the plate band switch and plate tuning capacitor are 2¾ and 6¼ inches from the left-hand end of the chassis in this view. A ventilating hole somewhat larger than the tube socket (829-B type) is centered 6½ inches from the right-hand end of the chassis and 6 inches from the rear. A piece of perforated aluminum covers the hole and supports the tube socket mounted on 1-inch ceramic cones. Feed-through insulators carry connections to the bottom terminals of the plate tank-coil unit, the plate r.f. choke and the neutralizing capacitor. The meter is enclosed in a 4 × 4 × 2-inch aluminum box.

Medium-Power Tetrode Amplifier

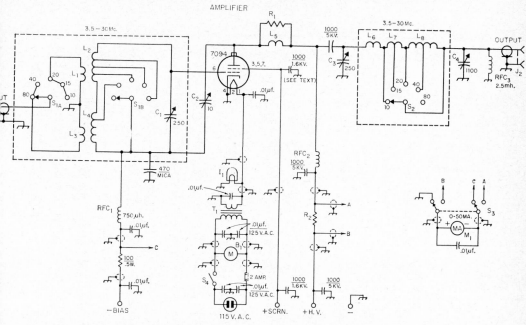

Fig. 6-65—Circuit of the 7094 amplifier. Unless specified otherwise, capacitances are in $\mu\mu$f. All fixed capacitors rated at less than 5 kv. are disk ceramic. The 5-kv. capacitors are TV-type ceramics (Centralab 858). Dashed lines in grid circuit enclose components of Harrington GP-50 multiband tank unit. Those in the plate circuit enclose components of the B & W 851 pi-network inductor.

B₁—Blower (Allied Radio Cat. No. 72P715).

C₁—250-$\mu\mu$f. midget variable (special).

C₂—Neutralizing capacitor—11 $\mu\mu$f. max. (Johnson N125).

C₃—250-$\mu\mu$f. 3000-volt variable (Johnson 250E30).

C₄—1100-$\mu\mu$f. variable—triple-gang broadcast replacement type, 365 $\mu\mu$f. (or more) per section, sections connected in parallel.

I₁—6.3-volt dial lamp.

J₁, J₂—Coax receptacle (SO-239).

L₁—2 turns No. 16, 1 inch diam., over ground end of L₂.

L₂—14 turns No. 16, ¾ inch diam., 2 inches long.

L₃—3 turns No. 16, 1 inch diam., over ground end of L₄

L₄—38 turns No. 22, ¾ inch diam., 1½ inches long.

L₅—3 turns No. 12, ⅜ inch diam., 1 inch long.

L₆—4 turns ³⁄₁₆ × ³⁄₁₆-inch copper strip, 1⅜ inches diameter, 2½ inches long.

L₇—4¾ turns No. 8, 2½ inches diam., 1¾ inches long,

tapped at 3 turns from the L₈ end.

L₈—9½ turns No. 12, 2½ inches diam., 1½ inches long, tapped at 6 turns from the output end (see text).

Note: L₇ and L₈ are mounted close together on the same axis; L₆ is mounted at right angles.

M₁—D.c. milliammeter, 0–50-ma. scale—3⅛-inch rectangular (Triplett Model 327-PL).

R₁—Three 150-ohm 1-watt carbon resistors in parallel.

R₂—Approx. 32 turns No. 24 on a ¼-inch diam. form (see measurements section for method of adjustment).

RFC₁—750-μh. r.f. choke (National R-33).

RFC₂—Plate r.f. choke 120μh (Raypar RL-101).

RFC₃—2.5-mh. r.f. choke (National R-50).

S₁—Two-wafer 5-position ceramic rotary switch.

S₂—Special heavy-duty 5-position rotary switch (component of B & W inductor unit).

T₁—Filament transformer: 6.3 volts, 3.5 amps. minimum (Thordarson 21F11).

output connector, a.c. power connector, fuse, screen-voltage, bias and ground terminals, high-voltage connector (Millen) and the coax input connector. Strips of ½-inch aluminum angle fastened to the panel provide a means of fastening the shielding enclosure to the panel. Paint should be removed where the angle rests against the panel so that there will be good electrical contact between the two.

Preliminary Adjustment

To maintain a tank Q of 10 at 4 and 7.3 Mc., 4 turns should be removed or shorted out at the front end of the B&W unit, and the 40-meter tap should be moved one turn toward the rear. (For operation at less than maximum ICAS ratings, see pi-network charts earlier in this chapter.)

Before applying excitation, the amplifier should be checked for v.h.f. parasitic oscillation as described earlier in this section. A resistor of about 20,000 ohms should be connected between the bias terminal and ground. Full plate voltage may be applied, but the screen should be operated from an adjustable 50,000-ohm 50-watt series resistor connected to the plate supply. The grid band switch should be turned to the 10-meter position and the plate switch to the 80-meter position. With the meter switched to read plate current, the screen resistance should be reduced until the plate power input is about 100 watts. The meter should then be switched to read grid current and the recommended procedure followed. The objective is to suppress the parasitic oscillation with the smallest possible coil to keep the parasitic-circuit

Fig. 6-66—Bottom view of the 7094 amplifier. The grid-tank assembly in the upper left-hand corner and the output loading capacitor in the lower right-hand corner are placed so that the shaft of the latter and the shaft of the grid band switch are 1½ inches from the ends of the chassis. Spacers between the chassis and the output capacitor bring its shaft level with those of the grid-tank unit. The meter switch is at the center. The filament transformer is mounted on an aluminum bracket. The ventilating fan is bolted against the rear wall of the chassis.

resonant frequency between the two v.h.f. TV bands. If oscillation is detected, additional loading resistors should be tried first. If this does not work, another turn should be added to the coil, or the turns squeezed closer together. With the parasitic coil described, the resonant frequency of the circuit is about 100 megacycles.

Neutralizing

Neutralizing should be done with excitation applied to produce rated grid current. The input and output circuits should be tuned to the same frequency. Plate and screen voltages should be disconnected at the transmitter terminals. The neutralizing capacitor should then be adjusted until a point is found where there is no change in grid current as the plate tank circuit is tuned through resonance. The output capacitor should be set at maximum capacitance for this check. After plate and screen voltages have been applied and the amplifier loaded, the neutralizing capacitor should be given a final adjustment to the point where minimum plate current and maximum grid and screen currents occur simultaneously.

Power Supply

Maximum ICAS ratings on the 7094 are 1500 volts, 330 ma. on c.w., 1500 volts, 200 ma. (max.) Class AB₁ s.s.b., and 1200 volts, 275 ma. for a.m. phone. However, the tube will work well at plate voltages down to at least 700 volts, provided appropriate values are used in the pi network as mentioned previously. The recommended screen voltage is 400 for all classes of operation at screen currents up to 30 ma., depending on the type of operation. Therefore a regulated screen voltage can be obtained using a pair of 0D3s and one 0C3 in series. If screen voltage is obtained from the plate supply, an adjustable 100-watt 75,000-ohm series resistor should be used and the value adjusted to obtain the desired operating plate current after initial tuning adjustments have been made.

Biasing

A fixed biasing voltage of 50 is required for s.s.b. operation. Batteries should last indefinitely. The biasing voltage may also be obtained from a voltage divider across a VR tube with suitable series resistor. A biasing voltage of 130 is recommended for plate-modulated Class C service, and 100 volts for c.w. operation. Recommended grid current is 5 ma. If the screen is operated from a fixed-voltage source, a source regulated by an 0A3 should provide plate-current cut off. The balance of the required operating bias may be obtained from a grid leak (5000 ohms for c.w. or 11,000 ohms for phone). In case the screen is supplied through a dropping resistor from the plate supply, fixed biasing voltages of 100 for c.w. or 130 for phone (no grid leak) should provide reasonable protection for the tube in case of failure of excitation.

The rated driving power is 5 watts, easily furnished by a 2E26 without pushing it. Existing transmitters using a 6L6, 6146 or 807 in the final may be used if provision is made for controlling the output of these units by adjustment of screen voltage.

Grounded-Grid Half Kilowatt

A Grounded-Grid Half Kilowatt

The amplifier shown in Figs. 6-67, 6-69 and 6-70 will run at about 500 watts input on c.w. — or p.e.p. input as an s.s.b. linear — on all bands from 80 through 10 meters. The unit is small enough to sit on the operating table right along with the rest of the station equipment; no need for big racks here.

Using a pair of 811As in parallel in the grounded-grid circuit, this rig is a good one to use following transmitters such as the Viking Ranger, DX-40, Globe Scout, and others of similar power class, for a worth-while increase in power output on c.w. As a linear amplifier following an s.s.b. exciter it requires no swamping because the 811A grids provide a fairly constant load in themselves, and also the fed-through power with grounded-grid presents an additional constant load to the driver. The total driving power needed on any band is less than 20 watts.

An additional useful feature is a built-in directional coupler using a version of the "Mickey Match." Besides its obvious application for checking the s.w.r. on the transmission line to the antenna or for help in tuning up a coax-coupled antenna coupler, it is practically indispensable as an indicator of relative power output in tuning the amplifier.

The Circuit

A number of tube types could be used in an amplifier of this power class, but the 811As are a good choice because they do not need a bias supply and are not expensive. (Surplus 811s can be used if you don't want to buy new tubes; the ratings are not quite as high but they can be pushed a bit in intermittent service such as c.w. and s.s.b.)

The complete circuit is shown in Fig. 6-68. To save trouble and work, standard components are used throughout — the only special construction is the shielding and a few simple r.f. chokes. The tube filaments are driven directly from coax input from the driver; no tuning is used or is needed in this circuit. The filaments are kept above ground by the B & W type FC15 filament choke.

The plate tank is the familiar pi network, using a B & W type 851 tapped coil and band-switch assembly. This assembly has been modified slightly in two respects: First, the copper-strip 10-meter coil normally mounted at the top of the rear plate is taken off and moved so that it is supported between the tank assembly and the stator of the tank tuning capacitor as shown in Fig. 6-69. A short length of copper strip is bolted between the free end of the coil and the right-hand stator connection of the tuning capacitor, to support the free end. This change is made in order to avoid the long lead that would have to be run from the capacitor to the regular input terminal on the tank assembly, since this terminal is at the right-hand side of the assembly as viewed from the top. The turns of the 10-meter coil are also squeezed together a bit to increase the inductance, because it was found that a rather large amount of capacitance had to be used to tune the circuit to the band with the coil at its original length. The length is now $1\frac{5}{8}$ inches between mounting holes.

The second modification is the addition of a pair of switch contacts on the rear switch plate of the tank assembly. There is an extra position on this plate with holes already provided for contacts, and the additional set of contacts is used to switch in fixed output loading capacitance on 80 meters, where a large output capacitance is needed. The variable loading capacitor, C_3, with the five fixed mica capacitors, C_5 to C_9 inclusive, give continuous variation of capacitance up to 1275 $\mu\mu$f. on all bands, including the regular switch position for the 80-meter band. However, if the switch is turned to the extra position an additional 1000-$\mu\mu$f. mica capacitor is connected in parallel, so that continuous variation of capacitance to over 2200 $\mu\mu$f. is possible on 80. This takes care of cases where the load resistance

Fig. 6-67—This amplifier operates at a plate input of approximately 500 watts, uses a pair of 811As in grounded-grid, and is complete with power supply on a 13 × 17 × 4-inch chassis. The rack panel is 10½ by 19 inches. Front-panel controls include the plate tuning capacitor and band switch in the center, filament and plate power switches with their pilot lights at the lower left, sensitivity control and forward-reflected power switch for the directional coupler at the lower right, variable loading capacitor and auxiliary loading-capacitor switch underneath the 0-1 milliammeter at the right, and the grid-cathode milliammeter with its switch at the upper left. The filter choke, 866As and plate transformer occupy the rear section of the chassis.

happens to be unusually low or reactive.[1]

A 500-ma. d.c. meter is used for reading either total cathode current or grid current alone. The cathode current is read in preference to plate

current because of safety considerations. Putting the meter in the hot d.c. plate lead leaves nothing but a little plastic insulation between the high voltage and the meter adjusting screw. It is a bit of a nuisance to have to subtract the grid current from the cathode current in order to find the plate current, but it isn't serious. The d.c. grid circuit has a jack, J_3, for introducing external bias either for blocked-grid keying or for cutting

[1]These contacts can be obtained directly from the manufacturer of the tank assembly. To secure a set of contacts with mounting hardware, send one dollar to Barker & Williamson, Beaver Dam and Canal, Bristol, Penna., specifying the type of tank assembly for which they are wanted. The contacts are not catalog items and are not available through dealers.

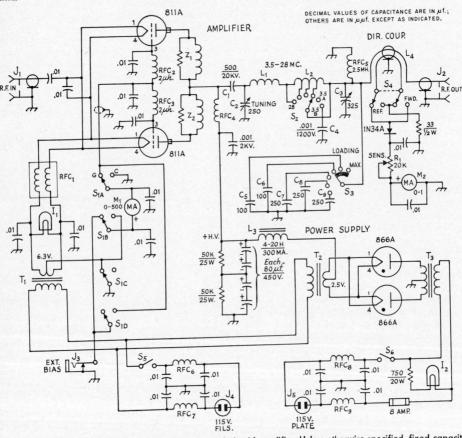

Fig. 6-68 — Circuit diagram of the parallel-811A grounded-grid amplifier. Unless otherwise specified, fixed capacitors are disk ceramic, 600-volt rating.

C_1—500 $\mu\mu$f., 20,000 volts (TV "doorknob" type).

C_2—250-$\mu\mu$f. variable, 2000 volts (Johnson 250E20).

C_3—325-$\mu\mu$f. variable, receiving type (Hammarlund) MC-325-M).

C_4–C_9, inc.—1200-volt mica, case style CM-45.

I_1, I_2—6.3-volt dial lamp, 150-ma. (No. 47).

J_1, J_2—Coax connector, chassis mounting.

J_3—Closed-circuit phone jack.

J_4, J_5—115-volt male connector, chassis mounting (Amphenol 61-M1).

L_1, L_2, S_2—5-band pi-network coil-switch assembly; see text (B & W 851).

L_3—Swinging choke, 4-20 henrys, 300 ma. (UTC S-34).

L_4—Section of coax line with extra conductor inserted; see Footnote 1 for construction references.

M_1, M_2—Milliammeter, 3½-inch plastic case (Triplett 327-PL).

R_1—20,000-ohm composition control, linear taper.

RFC_1—Filament-choke assembly, to carry 8 amp. (B & W FC15).

RFC_2, RFC_3—2 μh. (National R-60).

RFC_4—90 μh.; 4⅜-inch winding of No. 26, 40 t.p.i., on ¾-inch ceramic form (B & W 800).

RFC_5—2.5 mh., any type.

RFC_6–RFC_9, Incl.—18 turns No. 14 enam., close-wound, ½-inch diam., self-supporting.

S_1—4-pole 2-position rotary, nonshorting (Mallory 3242J or Centralab 1450).

S_2—Part of tank assembly; see L_1 L_2.

S_3—Miniature ceramic rotary, 1 section, 1 pole, 6 positions used, progressive shorting (Centralab 2042).

S_4—Miniature ceramic rotary, 1 section, 2 poles, 2 positions used, nonshorting (Centralab 2003).

S_5, S_6—S.p.s.t. toggle.

T_1—Filament transformer, 6.3 volts, 8 amp. min. (UTC S-61).

T_2—Filament transformer, 2.5 volts, 10 amp. (UTC S-57).

T_3—Plate transformer, 3000 volts center-tapped, 300 ma. d.c. (UTC S-47).

Grounded-Grid Half Kilowatt

off the plate current during receiving, and a four-pole switch, S_1, is therefore needed for handling the meter switching while keeping all circuits functioning normally.

The power supply uses 866As with a plate transformer giving 1500 volts each side of the center tap, and working into a single-section choke-input filter. The filter capacitor consists of four 80-μf. electrolytics connected in series to handle the voltage, giving an effective filter capacitance of 20 μf. This supply is running well below its capabilities in the intermittent type of operation represented by c.w. and s.s.b., and the amplifier is somewhat "over-powered" in this respect. A lighter plate transformer can be used since the average current in regular operation is only about half the maximum tube rating of 350 ma. for the pair.

The a.c. inputs to both filaments and plates have TVI filters installed right at the a.c. connectors. The chokes in these filters, RFC_6 to RFC_9 inclusive, are homemade by winding 18 turns of No. 14 enameled wire close-wound on a half-inch dowel or drill.

Construction

The only space available for the filament transformers is below chassis, so these are mounted on the front wall of the chassis as shown in Fig. 6-70. There is plenty of room for all other power-supply parts below chassis, and the photographs make any further comment on this section unnecessary.

The r.f. layout shown in Fig. 6-69 is almost an exact copy of the circuit layout as given in Fig. 6-68. The plate blocking capacitor, C_1, is mounted on a small right-angle bracket fastened to the left-hand stator connection of the tank capacitor, C_2. The tube plates are connected to C_1 through individual parasitic-suppressor assemblies, Z_1 and Z_2. The hot end of the plate choke, RFC_4, also connects to this same point. The tank capacitor is mounted on $\frac{3}{4}$-inch ceramic pillars to bring its shaft to the same height as the switch shaft on the tank-coil assembly. The

capacitor is grounded by connecting the bottom of its frame through a half-inch wide strip of aluminum to essentially the same point at which the plate-choke bypass capacitor, a 0.001-μf. 2000-volt disk, is grounded. The ground end of the aluminum strip actually is under the bottom of the plate choke, and the ground lug for the bypass capacitor is just to the left. This strip, plus short leads in the circuit from the tube plates through the tank capacitor to ground, keep the resonant frequency of the loop thus formed well up in the v.h.f. region; this is important because it permits using low-inductance parasitic chokes in shunt with the suppressor resistors, and thus tends to keep the r.f. plate current at the regular operating frequencies out of the resistors. With other tank grounding arrangements originally tried, larger parasitic chokes had to be used and it was impossible to prevent the resistors from burning up when operating on 10, 15 and even 20 meters. Now they do not overheat on any frequency, and v.h.f. parasitics are nonexistent — although without the suppressors the parasitics are only too much in evidence.

The output loading capacitors, C_3 through C_9, are mounted toward the rear so the leads from the tank coil can be kept as short as possible. A length of copper strip is used between the coil and the stator of C_3; originally this lead was No. 14 wire but on 10 meters the tank current was enough to heat it to the point of discoloration. The ground lead from the fixed units, made to the rear bearing connection of C_3, is also copper strip. C_3 and S_3 are operated through extension shafts, using Millen flexible couplings to simplify the alignment problem.

Underneath the chassis, each 811A grid is bypassed directly to the socket-mounting screw nearest the plate choke (right-hand side of the socket in Fig. 6-70). The d.c. leads have small chokes, RFC_2 and RFC_3, with additional bypasses for good r.f. filtering, particularly at v.h.f. since grid rectification generates harmonics in the TV bands. The filament choke, RFC_1, is mounted

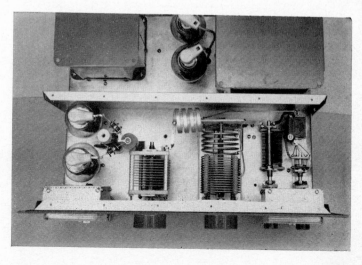

Fig. 6-69—The r.f. section with the shield cover removed. Components here are readily identifiable by reference to the circuit diagram. The meters are enclosed in rectangular boxes made from thin aluminum sheet, formed to be fastened by the meter mounting screws. The back covers on these boxes are made from perforated aluminum, folded over at the edges and held on the boxes by sheet-metal screws. The switch for shifting the 0-500 milliammeter (left) from grid to cathode is concealed by the box which encloses the meter.

so that the filament side is close to the filament terminals on the tube sockets; the other end is bypassed directly to the chassis.

The shielding around the amplifier consists of two pieces of sheet aluminum and a perforated aluminum ("do-it-yourself" type) cover having the shape of an inverted U. Fig. 6-69 shows how the rear wall is made. Its edges are bent to provide flanges for fastening the cover with sheet-metal screws, and there is a similar flange projecting to the rear at the bottom for fastening the wall to the chassis. The front piece extends the full height of the panel and is identically drilled and cut out for meters and controls. It has flanges at the top and extending down the sides from the top to the chassis. The cover itself extends down over the sides of the chassis for about one inch. Numerous screws are used for fastening the cover, to prevent leakage of harmonics.

The shields over the meters are made as described in the caption for the inside top view. Meter leads are bypassed to the shield boxes where they emerge.

Construction of the directional coupler parallels that given for the antenna coupler in Chapter Thirteen.

Operating Conditions and Tuning

The voltage delivered by the power supply is approximately 1500 volts with no drive and with the tubes taking only the no-bias static plate current, which is about 60 ma. At the full load of 350 ma. the voltage is slightly under 1400. Optimum operating conditions for 1400 volts at 350 ma. peak-envelope power input as an s.s.b. linear call for a peak-envelope grid current of 60 ma. The peak-envelope tube power output is close to 350 watts under these conditions. The same operating conditions are also about optimum for c.w.

The behavior of the cathode current when tuning a grounded-grid triode amplifier is somewhat confusing, and the meter is principally useful as a check on operating conditions rather than as a tuning indicator. The best indicator of proper tuning of the plate tank capacitor is the forward-power reading of the directional coupler. For any trial setting of the loading controls and driving power, *always* set the plate tank capacitor control at the point which results in a maximum reading on the power-output indicator.

The power indications are only relative, of course, and the sensitivity control should be set to give a reading in the upper half of the scale of the meter.

The objective in adjusting loading and drive is to arrive at maximum power output simultaneously with a plate current of 350 ma. and a grid current of 60 ma. — that is, a total cathode current of 410 ma. when the grid current reading is 60 ma. The loading is critical. If the amplifier is not loaded heavily enough the grid current will be too high and the right value of total cathode current either will not be reached or, if reached, the amplifier will be operating in the "flattening" region as an s.s.b. linear. (It can be operated this way on c.w., however, since linearity is unimportant here.) If the loading is too heavy, the grid current will be low when the cathode current reaches the proper value, but the efficiency will be low and the tubes will overheat.

Getting the knack of it takes a little practice, but when the job is done right the tubes will run cool on all bands in regular operation. Running key-down over a period of time may show just a trace of dark red color on the plates since the input and dissipation are somewhat over ratings under these operating conditions, although perfectly satisfactory with ordinary keying or s.s.b. voice.

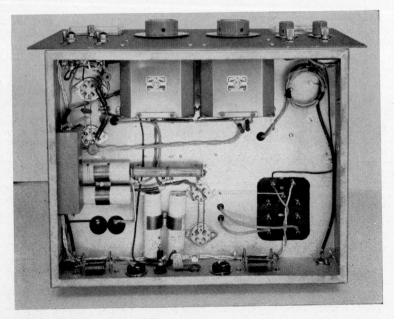

Fig. 6-70—In this below-chassis view, the two filament transformers are at the top, mounted on the chassis wall. The 811A sockets are at the upper left. The rectangular box on the left-hand wall contains the FC15 filament-choke assembly. The "Mickey Match" directional coupler is at the upper right. Filter capacitors and the bleeder resistors are in the lower section. A.c. inlets, fuse holder, bias jack, and the 115-volt line TVI filters are on the bottom chassis wall.

650-Watt Amplifier

A Compact 650-Watt Amplifier

Compactness in the high-power amplifier shown in Figs. 6-71 through 6-76 is achieved through the use of germanium rectifiers in the power supply and tubes of the radial-beam type. When driven by an exciter delivering about 30 watts output, the amplifier runs at about 650 watts input and gives an output of about 400 watts on c.w. or p.e.p. s.s.b. It covers 80 through 10 meters by means of band switching and has a fixed 50-ohm output impedance.

Two 4X250B tubes operating Class AB$_2$ are used in a grounded-cathode circuit (see Fig. 6-72). No grid tuning is used, since an exciter of the size mentioned will drive the grids directly across the 110-ohm resistance. L_1 is a series peaking coil to increase the drive on 10 meters. A parallel-tuned tank with fixed-link output coupling is used in the plate circuit. This system has the advantage that series plate feed can be used, and no large output capacitance is needed. Tuning is straightforward and the coupling, once adjusted holds over a wide frequency range.

The link circuit is grounded through a removable jumper at the output connector, so that a balanced load can be fed if desired.

The small 15-$\mu\mu$f. capacitor (CRL Type 850), from the plates to ground, provides a short path for harmonic currents and keeps them out of the output coil. On the 3.5- to 4-Mc. range a fixed 100-$\mu\mu$f. capacitor is connected across the coil, so that a proper L-to-C ratio can be maintained at 4 Mc. When switched out of the circuit, the coil and fixed capacitor resonate around 5 Mc., which is sufficiently removed from any of the other ranges to avoid any difficulty.

The 10-ohm resistor in the B + lead serves as a fuse in case of a shorted tube or other fault that might endanger the power supply.

Power Supply

The plate supply uses two voltage doublers in series; see Fig. 6-75. Two 325-volt windings on T_2 feed strings of germanium rectifiers in full-wave voltage-doubler connections. Each doubler capacitance is 160 μf., made up of two parallel 80-μf. 450-volt cartridge type units with cardboard sleeves. The chassis is lined with insulating material under the C_5 and C_6 capacitors, since their outer cans run as high as +1300 volts. The ripple is around 3 per cent r.m.s., and the regulation from no load to full load is about 15 per cent. Sixteen cells are used. Each group of four cells in one side of a voltage doubler has two 560 K resistors connected across pairs of cells to equalize the reverse voltage drop. Other 560 K resistors are connected as bleeders only as a safety measure, since no bleeders are needed for proper circuit operation. But even with the bleeders, the capacitors can retain a charge for several minutes, so be careful!

Grid bias is furnished by a 75-volt winding on T_1, a half-wave rectifier and an 80-μf. capacitor. About −90 volts is developed across C_9 and applied to the tubes during stand-by periods. The operating bias is adjustable from −30 to −60 volts by R_3.

Screen voltage is taken from the +375-volt point of the plate supply (junction C_7 and C_8). It is dropped through the 6BF5 regulator to deliver a low-impedance output adjustable from about 250 to 325 volts at up to 75 ma. Since this type of regulator will not handle reverse current, bleeder R_2 (Fig. 6-72) is provided to offset no-signal negative screen current to the 4X250Bs and make the screen meter read on scale.

When in operating condition, the "reference" voltage for the screen regulator is the −90 volt bias supply. In stand-by condition the reference is switched down to the tap on R_3, thus reducing the screen voltage from its nominal +300 or so to a lower value. This action, together with the increased grid bias, insures that the 4X250Bs

Fig. 6-71—The panel of this 650-watt amplifier built by W9LZY measures only 10 by 14 inches. Below the meter are the meter switch, high-voltage switch and filament/bias switch. To the right are controls for the band switch (above) and the tank capacitor (below).

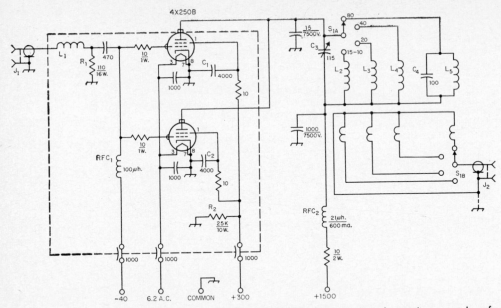

Fig. 6-72—Circuit diagram of the r.f. portion of the amplifier. Unless otherwise indicated, capacitances are in $\mu\mu$f., resistances are in ohms, resistors are ½ watt. The 1000-$\mu\mu$f. plate bypass is a CRL Type 858-S; the 1000-$\mu\mu$f. feed-through capacitors are 500-volt ceramic.

C_1, C_2—Four 1000-$\mu\mu$f. 500-volt disk ceramic capacitors in parallel.

C_3—115-$\mu\mu$f. variable, 2000-volt spacing. See text.

C_4—Two 25-$\mu\mu$f. NPO ceramic and one 50-$\mu\mu$f. N750 ceramic in parallel, 7500-volt rating.

J_1—UG-291/U BNC panel jack (Amphenol 31-001).

J_2—SO-239 UHF panel jack (Amphenol 83-1R).

L_1—6 turns No. 20, ⅜-inch diam., ½ inch long.

L_2—4½ turns ⅛-inch copper tubing, 1¼ inches long, 1⅛-inch diam. Link is 3 turns No. 16 wire, ¾ inch long, ¾-inch diam

L_3—6 turns ⅛-inch copper tubing, 1½ inch long, 1⅝-inch

diam. Link is 2 turns No. 12, ½ inch long, 1⅛-inch diam.

L_4—8½ turns No. 12, 1⅛ inches long, 2⅛-inch diam. Link is 3 turns No. 12, ⅝ inch long, 1½-inch diam.

L_5—Two coils, see text. Outer is 10 turns No. 12, 1⅜ inches long, 2⅛-inch diam. Inner coil is 6½ turns No. 12, ¾ inch long, 1¾-inch diam., inside plate end of outer coil. Link is 4 turns No. 12, ½ inch long, 1½-inch diam.

RFC_1—100-μh. r.f. choke (National R-33-4).

RFC_2—21-μh. 600-ma. r. f. choke (Ohmite Z-28).

draw no current in standby condition. In operation the grid, screen, and plate voltages all tend to vary in proportion to line-voltage changes.

The screen current is measured by switching the 0-75 milliammeter across 22 ohms in the lead

to the screen-voltage regulator. The resistor has negligible shunting effect. For measuring plate current the meter is switched across a low resistance R_6, connected between the two sections of the plate supply. R_5 was adjusted for

Fig. 6-73—Rear view of the 650-watt amplifier showing mounting of the 4X250Bs and the plate transformer. Shields in the foreground enclose voltage-regulator tubes and a relay. The shaft protruding from the rear edge of the chassis operates the bias potentiometer.

650-Watt Amplifier

Fig. 6-74—Side view of the 4X250B amplifier showing mounting of the band switch and tank coils. The chassis is perforated for ventilation.

full-scale meter reading at 750 ma. There is a maximum of 425 volts between switch contacts and 850 volts from contacts to ground.

The stand-by relay K_1 is one that plugs into a 7-pin miniature socket. It operates from 115 volts a.c. and a half-wave power supply. The input is brought out to two terminals on the rear of the chassis, where connection is made across the antenna relay coil.

Construction

The amplifier is built on an 8×14-inch chassis with a 10×14-inch panel. The chassis is $4\frac{1}{2}$ inches deep, to provide space for the filter capacitors and cooling fan underneath. As can be seen by studying the photographs, the plate power supply occupies the left end of the chassis, and the r.f. circuits take most of the remaining space. The heater and bias supply is stowed under the right rear corner of the chassis behind the plate tuning capacitor. The screen regulator and stand-by relay are at the rear of the chassis in the center.

The controls are few and simple. The band switch has four positions, for the 80-, 40-, 20- and 15- and 10-meter bands. Other controls are the plate tuning capacitor, plate-current/screen-current meter switch, power and plate voltage switches.

The plate tank capacitor is one from a BC-375 tuning unit, mounted under the chassis on four ceramic feed-through bushings. (Any other capacitor of equivalent rating, such as the Johnson 155-4 may be substituted.) Four holes were drilled and tapped in the $\frac{1}{4}$-inch square frame rods on the right-hand side of the capacitor, and 6-32 threaded rod was screwed into the holes and passed through the insulators. The four screws project above the insulators at

the top of the chassis, where the B+ ends of the plate coils connect to them via copper strips. An insulated shaft extension goes through the panel to the tuning knob.

The wire from each coil was wrapped around a pipe of suitable diameter. Four Plexiglass strips were drilled with clearance holes at the desired spacing, then the coil wire was fed through the holes. The 80-meter coil was made with two concentric sections in series to get enough inductance into the available space. The 80- and 40-meter links were also threaded through strips, while the 20- and 10-meter links are self-supporting. All links are a push fit inside the insulating strips of their respective coils, and are held with a drop or two of cement after adjustment.

The two band-switch wafers are each single-pole, 4-position, 60-degree throw (Communications Products Co., Type 86). A 60-degree index-and-shaft assembly from an Oak Type H switch was used. The rest of the switch was made up from 6-32 threaded brass rod, $\frac{1}{4}$-inch o.d. tubing, 1/16-inch aluminum sheet, and miscellaneous ceramic spacers and fiber washers from junked rotary switches.

The front wafer switches the plate coils. The links are connected to the rear wafer through RG-58/U cable, except the 80-meter link which goes direct. The cold sides of all links are soldered to a strip of copper running around the wafer, supported by 2-56 screws through the unused holes between contacts. The u.h.f.-type output connector is mounted on a strip of bakelite fastened to the rear switch bracket; its shell is grounded through a couple of solder lugs shown. T_2 weighs about twenty pounds; the chassis should be at least 0.08-inch aluminum to be strong enough to carry it.

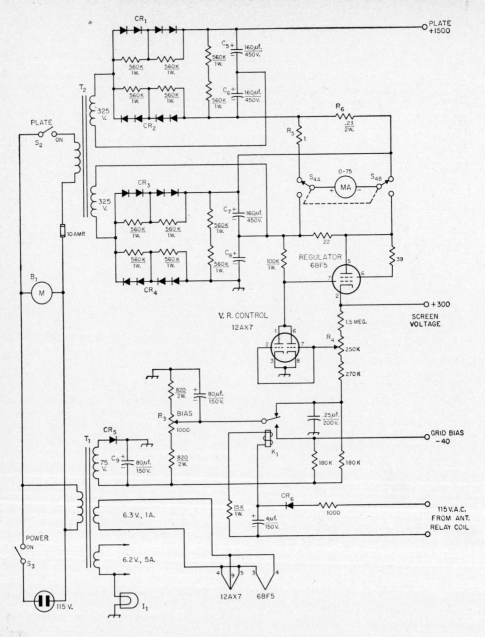

Fig. 6-75—Circuit of the power supply. Unless otherwise indicated, resistances are in ohms, resistors are ½ watt.

B₁—3250-r.p.m. motor with 4-inch fan blade (Rotron* 92-AS motor).

C₅ C₆, C₇, C₈—Two 80-μf. electrolytics in parallel (Sprague TVA-1716). Insulate as described in text.

CR₁—CR₄—Four 500-ma. 300-volt peak inverse (1N153 or equiv.).

CR₅—100-ma. 380-volt peak inverse.

CR₆—65-ma. 380-volt peak inverse (Federal 1002A).

I₁—150-ma. 6-8 volts (GE No. 47).

K₁—5000-ohm coil, 4 ma. pull-in (Terado Series 600 or *Rotron Mfg. Co., 7 Schoonmaker Lane, Woodstock, New York.

equivalent).

R₂—2-watt linear potentiometer (Ohmite CU-1021).

R₄—2-watt linear potentiometer (Ohmite CU-2541).

S₂, S₃—15-amp. 125-volt toggle (Cutler-Hammer 7501-K13).

S₄—Two-pole 2-throw 60-degree throw ceramic rotary switch, non-shorting. See text.

T₁—6.2 volts at 5.5 amp., 6.3 volts at 1 amp., 75 volts at 100 ma. (Forest Electric Co.** T-423).

T₂—Two-secondaries, each 325 volts, 1 amp. (Forest** T-412).

**Forest Electric Co., 7216 Circle Rd., Forest Park, Ill.

650-Watt Amplifier

Fig. 6-76—This bottom view show the ventilating fan, tank capacitor, rectifier stacks and filter capacitors.

A bottom cover and a perforated-metal shield over the top, sides and rear should be added, for safety as well as TVI-proofing. An opening should be cut above the r.f. tubes and covered with hardware cloth.

Cooling

Each 4X250B tube requires at least 3.6 cubic feet of air per minute through the anode cooler. The base also requires some air. The tube is ordinarily mounted in an Eimac "air-system" socket so that the air flows first over the base, then through the anode cooler. This leads to a fairly large pressure drop, which is ordinarily considered to require a centrifugal blower. Since a blower of this type requires considerable space, the design has been altered to permit the use of a fan. Only the insulating rings and contacts from Eimac sockets are used, mounted by the cathode tabs in oversized holes in the chassis. Many small holes are drilled in the chassis to provide additional air passage. A small aluminum housing above the chassis directs all the air through the anode coolers. It comes to within 1/4 inch of the anode coolers. The opening is closed by a piece of Fiberglas-base plastic fitting on top. It comes to within 1/16 inch of the tubes, so that a small amount of the air flows around the outside of the coolers.

All of the left end and part of the right end of the chassis are perforated by 3/8-inch holes. The air drawn in by the fan passes over the plate rectifier fins and past the heater transformer. The whole air path is direct and free from large obstructions and sharp bends.

The fan is a 4-inch blade driven by a Rotron Mfg. Co. Type 92-AS motor at 3250 r.p.m. It is mounted in a hole 4 1/8 inches in diameter in the grid housing, with about 1/8 of the blade thickness projecting into the housing. The motor is a capacitor-run type. The 1-μf. 600-volt phasing capacitor mounts on the side of the grid housing. The motor, housing and capacitor can be removed as a unit, leaving only the front and rear walls of the housing in place.

Under the conditions described, the pressure vs. flow curves of the fan and of the tubes indicate that somewhere around 10 c.f.m. of air is delivered. This is entirely ample for the pair of 4X250Bs. Since the only major source of heat is the tubes, and since this heat is quickly removed by the air, the whole amplifier runs at a satisfactorily low temperature.

Operation

For Class AB$_2$ operation, the screen voltage is set at 300 volts, and the grid bias at a point (about −40 volts) where the tubes draw 150 ma. without drive. When operating and fully loaded, full output from an HT-30 or similar exciter should swing the plate current to approximately 400 ma.

The various links are of approximately the right inductance to couple to a 50-ohm load. They must be quite tightly coupled to their plate coils. When properly positioned with a 50-ohm load connected, the plate current dips 10 or 15 ma. as the plate capacitor is tuned through resonance with r.f. drive applied. Once adjusted, these links are left alone. The antenna is tuned with the aid of an s.w.r. bridge to present a 50-ohm load to the amplifier. The amplifier should not be operated without a suitable load

Operation is now very simple. The heaters are warmed up for at least 30 seconds. With the plate power switch off, the band switch is set to the proper range. The exciter is tuned up to give c.w. output. (Not more than 40 volts r.m.s.) The plate power is turned on and the plate capacitor tuned to the plate current dip, or to maximum indicated output if a Micromatch is being used. The exciter is then set to give the type of output desired.

(Originally described in *QST* for Sept. 1958.)

4-250-A's in a 1-Kw. Final

The amplifier shown in the accompanying photographs uses two 4-250As in parallel and covers 3.5 to 28 Mc. with complete band-switching. The output circuit is a pi network designed for working into reasonably well-matched 52- to 75-ohm coaxial lines. The amplifier can handle a kilowatt input in Class C operation on either phone or c.w. without pushing the tubes to their limits. It can also be operated as a linear amplifier for single side band.

The various components are mounted on a 17 × 13 × 4-inch aluminum chassis attached to a standard 19-inch relay rack panel 15¾-inches high. The above-chassis section is enclosed in a 11½-inch high shield made from ⅟₁₆-inch sheet aluminum. An aluminum bottom plate completes the below-chassis shielding. Enclosing the amplifier in this way, plus the use of shielded wire and filters in the supply leads, takes care of the harmonic TVI question.

The 4-250As are cooled by forcing air into the chassis and thence up past the tubes by means of a 21 cu. ft. per minute blower. The air is exhausted through two 3-inch diameter circular openings over the tubes in the top cover. To maintain the shielding intact, these are covered with perforated aluminum.

A Barker and Williamson Model 850 band-switching pi-tank inductor is used in the output circuit. It is tuned by a vacuum variable capacitor operated through the counter dial (Groth TC-3) shown in the panel view

Circuit Details

The circuit, Fig. 6-78, is electrically the more-or-less standard arrangement of a parallel-tuned grid circuit and a pi-network output circuit. The amplifier is neutralized by the capacitive bridge method. A filament transformer is included, but all other voltages come from external supplies.

The grid input circuit of the amplifier uses a slightly modified B&W turret assembly. The grid coils are tuned by a 75-$\mu\mu$f. variable. The 20-, 15-, and 10-meter coils each must have a few turns removed for proper grid tuning on these bands.

The circuit includes a 2000-ohm grid leak and has provisions for external bias, which should be used in combination with the leak. The bypass capacitors on the screen leads all carry a rating of 1600 volts. This rating is necessary to avoid capacitor breakdowns when operating the amplifier screens at their rated voltages for AB$_1$ operation, and also with plate-modulated Class C operation where the 600-volt rating of the smaller ceramic capacitors would be exceeded on modulation peaks. All of the 0.001- and 0.003-μf. capacitors are the disk type, and aside from the screen bypasses are used mainly for filtering TV harmonics from the supply leads.

The bypass capacitors in the high-voltage lead

Fig. 6-77—A 1-kw. final using a pair of 4-250-A's in parallel.

1-Kw. Amplifier

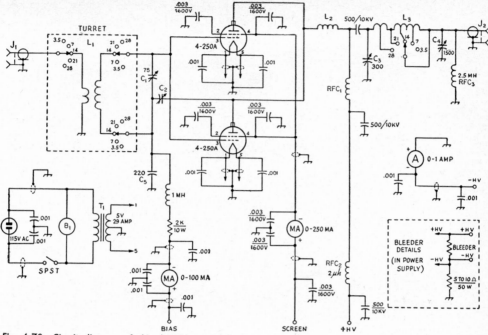

Fig. 6-78—Circuit diagram of the 4-250A amplifier.

B₁—Blower-motor assembly, 21 c.f.m. (Ripley model 8433).

C₁—75-μμf. variable, receiving spacing (Millen 19075).

C2—7-μμf. neutralizing capacitor (Cardwell type ADN).

C₃—300-μμf. vacuum variable (Jennings type UCS).

C₄—1500-μμf. variable (Cardwell type 8013).

C₅—220-μμf. mica or NPO ceramic.

J₁, J₂—Coax receptacle, chassis mounting.

L₁—Turret assembly (B&W BTEL with 14-, 21-, and 28-Mc. coils modified by removing turns).
3.5 Mc.: 39 turns No. 22, 1¼ inches diam., 1⅜ inches long, link 3 turns No. 18.
7 Mc.: 20 turns No. 20, 1¼ inches diam., 1W inches long, link 3 turns No. 18.

14 Mc.: 8 turns No. 18, 1¼ inches diam., ¾ inch long, link 2 turns No. 18.
21 Mc.: 4 turns No. 16, 1¼ inches diam., ½ inch long, link 1 turn No. 18.
28 Mc.: 2½ turns No. 16, 1¼ inches diam., ½ inch long, link 1 turn No. 18.

L₂—V.h.f. parasitic suppressor, 4 turns No. 12, ¼ inch dia., turns spaced wire diameter.

L₃—Pi-tank inductor (B&W Model 850). Inductances as follows: 3.5 Mc., 13.5 μh.; 7 Mc., 6.5 μh.; 14 Mc. 1.75 μ.; 21 Mc., 1 μh.; 28 Mc., 0.8 μh.

RFC₁—National type R175A r.f. choke.

RFC₂—2-μph. 500-ma. r.f. choke (National type R-60).

RFC₃—2.5-mh. r.f. choke.

T₁—Filament transformer, 5 volts, 29 amp. (Thordarson T-21FO7-A).

are the TV high-voltage ceramic type, as is also the blocking capacitor in the tank circuit. The loading capacitor, C_4, in the output circuit of the amplifier is a variable having enough range (1500 μμf. total capacitance) to give adequate loading on 80 through 10 meters when working into a 52- or 75-ohm resistive load.

Plate current is metered by a 0–1 ammeter shunted across a resistor in the negative high-voltage lead. As shown in Fig. 6-78, this resistor is incorporated in the power supply, not in the amplifier unit. A 50-watt rating represents an ample safety factor, since the power dissipated would not exceed a few watts should the ammeter open up.

Separate milliammeters are provided for the grid and screen circuits. The screen meter is quite essential since the screen current, and hence screen dissipation, is very sensitive to grid driving voltage and plate tuning.

Layout Details

Fig. 6-79 is a view looking into the amplifier with the top cover removed. The variable capaci-

tor at the right is the output loading control, C_4. To the left of C_4 is the Model 850 inductor unit. Immediately to the rear (below, in the photograph) of the inductor is the output lead, connected to a coaxial receptacle mounted on the rear cover. The vacuum variable, C_3, is mounted between the inductor and the 4-250As. It is supported by an aluminum bracket 6 inches high and 4 inches wide. The neutralizing capacitor C_2 is between the 4-250As and the front panel.

The grid turret and tuning capacitor are mounted underneath the chassis to take advantage of the shielding afforded thereby. To fit under the chassis the turret is mounted with the switch shaft vertical, necessitating a right-angle drive to the panel control. The shaft approaches the panel at an angle, so a flexible coupling of the ball type (Millen 39001) is used between the shaft and panel bearing.

The meters are in a separate enclosure measuring 11 × 3 × 3-inches. It is mounted to the front of the box by countersunk flat-head screws. The top lips of the meter box are drilled to take sheet-metal screws when the lid is in place.

Fig 6-79 (above)   Fig. 6-80 (below)

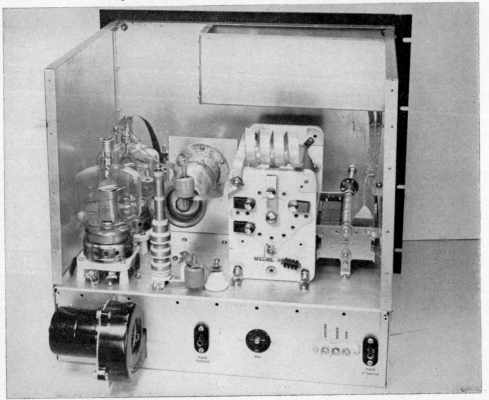

1-Kw. Amplifier

Fig. 6-81

Connections to the tube plates and neutralizing capacitor are made from flexible brass strip $\frac{1}{2}$ inch wide. A piece of $\frac{3}{4}$-inch wide brass strip is used for the connection between the stator terminal of the vacuum variable and the tank inductor. The blocking capacitor is mounted on this strip.

Fig. 6-80 shows the amplifier with the top and back panels removed. The blower assembly is mounted on the rear chassis wall. To the right of the motor is the high-voltage terminal, the 115-volt connector, the grid and screen terminals, and the high-voltage negative connector. Leads from these last three terminals run below chassis in shielded wire and then up to the meter box. These leads are visible in front of the loading capacitor. Belden 8885 shielded wire is used for the leads. The inner conductor is bypassed to the shield braid at each end. The 2.5-mh. "safety" choke, RFC_3, shunting the output end of the pi network is mounted on the back of the tank coil between the output lead and chassis ground.

The isolantite feedthrough insulator to the left of the inductor is used to bring the high voltage through the chassis. Adjacent to it is the bypass at the bottom of the plate choke, RFC_1.

Mounting details of the right-angle drive assembly for switching the grid circuit are clearly visible in Fig. 6-81. A $\frac{1}{2}$-inch square rod $2\frac{3}{4}$ inches long is drilled and tapped at both ends to support the drive.

The sockets for the 4-250As are mounted on one-inch isolantite pillars. The screen and filament terminals are bypassed directly at the socket terminals. The grid terminals on the sockets face each other, and a small feedthrough is used to bring the grid lead up through the chassis.

Fig. 6-82 is a bottom view of the amplifier and Fig. 6-83 is a close-up view of the grid circuit. A short length of RG-58/U is used to connect J_1 on the rear chassis wall to the link terminals on the turret assembly. The high-voltage lead is filtered by the 500-$\mu\mu$f. ceramic bypass and RFC_2. These two components are visible on the inside of the rear wall above the blower assembly. Two-terminal tie-points are used for the a.c. connections to the filament transformer and blower motor. Shielded leads are used between the tie-points and the 115-volt connector.

Fig. 6-83 shows the grid-circuit wiring in a bit more detail, particularly the grid choke, grid resistor and C_5 clustered just above the tuning capacitor. The modifications to the 10- and 15-meter coils also are somewhat more easily seen in this photograph.

Adjustment and Operating Data

The amplifier should be neutralized with the plate and screen supply leads disconnected and the bandswitch set to 28 Mc. An indicating wave meter should be coupled to the tank circuit and drive applied to the amplifier. Resonate the grid and plate tanks and adjust the neutralizing capacitor for minimum r.f. in the tank circuit as indicated by the wave meter. The same neutralizing adjustment should hold for all bands. Don't attempt to neutralize with the plate and screen supply leads connected — i.e., with a complete circuit for d.c. — because even with the power turned off this permits electrons to flow from the cathode to the plate and screen, and r.f. will be present that cannot be neutralized out.

The parasitic choke will, in general, resonate the plate lead in one of the low v.h.f. TV channels, and will tend to increase harmonic output in that channel. Measure the resonant frequency of the plate lead at L_2 with a grid-dip meter, and if it is in one of the channels received in your locality, either pull the turns apart, or squeeze them together to move the frequency to an unused channel. Any frequency from 70 to 100 Mc. should be satisfactory.

Fig. 6-83

Power Supply

For 1 kw. input, a plate voltage of at least 2000 is required. Screen voltage is obtained preferably from a separate 400-volt supply. For Class C operation, an external bias supply regulated by a VR-150, plus a grid leak of 2000 ohms is recommended. With this combination, the grid current should be 25 ma. Screen current should be about 60 ma. with the amplifier fully loaded.

Some sort of r.f. output indicator, such as a

Fig. 6-82

crystal-rectifier voltmeter or r.f. ammeter in the feed line, should be used in tuning. It is preferable to do the preliminary tuning with the plate voltage applied to the tubes but with the screen voltage at zero. Zero screen voltage, provided the d.c. screen circuit is complete, will give enough output for tuning adjustments. C_2 and C_4 are adjusted to give maximum output, and the screen voltage is then increased until the amplifier is running at the desired input. C_3 is of course tuned for the plate-current dip so that the amplifier tank is kept tuned to resonance.

The fixed values of inductance available in the B&W unit preclude the possibility of matching over a wide range of impedances. The circuit can handle an s.w.r. in the coax line of about 2 to 1, but with higher s.w.r. values it may not be possible to get the desired loading. Also, although the construction is such that the amplifier is "clean" insofar as direct radiation and leakage of harmonics in the TV bands are concerned, a good low-pass filter will be required in most installations. A low s.w.r. in the coax line is definitely a requirement if excessive build-up of currents or voltages in the filter is to be avoided. If the line cannot be matched at the antenna, an auxiliary antenna coupler will have to be used.

For plate modulation a choke coil may be connected in the d.c. screen lead so the screen voltage will follow the audio variations in plate voltage. The choke should have an inductance of about 10 henrys, and must be capable of carrying 125 ma. d.c. For Class AB₁ operation on single side band the circuit may be left intact, the only requirement being to supply the proper operating voltages from suitably well-regulated supplies. If the amplifier is to be operated in AB₂ on s.s.b. the grid-leak resistor should be shorted out; also, suitable loading should be applied to the grid tank to maintain good regulation of the r.f. driving voltage.

(From *QST*, June, 1956.)

A V.F.O. With Differential Keyer

Figs. 6-84 through 6-88 show a v.f.o. with output on either 3.5 or 7 Mc. Included is a differential system for keying the control grid of an amplifier. The diagram is shown in Fig. 6-86. One section of a 12AT7 is used in the Vackar oscillator circuit, while the second section is used as a cathode follower driving a 5763 amplifier/doubler. S_1 selects either of two frequency ranges — 3.5 to 4 Mc. for use in the 80-meter band, and 3.5 to 3.65 Mc. for multiplying to the higher-frequency bands. If only the first range is desired, C_1 and C_3 may be omitted and the stators of C_2 and C_4 connected to the junction of C_5 and L_1. If both 3.5- and 7-Mc. output is desired, the two coils can be put on a switch section ganged to S_1.

To avoid chirp and permit full break-in c.w. operation, a differential keying system is used. Grid-block keying of an amplifier stage beyond the v.f.o. unit is provided by the negative power supply (6X5 rectifier), the 470K resistor, the 33K resistor R_1, and the 0.1-μf. capacitor C_6. The 6J5 cathode follower and the 0A2 control the oscillator. A complete description of the circuit operation will be found in Chapter Eight. Opening S_2 turns on the oscillator for "frequency spotting" purposes.

Construction

The unit is built on a 7 $\times$ 12 $\times$ 2-inch aluminum chassis that will fit inside an 8 $\times$ 14½ $\times$ 8¼-inch cabinet (Bud C-1747). The panel is 8 by 12 inches and the dial is a Millen 10035. Before mounting the components, it is advisable to stiffen the chassis against vibration by fastening two lengths of aluminum angle stock running lengthwise against the under surface of the chassis. Several machine screws should be used with each.

The v.f.o. tuned-circuit components are enclosed in a 4 $\times$ 5 $\times$ 6-inch aluminum box. This should also be stiffened with lengths of angle stock, one strip running under the top of the box, and one externally along each of the side covers.

The coil is supported on 2½-inch ceramic pillars (Millen 31002). The tuning capacitor C_4 is elevated above the bottom of the box on an aluminum bracket so that its shaft will line up with the dial. The band spread switch S_1 is mounted in the bottom of the box, to the rear of the coil, with its shaft vertical. The shaft is controlled from the panel by means of a National RAD right-angle drive and a "universal-joint" type shaft coupler (Millen 39001), as shown in the bottom-view photograph.

The three trimmer capacitors are mounted in the top of the box. C_3 is submounted so that its shaft, which is at high r.f. potential, will not protrude from the box. It is adjusted with an insulated screwdriver through a hole in the top of the box. C_5 is an air trimmer used here as a fixed capacitor. It is mounted on a bracket fastened to the bottom of the box, under the coil, and set at maximum capacitance.

The box should be placed on the chassis so that an extension of the shaft of the tuning capacitor will line up with the dial. This places the box somewhat off center.

Power-supply components are mounted at the left-hand end of the chassis as viewed from the rear. The power transformer, plate and bias rectifiers, voltage-regulator tubes and filter choke L_5 are placed on the top side of the chassis. The

Fig. 6-84—The v.f.o. unit mounted in its cabinet. Holes are drilled in the dial cover to accommodate the switch shafts. At the right, a poker chip has been cemented to the v.f.o. set push-button switch so that it can be operated while tuning the v.f.o.; this makes frequency-spotting a one-handed operation.

Fig. 6-85—Rear view of the v.f.o. unit. Power-supply components are to the left of the tuned-circuit compartment, and r.f. and 6J5 tubes to the right. The three screws along the center line of the box are used to fasten a stiffening strip of angle stock inside. Similar strips should be fastened against the side covers.

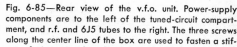

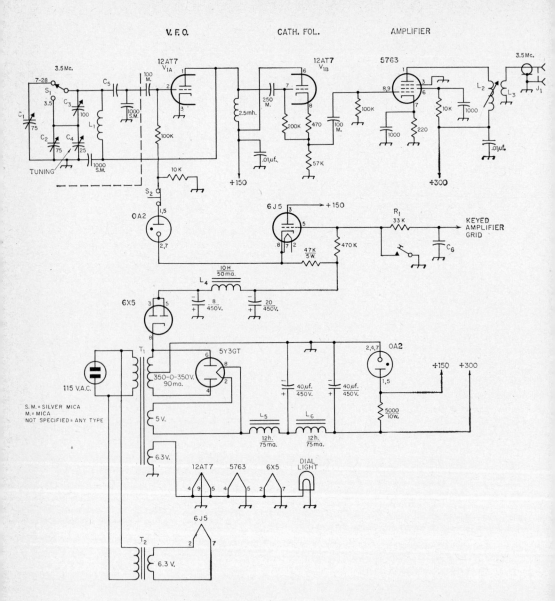

Fig. 6-86—Circuit diagram of the v.f.o., with its power supply and the keying system. Except as otherwise indicated, fixed resistors are ½ watt, capacitances are in μμf., resistances are in ohms. Capacitors marked with polarity are electrolytic.

C_1, C_2—75-μμf. variable (Hammarlund APC-75).

C_3—100-μμf. variable (Hammarlund APC-100).

C_4—25-μμf. variable (Millen 20025).

C_5—50-μμf. (Hammarlund APC-50); see text.

C_6—0.1-μf. 600-v. tubular, part of shaping circuit. Mounted in amplifier.

J_1—Coax connectors, chassis mounting.

L_1—30 turns No. 16, 1¾ inch diameter, 10 turns/inch (Airdux 1410T).

L_2—3.5 Mc.—72 turns No. 22 enam., close-wound on ⅜″ diameter slug-tuned form (Waters CSA-1012-1-WH).

7 Mc.—40 turns No. 22 close-wound on same form as above; 5-turn link.

L_3—10 turns, wound on cold end of, but insulated from, L_2.

L_4—10 hy., 50 ma. (Triad C-3X).

L_5, L_6—12 hy., 75 ma. (Triad C-5X).

R_1—33,000 ohms, part of shaping circuit. Mounted in amplifier.

S_1—Miniature rotary, 2-position (Centralab PA-2001).

S_2—Normally-closed push-button switch (Switchcraft 1002 modified with a longer shaft so as to extend through the main dial housing).

T_1—700 v. c.t., 90 ma.; 5 v., 3 amp.; 6.3 v., 3.5 amp. (Triad R-11A).

T_2—6.3-v. 0.6-ampere filament transformer.

A V.F.O.

Fig. 6-87—The v.f.o. coil is mounted on ceramic pillars. The tuning capacitor C_4 can be seen behind the rear pair of insulators. The air capacitor C_5 is partially hidden by the 1000-$\mu\mu$f. silver mica capacitor below the coil. No. 14 wire is used between the switch and the coil and capacitors. In the foreground, transformer and tubes have been removed to show the adjusting screw of L_2.

bias filter choke, the plate filter choke L_6 and the filter capacitors are underneath. L_6 mounts with the same screws used for mounting L_5 above. Several ¼-inch holes should be drilled in the chassis in the vicinity of the power-supply components to help ventilate the under side of the chassis.

The v.f.o./cathode follower, amplifier and 6J5 tubes and their associated circuit components are at the left hand end of the chassis. The v.f.o. tube is close to the panel, followed by the 5763 amplifier, T_2 and 6J5 cathode follower. The slug-

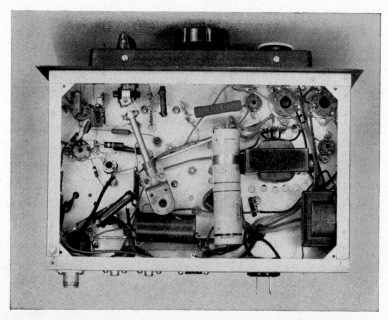

Fig. 6-88—Bottom view of the v.f.o. unit. The right-angle drive, right of center, drives the band-spread switch S_1. The small sections of aluminum angle stock are stiffeners added after the components were mounted. The method suggested in the text is preferable.

tuned coil L_2 is mounted alongside the 5763. It can be adjusted from the top of the chassis.

Along the rear edge of the chassis are a connector for the a.c. line, connectors for connecting a remote switch in parallel with S_2, for the key, for the keyed amplifier grid, and a coaxial connector for r.f. output.

Large rectangular ventilating holes are cut in the lid of the cabinet and then backed with patches of Reynolds perforated aluminum. If this detail is omitted, the temperature rise of the unit may cause considerable frequency drift.

Adjustment

In adjusting the v.f.o. frequency ranges, first set S_1 to the 80-meter position. With the dial set at zero (C_4 at maximum capacitance) adjust C_2 for a signal at 3500 kc. on a calibrated receiver. Then, with the dial of the v.f.o. set at the upper region of the scale, the signal should be heard at 4000 kc. If it is impossible to reach 4000 kc. with the v.f.o., the coil should be trimmed a part of a turn at a time.

In adjusting the second range (3500 to 3650 kc.), turn S_1 to the 7 — 28-Mc. position. Set C_3 temporarily at about half capacitance. Then, with the v.f.o. dial set at zero, adjust C_1 until a signal is heard at 3500 kc. Then check the v.f.o. frequency at the upper end of the dial. If the range does not go up to 3650 kc., C_3 should be increased a little and C_1 decreased to bring 3500 kc. at zero on the dial. If the tuning range goes above 3650 kc., C_3 should be decreased, and C_1 increased. A few trial settings should yield the correct range. The only other adjustment of the r.f. circuit is resonating the slug-tuned output coil. If set in the center of the tuning range, output should be reasonably constant over the entire range.

Adjustment of the keying circuit should be in accordance with the factors mentioned in Chapter Eight in connection with grid-block keying.

THE VACKAR VFO CIRCUIT

The Vackar variable-frequency oscillator appears to have some advantages over the usual Clapp circuit.[1] In the latter, the output amplitude varies greatly with frequency. In the Vackar circuit, the output varies only a little with frequency. The useful frequency range of the Clapp circuit is about 1.2 to 1; in the Vackar it is about 2.5 to 1. The first of these advantages should be of interest to amateurs.

My friend and colleague, Mr. James B. Ricks, W9TO, has pointed out that the 6AG7 is not the best tube to use for a series-tuned VFO; indeed the several papers originally describing these circuits invariably show triodes. The best tube is that one which has the lowest ratio of change of input capacitance to its mutual conductance. The operating mutual conductance for the cathode, control grid, and screen grid of a 6AG7 (as typically used as an oscillator) is low, despite its high value for the normal grid-to-plate circuitry. Also, it has a high input capacitance and high heater and plate power inputs. In consequence, this tube is not ideal for the purpose.

A small dual triode, the 12AT7, offers higher oscillator g_m in one triode section, lower input capacitance, and about one third the heater and plate power inputs required by the 6AG7. In consequence, it is a superior tube for series-tuned oscillators. The output voltage will be lower for the 12AT7, naturally, but a tube should not be evaluated for VFO use on the basis of power output.

W9TO has adapted the Vackar circuit to an amateur VFO with output on 80 meters using the 12AT7 in the circuit of Fig. 6-89. The first triode unit and its associated components form the oscillator proper; the other triode unit is a cathode follower which reduces loading effects on the oscillator frequency. Two of these VFO units have been made and tested; their frequency stability is excellent, and they key well. The output r.f. was measured as 1.2 volts r.m.s. using a General Radio v.t.v.m. The total current from the 255-volt regulated B supply was 16 ma., key down.

In series-tuned oscillators of the Clapp or Vackar type the characteristics of the series capacitor C_x are critical if the oscillator is to be keyed. An annoying chirp, slight but detectable, was finally traced to imperfection of this capacitor, even though it was a low temperature coefficient silvered mica one. Several silvered micas of good make were tried; they all produced slight chirp, some less than others. A so-called zero temperature coefficient (NPO) ceramic capacitor gave less chirp (very little, in fact), but the chirp was eliminated by using an APC air trimmer for C_x. Apparently, there is enough r.f. current through C_x to cause di-

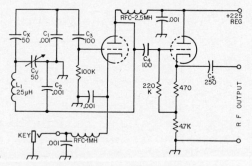

Fig. 6-89—Vackar series-tuned v.f.o. circuit at W9TO. The tube is a 12AT7 dual triode. R.f. output from the cathode-follower second section is 1.2 volts r.m.s.

C_1, C_2—Silver mica.
C_3, C_4, C_5—Mica.
C —APC air variable.
Other capacitors are ceramic.

electric heating and a small resulting change in capacity even in these high-grade capacitors. This was confirmed indirectly by using for C_x a negative temperature coefficient (N750) ceramic capacitor. The chirp was tremendous!

Of course, the series capacitor is not the only possible cause of chirp; poor plate voltage regulation or a long time constant in the keying circuit might also contribute. To avoid this, the plate supply should be regulated, and series resistances and shunt capacitances in the keying circuit should be kept to a minimum.[2]

The circuit shown will key cleanly without chirp; with the constants shown it will be somewhat clicky, due to turning on and off rapidly; this makes it very desirable for use in a differential keying system in which the oscillator is turned on before the amplifier, and the amplifier is turned off before the oscillator. — *W9IK*

---

[1] Clapp, J. K., "Frequency Stable *LC* Oscillators," *Proc. of the I.R.E.*, Aug., 1954, Vol. 42, No. 8, page 1295.

[2] The chirp discussed in the preceding paragraph evidently is a slow one attributable to temperature effects. A chirp of the "dynamic" type often manifests itself as a click when the time constant of the keying circuit is very short, becoming observable as a chirp when key-thump elimination methods are used. — ED.

This material originally appeared in *QST* for November, 1955. — ED.

Converting Surplus

Converting Surplus Transmitters for Novice Use

War-surplus radio equipment, available in many radio stores, is a good source of radio parts. Some of the transmitters and receivers can be made to operate in the amateur bands with little or no modification. It would be hard to find a more economical way for a Novice to get started on 40 or 80 meters than by adapting a normally-v.f.o.-controlled surplus "Command Set" to crystal control.

The "Command Sets" are parts of the SCR-274N and AN/ARC-5 equipments, transmitters and receivers designed for use in military aircraft. The two series are substantially identical in circuit and construction. Of the transmitters, two are of particular interest to the Novice. These are the BC-696 (part of 274N) or T19 (ARC-5) covering 3 to 4 Mc., and the BC-459 or T22, 7 to 9.1 Mc. The transmitter circuit consists of a 1626 triode variable-frequency oscillator that drives a pair of 1625s in parallel, which for Novice use can be run at 75 watts input. In addition to the 1626 and 1625s the transmitters include a 1629 magic-eye tube, which was used as a resonance indicator with a crystal for checking the dial calibration. The tubes have 12-volt heaters connected in series-parallel for 24-volt battery operation. The BC-696 and 459 are available from surplus dealers at prices ranging from five to fifteen dollars each, depending on condition.

Several methods have been described for converting the transmitters to crystal control for Novice use, but most of them didn't take into consideration the reconversion required to change back to v.f.o. when the Novice became a General-Class license holder.

In the modification to be described, the Novice requirement for crystal control is met by using a separate crystal-controlled oscillator. The output of the external oscillator is fed into the transmitter through a plug that fits into the 1626 oscillator socket. The 1626 is not used. The transmitter modifications are such that when it is desired to restore the transmitter to v.f.o. operation the external oscillator is unplugged and the 1626 is put back in its socket. No wiring changes are needed to go from crystal control to v.f.o.

In addition to the external oscillator, a power supply is required for the oscillator and transmitter (Fig. 6-90), and certain wiring changes are

needed to make the transmitter itself suitable for amateur use. These changes consist primarily of removing two relays, changing the tube heater circuit for operation on 12 volts instead of 24 volts, and the addition of a power plug.

Transmitter Modifications

The 80- and 40-meter transmitters are practically identical except for frequency range, and the modifications are the same in both. Remove the top cover and bottom plate. Remove the tubes and crystal from their sockets so there will be no danger of breaking them as you work on the transmitter. If the sockets are not marked by tube types, mark them yourself so you'll know which tube goes where.

The following modifications are required:

1) Remove the antenna relay (front panel) and control relay (side of chassis) and unsolder and remove all wires that were connected to the relays with the exception of the wire going to Pin 4 on the oscillator socket.

2) Remove the wire-wound resistor mounted on the rear wall of the transmitter.

3) Unsolder the wire from Pin 7 of the 1629 socket and move it to Pin 2. Ground Pin 7.

4) Unsolder the wires from Pin 1 of the 1625 closest to the drive shaft for the variable capacitors and solder the wires to Pin 7. Run a lead from the same Pin 1 to the nearest chassis ground.

5) Unsolder all leads from the power socket at the rear of the chassis and remove the socket. The socket can be pried off with a screwdriver.

6) Unsolder the end of the 20-ohm resistor (red-black-black) that is connected to Pin 4 on the oscillator socket and connect it to Pin 6

Fig. 6-90—The complete Novice setup, in this case using the 80-meter (BC-457) transmitter. Note the key jack at the lower-left corner of the transmitter panel. The crystal oscillator is connected to the transmitter oscillator-tube socket with a short length of cable terminating in an octal plug. A small notch should be cut in the transmitter cover to provide clearance for the cable when the cover is installed.

The power transformer, rectifier, and choke are mounted on top of the power-supply chassis at the rear, and the control switches are mounted on the wall as shown. Remaining components are underneath.

of the calibration crystal socket. There is also a lead on Pin 4 that was connected to the keying relay; connect this lead to the nearest chassis ground point.

7) Mount an octal socket (Amphenol 78-RS8) in the hole formerly occupied by the power socket. Install a solder lug under one of the nuts holding the socket mounting.

8) Wire the octal socket as shown in Fig. 6-91. One of the leads unsoldered from the original power socket is red with a white tracer. This is the B+ lead for the 1625s. The yellow lead is the screen lead for the 1625s and the white lead is the heater lead. Although the manuals covering this equipment specify these colors, it's safer not to take them for granted; check where each lead actually goes before connecting it to the new power socket. The lead from Pin 1 on the power socket to Pin 6 on the calibration-crystal socket is the oscillator plate-voltage lead. The leads from Pins 7 and 8 on the power plug to Pins 1 and 6 on the oscillator socket are new leads to carry power to the external crystal-controlled oscillator. The lead from Pin 4 of the power socket to Pin 2 on the 1629 (resonance indicator) socket is the 12-volt heater lead.

9) Mount a closed-circuit phone jack at the lower left-hand corner of the front panel. Connect a lead from the ungrounded phone jack terminal to Pin 6 (cathode) of either of the 1625 sockets. This completes the modification.

Crystal-Controlled Oscillator Details

The external crystal-controlled oscillator circuit, shown in Fig. 6-92, uses a 6AG7 in the grid-plate oscillator circuit. Either 80- or 40-meter crystals are required, depending on the band in use, A tuned plate circuit is not required in the

oscillator; it was found that more than adequate grid drive could be obtained with the setup as shown.

Output from the oscillator is fed to the transmitter through an 8-inch length of RG-58 coax cable. The cable is terminated in an octal plug, P_2, which is plugged into the oscillator tube socket in the transmitter. Power for the external oscillator is obtained through this socket.

The crystal-controlled oscillator is built in and on a $4 \times 2 \times 2\frac{3}{4}$-inch aluminum box. The tube and crystal sockets are mounted on top of the box and the remaining components inside. Layout of parts is not particularly critical but the general arrangement shown in Figs. 6-90 and 6-93 should be followed to insure good results.

In the completed setup, oscillator and amplifier, the cathodes of the 1625s are keyed and the crystal oscillator runs continuously during transmissions. It is thus necessary to turn the oscillator off during standby periods, and this is accomplished by opening the B-plus switch on the power supply. This method is used in preference to keying the oscillator and amplifier simultaneously because keying the oscillator is likely to make the signal chirpy. With amplifier keying the signal is a real T9X.

Power Supply

Fig. 6-91 shows the circuit of the power supply, which uses a 5U4G rectifier and a capacitor-input filter. The power transformer, T_1, is a type made by several manufacturers. To obtain the necessary 12.6 volts for the heaters, a 6.3-volt filament transformer is connected in series with the 6.3-volt winding on T_1. This setup also will provide 6.3 volts for the heater of the 6AG7. Current requirement for the 6AG7 heater is 0.65 amp. and for the 1625s, 0.9 amp. total.

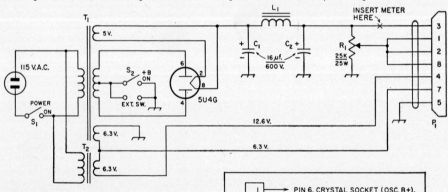

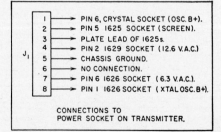

Fig. 6-91 — Circuit diagram of power socket and power supply.

C_1, C_2 — 16-μf., 600-volt electrolytic (Sprague TVA-1965, Aerovox PRS).

J_1 — Octal socket (Amphenol 78-RS8).

L_1 — 1- to 2-hy., 200-ma. filter choke, TV replacement type (Stancor C2325 or C2327, or equivalent).

P_1 — Octal cable plug (Amphenol 86-PM8).

R_1 — 25,000 ohms, 25 watts, with slider.

S_1, S_2 — Single-pole, single-throw toggle switch.

T_1 — Power transformer, 100 volts center-tapped, 200 ma.; 5 volts, 3 amp.; 6.3 volts, 6 amp. (Knight 61G414, Triad R-21A, or equivalent).

T_2 — Filament transformer, 6.3 volts, 3 amp. (Triad F·16X, Knight 62-G-031, or equivalent).

CONNECTIONS TO POWER SOCKET ON TRANSMITTER.

1	PIN 6, CRYSTAL SOCKET (OSC. B+).
2	PIN 5 1625 SOCKET (SCREEN).
3	PLATE LEAD OF 1625s.
4	PIN 2 1629 SOCKET (12.6 V.A.C.).
5	CHASSIS GROUND.
6	NO CONNECTION.
7	PIN 6 1626 SOCKET (6.3 V.A.C.).
8	PIN 1 1626 SOCKET (XTAL OSC. B+).

Converting Surplus

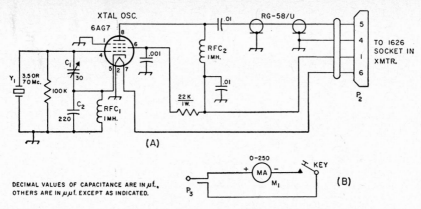

Fig. 6-92—(A) Circuit diagram of external crystal-controlled oscillator. Unless otherwise specified, resistances are in ohms, resistors are ½ watt. The 0.01- and 0.001-μf. capacitors are disk ceramic. (B) Method of connecting the milliammeter in series with the key.

C_1—3-30-μμf. trimmer.
C_2—220-μμf. fixed mica.
M_1—0-250 d.c. milliammeter.
P_2—Octal plug, male (Amphenol 86-PM8).

P_3—Phone plug.
RFC_1, RFC_2—1-mh. r.f. chokes.
Y_1—3.5- or 7-Mc. Novice-band crystal, as required.

To turn off the plate voltages on the transmitter during stand-by periods, the center tap of T_1 is opened. This can be done in two ways; by S_2, or by a remotely-mounted switch whose leads are connected in parallel with S_2. A two-terminal strip is mounted on the power-supply chassis, the terminals being connected to S_2 which is also on the chassis. The remotely-mounted switch can be installed in any convenient location at the operating position. A single-pole, single-throw switch can be used for this purpose or, if desired, a multicontact switch can be used to perform simultaneously this and other functions, such as controlling an antenna-changeover relay.

The high-voltage and heater leads are brought out in a cable to an octal plug, P_1, that connects to J_1 on the transmitter. The length of the cable will, of course, depend on where you want to install the power supply. Some amateurs prefer to have the supply on the floor under the operating desk rather than have it take up room at the operating position.

The supply shown here was constructed on a 3 × 6 × 10-inch chassis. The layout is not critical, nor are there any special precautions to take during construction other than to observe polarity in wiring the electrolytic capacitors and to see that the power leads are properly insulated. Never have P_1 unplugged from J_1 when the power supply is turned on; there is danger of electrical shock at several pins of P_1. Interchanging the inserts of P_1 and J_1 will remove this hazard.

When wiring P_1 don't connect the B-plus lines to Pins 2 or 3, the amplifier plates and screens, at first. It is more convenient to test the oscillator without plate and screen voltages on the amplifier.

When the supply is completed, check between chassis ground and the 12.6-volt lead with an a.c. voltmeter to see if the two 6.3-volt windings are connected correctly. If you find that the voltage is

zero, reverse one of the windings. If you don't have an a.c. meter you can check by observing the heaters in the 1625s. They will light up if you have the windings connected correctly. Incidentally, leave B plus off, by opening S_2, for this check.

Next, set the slider on the bleeder resistor, R_1, at about one-quarter of the total resistor length, measured from the B-plus end of the bleeder. Be sure to turn off the power when making this adjustment. With the tap set about one-quarter of the way from the B-plus end of the bleeder the oscillator plate and amplifier screen voltages will be approximately 250 volts.

Testing the Transmitter

A key and meter connected as shown in Fig. 6-92 are needed for checking the transmitter. When P_3 is plugged into the jack in the transmitter it will measure the cathode current of the 1625s. The cathode current is the sum of the plate, screen and control-grid currents. Some amateurs prefer to install the meter in the plate lead so it reads plate current only. This can be done by opening the B-plus line at the point marked "X" in Fig. 6-91, and inserting the meter in series with the line. However, unless more than one meter is available, don't install it in the power supply setup in this way until after the tests described below have been made.

Insert the external oscillator plug, P_2, into the 1626 socket and connect P_1 to the transmitter. Plug P_1 into the key jack on the front panel of the transmitter. With S_2 open, turn on the power and allow a minute or two for the tubes to warm up. Next, close the center-tap connection, S_2, on the power transformer. Set the transmitter dial to the same frequency as that of the crystal in use and close the key. A slight indication of grid current should show on the meter. There is no plate or screen current because there are no screen or plate voltages on the amplifier. If no grid current is obtained, adjust C_1 to the point where grid current shows, or try another crystal.

The next step is to peak the amplifier grid circuit — that is, the 1626 v.f.o. tank — for maximum grid-current reading. The v.f.o. trimmer capacitor is in an aluminum box on the top of the chassis at the rear. There is a $\frac{1}{2}$-inch diameter hole in the side of the box; loosen the small screw visible through this hole, thus unlocking the rotor shaft of the trimmer capacitor. Move the rotor-arm shaft in either direction, observing the meter reading, and find the position that gives the highest reading. This should be something more than 10 ma.

Now connect the plate and screen voltage leads to P_1. Be sure to turn off the power supply before making the connections!

The first test of the rig should be with a dummy load; a 115-volt, 60-watt light bulb can be used for this purpose. The lamp should be connected between the antenna terminal and chassis ground. However, to make the lamp take power it may be necessary to add capacitance in parallel with it. A receiving-type variable capacitor having 250 $\mu\mu f$. or more maximum capacitance will be adequate for the job.

Turn on the power and allow the tubes to warm up, but leave the key open. Set the antenna coupling control on the transmitter to 7 or 8, and set the variable capacitor connected across the dummy load to about maximum capacitance. Next, close the key and adjust the antenna inductance control for an increase in cathode current. Turn the frequency control for a dip in current reading. The indicated frequency will probably differ from that of the crystal in use, but don't worry about it.

Adjust the three transmitter controls, antenna inductance, antenna coupling, and frequency, along with the variable capacitor across the lamp load, until the lamp lights up to apparently full brilliance. The cathode current should be between 150 and 200 ma. With the transmitter fully loaded, adjust C_1 in the crystal oscillator so that the lamp brilliance just starts to decrease. This is the optimum setting for C_1 and it can be left at this setting, no further adjustments being required.

If a d.c. voltmeter is available, check the different voltages in the setup. Using the power supply shown here, the plate voltage on the 1625s is approximately 400 with the amplifier fully loaded. With the plate voltage on the oscillator and screen voltage on the 1625s adjusted to 250 volts (tap on R_1), the oscillator screen voltage is 160 volts. The oscillator takes approximately 30 ma. and the 1625 amplifier screens about 10 ma. when the amplifier is fully loaded.

Getting on the Air

To put the transmitter on the air it is necessary only to connect an antenna to the antenna post and connect a ground lead from the transmitter chassis to a water-pipe ground or to a metal stake driven in the ground. Almost any length of antenna will work, but for best results the minimum length should not be less than about $\frac{1}{8}$ wavelength for the band in use. This is approximately 33 feet for 80 meters and 16 feet for 40 meters. It is of course better to make the antenna longer — and to be sure to get the far end as high as possible.

An output indicator will prove to be a handy device for knowing when power is actually going into the antenna. For this purpose use a 6.3-volt, 150-ma. dial lamp. Connect two leads, each about one foot long, to the shell and base of the bulb, respectively. Clip one lead to the antenna post and the other lead on the antenna wire two feet from antenna post. A small amount of power will go through the bulb and this will provide a visual indication of output. Follow the same tuning procedure as outlined above for the dummy antenna. If the bulb gets so bright that it is in danger of burning out, move the leads closer together to reduce the pickup.

It may be found that certain antenna lengths won't work — that is, the amplifier won't load — no matter where the antenna coupling and inductance are set. In such a case, connect a variable capacitor — like the one used with the lamp dummy — between the antenna post and the transmitter chassis. Adjust the capacitor and antenna inductance for maximum brilliance of the output indicator; this will be the best setting for the controls.

A superior antenna system uses a two-wire feeder system and an antenna coupler; examples are given in Chapters 13 and 14. If a coupler is used, the transmitter and coupler should be connected together with coax line. The inner conductor of the coax should be connected to the antenna terminal and the outer braid to the transmitter case, as close to the antenna terminal as possible. If desired, the antenna terminal can be removed and a coax fitting substituted.

When the coveted General Class ticket is obtained, it is only necessary to unplug the crystal oscillator, put the original tube back in the rig, and move out of the Novice band.

Fig. 6-93—This bottom view of the crystal oscillator shows the arrangement of components. Terminal strips are used for the cable connections and also as a support for C_1, the feedback capacitor.

CHAPTER 7

Power Supplies

Essentially pure direct-current plate supply is required to prevent serious hum in the output of receivers, speech amplifiers, modulators and transmitters. In the case of transmitters, pure d.c. plate supply is also dictated by government regulation.

The filaments of tubes in a transmitter or modulator usually may be operated from a.c. However, the filament power for tubes in a receiver (excepting power audio tubes), or those in a speech amplifier may be a.c. only if the tubes are of the indirectly-heated-cathode type, if hum is to be avoided.

Wherever commercial a.c. lines are available, high-voltage d.c. plate supply is most cheaply and conveniently obtained by the use of a transformer-rectifier-filter system. An example of such a system is shown in Fig. 7-1.

In this circuit, the plate transformer, T_1, steps up the a.c. line voltage to the required high voltage. The a.c. is changed to pulsating d.c. by the rectifiers, V_1 and V_2. Pulsations in the d.c. appearing at the output of the rectifier (points A and B) are smoothed out by the filter composed of L_1 and C_1. R_1 is a *bleeder* resistor. Its chief function is to discharge C_1, as a safety measure, after the supply is turned off. By proper selection of value, R_1

also helps to minimize changes in output voltage with changes in the amount of current drawn from the supply. T_2 is a step-down transformer to provide filament voltage for the rectifier tubes. It must have sufficient insulation between the

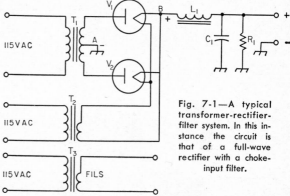

Fig. 7-1—A typical transformer-rectifier-filter system. In this instance the circuit is that of a full-wave rectifier with a choke-input filter.

filament winding and the core and primary winding to withstand the peak value of the rectified voltage. T_3 is a similar transformer to supply the filaments or heaters of the tubes in the equipment operating from the supply. Frequently, these three transformers are combined in a single unit having a single 115-volt primary winding and the required three secondary windings on one core.

Rectifier Circuits

Half-Wave Rectifier

Fig. 7-2 shows three rectifier circuits covering most of the common applications in amateur equipment. Fig. 7-2A is the circuit of a half-wave rectifier. During that half of the a.c. cycle when the rectifier plate is positive with respect to the cathode (or filament), current will flow through the rectifier and load. But during the other half of the cycle, when the plate is negative with respect to the cathode, no current can flow. The shape of the output wave is shown in (A) at the right. It shows that the current always flows in the same direction but that the flow of current is not continuous and is pulsating in amplitude.

The average output voltage — the voltage read by the usual d.c. voltmeter — with this circuit is 0.45 times the r.m.s. value of the a.c. voltage delivered by the transformer secondary. Because the frequency of the pulses in the output wave is relatively low (one pulsation per cycle), considerable filtering is required to

provide adequately smooth d.c. output, and for this reason this circuit is usually limited to applications where the current involved is small, such as in supplies for cathode-ray tubes and for protective bias in a transmitter.

Another disadvantage of the half-wave rectifier circuit is that the transformer must have a considerably higher primary volt-ampere rating (approximately 40 per cent greater), for the same d.c. power output, than in other rectifier circuits.

Full-Wave Center-Tap Rectifier

The most universally used rectifier circuit is shown in Fig. 7-2B. Being essentially an arrangement in which the outputs of two half-wave rectifiers are combined, it makes use of both halves of the a.c. cycle. A transformer with a center-tapped secondary is required with the circuit. When the plate of V_1 is positive, current flows through the load to the center tap. Current cannot flow through V_2 because at this instant its cathode (or filament) is positive in respect to its plate. When the polarity reverses, V_2 conducts and current again flows through the load to the center-tap, this time through V_2.

The average output voltage is 0.45 times the r.m.s. voltage of the entire transformer-secondary, or 0.9 times the voltage across *half* of the transformer secondary. For the same *total* secondary voltage, the average output voltage is the same as that delivered with a half-wave rectifier. However, as can be seen from the sketches of the output wave form in (B) to the right, the frequency of the output pulses is twice that of the half-wave rectifier. Therefore much less filtering is required. Since the rectifiers work alternately, each handles half of the average load current. Therefore the load-current rating of each rectifier need be only half the total load current drawn from the supply.

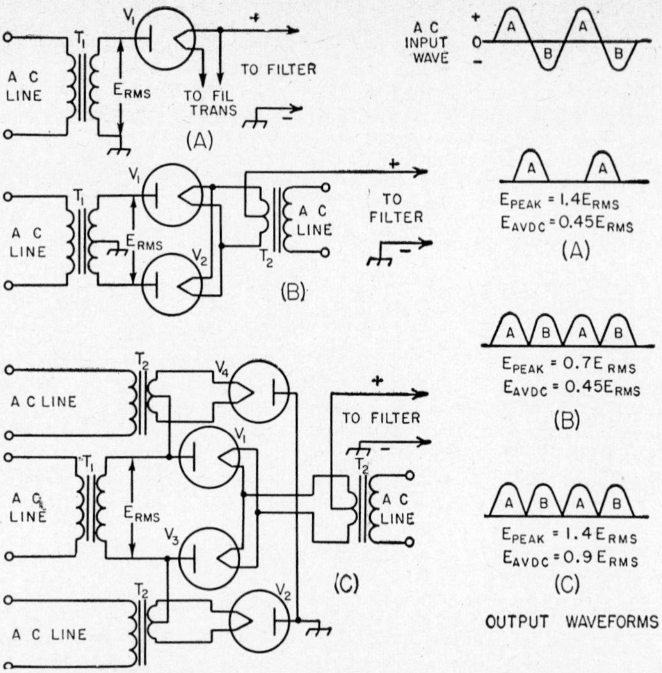

Two separate transformers, with their primaries connected in parallel and secondaries connected in series (with the proper polarity) may be used in this circuit. However, if this substitution is made, the primary volt-ampere rating must be reduced to about 40 per cent less than twice the rating of one transformer.

Fig. 7-2—Fundamental vacuum-tube rectifier circuits. A—Half-wave. B—Full-wave. C—Full-wave bridge. A.c.-input and pulsating-d.c. output wave forms are shown at the right. Output-voltage values indicated do not include rectifier drops. Other types of rectifiers may be substituted.

Full-Wave Bridge Rectifier

Another full-wave rectifier circuit is shown in Fig. 7-2C. In this arrangement, two rectifiers operate in series on each half of the cycle, one rectifier being in the lead to the load, the other being in the return lead. Over that portion of the cycle when the upper end of the transformer secondary is positive with respect to the other end, current flows through V_1, through the load and thence through V_2. During this period current cannot flow through rectifier V_4 because its plate is negative with respect to its cathode (or filament). Over the other half of the cycle, current flows through V_3, through the load and thence through V_4. Three filament transformers

are needed — one for V_1 and V_3 and one each for V_2 and V_4. The output wave shape (C), to the right, is the same as that from the simple center-tap rectifier circuit. The output voltage obtainable with this circuit is 0.9 times the r.m.s. voltage delivered by the transformer secondary. For the same total transformer-secondary voltage, the average output voltage when using the bridge rectifier will be twice that obtainable with the center-tap rectifier circuit. However, when comparing rectifier circuits for use *with the same transformer*, it should be remembered that the *power* which a given transformer will handle remains the same regardless of the rectifier circuit used. If the output voltage is doubled by substituting the bridge circuit for the center-tap rectifier circuit, only half the rated load current can be taken from the transformer without exceeding its normal rating. Each rectifier in a bridge circuit should have a minimum load-current rating of one half the total load current to be drawn from the supply.

Rectifiers

High-Vacuum Rectifiers

High-vacuum rectifiers depend entirely upon the thermionic emission from a heated filament and are characterized by a relatively high internal resistance. For this reason, their application usually is limited to low power, although there are a few types designed for medium and high power in cases where the relatively high

internal voltage drop may be tolerated. This high internal resistance makes them less susceptible to damage from temporary overload and they are free from the bothersome electrical noise sometimes associated with other types of rectifiers.

Some rectifiers of the high-vacuum full-wave type in the so-called receiver-tube class will handle up to 275 ma. at 400 to 500 volts d.c. out-

Rectifiers

put. Those in the higher-power class can be used to handle up to 500 ma. at 2000 volts d.c. in full-wave circuits. Most low-power high-vacuum rectifiers are produced in the full-wave type, while those for greater power are invariably of the half-wave type, two tubes being required for a full-wave rectifier circuit. A few of the lower-voltage types have indirectly heated cathodes, but are limited in heater-to-cathode voltage rating.

Mercury-Vapor Rectifiers

The voltage drop through a mercury-vapor rectifier is practically constant at approximately 15 volts regardless of the load current. For high power they have the advantage of cheapness. Rectifiers of this type, however, have a tendency toward a type of oscillation which produces noise in nearby receivers, sometimes difficult to eliminate. R.f. filtering in the primary circuit and at the rectifier plates as well as shielding may be required. As with high-vacuum rectifiers, full-wave types are available in the lower-power ratings only. For higher power, two tubes are required in a full-wave circuit.

Selenium and Other Semiconductor Rectifiers

Selenium, germanium and silicon rectifiers are finding increasing application in power supplies for amateur equipment. These units have the advantages of compactness, low internal voltage drop (about 5 volts per unit) and low operating temperature. Also, no filament transformers are required.

Individual units of all three types are available with input ratings of 130 volts r.m.s. Selenium units are rated at up to 1000 ma. or more d.c. load current; germanium units have ratings up to 400 ma., and silicon units up to 500 ma. In full-wave circuits these load-current figures can be doubled.

The extreme compactness of silicon types makes feasible the stacking of several units in series for higher voltages. Standard stacks are available that will handle up to 2000 volts r.m.s. input at a d.c. load current of 325 ma. Two of these stacks in a full-wave circuit will handle 650 ma., although they are comparatively expensive.

Semiconductor rectifiers may be substituted in any of the basic circuits shown in Fig. 7-2, the terminal marked " + " or "cathode" corresponding to the filament connection. Advantage may be taken of the voltage-multiplying circuits discussed in a later section of this chapter in adapting rectifiers of this type.

Rectifier Ratings

Vacuum-tube rectifiers are subject to limitations as to breakdown voltage and current-handling capability. Some types are rated in terms of the maximum r.m.s. voltage which should be applied to the rectifier plate. This is sometimes dependent on whether a choke- or capacitive-input filter is used. Others, particularly mercury-vapor types, are rated according to maximum inverse peak voltage — the peak voltage between plate and cathode while the tube is not con-

ducting. In the circuits of Fig. 7-2, the inverse peak voltage across each rectifier is 1.4 times the r.m.s. value of the voltage delivered by the *entire* transformer secondary, except that if a capacitive-input filter is used with the half-wave rectifier circuit of Fig. 7-2A, the multiplying factor becomes 2.8.

All rectifier tubes are rated also as to maximum d.c. load current and many, in addition, carry peak-current ratings, all of which should be carefully observed to assure normal tube life. With a capacitive-input filter, the peak current may run several times the d.c. current, while with a choke-input filter the peak value may not run more than twice the d.c. load current.

Operation of Rectifiers

In operating rectifiers requiring filament or cathode heating, care should be taken to provide the correct filament voltage at the tube terminals. Low filament voltage can cause excessive voltage drop in high-vacuum rectifiers and a considerable reduction in the inverse peak-voltage rating of a mercury-vapor tube. Filament connections to the rectifier socket should be firmly soldered, particularly in the case of the larger mercury-vapor tubes whose filaments operate at low voltage and high current. The socket should be selected with care, not only as to contact surface but also as to insulation, since the filament usually is at full output voltage to ground. Bakelite sockets will serve at voltages up to 500 or so, but ceramic sockets, well spaced from the chassis, always should be used at the higher voltages. Special filament transformers with high-voltage insulation between primary and secondary are required for rectifiers operating at potentials in excess of 1000 volts inverse peak.

The rectifier tubes should be placed in the equipment with adequate space surrounding them to provide for ventilation. When mercury-vapor tubes are first placed in service, and each time after the mercury has been disturbed, as by removal from the socket to a horizontal position, they should be run with filament voltage only for 30 minutes before applying high voltage. After

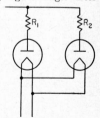

Fig. 7-3—Connecting mercury-vapor rectifiers in parallel for heavier currents. R_1 and R_2 should have the same value, between 50 and 100 ohms, and corresponding filament terminals should be connected together.

that, a delay of 30 seconds is recommended each time the filament is turned on.

Rectifiers may be connected in parallel for current higher than the rated current of a single unit. This includes the use of the sections of a double diode for this purpose. With mercury-vapor types, equalizing resistors of 50 to 100 ohms should be connected in series with each plate, as shown in Fig. 7-3, to help maintain an equal division of current between the two rectifiers.

Filters

The pulsating d.c. waves from the rectifiers shown in Fig. 7-2 are not sufficiently constant in amplitude to prevent hum corresponding to the pulsations. Filters consisting of capacitances and inductances are required between the rectifier and the load to smooth out the pulsations to an essentially constant d.c. voltage. Also, upon the design of the filter depends to a large extent the d.c. voltage output, the *voltage regulation* of the power supply and the maximum load current that can be drawn from the supply without exceeding the peak-current rating of the rectifier.

Power-supply filters fall into two classifications, depending upon whether the first filter element following the rectifier is a capacitor or a choke. Capacitive-input filters are characterized by relatively high output voltage in respect to the transformer voltage, but poor voltage regulation. Choke-input filters result in much better regulation, when properly designed, but the output voltage is less than would be obtained with a capacitive-input filter from the same transformer.

Voltage Regulation

The output voltage of a power supply always decreases as more current is drawn, not only because of increased voltage drops in the transformer, filter chokes and the rectifier (if high-vacuum rectifiers are used) but also because the output voltage at light loads tends to soar to the peak value of the transformer voltage as a result of charging the first capacitor. By proper filter design the latter effect can be eliminated. The change in output voltage with load is called *voltage regulation* and is expressed as a percentage.

$$Per\ cent\ regulation = \frac{100\ (E_1 - E_2)}{E_2}$$

Example: No-load voltage = E_1 = 1550 volts.
Full-load voltage = E_2 = 1230 volts.

Percentage regulation = $\dfrac{100\ (1550 - 1230)}{1230}$

$$= \frac{32,000}{1230} = 26 \text{ per cent.}$$

Regulation may be as great as 100% or more with a capacitive-input filter, but by proper design can be held to 20% or less with a choke-input filter.

Good regulation is desirable if the load current varies during operation, as in a keyed stage or a Class B modulator, because a large change in voltage may increase the tendency toward key clicks in the former case or distortion in the latter. On the other hand, a steady load, such as is represented by a receiver, speech amplifier or unkeyed stages in a transmitter, does not require good regulation so long as the proper voltage is obtained under load conditions. Another consideration that makes good voltage regulation desirable is that the filter capacitors must have a voltage rating safe for the highest value to which the voltage will soar when the external load is removed.

When essentially constant voltage, regardless of current variation is required (for stabilizing an oscillator, for example), special voltage-regulating circuits described elsewhere in this chapter are used.

Load Resistance

In discussing the performance of power-supply filters, it is sometimes convenient to express the load connected to the output terminals of the supply in terms of resistance. The load resistance is equal to the output voltage divided by the total current drawn, including the current drawn by the bleeder resistor.

Input Resistance

The sum of the transformer impedance and the rectifier resistance is called the input resistance. The approximate transformer impedance is given by

$$Z_{TR} = N^2 R_{PRI} + R_{SEC}$$

where N is the transformer turns ratio, primary to secondary (primary to $\frac{1}{2}$ secondary in the case of a full-wave rectifier), and R_{PRI} and R_{SEC} are the primary and secondary resistances respectively. R_{SEC} will be the resistance of half of the secondary in the case of a full-wave circuit.

Bleeder

A bleeder resistor is a resistance connected across the output terminals of the power supply (see Fig. 7-1). Its functions are to discharge the filter capacitors as a safety measure when the power is turned off and to improve voltage regulation by providing a minimum load resistance. When voltage regulation is not of importance, the resistance may be as high as 100 ohms per volt. The resistance value to be used for voltage-regulating purposes is discussed in later sections. From the consideration of safety, the power rating of the resistor should be as conservative as possible, since a burned-out bleeder resistor is more dangerous than none at all!

Ripple Frequency and Voltage

The pulsations in the output of the rectifier can be considered to be the resultant of an alternating current superimposed upon a steady direct current. From this viewpoint, the filter may be considered to consist of shunting capacitors which short-circuit the a.c. component while not interfering with the flow of the d.c. component, and series chokes which pass d.c. readily but which impede the flow of the a.c. component.

The alternating component is called the ripple. The effectiveness of the filter can be expressed in terms of per cent ripple, which is the ratio of the r.m.s. value of the ripple to the d.c. value in terms of percentage. For c.w. transmitters, the output ripple from the power supply should not exceed 5 per cent. The ripple in the output of supplies for voice transmitters should not exceed 1 per cent. Class B modulators require a ripple reduction to about 0.25%, while v.f.o.'s, high-

Filters

gain speech amplifiers, and receivers may require a reduction in ripple to 0.01%.

Ripple frequency is the frequency of the pulsations in the rectifier output wave — the number of pulsations per second. The frequency of the ripple with half-wave rectifiers is the same as the frequency of the line supply — 60 cycles with 60-cycle supply. Since the output pulses are doubled with a full-wave rectifier, the ripple frequency is doubled — to 120 cycles with 60-cycle supply.

The amount of filtering (values of inductance and capacitance) required to give adequate smoothing depends upon the ripple frequency, more filtering being required as the ripple frequency is lowered.

● CAPACITIVE-INPUT FILTERS

Capacitive-input filter systems are shown in Fig. 7-4. Disregarding voltage drops in the chokes, all have the same characteristics except

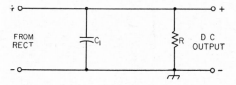

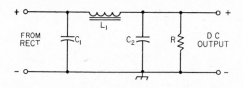

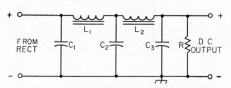

Fig. 7-4—Capacitive-input filter circuits. A—Simple capacative. B—Single-section. C—Double-section.

in respect to ripple. Better ripple reduction will be obtained when LC sections are added, as shown in Figs. 7-4B and C.

Output Voltage

To determine the approximate d.c. voltage output when a capacitive-input filter is used, reference should be made to the graph of Fig. 7-5.

Example:
Transformer r.m.s. voltage — 350
Input resistance — 200 ohms
Maximum load current, including bleeder current — 175 ma.
Load resistance $= \dfrac{350}{0.175} = 2000$ ohms approx.

From Fig. 7-5, for a load resistance of 2000 ohms and an input resistance of 200 ohms, the d.c. output voltage is given as slightly over 1

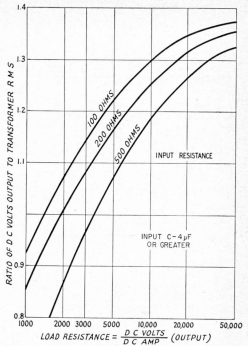

Fig. 7-5—Chart showing approximate ratio of d.c. output voltage across filter input capacitor to transformer r.m.s. secondary voltage for different load and input resistances.

times the transformer r.m.s. voltage, or about 350 volts.

Regulation

If a bleeder resistance of 50,000 ohms is used, the d.c. output voltage, as shown in Fig. 7-5, will rise to about 1.35 times the transformer r.m.s. value, or about 470 volts, when the external load is removed. For greater accuracy, the voltage drops through the input resistance and the resistance of the chokes should be subtracted from the values determined above. For best regulation with a capacitive-input filter, the bleeder resistance should be as low as possible without exceeding the transformer, rectifier or choke ratings when the external load is connected.

Maximum Rectifier Current

The maximum current that can be drawn from a supply with a capacitive-input filter without exceeding the peak-current rating of the rectifier may be estimated from the graph of Fig. 7-6. Using values from the preceding example, the ratio of peak rectifier current to d.c. load current for 2000 ohms, as shown in Fig. 7-6 is 3. Therefore, the maximum load current that can be drawn without exceeding the rectifier rating is ⅓ the peak rating of the rectifier. For a load current of 175 ma., as above, the rectifier peak current rating should be at least 3 × 175 = 525 ma.

With bleeder current only, Fig. 7-6 shows that the ratio will increase to over 8. But since the bleeder draws less than 10 ma. d.c., the rectifier peak current will be only 90 ma. or less.

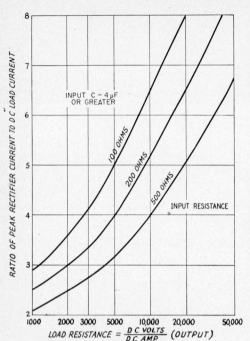

Fig. 7-6—Graph showing the relationship between the d.c. load current and the rectifier peak plate current with capacitive input for various values of load and input resistance.

Ripple Filtering

The approximate ripple percentage after the simple capacitive filter of Fig. 7-4A may be determined from Fig. 7-7. With a load resistance of 2000 ohms, for instance, the ripple will be approximately 10% with an 8-μf. capacitor or 20% with a 4-μf. capacitor. For other capacitances, the ripple will be in inverse proportion to

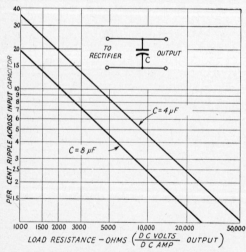

Fig. 7-7—Showing approximate 120-cycle percentage ripple across filter input capacitor for various loads.

the capacitance, e.g., 5% with 16 μf., 40% with 2 μf., and so forth.

The ripple can be reduced further by the addition of LC sections as shown in Figs. 7-4B and C. Fig. 7-8 shows the factor by which the ripple from any preceding section is reduced depending on the product of the capacitance and inductance added. For instance, if a section composed of a choke of 5 h. and a capacitor of 4 μf. were to be added to the simple capacitor of Fig. 7-4A, the product is $4 \times 5 = 20$. Fig. 7-8 shows that the original ripple (10% as above with 8 μf. for example) will be reduced by a factor of about 0.08. Therefore the ripple percentage after the new section will be

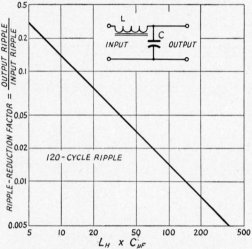

Fig. 7-8—Ripple-reduction factor for various values of L and C in filter section. Output ripple = input ripple × ripple factor.

approximately $0.08 \times 10 = 0.8\%$. If another section is added to the filter, its reduction factor from Fig. 7-8 will be applied to the 0.8% from the preceding section; $0.8 \times 0.08 = 0.064\%$ (if the second section has the same LC product as the first).

● CHOKE-INPUT FILTERS

Much better voltage regulation results when a choke-input filter, as shown in Fig. 7-9, is used. Choke input also permits better utilization of the rectifier, since a higher load current usually can be drawn without exceeding the peak current rating of the rectifier.

Minimum Choke Inductance

A choke-input filter will tend to act as a capacitive-input filter unless the input choke has at least a certain minimum value of inductance called the **critical** value. This critical value is given by

$$L_\mathrm{h} = \frac{E_\mathrm{VOLTS}}{I_\mathrm{MA.}}$$

where E is the output voltage of the supply, and I is the current being drawn from the supply.

If the choke has at least the critical value, the output voltage will be limited to the average value of the rectified wave at the input to the

Filters

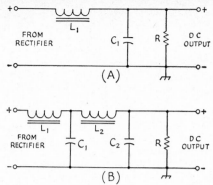

Fig. 7-9—Choke-input filter circuits. A—Single-section. B—Double-section.

choke (see Fig. 7-2) when the current drawn from the supply is small. This is in contrast to the capacitive-input filter in which the output voltage tends to soar toward the peak value of the rectified wave at light loads. Also, if the input choke has at least the critical value, the rectifier peak plate current will be limited to about twice the d.c. current drawn from the supply. Most rectifier tubes have peak-current ratings of three to four times their maximum d.c. output-current ratings. Therefore, with an input choke of at least critical inductance, current up to the maximum output-current rating of the rectifier may be drawn from the supply without exceeding the peak-current rating of the rectifier.

Minimum-Load—Bleeder Resistance

From the formula above for critical inductance, it is obvious that if no current is drawn from the supply, the critical inductance will be infinite. So that a practical value of inductance may be used, some current must be drawn from the supply at all times the supply is in use. From the formula we find that this minimum value of current is

$$I_{MA.} = \frac{E_{VOLTS}}{L_h}$$

Thus, if the choke has an inductance of 20 h., and the output voltage is 2000, the minimum load current should be 100 ma. This load may be provided, for example, by transmitter stages that draw current continuously (stages that are not keyed). However, in the majority of cases it will be most convenient to adjust the bleeder resistance so that the bleeder will draw the required minimum current. In the above example, the bleeder resistance should be 2000/0.1 = 20,000 ohms.

From the formula for critical inductance, it is seen that when more current is drawn from the supply, the critical inductance becomes less. Thus, as an example, when the total current, including the 100 ma. drawn by the bleeder rises to 400 ma., the choke need have an inductance of only 5 h. to maintain the critical value. This is fortunate, because chokes having the required inductance for the bleeder load only and that will maintain this value of inductance for much larger currents are very expensive.

Swinging Chokes

Less costly chokes are available that will maintain at least critical value of inductance over the range of current likely to be drawn from practical supplies. These chokes are called **swinging chokes**. As an example, a swinging choke may have an inductance rating of 5/25 h. and a current rating of 225 ma. If the supply delivers 1000 volts, the minimum load current should be 1000/25 = 40 ma. When the full load current of 225 ma. is drawn from the supply, the inductance will drop to 5 h. The critical inductance for 225 ma. at 1000 volts is 1000/225 = 4.5 h. Therefore the 5/25-h. choke maintains at least the critical inductance at the full current rating of 225 ma. At all load currents between 40 ma. and 225 ma., the choke will adjust its inductance to at least the approximate critical value.

Table 7-I shows the maximum supply output voltage that can be used with commonly-available swinging chokes to maintain critical inductance at the maximum current rating of the choke. These chokes will also maintain critical inductance for any *lower* values of voltage, or current down to the required minimum drawn by a proper bleeder as discussed above.

TABLE 7-I				
L_h	Max. ma.	Max. volts	Max. R^1	Min. ma.[2]
3.5/13.5	150	525	13.5K	39
5/25	175	875	25K	35
2/12	200	400	12K	33
5/25	200	1000	25K	40
5/25	225	1125	25K	45
2/12	250	500	12K	42
4/20	300	1200	20K	60
5/25	300	1500	25K	60
3/17	400	1200	17K	71
4/20	400	1600	20K	80
5/25	400	2000	25K	80
4/16	500	2000	16K	125
5/25	500	2500	25K	100
5/25	550	2750	25K	110

[1] Maximum bleeder resistance for critical inductance.
[2] Minimum current (bleeder) for critical inductance.

In the case of supplies for higher voltages in particular, the limitation on maximum load resistance may result in the wasting of an appreciable portion of the transformer power capacity in the bleeder resistance. Two input chokes in series will permit the use of a bleeder of twice the resistance, cutting the wasted current in half. Another alternative that can be used in a c.w. transmitter is to use a very high-resistance bleeder for protective purposes and only sufficient fixed bias on the tubes operating from the supply to bring the total current drawn from the supply, when the key is open, to the value of current that the required bleeder resistance should draw from the supply. Operating bias is brought back up to normal by increasing the grid-leak resistance. Thus the entire current capacity of the supply (with the exception of the small drain of the protective bleeder) can be used in operating the transmitter stages. With this system, it is advisable to operate the tubes at phone, rather than c.w., rating, since the average dissipation is increased.

Output Voltage

Provided the input-choke inductance is at least the critical value, the output voltage may be calculated quite closely by the following equation:

$$E_o = 0.9E_t - (I_B + I_L)(R_1 + R_2) - E_r$$

where E_o is the output voltage; E_t is the r.m.s. voltage applied to the rectifier (r.m.s. voltage between center-tap and one end of the secondary in the case of the center-tap rectifier); I_B and I_L are the bleeder and load currents, respectively, in amperes; R_1 and R_2 are the resistances of the first and second filter chokes; and E_r is the drop between rectifier plate and cathode. The various voltage drops are shown in Fig. 7-12. At no load I_L is zero, hence the no-load voltage may be calculated on the basis of bleeder current only. The voltage regulation may be determined from the no-load and full-load voltages using the formula previously given.

Ripple with Choke Input

The percentage ripple output from a single-section filter (Fig. 7-9A) may be determined to a close approximation, for a ripple frequency of 120 cycles, from Fig. 7-10.

Example: $L = 5$ h., $C = 4$ μf., $LC = 20$.

From Fig. 7-10, percentage ripple = 5 per cent.

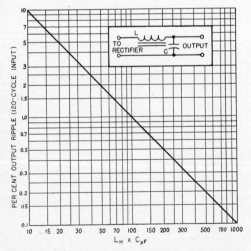

Fig. 7-10—Graph showing combinations of inductance and capacitance that may be used to reduce ripple with a single-section choke-input filter.

Example: $L = 5$ h. What capacitance is needed to reduce the ripple to 1 per cent? Following the 1-per-cent line to the right to its intersection with the diagonal, thence downward to the LC scale, read $LC = 100$. $100/5 = 20$ μf.

In selecting values for the first filter section, the inductance of the choke should be determined by the considerations discussed previously. Then the capacitor should be selected that when combined with the choke inductance (minimum inductance in the case of a swinging choke) will bring the ripple down to the desired value. If it is found impossible to bring the ripple down to the desired figure with practical values in a single section, a second section can be added, as shown in Fig. 7-9B and the reduction factor from Fig. 7-8 applied as discussed under capacitive-input filters. The second choke should not be of the swinging type, but one having a more or less constant inductance with changes in current (smoothing choke).

● OUTPUT CAPACITOR

If the supply is intended for use with an audio-frequency amplifier, the reactance of the last filter capacitor should be small (20 per cent or less) compared with the other audio-frequency resistance or impedance in the circuit, usually the tube plate resistance and load resistance. On the basis of a lower a.f. limit of 100 cycles for speech amplification, this condition usually is satisfied when the output capacitance (last filter capacitor) of the filter has a capacitance of 4 to 8 μf., the higher value of capacitance being used in the case of lower tube and load resistances.

● RESONANCE

Resonance effects in the series circuit across the output of the rectifier which is formed by the first choke (L_1) and first filter capacitor (C_1) must be avoided, since the ripple voltage would build up to large values. This not only is the opposite action to that for which the filter is intended, but also may cause excessive rectifier peak currents and abnormally high inverse peak voltages. For full-wave rectification the ripple frequency will be 120 cycles for a 60-cycle supply, and resonance will occur when the product of choke inductance in henrys times capacitor capacitance in microfarads is equal to 1.77. The corresponding figure for 50-cycle supply (100-cycle ripple frequency) is 2.53, and for 25-cycle supply (50-cycle ripple frequency) 13.5. At least twice these products of inductance and capacitance should be used to ensure against resonance effects. With a swinging choke, the minimum rated inductance of the choke should be used.

● RATINGS OF FILTER COMPONENTS

Although filter capacitors in a choke-input filter are subjected to smaller variations in d.c. voltage than in the capacitive-input filter, it is

Transformers

advisable to use capacitors rated for the peak transformer voltage in case the bleeder resistor should burn out when there is no load on the power supply, since the voltage then will rise to the same maximum value as it would with a filter of the capacitive-input type.

In a capacitive-input filter, the capacitors should have a working-voltage rating at least as high, and preferably somewhat higher, than the peak-voltage rating of the transformer. Thus, in the case of a center-tap rectifier having a transformer delivering 550 volts each side of the center-tap, the minimum safe capacitor voltage rating will be 550 × 1.41 or 775 volts. An 800-volt capacitor should be used, or preferably a 1000-volt unit.

Filter Capacitors in Series

Filter capacitors are made in several different types. Electrolytic capacitors, which are available for peak voltages up to about 800, combine high capacitance with small size, since the dielectric is an extremely thin film of oxide on aluminum foil. Capacitors of this type may be connected in series for higher voltages, although the filtering capacitance will be reduced to the resultant of the two capacitances in series. If this arrangement is used, it is important that *each* of the capacitors be shunted with a resistor of about 100 ohms per volt of supply voltage, with a power rating adequate for the total resistor current at that voltage. These resistors may serve as all or part of the bleeder resistance (see choke-input filters). Capacitors with higher-voltage ratings usually are made with a dielectric of thin paper impregnated with oil. The **working voltage** of a capacitor is the voltage that it will withstand continuously.

Filter Chokes

The input choke may be of the swinging type, the required minimum no-load and full-load inductance values being calculated, as described above. For the second choke (**smoothing choke**) values of 4 to 20 henrys ordinarily are used. When filter chokes are placed in the positive leads, the negative being grounded, the windings should be insulated from the core to withstand the full d.c. output voltage of the supply and be capable of handling the required load current.

Filter chokes or inductances are wound on iron cores, with a small gap in the core to prevent magnetic saturation of the iron at high currents. When the iron becomes saturated its

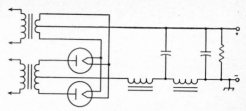

Fig. 7-11—In most applications, the filter chokes may be placed in the negative instead of the positive side of the circuit. This reduces the danger of a voltage breakdown between the choke winding and core.

permeability decreases, consequently the inductance also decreases. Despite the air gap, the inductance of a choke usually varies to some extent with the direct current flowing in the winding; hence it is necessary to specify the inductance at the current which the choke is intended to carry. Its inductance with little or no direct current flowing in the winding may be considerably higher than the value when full load current is flowing.

● NEGATIVE-LEAD FILTERING

For many years it has been almost universal practice to place filter chokes in the positive leads of plate power supplies. This means that the insulation between the choke winding and its core (which should be grounded to chassis as a safety measure) must be adequate to withstand the output voltage of the supply. This voltage requirement is removed if the chokes are placed in the negative lead as shown in Fig. 7-11. With this connection, the capacitance of the transformer secondary to ground appears in parallel with the filter chokes tending to bypass the chokes. However, this effect will be negligible in practical application except in cases where the output ripple must be reduced to a very low figure. Such applications are usually limited to low-voltage devices such as receivers, speech amplifiers and v.f.o.'s where insulation is no problem and the chokes may be placed in the positive side in the conventional manner. In higher-voltage applications, there is no reason why the filter chokes should not be placed in the negative lead to reduce insulation requirements. Choke terminals, negative capacitor terminals and the transformer center-tap terminal should be well protected against accidental contact, since these will assume full supply voltage to chassis should a choke burn out or the chassis connection fail.

Plate and Filament Transformers

Output Voltage

The output voltage which the plate transformer must deliver depends upon the required d.c. load voltage and the type of filter circuit.

With a choke-input filter, the required r.m.s. secondary voltage (each side of center-tap for a center-tap rectifier) can be calculated by the equation:

$$E_t = 1.1\left[E_o + I(R_1 + R_2) + E_r \right]$$

where E_o is the required d.c. output voltage, I is the load current (including bleeder current) in amperes, R_1 and R_2 are the d.c. resistances of the chokes, and E_r is the voltage drop in the rectifier. E_t is the full-load r.m.s. secondary voltage; the open-circuit voltage usually will be

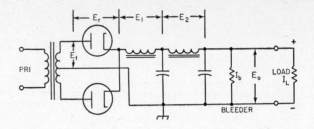

Fig. 7-12—Diagram showing various voltage drops that must be taken into consideration in determining the required transformer voltage to deliver the desired output voltage.

5 to 10 per cent higher than the full-load value.

The approximate transformer output voltage required to give a desired d.c. output voltage with a given load with a capacitive-input filter system can be calculated with Fig. 7-12.

Example:
Required d.c. output volts — 500
Load current to be drawn — 100 ma. (0.1 amp)

$$\text{Load resistance} = \frac{500}{0.1} = 5000 \text{ ohms.}$$

If the rectifier resistance is 200 ohms, Fig. 7-5 shows that the ratio of d.c. volts to the required transformer r.m.s. voltage is approximately 1.15.

The required transformer terminal voltage under load with chokes of 200 and 300 ohms is

$$E_t = \frac{E_o + I\left(R_1 + R_2 + R_r\right)}{1.15}$$

$$= \frac{500 + 0.1\left(200 + 300 + 200\right)}{1.15}$$

$$= \frac{570}{1.15} = 495 \text{ volts.}$$

Volt-Ampere Rating

The volt-ampere rating of the transformer depends upon the type of filter (capacitive or choke input). With a capacitive-input filter the heating effect in the secondary is higher because of the high ratio of peak to average current, consequently the volt-amperes consumed by the transformer may be several times the watts delivered to the load. With a choke-input filter, provided the input choke has at least the critical inductance, the secondary volt-amperes can be calculated quite closely by the equation:

$$\text{Sec. V.A.} = 0.00075EI$$

where E is the *total* r.m.s. voltage of the secondary (between the outside ends in the case of a center-tapped winding) and I is the d.c. output current in milliamperes (load current plus bleeder current). The primary volt-amperes will be 10 to 20 per cent higher because of transformer losses.

Broadcast & Television Replacement Transformers in Amateur Transmitter Service

Small power transformers of the type sold for replacement in broadcast and television receivers are usually designed for service in terms of use for several hours continuously with capacitor-input filters. In the usual type of amateur transmitter service, where most of the power is drawn intermittently for periods of several minutes with equivalent intervals in between, the published ratings can be exceeded without excessive transformer heating.

With capacitor input, it should be safe to draw 20 to 30 per cent more current than the rated value. With a choke-input filter, an increase in current of about 50 per cent is permissible. If a bridge rectifier is used (with a choke-input filter) the output voltage will be approximately doubled. In this case, it should be possible in amateur transmitter service to draw the rated current, thus obtaining about twice the rated output power from the transformer.

This does not apply, of course, to amateur transmitter plate transformers which are usually already rated for intermittent service.

Filament Supply

Except for tubes designed for battery operation, the filaments or heaters of vacuum tubes used in both transmitters and receivers are universally operated on alternating current obtained from the power line through a step-down transformer delivering a secondary voltage equal to the rated voltage of the tubes used. The transformer should be designed to carry the current taken by the number of tubes which may be connected in parallel across it. The filament or heater transformer generally is center-tapped, to provide a balanced circuit for eliminating hum.

For medium- and high-power r.f. stages of transmitters, and for high-power audio stages, it is desirable to use a separate filament transformer for each section of the transmitter, installed near the tube sockets. This avoids the necessity for abnormally large wires to carry the total filament current for all stages without appreciable voltage drop. Maintenance of rated filament voltage is highly important, especially with thoriated-filament tubes, since under- or over-voltage may reduce filament life.

Typical Power Supplies

Figs. 7-13 and 7-14 show typical power-supply circuits. Fig. 7-13 is for use with trans-

formers commonly listed as broadcast or television replacement power transformers. In addi-

Typical Power Supplies

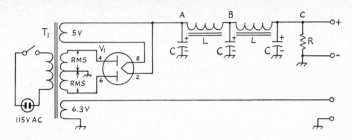

Fig. 7-13—Typical a.c. power-supply circuit for receivers, exciters, or low-power transmitters. Representative values will be found in Table 7-II. The 5-volt winding of T_1 should have a current rating of at least 2 amp. for types 5Y3-GT and 5V4-GA, and 3 amp. for 5U4-GB.

tion to the high-voltage winding for plate supply, these transformers have windings that supply filament voltages for both the rectifier tube and the 6.3-volt tubes in the receiver or low-power transmitter or exciter. Transformers of this type may be obtained in ratings up to 1200 volts r.m.s. center-tapped, 200 d.c. ma. output.

Fig. 7-13 shows a two-section filter with capacitor input. However, depending upon the maximum hum level that may be allowable for a particular application, the last capacitor and choke may not be needed. In some low-current applications, the first capacitor alone may provide adequate filtering. Table 7-II shows the approximate full-load and bleeder-load output voltages and a.c. ripple percentages for several representative sets of components. Voltage and ripple values are given for three points in the circuit — Point A (first capacitor only used), Point B (last capacitor and choke omitted), and Point C (complete two-section filter in use).

In each case, the bleeder resistor R should be used across the output.

Table 7-II also shows approximate output voltages and ripple percentages for choke-input filters (first filter capacitor omitted), for Point B (last capacitor and choke omitted), and Point C (complete two-section filter, first capacitor omitted).

Actual full-load output voltages may be somewhat lower than those shown in the table, since the voltage drop through the resistance of the transformer secondary has not been included.

Fig. 7-14 shows the conventional circuit of a transmitter plate supply for higher powers. A full-wave rectifier circuit, half-wave rectifier tubes, and separate transformers for high voltage, rectifier filaments and transmitter filaments are used. The high-voltage transformers used in this circuit are usually rated directly in terms of d.c. output voltage, assuming rectifiers and filters of the type shown in Fig. 7-14. Table 7-III shows typical values for representative supplies, based on commonly available components. Transformer

TABLE 7-II

Capacitor-Input Power Supplies

T_1 Rating		V_1 Tube Type	C		L		R		Approximate Full-load d.c. Volts at			Approximate Ripple % at			Approx. Output Volts Bleeder Load	Useful Output Ma.*
Volts R.M.S. (C.T.)	Ma. D.C.		μf.	Volts	H.	Ohms	Ohms	Watts	A	B	C	A	B	C		
650	40	5Y3-GT	8	600	8	400	90K	5	375	360	345	2.5	0.08	0.002	450	36
650	40	5V4-GA	8	600	8	400	90K	5	410	395	375	2.5	0.08	0.002	450	36
700	90	5Y3-GT	8	600	10	225	46K	10	370	350	330	6	0.1	0.002	460	82
700	90	5V4-GA	8	600	10	225	46K	10	410	390	370	6	0.1	0.002	460	82
750	150	5U4-GB	8	700	8	145	25K	10	375	350	330	9	0.2	0.006	500	136
750	150	5V4-GA	8	700	8	145	25K	10	425	400	380	9	0.2	0.006	500	136
800	200	5U4-GB	8	700	8	120	22K	20	375	350	325	12	0.3	0.008	550	184
Choke-Input Power Supplies																
650	40	5Y3-GT	8	450	15	420	18K	10	—	240	225	—	0.8	0.01	265	25
650	40	5V4-GA	8	450	15	420	18K	10	—	255	240	—	0.8	0.01	280	25
700	90	5Y3-GT	8	450	10	225	11K	10	—	240	220	—	1.25	0.02	250	68
700	90	5V4-GA	8	450	10	225	11K	10	—	270	250	—	1.25	0.02	280	68
750	150	5Y3-GT	8	450	12	150	13K	20	—	265	245	—	1	0.015	325	125
750	150	5V4-GA	8	450	12	150	13K	20	—	280	260	—	1	0.015	340	125
800	200	5U4-GB	8	450	12	140	14K	20	—	275	250	—	1	0.015	350	175

* Balance of transformer current capacity consumed by bleeder resistor.

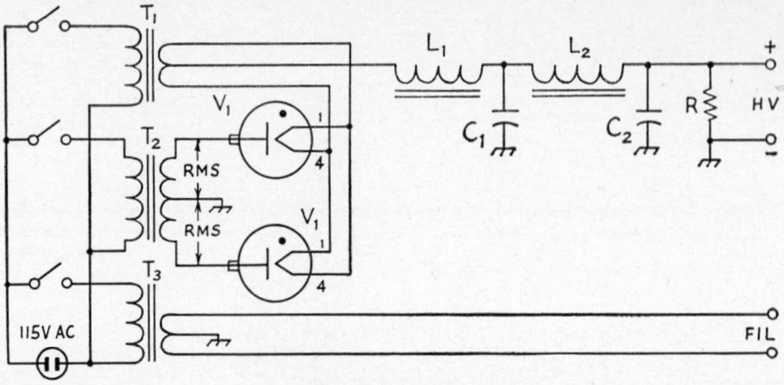

Fig. 7-14—Conventional power-supply circuit for higher-power transmitters.

C₁, C₂—4 μf. for approximately 0.5% output ripple; 2 μf. for approximately 1.5% output ripple. C₂ should be 4 μf. if supply is for modulator.

R—25,000 ohms.

L₁—Swinging choke: 5/25 h., current rating same as T₂.

L₂—Smoothing choke: current rating same as T₂.

T₁—2.5 volts, 4 amp. for type 816; 2.5 volts, 10 amp. for 866A.

T₂—D.c. voltage rating same as output voltage.

T₃—Voltage and current rating to suit transmitter-tube requirements.

V₁—Type 816 for 400/500-volt supply; 866A for others shown in Table 7-III. See Table 7-III for other values.

TABLE 7-III								
Approx. D.C. Output		T₂ Rating		L₂ H.	Voltage Rating C₁, C₂	R Watts	Approx. Bleeder-Load Output Volts
Volts	Ma.[1]	Approx. V.R.M.S.	Ma.				
400/500	230	520/615	250	4	700	20	440/540
600/750	260	750/950	300	8	1000	50	650/800
1250/1500	240	1500/1750	300	8	2000	150	1300/1600
1250/1500	440	1500/1750	500	6	2000	150	1315/1615
2000/2500	200	2400/2900	300[4]	8	3000	320[2]	2050/2550
2000/2500	400	2400/2900	500	6	3000	320[2]	2065/2565
2500/3000	380	2500/3450	500[5]	6	4000	500[3]	2565/3065

[1] Balance of transformer current rating consumed by bleeder resistor.
[2] Use two 160-watt, 12,500-ohm units in series.
[3] Use five 100-watt, 5000-ohm units in series.
[4] Regulation will be somewhat better with a 400- or 500-ma. choke.
[5] Regulation will be somewhat better with a 550-ma. choke.

voltages shown are reppresentative for units with dual-voltage secondaries. The bleeder-load voltages shown may be somewhat lower than actually found in practice, because transformer resistance has not been included. Ripple at the output of the first filter section will be approximately 5 per cent with a 4-μf. capacitor, or 10 per cent with a 2-μf. capacitor. Transformers made for amateur service are designed for choke-input. If a capacitor-input is used rating should be reduced about 30%.

Voltage Dropping

Series Voltage-Dropping Resistor

Certain plates and screens of the various tubes in a transmitter or receiver often require a variety of operating voltages differing from the output voltage of an available power supply. In most cases, it is not economically feasible to provide a separate power supply for each of the required voltages. If the current drawn by an electrode, or combination of electrodes operating at the same voltage, is reasonably constant under normal operating conditions, the required voltage may be obtained from a supply of higher voltage by means of a voltage-dropping resistor in series, as shown in Fig. 7-15A. The value of the series, resistor, R_1, may be obtained from Ohm's Law, $R = \dfrac{E_d}{I}$, where

E_d is the voltage *drop* required from the supply voltage to the desired voltage and I is the total rated current of the load.

Example: The plate of the tube in one stage and the screens of the tubes in two other stages require an operating voltage of 250. The nearest available supply voltage is 400 and the total of the rated plate and screen currents is 75 ma. The required resistance is

$$R = \frac{400 - 250}{0.075} = \frac{150}{0.075} = 2000 \text{ ohms.}$$

The power rating of the resistor is obtained from P (watts) = I^2R = $(0.075)^2$ (2000) = 11.2 watts. A 20-watt resistor is the nearest safe rating to be used.

Voltage Dividers

The regulation of the voltage obtained in this manner obviously is poor, since any change in current through the resistor will cause a directly proportional change in the voltage drop across the resistor. The regulation can be im-

Voltage Stabilization

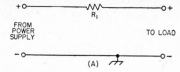

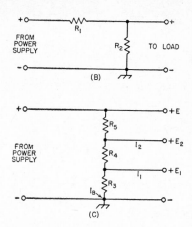

Fig. 7-15—A—Series voltage-dropping resistor. B—Simple voltage divider. C—Multiple divider circuit.

$$R_3 = \frac{E_1}{I_b}; \quad R_4 = \frac{E_2 - E_1}{I_b + I_1}; \quad R_5 = \frac{E - E_2}{I_b + I_1 + I_2}$$

proved somewhat by connecting a second resistor from the low-voltage end of the first to the negative power-supply terminal, as shown in Fig. 7-15B. Such an arrangement constitutes a **voltage divider.** The second resistor, R_2, acts as a constant load for the first, R_1, so that any variation in current from the tap becomes a smaller percentage of the total current through R_1. The heavier the current drawn by the resistors when they alone are connected across the supply, the better will be the voltage regulation at the tap.

Such a voltage divider may have more than a single tap for the purpose of obtaining more than one value of voltage. A typical arrangement is shown in Fig. 7-15C. The terminal voltage is E, and two taps are provided to give lower voltages, E_1 and E_2, at currents I_1 and I_2 respectively. The smaller the resistance between taps in proportion to the total resistance, the smaller the voltage between the taps. For convenience, the voltage divider in the figure is considered to be made up of separate resistances R_3, R_4, R_5, between taps. R_3 carries only the bleeder current, I_b; R_4 carries I_1 in addition to I_b; R_5 carries I_2, I_1 and I_b. To calculate the resistances required, a bleeder current, I_b, must be assumed; generally it is low compared with the total load current (10 per cent or so). Then the required values can be calculated as shown in the caption of Fig. 7-15C, I being in decimal parts of an ampere.

The method may be extended to any desired number of taps, each resistance section being calculated by Ohm's Law using the needed voltage drop across it and the total current through it. The power dissipated by each section may be calculated either by multiplying I and E or I^2 and R.

Voltage Stabilization

Gaseous Regulator Tubes

There is frequent need for maintaining the voltage applied to a low-voltage low-current circuit at a practically constant value, regardless of the voltage regulation of the power supply or variations in load current. In such applications, gaseous regulator tubes (0C3/VR105, 0D3/VR150, etc.) can be used to good advantage. The voltage drop across such tubes is constant over a moderately wide current range. Tubes are available for regulated voltages near 150, 105, 90 and 75 volts.

The fundamental circuit for a gaseous regulator is shown in Fig. 7-16A. The tube is connected in series with a **limiting resistor**, R_1, across a source of voltage that must be higher than the **starting** voltage. The starting voltage is about 30 to 40 per cent higher than the operating voltage. The load is connected in parallel with the tube. For stable operation, a minimum tube current of 5 to 10 ma. is required. The maximum permissible current with most types is 40 ma.; consequently, the load current cannot exceed 30 to 35 ma. if the voltage is to be stabilized over a range from zero to maximum load current.

The value of the limiting resistor must lie between that which just permits minimum tube current to flow and that which just passes the maximum permissible tube current when there is no load current. The latter value is generally used. It is given by the equation:

$$R = \frac{(E_s - E_r)}{I}$$

where R is the limiting resistance in ohms, E_s is the voltage of the source across which the tube and resistor are connected, E_r is the rated voltage drop across the regulator tube, and

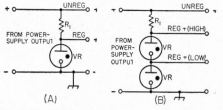

Fig. 7-16—Voltage-stabilizing circuits using VR tubes.

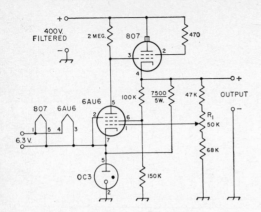

Fig. 7-17—Electronic voltage-regulator circuit. Resistors are ½ watt unless specified otherwise.

I is the maximum tube current in amperes, (usually 40 ma., or 0.04 amp.).

Fig. 7-16B shows how two tubes may be used in series to give a higher regulated voltage than is obtainable with one, and also to give two values of regulated voltage. The limiting resistor may be calculated as above, using the sum of the voltage drops across the two tubes for E_r. Since the upper tube must carry more current than the lower, the load connected to the low-voltage tap must take small current. The total current taken by the loads on both the high and low taps should not exceed 30 to 35 milliamperes.

Voltage regulation of the order of 1 per cent can be obtained with these regulator circuits.

A single VR tube may also be used to regulate the voltage to a load current of almost any value

so long as the *variation* in the current does not exceed 30 to 35 ma. If, for example, the average load current is 100 ma., a VR tube may be used to hold the voltage constant provided the current does not fall below 85 ma. or rise above 115 ma. In this case, the resistance should be calculated to drop the voltage to the VR-tube rating at the maximum load current to be expected plus about 5 ma. If the load resistance is constant, the effects of variations in line voltage may be eliminated by basing the resistance on the load current plus 15 ma. Voltage-regulator tubes may also be connected in parallel as described later in this chapter.

Electronic Voltage Regulation

Several circuits have been developed for regulating the voltage output of a power supply elec-

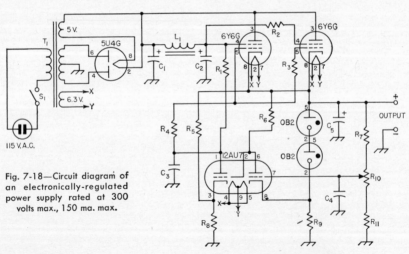

Fig. 7-18—Circuit diagram of an electronically-regulated power supply rated at 300 volts max., 150 ma. max.

C_1, C_2, C_5—16-μf. 600-volt electrolytic.
C_3—0.015-μf. paper.
C_4—0.1-μf. paper.
R_1—0.3 megohm, ½ watt.
R_2, R_3—100 ohms, ½ watt.
R_4—510 ohms, ½ watt.
R_5, R_8—30,000 ohms, 2 watts.
R_6—0.24 megohm, ½ watt.
R_7—0.15 megohm, ½ watt.

R_9—9100 ohms, 1 watt.
R_{10}—0.1-megohm potentiometer.
R_{11}—43,000 ohms, ½ watt.
L_1—8-hy., 40-ma. filter choke.
S_1—S.p.s.t. toggle.
T_1—Power transformer: 375-375 volts r.m.s., 160 ma.; 6.3 volts, 3 amps.; 5 volts, 3 amps. (Thor. 22R33).

Voltage Stabilization

tronically. While more complicated than the VR-tube circuits, they will handle higher voltages and currents and the output voltage may be varied continuously over a wide range. In the circuit of Fig. 7-17, the 0C3 regulator tube supplies a reference of approximately 105 volts for the 6AU6 control tube. When the load connected across the output terminals increases, the output voltage tends to decrease. This drops the voltage on the control grid of the 6AU6, causing the tube to draw less current through the 2-megohm plate resistor. As a consequence the grid voltage on the 807 series regulator rises and the voltage drop across the 807 decreases, compensating for the reduction in output voltage. With the values shown, adjustment of R_1 will give a regulated output from 150 to 250 volts, at up to 60 or 70 ma. A 6L6-GB can be substituted for the type 807; the available output current can be increased by adding one or more tubes in parallel with the series regulator tube. When tubes are connected in parallel, 100-ohm resistors should be wired to each control grid and plate terminal, to reduce the chances for parasitic oscillations.

Another similar regulator circuit is shown in Fig. 7-18. The principal difference is that screen-grid regulator tubes are used. The fact that a screen-grid tube is relatively insensitive to changes in plate voltage makes it possible to obtain a reduction in ripple voltage adequate for many purposes simply by supplying filtered d.c. to the screens with a consequent saving in weight and cost. The accompanying table shows the performance of the circuit of Fig. 7-18. Column I shows various output voltages, while Column II shows the maximum current that can be drawn at that voltage with negligible variation in output voltage. Column III shows the measured ripple at the maximum current. The second part of the

Table of Performance for Circuit of Fig. 7-18					
I	II	III	Output voltage — 300		
450 v.	22 ma.	3 mv.	150 ma.	2.3 mv.	
425 v.	45 ma.	4 mv.	125 ma.	2.8 mv.	
400 v.	72 ma.	6 mv.	100 ma.	2.6 mv.	
375 v.	97 ma.	8 mv.	75 ma.	2.5 mv.	
350 v.	122 ma.	9.5 mv.	50 ma.	3.0 mv.	
325 v.	150 ma.	3 mv.	25 ma.	3.0 mv.	
300 v.	150 ma.	2.3 mv.	10 ma.	2.5 mv.	

table shows the variation in ripple with load current at 300 volts output.

High-Voltage Regulators

Regulated screen voltage is required for screen-grid tubes used as linear amplifiers in single-sideband operation. Figs. 7-19 through 7-22 show various different circuits for supplying regulated voltages up to 1200 volts or more.

In the circuit of Fig. 7-19, gas-filled regulator tubes are used to establish a fixed reference voltage to which is added an electronically regulated variable voltage. The design can be modified to give any voltage from 225 volts to 1200 volts, with each design-center voltage variable by plus or minus 60 volts.

The output voltage will depend upon the number and voltage ratings of the VR tubes in the string between the 991 and ground. The total VR-tube voltage rating needed can be determined by subtracting 250 volts from the desired output voltage. As examples, if the desired output voltage is 350, the total VR-tube voltage rating should be $350 - 250 = 100$ volts. In this case, a VR-105 would be used. For an output voltage of 1000, the VR-tube voltage rating should be $1000 - 250 = 750$ volts. In this case, five VR-150s would be used in series.

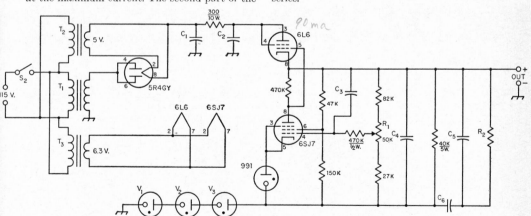

Fig. 7-19—High-voltage regulator circuit by W4PRM. Resistors are 1 watt unless indicated otherwise.

C₁, C₂—4-µf. paper, voltage rating above peak-voltage output of T₁.
C₃—0.1-µf. paper, 600 volts.
C₄—12-µf. electrolytic, 450 volts.
C₅—40 µf., voltage rating above d.c. output voltage. Can be made up of a combination of electrolytics in series with equalizing resistor. (See section on ratings of filter components.)
C₆—4-µf. paper, voltage rating above voltage rating of

VR string.
R₁—50,000-ohm, 4-watt potentiometer.
R₂—Bleeder resistor, 50,000 to 100,000 ohms, 25 watts (not needed if equalizing resistors mentioned above are used).
T₁—See text.
T₂—Filament transformer; 5 volts, 2 amp.
T₃—Filament transformer; 6.3 volts, 1.2 amp.
V₁, V₂, V₃—See text.

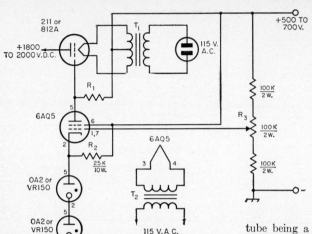

R_1—6000 ohms for 211; 2300 ohms for 812A, 20 watts.

R_2—25,000 ohms, 10 watts.

R_3—Output voltage control, 0.1- megohm, 2-watt potentiometer.

T_1—Filament transformer: 10 volts, 3.25 amp. for 211; 6.3 volts, 4 amp. for 812A.

T_2—Filament transformer: 6.3 volts, 1 amp.

tube being a 6AQ5. With an input voltage of 1800 to 2000, an output voltage of 500 to 700 can be obtained with a regulation better than 1 per cent over a current range of 0 to 100 ma.

In the circuit of Fig. 7-21, a V-70D (or 8005) is used as the regulator, and the control tube is an 807 which can take the full output voltage, making it unnecessary to raise it above ground with VR tubes. If taps are switched on R_1, the output voltage can be varied over a wide range. Increasing the screen voltage decreases the output voltage. For each position of the tap on R_1, decreasing the value of R_3 will lower the minimum output voltage as R_2 is varied, and decreasing the

The maximum voltage output that can be obtained is approximately equal to 0.7 times the r.m.s. voltage of the transformer T_1. The current rating of the transformer must be somewhat above the load current to take care of the voltage dividers and bleeder resistances.

A single 6L6 will handle 90 ma. For larger currents, 6L6s may be added in parallel.

The heater circuit supplying the 6L6 and 6SJ7 should *not* be grounded. The shaft of R_1 should be grounded. When the output voltage is above 300 or 400, the potentiometer should be provided with an insulating mounting, and should be controlled from the panel by an extension shaft with an insulated coupling and grounded control.

In some cases where the plate transformer has sufficient current-handling capacity, it may be desirable to operate a screen regulator from the plate supply, rather than from a separate supply. This can be done if a regulator tube is used that can take the required voltage drop. In Fig. 7-20, a type 211 or 812A is used, the control

Fig. 7-21—This regulator circuit used by W1SUN operates from the plate supply and requires no VR string. A small supply provides screen voltage and reference bias for the control tube.

Unless otherwise marked, resistances are in ohms. (K = 1000). Capacitors are electrolytic.

R_1—50,000-ohm, 50-watt adjustable resistor.

R_2—0.1-megohm 2-watt potentiometer.

R_3—4.7 megohms, 2 watts.

R_4—0.1 megohm, ½ watt.

T_1—Power transformer: 470 volts center tapped, 40 ma.; 5 volts, 2 amps.; 6.3 volts, 2 amps.

T_2—Filament transformer: 7.5 volts, 3.25 amp. (for V-70D).

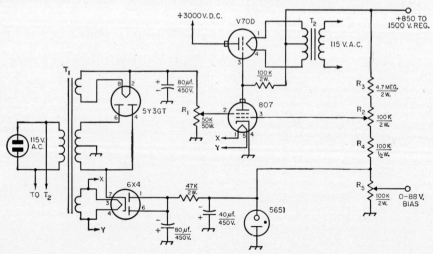

Bias Supplies

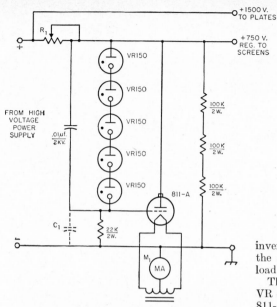

+1500 V. TO PLATES

+750 V. REG. TO SCREENS

R₁

VR150

VR150

VR150

VR150

VR150

811-A

FROM HIGH VOLTAGE POWER SUPPLY

.01 μf. 2KV.

100K 2W.

100K 2W.

100K 2W.

C₁

22K 2W.

M₁ MA

Fig. 7-22—Shunt screen regulator used by W2AZW. Resistances are in ohms (K = 1000).

C_1—0.01 μf., 400 volts if needed to suppress oscillation.

M_1—See text.

R_1—Adjustable wire-wound resistor, resistance and wattage as required.

value of R_4 will raise the maximum output voltage. However, if these values are made too small, the 807 will lose control.

At 850 volts output, the variation over a current change of 20 to 80 ma. should be negligible. At 1500 volts output with the same current change, the variation in output voltage should be less than three per cent. Up to 88 volts of grid bias for a Class A or Class AB₁ amplifier may be taken from the potentiometer across the reference-voltage source. This bias cannot, of course, be used for biasing a stage that is drawing grid current.

A somewhat different type of regulator is the shunt regulator shown in Fig. 7–22. The VR tubes and R_2 in series are across the output. Since the voltage drop across the VR tubes is constant, any change in output voltage appears across R_2. This causes a change in grid bias on the 811-A grid, causing it to draw more or less current in inverse proportion to the current being drawn by the amplifier screen. This provides a constant load for the series resistor R_1.

The output voltage is equal to the sum of the VR drops plus the grid-to-ground voltage of the 811-A. This varies from 5 to 20 volts between full load and no load. The initial adjustment is made by placing a milliammeter in the filament center-tap lead, as shown, and adjusting R_1 for a reading of 15 to 20 ma. higher than the normal peak screen current. This adjustment should be made with the amplifier connected but with no excitation, so that the amplifier draws idling current. After the adjustment is complete, the meter may be removed from the circuit and the filament center tap connected directly to ground. Adjustment of the tap on R_1 should, of course, be made with the high voltage turned off.

Any number of VR tubes may be used to provide a regulated voltage near the desired value. The maximum current through the 811-A should be limited to the maximum plate-current rating of the tube. If larger currents are necessary, two 811-As may be connected in parallel. Over a current range of 5 to 60 ma., the regulator holds the output voltage constant within 10 or 15 volts.

Bias Supplies

As discussed in Chapter 6 on high-frequency transmitters, the chief function of a bias supply for the r.f. stages of a transmitter is that of providing protective bias, although under certain circumstances, a bias supply, or pack, as it is sometimes called, can provide the operating bias if desired.

Simple Bias Packs

Fig. 7-23A shows the diagram of a simple bias supply. R_1 should be the recommended grid leak for the amplifier tube. No grid leak should be used in the transmitter with this type of supply. The output voltage of the supply, when amplifier grid current is not flowing, should be some value between the bias required for plate-current cut-off and the recommended operating bias for the amplifier tube. The transformer peak voltage (1.4 times the r.m.s. value) should not exceed the recommended operating-bias value, otherwise the output voltage of the pack will soar above the operating-bias value with rated grid current.

This soaring can be reduced to a considerable extent by the use of a voltage divider across the transformer secondary, as shown at B. Such a system can be used when the transformer voltage is higher than the operating-bias value. The tap on R_2 should be adjusted to give amplifier cut-off bias at the output terminals. The lower the total value of R_2, the less the soaring will be when grid current flows.

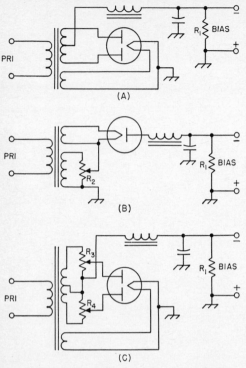

A full-wave circuit is shown in Fig. 7-23C. R_3 and R_4 should have the same total resistance and the taps should be adjusted symmetrically. In all cases, the transformer must be designed to furnish the current drawn by these resistors plus the current drawn by R_1.

Regulated Bias Supplies

The inconvenience of the circuits shown in Fig. 7-23 and the difficulty of predicting values in practical application can be avoided in most cases by the use of gaseous voltage-regulator tubes across the output of the bias supply, as shown in Fig. 7-24A. A VR tube with a voltage rating anywhere between the biasing-voltage value which will reduce the input to the amplifier to a safe level when excitation is removed, and the operating value of bias, should be chosen. R_1 is adjusted, without amplifier excitation, until the VR tube ignites and draws about 5 ma. Additional voltage to bring the bias up to the operating value when excitation is applied can be obtained from a grid leak resistor, as discussed in the transmitter chapter.

Each VR tube will handle 40 ma. of grid current. If the grid current exceeds this value under any condition, similar VR tubes should be added in parallel, as shown in Fig. 7-24B, for each 40 ma., or less, of additional grid current. The

Fig. 7-23—Simple bias-supply circuits. In A, the peak transformer voltage must not exceed the operating value of bias. The circuits of B (half-wave) and C (full-wave) may be used to reduce transformer voltage to the rectifier. R_1 is the recommended grid-leak resistance.

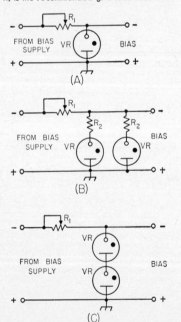

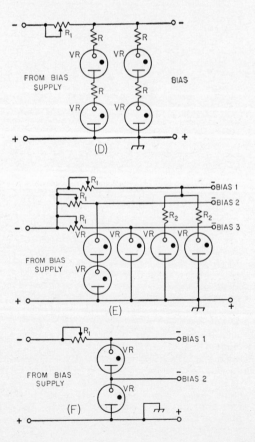

Fig. 7-24—Illustrating the use of VR tubes in stabilizing protective-bias supplies. R_1 is a resistor whose value is adjusted to limit the current through each VR tube to 5 ma. before amplifier excitation is applied. R and R_2 are current-equalizing resistors of 50 to 1000 ohms.

Bias Supplies

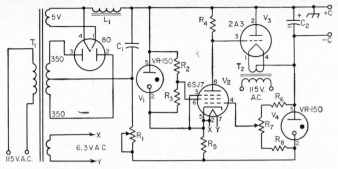

Fig. 7-25—Circuit diagram of an electronically-regulated bias supply.

C_1—20-μf. 450-volt electrolytic.
C_2—20-μf. 150-volt electrolytic.
R_1—5000 ohms, 25 watts.
R_2—22,000 ohms, 1/2 watt.
R_3—68,000 ohms, 1/2 watt.
R_4—0.27 megohm, 1/2 watt.
R_5—3000 ohms, 5 watts.
R_6—0.12 megohm, 1/2 watt.

R_7—0.1-megohm potentiometer.
R_8—27,000 ohms, 1/2 watt.
L_1—20-hy. 50-ma. filter choke.
T_1—Power transformer: 350 volts
r.m.s. each side of center
50 ma.; 5 volts, 2 amp.;
6.3 volts, 3 amp.
T_2—2.5-volt filament transformer
(Thordarson 21F00).

resistors R_2 are for the purpose of helping to maintain equal currents through each VR tube, and should have a value of 50 to 1000 ohms or more.

If the voltage rating of a single VR tube is not sufficiently high for the purpose, other VR tubes may be used in series (or series-parallel if required to satisfy grid-current requirements) as shown in the diagrams of Fig. 7-24C and D.

If a single value of fixed bias will serve for more than one stage, the biasing terminal of each such stage may be connected to a single supply of this type, provided only that the total grid current of all stages so connected does not exceed the current rating of the VR tube or tubes. Alternatively, other separate VR-tube branches may be added in any desired combination to the same supply, as in Fig. 7-24E, to adapt them to the needs of each stage. Providing the VR-tube current rating is not exceeded, a series arrangement may be tapped for lower voltage, as shown at F.

The circuit diagram of an electronically regulated bias-supply is shown in Fig. 7-25. The output voltage may be adjusted to any value between 40 volts and 80 volts and the unit will handle grid currents up to 35 ma. over the range of 50 to 80 volts, and 25 ma. over the remainder of the range. If higher current-handling capacity is required, more 2A3s can be connected in parallel with V_3. The regulation will hold to about 0.01 volt per milliampere of grid current. The regulator operates as follows: Since the voltage drop across V_3 and V_4 is in parallel with the voltage drop across V_1 and R_5, any change in voltage across V_3 will appear across R_5 because the voltage drops across both VR tubes remain constant. R_5 is a cathode biasing resistor for V_2, so any voltage change across it appears as a grid-voltage change on V_2. This change in grid voltage is amplified by V_2 and appears across R_4 which is connected to the plate of V_2 and the grids of V_3. This change in

voltage swings the grids of V_3 more positive or negative, and thus varies the internal resistance of V_3, maintaining the voltage drop across V_3 practically constant.

Other Sources of Biasing Voltage

In some cases, it may be convenient to obtain the biasing voltage from a source other than a separate supply. A half-wave rectifier may be connected with reversed polarization to obtain biasing voltage from a low-voltage plate supply, as shown in Fig. 7-26A. In an-

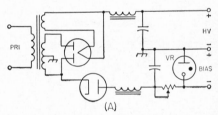

(A)

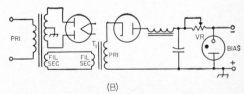

(B)

Fig. 7-26—Convenient means of obtaining biasing voltage. A—From a low-voltage plate supply. B—From spare filament winding. T_1 is a filament transformer, of a voltage output similar to that of the spare filament winding, connected in reverse to give 115 volts r.m.s. output. If cold-cathode or selenium rectifiers are used, no additional filament supply is required.

other arrangement, shown at B, a spare filament winding can be used to operate a filament transformer of similar voltage rating in reverse to obtain a voltage of about 130 from the winding that is customarily the primary. This will be sufficient to operate a VR75 or VR90 regulator tube.

A bias supply of any of the types discussed requires relatively little filtering, if the output-terminal peak voltage does not approach the operating-bias value, because the effect of the supply is entirely or largely "washed out" when grid current flows.

Selenium-Rectifier Circuits

While the circuits shown in Figs. 7-27, 7-28 and 7-29 may be used with any type of rectifier, they find their greatest advantage when used with selenium rectifiers which require no filament transformer. These circuits must be used with caution, observing line polarity in the circuits so marked, to avoid shorting the line, since the negative output terminal should always be grounded. In circuits showing isolating transformers, the transformer is a requirement, since without the transformer, the negative output terminal cannot be grounded in following good practice for safety without shorting out part of the rectifier circuit. In the circuits which do not show a transformer, the transformer is preferable, since it avoids the need for a correctly polarized power-line connection to prevent a short circuit.

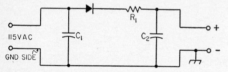

Fig. 7-27—Simple half-wave circuit for selenium rectifier.
C_1—0.05-μf. 600-volt paper.
C_2—40-μf. 200-volt electrolytic.
R_1—25 to 100 ohms.

Fig. 7-27 is a straightforward half-wave rectifier circuit which may be used in applications where 115 to 130 volts d.c. is desired. It can be used as a bias supply by reversing the polarity of the rectifier and capacitors.

Three voltage-doubler circuits are shown in Fig. 7-28. At A is a full-wave circuit, while the other two, at A and B, are half-wave circuits. Although easier to filter, the circuit of A has the disadvantage that the output cannot be grounded directly unless an isolation transformer is used. B and C are similar, except that the series capacitor is in different sides of the circuit. The output of B can be grounded directly if proper line polarity is observed. Circuit C, which includes a filter for illustration purposes, requires an isolation transformer if the output is to be grounded, but since all three capacitors, including the filter capacitor, have a common negative connection, a triple-unit capacitor may be used where space must be conserved.

Fig. 7-29 shows voltage tripler and quadrupler circuits. The circuit of A is a halfwave tripler. A full-wave tripler, requiring an additional rectifier element, is shown at B. The circuit of Fig. 7-29C is a half-wave voltage quadrupler. The full-wave version is shown at D. Both full-wave circuits require an isolation transformer to permit grounding of the output.

In the circuits of Figs. 7-28 and 7-29 where an isolation transformer is not shown, it is essential that the indicated line polarity be observed if the output is to be grounded. Otherwise part of the circuit will be shorted out.

The resistors R_1 are for rectifier protective purposes, and recommended minimum values are given in the table at the end of this section. The value of capacitance given is representative. Larger values will improve voltage regulation. Smaller values may be used at a sacrifice in regulation.

Fig. 7-28—Voltage-doubling circuits for use with selenium rectifiers. Maximum back voltage on rectifiers is 2.8 E_{rms}. Voltage rating at least 1.4 E_{rms} for C_1, at least 2.8 E_{rms} for C_2.
C_1—40-μf. electrolytic.
C_2—40-μf. electrolytic.
R_1—25 to 100 ohms.
L_1—Filter choke.
T_1—Isolation transformer.

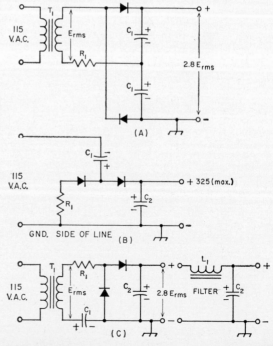

Selenium Rectifiers

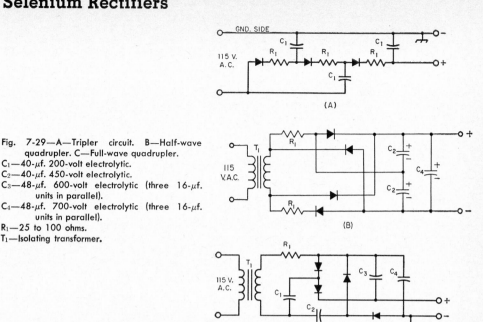

Fig. 7-29—A—Tripler circuit. B—Half-wave quadrupler. C—Full-wave quadrupler.
C₁—40-μf. 200-volt electrolytic.
C₂—40-μf. 450-volt electrolytic.
C₃—48-μf. 600-volt electrolytic (three 16-μf. units in parallel).
C₄—48-μf. 700-volt electrolytic (three 16-μf. units in parallel).
R₁—25 to 100 ohms.
T₁—Isolating transformer.

Power-Line Considerations

● POWER-LINE CONNECTIONS

If the transmitter is rated at much more than 100 watts, special consideration should be given to the a.c. line running into the station. In some residential systems, three wires are brought in from the outside to the distribution board, while in other systems there are only two wires. In the three-wire system, the third wire is the **neutral** which is grounded. The voltage between the other two wires normally is 230, while half of this voltage (115) appears between each of these wires and neutral, as indicated in Fig. 7-30A. In systems of this type, usually it will be found that the 115-volt household load is divided as evenly as possible between the two sides of the circuit, half of the load being connected between one wire and the neutral, while the other half of the load is connected between the other wire and neutral. Heavy appliances, such as electric stoves and heaters, normally are designed for 230-volt operation and therefore are connected across the two ungrounded wires. While both ungrounded wires should be fused, a fuse should never be used in the wire to the neutral, nor should a switch be used in this side of the line. The reason for this is that opening the neutral wire does not disconnect the equipment. It simply leaves the equipment on one side of the 230-volt circuit in series with whatever load may be across the other side of the circuit, as shown in Fig. 7-30B. Furthermore, with the neutral open, the voltage will then be divided between the two sides in inverse proportion to the load resistance, the voltage on one side dropping below normal, while it soars on the other side, unless the loads happen to be equal.

The usual line running to baseboard outlets is rated at 15 amperes. Considering the power consumed by filaments, lamps, modulator, receiver and other auxiliary equipment, it is not

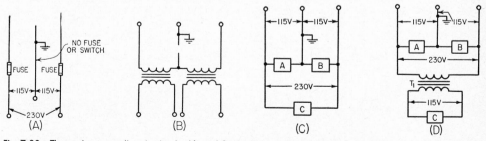

Fig. 7-30—Three-wire power-line circuits. A—Normal 3-wire-line termination. No fuse should be used in the grounded (neutral) line. B—Showing that a switch in the neutral does not remove voltage from ether side of the line. C—Connections for both 115- and 230-volt transformers. D—Operating a 115-volt plate transformer from the 230-volt line to avoid light blinking. T₁ is a 2-to-1 step-down transformer.

unusual to find this 15-ampere rating exceeded by the requirements of a station of only moderate power. It must also be kept in mind that the same branch may be in use for other household purposes through another outlet. For this reason, and to minimize light blinking when keying or modulating the transmitter, a separate heavier line should be run from the distribution board to the station whenever possible. (A three-volt drop in line voltage will cause noticeable light blinking.)

If the system is of the three-wire type, the three wires should be brought into the station so that the load can be distributed to keep the line balanced. The voltage across a fixed load on one side of the circuit will increase as the load current on the other side is increased. The rate of increase will depend upon the resistance introduced by the neutral wire. If the resistance of the neutral is low, the increase will be correspondingly small. When the currents in the two circuits are balanced, no current flows in the neutral wire and the system is operating at maximum efficiency.

Light blinking can be minimized by using transformers with 230-volt primaries in the power supplies for the keyed or intermittent part of the load, connecting them across the two ungrounded wires with no connection to the neutral, as shown in Fig. 7-30C. The same can be accomplished by the insertion of a step-down transformer whose primary operates at 230 volts and whose secondary delivers 115 volts. Conventional 115-volt transformers may be operated from the secondary of the step-down transformer (see Fig. 7-30D).

When a special heavy-duty line is to be installed, the local power company should be consulted as to local requirements. In some localities it is necessary to have such a job done by a licensed electrician, and there may be special requirements to be met in regard to fittings and the manner of installation. Some amateurs terminate the special line to the station at a switch box, while others may use electric-stove receptacles as the termination. The power is then distributed around the station by means of conventional outlets at convenient points. All circuits should be properly fused.

Fusing

All transformer primary circuits should be properly fused. To determine the approximate current rating of the fuse to be used, multiply each current being drawn from the supply in amperes by the voltage at which the current is being drawn. Include the current taken by bleeder resistances and voltage dividers. In the case of series resistors, use the source voltage, not the voltage at the equipment end of the resistor. Include filament power if the transformer is supplying filaments. After multiplying the various voltages and currents, add the individual products. Then divide by the line voltage and add 10 or 20 per cent. Use a fuse with the nearest larger current rating.

● LINE-VOLTAGE ADJUSTMENT

In certain communities trouble is sometimes experienced from fluctuations in line voltage. Usually these fluctuations are caused by a variation in the load on the line and, since most of the variation comes at certain fixed times of the day or night, such as the times when lights are turned on at evening, they may be taken care of by the use of a manually operated compensating device. A simple arrangement is shown in Fig. 7-31A. A toy transformer is used to boost or buck the line voltage

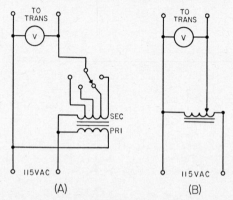

Fig. 7-31—Two methods of transformer primary control. At A is a tapped toy transformer which may be connected so as to boost or buck the line voltage as required. At B is indicated a variable transformer or autotransformer (Variac) which feeds the transformer primaries.

as required. The transformer should have a tapped secondary varying between 6 and 20 volts in steps of 2 or 3 volts and its secondary should be capable of carrying the full load current of the entire transmitter, or that portion of it fed by the toy transformer.

The secondary is connected in series with the line voltage and, if the phasing of the windings is correct, the voltage applied to the primaries of the transmitter transformers can be brought up to the rated 115 volts by setting the toy-transformer tap switch on the right tap. If the phasing of the two windings of the toy transformer happens to be reversed, the voltage will be reduced instead of increased. This connection may be used in cases where the line voltage may be above 115 volts. This method is preferable to using a resistor in the primary of a power transformer since it does not affect the voltage regulation as seriously. The circuit of 7-31B illustrates the use of a variable autotransformer (Variac) for adjusting line voltage.

Another scheme by which the primary voltage of each transformer in the transmitter may be adjusted to give a desired secondary voltage, with a master control for compensating for changes in line voltage, is shown in Fig. 7-32.

This arrangement has the following features:
1) Adjustment of the switch S_1 to make the voltmeter read 105 volts automatically adjusts all transformer primaries to the predetermined correct voltage.

Power Supply Construction

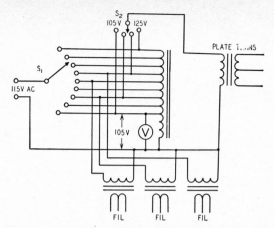

Fig. 7-32—With this circuit, a single adjustment of the tap switch S₁ places the correct primary voltage on all transformers in the transmitter.

2) The necessity for having all primaries work at the same voltage is eliminated. Thus, 110 volts can be applied to the primary of one transformer, 115 to another, etc., as required to obtain the desired output voltage.

3) Independent control of the plate transformer is afforded by the tap switch S_2. This permits power-input control and does not require an extra autotransformer.

Constant-Voltage Transformers

Although comparatively expensive, special transformers called **constant-voltage transformers** are available for use in cases where it is necessary to hold line voltage and/or filament voltage constant with fluctuating supply-line voltage. They are rated over a range of 17 v.a. at 6.3 volts output, for small tube-heater demands, up to several thousand volt-amperes at 115 or 230 volts. In average figures, such transformers will hold their output voltages within one per cent under an input-voltage variation of 30 per cent.

Construction of Power Supplies

The length of most leads in a power supply is unimportant, so that the arrangement of components from this consideration is not a factor in construction. More important are the points of good high-voltage insulation, adequate conductor size for filament wiring, proper ventilation for rectifier tubes and — most important of all — safety to the operator. Exposed high-voltage terminals or wiring which might be bumped into accidentally should not be permitted to exist. They should be covered with adequate insulation or placed inaccessible to contact during normal operation and adjustment of the transmitter. Power-supply units should be fused individually. All negative terminals of plate supplies and positive terminals of bias supplies should be securely grounded to the chassis, and the chassis connected to a waterpipe or radiator ground. All transformer, choke, and capacitor cases should also be grounded to the chassis. A.c. power cords and chassis connectors should be arranged so that exposed contacts are never "live." Starting at the conventional a.c. wall outlet which is female, one end of the cord should be fitted with a male plug. The other end of the cord should have a female receptacle. The input connector of the power supply should have a male receptacle to fit the female receptacle of the cord. The power-output connector on the power supply should be a female socket. A male plug to fit this socket should be connected to the cable going to the equipment. The opposite end of the cable should be fitted with a female connector, and the series should terminate with a male connector on the equipment. If connections are made in this manner, there should be no "live" exposed contacts at any point, regardless of where a disconnection may be made.

Rectifier filament leads should be kept short

Fig. 7-33—A typical low-voltage power supply. The two a.c. connectors permit independent control of filament and high voltage.

to assure proper voltage at the rectifier socket, through a metal chassis, grommet-lined clearance holes will serve for voltages up to 500 or 750, but ceramic feed-through insulators should be used for higher voltages. Bleeder and voltage-dropping resistors should be placed where they are open to air circulation. Placing them in confined space reduces the rating.

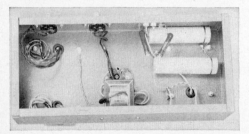

Fig. 7-34. A bottom view of the low-voltage power supply. The separate filament transformer is mounted against the lower wall of the chassis. The electrolytic filter capacitors are mounted on terminal strips. Rubber grommets are used where wires pass through the chassis.

It is highly preferable from the standpoint of operating convenience to have separate filament transformers for the rectifier tubes, rather than to use combination filament and plate transformers, such as those used in receivers. This permits the transmitter plate voltage to be switched on without the necessity for waiting for rectifier filaments to come up to temperature after each time the high voltage has been turned off. When using a combination power transformer, high voltage may be turned off without turning the filaments off by using a switch between the transformer center tap and chassis. This switch should be of the rotary

type with good insulation between contacts. The shaft of the switch *must* be grounded.

● **SAFETY PRECAUTIONS**

All power supplies in an installation should be fed through a single main power-line switch so that all power may be cut off quickly, either before working on the equipment, or in case of an accident. Spring-operated switches or relays are not sufficiently reliable for this important service. Foolproof devices for cutting off all power to the transmitter and other equipment are shown in Fig. 7-37. The arrangements shown in Fig. 7-37A and B are similar circuits for two-wire (115-volt) and three-wire (230-volt) systems. S is an enclosed double-throw knife switch of the sort usually used as the entrance switch in house installations. J is a standard a.c. outlet and P a shorted plug to fit the outlet. The switch should be located prominently in plain sight and mem-

Fig. 7-36—Bottom view of the high-voltage supply. The electrolytic capacitors (connected in series) are mounted on an insulating board. Voltage-equalizing resistors are connected across each capacitor. Separate input connectors are provided for filament and plate power.

Fig. 7-35—A typical high-voltage supply. The sockets for the 866A mercury-vapor rectifier tubes are spaced from the metal chassis by small cone insulators. Note the insulated tube plate connectors, the safety high-voltage output terminal and the fuse.

Power-Supply Construction

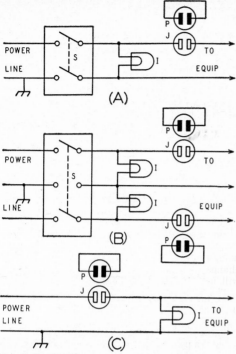

Fig. 7-37—Reliable arrangements for cutting off all power to the transmitter. S is an enclosed double-pole knife-type switch, J a standard a.c. outlet. P a shorted plug to fit the outlet and I a red lamp.

A is for a two-wire 115-volt line, B for a three-wire 230-volt system, and C a simplified arrangement for low-power stations.

in his absence and either injuring themselves or the equipment or perhaps starting a fire. Of utmost importance is the fact that the outlet J *must* be placed in the *ungrounded* side of the line.

Those who are operating low power and feel that the expense or complication of the switch isn't warranted can use the shorted-plug idea as the main power switch. In this case, the outlet should be located prominently and identified by a signal light, as shown in Fig. 7-37C.

The test bench ought to be fed through the main power switch, or a similar arrangement at the bench, if the bench is located remote from the transmitter.

A bleeder resistor with a power rating giving a considerable margin of safety should be used across the output of all transmitter power supplies so that the filter capacitors will be discharged when the high-voltage transformer is turned off.

bers of the household should be instructed in its location and use. I is a red lamp located alongside the switch. Its purpose is not so much to serve as a warning that the power is on as it is to help in identifying and quickly locating the switch should it become necessary for someone else to cut the power off in an emergency.

The outlet J should be placed in some corner out of sight where it will not be a temptation for children or others to play with. The shorting plug can be removed to open the power circuit if there are others around who might inadvertently throw the switch while the operator is working on the rig. If the operator takes the plug with him, it will prevent someone from turning on the power

Selenium-Rectifier Table

All types listed below are rated as follows: Max. input r.m.s. volts — 130, Max. peak inverse volts — 380. Series resistors of 47 ohms are recommended for units rated at less than 65 ma., 22 ohms for 75- and 100-ma. units, 15 ohms for 150-ma. units, and 5 ohms for all higher-current units.

D.C. Ma. Output	Manufacturer					
	A	B	C	D	E	F
20	1159	....	8S20	....	...	....
30	....	....	....	8Y1	...	....
35	....	....	8S35	....	...	....
50	....	RS65Q	....	....	50	....
65	1002A	RS65	6S65	8J1	65	NA-5
75	1003A	RS75	6S75	5M4	75	NB-5
100	1004A	RS100	6S100	5M1	100	NC-5
150	1005A	RS150	6S150	5P1	150	ND-5
200	1006A	RS200	6S200	5R1	200	NE-5
250	1028A	RS250	6S250	5Q1	250	NF-5
300	1090A	RS300	6S300	6Q4	300	....
350	1023	RS350	6S350	5QS1	...	NK-5
400	1130	RS400	6S400	5S2	400	NH-5
450	....	RS450	6S450	....	...	NJ-5
500	1179	RS500	6S500	5S1	500	....
600	....	....	....	....	600	....
1000	....	RS1000	....	....	...	....

A — Federal.   B — International.   C — Mallory. D — Radio Receptor.   E — Sarkes-Tarzian.   F — Sylvania.

Silicon Rectifier Table

JETEC Type	Max. R.M.S. Input Volts	Max. D.C. Load Current
1N1082	140	500 ma.
1N1084	280	500 ma.
1N1109	840	425 ma.
1N1110	1120	400 ma.
1N1113	1960	325 ma.
*M150	130	150 ma.
*M500	130	500 ma.

* Sarkes-Tarzian type number.

Germanium Rectifier Table

(All 300 ma. d.c. output)

JETEC Type	Max. R.M.S. Volts Input	JETEC Type	Max. R.M.S. Volts Input	JETEC Type	Max. R.M.S. Volts Input
1N600	70	1N600A	70	1N611	210
1N601	105	1N603A	210	1N613	350
1N602	140	1N604A	280	1N607A	35
1N604	280	1N605A	350	1N608A	70
1N605	350	1N607	35	1N611A	210
1N599A	35	1N608	70	1N612A	280

CHAPTER 8

Keying and Break-In

Section 12.133 of the FCC regulations says ". . . The frequency of the emitted . . . wave shall be as constant as the state of the art permits." It also says ". . . spurious radiation shall not be of sufficient intensity to cause interference in receiving equipment of good engineering design including adequate selectivity characteristics, which is tuned to a frequency or frequencies outside the frequency band of emission normally required for the type of emission being employed by the amateur station."

The state of the art is such that an emitted wave can be mighty stable, yet many code (and phone) stations show f.m. and chirp that leaves them open to a citation by the Commission. Key clicks (and splatter) represent violations of the spurious radiation clause, and it isn't hard to find evidences of them in any of the ham bands.

There are four factors that have to be considered in the keying of a transmitter. They are r.f. clicks, envelope shape, chirp and backwave.

R.F. Clicks

When any circuit carrying d.c. or a.c. is closed or broken, the small or large spark (depending upon the voltage and current) generates r.f. during the instant of make or break. This r.f. covers a frequency range of many megacycles. When a transmitter is keyed, the spark at the key (and relay, if used) causes a click in the receiver. *This click has no effect on the transmitted signal.* Since it occurs at the same time that a click (if any) appears on the transmitter output, it must be removed if one is to listen critically to his own signal within the shack. A small r.f. filter is required at the contacts of the key (and relay); typical circuits and values are shown in Fig. 8-1. To check the effectiveness of the r.f. filter, listen on a lower-frequency band than the transmitter is tuned to, with a short antenna and the gain backed off.

Envelope Shape

The key clicks that go out on the air with the signal are controlled by the shape of the envelope of the signal. The envelope is the outline of the oscilloscope pattern of your transmitter output, but an oscilloscope isn't needed to observe the effects. Fig. 8-2 shows representative scope patterns that might be obtained with a given transmitter under various conditions.

One should understand that the *on-the-air* clicks are determined by the shaping, while the r.f. clicks caused by the spark at the key can only be heard in the station receiver and possibly a broadcast receiver in the same house or apartment.

Chirp

The frequency-stability reference in the opening paragraph refers to the "chirp" observed on many signals. This is caused by a change in frequency of the signal during a single dot or dash. Chirp is an easy thing to detect if you know how to listen for it, although it is amazing how some operators will listen to a signal and say it has no chirp when it actually has. The easiest way to detect chirp is to tune in the code signal at a low beat note and listen for any change in frequency during a dash. The lower the beat note, the easier it is to detect the frequency change. Listening to a harmonic of the signal will accentuate the frequency change.

The main reason for minimizing chirp, aside from complying with the letter of the regulations, is one of pride, since a properly shaped chirp-free signal is a pleasure to copy and is likely to attract attention by its rarity. Chirps cannot be observed on an oscilloscope pattern of the envelope.

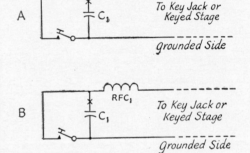

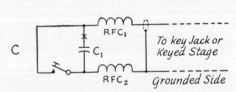

Fig. 8-1—Typical filter circuits to apply at the key (and relay, if used) to minimize r.f. clicks. The simplest circuit (A) is a small capacitor mounted at the key. If this proves insufficient, an r.f. choke can be added to the ungrounded lead (B) or in both leads (C). The value of C_1 is .001 to .01 μf., RFC_1 and RFC_2 can be 0.5 to 2.5 mh., with a current-carrying ability sufficient for the current in the keyed circuit. In difficult cases another small capacitor may be required on the other side of the r.f. choke or chokes. In all cases the r.f. filter should be mounted right at the key or relay terminals; sometimes the filter can be concealed under the key. When cathode or center-tap keying is used, the resistance of the r.f. choke or chokes will add cathode bias to the keyed stage, and in this case a high-current low-resistance choke may be required, or compensating reduction of the grid-leak bias (if it is used) may be needed.

A visible spark on "make" can often be reduced by the addition of a small (10 to 100 ohms) resistor in series with C_1 (inserted at point "x"). Too high a value of resistor reduces the arc-suppressing effect on "break."

Keying Factors

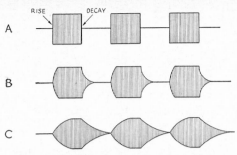

RISE DECAY

A

B

C

Fig. 8-2—Typical oscilloscope displays of a code transmitter. The rectangular-shaped dots (A) have serious key clicks extending many kc. either side of the transmitter frequency. Using proper shaping circuits increases the rise and decay times to give signals with the envelope form of B. This signal would have practically no key clicks. Carrying the shaping process too far, as in C, results in a signal that is too "soft" and is not easy to copy.

Backwave

The last factor is "backwave," a signal during key-up conditions from some amplifier-keyed transmitters. Some operators listening in the shack to their own signals and hearing a backwave think that the backwave can be heard on the air. It isn't necessarily so, and the best way to check is with an amateur a mile or more away. If he can't hear a backwave on the S9+ signal, you can be sure that it isn't there when the signal is weaker. Backwave is undesirable because it makes a signal harder to copy, even with acceptable shaping and no chirp.

Amplifier Keying

Many two-, three- and even four-stage transmitters are utterly incapable of completely chirp-free amplifier keying because the severe "modulation" of the output stage has an effect on the oscillator frequency and "pulls" through the several stages. This is particularly true when the oscillator stage is on the same frequency as the keyed output stage, but it can also happen when frequency multiplying is involved. Another source of reaction is the variation in oscillator supply voltage under keying conditions, although this can usually be handled by stabilizing the oscillator supply with a VR tube. If the objective is a completely chirp-free transmitter, the very first step is to make sure that keying the contemplated amplifier stage (or stages) has no effect on the oscillator frequency. This can be checked by listening on the oscillator frequency while the amplifier stage is keyed. Listen for chirp on either side of zero beat to eliminate the possible effect of a chirpy receiver caused by line-voltage changes or pulling. If no chirp of the steadily running oscillator can be detected, the transmitter can be keyed without chirp in the stage or stages used for the test. This is no assurance that the transmitter can be keyed without chirp in an earlier stage until the same test is passed by the earlier stage.

An amplifier can be keyed by any method that reduces the output to zero. Neutralized stages

can be keyed in the cathode circuit, although where powers over 50 or 75 watts are involved it is often desirable to use a keying relay or vacuum tube keyer, to minimize the chances for electrical shock. Tube keying drops the supply voltages and adds cathode bias, points to be considered where maximum output is required. Blocked-grid keying is applicable to many neutralized stages, but it presents problems in high-powered amplifiers and requires a source of negative voltage. Output stages that aren't neutralized, such as many of the tetrodes and pentodes in widespread use, will usually leak a little and show some backwave regardless of how they are keyed. In a case like this it may be necessary to key two stages to eliminate backwave. They can be keyed in the cathodes, with blocked-grid keying, or in the screens. When screen keying is used, it is not always sufficient to reduce the screen voltage to zero; it may have to be pulled to some negative value to bring the key-up plate current to zero, unless fixed negative control-grid bias is used. It should be apparent that where two stages are keyed, keying the earlier stage must have no effect on the oscillator frequency if completely chirp-free output is the goal.

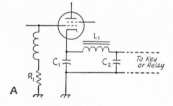

A

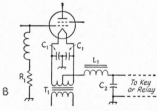

B

Fig. 8-3—The basic cathode (A) and center-tap (B) keying circuits. In either case C_1 is the r.f. return to ground, shunted by a larger capacitor for shaping. Voltage ratings at least equal to the cut-off voltage of the tube are required. T_1 is the normal filament transformer. C_2 can be about 0.01 µf.

The shaping of the signal is controlled by the values of L_1 and C_1. Increased capacitance at C_1 will make the signal softer on break; increased inductance at L_1 will make the signal softer on make. In many cases the make will be satisfactory without any inductance.

Values at C_1 will range from 0.5 to 4 µf., depending upon the tube type and operating conditions. The value of L_1 will also vary with tube type and conditions, and may range from a fraction of a henry to several henrys. When tetrodes or pentodes are keyed in this manner, a smaller value can sometimes be used at C_1 if the screen-voltage supply is fixed and not obtained from the plate supply through a dropping resistor.

Oscillators keyed in the cathode circuit cannot be softened on break indefinitely by increasing the value of C_1 because the grid-circuit time constant enters into the action.

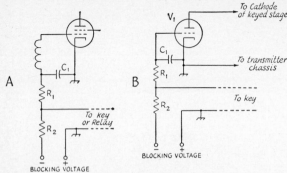

Fig. 8-4—The basic circuit for blocked-grid keying is shown at A. R_1 is the normal grid leak, and the blocking voltage must be at least several times the normal grid bias. The click on make can be reduced by making C_1 larger, and the click on break can be reduced by making R_2 larger. Usually the value of R_2 will be 5 to 20 times the resistance of R_1. The power supply current requirement depends upon the value of R_2, since closing the key circuit places R_2 across the blocking voltage supply.

An allied circuit is the vacuum-tube keyer of B. The tube V_1 is connected in the cathode circuit of the stage to be keyed. The values of C_1, R_1 and R_2 determine the keying envelope in the same way that they do for blocked-grid keying. Values to start with might be 0.47 megohm for R_1, 4.7 megohm for R_2 and 0.0047 μf. for C_1.

The blocking voltage supply must deliver several hundred volts, but the current drain is very low. The 6B4-G or other low plate-resistance triode is suitable for V_1. To increase the current-carrying ability of a tube keyer, several tubes can be connected in parallel.

A vacuum-tube keyer adds cathode bias and drops the supply voltages to the keyed stage and will reduce the output of the stage.

Shaping of the keying is obtained in several ways. Blocked-grid and vacuum-tube keyers get suitable shaping with proper choice of resistor and capacitor values, while cathode and screen-grid keying can be shaped by using inductors and capacitors. Sample circuits are shown in Figs. 8-3, 8-4 and 8-5, together with instructions for their adjustment. There is no "best" adjustment, since this is a matter of personal preference and what you want your signal to sound like. Most operators seem to like the make to be heavier than the break. All of the circuits shown here are capable of a wide range of adjustment.

If the negative supply in a grid-block keyed stage fails, the tube will draw excessive key-up current. To protect against tube damage in this eventuality, an overload relay can be used or, more simply, a fast-acting fuse can be included in the cathode circuit.

Oscillator Keying

The reader may wonder why oscillator keying hasn't been mentioned earlier, since it is widely used. The sad fact of life is that excellent oscillator keying is infinitely more difficult to obtain than is excellent amplifier keying. If the objective is no detectable chirp, it is probably *impossible* to obtain with oscillator keying, particularly on the higher frequencies. The reasons are simple. Any keyed-oscillator transmitter requires shaping at the oscillator, which involves changing the operating conditions of the oscillator over a significant period of time. The output of the

oscillator doesn't rise to full value immediately, so the drive on the following stage is changing, which in turn may reflect a variable load on the oscillator. No oscillator has been devised that has no change in frequency over its entire operating voltage range and with a changing load. Furthermore, the shaping of the keyed-oscillator envelope usually has to be exaggerated, because the following stages will tend to sharpen up the keying and introduce clicks unless they are operated as linear amplifiers (as described in detail later).

Acceptable oscillator keying can be obtained on the lower-frequency bands, and the methods used to key amplifiers can be used, but chirp-free clickless oscillator keying is probably not possible at the higher frequencies, unless at some future date a completely voltage-insensitive oscillator circuit is devised. Often some additional shaping of the signal will be introduced on "make" through the use of a clamp tube in the output amplifier stage, because the time constant of the screen bypass capacitor plus screen dropping resistor increases the screen-voltage rise time, but it is of no help on the "break" portion of the signal.

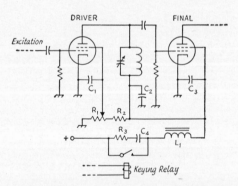

Fig. 8-5—When the driver stage plate voltage is roughly the same as the screen voltage of a tetrode final amplifier, combined screen and driver keying is an excellent system. The envelope shaping is determined by the values of L_1, C_1, and R_3, although the r.f. bypass capacitors C_1, C_2 and C_3 also have a slight effect. R_1 serves as an excitation control for the final amplifier, by controlling the screen voltage of the driver stage. If a triode driver is used, its plate voltage can be varied for excitation control.

The inductor L_1 will not be too critical, and the secondary of a spare filament transformer can be used if a low-inductance choke is not available. The values of C_1 and R_3 will depend upon the inductance and the voltage and current levels, but good starting values are 0.1 μf. and 50 ohms.

To minimize the possibility of electrical shock, it is recommended that a keying relay be used in this circuit, since both sides of the circuit are "hot." As in any transmitter, the signal will be chirp-free only if keying the driver stage has no effect on the oscillator frequency.

Stages to Key

Break-In Keying

The usual argument for oscillator keying is that it permits break-in operation, which is true. If break-in operation is not contemplated and as near perfect keying as possible is the objective, then keying an amplifier or two by the methods outlined earlier is the solution. For operating convenience, an automatic transmitter "turner-onner" (see Campbell, *QST*, Aug., 1956), which will turn on the power supplies and switch antenna relays and receiver muting devices, can be used. The station switches over to the complete "transmit" condition where the first dot is sent, and it holds in for a length of time dependent upon the setting of the delay. It is equivalent to voice-operated phone of the type commonly used by s.s.b. stations. It does not permit hearing the other station whenever the key is up, as does full break-in.

Full break-in with excellent keying is not easy to come by, but it is easier than many amateurs think. Many use oscillator keying and put up with a second-best signal.

Three solutions to chirp-free break-in keying have been developed. One is the "silent v.f.o.," which consists of a well-shielded oscillator and buffer stage running continuously at a low frequency. The output is keyed before it gets out of the shielded compartment, and in some applications several subsequent stages are also keyed.

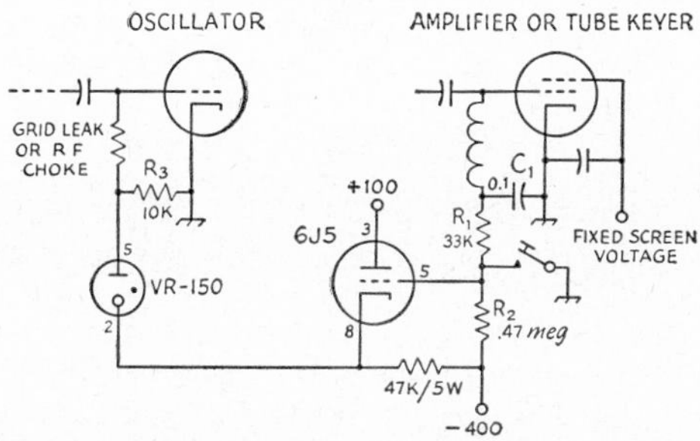

A second approach is to use a conversion exciter, in which two oscillators (one crystal-controlled, one v.f.o.) run continuously and their outputs, with suitable buffer stages intervening, are fed to a mixer stage. The mixer stage output is the sum or difference frequency of the two oscillator frequencies, which have been selected to give a sum or difference in an amateur band. When the mixer stage is turned off by keying, no output appears in the amateur band, and the effect is the same as keying an oscillator stage that cannot possibly chirp. The oscillator frequencies must be selected carefully so that none of their harmonics fall within an amateur band, and sufficient selectivity must be present in stages following the mixer to insure that no spurious signals are amplified.

Differential Keying

A third approach is to turn the oscillator on fast before a keyed amplifier stage can pass any signal and turn off the oscillator fast after the keyed amplifier stage has cut off. The principle is called "differential keying" and a number of circuits have been devised for accomplishing the action. One of the simplest can be applied to any grid-block keyed amplifier or tube-keyed stage by the addition of a triode and a VR tube, as in Fig. 8-6. Using this keying system for break-in, the keying will be chirp-free if it is chirp-free with the VR tube removed from its socket, to permit the oscillator to run all of the time. If the transmitter can't pass this test, it indicates that more isolation is required between keyed stage and oscillator.

Another VR-tube differential keying circuit, useful when the screen-grid circuit of an amplifier is keyed, is shown in Fig. 8-7. The normal screen keying circuit is made up of the shaping capacitor C_1, the keying relay (to remove dangerous volt-

Fig. 8-6—When satisfactory blocked-grid or tube keying of an amplifier stage has been obtained, this VR-tube break-in circuit can be applied to the transmitter to furnish differential keying. The constants shown here are suitable for blocked-grid keying of a 6146 amplifier; with a tube keyer the 6J5 and VR tube circuitry would be the same.

With the key up, sufficient current flows through R_3 to give a voltage that will cut off the oscillator tube. When the key is closed, the cathode voltage of the 6J5 becomes close to ground potential, extinguishing the VR tube and permitting the oscillator to operate. Too much shunt capacity on the leads to the VR tube, and too large a value of grid capacitor in the oscillator, may slow down this action, and best performance will be obtained when the oscillator (turned on and off this way) sounds "clicky." The output envelope shaping is obtained in the amplifier, and it can be made softer by increasing the value of C_1. If the keyed amplifier is a tetrode or pentode, the screen voltage should be obtained from a fixed voltage source or stiff voltage divider, not from the plate supply through a dropping resistor.

A switch connected in series with the VR tube will, when opened, turn on the oscillator for "frequency spotting."

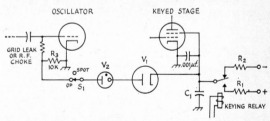

Fig. 8-7—VR-tube differential keying in an amplifier screen circuit.

With key up and current flowing through V_1 and V_2, the oscillator is cut off by the drop through R_3. The keyed stage draws no current because its screen grid is negative. C_1 is charged negatively to the value of the $-$source. When the relay is energized, C_1 charges through R_1 to a $+$ value. Before reaching zero (on its way $+$) there is insufficient voltage to maintain ionization in V_2, and the current is broken in R_3, turning on the oscillator stage. As the screen voltage goes positive, the VR tube, V_2, cannot reignite because the diode, V_1, will not conduct in that direction. The oscillator and keyed stage remain on as long as the relay is closed. When the relay opens, the voltage across C_1 must be sufficiently negative for V_2 to ionize before any bleeder current will pass through R_3. By this time the screen of the keyed stage is so far negative that the tube has stopped conducting.

247

ages from the key), and the resistors R_1 and R_2. The + supply should be 50 to 100 volts higher than the normal screen voltage, and the − voltage should be sufficient to ignite the VR tube, V_2, through the drop in R_2 and R_3. Current through R_2 will be determined by voltage required to cut off oscillator; if 10 volts will do it the current will be 1 ma. For a desirable keying characteristic, R_2 will usually have a higher value than R_1. Increasing the value of C_1 will soften both "make" and "break."

The tube used at V_2 will depend upon the available negative supply voltage. If it is between 120 and 150, a 0A3/VR75 is recommended. Above this a 0C3/VR105 can be used. The diode, V_1, can be any diode operated within ratings. A 6AL5 will suffice with screen voltages under 250 and bleeder currents under 5 ma. For maximum life a separate heater transformer should be used for the diode, with the cathode connected to one side of the heater winding.

Clicks in Later Stages

It was mentioned earlier that key clicks can be generated in amplifier stages following the keyed stage or stages. This is often a puzzling problem to an operator who has spent considerable time adjusting the keying in his exciter unit for clickless keying, only to find that the clicks are bad when the amplifier unit is added. There are two possible causes for the clicks: low-frequency parasitic oscillations and amplifier "clipping."

Under some conditions an amplifier will be momentarily triggered into low-frequency para-sitic oscillations, and clicks will be generated when the amplifier is driven by a keyed exciter. If these clicks are the result of low-frequency parasitic oscillations, they will be found in "groups" of clicks occurring at 50- to 150-kc. intervals either side of the transmitter frequency. Of course low-frequency parasitic oscillations can be generated in a keyed stage, and the operator should listen carefully to make sure that the output of the exciter is clean before he blames a later amplifier. Low-frequency parasitic oscillations are usually caused by poor choice in r.f. choke values, and the use of more inductance in the plate choke than in the grid choke for the same stage is recommended. (See Chapter Six and "low-frequency parasitic oscillations.")

When the clicks introduced by the addition of an amplifier stage are found only near the transmitter frequency, amplifier "clipping" is indicated. It is quite common when fixed bias is used on the amplifier and the bias is well past the "cut-off" value. The effect can usually be minimized or eliminated by using a combination of fixed and grid-leak bias for the amplifier stage. The fixed bias should be sufficient to hold the key-up plate current only to a low level and not to zero. In a triode amplifier, overdriving the amplifier can also result in clipping that will add key clicks, and the cure is to reduce the drive. The output won't suffer appreciably.

A linear amplifier (Class AB_1, AB_2 or B) will amplify the excitation without adding any clicks, and if clicks show up a low-frequency parasitic oscillation is probably the reason.

Testing Your Keying

The choice of a keying circuit is not as important as its testing. Any of the circuits shown in this chapter can be made to give satisfactory keying, but must be adjusted properly.

The easiest way to find out what your keyed signal sounds like on the air is to trade stations with a near-by ham friend some evening for a short QSO. If he is a half mile or so away, that's fine, but any distance where the signals are still S9 will be satisfactory.

After you have found out how to work his rig, make contact and then have him send slow dashes, with dash spacing. (The letter "T" at about 5 w.p.m.) With minimum selectivity, cut the r.f. gain back just enough to avoid receiver overloading (the condition where you get crisp signals instead of mushy ones) and tune slowly from out of beat-note range on one side of the signal through to zero and out the other side. Knowing the tempo of the dashes, you can readily identify any clicks in the vicinity as yours or someone else's. A good signal will have a thump on "make" that is perceptible only where you can also hear the beat note, and the click on "break" should be practically negligible at any point. Fig. 8-8A shows how it should sound. If your signal is like that, it will sound good, provided there are no chirps. Then have him run off a string of 35- or 40-w.p.m. dots with the bug — if they are easy to copy, your signal has no "tails" worth worrying about and is a good one for any speed up to the limit of manual keying. Make one last check with the selectivity in (Fig. 8-8B), to see that the clicks off the signal are negligible even at high signal level.

If you don't have any convenient friends with whom to trade stations, you can still check your keying, although you have to be a little more careful. The first step is to get rid of the r.f. click at the key, as described earlier, because if you don't you cannot make further observations.

So far you haven't done a thing for your signal on the air and you still don't know what it sounds like, but you may have cleaned up some clicks in the broadcast set. Now disconnect the antenna from your receiver and short the antenna terminals with a short piece of wire. Tune in your own signal and reduce the r.f. gain to the point where your receiver doesn't overload. Detune any antenna trimmer the receiver may have. If you can't avoid overload within the r.f. gain-control range, pull out the r.f. amplifier tube and try again. If you still can't avoid overload, listen to the second

Keying Tests

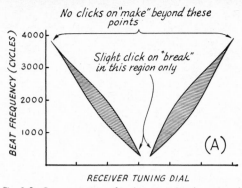

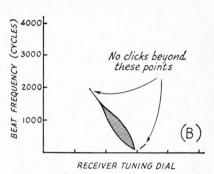

Fig. 8-8—Representations of a clean c.w. signal as a receiver is tuned through it. (A) shows a receiver with no selectivity and the b.f.o. set in the center of the pass band, and (B) shows the selectivity in and the receiver adjusted for single-signal reception. The variation in thickness of the lines represents the relative signal intensity. The audio frequency where the signal disappears will depend upon the receiver selectivity characteristic and the strength of the signal.

harmonic as a last resort. An overloaded receiver can generate clicks.

Describing the volume level at which you should set your receiver for these "shack" tests is a little difficult. The r.f. filter should be effective with the receiver running wide open and with an antenna connected. When you turn on the transmitter and take the other steps mentioned to reduce the signal in the receiver, run the audio up and the r.f. down to the point where you can just hear a little "rushing" sound with the b.f.o. off and the receiver tuned to the signal. This is with the selectivity in. At this level, a properly adjusted keying circuit will show no clicks off the rushing-sound range. With the b.f.o. on and the same gain setting, there should be no clicks outside the beat-note range. When observing clicks, make the slow-dash and fast-dot tests outlined previously.

Now you know how your signal sounds on the air, with one possible exception. If keying your

transmitter makes the lights blink, you may not be able to tell too accurately about the chirp on your signal. However, if you are satisfied with the absence of chirp when tuning *either side of zero beat*, it is safe to assume that your receiver isn't chirping with the light flicker and that the observed signal is a true representation. No chirp either side of zero beat is fine. Don't try to make these tests without first getting rid of the r.f. click at the key, because clicks can mask a chirp.

Exchanging stations temporarily with another interested amateur is probably the best way to check your keying. The second-best method is to check it in the shack as outlined above. The least satisfactory way is to ask another ham on the air how your keying sounds. The reason it is the least satisfactory is that most hams are reluctant to be highly critical of another amateur's signal. In a great many cases they don't actually know what to look for or how to describe any aberrations they may observe.

Vacuum-Tube Keyers

The practical tube-keyer circuit of Fig. 8-9 can be used for keying any stage of any transmitter. Depending upon the power level of the keyed stage, more or fewer Type 2A3 tubes can be connected in parallel to handle the necessary current. The voltage drop through a single 2A3 varies from about 70 volts at 50 ma. to 40 volts at

20 ma. Tubes added in parallel will reduce the drop in proportion to the number of tubes used.

When connecting the output terminals of the keyer to the circuit to be keyed, the grounded output terminal of the keyer must be connected to the transmitter ground. Thus the keyer can be used only in negative-lead or cathode keying.

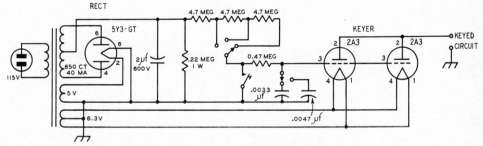

Fig. 8-9—Wiring diagram of a practical vacuum-tube keyer.

249

When used in cathode keying, it will introduce cathode bias to the stage and reduce the output. This can be compensated for by a reduction in the grid-leak bias of the stage.

The negative-voltage supply can be eliminated if a negative voltage is available from some other source, such as a bias supply. A simplified version of this circuit could eliminate the switches and associated resistors and capacitors, since they are incorporated only to allow the operator to select the combination he prefers. But once the values have been selected, they can be soldered permanently in place. The rule for adjusting the keying characteristic is the same as for blocked-grid keying.

A Low-Power Keyer

If a low-level stage running only a few watts is to be keyed, the tube-keyer circuit of Fig. 8-10 offers a simple solution. By using a 117L7 type tube, which incorporates its own rectifier, it is only necessary to connect to some existing power supply at the point marked "X". The keying characteristic will vary with many factors, so the values of R_1 and R_2 only represent starting points for experimentation.

When the key or keying lead has poor insulation, the resistance may become low enough (particularly in humid weather) to reduce the blocking voltage and allow the keyer tube to pass some current. This may cause a slight backwave, but it can be cured by better insulation, or by reduced values of resistors and increased values of capacitors.

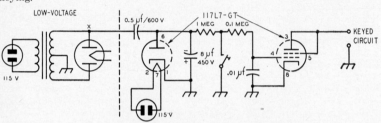

Fig. 8-10—Simple low-power vacuum-tube keyer. Connect keyer to a low-voltage power supply at point "X".

Monitoring of Keying

In general, there are two common methods for monitoring one's "fist" and signal. The first, and perhaps less common type, involves the use of an audio oscillator that is keyed simultaneously with the transmitter.

The second method is one that permits receiving the signal through one's receiver, and this generally requires that the receiver be tuned to

the transmitter (not always convenient unless working on the same frequency) and that some method be provided for preventing overloading of the receiver, so that a good replica of the transmitted signal will be received. Except where quite low power is used, this usually involves a relay for simultaneously shorting the receiver input terminals and reducing the receiver gain.

Break-In Operation

Break-in operation requires a separate receiving antenna, since none of the available antenna change-over relays is fast enough to follow keying. The receiving antenna should be installed as far as possible from the transmitting antenna. It should be mounted at right angles to the transmitting antenna and fed with low pick-up lead-in material such as co-axial cable or 300-ohm Twin-Lead, to minimize pick-up.

If a low-powered transmitter is used, it is often quite satisfactory to use no special equipment for break-in operation other than the separate receiving antenna, since the transmitter will not block the receiver too seriously. Even if the transmitter keys without clicks, some clicks will be heard when the receiver is tuned to the transmitter frequency because of overload in the receiver. An output limiter, as described in Chapter Five, will wash out these

clicks and permit good break-in operation even on your transmitter frequency.

When powers above 25 or 50 watts are used, special treatment is required for quiet break-in on the transmitter frequency. A means should be provided for shorting the input of the receiver when the code characters are sent, and a means for reducing the gain of the receiver at the same time is often necessary. The system shown in Fig. 8-11 permits quiet break-in operation for higher-powered stations. It requires a simple operation on the receiver but otherwise is perfectly straightforward. R_1 is the regular receiver r.f. and i.f. gain control. The ground lead is lifted on this control and run to a rheostat, R_2, that goes to ground. A wire from the junction runs outside the receiver to the keying relay, K_1. When the key is up, the ground side of R_1 is connected to ground through the relay arm, and the receiver is in its normal operating

Break-In

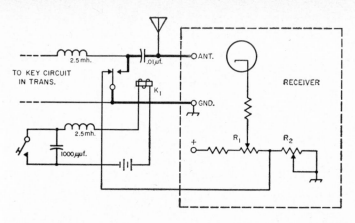

Fig. 8-11—Wiring diagram for smooth break-in operation. The lead shown as a heavy line and the lead from bottom relay contact to ANT post on receiver should be kept as short as possible for minimum pickup of the transmitter signal.

R₁—Receiver manual gain control.

R₂—5000- or 10,000-ohm wire-wound potentiometer.

K₁—S.p.d.t. keying relay. Although battery and d.c. relay are shown, any suitable a.c. or d.c. relay and power source can be used.

condition. When the key is closed, the relay closes, which breaks the ground connection from R_1 and applies additional bias to the tubes in the receiver. This bias is controlled by R_2. When the relay closes, it also closes the circuit to the transmitter oscillator. A filter at the key suppresses the clicks caused by the relay current.

The keying relay should be mounted on the receiver as close to the antenna terminals as possible, and the leads shown heavy in the diagram should be kept short, since long leads will allow too much signal to get through into the receiver. A good high-speed keying relay should be used.

A few of the recent communications receivers bring the return lead from the r.f. gain control to a normally shorted terminal at the rear of the receiver. The preceding break-in system can be readily applied to a receiver of this type, and it will repay the receiver owner to study the instruction book and determine if his receiver already has this connection made in it. Other receivers have provision for reducing the gain or for blanking the receiver; one popular model has provision for bringing in negative bias from a transmitter grid leak to cut off an audio stage during transmit periods.

Full descriptions of systems for break-in operation can be found in the following *QST* articles:

Crawfis, "Simplified 'Break-In with One Antenna,'" Nov., 1954.

Goodman, "VR Break-In Keying," Feb., 1954.

Hays, "Selenium Break-In Keying," July, 1955.

Miller and Meichner, "TVG — An Aid to Break-In," March, 1953.

Puckett, "'De Luxe' Keying Without Relays," September, 1953; Part II, Dec., 1953.

Puckett, "C.W. Man's Control Unit," Feb., 1955.

Receiver Muting and Grid-Block Keying

The muting system shown in Fig. 8-12 can be used with any grid-block or tube-keyed transmitter, and it is particularly applicable to the VR-tube differential keying circuit of Fig. 8-6. Referring to Fig. 8-12, R_1, R_2 and C_1 have the same values and functions that the similarly designated components in Figs. 8-4 and 8-6 have. When the key is open, a small current will flow through R_3, the 0A2 and R_2, and the voltage drop across R_3 will be sufficient to cut off the 6C4. With the 6C4 cut off, there is no current through R_4 and consequently no voltage appearing across R_4. The voltage of the receiver a.v.c. bus is zero with respect to ground.

When the key is closed, there is insufficient voltage across the 0A2 to maintain conduction, and consequently there is no current flow through R_3. With zero voltage between grid and cathode, the 6C4 passes current. The drop across R_4, and thus the negative voltage applied to the a.v.c. line in the receiver, is determined by the value of R_4. Thus the key-down gain of the receiver can be adjusted to permit listening to one's own signal, by increasing the value of R_4 until the receiver output level is a comfortable one. To utilize the same antenna for transmitting and receiving, and thus benefit during receiving from

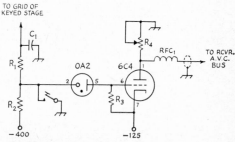

Fig. 8-12—Circuit diagram of a receiver muter for use with grid-block or tube keying.

C₁—Shaping capacitor, see text.

R₁, R₂—Shaping resistors, see text.

R₃—0.1 megohm.

R₄—15,000-ohm 2-watt potentiometer

RFC₁—1 mh. or less.

any directional properties of the antenna, an electronic transmit-receive switch can be used (see later in this chapter).

The receiver a.v.c. bus can be located by reference to the receiver instruction manual, and connection be made to it through a length of shielded wire. The a.v.c. switch in the receiver must be turned to ON for the muter to be effective.

If desired, the muting circuit can be built into the transmitter, or it can be mounted on a shelf or small chassis behind the receiver. The two negative voltages can be furnished by one supply and a reasonably heavy voltage divider; the main requirement of the supply is that the nominal −125 volts remain below the normal voltage drop of the 0A2 (150 volts). Installation of the muting circuits should have little or no effect on the keying characteristic of the transmitter; if it does the characteristic can be restored by proper values for R_1, R_2 and C_1.

The "Matchtone"

The "Matchtone" is a combination of the Monimatch (see Chapter 21) and a c.w. tone-generating monitor. It consists of a transistor audio oscillator which uses the Monimatch as a keyed source of d.c. power. In addition to the usual function it can be used by the sightless amateur as an audible transmitter-antenna tuning indicator.

While direct monitoring of c.w. transmissions via the receiver is a preferred method because it can reveal much about the keying characteristics, transmissions offset from the receiving frequency call for a separate monitor. The self-powered transistorized monitor fills the bill nicely. The use of the r.f. bridge, already connected in the r.f. transmission line, as a source of power for the monitor is a logical choice.

The circuit of the Matchtone and the connections to the Monimatch and the receiver are shown in Fig. 8-13. A small 2- or 3-to-1 push-pull grid-to-plate audio interstage transformer is used for feedback as well as for coupling to the receiver. If a transformer having a p.p. grid winding is not available from the junk box, the audio coupling to the receiver can be obtained by connecting C_2 to the ungrounded end of R_1. While use of a low value of capacitance for C_2 is necessary to avoid excessive shunting of the high-impedance receiver audio circuit, the value shown will provide sufficient coupling for a good audio tone level from the monitor. A third possibility for the audio output connection from the monitor is to substitute the headphones for R_1, together with a single-pole double-throw switch or relay to switch the phones between the monitor and the receiver. The on-off switch, S_1, can be made a part of R_2 by use of a volume control switch attachment.

The value shown for C_1 gives an audio pitch in the 500–1000 cycle range, depending somewhat on the particular transformer, the setting of R_2 and the transmitter output power. Other values of C_1 can be used to adjust the pitch to the operator's individual preference. R_2 may be adjusted to compensate for the changes in the d.c. current from the Monimatch caused by a change in transmitter frequency band or power. Using either a 2N109 or a CK722 transistor, the circuit should oscillate with usable audio level with as little as 0.1 ma. d.c. flowing to ground through the monitor. Other low-cost transistors such as the 2N107 and the 2N170 should work equally well.

Because the pitch of the audio tone is to some degree dependent upon the d.c. voltage obtained from the Monimatch, the pitch gives a reasonably accurate indication of correct final amplifier plate circuit tuning (maximum power output) and, if an antenna tuner is used, will also indicate resonance of the tuner to the transmitter output frequency. This characteristic of the Matchtone should be of considerable aid to sightless amateurs. (From *QST*, January, 1958.)

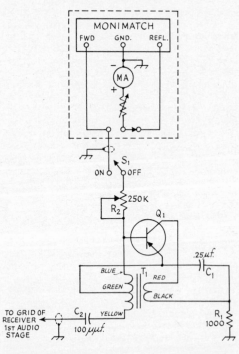

Fig. 8-13—Circuit of the Matchtone. Section enclosed in dashed line is the Monimatch and its indicating circuit. Braid of shielded lead to audio grid should connect to receiver chassis.

C_1—Paper.
C_2—Mica or ceramic.
Q_1—2N109, CK722 or similar.
R_1—1000 ohms, ½ watt.
R_2—0.25-megohm volume control.
S_1—S.p.s.t. toggle.
T_1—Push-pull interstage audio transformer, 2:1 or 3:1 total grid to plate.

T.R. Switches

Electronic Transmit-Receive Switches

No antenna relay is fast enough to switch an antenna from transmitter to receiver and back at normal keying speeds. As a consequence, when it is desired to use the same antenna for transmitting and receiving (a "must" when directional antennas are used) and to operate c.w. break-in or voice-controlled sideband, an electronic switch is used in the antenna. The word "switch" is a misnomer in this case; the transmitter is connected to the antenna at all times and the t.r. "switch" is a device for preventing burn-out of the receiver by the transmitter.

One of the simplest approaches is the circuit shown in Fig. 8–14. The 6C4 cathode follower couples the incoming signal on the line to the receiver input with only a slight reduction in gain. When the transmitter is "on," the grid of the 6C4 is driven positive and the rectified current biases the 6C4 so that it can pass very little power on to the receiver. The factors that limit the r.f. voltage the circuit can handle are the voltage break-down rating of the 47-$\mu\mu$f. capacitor and the voltage that may be safely applied between the grid and cathode of the tube.

To avoid stray pick-up on the lead between the cathode and the antenna terminal of the receiver, this lead should be kept as short as possible. The entire unit should be shielded and mounted on the receiver near the antenna terminals. In wiring the tube socket, input and output circuit components and wiring should be separated to reduce feed-through by stray coupling.

The t.r. switch of Fig. 8–15 differs in two ways from the preceding example. By using a grounded cathode and a tuned plate circuit, a voltage gain is obtained through the tube. The input is taken from the plate of the transmitter output stage instead of from the transmission line, and as a result the voltage build-up in the transmitter tank is utilized. Unlike the preceding t.r. switch, which permits listening on frequencies or bands to which the transmitter is not tuned, this switch will not permit much receiver response at frequencies removed from the transmitter frequency. Usually this is no problem, since most operation is around one's transmitter frequency. The 2.2K resistor across the plate circuit broadens the frequency response and reduces the need for retuning over a band. In a commercial version of this switch, a broadband output transformer replaces L_1 and the variable capacitor, and no coil changes are required in the range 3.5 to 30 Mc.

The switch of Fig. 8–15 can be built in a small metal box and mounted in the transmitter close to the output stage. The plate and heater power can be "borrowed" from the transmitter; the plate power will be less than 15 ma. at 100 to 150 volts. The coaxial line to the receiver can be any convenient length.

The capacitive voltage divider for feeding the t.r. switch is composed of the t.r. switch input

capacitance (about 10 $\mu\mu$f.) and a series capacitor for connection to the plate tank. A conservative value of the series capacitor for an a.m. plate-modulated final can be calculated by the following formula:

$$C_1(\mu\mu f.) = \frac{2500}{d.c.\ plate\ volts}$$

The series capacitance as calculated above may be doubled in value when the final is not modulated, as in c.w., grid modulation or in a linear power amplifier.

The series capacitance is generally less than 20 $\mu\mu$f. The capacitor should be of the low-loss variety and should be capable of withstanding the tank voltage. For plate voltages of 800 volts or less, the disk type ceramic capacitors have been found to be adequate. For greater voltages, an inexpensive capacitor may be fabricated from RG-8/U coaxial cable. This cable has a rating of approximately 6000 peak r.f. volts, and in the laboratory it withstands in excess of 20,000 volts of d.c. Actually, in normal use it is usually limited by current rather than voltage. The capacitance of the cable is 30 $\mu\mu$f. per foot, so that one may measure off the required capacitance by the inch, and end up with a really low-loss and practical unit.

The t.r. switch input is a high impedance for low frequencies. It is advantageous, therefore, to have the tank circuit at d.c. ground potential so that crosstalk at power-line frequencies will be eliminated. Fortunately, this is the case in practically all modern transmitters. A type of noise customarily picked up with electronic t.r. switches is that caused by plate current flowing in the power amplifier. It is necessary, therefore, to bias the tubes beyond cutoff when receiving.

TVI and T.R. Switches

The preceding t.r. switches generate harmonics when their grid circuits are driven positive, and these harmonics can cause TVI if steps are not

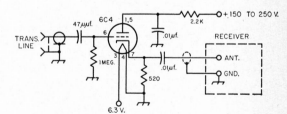

Fig. 8-14—Schematic diagram of cathode-follower t.r. switch. Resistors are ½-watt. The unit should be assembled in a small chassis or shield can and mounted on or very close to the receiver antenna terminals. The transmitter transmission line can be connected at the coaxial jack with an M-358 Tee adapter.

The heater and plate power can be "borrowed" from the receiver in most cases.

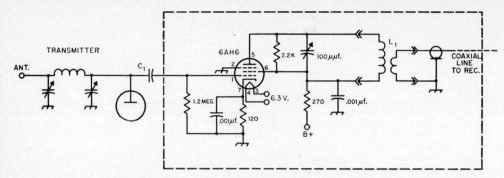

Fig. 8-15—A t.r. switch that mounts in the transmitter. Resistors are ½-watt.

C_1—Depends upon transmitter. See text.

L_1—Plug-in coil to tune to band in use. Coupling coil to receiver, 20 per cent turns in L_1 wound tight over "cold" end of L_1.

taken to prevent it. The switch of Fig. 8–14 should be well-shielded and used in the antenna transmission line between transmitter and low-pass filter. The switch of Fig. 8–15, when mounted in a transmitter that was TVI-free, should not introduce any TVI because the filtering that is successful for the transmitter should be successful for the harmonics generated by the t.r. switch.

Speed Keys

The average operator finds that a speed of 20 to 25 words per minute is the limit of his ability with a straight hand key. However, he can increase his speed to 30 to 40 w.p.m. by the use of a "speed key." The mechanical speed keys, available in most radio stores, give additional speed by making strings of dots when the key lever is pushed to the right; dashes are made manually by closing the key to the left. After practicing with the speed key, the operator obtains the correct "feel" for the key, which allows him to release the dot lever at exactly the right time to make the required number of dots. A speed key can deliver practically perfect code characters when used by an operator who knows what good code sounds like; however, one will not compensate for an operator's poor code ability.

An electronic speed key will not compensate for an operator's poor sending ability, either. However, the electronic speed key has the feature that it makes strings of both dots *and* of dashes, by proper manipulation of the key lever, and in current designs the dashes are *self-completing*. This means that it is impossible to send anything but the correct length of dash when the key lever is closed on the dash side. It is, of course, possible to send an incorrect number of dashes through poor operator timing.

An Electronic Speed Key

Fig. 8-16—This electronic speed key has a range of approximately 8 to 35 w.p.m., set by the speed control at top center. It has relay output and can be used with any transmitter that can be keyed by a hand key. The key (left) is made from two telegraph keys and a pair of ⅛-inch thick sheet plastic paddles.

The unit shown in Figs. 8-16 and 8-18 represents one of the simpler designs of an electronic key. The total cost of the key, in dollars and construction time, is quite low. The keying lever is made from parts taken from two straight telegraph keys; these are available at less than a dollar each in the war-surplus version (J-38). A more elegant keying lever can be built from a (more-expensive) war-surplus mechanical speed key.

Referring to Fig. 8-17, the timing of the key is provided by the oscillator V_{1A}. When the key is closed, a sawtooth wave is generated by the fast charge and slow discharge of the .25-μf. capacitor in the cathode circuit. The rate of discharge is set by the total resistance across the capacitor, and the voltage to which the capacitor is charged is determined by the setting of R_1. The sawtooth wave, applied to the grid of V_{2A}, cannot drive the grid very positive because the 3.3-megohm resistor limits the current; the effect is to "clip the tops" of the sawtooth cycles. The

An Electronic Speed Key

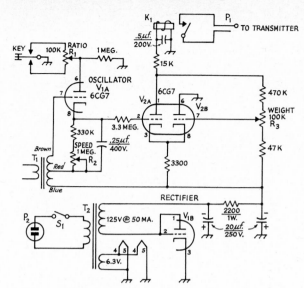

Fig. 8-17—Circuit diagram of the electronic speed key. Unless otherwise specified, resistors are ½ watt. Polarity-marked capacitors are electrolytic, others are tubular paper.

K_1—5000-ohm 3-ma. relay (Sigma 41F-5000S-SIL).

P_1—Phone plug.

P_2—A.c. line plug.

R_1, R_3—100,000-ohm potentiometer, linear taper.

R_2—1-megohm potentiometer, linear taper.

S_1—S.p.s.t. toggle.

T_1—5-watt 25,000-to-4-ohm output transformer, secondary not used (Stancor A-3857).

T_2—125-v. 50-ma. and 6.3-v. 2-amp. transformer (Thordarson 26R38 or similar).

voltage at which V_{2A} passes enough current to close the relay is set by the position of the arm of R_3.

Except for the tubes, the keyer circuit is housed in a grey Hammertone 6 × 5 × 4-inch Minibox (Bud CU-2107), as shown in Fig. 8-16. The tube sockets are mounted so that the two tubes project outside at the rear of the unit. The power transformer is mounted on the rear wall, and the toggle switch and the three controls are mounted on the "front" panel. The power line to P_2, the two-wire cable to P_1, and the three-wire cable to the key leave the cabinet at the rear through individual rubber grommets. Use multiple tie points generously for the support of the fixed resistors and capacitors.

To make the key, first remove the keys from their bases and strip the bases of their remaining hardware. The four support legs for the key are

Fig. 8-18—Components for the electronic speed key are mounted on the three walls of a Minibox section, with the tubes projecting out the back. Keep wires away from screw holes, to prevent short circuits when the box is assembled.

formed from the original tie strips and shorting switch arms. At the front they bolt to the key frame at the countersunk holes; at the rear they make up to the binding posts. The three-wire cable connects to two binding posts and a supporting leg. A heavy base of ½-inch thick steel adds weight to the structure, and rubber or cork feet glued to the steel prevent its scratching the table.

Adjustment of Electronic Speed Key

In operation, the three controls will serve as their labels indicate. There is a unique (but not highly critical) combination of settings of the weight and ratio controls that will give automatic dots and dashes at the same speed; this setting can only be determined by ear and will be dependent on how well the operator can recognize good code. If the operator taps his foot to count groups of four dots or two dashes, the dots and dashes will have the same speed when the beat is the same. It is easy to determine whether dots or dashes are too heavy or too light. Connect an ohmmeter to P_1; holding the dot lever closed should make the ohmmeter needle hover around half scale, and holding the dash lever closed should make the ohmmeter hover around 75 per cent of the short-circuit reading. Lacking an ohmmeter, the transmitter plate milliammeter can be used; dots and dashes should give 50 per cent and 75 per cent of the key-down value when the keyer controls have been properly adjusted.

QST articles describing other types of electronic speed keys include:

Brann, "In Search of the Ideal Electronic Key," Feb., 1951

Bartlett, "Compact Automatic Key Design," Dec., 1951

Kaye, "All-Electronic 'Ultimatic' Keyer," April, May, 1955

CHAPTER 9

Speech Amplifiers and Modulators

The audio amplifiers used in radiotelephone transmitters operate on the principles outlined earlier in this book in the chapter on vacuum tubes. The design requirements are determined principally by the type of modulation system to be used and by the type of microphone to be employed. It is necessary to have a clear understanding of modulation principles before the problem of laying out a speech system can be approached successfully. Those principles are discussed under appropriate chapter headings.

The present chapter deals with the design of audio amplifier systems for communication purposes. In voice communication the primary objective is to obtain the most *effective* transmission; i.e., to make the message be understood at the receiving point in spite of adverse conditions created by noise and interference. The methods used to accomplish this do not necessarily coincide with the methods used for other purposes, such as the reproduction of music or other program material. In other words, "naturalness" in reproduction is distinctly secondary to intelligibility.

The fact that satisfactory intelligibility can be maintained in a relatively narrow band of frequencies is particularly fortunate, because the width of the channel occupied by a phone transmitter is directly proportional to the width of the audio-frequency band. If the channel width is reduced, more stations can occupy a given band of frequencies without mutual interference.

In speech transmission, amplitude distortion of the voice wave has very little effect on intelligibility. The importance of such distortion in communication lies almost wholly in the fact that many of the audio-frequency harmonics caused by it lie outside the channel needed for intelligible speech, and thus will create unnecessary interference to other stations.

Speech Equipment

In designing speech equipment it is necessary to know (1) the amount of audio power the modulation system must furnish and (2) the output voltage developed by the microphone when it is spoken into from normal distance (a few inches) with ordinary loudness. It then becomes possible to choose the number and type of amplifier stages needed to generate the required audio power without overloading or undue distortion anywhere in the system.

● MICROPHONES

The level of a microphone is its electrical output for a given sound intensity. Level varies greatly with microphones of different types, and depends on the distance of the speaker's lips from the microphone. Only approximate values based on averages of "normal" speaking voices can be given. The values given later are based on close talking; that is, with the microphone about an inch from the speaker's lips.

The frequency response or fidelity of a microphone is its relative ability to convert sounds of different frequencies into alternating current. For understandable speech transmission only a limited frequency range is necessary, and intelligible speech can be obtained if the output of the microphone does not vary more than a few decibels at any frequency within a range of about 200 to 2500 cycles. When the variation expressed in terms of decibels is small between two frequency limits, the microphone is said to be **flat** between those limits.

Carbon Microphones

The **carbon microphone** consists of a metal diaphragm placed against an insulating cup containing loosely packed carbon granules **(microphone button)**. When used with a vacuum-tube amplifier, the microphone is connected in the cathode circuit of a low-μ triode, as shown in Fig. 9-1A.

Sound waves striking the diaphragm cause it to vibrate in accordance with the sound, and the pressure on the granules alternately increases and decreases, causing a corresponding decrease and increase in the electrical resistance of the microphone. The instantaneous value of this resistance determines the instantaneous value of plate current through the tube, and as a consequent the voltage drop across the plate load resistor increases and decreases with the increases and decreases in granule pressure.

The carbon microphone finds its major amateur application in mobile and portable work; a good microphone in the circuit of Fig. 9-1A will deliver 25 to 35 volts peak output.

Piezo-electric Microphones

The **crystal microphone** makes use of the piezoelectric properties of Rochelle salts crystals. This type of microphone requires no battery or transformer and can be connected directly to the

Speech Equipment

grid of an amplifier tube. It is a popular type of microphone among amateurs, for these reasons as well as the fact that it has good frequency response and is available in inexpensive models. The input circuit for the crystal microphone is shown in Fig. 9-1B.

Although the level of crystal microphones varies with different models, an output of 0.03 volt or so is representative for communication types. The level is affected by the length of the cable connecting the microphone to the first amplifier stage; the above figure is for lengths of 6 or 7 feet. The frequency characteristic is unaffected by the cable, but the load resistance (amplifier grid resistor) does affect it; the lower frequencies are attenuated as the value of load resistance is lowered. A grid-resistor value of at least 1 megohm should be used for reasonably flat response, 5 megohms being a customary figure.

The **ceramic microphone** utilizes the piezoelectric effect in certain types of ceramic materials to achieve performance very similar to that of the crystal microphone. It is less affected by temperature and humidity. Output levels are similar to those of crystal microphones for the same type of frequency response.

Velocity and Dynamic Microphones

In a **velocity** or "ribbon" microphone, the element acted upon by the sound waves is a thin corrugated metallic ribbon suspended between the poles of a magnet.

Velocity microphones are built in two types, high impedance and low impedance, the former being used in most applications. A high-impedance microphone can be directly connected to the grid of an amplifier tube, shunted by a resistance of 0.5 to 5 megohms (Fig. 9-1C). Low-impedance microphones are used when a long connecting cable (75 feet or more) must be employed. In such a case the output of the microphone is coupled to the first amplifier stage through a suitable step-up transformer, as shown in Fig. 9-1D.

The level of the velocity microphone is about 0.03 to 0.05 volt. This figure applies directly to the high-impedance type, and to the low-impedance type when the voltage is measured across the secondary of the coupling transformer.

The **dynamic microphone** somewhat resembles a dynamic loud-speaker. A lightweight voice coil is rigidly attached to a diaphragm, the coil being suspended between the poles of a permanent magnet. Sound causes the diaphragm to vibrate, thus moving the coil back and forth between the magnet poles and generating an alternating voltage.

The dynamic microphone usually is built with high-impedance output, suitable for working directly into the grid of an amplifier tube. If the connecting cable must be unusually long, a low-impedance type should be used, with a step-up transformer at the end of the cable.

In general, the dynamic microphones have the smoothest peak-free response and widest frequency range, and they are also the least susceptible to damage from shock and extremes of temperature and humidity.

● THE SPEECH AMPLIFIER

The audio-frequency amplifier stage that causes the r.f. carrier output to be varied is called the **modulator,** and all the amplifier stages preceding it comprise the **speech amplifier.** Depending on the modulator used, the speech amplifier may be called upon to deliver a power output ranging from practically zero (only voltage required) to 20 or 30 watts.

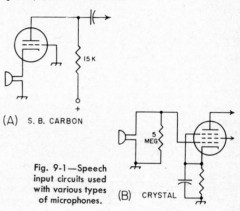

(A)   S. B. CARBON

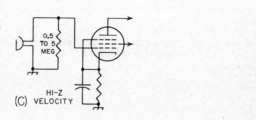

Fig. 9-1—Speech input circuits used with various types of microphones.   (B)   CRYSTAL

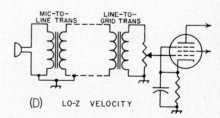

(C)   HI-Z VELOCITY

(D)   LO-Z VELOCITY

Before starting the design of a speech amplifier, therefore, it is necessary to have selected a suitable modulator for the transmitter. This selection must be based on the power required to modulate the transmitter, and this power in turn depends on the type of modulation system selected, as described in Chapter 10. With the modulator picked out, its **driving-power** requirements (audio power required to excite the modulator to full output) can be determined from the tube tables in a later chapter. Generally speaking, it is advisable to choose a tube or tubes for the last stage of the speech amplifier that will be capable of

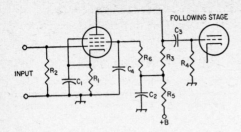

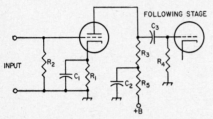

Fig. 9-2—Resistance-coupled voltage-amplifier circuits. A, pentode; B, triode. Designations are as follows:

C_1—Cathode bypass capacitor.
C_2—Plate bypass capacitor.
C_3—Output coupling capacitor (blocking capacitor).
C_4—Screen bypass capacitor.
R_1—Cathode resistor.
R_2—Grid resistor.
R_3—Plate resistor.
R_4—Next-stage grid resistor.
R_5—Plate decoupling resistor.
R_6—Screen resistor.

Values for suitable tubes are given in Table 9-I. Values in the decoupling circuit, C_2R_5, are not critical. R_5 may be about 10% of R_3; an 8- or 10-μf. electrolytic capacitor is usually large enough at C_2.

developing at least 50 per cent more power than the rated driving power of the modulator. This will provide a factor of safety so that losses in coupling transformers, etc., will not upset the calculations.

Voltage Amplifiers

If the last stage in the speech amplifier is a Class AB_2 or Class B amplifier, the stage ahead of it must be capable of sufficient power output to drive it. However, if the last stage is a Class AB_1 or Class A amplifier the preceding stage can be simply a voltage amplifier. From there on back to the microphone, all stages are voltage amplifiers.

The important characteristics of a voltage amplifier are its **voltage gain**, maximum undistorted **output voltage**, and its **frequency response**. The voltage gain is the voltage-amplification ratio of the stage. The output voltage is the maximum a.f. voltage that can be secured from the stage without distortion. The amplifier frequency response should be adequate for voice reproduction; this requirement is easily satisfied.

The voltage gain and maximum undistorted output voltage depend on the operating conditions of the amplifier. Data on the popular types of tubes used in speech amplifiers are given in Table 9-I, for resistance-coupled amplification.

The output voltage is in terms of *peak* voltage rather than r.m.s.; this makes the rating independent of the waveform. Exceeding the peak value causes the amplifier to distort, so it is more useful to consider only peak values in working with amplifiers.

Resistance Coupling

Resistance coupling generally is used in voltage-amplifier stages. It is relatively inexpensive, good frequency response can be secured, and there is little danger of hum pick-up from stray magnetic fields associated with heater wiring. It is the most satisfactory type of coupling for the output circuits of pentodes and high-μ triodes, because with transformers a sufficiently high load impedance cannot be obtained without considerable frequency distortion. Typical circuits are given in Fig. 9-2 and design data in Table 9-I.

Transformer Coupling

Transformer coupling between stages ordinarily is used only when power is to be transferred (in such a case resistance coupling is very inefficient), or when it is necessary to couple between a single-ended and a push-pull stage. Triodes having an amplification factor of 20 or less are used in transformer-coupled voltage amplifiers. With transformer coupling, tubes should be operated under the Class A conditions given in the tube tables at the end of this book.

Representative circuits for coupling single-ended to push-pull stages are shown in Fig. 9-3. The circuit at A combines resistance and transformer coupling, and may be used for exciting the

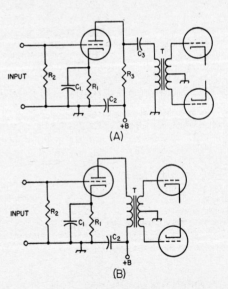

Fig. 9-3—Transformer-coupled amplifier circuits for driving a push-pull amplifier. A is for resistance-transformer coupling; B for transformer coupling. Designations correspond to those in Fig. 9-2. In A, values can be taken from Table 9-I. In B, the cathode resistor is calculated from the rated plate current and grid bias as given in the tube tables for the particular type of tube used.

Table 9–I

TABLE 9–I — RESISTANCE-COUPLED VOLTAGE-AMPLIFIER DATA

Data are given for a plate supply of 300 volts. Departures of as much as 50 per cent from this supply voltage will not materially change the operating conditions or the voltage gain, but the output voltage will be in proportion to the ratio of the new voltage to 300 volts. Voltage gain is measured at 400 cycles. Capacitor values given are based on 100-cycle cutoff. For increased low-frequency response, all capacitors may be made larger than specified (cut-off frequency in inverse proportion to capacitor values provided all are changed in the same proportion). A variation of 10 per cent in the values given has negligible effect on the performance.

	Plate Resistor Megohms	Next-Stage Grid Resistor Megohms	Screen Resistor Megohms	Cathode Resistor Ohms	Screen Bypass µf.	Cathode Bypass µf.	Blocking Capacitor µf.	Output Volts (Peak)[1]	Voltage Gain[2]
6SJ7, 12SJ7	0.1	0.1	0.35	500	0.10	11.6	0.019	72	67
		0.25	0.37	530	0.09	10.9	0.016	96	98
		0.5	0.47	590	0.09	9.9	0.007	101	104
	0.25	0.25	0.89	850	0.07	8.5	0.011	79	139
		0.5	1.10	860	0.06	7.4	0.004	88	167
		1.0	1.18	910	0.06	6.9	0.003	98	185
	0.5	0.5	2.0	1300	0.06	6.0	0.004	64	200
		1.0	2.2	1410	0.05	5.8	0.002	79	238
		2.0	2.5	1530	0.04	5.2	0.0015	89	263
6J7, 7C7, 12J7-GT	0.1	0.1	0.44	500	0.07	8.5	0.02	55	61
		0.25	0.5	450	0.07	8.3	0.01	81	82
		0.5	0.53	600	0.06	8.0	0.006	96	94
	0.25	0.25	1.18	1100	0.04	5.5	0.008	81	104
		0.5	1.18	1200	0.04	5.4	0.005	104	140
		1.0	1.45	1300	0.05	5.8	0.005	110	185
	0.5	0.5	2.45	1700	0.04	4.2	0.005	75	161
		1.0	2.9	2200	0.04	4.1	0.003	97	200
		2.0	2.95	2300	0.04	4.0	0.0025	100	230
6AU6, 6SH7, 12AU6, 12SH7	0.1	0.1	0.2	500	0.13	18.0	0.019	76	109
		0.22	0.24	600	0.11	16.4	0.011	103	145
		0.47	0.26	700	0.11	15.3	0.006	129	168
	0.22	0.22	0.42	1000	0.1	12.4	0.009	92	164
		0.47	0.5	1000	0.098	12.0	0.007	108	230
		1.0	0.55	1100	0.09	11.0	0.003	122	262
	0.47	0.47	1.0	1800	0.075	8.0	0.0045	94	248
		1.0	1.1	1900	0.065	7.6	0.0028	105	318
		2.2	1.2	2100	0.06	7.3	0.0018	122	371
6AQ6, 6AQ7, 6AT6, 6Q7, 6SL7GT, 6T8, 12AT6, 12Q7-GT, 12SL7,-GT (one triode)	0.1	0.1	——	1500	——	4.4	0.027	40	34
		0.22	——	1800	——	3.6	0.014	54	38
		0.47	——	2100	——	3.0	0.0065	63	41
	0.22	0.22	——	2600	——	2.5	0.013	51	42
		0.47	——	3200	——	1.9	0.0065	65	46
		1.0	——	3700	——	1.6	0.0035	77	48
	0.47	0.47	——	5200	——	1.2	0.006	61	48
		1.0	——	6300	——	1.0	0.0035	74	50
		2.2	——	7200	——	0.9	0.002	85	51
6AV6, 12AV6, 12AX7 (one triode)	0.1	0.1	——	1300	——	4.6	0.027	43	45
		0.22	——	1500	——	4.0	0.013	57	52
		0.47	——	1700	——	3.6	0.006	66	57
	0.22	0.22	——	2200	——	3.0	0.013	54	59
		0.47	——	2800	——	2.3	0.006	69	65
		1.0	——	3100	——	2.1	0.003	79	68
	0.47	0.47	——	4300	——	1.6	0.006	62	69
		1.0	——	5200	——	1.3	0.003	77	73
		2.2	——	5900	——	1.1	0.002	92	75
6SC7, 12SC7[3] (one triode)	0.1	0.1	——	750	——	——	0.033	35	29
		0.25	——	930	——	——	0.014	50	34
		0.5	——	1040	——	——	0.007	54	36
	0.25	0.25	——	1400	——	——	0.012	45	39
		0.5	——	1680	——	——	0.006	55	42
		1.0	——	1840	——	——	0.003	64	45
	0.5	0.5	——	2330	——	——	0.006	50	45
		1.0	——	2980	——	——	0.003	62	48
		2.0	——	3280	——	——	0.002	72	49
6CG7, 6J5, 7A4, 7N7, 6SN7-GT, 12J5-GT, 12SN7-GT (one triode)	0.047	0.047	——	1300	——	3.6	0.061	59	14
		0.1	——	1580	——	3.0	0.032	73	15
		0.22	——	1800	——	2.5	0.015	83	16
	0.1	0.1	——	2500	——	1.9	0.031	68	16
		0.22	——	3130	——	1.4	0.014	82	16
		0.47	——	3900	——	1.2	0.0065	96	16
	0.22	0.22	——	4800	——	0.95	0.015	68	16
		0.47	——	6500	——	0.69	0.0065	85	16
		1.0	——	7800	——	0.58	0.0035	96	16
6C4, 12AU7 (one triode)	0.047	0.047	——	870	——	4.1	0.065	38	12
		0.1	——	1200	——	3.0	0.034	52	12
		0.22	——	1500	——	2.4	0.016	68	12
	0.1	0.1	——	1900	——	1.9	0.032	44	12
		0.22	——	3000	——	1.3	0.016	68	12
		0.47	——	4000	——	1.1	0.007	80	12
	0.22	0.22	——	5300	——	0.9	0.015	57	12
		0.47	——	8800	——	0.52	0.007	82	12
		1.0	——	11000	——	0.46	0.0035	92	12

[1] Voltage across next-stage grid resistor at grid-current point.
[2] At 5 volts r.m.s. output.
[3] Cathode-resistor values are for phase-inverter service

grids of a Class A or AB$_1$ following stage. The resistance coupling is used to keep the d.c. plate current from flowing through the transformer primary, thereby preventing a reduction in primary inductance below its no-current value; this improves the low-frequency response. With low-μ triodes (6C5, 6J5, etc.), the gain is equal to that with resistance coupling multiplied by the secondary-to-primary turns ratio of the transformer.

In B the transformer primary is in series with the plate of the tube, and thus must carry the tube plate current. When the following amplifier operates without grid current, the voltage gain of the stage is practically equal to the μ of the tube multiplied by the transformer ratio. This circuit also is suitable for transferring power (within the capabilities of the tube) to a following Class AB$_2$ or Class B stage.

Phase Inversion

Push-pull output may be secured with resistance coupling by using **phase-inverter** or **phase-splitter** circuits as shown in Fig. 9-4.

The circuits shown in Fig. 9-4 are of the "self-balancing" type. In A, the amplified voltage

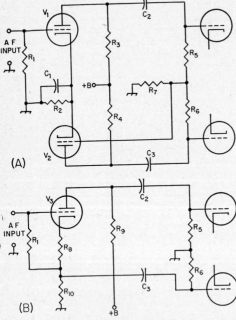

(A)

(B)

Fig. 9-4—Self-balancing phase-inverter circuits. V_1 and V_2 may be a double triode such as the 12AU7 or 12AX7. V_3 may be any of the triodes listed in Table 9-I, or one section of a double triode.

R_1—Grid resistor (1 megohm or less).

R_2—Cathode resistor; use one-half value given in Table 9-I for tube and operating conditions chosen.

R_3, R_4—Plate resistor; select from Table 9-I.

R_5, R_6—Following-stage grid resistor (0.22 to 0.47 megohm).

R_7—0.22 megohm.

R_8—Cathode resistor; select from Table 9-I.

R_9, R_{10}—Each one-half of plate load resistor given in Table 9-I.

C_1—10-μf. electrolytic.

C_2, C_3—0.01- to 0.1-μf. paper.

from V_1 appears across R_5 and R_7 in series. The drop across R_7 is applied to the grid of V_2, and the amplified voltage from V_2 appears across R_6 and R_7 in series. This voltage is 180 degrees out of phase with the voltage from V_1, thus giving push-pull output. The part that appears across R_7 from V_2 opposes the voltage from V_1 across R_7, thus reducing the signal applied to the grid of V_2. The negative feedback so obtained tends to regulate the voltage applied to the phase-inverter tube so that the output voltages from both tubes are substantially equal. The gain is slightly less than twice the gain of a single-tube amplifier using the same operating conditions.

In the single-tube circuit shown in Fig. 9-4B the plate load resistor is divided into two equal parts, R_9 and R_{10}, one being connected to the plate in the normal way and the other between cathode and ground. Since the voltages at the plate and cathode are 180 degrees out of phase, the grids of the following tubes are fed equal a.f. voltages in push-pull. The grid return of V_3 is made to the junction of R_8 and R_{10} so normal bias will be applied to the grid. This circuit is highly degenerative because of the way R_{10} is connected. The voltage gain is less than 2 even when a high-μ triode is used at V_3.

Gain Control

A means for varying the over-all gain of the amplifier is necessary for keeping the final output at the proper level for modulating the transmitter. The common method of gain control is to adjust the value of a.c. voltage applied to the grid of one of the amplifiers by means of a voltage divider or potentiometer.

The gain-control potentiometer should be near the input end of the amplifier, at a point where the signal voltage level is so low there is no danger that the stages ahead of the gain control will be overloaded by the full microphone output. With carbon microphones the gain control may be placed directly across the microphone-transformer secondary. With other types of microphones, however, the gain control usually will affect the frequency response of the microphone when connected directly across it. Also, in a high-gain amplifier it is better to operate the first tube at maximum gain, since this gives the best signal-to-hum ratio. The control therefore is usually placed in the grid circuit of the second stage.

● DESIGNING THE SPEECH AMPLIFIER

The steps in designing a speech amplifier are as follows:

1) Determine the power needed to modulate the transmitter and select the modulator. In the case of plate modulation, a Class B amplifier may be required. Select a suitable tube type and determine from the tube tables at the end of this book the grid driving power required, if any.

2) As a safety factor, multiply the required driver power by at least 1.5.

Speech Amplifier Design and Construction

3) Select a tube, or pair of tubes, that will deliver the power determined in the second step. This is the last or output stage of the speech-amplifier. Receiver-type power tubes can be used (beam tubes such as the 6L6 may be needed in some cases) as determined from the receiving-tube tables. If the speech amplifier is to drive a Class B modulator, use a Class A or AB_1 amplifier.

4) If the speech-amplifier output stage is also the modulator and must operate Class AB_2 to develop the required power output, use a low- or medium-μ triode to drive it. If more power is needed than can be obtained from one tube, use two in push-pull, in the driver. In either case transformer coupling will have to be used, and transformer manufacturers' catalogs should be consulted for a suitable type.

5) If the speech-amplifier output stage operates Class A or AB_1, it may be driven by a voltage amplifier. If the output stage is push-pull, the driver may be a single tube coupled through a transformer with a balanced secondary, or may be a dual-triode phase inverter. Determine the signal voltage required for full output from the last stage. If the last stage is a single-tube Class A amplifier, the peak signal is equal to the grid-bias voltage; if push-pull Class A, the peak-to-peak signal voltage is equal to twice the grid bias; if Class AB_1, twice the bias voltage when fixed bias is used; if cathode bias is used, twice the bias figured from the cathode resistance and the maximum-signal cathode current.

6) From Table 9-I, select a tube capable of giving the required output voltage and note its rated voltage gain. A double-triode phase inverter (Fig. 9-4A) will have approximately twice the output voltage and twice the gain of one triode operating as an ordinary amplifier. If the driver is to be transformer-coupled to the last stage, select a medium-μ triode and calculate the gain and output voltage as described earlier in this chapter.

7) Divide the voltage required to drive the output stage by the gain of the preceding stage. This gives the peak voltage required at the grid of the next-to-the-last stage.

8) Find the output voltage, under ordinary conditions, of the microphone to be used. This information should be obtained from the manufacturer's catalog. If not available, the figures given in the section on microphones in this chapter will serve.

9) Divide the voltage found in (7) by the output voltage of the microphone. The result is the over-all gain required from the microphone to the grid of the next-to-the-last stage. To be on the safe side, double or triple this figure.

10) From Table 9-I, select a combination of tubes whose gains, when multiplied together, give approximately the figure arrived at in (9). These amplifiers will be used in cascade. If high gain is required, a pentode may be used for the first speech-amplifier stage, but it is *not* advisable to use a second pentode because of the possibility of feedback and self-oscillation. In most cases a triode will give enough gain, as a second stage, to make up the total gain required. If not, a medium-μ triode may be used as a third stage.

A high-μ double triode with the sections in cascade makes a good low-level amplifier, and will give somewhat greater gain than a pentode followed by a medium-μ triode. With resistance-coupled input to the first section the cathode of that section may be grounded (contact potential bias), which is helpful in reducing hum.

● SPEECH-AMPLIFIER CONSTRUCTION

Once a suitable circuit has been selected for a speech amplifier, the construction problem resolves itself into avoiding two difficulties — excessive hum, and unwanted feedback. For reasonably humless operation, the hum voltage should not exceed about 1 per cent of the maximum audio output voltage — that is, the hum and noise should be at least 40 db. below the output level.

Unwanted feedback, if negative, will reduce the gain below the calculated value; if positive, is likely to cause self-oscillation or "howls." Feedback can be minimized by isolating each stage with decoupling resistors and capacitors, by avoiding layouts that bring the first and last stages near each other, and by shielding of "hot" points in the circuit, such as grid leads in low-level stages.

Speech-amplifier equipment, especially voltage amplifiers, should be constructed on steel chassis, with all wiring kept below the chassis to take advantage of the shielding afforded. Exposed leads, particularly to the grids of low-level high-gain tubes, are likely to pick up hum from the electric field that usually exists in the vicinity of house wiring. Even with the chassis, additional shielding of the input circuit of the first tube in a high-gain amplifier usually is necessary. In addition, such circuits should be separated as much as possible from power-supply transformers and chokes and also from any audio transformers that operate at fairly high power levels; this will minimize magnetic coupling to the grid circuit and thus reduce hum or audio-frequency feedback. It is always safe, although not absolutely necessary, to separate the speech amplifier and its power supply, building them on separate chassis.

If a low-level microphone such as the crystal type is used, the microphone, its connecting cable, and the plug or connector by which it is attached to the speech amplifier, all should be shielded. The microphone and cable usually are constructed with suitable shielding; this should be connected to the speech-amplifier chassis, and it is advisable — as well as usually necessary — to connect the chassis to a ground such as a water pipe. With the top-cap tubes, complete shielding of the grid lead and grid cap is a necessity.

Heater wiring should be kept as far as possible from grid leads, and either the center-tap or one side of the heater-transformer secondary winding should be connected to the chassis. If the center-tap is grounded, the heater leads to each tube should be twisted together to reduce the magnetic field from the heater current. With either type of connection, it is advisable to lay heater leads in the corner formed by a fold in the chassis, bringing them out from the corner to the tube socket by the shortest possible path.

When metal tubes are used, always ground the shell connection to the chassis. Glass tubes used in the low-level stages of high-gain amplifiers must be shielded; tube shields are obtainable for that purpose. It is a good plan to enclose the entire amplifier in a metal box, or at least provide it with a cane-metal cover, to avoid feedback difficulties caused by the r.f. field of the transmitter. R.f. picked up on exposed wiring, leads or tube elements causes overloading, distortion, and self-oscillation of the amplifier.

When using paper capacitors as bypasses, be sure that the terminal marked "outside foil" is connected to ground. This utilizes the outside foil of the capacitor as a shield around the "hot" foil. When paper capacitors are used for coupling between stages, always connect the outside foil terminal to the side of the circuit having the lowest impedance to ground. Usually, this will be the plate side rather than the following-grid side.

Modulators and Drivers

● CLASS AB AND B MODULATORS

Class AB or B modulator circuits are basically identical no matter what the power output of the modulator. The diagrams of Fig. 9-5 therefore will serve for any modulator of this type that the amateur may elect to build. The triode circuit is given at A and the circuit for tetrodes at B. When small tubes with indirectly heated cathodes are used, the cathodes should be connected to ground.

Modulator Tubes

The audio ratings of various types of transmitting tubes are given in the chapter containing the tube tables. Choose a pair of tubes that is capable of delivering sine-wave audio power equal to somewhat more than half the d.c. input to the modulated Class C amplifier. It is sometimes convenient to use tubes that will operate at the same plate voltage as that applied to the Class C stage, because one power supply of adequate current capacity may then suffice for both stages.

In estimating the output of the modulator, remember that the figures given in the tables are for the tube output only, and do not include output-transformer losses. To be adequate for modulating the transmitter, the modulator should have a theoretical power capability 15 to 25 per cent greater than the actual power needed for modulation.

Matching to Load

In giving audio ratings on power tubes, manufacturers specify the plate-to-plate load impedance into which the tubes must operate to deliver the rated audio power output. This load impedance seldom is the same as the modulating impedance of the Class C r.f. stage, so a match must be brought about by adjusting the turns ratio of the coupling transformer. The required turns ratio, primary to secondary, is

$$N = \sqrt{\frac{Z_p}{Z_m}}$$

where N = Turns ratio, primary to secondary

Z_m = Modulating impedance of Class C r.f. amplifier

Z_p = Plate-to-plate load impedance for Class B tubes

Example: The modulated r.f. amplifier is to operate at 1250 volts and 250 ma. The power input is

$$P = EI = 1250 \times 0.25 = 312 \text{ watts}$$

so the modulating power required is 312/2 = 156 watts. Increasing this by 25% to allow for losses and a reasonable operating margin gives

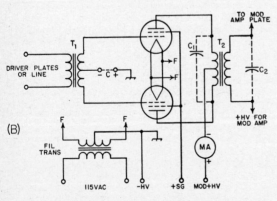

Fig. 9-5—Modulator circuit diagrams. Tubes and circuit considerations are discussed in the text.

Modulators and Drivers

$156 \times 1.25 = 195$ watts. The modulating impedance of the Class C stage is

$$Z_m = \frac{E}{I} = \frac{1250}{0.25} = 5000 \text{ ohms}.$$

From the tube tables a pair of Class B tubes is selected that will give 200 watts output when working into a 6900-ohm load, plate-to-plate. The primary-to-secondary turns ratio of the modulation transformer therefore should be

$$N = \sqrt{\frac{Z_p}{Z_m}} = \sqrt{\frac{6900}{5000}} = \sqrt{1.38} = 1.175{:}1.$$

The required transformer ratios for the ordinary range of impedances are shown graphically in Fig. 9-6.

Many modulation transformers are provided with primary and secondary taps, so that various turns ratios can be obtained to meet the requirements of particular tube combinations. However, it may be that the exact turns ratio required cannot be secured, even with a tapped modulation transformer. *Small* departures from the proper turns ratio will have no serious effect if the modulator is operating well within its capabilities; if the actual turns ratio is within 10 per cent of the ideal value the system will operate satisfactorily. Where the discrepancy is larger, it is usually possible to choose a new set of operating conditions for the Class C stage to give a modulating impedance that can be matched by the turns ratio of the available transformer. This may require operating the Class C amplifier at higher voltage and less plate current, if the modulating impedance must be increased, or at lower voltage and higher current if the modulating impedance must be decreased. However, this process cannot be carried very far without exceeding the ratings of the Class C tubes for either plate voltage or plate current, even though the power input is kept at the same figure.

Suppressing Audio Harmonics

Distortion in either the driver or Class B modulator will cause a.f. harmonics that may lie outside the frequency band needed for intelligible speech transmission. While it is almost impossible to avoid some distortion, it *is* possible to cut down the amplitude of the higher-frequency harmonics.

The purpose of capacitors C_1 and C_2 across the primary and secondary, respectively, of the Class B output transformer in Fig. 9-5 is to reduce the strength of harmonics and unnecessary high-frequency components existing in the modulation. The capacitors act with the leakage inductance of the transformer winding to form a rudimentary low-pass filter. The values of capacitance required will depend on the load resistance (modulating impedance of the Class C amplifier) and the leakage inductance of the particular transformer used. In general, capacitances between about 0.001 and 0.01 μf. will be required; the larger values are necessary with the lower values of load resistance. The voltage rating of each capacitor should at least be equal to the d.c. voltage at the transformer winding with which it is associated. In the case of C_2, part of the total capacitance re-

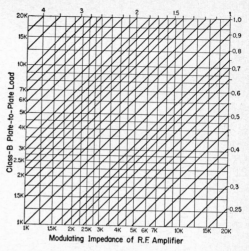

Fig. 9-6—Transformer ratios for matching a Class C modulating impedance to the required plate-to-plate load for the Class B modulator. The ratios given on the curves are from total primary to secondary. Resistance values are in kilohms.

quired will be supplied by the plate bypass or blocking capacitor in the modulated amplifier.

A still better arrangement is to use a low-pass filter as shown later, even though clipping is not deliberately employed.

Grid Bias

Certain triodes designed for Class B audio work can be operated without grid bias. Besides eliminating the grid-bias supply, the fact that grid current flows over the whole audio cycle means that the load resistance for the driver is fairly constant. With these tubes the grid-return lead from the center-tap of the input transformer secondary is simply connected to the filament center-tap or cathode.

When the modulator tubes require bias, it should always be supplied from a *fixed* voltage source. Cathode bias or grid-leak bias cannot be used with a Class B amplifier; with both types the bias changes with the amplitude of the signal voltage, whereas proper operation demands that the bias voltage be unvarying no matter what the strength of the signal. When only a small amount of bias is required it can be obtained conveniently from a few dry cells. For larger bias voltages a heavy-duty "B" battery may be used if the grid current does not exceed 40 or 50 milliamperes on voice peaks. The batteries are charged by the grid current rather than discharged, but a battery nevertheless will deteriorate with time and its internal resistance will increase. When the increase in internal resistance becomes appreciable, the battery tends to act like a grid-leak resistor and the bias varies with the applied signal. Batteries should be checked with a voltmeter occasionally while the amplifier is operating. If the bias varies more than 10 per cent or so with voice excitation the battery should be replaced.

9 – SPEECH AMPLIFIERS AND MODULATORS

As an alternative to batteries, a regulated bias supply may be used. This type of supply is described in the power supply chapter.

Plate Supply

In addition to adequate filtering, the voltage regulation of the plate supply should be as good as it can be made. If the d.c. output voltage of the supply varies with the load current, the voltage at *maximum* current determines the amount of power that can be taken from the modulator without distortion. A supply whose voltage drops from 1500 at no load to 1250 at the full modulator plate current is a 1250-volt supply, so far as the modulator is concerned, and any estimate of the power output available should be based on the lower figure.

Good dynamic regulation — i.e., with suddenly applied loads — is equally as important as good regulation under steady loads, since an instantaneous drop in voltage on voice peaks also will limit the output and cause distortion. The output capacitor of the supply should have as much capacitance as conditions permit. A value of at least 10 μf. should be used, and still larger values are desirable. It is better to use all the available capacitance in a single-section filter rather than to distribute it between two sections.

It is particularly important, in the case of a tetrode Class B stage, that the screen-voltage power-supply source have excellent regulation, to prevent distortion. The screen voltage should be set as exactly as possible to the recommended value for the tube. The audio impedance between screen and cathode also must be low.

Overexcitation

When a Class B amplifier is overdriven in an attempt to secure more than the rated power, distortion increases rapidly. The high-frequency harmonics which result from the distortion modulate the transmitter, producing spurious sidebands which can cause serious interference over a band of frequencies several times the channel width required for speech. (This can happen even though the modulation percentage, as defined in the chapter on amplitude modulation, is less than 100 per cent, if the modulator is incapable of delivering the audio power required to modulate the transmitter.)

As shown later, such a condition may be reached by deliberate design, in case the modulator is to be adjusted for peak

clipping. But whether it happens by accident or intention, the splatter and spurious sidebands can be eliminated by inserting a low-pass filter (Fig. 9-13) between the modulator and the modulated amplifier, and then taking care to see that the actual modulation of the r.f. amplifier does not exceed 100 per cent.

Operation Without Load

Excitation should never be applied to a Class B modulator until after the Class C amplifier is turned on and is drawing the value of plate current required to present the rated load to the modulator. With no load to absorb the power, the primary impedance of the transformer rises to a high value and excessive audio voltages may be developed in the primary — frequently high enough to break down the transformer insulation.

● **DRIVERS FOR CLASS-B MODULATORS**

Class AB$_2$ and Class B amplifiers are driven into the grid-current region, so power is con-

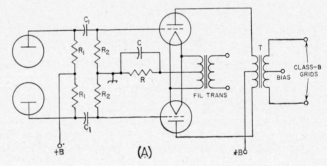

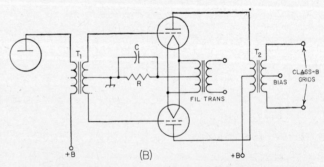

Fig. 9-7—Triode driver circuits for Class B modulators. A, resistance coupling to grids; B, transformer coupling. R_1 in A is the plate resistor for the preceding stage, value determined by the type of tube and operating conditions as given in Table 9-I. C_1 and R_2 are the coupling capacitor and grid resistor, respectively; values also may be taken from Table 9-I.

In both circuits the output transformer, (T_1T_2,) should have the proper turns ratio to couple between the driver tubes and the Class B grids. T_1 in B is usually a 2:1 transformer, secondary to primary. R, the cathode resistor, should be calculated for the particular tubes used. The value of C the cathode bypass, is determined as described in the text.

Modulators and Drivers

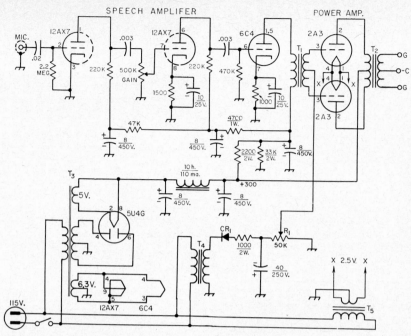

SPEECH AMPLIFIER

POWER AMP.

Fig. 9-8—Speech-amplifier driver for 10-15 watts output. Capacitances are in μf. Resistors are $\frac{1}{2}$ watt unless specified otherwise. Capacitors with polarity indicated are electrolytic; others may be paper or ceramic.

CR₁—Selenium rectifier, 20 ma.

R₁—50,000-ohm potentiometer, preferably wire wound.

T₁—Interstage audio transformer, single plate to push-pull grids, turns ratio 2 to 1 or 3 to 1, total secondary to primary.

T₂—Class-B driver transformer, 3000 ohms plate-to-plate; secondary impedance as required by

Class-B tubes used; 15 watt rating.

T₃—Power transformer, 700 volts c.t., 110 ma.; 5 volts, 3 amp.; 6.3 volts, 4 amp.

T₄—Power transformer, 125 volts, 20 ma.; 6.3 volts, 0.6 amp.

T₅—2.5-volt 5-ampere filament transformer (Thordarson 21F00).

sumed in the grid circuit. The preceding stage or driver must be capable of supplying this power at the required peak audio-frequency grid-to-grid voltage. Both of these quantities are given in the manufacturer's tube ratings. The grids of the Class B tubes represent a varying load resistance over the audio-frequency cycle, because the grid current does not increase directly with the grid voltage. To prevent distortion, therefore, it is necessary to have a driving source that will maintain the wave form of the signal without distortion even though the load varies. That is, the driver stage must have good regulation. To this end, it should be capable of delivering somewhat more power than is consumed by the Class B grids, as previously described in the discussion on speech amplifiers.

Driver Tubes

To secure good voltage regulation the internal impedance of the driver, as seen by the modulator grids, must be low. The principal component of this impedance is the plate resistance of the driver tube or tubes as reflected through the driver transformer. Hence for low driving-source impedance the effective plate resistance of the driver tubes should be low and the turns ratio of the driver transformer, primary to secondary,

should be as large as possible. The maximum turns ratio that can be used is that value which just permits developing the modulator grid-to-grid a.f. voltage required for the desired power output. The rated tube output as shown by the tube tables should be reduced by about 20 per cent to allow for losses in the Class B input transformer.

Low-μ triodes such as the 2A3 have low plate resistance and are therefore good tubes to use as drivers for Class AB₂ or Class B modulators. Tetrodes such as the 6V6 and 6L6 make very poor drivers in this respect when used without negative feedback, but with such feedback the effective plate resistance can be reduced to a value comparable with low-μ triodes.

Fig. 9-7 shows representative circuits for a push-pull triode driver using cathode bias. If the amplifier operates Class A the cathode resistor need not be bypassed, because the a.f. currents from each tube flowing in the cathode resistor are out of phase and cancel each other. However, in Class AB operation this is not true; considerable distortion will be generated at high signal levels if the cathode resistor is not bypassed. The bypass capacitance required can be calculated by a simple rule: the cathode resistance in ohms multiplied by the bypass capacitance in microfarads should equal at least 25,000. The voltage rating of the capacitor should be equal to the maximum bias voltage. This can be found from the maximum-signal plate current and the cathode resistance.

> *Example:* A pair of 2A3s is to be used in Class AB₁ self-biased. From the tube tables, the cathode resistance should be 780 ohms and the maximum-signal plate current 100 ma. From Ohm's Law,
>
> $$E = RI = 780 \times 0.10 = 78.6 \text{ volts}$$
>
> From the rule mentioned previously, the by-pass capacitance required is
>
> $$C = 25{,}000/R = 25{,}000/780 = 32 \ \mu f.$$
>
> A 40- or 50-μf. 100-volt electrolytic capacitor would be satisfactory

Fig. 9-8 is a typical circuit for a speech amplifier suitable for use as a driver for a Class AB₂ or Class B modulator. An output of about 13 watts can be realized with the power supply circuit shown (or any similar well-filtered supply delivering 300 volts under load). This is sufficient for driving any of the power triodes commonly used as modulators. The 2A3s in the output stage are operated Class AB₁. The circuit provides several times the voltage gain needed for communications-type crystal or ceramic microphones.

The two sections of a 12AX7 tube are used in the first two stages of the amplifier. These are resistance coupled, the gain control being in the grid circuit of the second stage. Although the cathode of the first stage is grounded and there is no separate bias supply for the grid, the grid

bias actually is about one volt because of "contact potential."

The third stage uses a medium-μ triode which is coupled to the 2A3 grids through a transformer having a push-pull secondary. The ratio may be of the order of 2 to 1 (total secondary to primary) or higher; it is not critical since the gain is sufficient without a high step-up ratio.

The output transformer, T_2, should be selected to couple between push-pull 2A3s and the grids of the particular modulator tubes used.

The power supply has a capacitor-input filter the output of which is applied to the 2A3 plates through T_2. For the lower-level stages, additional filtering is provided by successive RC filters which also serve to prevent audio feedback through the plate supply.

Grid bias for the 2A3s is furnished by a separate supply using a small selenium rectifier and a TV "booster" transformer, T_4. The bias may be adjusted by means of R_1, and should be set to −62 volts or to obtain a total plate current of 80 ma. (as measured in the lead to the primary center tap of T_2) for the 2A3s.

In building an amplifier of this type the constructional precautions outlined earlier should be observed. The Class AB₁ modulators described subsequently in this chapter are representative of good constructional practice.

Negative Feedback

Whenever tetrodes or pentodes are used as drivers for Class B modulators, negative feedback should be used in the driver stage, for the reason already discussed.

Suitable circuits for single-ended and push-pull tetrodes are shown in Fig. 9-9. Fig. 9-9A shows resistance coupling between the preceding stage and a single tetrode, such as the 6V6, that operates at the same plate voltage as the preceding stage. Part of the a.f. voltage across the primary of the output transformer is fed back to the grid of the tetrode, V_2, through the plate resistor of the preceding tube, V_1. The total resistance of R_4 and R_5 in series should be ten or more times the rated load resistance of V_2. Instead of the voltage divider, a tap on the transformer primary can be used to supply the feedback voltage, if such a tap is available.

The amount of feedback voltage that appears at the grid of tube V_2 is determined by R_1, R_2 and the plate resistance of V_1, as well as by the relationship between R_4 and R_5. Circuit values for typical tube combinations are given in detail in Fig. 9-9.

The push-pull circuit in Fig. 9-9B requires an audio transformer with a split secondary. The feedback

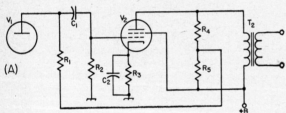

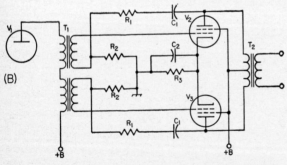

Fig. 9-9—Negative-feedback circuits for drivers for Class B modulators. A—Single-ended beam-tetrode driver. If V_1 and V_2 are a 6J5 and 6V6, respectively, or one section of a 6CG7 and a 6AQ5, the following values are suggested: R_1, 47,000 ohms; R_2, 0.47 megohm; R_3, 250 ohms; R_4, R_5, 22,000 ohms; C_1, 0.01 μf.; C_2, 50 μf.

B—Push-pull beam-tetrode driver. If V_1 is a 6J5 or 6CG7 and V_2 and V_3 6L6s, the following values are suggested: R_1, 0.1 megohm; R_2, 22,000 ohms; R_3, 250 ohms; C_1, 0.1 μf.; C_2, 100 μf.

Modulators and Drivers

voltage is obtained from the plate of each output tube by means of the voltage divider, R_1, R_2. The blocking capacitor, C_1, prevents the d.c. plate voltage from being applied to R_1R_2; the reactance of this capacitor should be low, compared with the sum of R_1 and R_2, at the lowest audio frequency to be amplified. Also, the sum of R_1 and R_2 should be high (ten times or more) compared with the rated load resistance for V_2 and V_3.

In this circuit the feedback voltage that is developed across R_2 appears at the grid of V_2 (or V_3) through the transformer secondary and grid-cathode circuit of the tube, provided the tubes are not driven to grid current. The per cent feedback is

$$n = \frac{R_2}{R_1 + R_2} \times 100$$

where n is the feedback percentage, and R_1 and R_2 are connected as shown in the diagram. The higher the feedback percentage, the lower the effective plate resistance. However, if the percentage is made too high the preceding tube, V_1, may not be able to develop enough voltage, through T_1, to drive the push-pull stage to maximum output without itself generating harmonic distortion. Distortion in V_1 is not compensated for by the feedback circuit.

If V_2 and V_3 are 6L6s operated self-biased in Class AB_1 with a load resistance of 9000 ohms, V_1 is a 6J5 or similar triode, and T_1 has a turns ratio of 2-to-1, total secondary to primary, it is possible to use over 30 per cent feedback without going beyond the output-voltage capabilities of the triode. Twenty per cent feedback will reduce the effective plate resistance to the point where the output voltage regulation is better than that of 2A3s without feedback. The power output under these conditions is about 20 watts.

Increasing the Effectiveness of the Phone Transmitter

The effectiveness of an amateur phone transmitter can be increased to a considerable extent by taking advantage of speech characteristics. Measures that may be taken to make the modulation more effective include band compression (filtering), volume compression, and speech clipping.

Compressing the Frequency Band

Most of the intelligibility in speech is contained in the medium band of frequencies; that is, between about 500 and 2500 cycles. On the other hand, a large portion of speech power is normally found below 500 cycles. If these low frequencies are attenuated, the frequencies that carry most of the actual communication can be increased in amplitude without exceeding 100-per cent modulation, and the effectiveness of the transmitter is correspondingly increased.

One simple way to reduce low-frequency response is to use small values of coupling capacitance between resistance-coupled stages, as shown in Fig. 9-10A. A time constant of 0.0005 second for the coupling capacitor and following-stage grid resistor will have little effect on the amplification at 500 cycles, but will practically halve it at 100 cycles. In two cascaded stages the gain will be down about 5 db. at 200 cycles and 10 db. at 100 cycles. When the grid resistor is ½ megohm a coupling capacitor of 0.001 μf. will give the required time constant.

The high-frequency response can be reduced by using "tone control" methods, utilizing a capacitor in series with a variable resistor connected across an audio impedance at some point in the speech amplifier. The best spot for the tone control is across the primary of the output transformer of the speech amplifier, as in Fig. 9-10B. The capacitor should have a reactance at 1000 cycles about equal to the load resistance required by the amplifier tube or tubes, while the variable resistor in series may have a value equal to four or five times the load resistance. The control can

be adjusted while listening to the amplifier, the object being to cut the high-frequency response without unduly sacrificing intelligibility.

Restricting the frequency response not only puts more modulation power in the optimum frequency band but also reduces hum, because the low-frequency response is reduced, and helps reduce the width of the channel occupied by the transmission, because of the reduction in the amplitude of the high audio frequencies.

Volume Compression

Although it is obviously desirable to modulate

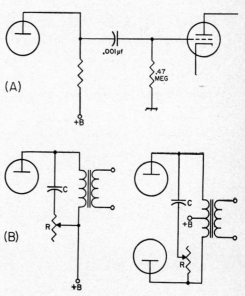

(A)

(B)

Fig. 9-10—A, use of a small coupling capacitor to reduce low-frequency response; B, tone-control circuits for reducing high-frequency response. Values for C and R are discussed in the text; 0.01 μf. and 25,000 ohms are typical.

the transmitter as completely as possible, it is difficult to maintain constant voice intensity when speaking into the microphone. To overcome this variable output level, it is possible to use automatic gain control that follows the *average* (not instantaneous) variations in speech amplitude. This can be done by rectifying and filtering some of the audio output and applying the rectified and filtered d.c. to a control electrode in an early stage in the amplifier.

A practical circuit for this purpose is shown in Fig. 9-11. V_1, a medium-μ triode, has its grid connected in parallel with the grid of the last speech amplifier tube (the stage preceding the power stage) through the gain control R_1. The amplified output is coupled to a full-wave rectifier, V_2. The rectified audio output develops a negative d.c. voltage across C_1R_3, which has a sufficiently long time constant to hold the voltage at a reasonably steady value between syllables and words. The negative d.c. voltage is applied as control bias to the suppressor grid of the first tube in the speech amplifier (this circuit requires a pentode first stage), effecting a reduction in gain. The gain reduction is substantially proportional to the average microphone output and thus tends to hold the amplifier output at a constant level.

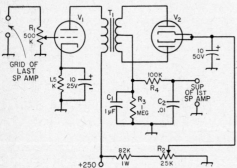

Fig. 9-11—Speech-amplifier output limiting circuit.

V_1—6C4, 6C5, 6CG7, 6J5, 12AU7, etc.

V_2—6H6, 6AL5, etc.

T_1 — Interstage audio, single plate to p. p. grids.

An adjustable bias is applied to the cathodes of V_2 to cut off the tube at low levels and thus prevent rectification until a desired output level is reached. R_2 is the "threshold control" which sets this level. R_1, the gain control, determines the rate at which the gain is reduced with increasing signal level.

The hold-in time can be increased by increasing the resistance of R_3. C_2 and R_4 may not be necessary in all cases; their function is to prevent too-rapid gain reduction on a sudden voice peak. The "rise time" of this circuit can be increased by increasing C_2 or R_4, or both.

The over-all gain of the system must be high enough so that full output can be secured at a moderately low voice level.

Speech Clipping and Filtering

In speech wave forms the average power con-

tent is considerably less than in a sine wave of the same peak amplitude. Since modulation percentage is based on peak values, the modulation or sideband power in a transmitter modulated 100 per cent by an ordinary voice wave form will be considerably less than the sideband power in the same transmitter modulated 100 per cent by a sine wave. In other words, the modulation percentage with voice wave forms is determined by peaks having relatively low average power content.

If the low-energy peaks are clipped off, the remaining wave form will have a considerably higher ratio of average power to peak amplitude. More sideband power will result, therefore, when such a clipped wave is used to modulate the transmitter 100 per cent. Although clipping distorts the wave form and the result therefore does not sound exactly like the original, it is possible to secure a worth-while increase in modulation power without sacrificing intelligibility. Once the system is properly adjusted *it will be impossible to overmodulate the transmitter* because the maximum output amplitude is fixed.

By itself, clipping generates the same high-order harmonics that overmodulation does, and therefore will cause splatter. To prevent this, the audio frequencies above those needed for intelligible speech must be filtered out, *after* clipping and *before* modulation. The filter required for this purpose should have relatively little attenuation at frequencies below about 2500 cycles, but high attenuation for all frequencies above 3000 cycles.

It is possible to use as much as 25 db. of clipping before intelligibility suffers; that is, if the original peak amplitude is 10 volts, the signal can be clipped to such an extent that the resulting maximum amplitude is less than one volt. If the original 10-volt signal represented the amplitude that caused 100-per-cent modulation on peaks, the clipped and filtered signal can then be amplified up to the same 10-volt peak level for modulating the transmitter.

There is a loss in naturalness with "deep" clipping, even though the voice is highly intelligible. With moderate clipping levels (6 to 12 db.) there is almost no change in "quality" but the voice power is increased considerably.

Before drastic clipping can be used, the speech signal must be amplified several times more than is necessary for normal modulation. Also, the hum and noise must be much lower than the tolerable level in ordinary amplification, because the noise in the output of the amplifier increases in proportion to the gain.

One type of clipper-filter system is shown in block form in Fig. 9-12A. The clipper is a peak-limiting rectifier of the same general type that is used in receiver noise limiters. It must clip both positive and negative peaks. The gain or clipping control sets the amplitude at which clipping starts. Following the low-pass filter for eliminating the harmonic distortion frequencies is a second gain control, the "level" or modulation control. This control is set initially so that the

Speech Clipping

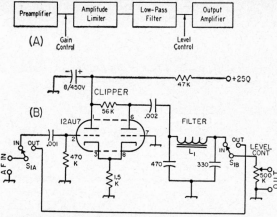

(A) Gain Control   Level Control

(B)

Fig. 9-12—(A) Block diagram of speech-clipping and filtering amplifier. (B) Practical speech clipper circuit with low-pass filter. Capacitances below 0.001 μf. are in μμf. Resistors are ½ watt.

L_1—20 henrys, 900 ohms (Stancor C-1515).
S_1—D.p.d.t. toggle or rotary.

amplitude-limited output of the clipper-filter
cannot cause more than 100 per cent modulation.

It should be noted that the peak amplitude
of the audio wave form actually applied to the
modulated stage in the transmitter is not necessarily held at the same relative level as the peak
amplitude of the signal coming out of the clipper
stage. When the clipped signal goes through the
filter, the relative phases of the various frequency components that pass through the filter
are shifted, particularly those components near
the cut-off frequency. This may cause the peak
amplitude out of the filter to exceed the peak
amplitude of the clipped signal applied to the
filter input terminals. Similar phase shifts can
occur in amplifiers following the filter, especially
if these amplifiers, including the modulator, do
not have good low-frequency response. With
poor low-frequency response the more-or-less
"square" waves resulting from clipping tend to
be changed into triangular waves having higher
peak amplitude. Best practice is to cut the low-
frequency response *before* clipping and to make
all amplifiers following the clipper-filter as flat
and distortion-free as possible.

The best way to set the modulation control
in such a system is to check the actual modulation
percentage with an oscilloscope connected as described in the section on modulation. With the
gain control set to give a desired clipping level
with normal voice intensity, the level control
should be adjusted so that the maximum modulation does not exceed 100 per cent no matter how
much sound is applied to the microphone.

A practical clipper-filter circuit is shown in
Fig. 9-12B. It may be inserted between two
speech-amplifier stages (but after the one having
the gain control) where the level is normally a few
volts. The cathode-coupled clipper circuit gives
some over-all voltage gain in addition to performing the clipping function. The filter constants
are such as to give a cut-off characteristic that

combines reasonably good fidelity with
adequate high-frequency suppression.

High-Level Clipping and Filtering

Clipping and filtering also can be
done at high level — that is, at the point
where the modulation is applied to the
r.f. amplifier — instead of in the low-
level stages of the speech amplifier. In
one rather simple but effective arrangement of this type the clipping takes
place in the Class-B modulator itself.
This is accomplished by carefully adjusting the plate-to-plate load resistance
for the modulator tubes so that they
saturate or clip peaks at the amplitude
level that represents 100 per cent
modulation. The load adjustment can
be made by choice of output transformer ratio or by adjusting the plate-
voltage/plate-current ratio of the modulated r.f. amplifier. It is best done by
examining the output wave form with
an oscilloscope.

The filter for such a system consists of a choke
coil and capacitors as shown in Fig. 9-13. The
values of L and C should be chosen to form a low-
pass filter section having a cut-off frequency of
about 2500 cycles, using the modulating impedance of the r.f. amplifier as the load resistance.
For this cut-off frequency the formulas are

$$L_1 = \frac{R}{7850} \quad \text{and} \quad C_1 = C_2 = \frac{63.6}{R}$$

where R is in ohms, L_1 in henrys, and C_1 and C_2
in microfarads. For example, with a plate-modulated amplifier operating at 1500 volts and 200
ma. (modulating impedance 7500 ohms) L_1
would be 7500/7850 = 0.96 henry and C_1 or
C_2 would be 63.6/7500 = 0.0085 μf. By-pass
capacitors in the plate circuit of the r.f. amplifier
should be included in C_2. Voltage ratings for C_1
and C_2 when connected as shown must be the same
as for the plate blocking capacitor — i.e., at least
twice the d.c. voltage applied to the plate of the
modulated amplifier. L and C values can vary 10
per cent or so without seriously affecting the operation of the filter.

Besides simplicity, the high-level system has
the advantage that high-frequency components

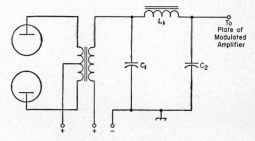

Fig. 9-13—Splatter-suppression filter for use at high
level, shown here connected between a Class B modulator
and plate-modulated r.f. amplifier. Values for L_1, C_1
and C_2 are determined as described in the text.

269

of the audio signal fed to the modulator grids, whether present legitimately or as a result of amplitude distortion in lower-level stages, are suppressed along with the distortion components that arise in clipping. Also, the undesirable effects of poor low-frequency response following clipping and filtering, mentioned in the preceding section, are avoided. Phase shifts can still occur in the high-level filter, however, so adjustments preferably should be made by using an oscilloscope to check the actual modulation percentage under all conditions of speech intensity. (For further discussion see Bruene, "High-Level Clipping and Filtering", QST, November, 1951.)

Low-Power Modulator

A modulator suitable for plate modulation of low-power transmitters or for screen or control-grid modulation of high-power amplifiers is pictured in Figs. 9-14 and 9-16. As shown in Fig. 9-15, it uses a pair of 6AQ5's in push-pull in the output stage. These are driven by a 6C4 phase inverter. A two-stage preamplifier using a 12AX7 brings the output voltage of a crystal or ceramic microphone up to the proper level for the 6C4 grid. A power supply is included on the same chassis.

The undistorted audio output of the amplifier is 7-8 watts. This is sufficient for modulating the plate of an r.f. amplifier running 10 to 15 watts input, or for modulating the control grids or screens of r.f. amplifiers using tubes having plate-dissipation ratings up to 250 watts. When screen modulation is used the screen power for the modulated amplifier (up to 250 volts) can be taken from the modulator power supply. The wiring shown in Fig. 9-15 provides for this, through an adjustable tap on the 25,000-ohm bleeder resistor, R_5, in the power supply. If a separate screen supply is used, or if the modulator is used for grid-bias or plate modulation of an r.f. amplifier, the d.c. circuit should be opened at point "X" in Fig. 9-15.

The amplifier uses resistance coupling up to the output-stage grids. The first section, V_{1A}, of the 12AX7 has "contact-potential" bias. The gain control, R_1, is in the grid circuit of the second section, V_{1B}, of the 12AX7. Negative feedback from the secondary of the output transformer, T_1, is introduced at the cathode of this tube section. The feedback voltage is dependent on

the ratio of R_2 to R_3, approximately, and with the constants given is sufficient to result in a considerable reduction in distortion along with improved regulation of the audio output voltage. The latter is important when the unit is used for modulating a screen or control grid, as described in the chapter on amplitude modulation.

The phase inverter is of the split-load type described earlier in this chapter. It drives the push-pull 6AQ5's in the power amplifier. The output transformer used in the power stage is a multitap modulation transformer suitable for any of the types of modulation mentioned above.

Capacitor C_1 across the secondary of the output transformer, T_1, is used to reduce the high-frequency response of the amplifier. Without it, self-oscillation is likely to occur at a high audio frequency (usually above audibility) because phase shift in the output transformer at the end of its useful frequency range causes the feedback to become positive.

The power supply uses a replacement-type transformer and choke with a capacitor-input filter. Voltage under the modulator and speech-amplifier load is 250. The decoupling resistance-capacitance networks in the plate circuits of V_{1A} and V_{1B} contribute additional smoothing of the d.c. for these low-level stages.

The unit includes provision for send-receive switching, S_1 being used for that purpose. S_{1B} can be used to control the r.f. section — for example, by being connected in parallel with the key used for c.w. operation. Simultaneously S_{1A} short-circuits the secondary of T_1 so the transformer will not be damaged by being left

Fig. 9-14—Speech amplifier and low-power modulator suitable for screen or control-grid modulation of high-power amplifiers, or for plate modulation of an r.f. stage with up to 15 watts plate input. It is assembled on a 7 × 9 × 2-inch steel chassis, with the power supply occupying the left-hand section and the audio circuits the right. The 12AX7 preamplifier is at the lower right-hand corner, the 6C4 phase inverter is to its left, and the 6AQ5 power amplifiers are behind the two. Controls along the chassis edge are, left to right, the power switch, send-receive switch, gain control, and microphone jack.

A Low-Power Modulator

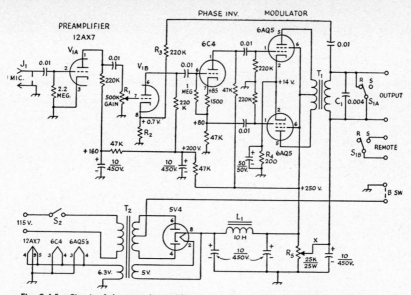

Fig. 9-15—Circuit of the speech amplifier and modulator. All capacitances are in $\mu f.$; capacitors with polarities marked are electrolytic, others are ceramic. Resistors are ½ watt except as noted below. Voltages measured to chassis with v.t. voltmeter.

J_1—Microphone connector (Amphenol 75-PC1M).

L_1—10 henrys, 90 ma. (Triad C-7X).

S_1—D.p.d.t. toggle.

S_2—S.p.s.t. toggle.

T_1—Modulation transformer, tapped secondary, primary 10,000 ohms plate to plate (Thordarson 21M68).

T_2—Power transformer, 525 v.c.t., 90 ma.; 6.3 v., 5 amp.; 5 v., 2 amp. (Triad R-10A).

R_2—1500 ohms, ½ watt.

R_4—App. 200 ohms, 2 watts (two 390-ohm 1-watt resistors in parallel).

without load. If S_{1B} is connected across the transmitter key, S_1 also can be used as a phone-c.w. switch, being left in the "R" position for c.w. operation.

The terminals marked "B Switch" should be short circuited (indicated by the dashed line) if S_1 is used as a send-receive switch. If a switch on the transmitter is used for send-receive, these terminals may be used for turning the plate voltage in the modulator on and off through

an extra pair of contacts on the transmitter send-receive switch. In that case S_1 should be left in the "send" position for phone operation.

The proper secondary taps to use on T_1 will depend on the impedance of the load to which the amplifier is connected. Methods for determining the modulating impedance with various types of modulation are given in the section on amplitude modulation, together with information on connecting the modulator to the r.f. stage.

Fig. 9-16—Below-chassis view of the modulator. The rectifier-tube socket and electrolytic filter capacitors are at the right in this view. The 12AX7 socket is at the lower left. Bleeder resistor R_5 is at the upper left, near the 6-terminal connection strip on the rear edge of the chassis. Placement of components is not critical, but the leads in the first two stages should be kept short and close to the chassis to minimize hum troubles.

25-Watt Modulator using Push-Pull 6BQ6GTs

The speech amplifier-modulator shown in Figs. 9-17 to 9-19, inclusive, can be used for plate modulation of low-power transmitters running 25 to 50 watts input to the final stage. The circuit as shown is capable of an audio output of 25 watts, but this can be increased to 30 watts by a simple modification. The 6BQ6s in the output stage are operated in Class AB$_1$. Inexpensive receiver-type replacement components are used throughout, except for the modulation transformer.

Circuit

The speech amplifier uses a pentode first stage resistance-coupled to a triode second stage. This combination gives sufficient gain for a crystal microphone. The pentode and triode are the two sections of a dual tube, the 6AN8. Transformer coupling is used between the triode and the modulator tubes, in order to get push-pull voltage for the 6BQ6GT grids. Cathode bias is used on the final stage.

The coupling capacitance between the first and second stages is purposely made small to reduce the low-frequency response, and the primary of the output transformer is shunted by C_2 to reduce the amplification at the high-frequency end. C_1, on the first stage, also tends to reduce high-frequency response in addition to bypassing any r.f. that might be picked up on the microphone cord. These measures confine the frequency response to the most useful portion of the voice range.

S_2 is the "send-receive" switch. One section opens the power transformer center tap, thus cutting off the plate voltage during receiving periods. The other section can be connected to the key terminals on the transmitter, as indicated in the circuit diagram, to turn the transmitter on and off along with the modulator. If the transmitter is one in which the oscillator is not keyed, S_{2B} may be used to control the transmitter plate voltage, usually by being connected in the 115-volt circuit to the plate-supply transformer.

The "phone-c.w." switch, S_3, short-circuits the secondary of the modulation transformer, T_3, when the transmitter is to be keyed, and also opens the center-tap of T_1 so plate voltage cannot be applied to the modulator.

The power supply uses a receiver replacement-type transformer with a capacitor-input filter. Additional filtering for the speech-amplifier stages is provided by the 10-μf. capacitors and the series resistors in the plate circuits. Hum is also reduced by the VR-150 used to regulate the modulator screen voltage. Note that the regulator tube is connected between the screens and cathodes so that the actual screen voltage is 150 and is not reduced by the drop in the cathode bias resistor. Maintaining full screen voltage is important if the rated output is to be secured.

Operating

The 6BQ6GT amplifier requires a plate-to-plate load of 4000 ohms, and the output transformer ratio must be chosen to reflect this load to the plates (see later section on matching a modulator to its load). For most small transmitters running 30 to 50 watts input to the final stage a 1-to-1 transformer ratio will be satisfactory, since the modulating impedance of such transmitters usually is in the neighborhood of 4000 ohms. The secondary of T_3 is connected in series with the d.c. lead to the plate (and screen, if a screen-grid tube) of the Class C amplifier to be modulated. For further details, see the chapter on amplitude modulation.

For checking the modulator operation a milliammeter (0–200 range satisfactory) may be connected in the lead to the center-tap of the

Fig. 9-17—A modulator for transmitters operating at plate inputs up to 50 watts. The speech amplifier and modulator are at the left in this view; power supply components are at the right. The chassis is 7 × 11 × 2 inches.

25-Watt Modulator

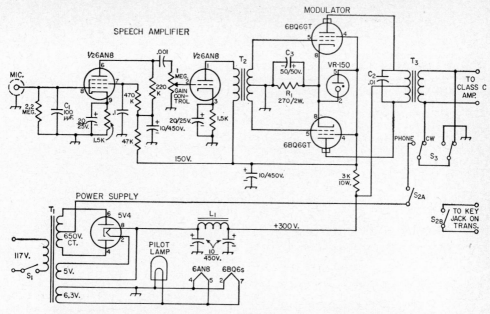

Fig. 9-18—Circuit diagram of the 25-watt modulator. Capacitances below 0.001 μf. are in μμf. Capacitors up to 0.01 μf. are ceramic. Resistors are ½ watt unless otherwise specified.

L_1—8 henrys, 150 ma.
S_1—S.p.s.t. toggle.
S_2—D.p.d.t. toggle.
S_3—2-pole 2-position rotary (Centralab PA-2003).

T_1—Power transformer, 650 volts c.t., 150 ma. 5 volts 3 amp.; 6.3 volts, 5 amp.
T_2—Interstage audio, single plate to p.p. grids, pri. to total sec. ratio 1 to 3.
T_3—Modulation transformer, multimatch type (UTC S-19).

primary of T_3. Without voice input to the microphone the plate current should be approximately 50 ma. When modulating the transmitter, the current should "kick" to 60 or 70 ma.; this will usually represent 100 per cent modulation. If the amplifier can be tested with a single-tone signal replacing the microphone, the plate current will be about 165 ma. at full output.

The audio power output can be increased to about 30 watts, sufficient for modulating an 807 at its full phone rating, if the 6BQ6GT cathodes are grounded and bias of about 30 volts from a fixed source such as a small battery is applied to the grids. The battery may be substituted for the cathode resistor if the ground connection is moved from the center tap of the secondary of T_2 to the cathodes of the 6BQ6GTs.

(From *QST*, December, 1955.)

Fig. 9-19—Under-chassis view of the 6BQ6GT modulator. The two large capacitors at the right are the filter capacitors in the power supply. The modulator bias resistor and bypass capacitor (R_1C_3) are at lower left. Leads from the modulation transformer go through the three holes in the chassis. Shielded wire is used for heater, microphone input, and gain-control leads.

9 — SPEECH AMPLIFIERS AND MODULATORS

Class AB₁ Modulator Using 807s

The modulator unit shown in Figs. 9-20 to 9-22, inclusive, uses a pair of 807s as Class AB₁ power amplifiers. Its audio power output depends on the plate voltage applied to the 807s; approximate values and optimum plate-to-plate load resistances are as follows:

Plate Voltage	Plate-to-Plate Load	Power Output
400	6200 ohms	30 watts
500	8000 ohms	40 watts
600	9800 ohms	45 watts
750	12,500 ohms	60 watts

The power-output figures are conservative, and will vary somewhat with the losses in the output transformer. These in turn may vary with different combinations of tap connections. The nominal tube output (without transformer losses) is 20 to 25 per cent higher than the figures given.

The modulator is intended for use with an external plate and screen supply for the 807s, but includes a screen regulator circuit. The unit has a built-in power supply for the speech amplifier section. Fixed bias for the 807s is taken from this supply.

Speech Circuit

The speech amplifier uses a high-μ dual triode as a two-stage resistance-coupled amplifier, followed by a medium-μ triode. The latter is transformer-coupled to the modulator grids. The gain from the microphone input to the 807 grids is more than ample for crystal microphones and others of similar output level.

The frequency response of the amplifier is adjusted to put maximum energy in the range where it contributes most to speech intelligibility; that is, the output is highest between 500 and 1200 cycles and drops off gradually on either side. The lower frequencies are reduced by using low

values of coupling capacitance between the resistance-coupled stages, and the high-frequency end is attenuated by C_1. Further high-frequency attenuation, particularly for such components generated in the modulator itself, is provided by capacitor C_2, connected across the output terminals of the modulation transformer.

Power Supply

The plate-supply requirements of the 12AX7 and 6C4 in the speech amplifier are quite small and easily can be supplied by a small "TV booster" type transformer, T_3. As shown in the diagram, a half-wave selenium rectifier works into a capacitor-input filter from this transformer. Bias for the 807s is obtained from this supply by making the output current flow through R_2 and R_3 in series, these resistors being connected between the negative output terminal of the supply and ground so that a negative voltage is developed with respect to chassis. The bias is adjustable by varying R_2. A single variable resistor having a total resistance of 10,000 ohms can be used instead of the two 5000-ohm units in series; the adjustment becomes somewhat more critical with the larger resistor but the operation is otherwise the same.

Heater power for the speech amplifier and modulator tubes is supplied by a separate filament transformer, T_4.

Plate power for the 807s is intended to be taken from an external source at a voltage level suitable for the output power desired. Screen voltage for the 807s comes from the same source, but is regulated at 300 volts by means of two 0A2 voltage-regulator tubes in series. Such regulation is essential for proper operation of the modulator tubes. The current through the 0A2s should be adjusted to 25 to 30 ma., with no signal on the

Fig. 9-20—Speech amplifier and modulator using Class AB₁ 807s. Depending on plate voltage used, audio power outputs up to at least 60 watts may be obtained.

807 Modulator

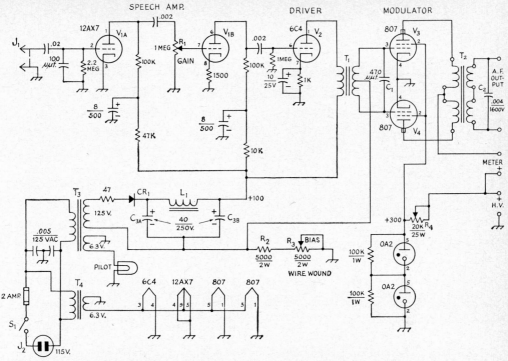

Fig. 9-21—Circuit diagram of the 807 modulator. Capacitances are in μf. unless otherwise specified; electrolytics are marked with polarity; others may be either ceramic or paper. Resistors are ½ watt except as indicated.

C_1—470-μμf. mica or ceramic.

C_2—App. 0.005 μf., 1600 volts (see discussion on modulators earlier in this chapter).

C_3—Dual 40-μf. electrolytic, 250 volts. Must be type that can be insulated from chassis.

CR_1—Selenium rectifier, 20-ma. or higher rating, 130 volts.

J_1—Chassis-type microphone connector (Amphenol 75-PC1M).

L_1—10 henrys, 50 ma. (Triad C-3X).

R_1—1-megohm control, audio taper.

R_2—5000 ohms, 2 watts.

R_3—5000-ohm wire-wound control, 2 watts.

R_4—20,000-ohm adjustable wire-wound, 25 watts.

S_1—S.p.s.t. toggle.

T_1—Interstage audio transformer, single plate to push-pull grids; 10-ma. primary; 3-to-1 turns ratio, total secondary to primary (Merit A-2914).

T_2—Multimatch modulation transformer, 30-watt rating adequate for voice work (UTC CVM-1).

T_3—Power transformer, 125 volts at 15 ma.; 6.3 volts at 0.6 amp. (Stancor PS8415).

T_4—Filament transformer, 6.3 volts at 3 amp.

grids of the 807s, by setting the slider on the 20,000-ohm adjustable resistor, R_4.

A pair of terminals is provided for connecting a d.c. milliammeter (0–200 ma. range is suitable) in series with the 807 plates for measuring plate current. Such a meter is useful as a check on the operation of the modulator during initial testing, and as a modulation indicator during actual operation. If a meter is not used the meter terminals should be connected together through a jumper.

Construction

The modulator shown is built on a 7 × 11 × 2-inch steel chassis, but other chassis sizes and layouts may be used if the builder prefers. The principal constructional precaution to be observed is to keep the modulation transformer, T_2, reasonably well separated from the low-level speech components so stray coupling between the wiring of these stages is minimized. The interstage transformer, T_1, should not be mounted too close to the power transformer, T_3, since there is a pos-

sibility of hum pickup in T_1 if these two units are close together.

It is necessary to cut a large hole — about 3 inches in diameter — for mounting the particular type of modulation transformer used in the unit shown. The connection terminals on this transformer are lugs on the bottom of the case, so the chassis opening must be large enough to permit making connections without danger of a short-circuit to chassis.

In wiring the speech-amplifier section, the leads to grids and plates should be kept short and separated as much as possible from heater wiring. The heater leads should be run along a fold in the edge of the chassis except where they must be brought out to reach the tube sockets. In this unit shielded wire was used for the heater wiring, but this is not necessary as a hum-reducing precaution. The principal reason here was mechanical; the shielded wire stays in place better and the shields can be "tacked" together with a spot of solder as a simple method of cabling.

Fig. 9-22—Below-chassis view of the 807 modulator.

In the top view, Fig. 9-20, the speech-amplifier section is along the right-hand edge of the chassis. The tube near the front is the 12AX7 dual-triode amplifier. The 6C4 driver is just behind it, and the filament transformer, T_4, is on the rear right-hand corner. The modulation transformer is in the left center alongside the 807 modulator tubes. Along the left edge of the chassis are the power transformer, T_3, the dual filter capacitor, C_3, and the two gas regulator tubes. The negative terminal of C_3 must be insulated from the chassis; the capacitor shown is a "twist-lok" type with a bakelite socket.

In the below-chassis view, Fig. 9-22, the power-supply components are at the right. L_1 is mounted on the right-hand wall of the chassis, with the selenium rectifier, CR_1, just to its left. The dropping resistor for the VR-regulated screen circuit is near the upper right corner, close to the 0A2 sockets. The 115-volt socket and fuse are on the chassis wall near the regulator tubes. The speech-amplifier section is at the lower left in this view, with components laid in as convenient. The interstage audio transformer, T_1, is mounted between the 807 sockets at the left. The control on the top wall is R_3, for setting the grid bias on the 807s. Audio output, high voltage, and meter connections are made through the terminal strip (Millen 37306) between the fuse and bias control.

Operating Notes

The speech amplifier section may be tested independently of the modulator, since it has its own power supply. Testing may be done as described later in the chapter, preferably with an audio oscillator and oscilloscope to check wave form.

The modulation transformer taps to be used will depend on the plate-to-plate load resistance required for the desired power output and on the modulating impedance of the r.f. amplifier. The chart furnished with the transformer should be consulted for this information.

If the Class-C amplifier plate supply has the proper voltage and has sufficient excess capacity to furnish an average current of 70 to 100 ma. in addition to its normal Class C load, it may be used for this modulator as well. If not, a separate supply of conventional design (see chapter on power supply) may be used. It should have a choke-input filter and should have a minimum output capacitance of about 10 μf. for good dynamic regulation.

Before attempting to test the modulator, remove the 807s from their sockets and adjust R_4 (shut off the voltage before making each adjustment) for a current of 25 to 30 ma. through the VR tubes. The current may be measured by connecting a milliammeter of suitable range in series with the positive high-voltage lead between the external power supply and this unit, since with the 807s out of their sockets the only current is that through R_4 and the VR tubes.

After R_4 is properly adjusted, replace the 807s and with R_3 at maximum resistance (maximum bias) connect the plate milliammeter to the meter terminals. Then apply plate power and adjust R_3 for a plate current of 40 to 50 ma.; the value is not especially critical, but should not be too near cutoff and should not be so large as to cause the rated plate dissipation of the tubes to be exceeded. With the Class-C load connected the plate current should rise to approximately 140 ma. at full output, using a sine-wave signal. With voice input the current should kick to 65–75 ma. on peaks. These figures for plate current are the same regardless of the plate voltage used, so long as the screen is maintained at 300 volts.

If c.w. as well as phone operation is to be employed, provision should be made either in the modulator or the r.f. unit for short-circuiting the secondary of the modulation transformer when the transmitter is being keyed.

6146 Modulator and Speech Amplifier

The modulator shown in Figs. 9-23 to 9-25, inclusive, uses a pair of 6146s in AB₁, and is complete with power and bias supplies on a $10 \times 17 \times 3$-inch chassis. The modulator also is equipped with an audio take-off for scope monitoring.

The audio power that can be obtained (based on measurements) is as follows:

Nominal Plate Voltage	Power Output	Plate-to-Plate Load Resistance
500 volts	75 watts	4200 ohms
600 volts	95 watts	5200 ohms
750 volts	120 watts	6700 ohms

Suitable sets of components for all three of the voltages listed above are readily available, so the power level can be selected to suit the Class C amplifier to be modulated. The modulator shown in the photographs is set up for 750-volt operation, but aside from the power and modulation transformers all components are the same regardless of the voltage level.

Audio Circuits

As shown in the circuit diagram, Fig. 9-24, the audio system consists of a 12AX7 preamplifier with the two tube sections in cascade, followed by a 6C4 voltage amplifier which is transformer-coupled to the grids of the Class AB₁ modulator tubes. The combination provides ample gain for a communications-type crystal, ceramic, or dynamic microphone.

The first stage of the amplifier is "contact-potential" biased, and is resistance-coupled to the second stage. The gain control, R_1, is in the grid circuit of the second stage. Decoupling resistors and capacitors are included in the plate-supply circuits of these two stages; these decoupling circuits also provide additional plate-supply hum filtering for the two low-level stages.

The secondary of T_1, the transformer coupling the third speech stage to the modulator grids, is shunted by a 470-μμf. capacitor to reduce high-frequency response. The optimum value of capacitance will depend on the particular type of audio transformer selected, as well as on the high-frequency characteristics of the microphone employed. Different values should be tried with the object of cutting the high-frequency response as much as possible, consistent with intelligibility.

The modulation transformer is of the multi-match type, and the taps should be selected to reflect the proper plate-to-plate load impedance, as given earlier, for the desired power output. The impedance ratio, secondary to primary, will depend on the modulating impedance of the modulated r.f. amplifier, as described earlier in this chapter. The secondary of the modulation transformer is shunted by C_1 to reduce output at the higher audio frequencies, particularly for attenuating high-frequency harmonics that might be generated in the modulator at high output levels. The value suggested (0.005 μf.) is an average figure and should be modified according to the modulating impedance of the Class-C stage as discussed earlier in this chapter.

Power Supply

Plate power for all tubes in the unit is supplied by a single power transformer. Mercury-vapor rectifiers are used because good voltage regulation is desirable. The filter is a single section with choke input and a large (over 25 μf.) output capacitance. The filter capacitor consists of three 80-μf. 450-volt electrolytic capacitors in series for 750-volt d.c. output. If the output voltage is 600 or less only two capacitors in series will be needed. These capacitors are shunted by 0.1-megohm resistors to help equalize the d.c. voltages across them.

The 200-volt (approximately) supply for the 6146 screens and the plates of the speech-amplifier tubes is taken from the main supply through a dropping resistor, and is regulated by two 0B2 voltage-regulator tubes in series. A 20-μf. ca-

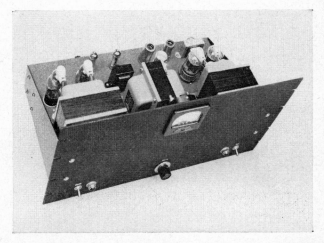

Fig. 9-23—Class-AB₁ modulator using 6146s, complete with speech amplifier and power supply. The relay-rack panel is 10½-inches high. Plate- and filament-supply primary switches, each with its own pilot lamp, are near the lower edge of the panel. The gain control is at lower center. Along the front of the chassis, just behind the panel, are the plate power transformer, filter choke, and modulation transformer, going from left to right. The tubes at the left are the 816 rectifiers, with the 6146s at the right. Along the rear edge are the two voltage-regulator tubes, the 12AX7 and 6C4 speech amplifier tubes, and the interstage audio transformer, T_1.

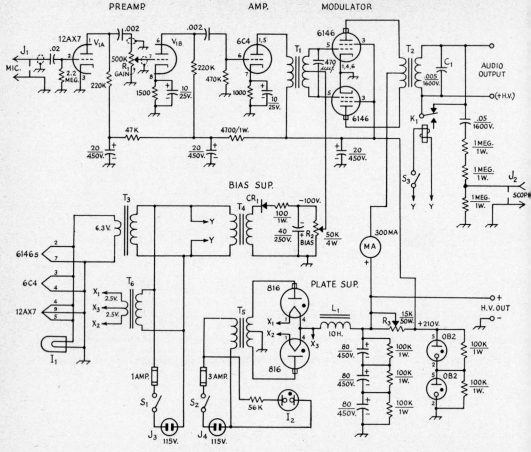

Fig. 9-24—Circuit diagram of the 6146 modulator and power supply. Capacitances are in μf. unless indicated otherwise; capacitors marked with polarity are electrolytic, others may be paper or ceramic as convenient. Resistances are in ohms; resistors are ½ watt except as indicated.

C_1—See text.

CR_1—Selenium rectifier, 20 ma. or higher rating, 130 volts.

I_1—6.3-volt pilot lamp.

I_2—Neon lamp, NE-51.

J_1—Microphone connector (Amphenol 75-PC1M).

J_2—Phono jack.

J_3, J_4—115-volt chassis-mounting plug (Amphenol 61-M1).

K_1—Antenna changeover relay, 115-volt coil (Advance AH/2C/115VA; type AM also suitable).

L_1—Filter choke, 10 henrys, 300 ma. (Triad C-19A).

R_1—0.5-megohm control, audio taper.

R_2—50,000-ohm wire-wound control, 4 watts.

R_3—15,000-ohm adjustable, 50 watts.

S_1, S_2—S.p.s.t. toggle.

S_3—S.p.s.t., mounted on R_1.

T_1—Interstage audio, single plate to p.p. grids, 3-to-1 secondary-to-primary ratio (Stancor A-63-C).

T_2—Multimatch modulation transformer, 125 watts (Triad M-12AL).

T_3—Filament transformer, 6.3 volts at 4 amp. (Triad F-53X).

T_4—Power transformer, 117 volts at 20 ma.; 6.3-volt winding unused (Thordarson 26R32).

T_5—Plate transformer. For 500 volts d.c.: 1235 volts c.t., 310 ma. (Triad P-7A); for 600 volts d.c.: 1455 volts c.t., 310 ma. (Triad P-11A). Transformer shown is for either 600 or 750 volts d.c. output at 310 ma.; sec. voltage 1780 c.t. for 750 volts (Triad P-14A).

T_6—Filament transformer, 5 volts at 3 amp., 2500-volt insulation (Stancor P-4088).

pacitor is connected across the VR tubes to improve the dynamic regulation in the 6146 screen circuit, since the peak instantaneous screen current exceeds the regulating capacity (30 ma.) of the VR tubes when the modulator is driven to maximum output.

Fixed bias for the 6146 grids is taken from a built-in bias supply using a TV "booster" transformer with a selenium rectifier. This bias is adjustable by means of R_2. The bias supply and filament transformer are on the same a.c. circuit so that bias is applied to the modulator grids whenever the tube heaters are energized.

Control and Auxiliary Circuits

The modulator includes an oscilloscope take-off circuit consisting of the 0.05-μf. capacitor and three 1-megohm resistors in series. This can be

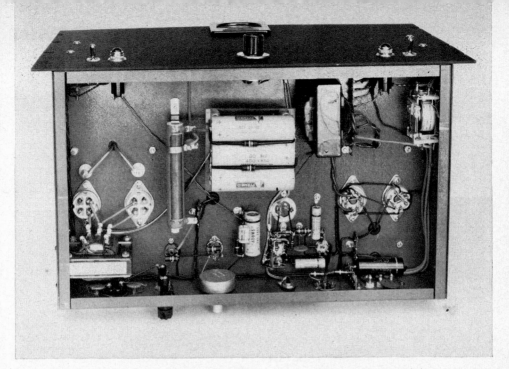

Fig. 9-25—Below-chassis view of the 6146 modulator. The 816 sockets and filament transformer (T_6) are at the lower left. The chassis wall at the bottom has on it, left to right, the 115-volt a.c. plugs, fuse holders, bias control (R_2), microphone input connector (J_1), scope take-off connector (J_2) and a three-terminal strip (Millen 37303) for audio output and positive high voltage connections. The high-voltage filter capacitor bank is in the center, mounted on a plate of plastic insulation which is supported away from the chassis on small pillars. The 6.3-volt transformer (T_3) is to the right of the capacitors. The antenna changeover relay used for shorting the modulation-transformer secondary is on the right-hand chassis wall.

used for horizontal deflection of a c.r. tube to give the trapezoidal modulation pattern (see chapter on amplitude modulation). Usually, it will be necessary to use an external control for adjusting the amplitude of the sweep voltage so obtained. If desired, a 1-megohm control can be substituted for the fixed resistor at the bottom of the string, thus avoiding the necessity for an external control.

The normally closed contacts of an antenna-type relay, K_1, are used to short-circuit the secondary of the modulation transformer when the transmitter is to be used for c.w. work. The switch, S_3, that controls the relay is mounted on the gain control, R_1, so that when the gain is turned all the way off, thus opening the switch, the relay contacts close. This insures that the modulator is inoperative and cannot be driven by accidental voice input (which would result in excessive plate current) when the transformer secondary is short-circuited.

Separate a.c. inputs are provided for the filament-bias and plate power circuits. The plate supply can thus be controlled by an external switch without disturbing the operation of the filament circuits or requiring a modification of the 115-volt wiring.

Terminals are provided for taking out high-voltage d.c. for an external unit. The power-supply equipment has more capacity than is needed by the modulator unit itself (the rating for amateur-type service is somewhat over 300

ma.) and may in some cases be sufficient for operation of the modulated r.f. amplifier as well. At least 200 ma. should be available for this purpose, since the average plate-supply current in the modulator unit alone is less than 100 ma., including the speech-amplifier and VR-tube drain.

Operating Data

The dropping resistor in the screen-supply circuit should be adjusted so that the current through 0B2s is 30 ma. with the bias on the 6146 grids adjusted so that the no-signal plate current is approximately 50 ma. The current through the VR tubes may be measured by temporarily opening the lead to the upper 0B2 at pin 5 and inserting a milliammeter of appropriate range.

If a sine-wave signal is used for testing the modulator, full output should be secured with a modulator plate current of approximately 240 ma. This value will be the same for all plate voltages, provided the screen voltage is maintained at approximately 200 volts and the values of plate-to-plate load resistance as specified earlier are used. With voice input the plate current will kick up to about 100 ma. on peaks, depending on the characteristics of the speaker's voice and those of the microphone used. This peak value should be determined under actual operating conditions with an oscilloscope, after which the plate milliammeter can be used as a modulation indicator.

Class B Modulator with Filter

Representative Class B modulator construction is illustrated by the unit shown in Figs. 9-26 and 9-28. This modulator includes a splatter

Fig. 9-26—A typical Class B modulator arrangement. This unit uses a pair of 811As, capable of an audio power output of 340 watts, and includes a splatter filter. The modulation transformer is at the left and the splatter choke at the right. All high-voltage terminals are covered so they cannot be touched accidentally.

filter, $C_1C_2L_1$ in the circuit diagram, Fig. 9-27, and also has provision for short-circuiting the modulation transformer secondary when c.w. is to be used.

The audio input transformer is not built into this unit, it being assumed that this transformer

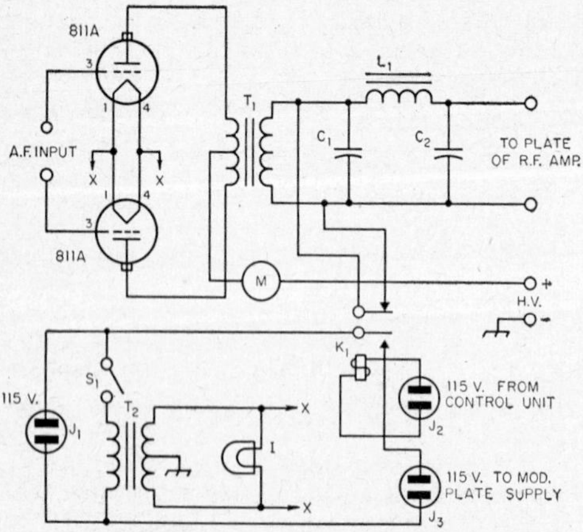

will be included in the driver assembly as is customary. If the modulator and speech amplifier-driver are mounted in the same rack or cabinet, the length of leads from the driver to the modulator grids presents no problem. The bias required by the modulator tubes at their higher plate-voltage ratings should be fed through the center tap on the secondary of the driver transformer. At a plate voltage of 1250 or less no bias is needed and the center-tap connection on the transformer can be grounded.

The values of C_1, C_2 and L_1 depend on the modulating impedance of the Class C r.f. amplifier. They can be determined from the formulas given in this chapter in the section on high-level clipping and filtering. The splatter filter will be effective regardless of whether the modulator operating conditions are chosen to give high-level clipping, but it is worth while to design the system for clipping at 100 per cent modulation if the tube curves are available for that purpose. The voltage ratings for C_1 and C_2 should at least equal the d.c. voltage applied to the modulated r.f. amplifier.

A relay with high-voltage insulation is used to short-circuit the secondary of T_1 when the

Fig. 9-28—The relay and filament transformer are mounted below the chassis. C_1, C_2 and K_1 are mounted on small stand-off insulators.

relay coil is not energized. A normally closed contact is used for this purpose. The other arm is used to close the primary circuit of the modulator plate supply when the relay is energized. Shorting the transformer secondary is necessary when the r.f. amplifier is keyed, to prevent an inductive discharge from the transformer winding that would put "tails" on the keyed characters and, with cathode keying of the amplifier, would cause excessive sparking at the key contacts. The control circuit should be arranged in such a way that K_1 is not energized during c.w. operation but is energized by the send-receive switch during phone operation.

Careful attention should be paid to insulation since the instantaneous voltages in the secondary circuit of the transformer will be at least twice the d.c. voltage on the r.f. amplifier. If a "hi-fi" amplifier of 10 watts or more output is available, it can be used as the driver for the 811As by coupling as shown in Fig. 9-29.

Fig. 9-27—Circuit diagram of the Class B modulator.

C_1, C_2, L_1—See text. (L_1 is Chicago Transformer type SR-300).

K_1—D.p.d.t. relay, high-voltage insulation (Advance type 400).

M—0–500 d.c. milliammeter, bakelite case.

T_1—Variable-ratio modulation transformer (Chicago Transformer type CMS-1).

T_2—Filament transformer, 6.3 v., 8 amp.

I_1—6.3-volt pilot light.

X_1, X_2—Chassis-type 115-volt plugs, male.

X_3—Chassis-type 115-volt receptacle, female.

S_1—S.p.s.t. toggle.

Checking Speech Equipment

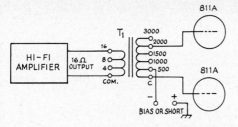

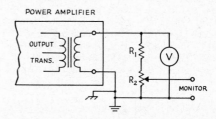

Fig. 9-29—A "hi-fi" audio amplifier will drive a Class-B modulator; a suitable coupling transformer is required. The connections shown here are for a pair of 811As. The amplifier should have an output rating of at least 10 watts.

T_1—10-watt line-to-voice-coil transformer (Stancor A-8104).

Checking Amplifier Operation

An adequate job of checking speech equipment can be done with equipment that is neither elaborate nor expensive. A typical setup is shown in Fig. 9-30. The construction of a simple audio oscillator is described in the chapter on measurements. The audio-frequency voltmeter can be either a vacuum-tube voltmeter or a multirange volt-ohm-milliammeter that has a rectifier-type a.c. range. The headset is included for aural checking of the amplifier performance.

An audio oscillator usually will have an output control, but if the maximum output voltage is in excess of a volt or so the output setting may be rather critical when a high-gain speech amplifier is being tested. In such cases an attenuator such as is shown in Fig. 9-30 is a convenience.

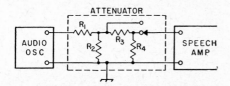

Fig. 9-30—Simple oscillator-attenuator test setup for checking a speech amplifier. It is not necessary that the frequency range of the audio oscillator be continuously variable; one or more "spot frequencies" will be satisfactory. Suitable resistor values are: R_1 and R_3, 10,000 ohms; R_2 and R_4, 1000 ohms.

Each of the two voltage dividers reduces the voltage by a factor of roughly 10 to 1, so that the over-all attenuation is about 100 to 1. The relatively low value of resistance, R_4, connected across the input terminals of the amplifier also will minimize stray hum pickup on the connecting leads.

The output of a power amplifier such as a modulator or driver for a Class B stage may be checked by using a resistance load of the rated value for the amplifier. A useful circuit arrangement is shown in Fig. 9-31. The load resistance, R_1, may be a single adjustable unit of appropriate power rating or may be made up of several resistors in series or parallel to give the required resistance. If measurement of the resistance is necessary an ohmmeter will be sufficiently accurate. In the case of a multimatch output transformer the taps should be those that will actually be used with the Class C amplifier with which the modulator is intended to work. R_1 then should have a value equal to the modulating impedance of the r.f. amplifier.

Fig. 9-31—Circuit for measuring power and making qualitative checks of the amplifier output. Values to be used for R_1 and R_2 are discussed in the text. The secondary winding of the output transformer in the amplifier should be disconnected from any d.c. source in the unit and one end connected to chassis as shown. An earth ground should be used on the system.

If an audio oscillator generating a good sine wave is used as the signal source the output power of the amplifier may be measured by an audio-frequency voltmeter as indicated by V. Either a vacuum-tube voltmeter on its a.c. scale or a rectifier-type a.c. voltmeter will be satisfactory, the principal requirements being relatively high impedance (1000 ohms per volt or more) and a reasonably accurate calibration. The power output will be equal to E^2/R_1, where E is the r.m.s. value of the voltage across the resistor (a.c. instruments usually are calibrated in r.m.s. values). This assumes that the distortion generated in the amplifier is small; if distortion is high, the voltmeter reading will be inaccurate.

If the amplifier is a driver for a Class B modulator, the value of R_1 should be calculated from R/N^2, where N is the turns ratio, primary to total secondary, of the class B input transformer, and R is the rated plate-to-plate load for the driver tube or tubes. R_1 should of course be connected across the total secondary in this case.

For a qualitative check on distortion, provision is made in Fig. 9-31 for monitoring the output of the amplifier. R_2 should be a wire-wound potentiometer having a resistance of 10 or 20 ohms. A headset may be connected to the "Monitor" terminals. Using the audio oscillator as a signal source, start with the gain control at minimum and then advance it slowly while listening carefully to the tone signal in the headset. When it begins to sound like a musical octave instead of a single tone, or when higher harmonically related tones can be heard along with the

281

desired one, distortion is starting to become appreciable. This effect usually will be detectable, but not serious, at full output of the amplifier as indicated by the voltmeter reading. Keep the signal in the headset at a moderate level by adjusting R_2 when necessary. If the amplifier passes the distortion test satisfactorily, reduce the audio input to zero and note whether any hum is audible in the headset. There should be none, if the tone level in the headset at full sine-wave output was no more than moderately high.

After completing these checks with satisfactory results, substitute the microphone for the oscillator input to the amplifier and have someone speak into it at a moderate level. The headset will serve to indicate the speech quality at various output levels. A tape recorder, if available, is useful at this stage since it can be substituted for the headset and will provide a means for comparing the effect of changes and adjustments

in which it is occurring can be located by working from the last stage toward the front end of the amplifier, applying a signal to each grid in turn from the audio oscillator and adjusting the signal voltage for maximum output. In the case of push-pull stages, the signal may be applied to the primary of the interstage transformer — *after* disconnecting it from the plate-voltage source and the amplifier tube. Assuming that normal design principles have been followed and that all stages are theoretically working within their capabilities, the probable causes of distortion are wiring errors (such as accidental short-circuit of a cathode resistor), defective components, or use of wrong values of resistance in cathode and plate circuits.

Using the Oscilloscope

Speech-amplifier checking is facilitated considerably if an oscilloscope of the type having

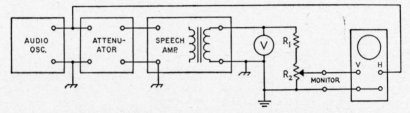

Fig. 9-32—Test setup using the oscilloscope to check for distortion. These connections will result in the type of pattern shown in Fig. 9-33, the horizontal sweep being provided by the audio input signal. For wave-form patterns, omit the connection between the audio oscillator and the horizontal amplifier in the scope, and use the horizontal linear sweep.

in the amplifier as well as giving a better over-all check on speech quality than the average headset. The effect of measures taken to attenuate high- or low-frequency response in the amplifier is readily observed by comparing recordings made before and after changes. The output quality of the amplifier also can be compared with the original output of the microphone as registered on the recorder. In using a recorder care must be taken to set R_2 so that the first stage in the recorder amplifier is not overloaded. Use the normal gain setting of the recorder and adjust R_2 to give normal level indications.

Amplifier Troubles

If the hum level is too high, the amplifier stage that is causing the trouble can be located by temporarily short-circuiting the grid of each tube to ground, starting with the output amplifier. When shorting a particular grid makes a marked decrease in hum, the hum presumably is coming from a *preceding* stage, although it is possible that it is getting its start in that particular grid circuit. If shorting a grid does *not* decrease the hum, the hum is originating either in the plate circuit of that tube or the grid circuit of the next. Aside from wiring errors, a defective tube, or inadequate plate-supply filtering, objectionable hum usually originates in the first stage of the amplifier.

If distortion occurs below the point at which the expected power output is secured the stage

amplifiers and a linear sweep circuit is available. A typical setup for using the oscilloscope is shown in Fig. 9-32. With the connections shown, the sweep circuit is not required but horizontal and vertical amplifiers are necessary. Audio voltage from the oscillator is fed directly to one oscilloscope amplifier (horizontal in this case) and the output of the speech amplifier is connected to the other. The scope amplifier gains should be adjusted so that each signal gives the same line length with the other signal shut off.

Under these conditions, when the input and output signals are applied simultaneously they are compared directly. If the speech amplifier is distortion-free and introduces no phase shift, the resulting pattern is simply a straight line, as shown at the upper left in Fig. 9-33, making an angle of about 45 degrees with the horizontal and vertical axes. If there is no distortion but there is phase shift, the pattern will be a smooth ellipse, as shown at the upper right. The greater the phase shift the greater the tendency of the ellipse to grow into a circle. When there is even-harmonic distortion in the amplifier one end of the line or ellipse becomes curved, as shown in the second row in Fig. 9-33. With odd-harmonic distortion such as is characteristic of overdriven push-pull stages, the line or ellipse is curved at both ends.

Patterns such as these will be obtained when the input signal is a fairly good sine wave. They will tend to become complicated if the input

Checking Speech Equipment

wave form is complex and the speech amplifier introduces appreciable phase shifts. It is therefore advisable to test for distortion with an input signal that is as nearly as possible a sine wave. Also, it is best to use a frequency in the 500-1000 cycle range, since improper phase shift in the amplifier is usually least in this region. Phase shift in itself is not of great importance in an audio amplifier of ordinary design because it does not change the character of speech so far as the ear is concerned. However, if a complex signal is used for testing, phase shift may make it difficult to detect distortion in the oscilloscope pattern.

Since the oscilloscope amplifiers themselves may introduce phase shift and possibly distortion as well, it is advisable to check the scope before attempting to make checks on the speech amplifier. Apply the signal from the audio oscillator simultaneously to the horizontal and vertical amplifier input terminals. If both amplifiers have the same phase characteristics and negligible distortion the pattern, after suitable adjustment of the gains, will be a straight line as shown at the upper left in Fig. 9-33. If distortion is visible, note whether it changes when the scope gain controls are reduced; if not, the signal voltage from the audio oscillator is too great and should be reduced to the point where the input amplifiers are not overloaded. After finding the proper settings for signal input and scope gains, leave the latter alone in making checks on the speech equipment and adjust the input to the scope by means of R_2 and the output of the audio oscillator. Phase shift in the scope itself is not serious since the presence of distortion in the speech amplifier can be detected by the patterns shown at the right in Fig. 9-33.

In amplifiers having negative feedback, excessive phase shift within the feed-back loop may cause self-oscillation, since the signal fed back may arrive at the grid in phase with the applied signal voltage instead of out of phase with it. Such a phase shift is most likely to be associated with the output transformer. Oscillation usually occurs at some frequency above 10,000 cycles, although occasionally it will occur at a very low frequency. If the pass band in the stage in which the phase shift occurs is deliberately restricted to the optimum voice range, as described earlier, the gain at both very high and very low frequencies will be so low that self-oscillation is unlikely, even with large amounts of feedback.

Generally speaking, it is easier to detect small amounts of distortion with the type of pattern shown in Fig. 9-33 than it is with the wave-form pattern obtained by feeding the output signal to the vertical plates and making use of the linear sweep in the scope. However, the wave-form pattern can be used satisfactorily if the signal from the audio oscillator is a reasonably good sine wave. One simple method is to examine the output of the oscillator alone and trace the pattern on a sheet of transparent paper. The pattern given by the output of the amplifier can then be

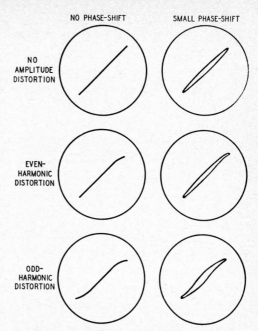

Fig. 9-33—Typical patterns obtained with the connections shown in Fig. 9-32. Depending on the number of stages in the amplifier, the pattern may slope upward to the right, as shown, or upward to the left. Also, depending on where the distortion originates, the curvature in the second row may appear either at the top or bottom of the line or ellipse.

compared with the "standard" pattern by adjusting the oscilloscope gains to make the two patterns coincide as closely as possible. The pattern discrepancies are a measure of the distortion.

In using the oscilloscope care must be taken to avoid introducing hum voltages that will upset the measurements. Hum pickup on the scope leads or other exposed parts such as the amplifier load resistor or the voltmeter can be detected by shutting off the audio oscillator and speech amplifier and connecting first one and then the other to the vertical plates of the scope, setting the internal horizontal sweep to an appropriate width. The trace should be a straight horizontal line when the vertical gain control is set at the position used in the actual measurements. Waviness in the line indicates hum. If the hum is not in the scope itself (check by disconnecting the leads at the instrument) make sure that there is a good ground connection on all the equipment and, if necessary, shield the hot leads.

The oscilloscope can be used to good advantage in stage-by-stage testing to check wave forms at the grid and plate of each stage and thus to determine rapidly where a source of trouble may be located. When the scope is connected to circuits that are not at ground potential for d.c., a capacitor of about 0.1 μf. should be connected in series with the hot oscilloscope lead. The probe lead should be shielded to prevent hum pickup.

CHAPTER 10

Amplitude Modulation

As described in the chapter on circuit fundamentals, the process of modulation sets up groups of frequencies called **sidebands,** which appear symmetrically above and below the frequency of the unmodulated signal or **carrier.** If the instantaneous values of the amplitudes of all these separate frequencies are added together, the result is called the **modulation envelope.** In **amplitude modulation (a.m.)** the modulation envelope follows the amplitude variations of the audio-frequency signal that is being used to modulate the wave.

For example, modulation by a 1000-cycle tone will result in a modulation envelope that varies in amplitude at a 1000-cycle rate. The actual r.f. signal that produces such an envelope consists of three frequencies — the carrier, a side frequency 1000 cycles higher, and a side frequency 1000 cycles lower than the carrier. These three frequencies easily can be separated by a receiver having high selectivity. In order to reproduce the original modulation the receiver must have enough bandwidth to accept the carrier and the sidebands simultaneously. This is because an a.m. detector responds to the modulation envelope rather than to the individual signal components, and the envelope will be distorted in the receiver unless all the frequency components in the signal go through without change in their relative amplitudes.

In the simple case of tone modulation the two side frequencies and the carrier are constant in amplitude — it is only the envelope amplitude that varies at the modulation rate. With more complex modulation such as voice or music the amplitudes and frequencies of the side frequencies vary from instant to instant. The amplitude of the modulation envelope varies from instant to instant in the same way as the complex audio-frequency signal causing the modulation. Nevertheless, even in this case the *carrier* amplitude is constant if the transmitter is properly modulated.

A.M. Sidebands and Channel Width

Speech can be electrically reproduced, with high intelligibility, in a band of frequencies lying between approximately 100 and 3000 cycles. When these frequencies are combined with a radio-frequency carrier, the sidebands occupy the frequency spectrum from about 3000 cycles below the carrier frequency to 3000 cycles above — a total band or **channel** of about 6 kilocycles.

Actual speech frequencies extend up to 10,000 cycles or more, so it is possible to occupy a 20-kc. channel if no provision is made for reducing its width. For communication purposes such a channel width represents a waste of valuable spectrum space, since a 6-kc. channel is fully adequate for intelligibility. Occupying more than the minimum channel creates unnecessary interference. Thus speech equipment design and transmitter adjustment and operation should be pointed toward maintaining the channel width at the minimum.

● THE MODULATION ENVELOPE

In Fig. 10-1, the drawing at A shows the unmodulated r.f. signal, assumed to be a sine wave of the desired radio frequency. The graph can be taken to represent either voltage or current.

In B, the signal is assumed to be modulated by the audio frequency shown in the small drawing above. This frequency is much lower than the carrier frequency, a necessary condition for good modulation. When the modulating voltage is "positive" (above its axis) the envelope amplitude is increased *above* its unmodulated amplitude; when the modulating voltage is "negative" the envelope amplitude is *decreased*. Thus the envelope grows larger and smaller with the polarity and amplitude of the modulating voltage.

The drawings at C shows what happens with stronger modulation. The envelope amplitude is doubled at the instant the modulating voltage reaches its positive peak. On the negative peak of the modulating voltage the envelope amplitude just reaches zero; in other words, the signal is completely modulated.

Percentage of Modulation

When a modulated signal is detected in a receiver, the detector output follows the modulation envelope. The stronger the modulation, therefore, the greater is the useful receiver output. Obviously, it is desirable to make the modulation as strong or "heavy" as possible. A wave modulated as in Fig. 10-1C would produce considerably more useful audio output than the one shown at B.

The "depth" of the modulation is expressed as a percentage of the unmodulated carrier amplitude. In either B or C, Fig. 10-1, X represents the unmodulated carrier amplitude, Y is the maximum envelope amplitude on the modulation up-peak, and Z is the minimum envelope amplitude on the modulation downpeak.

In a properly operating modulation system the modulation envelope is an accurate reproduction of the modulating wave, as can be seen in Fig. 10-1 at B and C by comparing one side of the outline with the shape of the modulating wave. (The lower outline duplicates the upper, but simply appears upside down in the drawing.)

The **percentage of modulation** is

$$\% \text{ Mod.} = \frac{Y - X}{X} \times 100 \text{ (upward modulation), or}$$

$$\% \text{ Mod.} = \frac{X - Z}{X} \times 100 \text{ (downward modulation)}$$

The Modulation Envelope

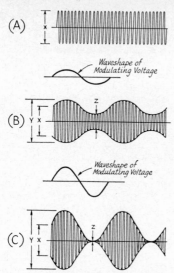

(A)

Waveshape of Modulating Voltage

(B)

Waveshape of Modulating Voltage

(C)

Fig. 10-1—Graphical representation of (A) r.f. output unmodulated, (B) modulated 50%, (C) modulated 100%. The modulation envelope is shown by the thin outline on the modulated wave.

If the wave shape of the modulation is such that its peak positive and negative amplitudes are equal, then the modulation percentage will be the same both up and down. If the two percentages differ, the larger of the two is customarily specified.

Power in Modulated Wave

The amplitude values shown in Fig. 10-1 correspond to current or voltage, so the drawings may be taken to represent instantaneous values of either. The power in the wave varies as the *square* of either the current or voltage, so at the peak of the modulation up-swing the instantaneous power in the envelope of Fig. 10-1C is four times the unmodulated carrier power (because the current and voltage both are doubled). At the peak of the down-swing the power is zero, since the amplitude is zero. These statements are true of 100 per cent modulation no matter what the wave form of the modulation. The instantaneous envelope power in the modulated signal is proportional to the square of its envelope amplitude at every instant. This fact is highly important in the operation of every method of amplitude modulation.

It is convenient, and customary, to describe the operation of modulation systems in terms of sine-wave modulation. Although this wave shape is seldom actually used in practice (voice wave shapes depart very considerably from the sine form) it lends itself to simple calculations and its use as a standard permits comparison between systems on a common basis. With sine-wave modulation the *average* power in the modulated signal over any number of full cycles of the modulation frequency is found to be 1½ times the power in the unmodulated carrier. In other words, the power output increases 50 per cent with 100 per cent modulation by a sine wave.

This relationship is very useful in the design of modulation systems and modulators, because any such system that is capable of increasing the *average* power output by 50 per cent with sine-wave modulation automatically fulfills the requirement that the *instantaneous* power at the modulation up-peak be four times the carrier power. Consequently, systems in which the additional power is supplied from outside the modulated r.f. stage (e.g., plate modulation) usually are designed on a sine-wave basis as a matter of convenience. Modulation systems in which the additional power is secured from the modulated r.f. amplifier (e.g., grid modulation) usually are more conveniently designed on the basis of peak envelope power rather than average power.

The extra power that is contained in a modulated signal goes entirely into the sidebands, half in the upper sideband and half in the lower. As a numerical example, full modulation of a 100-watt carrier by a sine wave will add 50 watts of sideband power, 25 in the lower and 25 in the upper sideband. Supplying this additional power for the sidebands is the object of all of the various systems devised for amplitude modulation.

No such simple relationship exists with complex wave forms. Complex wave forms such as speech do not, as a rule, contain as much average power as a sine wave. Ordinary speech wave forms have about half as much average power as a sine wave, for the same peak amplitude in both wave forms. Thus for the same modulation percentage, the sideband power with ordinary speech will average only about half the power with sine-wave modulation, since it is the peak envelope amplitude, not the average power, that determines the percentage of modulation.

Unsymmetrical Modulation

In an ordinary electric circuit it is possible to increase the amplitude of current flow indefinitely, up to the limit of the power-handling capability of the components, but it cannot very well be decreased to less than zero. The same thing is true of the amplitude of an r.f. signal; it can be modulated *upward* to any desired extent, but it cannot be modulated *downward* more than 100 per cent.

When the modulating wave form is unsymmetrical it is possible for the upward and downward modulation percentages to be different. A simple case is shown in Fig. 10-2. The positive peak of the modulating signal is about 3 times the amplitude of the negative peak. If, as shown in the drawing, the modulating amplitude is adjusted so that the peak downward modulation is just 100 per cent $(Z = 0)$ the peak upward modulation is 300 per cent $(Y = 4X)$. The carrier amplitude is represented by X, as in Fig. 10-1. The modulation envelope reproduces the wave form of the modulating signal accurately, hence there is no distortion. In such a modulated signal the increase in power output with modulation is considerably greater than it is when the modulation is symmetrical and therefore has to be limited to 100 per cent both up and down.

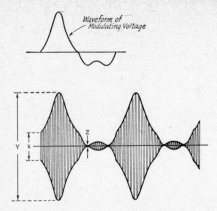

Fig. 10-2—Modulation by an unsymmetrical wave form. This drawing shows 100% downward modulation along with 300% upward modulation. There is no distortion, since the modulation envelope is an accurate reproduction of the wave form of the modulating voltage.

occupied by an amplitude-modulated signal is dependent *on the shape of the modulation envelope.* If this wave shape is complex and can be resolved into a wide band of audio frequencies, then the channel occupied will be correspondingly large. An overmodulated signal splatters and occupies a much wider channel than is necessary because the "clipping" of the modulating wave that occurs at the zero axis changes the envelope wave shape to one that contains high-order harmonics of the original modulating frequency. These harmonics appear as side frequencies separated by, in some cases, many kilocycles from the carrier frequency.

Because of this clipping action at the zero axis, it is important that care be taken to prevent applying too large a modulating signal in the downward direction. Overmodulation downward results in more splatter than is caused by most other types of distortion in a phone transmitter.

In Fig. 10-2 the peak envelope amplitude, Y, is four times the carrier amplitude, X, so the peak-envelope power is 16 times the carrier power. When the upward modulation is more than 100 per cent the power capacity of the modulating system obviously must be increased sufficiently to take care of the much larger peak amplitudes.

● GENERAL REQUIREMENTS

For proper operation of an amplitude-modulated transmitter there are a few general requirements that must be met no matter what particular method of modulation may be used. Failure to meet these requirements is accompanied by distortion of the modulation envelope. This in turn increases the channel width as compared with that required by the legitimate frequencies contained in the original modulating wave.

Overmodulation

If the amplitude of the modulation on the downward swing becomes too great, there will be a period of time during which the r.f. output is entirely cut off. This is shown in Fig. 10-3. The shape of the downward half of the modulating wave is no longer accurately reproduced by the modulation envelope, consequently the modulation is distorted. Operation of this type is called **overmodulation.** The distortion of the modulation envelope causes new frequencies (harmonics of the modulating frequency) to be generated. These combine with the carrier to form new side frequencies that widen the channel occupied by the modulated signal. These spurious frequencies are commonly called "splatter."

It is important to realize that the channel

Frequency Stability

For satisfactory amplitude modulation, the carrier *frequency* must be entirely unaffected by modulation. If the application of modulation causes a change in the carrier frequency, the frequency will wobble back and forth with the modulation. This causes distortion and widens the channel taken by the signal. Thus unnecessary interference is caused to other transmissions.

In practice, this undesirable frequency modulation is prevented by applying the modulation to an r.f. amplifier stage that is isolated from the frequency-controlling oscillator by a **buffer amplifier.** Amplitude modulation applied directly to an oscillator always is accompanied by frequency modulation. Under existing FCC regulations amplitude modulation of an oscillator is permitted only on frequencies above 144 Mc. Below that frequency the regulations require that an amplitude-modulated transmitter be completely free from frequency modulation.

Linearity

At least up to the limit of 100 per cent upward modulation, the amplitude of the r.f. output should be directly proportional to the amplitude of the modulating wave. Fig. 10-4 is a graph of an ideal **modulation characteristic,** or curve showing the relationship between r.f. output amplitude and instantaneous modulation amplitude. The modulation swings the r.f. ampli-

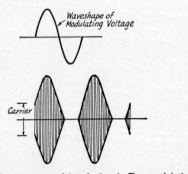

Fig. 10-3—An overmodulated signal. The modulation envelope is not an accurate reproduction of the wave form of the modulating voltage. This or any type of distortion occurring during the modulation process generates spurious sidebands or "splatter."

Methods

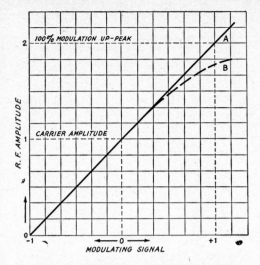

100% MODULATION UP-PEAK

CARRIER AMPLITUDE

R. F. AMPLITUDE

MODULATING SIGNAL

Fig. 10-4—The modulation characteristic shows the relationship between the instantaneous envelope amplitude of the r.f. output current (or voltage) and the instantaneous amplitude of the modulating voltage. The ideal characteristic is a straight line, as shown by curve A.

tude back and forth along the curve A, as the modulating voltage alternately swings positive and negative. Assuming that the negative peak of the modulating wave is just sufficient to reduce the r.f. output to zero (modulating voltage equal to -1 in the drawing), the same modulating voltage peak in the *positive* direction ($+1$) should cause the r.f. amplitude to reach twice its unmodulated value. The ideal is a straight line, as shown by curve A. Such a modulation characteristic is perfectly **linear**.

A **nonlinear** characteristic is shown by curve B. The r.f. amplitude does not reach twice the unmodulated carrier amplitude when the modulating voltage reaches its positive peak. A modulation characteristic of this type gives a modulation envelope that is "flattened" on the up-peak; in other words, the modulation envelope is not an exact reproduction of the modulating wave. It is therefore distorted and harmonics are generated, causing the transmitted signal to

occupy a wider channel than is necessary. A nonlinear modulation characteristic can easily result when a transmitter is not properly designed or is misadjusted.

The **modulation capability** of the transmitter is the maximum percentage of modulation that is possible without objectionable distortion from nonlinearity. The maximum capability can never exceed 100 per cent on the down-peak, but it is possible for it to be higher on the up-peak. The modulation capability should be as close to 100 per cent as possible, so that the most effective signal can be transmitted.

Plate Power Supply

The d.c. power supply for the plate or plates of the modulated amplifier should be well filtered; if it is not, plate-supply ripple will modulate the carrier and cause annoying hum. The ripple voltage should not be more than about 1 per cent of the d.c. output voltage.

In amplitude modulation the plate current of the modulated r.f. amplifier varies at an audio-frequency rate; in other words, an alternating current is superimposed on the d.c. plate current. The output filter capacitor in the plate supply must have low reactance, at the lowest audio frequency in the modulation, if the transmitter is to modulate equally well at all audio frequencies. The capacitance required depends on the ratio of d.c. plate current to plate voltage in the modulated amplifier. The requirements will be met satisfactorily if the capacitance of the output capacitor is at least equal to

$$C = 25 \frac{I}{E}$$

where C = Capacitance of output capacitor in μf.
I = D.c. plate current of modulated amplifier in milliamperes
E = Plate voltage of modulated amplifier

Example: A modulated amplifier operates at 1250 volts and 275 ma. The capacitance of the output capacitor in the plate-supply filter should be at least

$$C = 25 \frac{I}{E} = 25 \times \frac{275}{1250} = 25 \times 0.22 = 5.5 \ \mu\text{f}.$$

Amplitude Modulation Methods

● MODULATION SYSTEMS

As explained in the preceding section, amplitude modulation of a carrier is accompanied by an increase in power output, the additional power being the "useful" or "talk power" in the sidebands. This additional power may be supplied from an external source in the form of audio-frequency power. It is then added to the unmodulated power input to the amplifier to be modulated, after which the combined power is converted to r.f. This is the method used in plate modulation. It has the advantage that the r.f. power is generated at the high efficiency

characteristic of Class C amplifiers — of the order of 65 to 75 per cent — but has the accompanying disadvantage that generating the audio-frequency power is rather expensive.

An alternative that does not require relatively large amounts of audio-frequency power makes use of the fact that the power output of an amplifier can be controlled by varying the potential of a tube element — such as a control grid or a screen grid — that does not, in itself, consume appreciable power. In this case the additional power during modulation is secured by sacrificing carrier power; in other words, a tube is capable of delivering only so much total power

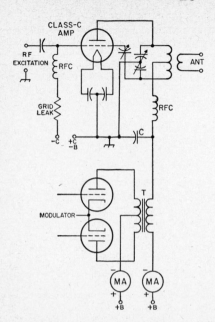

Fig. 10-5—Plate modulation of a Class C r.f. amplifier. The r.f. plate bypass capacitor, C, in the amplifier stage should have reasonably high reactance at audio frequencies. A value of the order of 0.001 μf. to 0.005 μf. is satisfactory in practically all cases. (See chapter on modulators.)

within its ratings, and if more must be delivered at full modulation, then less is available for the unmodulated carrier. Systems of this type must of necessity work at rather low efficiency at the unmodulated carrier level. As a practical working rule, the efficiency of the modulated r.f. amplifier is of the order of 30 to 35 per cent, and the unmodulated carrier power output obtainable with such a system is only about one-fourth to one-third that obtainable from the same amplifier with plate modulation.

It is well to appreciate that no simple modulation scheme that purports to get around this limitation of grid modulation ever has actually done so. Methods have been devised that have resulted in modulation at high over-all efficiency, without requiring audio power, by obtaining the necessary additional power from an auxiliary r.f. amplifier. This leads to circuit and operating complexities that make the systems unsuitable for amateur work, where rapid frequency change and simplicity of operation are almost always essential.

The methods discussed in this section are the basic ones. Variants that from time to time attain passing popularity can readily be appraised on the basis of the preceding paragraphs. A simple grid modulation system that claims high efficiency should be looked upon with suspicion, since it is almost certain that the high efficiency, if actually achieved, is obtained by sacrificing the linear relationship between modulating signal and modulation envelope that is the first essential of a good modulation method.

● PLATE MODULATION

Fig. 10-5 shows the most widely used system of plate modulation, in this case with a triode r.f. tube. A balanced (push-pull Class A, Class AB or Class B) **modulator** is transformer-coupled to the plate circuit of the modulated r.f. amplifier. The audio-frequency power generated by the modulator is combined with the d.c. power in the modulated-amplifier plate circuit by transfer through the coupling transformer, T. For 100 per cent modulation the audio-frequency power output of the modulator and the turns ratio of the coupling transformer must be such that the voltage at the plate of the modulated amplifier varies between zero and twice the d.c. operating plate voltage, thus causing corresponding variations in the amplitude of the r.f. output.

Audio Power

As stated earlier, the average power output of the modulated stage must increase during modulation. The modulator must be capable of supplying to the modulated r.f. stage sine-wave audio power equal to 50 per cent of the d.c. plate input. For example, if the d.c. plate power input to the r.f. stage is 100 watts, the sine-wave audio power output of the modulator must be 50 watts.

Modulating Impedance; Linearity

The **modulating impedance,** or load resistance presented to the modulator by the modulated r.f. amplifier, is equal to

$$Z_m = \frac{E_b}{I_p} \times 1000 \text{ ohms}$$

where E_b = D.c. plate voltage
I_p = D.c. plate current (ma.)

E_b and I_p are measured without modulation.

The power output of the r.f. amplifier must vary as the square of the instantaneous plate voltage (the r.f. output voltage must be proportional to the plate voltage) for the modulation to be linear. This will be the case when the amplifier operates under Class C conditions. The linearity depends upon having sufficient grid excitation and proper bias, and upon the adjustment of circuit constants to the proper values.

Adjustment of Plate-Modulated Amplifiers

The general operating conditions for Class C operation are described in the chapter on transmitters. The grid bias and grid current required for plate modulation usually are given in the operating data supplied by the tube manufacturer; in general, the bias should be such as to give an operating angle of about 120 degrees at the d.c. plate voltage used, and the grid excitation should be great enough so that the amplifier's plate efficiency will stay constant when the plate voltage is varied over the range from zero to twice the unmodulated value. For best linearity, the grid bias should be obtained from a fixed-bias source of about the cut-off value, supplemented by enough grid-leak bias to bring the total up to the required operating bias.

Plate Modulation

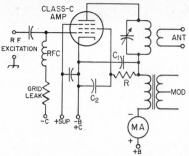

Fig. 10-6—Plate and screen modulation of a Class C r.f. amplifier using a screen-grid tube. The plate r.f. bypass capacitor, C_1, should have reasonably high reactance at all audio frequencies; a value of 0.001 to 0.005 μf. is generally satisfactory. The screen bypass, C_2, should not exceed 0.002 μf. in the usual case.

When the modulated amplifier is a beam tetrode the suppressor connection shown in this diagram may be ignored. If a base terminal is provided on the tube for the beam-forming plates, it should be connected as recommended by the tube manufacturer.

The maximum permissible d.c. plate power input for 100 per cent modulation is twice the sine-wave audio-frequency power output available from the modulator. This input is obtained by varying the loading on the amplifier (keeping its tank circuit tuned to resonance) until the product of d.c. plate voltage and plate current is the desired power. The modulating impedance under these conditions must be transformed to the proper value for the modulator by using the correct output-transformer turns ratio. This point is considered in detail in the chapter on modulator design.

Neutralization, when triodes are used, should be as nearly perfect as possible, since regeneration may cause nonlinearity. The amplifier also must be completely free from parasitic oscillations.

Although the total power input (d.c. plus audio-frequency a.c.) increases with modulation, the d.c. plate current of a plate-modulated amplifier should not change when the stage is modulated. This is because each increase in plate voltage and plate current is balanced by an equivalent decrease in voltage and current on the next

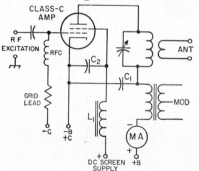

Fig. 10-7—Plate modulation of a beam tetrode, using an audio impedance in the screen circuit. The value of L_1 is discussed in the text. See Fig. 10-6 for data on bypass capacitors C_1 and C_2.

half-cycle of the modulating wave. D.c. instruments cannot follow the a.f. variations, and since the average d.c. plate current and plate voltage of a properly operated amplifier do not change, neither do the meter readings. A change in plate current with modulation indicates nonlinearity. On the other hand, a thermocouple r.f. ammeter connected in the antenna or transmission line will show an increase in r.f. current with modulation, because instruments of this type respond to power rather than to current or voltage.

Screen-Grid Amplifiers

Screen-grid tubes of the pentode or beam-tetrode type can be used as Class C plate-modulated amplifiers by applying the modulation to both the plate and screen grid. The usual method of feeding the screen grid with the necessary d.c. and modulation voltages is shown in Fig. 10-6. The dropping resistor, R, should be of the proper value to apply normal d.c. voltage to the screen under steady carrier conditions. Its value can be calculated by taking the difference between plate and screen voltages and dividing it by the rated screen current.

The modulating impedance is found by dividing the d.c. plate voltage by the sum of the plate and screen currents. The plate voltage multiplied by the sum of the two currents gives the power input to be used as the basis for determining the audio power required from the modulator.

Modulation of the screen along with the plate is necessary because the screen voltage has a much greater effect on the plate current than the plate voltage does. The modulation characteristic is nonlinear if the plate alone is modulated. However, some beam tetrodes can be modulated satisfactorily by applying the modulating power to the plate circuit alone, provided the screen is connected to its d.c. supply through an audio impedance. Under these conditions the screen becomes self-modulating, because of the variations in screen current that occur when the plate voltage is varied. The circuit is shown in Fig. 10-7. The choke coil L_1 is the audio impedance in the screen circuit; its inductance should be large enough to have a reactance (at the lowest desired audio frequency) that is not less than the impedance of the screen. The screen impedance can be taken to be approximately equal to the d.c. screen voltage divided by the d.c. screen current in amperes.

Choke-Coupled Modulator

The choke-coupled Class A modulator is shown in Fig. 10-8. Because of the relatively low power output and plate efficiency of a Class A amplifier, this method is seldom used except for a few special applications. The audio power output of the modulator is combined with the d.c. power in the plate circuit, as in the case of the transformer-coupled modulator. But there is considerably less freedom in adjustment, since no transformer is available for matching impedances.

The modulating impedance of the r.f. amplifier must be adjusted to the value of load impedance required by the particular modulator tube used, and the power input to the r.f. stage should not exceed twice the rated a.f. power output of the modulator for 100 per cent modulation. A complication is the fact that the plate voltage on the

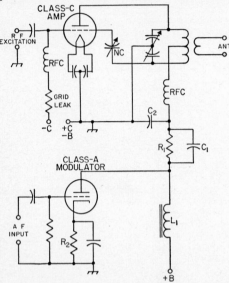

Fig. 10-8—Choke-coupled Class A modulator. The cathode resistor, R_2, should have the normal value for operation of the modulator tube as a Class A power amplifier. The modulation choke, L_1, should be 5 henrys or more. A value of 0.001 to 0.005 μf. is satisfactory at C_2, the r.f. amplifier plate bypass capacitor. See text for discussion of C_1 and R_1.

modulator must be higher than the plate voltage on the r.f. amplifier, for 100 per cent modulation. This is because the a.f. voltage developed by the modulator cannot swing to zero without a great deal of distortion. R_1 provides the necessary d.c. voltage drop between the modulator and r.f. amplifier, but its value cannot be calculated without using the published plate family of curves for the modulator tube used. The d.c. voltage drop through R_1 must equal the minimum instantaneous plate voltage on the modulator tube under normal operating conditions. C_1, an audio-frequency bypass across R_1, should have a capacitance such that its reactance at 100 cycles is not more than about one-tenth the resistance of R_1. Without R_1C_1 the percentage of modulation is limited to 70 to 80 per cent in the average case.

● GRID MODULATION

The principal disadvantage of plate modulation is that a considerable amount of audio power is necessary. This requirement can be avoided by applying the modulation to a grid element in the modulated amplifier. However, the convenience and economy of the low-power modulator must be paid for, since no modulation system gives something for nothing. The increased power output that accompanies modulation is paid for, in the case of grid modulation, by a reduction in the carrier power output obtainable from a given r.f.

amplifier tube, and by more rigorous operating requirements and more complicated adjustment.

The term "grid modulation" as used here applies to all types — control grid, screen, or suppressor — since the operating principles are exactly the same no matter which grid is actually modulated. With grid modulation the plate voltage is constant, and the increase in power output with modulation is obtained by making both the plate current and plate efficiency vary with the modulating signal as shown in Fig. 10-9. For

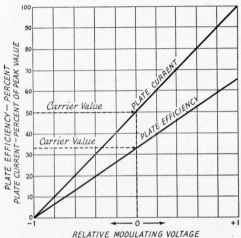

Fig. 10-9—In a perfect grid-modulated amplifier both plate current and plate efficiency would vary with the instantaneous modulating voltage as shown. When this is so the modulation characteristic is as given by curve A in Fig. 10-4, and the peak envelope output power is four times the unmodulated carrier power. The variations in plate current with modulation, indicated above, do not register on a d.c. meter, so the plate meter shows no change when the signal is modulated.

100 per cent modulation, both plate current and efficiency must, at the peak of the modulation up-swing, be twice their carrier values. Thus at the modulation-envelope peak the power input is doubled, and since the plate efficiency also is doubled at the same instant the peak envelope output power will be four times the carrier power. The efficiency obtainable at the envelope peak depends on how carefully the modulated amplifier is adjusted, and sometimes can be as high as 80 per cent. It is generally less when the amplifier is adjusted for good linearity, and under average conditions a round figure of $\frac{2}{3}$, or 66 per cent, is representative. The efficiency without modulation is only half the peak efficiency, or about 33 per cent. This low average efficiency reduces the permissible carrier output to about one-fourth the power obtainable from the same tube in c.w. operation, and to about one-third the carrier output obtainable from the tube with plate modulation.

The modulator is required to furnish only the audio power dissipated in the modulated grid under the operating conditions chosen. A speech amplifier capable of delivering 3 to 10 watts is usually sufficient.

Grid Modulation

Generally speaking, grid modulation does not give quite as linear a modulation characteristic as plate modulation, even under optimum operating conditions. When misadjusted the nonlinearity may be severe, resulting in bad distortion and splatter. However, with careful adjustment it is capable of satisfactory results.

Plate-Circuit Operating Conditions

The d.c. plate power input to the modulated amplifier, assuming a round figure of ⅓ (33 per cent) for the plate efficiency, should not exceed 1½ times the plate dissipation rating of the tube or tubes used in the modulated stage. It is generally best to use the maximum plate voltage permitted by the manufacturer's ratings, because the optimum operating conditions are more easily achieved with high plate voltage and the linearity also is improved.

> Example: Two tubes having plate dissipation ratings of 55 watts each are to be used with grid modulation.
> The maximum permissible power input, at 33% efficiency, is
> $P = 1.5 \times (2 \times 55) = 1.5 \times 110 = 165$ watts
> The maximum recommended plate voltage for these tubes is 1500 volts. Using this figure, the average plate current for the two tubes will be
> $$I = \frac{P}{E} = \frac{165}{1500} = 0.11 \text{ amp.} = 110 \text{ ma.}$$
> At 33% efficiency, the carrier output to be expected is 55 watts.
> The plate-voltage/plate-current ratio at *twice* carrier plate current is
> $$\frac{1500}{220} = 6.8$$

The tank-circuit L/C ratio should be chosen on the basis of *twice* the average or carrier plate current. If the L/C ratio is based on the plate voltage/plate current ratio under carrier conditions the Q may be too low for good coupling to the output circuit.

Screen Grid Modulation

Screen modulation is probably the simplest form of grid modulation and the least critical of adjustment. The most satisfactory way to apply the modulating voltage to the screen is through a transformer, as shown in Fig. 10-10. With practical tubes it is necessary to drive the screen somewhat negative with respect to the cathode to get complete cut-off of r.f. output. For this reason the peak modulating voltage required for 100 per cent modulation is usually 10 per cent or so greater than the d.c. screen voltage. The latter, in turn, is approximately half the rated screen voltage recommended under maximum ratings for c.w. operation.

The audio power required for 100 per cent modulation is approximately one-fourth the d.c. power input to the screen in c.w. operation, but varies somewhat with the operating conditions. A receiving-type audio power amplifier will suffice as the modulator for most transmitting tubes. The relationship between screen voltage and screen current is not linear, which means that the load on the modulator varies over the

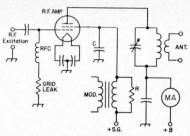

Fig. 10-10—Screen-grid modulation of beam tetrode. Capacitor C is an r.f. bypass capacitor and should have high reactance at audio frequencies. A value of 0.002 μf. is satisfactory. The grid leak can have the same value that is used for c.w. operation of the tube.

audio-frequency cycle. It is therefore highly advisable to use negative feedback in the modulator circuit. If excess audio power is available, it is also advisable to load the modulator with a resistance (R in Fig. 10-10) its value being adjusted to dissipate the excess power. Unfortunately, there is no simple way to determine the proper resistance except experimentally, by observing its effect on the modulation envelope with the aid of an oscilloscope.

On the assumption that the modulator will be fully loaded by the screen plus the additional load resistor R, the turns ratio required in the coupling transformer may be calculated as follows:

$$N = \frac{E_d}{2.5\sqrt{PR_L}}$$

where N is the turns ratio, secondary to primary; E_d is the rated screen voltage for c.w. operation; P is the rated audio power output of the modulator; and R_L is the rated load resistance for the modulator.

Adjustment

A screen-modulated amplifier should be adjusted with the aid of an oscilloscope connected as shown in Fig. 10-11. A tone source for modulating the transmitter is a convenience, since a steady tone will give a steady pattern on the oscilloscope. A steady pattern is easier to study than one that flickers with voice modulation.

Having determined the permissible carrier plate current as previously described, apply r.f. excitation and d.c. plate and screen voltages. Without modulation, adjust the plate loading to give the required plate current, keeping the plate tank circuit tuned to resonance. Next, apply modulation and increase the modulating voltage until the modulation characteristic shows curvature (see later in this chapter for use of the oscilloscope). If curvature occurs well below 100 per cent modulation, the plate efficiency is too high at the carrier level. Increase the plate loading slightly and readjust the r.f. grid excitation to maintain the same plate current; then apply modulation and check the characteristic again. Continue until the characteristic is as linear as possible from zero to twice the carrier amplitude.

In general, the amplifier should be heavily

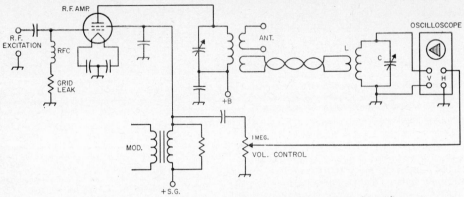

Fig. 10-11—Using the oscilloscope for adjustment of a screen-modulated amplifier.
L and *C* should tune to the operating frequency, and may be coupled to the transmitter tank circuit through a twisted pair or coax, using single-turn links at each end. The blocking capacitor (0.05 μf.) that couples the audio voltage from the screen grid to the horizontal plates of the oscilloscope should have a voltage rating equal to at least twice the d.c. voltage on the grid that is being modulated. The r.f. and audio voltages should be fed directly to the deflection plates of the scope tube (through blocking capacitors if necessary or desirable), not through any vertical or horizontal amplifiers that may be in the instrument.

loaded. Under proper operating conditions the plate-current dip as the amplifier plate circuit is tuned through resonance will be little more than just discernible. It is desirable to operate with the grid current as low as possible, since this reduces the screen current and thus reduces the amount of power required from the modulator.

With proper adjustment the linearity is good up to about 90 per cent modulation. When the screen is driven negative for 100 per cent modulation there is a kink in the modulation characteristic at the zero-voltage point. This introduces a small amount of envelope distortion. The kink can be removed and the over-all linearity improved by applying a small amount of modulating voltage to the control grid simultaneously with screen modulation.

In an alternative adjustment method not requiring an oscilloscope the r.f. amplifier is first tuned up for maximum output without modulation and the rated d.c. screen voltage (from a fixed-voltage supply) for c.w. operation applied. Use heavy loading and reduce the grid excitation until the output just starts to fall off, at which point the resonance dip in plate current should be small. Note the plate current and, if possible, the r.f. antenna or feeder current, and then reduce the d.c. screen voltage until the plate current is one-half its previous value. The r.f. output current should also be one-half its previous value at this screen voltage. The amplifier is then ready for modulation, and the modulating voltage may be increased until the plate current just starts to shift upward, which indicates that the amplifier is modulated 100 per cent. With voice modulation the plate current should remain steady, or show just an occasional small upward kick on intermittent peaks.

''Clamp-Tube'' Modulation

A method of screen-grid modulation that is convenient in transmitters provided with a screen protective tube ("clamp" tube) is shown in Fig.

10-12. An audio-frequency signal is applied to the grid of the clamp tube, which then becomes a modulator. The simplicity of the circuit is somewhat deceptive, since it is considerably more difficult from a design standpoint than the transformer-coupled arrangement of Fig. 10-10.

For proper modulation the clamp tube must be operated as a triode Class A amplifier, and it will be recognized that the method is essentially identical with the choke-coupled Class A plate modulator of Fig. 10-8 except that a resistance, R_2, is substituted for the choke. R_2 in the usual case is the screen dropping resistor normally used for c.w. operation. Its value should be at least two or three times the load resistance required by the Class A modulator tube for optimum audio-frequency output. Unfortunately, relatively little

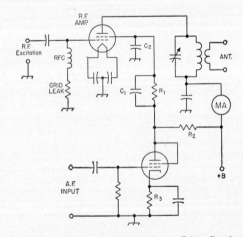

Fig. 10-12—Screen modulation by a "clamp" tube. The grid leak is the normal value for c.w. operation and C_2 should be 0.002 μf. or less. See text for discussion of C_1, R_1, R_2 and R_3. R_3 should have the proper value for Class A operation of the modulator tube, but cannot be calculated unless triode curves for the tube are available.

Clamp Tube Modulation

information is available on the triode operation of the tubes most frequently used for screen-protective purposes.

Like the choke-coupled modulator, the clamp-tube modulator is incapable of modulating the r.f. stage 100 per cent unless the dropping resistor, R_1, and audio bypass, C_1, are incorporated in the circuit. The same design considerations hold, with the addition of the fact that the screen must be driven negative, not just to zero voltage, for 100 per cent modulation. The modulator tube must thus be operated at a voltage ranging from 20 to 40 per cent higher than the screen that it modulates. Proper design requires knowledge of the screen characteristics of the r.f. amplifier and a set of plate-voltage plate-current curves on the modulator tube as a triode.

Adjustment with this system, once the design voltages have been determined, is carried out in the same way as with transformer-coupled screen modulation, preferably with the oscilloscope. Without the oscilloscope, the amplifier may first be adjusted for c.w. operation as described earlier, but with the modulator tube removed from its socket. The modulator is then replaced, and the cathode resistance, R_3, adjusted to reduce the amplifier plate current to one-half its c.w. value. The amplifier plate current should remain constant with modulation, or show just a small upward flicker on occasional voice peaks.

Controlled Carrier

As explained earlier, a limit is placed on the output obtainable from a grid-modulation system by the low r.f. amplifier plate efficiency (approximately 33 per cent) under unmodulated carrier conditions. The plate efficiency increases with modulation, since the output increases while the d.c. input remains constant, and reaches a maximum in the neighborhood of 50 per cent with 100 per cent sine-wave modulation. If the power input to the amplifier can be reduced during periods when there is little or no modulation, thus reducing the plate loss, advantage can be taken of the higher efficiency at full modulation to obtain higher effective output. This can be done by varying the d.c. power input to the modulated stage in accordance with *average* variations in voice intensity, in such a way as to maintain just sufficient carrier power to keep the modulation high, but not exceeding 100 per cent, under all conditions. Thus the carrier amplitude is controlled by the average voice intensity. Properly utilized, controlled carrier permits increasing the effective carrier output at maximum level to a value about equal to the rated plate dissipation of the tube, or twice the output obtainable with constant carrier.

It is desirable to control the power input just enough so that the plate loss, without modulation, is safely below the tube rating. Excessive control is disadvantageous because the distant receiver's a.v.c. system must continually follow the variations in average signal level. The circuit of Fig. 10-13 permits adjustment of both the maximum and minimum power input, and al-

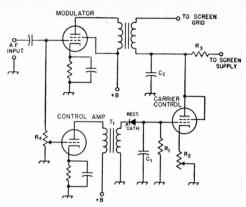

Fig. 10-13—Circuit for carrier control with screen modulation. A small triode such as the 6C4 can be used as the control amplifier and a 6Y6G is suitable as a carrier-control tube. T_1 is an interstage audio transformer having a 1-to-1 or larger turns ratio. R_4 is a 0.5-megohm volume control and also serves as the grid resistor for the modulator. A germanium crystal may be used as the rectifier. Other values are discussed in the text.

though somewhat more complicated than some circuits that have been used is actually simpler to operate because it separates the functions of modulation and carrier control. A portion of the audio voltage at the modulator grid is applied to a Class A "control amplifier" which drives a rectifier circuit to produce a d.c. voltage negative with respect to ground. C_1 filters out the audio variations, leaving a d.c. voltage proportional to the average voice level. This voltage is applied to the grid of a "clamp" tube to control the d.c. screen voltage and thus the r.f. carrier level. Maximum output is obtained when the carrier-control tube grid is driven to cut-off, the voice level at which this occurs being determined by the setting of R_4. The input without modulation is set to the desired level (usually about equal to the plate dissipation rating of the modulated stage) by adjusting R_2. R_3 may be the normal screen-dropping resistor for the modulated beam tetrode, but in case a separate screen supply is used the resistance need be just large enough to give sufficient voltage drop to reduce the no-modulation power input to the desired value.

C_1R_1 should have a time constant of about 0.1 second. The time constant of C_2R_3 should be no larger. Further details may be found in *QST* for April, 1951, page 64. An oscilloscope is required for proper adjustment.

Suppressor Modulation

Pentode-type tubes do not, in general, modulate well when the modulating voltage is applied to the screen grid. However, a satisfactory modulation characteristic can be obtained by applying the modulation to the suppressor grid. The circuit arrangement for suppressor-grid modulation of a pentode tube is shown in Fig. 10-14.

The method of adjustment closely resembles that used with screen-grid modulation. If an oscilloscope is not available, the amplifier is first adjusted for optimum c.w. output with zero bias

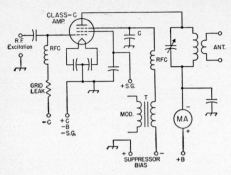

Fig. 10-14—Suppressor-grid modulation of an r.f. amplifier using a pentode-type tube. The suppressor-grid r.f. bypass capacitor, C, should be the same as the grid bypass capacitor in control-grid modulation.

on the suppressor grid. Negative bias is then applied to the suppressor and increased in value until the plate current and r.f. output current drop to half their original values. When this condition has been reached the amplifier is ready for modulation.

Since the suppressor is always negatively biased, the modulator is not required to furnish any power and a voltage amplifier can be used. The suppressor bias will vary with the type of pentode and the operating conditions, but usually will be of the order of −100 volts. The peak a.f. voltage required from the modulator is equal to the suppressor bias.

Control-Grid Modulation

Although control-grid modulation may be used with any type of r.f. amplifier tube, it is seldom used with tetrodes and pentodes because screen or suppressor modulation is generally simpler to adjust. However, control-grid modulation is the only form of grid modulation that is

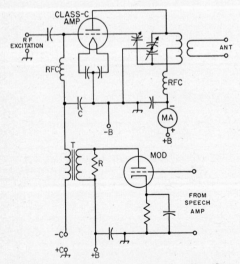

Fig. 10-15—Control-grid modulation of a Class C amplifier. The r.f. grid bypass capacitor, C, should have high reactance at audio frequencies (0.005 µf. or less).

applicable to triode amplifiers. A typical triode circuit is given in Fig. 10-15.

In control-grid modulation the d.c. grid bias is the same as in normal Class C amplifier service, but the r.f. grid excitation is somewhat smaller. The audio voltage superimposed on the d.c. bias changes the instantaneous grid bias at an audio rate, thus varying the operating conditions in the grid circuit and controlling the output and efficiency of the amplifier.

The change in instantaneous bias voltage with modulation causes the rectified grid current of the amplifier to vary, which places a variable load on the modulator. To reduce distortion, resistor R in Fig. 10-15 is connected in the output circuit of the modulator as a constant load, so that the over-all load variations will be minimized. This resistor should be equal to or somewhat higher than the load into which the modulator tube is rated to work at normal audio output. It is also recommended that the modulator circuit incorporate as much negative feedback as possible, as a further aid in reducing the internal resistance of the modulator and thus improving the "regulation" — that is, reducing the effect of load variations on the audio output voltage. The turns ratio of transformer T should be about 1 to 1 in most cases.

The load on the r.f. driving stage also varies with modulation. This in turn will cause the excitation voltage to vary and may cause the modulation characteristic to be nonlinear. To overcome it, the driver should be capable of two or three times the r.f. power output actually required to drive the amplifier. The excess power may be dissipated in a dummy load (such as an incandescent lamp of appropriate power rating) that then performs the same function in the r.f. circuit that resistor R does in the audio circuit.

The d.c. bias source in this system should have low internal resistance. Batteries or a voltage-regulated supply are suitable. Grid-leak bias should not be used.

Satisfactory adjustment of a control-grid modulated amplifier requires an oscilloscope. The scope connections are similar to those shown for screen-grid modulation in Fig. 10-11, with audio from the modulator's output transformer secondary applied to the horizontal plates through a blocking capacitor and volume control, and with r.f. from the plate tank circuits coupled to the vertical plates. The adjustment procedure follows that for screen modulation as previously described.

● CATHODE MODULATION

Circuit

The fundamental circuit for cathode modulation is shown in Fig. 10-16. It is a combination of the plate and grid methods, and permits a carrier efficiency midway between the two. The audio power is introduced in the cathode circuit, and both grid bias and plate voltage are modulated.

Because part of the modulation is by the

Cathode Modulation

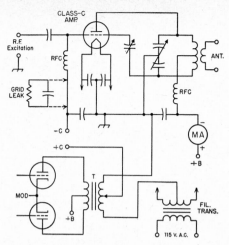

Fig. 10-16—Circuit arrangement for cathode modulation of a Class C r.f. amplifier. Values of bypass capacitors in the r.f. circuits should be the same as for other modulation methods.

control-grid method, the plate efficiency of the modulated amplifier must vary during modulation. The carrier efficiency therefore must be lower than the efficiency at the modulation peak. The required reduction in efficiency depends upon the proportion of grid modulation to plate modulation; the higher the percentage of plate modulation, the higher the permissible carrier efficiency, and vice versa. The audio power required from the modulator also varies with the percentage of plate modulation, being greater as this percentage is increased.

The way in which the various quantities vary is illustrated by the curves of Fig. 10-17. In these curves the performance of the cathode-modulated r.f. amplifier is plotted in terms

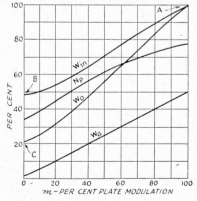

Fig. 10-17—Cathode-modulation performance curves, in terms of percentage of plate modulation plotted against percentage of Class C telephony tube ratings.

W_{in}—D.c. plate input watts in terms of percentage of plate-modulation rating.
W_o —Carrier output watts in per cent of plate-modulation rating (based on plate efficiency of 77.5%).
W_a —Audio power in per cent of d.c. watts input.
N_p —Plate efficiency of the amplifier in percentage.

of the tube ratings for plate-modulated telephony, with the percentage of plate modulation as a base. As the percentage of plate modulation is decreased, it is assumed that the grid modulation is increased to make the over-all modulation reach 100 per cent. The limiting condition, 100 per cent plate modulation and no grid modulation, is at the right (A); pure grid modulation is represented by the left-hand ordinate (B and C).

Example: Assume that the r.f. tube to be used has a 100% plate-modulation rating of 250 watts input and will give a carrier power output of 190 watts at that input. Cathode modulation with 40% plate modulation is to be used. From Fig. 10-17, the carrier efficiency will be 56% with 40% plate modulation, the permissible d.c. input will be 65% of the plate-modulation rating, and the r.f. output will be 48% of the plate-modulation rating. That is,

Power input = 250 × 0.65 = 162.5 watts
Power output = 190 × 0.48 = 91.2 watts

The required audio power, from the chart, is equal to 20% of the d.c. input to the modulated amplifier. Therefore

Audio power = 162.5 × 0.2 = 32.5 watts

The modulator should supply a small amount of extra power to take care of losses in the grid circuit. These should not exceed four or five watts.

Modulating Impedance

The modulating impedance of a cathode-modulated amplifier is approximately equal to

$$m\frac{E_b}{I_b}$$

where m = Percentage of plate modulation (expressed as a decimal)

E_b = D.c. plate voltage on modulated amplifier

I_b = D.c. plate current of modulated amplifier

Example: Assume that the modulated amplifier in the example above is to operate at a plate potential of 1250 volts. Then the d.c. plate current is

$$I = \frac{P}{E} = \frac{162.5}{1250} = 0.13 \text{ amp. (130 ma.)}$$

The modulating impedance is

$$m\frac{E_b}{I_b} = 0.4\frac{1250}{0.13} = 3846 \text{ ohms}$$

The modulating impedance is the load into which the modulator must work, just as in the case of pure plate modulation. This load must be matched to the load required by the modulator tubes by proper choice of the turns ratio of the modulation transformer, as described in the chapter on speech equipment.

Conditions for Linearity

R.f. excitation requirements for the cathode-modulated amplifier are midway between those for plate modulation and control-grid modulation. More excitation is required as the percentage of plate modulation is increased. Grid bias should be considerably beyond cut-off; fixed bias from a supply having good voltage regulation is preferred, especially when the percentage of plate modulation is small and the amplifier is operating more nearly like a grid-bias modulated stage. At the higher percentages of plate modulation a combination of fixed and grid-leak bias can be used, since the variation in rectified grid current is smaller. The grid leak should be bypassed for audio frequencies. The percentage of grid modulation may be regulated by choice of a suitable tap on the modulation-transformer secondary.

The cathode circuit of the modulated stage must be independent of other stages in the transmitter. When directly heated tubes are modulated their filaments must be supplied from a separate transformer. The filament bypass capacitors should not be larger than about 0.002 μf., to avoid bypassing the audio-frequency modulation.

Adjustment of Cathode-Modulated Amplifiers

In most respects, the adjustment procedure is similar to that for grid-bias modulation. The critical adjustments are antenna loading, grid bias, and excitation. The proportion of grid-bias to plate modulation will determine the operating conditions.

Adjustments should be made with the aid of an oscilloscope connected in the same way as for grid-bias modulation. With proper antenna loading and excitation, the normal wedge-shaped pattern will be obtained at 100 per cent modulation. As in the case of grid-bias modulation, too light antenna loading will cause flattening of the upward peaks of modulation as also will too high excitation. The cathode current will be practically constant with or without modulation when the proper operating conditions have been established.

● LINEAR AMPLIFIERS

If a signal is to be amplified after modulation has taken place, the shape of the modulation envelope must be preserved if distortion is to be avoided. This requires the use of a **linear amplifier** — that is, one that will reproduce, in its output circuit, the exact form of the signal envelope applied to its grid.

Linear amplifiers for amplitude-modulated r.f. signals cannot be operated with the grid bias beyond cut-off. To do so would mean that the part of the modulation envelope near the zero axis (see Fig. 10-1C) would be clipped, since there would be times when the instantaneous signal voltage would be below the minimum value that would cause plate-current flow. The result would be overmodulation of the type shown in Fig. 10-3.

However, the grid bias may be set at any value less than cutoff. Usually, such amplifiers are operated at or near the Class B condition — that is, with the grid bias at or somewhat less than cutoff. Although Class B operation results in considerable distortion of the individual r.f. cycles applied to the grid, the modulation *envelope* is not distorted if the operating conditions are chosen properly. The r.f. distortion produces only r.f. harmonics, and these can be eliminated by the selectivity of the output tank circuit.

A linear amplifier used for a.m. has the same disadvantages with respect to efficiency that grid modulation does. The reason also is much the same: since the amplifier must handle a peak-envelope power four times as great as the unmodulated carrier power, it cannot be operated at its full capabilities when it is amplifying only the unmodulated carrier. The plate efficiency of the amplifier varies with the instantaneous value of the modulation envelope in the same way that it varies with the instantaneous modulating voltage in grid modulation (Fig. 10-9). Hence the efficiency at the unmodulated carrier level is only of the order of 30-35 per cent.

Because of this low efficiency, linear amplifiers have not had much application in amateur transmitters, especially since equivalent efficiency can be obtained with grid modulation, along with a less critical adjustment procedure. Recently there has been some increase in use of a.m. linears, particularly at v.h.f., as a means of stepping up the modulated power output of very low power transmitters with a minimum of complication in over-all equipment and operation. To obtain a useful increase in power output by this means the linear amplifier must use a tube or tubes capable of relatively large plate dissipation, since about two-thirds of the d.c. power input to the amplifier is consumed in heating the plate and only about one-third is converted to useful carrier output.

Checking A.M. Phone Operation

● USING THE OSCILLOSCOPE

Proper adjustment of a phone transmitter is aided immeasurably by the oscilloscope. The scope will give more information, more accurately, than almost any collection of other instruments that might be named. Furthermore, an oscilloscope that is entirely satisfactory for the purpose is not necessarily an expensive instrument; the cathode-ray tube and its power supply are about all that are needed. Amplifiers and linear sweep circuits are by no means necessary.

In the simplest scope circuit, radio-frequency voltage from the modulated amplifier is applied to the vertical deflection plates of the tube, usually through blocking capacitors as shown in the oscilloscope circuit in the chapter on measurements, and audio-frequency voltage from the modulator is applied to the horizontal deflection plates. As the instantaneous amplitude of the audio signal varies, the r.f. output of the transmitter likewise varies, and this produces a wedge-shaped pattern or **trapezoid** on the screen. If the oscilloscope has a built-in horizontal sweep, the

Checking A.M. Phone Operation

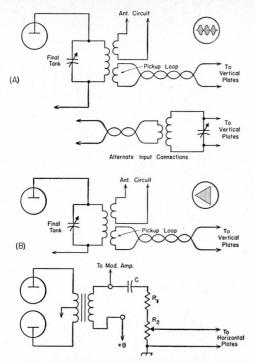

Fig. 10-18—Methods of connecting the oscilloscope for modulation checking. A—connections for wave-envelope pattern with any modulation method; B—connections for trapezoidal pattern with plate modulation. See Fig. 10-11 for scope connections for trapezoidal pattern with screen modulation.

r.f. voltage can be applied to the vertical plates as before (never through an amplifier) and the sweep will produce a pattern that follows the modulation envelope of the transmitter output, provided the sweep frequency is lower than the modulation frequency. This produces a **wave-envelope** modulation pattern.

The Wave-Envelope Pattern

The connections for the wave-envelope pattern are shown in Fig. 10-18A. The vertical deflection plates are coupled to the amplifier tank coil (or an antenna coil) through a low-impedance (coax, twisted pair, etc.) line and pick-up coil. As shown in the alternative drawing, a resonant circuit tuned to the operating frequency may be connected to the vertical plates, using link coupling between it and the transmitter. This will eliminate r.f. harmonics, and the tuning control provides a convenient means for adjustment of the pattern height.

If it is inconvenient to couple to the final tank coil, as may be the case if the transmitter is tightly shielded to prevent TVI, the pick-up loop may be coupled to the tuned tank of a matching circuit or antenna coupler. Any method (even a short antenna coupled to the tuned circuit shown in the "alternate input connections" of Fig. 10-18A) that will pick up

enough r.f. to give a suitable pattern height may be used.

The position of the pick-up coil should be varied until an unmodulated carrier pattern, Fig. 10-19B, of suitable height is obtained. The horizontal sweep voltage should be adjusted to make the width of the pattern somewhat more than half the diameter of the screen. When voice modulation is applied, a rapidly changing pattern of varying height will be obtained. When the maximum height of this pattern is just twice that of the carrier alone, the wave is being modulated 100 per cent. This is illustrated by Fig. 10-19D, where the point X represents the horizontal sweep line (reference line) alone, YZ is the carrier height, and PQ is the maximum height of the modulated wave.

If the height is greater than the distance PQ, as illustrated in E, the wave is overmodulated in the upward direction. Overmodulation in the downward direction is indicated by a gap in the pattern at the reference axis, where a single bright line appears on the screen. Overmodulation in either direction may take place even when the modulation in the other direction is less than 100 per cent.

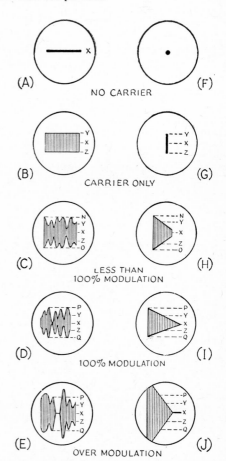

Fig. 10-19—Wave-envelope and trapezoidal patterns representing different conditions of modulation.

The Trapezoidal Pattern

Connections for the trapezoid or wedge pattern as used for checking plate modulation are shown in Fig. 10-18B. The vertical plates of the c.r. tube are coupled to the transmitter tank through a pick-up loop, preferably using a tuned circuit, as shown in the upper drawing, adjustable to the operating frequency. Audio voltage from the modulator is applied to the horizontal plates through a voltage divider, R_1R_2. This voltage should be adjustable so a suitable pattern width can be obtained; a 0.25-megohm volume control can be used at R_2 for this purpose.

The resistance required at R_1 will depend on the d.c. plate voltage on the modulated amplifier. The total resistance of R_1 and R_2 in series should be about 0.25 megohm for each 100 volts of d.c. plate voltage. For example, if the modulated amplifier operates at 1500 volts, the total resistance should be 3.75 megohms, 0.25 megohm at R_2 and the remainder, 3.5 megohms, in R_1. R_1 should be composed of individual resistors not larger than 0.5 megohm each, in which case 1-watt resistors will be satisfactory.

For adequate coupling at 100 cycles the capacitance, in microfarads, of the blocking capacitor, C, should be at least $0.05/R$, where R is the total resistance $(R_1 + R_2)$ in megohms. In the example above, where R is 3.75 megohms, the capacitance should be $0.05/3.75 = 0.013$ μf. or more. The voltage rating of the capacitor should be at least twice the d.c. voltage applied to the modulated amplifier. The capacitance can be made up of two or more similar units in series, so long as the total capacitance is equal to that required, in case a single unit of sufficient voltage rating is not available. Two or more units may be used in parallel if capacitors having adequate voltage rating but insufficient capacitance are available.

The corresponding scope connections for screen modulation were given in Fig. 10-11. This circuit will be satisfactory for d.c. screen voltages up to 200 volts or so, which will include most beam tetrodes. If the d.c. screen voltage, adjusted for proper modulation, exceeds 200 volts a voltage divider similar to that shown in Fig. 10-18 should be used, the values being calculated as described above using the screen voltage instead of the plate voltage.

Trapezoidal patterns for various conditions of modulation are shown in Fig. 10-19 at F to J, each alongside the corresponding wave-envelope pattern. With no signal, only the cathode-ray spot appears on the screen. When the un-modulated carrier is applied, a vertical line appears; the length of the line should be adjusted, by means of the pick-up coil coupling, to a convenient value. When the carrier is modulated, the wedge-shaped pattern appears; the higher the modulation percentage, the wider and more pointed the wedge becomes. At 100 per cent modulation it just makes a point on the axis, X, at one end, and the height, PQ, at the other end is equal to twice the carrier height, YZ. Over-

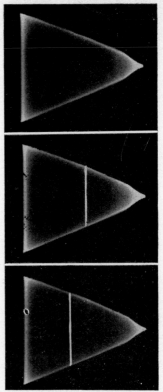

Fig. 10-20—*Top*—A typical trapezoidal pattern obtained with screen modulation adjusted for optimum conditions. The sudden change in slope near the point of the wedge occurs when the screen voltage passes through zero. *Center*—If there is no audio distortion, the unmodulated carrier will have the height and position shown by the white line superimposed on the sine-wave modulation pattern. *Bottom*—Even-harmonic distortion in the audio system, when the audio signal applied to the speech amplifier is a sine wave, is indicated by the fact that the modulation pattern does not extend equal horizontal distances on both sides of the unmodulated carrier.

modulation in the upward direction is indicated by increased height over PQ, and downward by an extension along the axis X at the pointed end.

● CHECKING TRANSMITTER PERFORMANCE

The trapezoidal pattern is generally more useful than the wave-envelope pattern for checking the operation of a phone transmitter. However, both types of patterns have their special virtues, and the best test setup is one that makes both available. The trapezoidal pattern is better adapted to showing the performance of a modulated amplifier from the standpoint of inherent linearity, without regard to the wave form of the audio modulating signal, than is the wave-envelope pattern. Distortion in the audio signal also can be detected in the trapezoidal pattern, although considerable experience in analyzing scope patterns is sometimes required to recognize it.

If the wave-envelope pattern is used with a

Checking Modulation

sine-wave audio modulating signal, distortion in the modulation envelope is easily recognizable; however, it is difficult to determine whether the distortion is caused by lack of linearity of the r.f. stage or by a.f. distortion in the modulator. If the trapezoidal pattern shows good linearity in such a case the trouble obviously is in the audio system. It is possible, of course, for both defects to be present simultaneously. If they are, the r.f. amplifier should be made linear first; then any distortion in the modulation envelope will be the result of some type of improper operation in the speech amplifier or modulator, or in coupling the modulator to the modulated r.f. stage.

R. F. Linearity

The trapezoidal pattern is actually a graph of the modulation characteristic of the modulated amplifier. The sloping sides of the wedge show the r.f. amplitude for every value of instantaneous modulating voltage, exactly the type of curve plotted in Fig. 10-4. If these sides are perfectly straight lines, as drawn in Fig. 10-19 at H and I, the modulation characteristic is linear. If the sides show curvature, the characteristic is nonlinear to an extent that is shown by the degree to which the sides depart from perfect straightness. This is true regardless of the wave form of the modulating voltage.

Audio Distortion

If the speech system can be driven by a good audio sine-wave signal instead of a microphone, the trapezoidal pattern also will show the presence of even-harmonic distortion (the most common type, especially when the modulator is over-loaded) in the speech amplifier or modulator. If there is no distortion in the audio system, the trapezoid will extend horizontally equal distances on each side of the vertical line representing the unmodulated carrier. If there is even-harmonic distortion the trapezoid will extend farther to one side of the unmodulated-carrier position than to the other. This is shown in Fig. 10-20. The probable cause is inadequate power output from the modulator, or incorrect load on the modulator.

An audio oscillator having reasonably good sine-wave output is highly desirable for testing both speech equipment and the phone transmitter as a whole. A very simple audio oscillator such as is shown in Chapter 21 on measurements is quite adequate. With such an oscillator and the scope, the pattern is steady and can be studied closely to determine the effects of various operating adjustments.

In the case of the wave-envelope pattern, distortion in the audio system will show up in the modulation envelope (with a sine-wave input signal) as a departure from the sine-wave form, and may be checked by comparing the envelope with a drawing of a sine wave. Attributing any such distortion to the audio system assumes, of course, that a check has been made on the linearity of the modulated r.f. amplifier, preferably by use of the trapezoidal pattern.

Typical Patterns

Figs. 10-20, 10-21 and 10-22 show some typical scope patterns of modulated signals for different conditions of operation. The screen-modulation patterns, Fig. 10-20, also show how the presence of even-harmonic audio distortion can be detected in the trapezoidal pattern. The pattern

Fig. 10-21—Oscilloscope patterns showing proper modulation of a plate-and-screen modulated tetrode r.f. amplifier. Upper row, trapezoidal patterns; lower row, corresponding wave-envelope patterns. In the latter a linear sweep having a frequency one-third that of the sine-wave audio modulating frequency was used, so that three cycles of the modulation envelope show in the pattern.

| Unmodulated carrier. | Approximately 50 per cent modulation. | 100 per cent modulation. |

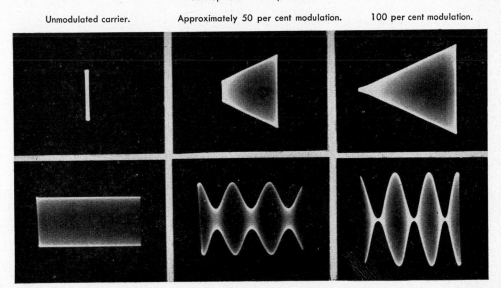

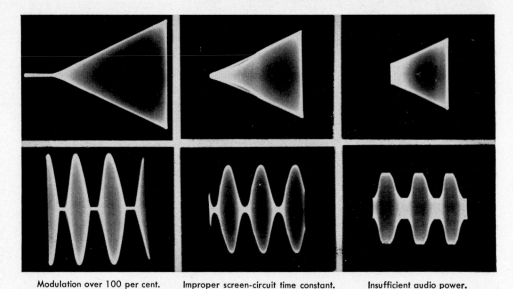

| Modulation over 100 per cent. | Improper screen-circuit time constant. | Insufficient audio power. |

Fig. 10-22—Improper operation or design. These pictures are to the same scale as those in Fig. 10-21, on the same transmitter and with the same test setup.

to be sought in adjusting the transmitter is the one at the top in Fig. 10-20, where the top and bottom edges of the pattern continue in straight lines up to the point representing 100 per cent modulation. If these edges tend to bend over toward the horizontal at the maximum height of the wedge the amplifier is "flattening" on the modulation up-peaks. This is usually caused by attempting to get too large a carrier output, and can be corrected by tighter coupling to the antenna or by reducing the d.c. screen voltage.

Fig. 10-21 shows patterns indicating proper operation of a plate-and-screen modulated tetrode r.f. amplifier. The corresponding wave-envelope pattern is shown with each trapezoidal pattern. The slight "tailing off" at the modulation down peak (point of the wedge) can be minimized by careful adjustment of r.f. grid excitation and plate loading.

Several types of improper operation are shown in Fig. 10-22. In the photos at the left the linearity of the r.f. stage is good but the amplifier is being modulated over 100 per cent. This is shown by the maximum height of the pattern (compare with the unmodulated carrier of Fig. 10-21) and by the bright line extending from the point of the wedge (or between sections of the envelope).

The patterns in the center, Fig. 10-22, show the effect of a too-long time constant in the screen circuit, in an amplifier getting its screen voltage through a dropping resistor, both plate and screen being modulated. The "double-edged" pattern is the result of audio phase shift in the screen circuit combined with varying screen-to-cathode resistance during modulation. The over-all effect is to delay the rise in output amplitude during the up-sweep of the modulation cycle, slightly distorting the modula-

tion envelope as shown in the wave-envelope pattern. This effect, which becomes more pronounced as the audio modulating frequency is increased, is usually absent at low modulation percentages but develops rapidly as the modulation approaches 100 per cent. It can be reduced by reducing the screen bypass capacitance, and also by connecting resistance (to be determined experimentally, but of the same order as the screen dropping resistance) between screen and cathode.

The right-hand pictures in Fig. 10-22 show the effect of insufficient audio power. Although the trapezoidal pattern shows good linearity in the r.f. amplifier, the wave-envelope pattern shows flattened peaks (both positive and negative) in the modulation envelope even though the audio signal applied to the amplifier was a sine wave. More speech-amplifier gain merely increases the flattening without increasing the modulation percentage in such a case. The remedy is to use a larger modulator or less input to the modulated r.f. stage. In some cases the trouble may be caused by an incorrect modulation-transformer turns ratio, causing the modulator to be overloaded before its maximum power output capabilities are reached.

Faulty Patterns

The pattern defects shown in Fig. 10-22 are only a few out of many that might be observed in the testing of a phone transmitter, all capable of being interpreted in terms of improper operation in some part of the transmitter. It is well to keep in mind, however, that it is not always the transmitter that is at fault when the scope shows an unusual pattern The trouble may be in some defect in the test setup.

Patterns representative of two common faults

Checking Modulation

of this nature are shown in Fig. 10-23. The upper picture shows what happens to the trapezoidal pattern when the audio voltage applied to the horizontal plates of the c.r. tube is not exactly in phase with the modulation envelope. The normal straight edges of the wedge are transformed into ellipses which in the case of 100 per cent modulation (shown) touch at the horizontal axis and reach maximum heights equal to the height of the normal wedge at the modulation up-peak. Such a phase shift can occur (and usually will) if the audio voltage applied to the c.r. tube deflection plates is taken from any point in the audio system other than where it is applied to the modulated r.f. stage. The coupling capacitor shown in the recommended circuit of Fig. 10-18 must have very low reactance compared with the resistance of R_1 and R_2 in series — not larger than a few per cent of the resistance.

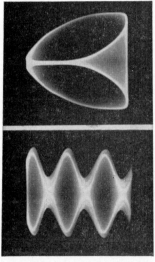

Fig. 10-23—Upper photo—Audio phase shift in coupling circuit between transmitter and horizontal deflection plates. Lower photo—Hum on vertical deflection plates.

The wave-envelope pattern in Fig. 10-23 shows the effect of hum on the vertical deflection plates. This may actually be on the carrier (poor power-supply filtering) or may be introduced in some way from the a.c. line through stray coupling between the scope and the line or because of poor grounding of the scope, transmitter or modulator.

It is important that r.f. from the *modulated stage only* be coupled to the oscilloscope, and then only to the vertical plates. If r.f. is present also on the horizontal plates, the pattern will lean to one side instead of being upright. If the oscilloscope cannot be moved to a position where the unwanted pick-up disappears, a small bypass capacitor (10 $\mu\mu$f. or more) should be connected across the horizontal plates as close to the cathode-ray tube as possible. An r.f.

choke (2.5 mh. or smaller) may also be connected in series with the ungrounded horizontal plate.

● MODULATION CHECKING WITH THE PLATE METER

The plate milliammeter of the modulated amplifier provides a simple and fairly reliable means for checking the performance of a phone transmitter, although it does not give nearly as definite information as the oscilloscope does. If the modulated amplifier is perfectly linear, its plate current will not change when modulation is applied if

1) the upward modulation percentage does not exceed the modulation capability of the amplifier,

2) the downward modulation does not exceed 100 per cent, and

3) there is no change in the d.c. operating voltages on the transmitter when modulation is applied.

The plate current should be constant, ideally, with any of the methods of modulation discussed in this chapter, with the single exception of the controlled-carrier system. The plate meter cannot give a reliable check on the performance of the latter system because the plate current increases with the intensity of modulation. With this system the plate-current variations should be correlated with the transmitter performance as observed on an oscilloscope, if the plate meter is to be used for checking modulation.

Plate Modulation

With plate modulation, a downward shift in plate current may indicate one or more of the following:

1) Insufficient excitation to the modulated r.f. amplifier.

2) Insufficient grid bias on the modulated stage.

3) R.f. amplifier not loaded properly to present the required value of modulating impedance to the modulator.

4) Insufficient output capacitance in the filter of the modulated-amplifier plate supply.

5) D.c. input to the r.f. amplifier, under carrier conditions, is in excess of the manufacturer's ratings for plate modulation. Alternatively, the cathode emission of the amplifier tubes may be low.

6) In plate-and-screen modulation of tetrodes or pentodes, the screen is not being sufficiently modulated along with the plate. In systems in which the d.c. screen voltage is obtained through a dropping resistor, a downward dip in plate current may occur if the screen bypass capacitance is large enough to bypass audio frequencies.

7) Poor voltage regulation of the modulated-amplifier plate supply. This may be caused by voltage drop in the supply itself, when the modulated amplifier and a Class B amplifier are operated from the same supply, or may be caused by voltage drop in the primary supply from the power line when the modulator load is thrown on. It is readily

checked by measuring the voltage with and without modulation. Poor line regulation will be shown by a drop in filament voltage with modulation.

Any of the following may cause an upward shift in plate current:

1) Overmodulation (excessive audio power, audio gain too high).
2) Incomplete neutralization of the modulated amplifier.
3) Parasitic oscillation in the modulated amplifier.

Grid Modulation

With any type of grid modulation, any of the following may cause a downward shift in modulated-amplifier plate current:

1) Too much r.f. excitation.
2) Insufficient grid bias, particularly with control-grid modulation. Grid bias is usually not critical with screen and suppressor modulation, the value of grid leak recommended for c.w. operation being satisfactory.
3) With control-grid modulation, excessive resistance in the bias supply.
4) Insufficient output capacitance in plate-supply filter.
5) Plate efficiency too high under carrier conditions; amplifier is not loaded heavily enough.

Because grid modulation is not perfectly linear (always less so than plate modulation) an amplifier that is properly designed and operated may show a small upward plate-current shift with modulation, 10 per cent or less with sine-wave modulation and amounting to an occasional upward flicker with voice. An upward plate current shift in excess of this may be caused by

1) Overmodulation (excessive modulating voltage).
2) Regeneration (incomplete neutralization).
3) With control-grid or suppressor modulation, bias too great.
4) With screen modulation, d.c. screen voltage too low.
5) Audio distortion in modulator.

In grid-modulation systems the modulator is not *necessarily* operating linearly if the plate current stays constant with or without modulation. It is readily possible to arrive at a set of operating conditions in which flattening of the up-peaks is just balanced by overmodulation downward, resulting in practically the same plate current as when the transmitter is unmodulated. The oscilloscope provides the only certain check on grid modulation.

● COMMON TROUBLES IN THE PHONE TRANSMITTER

Noise and Hum on Carrier

Noise and hum may be detected by listening to the signal on a receiver, provided the receiver is far enough away from the transmitter to avoid overloading. The hum level should be low compared with the voice at 100 per cent modulation. Hum may come either from the speech amplifier and modulator or from the r.f. section of the transmitter. Hum from the r.f. section can be detected by completely shutting off the modulator; if hum remains when this is done, the power-supply filters for one or more of the r.f. stages have insufficient smoothing. With a hum-free carrier, hum introduced by the modulator can be checked by turning on the modulator but leaving the speech amplifier off; power-supply filtering is the likely source of such hum. If carrier and modulator are both clean, connect the speech amplifier and observe the increase in hum level. If the hum disappears with the gain control at minimum, the hum is being introduced in the stage or stages preceding the gain control. The microphone also may pick up hum, a condition that can be checked by removing the microphone from the circuit but leaving the first speech-amplifier grid circuit otherwise unchanged. A good ground (to a cold water pipe, for example) on the microphone and speech system usually is essential to hum-free operation.

Spurious Sidebands

A superheterodyne receiver having a variable-selectivity crystal filter is needed for checking spurious sidebands outside the normal communication channel. The r.f. input to the receiver must be kept low enough, by removing the antenna or by adequate separation from the transmitter, to avoid overloading and consequent spurious receiver responses. An "S"-meter reading of about half scale is satisfactory. With the crystal filter in its sharpest position tune through the region outside the normal channel limits (3 to 4 kilocycles each side of the carrier) while another person talks into the microphone. Spurious sidebands will be observed as intermittent "clicks" or crackles well away from the carrier frequency. Sidebands more than 3 to 4 kilocycles from the carrier should be of negligible strength, compared with the carrier, in a properly modulated phone transmitter. The causes are overmodulation or nonlinear operation.

With sine-wave modulation the relative intensities of sidebands can be observed if a tone of 1000 cycles or so is used, since the crystal filter readily can separate frequencies of this order. The "S"-meter will show how the spurious side frequencies (those spaced more than the modulating frequency from the carrier) compare with the carrier itself. Without an "S"-meter, the a.v.c. should be turned off and the b.f.o. turned on; then the r.f. gain should be set to give a moderately strong beat note with the carrier. The intensity of side frequencies can be estimated from the relative strength of the beats as the receiver is tuned through the spectrum adjacent to the carrier.

As an alternative to the sharp crystal filter, a Q-multiplier adjusted for sharpest selectivity can give equivalent results in analyzing the spectrum of the signal if the same care is used to prevent overloading and spurious receiver responses. This generally requires keeping the r.f. and i.f. gain low.

Receivers having steep-sided band-pass filters for single-sideband reception can be used, but the technique is more difficult. If the band pass is, say, 3 kc., the signal should first be tuned in with the carrier placed at one edge of the pass band. If it is placed at the low edge, for example, the receiver should then be tuned 3 kc. *higher* so its response will be in the region just outside the normal spectrum space occupied by one sideband. Any "crackles" heard in this region represent the results of nonlinearity or overmodulation. This assumes that the precautions mentioned above with respect to receiver overloading have been carefully observed.

R.F. in Speech Amplifier

A small amount of r.f. current in the speech amplifier — particularly in the first stage, which is most susceptible to such r.f. pickup — will cause overloading and distortion in the low-level stages. Frequently also there is a regenerative effect which causes an audio-frequency oscillation or "howl" to be set up in the audio system. In such cases the gain control cannot be advanced very far before the howl builds up, even though the amplifier may be perfectly stable when the r.f. section of the transmitter is not turned on.

Complete shielding of the microphone, microphone cord, and speech amplifier is necessary to prevent r.f. pickup, and a ground connection separate from that to which the transmitter is connected is advisable.

If the transmitter is "hot" with r.f., the cause usually is to be found in the method of coupling to the antenna. Any form of coupling that involves either a direct or capacitive connection between the transmitter and the transmission line is likely to cause the transmitter chassis to assume an r.f. potential above ground because of "parallel" type currents on the line. An earth connection to the transmitter does not always help in such a case. The best remedy is to use inductive coupling between the transmitter and line, a matching circuit such as is described in the chapter on transmission lines being suitable.

● MODULATION MONITORING

It is always desirable to modulate as fully as possible, but 100 per cent modulation should not be exceeded — particularly in the downward direction — because harmonic distortion will be generated and the channel width increased. This causes unnecessary interference to other stations. The oscilloscope is the best instrument for continuously checking the modulation. However, simpler indicators may be used for the purpose, once calibrated.

A convenient indicator, when a Class B modulator is used, is the plate milliammeter in the Class B stage, since the plate current of the modulator fluctuates with the voice intensity. Using the oscilloscope, determine the gain-control setting and voice intensity that give 100 per cent modulation on voice peaks, and simultaneously observe the maximum Class B plate-milliammeter reading on the peaks. When this maximum reading is obtained, it will suffice to adjust the gain so that it is not exceeded.

A high-resistance (1000-ohms-per-volt or more) rectifier-type voltmeter (copper-oxide or germanium type) also can be used for modulation monitoring. It should be connected across the output circuit of an audio driver stage where the power level is a few watts, and similarly calibrated against the oscilloscope to determine the reading that represents 100 per cent modulation.

The plate milliammeter of the modulated r.f. stage also is of value as an indicator of overmodulation. As explained earlier, the d.c. plate current stays constant if the amplifier is linear. When the amplifier is overmodulated, especially in the downward direction, the operation is no longer linear and the average plate current will change. A flicker of the pointer may therefore be taken as an indication of overmodulation or nonlinearity. However, since it is possible that under some operating conditions the plate current will remain constant even though the amplifier is considerably overmodulated, an indicator of this type is not wholly reliable unless it has been checked against an oscilloscope.

CHAPTER 11

Suppressed-Carrier and
Single-Sideband Techniques

A fully modulated a.m. signal has two-thirds of its power in the carrier and only one-third in the sidebands. The sidebands carry the intelligence to be transmitted; the carrier "goes along for the ride" and serves only to demodulate the signal at the receiver. By eliminating the carrier and transmitting only the sidebands or just one sideband, the available transmitter power is used to greater advantage. The carrier must be reinserted at the receiver, but this is no great problem, as explained later under "Receiving Suppressed-Carrier Signals."

Assuming that the same final-amplifier tube or tubes are used either for normal a.m. or for single sideband, carrier suppressed, it can be shown that the use of s.s.b. can give an effective gain of up to 9 db. over a.m. — equivalent to increasing the transmitter power 8 times. Eliminating the carrier also eliminates the heterodyne interference that so often spoils communication in congested phone bands.

● DOUBLE-SIDEBAND GENERATORS

The carrier can be suppressed or nearly eliminated by an extremely sharp filter or by using a **balanced modulator.** The basic principle in any balanced modulator is to introduce the carrier in such a way that it does not appear in the output but so that the sidebands will. This requirement is satisfied by introducing the audio in push-pull and the r.f. drive in parallel, and connecting the output in push-pull. Balanced modulators can also be connected with the r.f. drive and audio inputs in push-pull and the output in parallel with equal effectiveness. The choice of a balanced modulator circuit is generally determined by constructional considerations and the method of modulation preferred by the builder. Vacuum-tube balanced modulators can be operated at high power levels and the double-sideband output can be used directly into the antenna. A d.s.b. signal can be copied by the same methods that are used for single-sideband signals, provided the receiver has sufficient selectivity to reject one of the sidebands.

In any balanced-modulator circuit there will be no output with no audio signal. When push-pull audio is applied, the balance is upset, and one branch will conduct more than the other. Since any modulation process is the same as "mixing" in receivers, sum and difference frequencies (sidebands) will be generated. The modulator is not balanced for the sidebands, and they will appear in the output.

In the rectifier-type balanced modulators shown in Fig. 11-1, the diode rectifiers are connected in such a manner that, if they have equal forward resistances, no r.f. can pass from the carrier source to the output circuit via either of

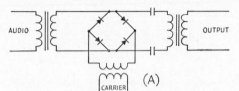

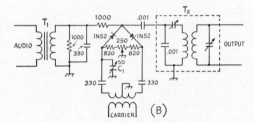

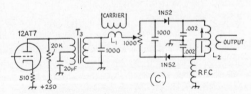

Fig. 11-1—Typical rectifier-type balanced modulators.

The circuit at A is called a "bridge" balanced modulator and has been widely used in commercial work.

The balanced modulator at B is shown with constants suitable for operation at 450 kc. It is useful for working into a crystal bandpass filter. T_1 is a transformer designed to work from the audio source into a 600-ohm load, and T_2 is an ordinary i.f. transformer with the trimmer reconnected in series with a 0.001-μf. capacitor, for impedance-matching purposes from the modulator. The capacitor C_1 is for carrier balance and may be found unnecessary in some instances—it should be tried connected on either side of the carrier input circuit and used where it is more effective. The 250-ohm potentiometer is normally all that is required for carrier balance. The carrier input should be sufficient to develop several volts across the resistor string.

The balanced modulator circuit at C is shown with constants suitable for operation at 3.9 Mc. T_3 is a small step-down output transformer (UTC R-38A), shunt-fed to eliminate d.c. from the windings. L_1 can be a small coupling coil wound on the "cold" end of the carrier-oscillator tank coil, with sufficient coupling to give two or three volts of r.f. across its output. L_2 is a slug-tuned coil that resonates to the carrier frequency with the effective 0.001 μf. across it. The 1000-ohm potentiometer is for carrier balance.

Suppressing the Carrier

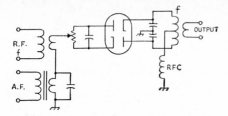

Fig. 11-2—A twin-diode balanced-modulator circuit. This is essentially the same as the circuit in Fig. 11-1C, and differs only in that a twin diode is used instead of dry rectifiers. The heater circuit for the twin diode can be connected in the usual way (one side grounded or center tap grounded).

the two possible paths. The net effect is that no r.f. energy appears in the output. When audio is applied, it unbalances the circuit by biasing the diode (or diodes) in one path, depending upon the instantaneous polarity of the audio, and hence some r.f. will appear in the output. The r.f. in the output will appear as a double-sideband suppressed-carrier signal. (For a more complete description of diode-modulator operation, see "Diode Modulators," *QST*, April, 1953, p. 39.)

In any diode modulator, the r.f. voltage should be at least 6 or 8 times the peak audio voltage, for minimum distortion. The usual operation involves a fraction of a volt of audio and several volts of r.f. The diodes should be matched as closely as possible — ohmmeter measurements of their forward resistances is the usual test.

(The circuit of Fig. 11-1B is described more fully in Weaver and Brown, "Crystal Lattice Filters for Transmitting and Receiving," *QST*, August, 1951. The circuit of Fig. 11-1C is suitable for use in a double-balanced-modulator circuit and is so described in "SSB, Jr.," *General Electric Ham News*, September, 1950.)

Vacuum-tube diodes can also be used in the two- and four-diode balanced-modulator circuits, and many operators consider them superior to the dry rectifier circuits. A typical balanced modulator circuit using a twin diode (6AL5, 6H6, etc.) is shown in Fig. 11-2. In phasing-type s.s.b. generators (described later) two of these modulators are required, and they are usually worked into a common output circuit. (For a description of a complete s.s.b. exciter using 6AL5 balanced modulators, see Vitale, "Cheap and Easy S.S.B.," *QST*, March, 1956, and May, 1958.)

Another form of balanced modulator uses a "beam-deflection" tube, and it is capable of high degrees of carrier suppression (60 db.) with good output (4 volts peak-to-peak) and low distortion (45 db.). A typical circuit, useful in the frequency range 250 to 5000 kc., is shown in Fig 11-3. A carrier signal of 10 volts peak-to-peak is applied to the No. 1 grid, and a maximum audio signal of 2.8 volts peak-to-peak is introduced at one of the deflector electrodes; the other deflector is bypassed. With no audio signal, the output can be minimized by adjustment of the balance controls R_1 and R_2. When the balance is upset by

an audio signal, the beam is deflected back and forth between the two plates, and a double-sideband suppressed-carrier signal appears in the output.

Since stray magnetic fields may upset the balance, the 7360 should be mounted as far as possible from components with magnetic fields. Plate and deflection-electrode circuits should be symmetrical to minimize capacitive unbalance.

● SINGLE-SIDEBAND GENERATORS

Two basic systems for generating s.s.b. signals are shown in Fig. 11-4. One involves the use of a bandpass filter having sufficient selectivity to pass one sideband and reject the other. Filters having such characteristics can only be constructed for relatively low frequencies, and most filters used by amateurs are designed to work somewhere around 500 kc. Good sideband filtering can be done at frequencies as high as 5 Mc. by using multiple-crystal filters. The low-frequency oscillator output is combined with the audio output of a speech amplifier in a balanced modulator, and only the upper and lower sidebands appear in the output. One of the sidebands is passed by the filter and the other rejected, so that an s.s.b. signal is fed to the mixer. The signal is there mixed with the output of a high-frequency r.f. oscillator to produce the desired output frequency. For additional amplification a linear r.f. amplifier (Class A or Class B) must be used. When the s.s.b. signal is generated around 500 kc. it may be necessary to convert twice to reach the operating frequency, since this sim-

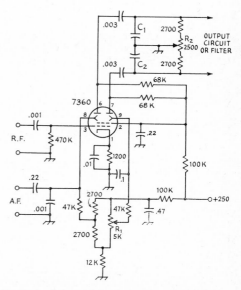

Fig. 11-3—A beam-deflection balanced modulator works well to 5 Mc., giving excellent carrier suppression with low distortion. Capacitances are in μf.

C_1, C_2—To resonate output circuit or filter.
R_1—Carrier balance control.
R_2—Quadrature balance control.

plifies the problem of rejecting the "image" frequencies resulting from the heterodyne process. The problem of image frequencies in the frequency conversions of s.s.b. signals differs from the problem in receivers because the beating-oscillator frequency becomes important. Either balanced modulators or sufficient selectivity must be used to attenuate these frequencies in the output and hence minimize the possibility of unwanted radiations. (Examples of filter-type exciters can be found in *QST* for June, 1958, and January, 1956.)

The second system is based on the phase relationships between the carrier and sidebands in a modulated signal. As shown in the diagram, the audio signal is split into two components that are identical except for a phase difference of 90 de-

level can be increased in a following amplifier.

Properly adjusted, either system is capable of good results. Arguments in favor of the filter system are that it is somewhat easier to adjust without an oscilloscope, since it requires only a receiver and a v.t.v.m. for alignment, and it is more likely to remain in adjustment over a long period of time. The chief argument against it, from the amateur viewpoint, is that it requires quite a few stages and at least one frequency conversion after modulation. The phasing system requires fewer stages and can be designed to require no frequency conversion, but its alignment and adjustment are often considered to be a little "trickier" than that of the filter system. This probably stems from lack of familiarity with the system rather than any actual difficulty, and now that

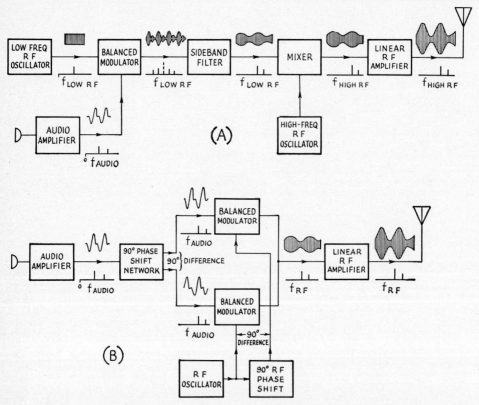

Fig. 11-4—Two basic systems for generating single-sideband suppressed-carrier signals. Representations of a typical envelope picture (as seen on an oscilloscope) and spectrum picture (as seen on a very selective panoramic receiver) are shown above and below the connecting links.

grees. The output of the r.f. oscillator (which may be at the operating frequency, if desired) is likewise split into two separate components having a 90-degree phase difference. One r.f. and one audio component are combined in each of two separate balanced modulators. The carrier is suppressed in the modulators, and the relative phases of the sidebands are such that one sideband is balanced out and the other is augmented in the combined output. If the output from the balanced modulators is high enough, such an s.s.b. exciter can work directly into the antenna, or the power

commercial preadjusted audio-phasing networks are available, most of the alignment difficulty has been eliminated. In most cases the phasing system will cost less to apply to an existing transmitter.

Regardless of the method used to generate a s.s.b. signal of 5 or 10 watts, the minimum cost will be found to be higher than for an a.m. transmitter of the same low power. However, as the power level is increased, the s.s.b. transmitter becomes more economical than the a.m. rig, both initially and from an operating standpoint.

Phasing-Type Exciters

Phasing-Type S.S.B. Exciters

It should be obvious that a phasing-type s.s.b. exciter can take many forms, but in general it will consist of a speech amplifier, audio phase-shift network, audio amplifier, balanced modulators, r.f. source, r.f. phase-shift network, and r.f. amplifier. If operation on a band other than that of the r.f. source, a mixer stage will also be required, for heterodyning the signal to the desired frequency. Since there are several balanced-modulator, audio- and r.f. phasing circuits, it is apparent that many different combinations are available. One of the simplest of all combinations is that shown in Fig. 11-5.

Referring to Fig. 11-5, the speech amplifier builds up the signal from a crystal microphone to a useful level. The audio signal is then fed to an audio phase-shift network, *PSN*, which applies equal-amplitude audio signals 90 degrees out of phase to the grids of the 12AT7 audio amplifier. The two audio signals, 90 degrees out of phase, are applied to two balanced modulators that have their outputs in parallel (L_3). The r.f. excitation to the balanced modulators is also 90 degrees out of phase, obtained by coupling from the two tuned circuits at L_1 and L_2. A 6AG7 linear amplifier, operating Class AB_1, follows the balanced-modulator stage and provides about 5 watts peak envelope output.

The gain control in the speech amplifier sets the gain to the proper level, depending upon the

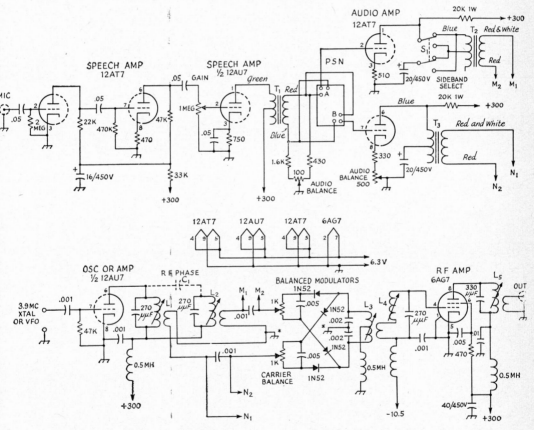

Fig. 11-5—Schematic of a phasing-type s.s.b. exciter. Capacitance in μf. unless otherwise noted—resistors are ½-watt unless otherwise noted. Chassis grounds marked * should be the same.

C_1—5 or 10 μμf. if inductive coupling between L_1 and L_2 not sufficient.

T_1—Single plate to push-pull grid, 1:3 ratio (Stancor A53C).

T_2, T_3—6-watt universal output transformer, 30 ohms output (UTC R-38A).

L_1, L_2—32 turns No. 22 enam. closewound on ½-inch diameter iron-core tuned form (Millen 69046). Link turn is 6 turns hook-up wire wound adjacent to cold end.

L_3—16 turns No. 22 enam., spaced to occupy 1-inch length on ½-inch diameter iron-core-tuned form (Millen 69046), tapped at center. One-turn link wound at center.

L_4—Same as L_1; no link.

L_5—25 turns No. 22 enam. closewound on ½-inch iron-core-tuned form (Millen 69046). Link of 4 turns at cold end.

S_1—D.p.d.t. toggle or rotary.

PSN—Audio phase-shift network (Millen 75012). See Fig. 11-6.

microphone and how the operator uses it. Since the audio phase-shift network, *PSN*, has unequal gains through its two channels, unequal-amplitude audio is required at the input to

obtain equal signals in the output. This is obtained through proper adjustment of the 100-ohm input audio balance control. To compensate for lack of uniformity in audio-amplifier gains, a 500-ohm audio balance control is provided in the cathode of a 12AT7 section. R.f. carrier balance is obtained by proper setting of the 1000-ohm carrier balance controls. The sideband in use (upper or lower) is selected by S_1, which reverses the audio signal in one of the channels. The r.f. phasing adjustment is obtained by the tuning of L_1 and L_2.

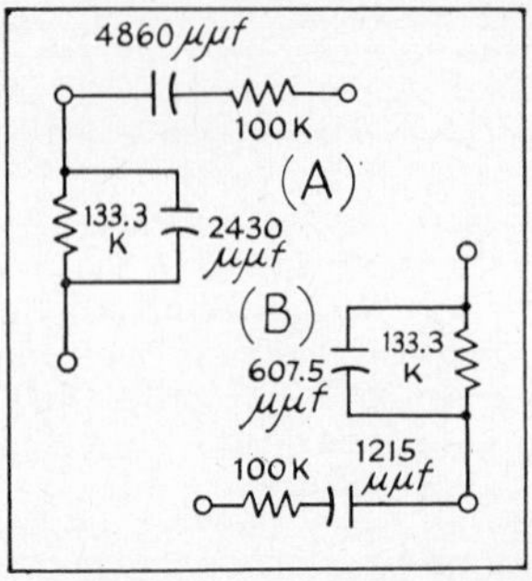

Construction

There are a few constructional precautions that should be observed in a unit of this type. Transformers T_2 and T_3 should preferably be mounted at right angles to each other, to minimize stray coupling. The 1N52 germanium diodes used in the balanced modulator should be checked for forward and back resistance with an ohmmeter, and the forward resistances (the lower readings) should agree within 10 per cent. The leads from the coupling loops at L_1 and L_2 should return to the balanced modulator stage in twisted pairs, and the grounding precaution mentioned in Fig. 11-5 should be observed. Coils L_1 and L_2 should be mounted parallel to each other and with a separation of about $1\frac{1}{2}$ diameters — L_3 and L_4 should be mounted to minimize coupling between them and L_5 and the oscillator coils. This can be accomplished by providing shielding or using the chassis deck to separate them.

Although slug-tuned coils are shown in the schematic, capacitance-tuned circuits can of course be used. Approximately the same L/C ratios should be retained, however. If operation on another amateur band is desired, the tuned circuits can be modified accordingly, retaining the same L/C ratios,

Fig. 11-6—Schematic of the phase-shift network marked PSN in Fig. 11-5. Resistors and capacitors should be within 1 per cent of values shown.

or the output of this unit can be heterodyned to the different band.

Adjustment

If v.f.o. operation is to be used, the v.f.o. signal should furnish at least 10 volts r.m.s. at the terminals. With crystal control, plug in a crystal and tune L_1 until the circuit oscillates, as indicated by a signal in a receiver tuned to the proper frequency, and then tune the circuit to a slightly higher frequency. With v.f.o. operation, the circuit is resonated in the usual manner, as indicated by a plate-current minimum.

The output from the 6AG7 stage can be checked on an oscilloscope or on a receiver. The method of coupling an oscilloscope or receiver to the exciter is shown in Fig. 11-7. When connecting to an oscilloscope, a tuned circuit is required, and the r.f. voltage developed across the tuned circuit is applied directly to the vertical deflection plates. The receiver is connected by coupling loosely through a loop and length of shielded cable; when further attenuation is required it is obtained through the use of resistors at the receiver input terminals.

With the oscillator running, tune the balanced modulator and 6AG7 circuits for maximum output — this resonates these circuits. Next adjust the carrier balance potentiometers for minimum output. Then introduce a single audio tone of around 1000 cycles at the microphone terminal. Here again it may be necessary to use a resistance voltage divider to hold the signal down and prevent overload. Advance the gain control and check the voltage at Pins 2 and 7 of the 12AT7 audio amplifier with a v.t.v.m. If they are not

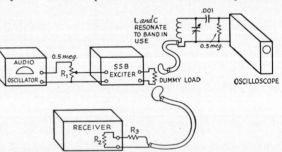

Fig. 11-7—Fundamental arrangement for using an oscilloscope and/or receiver when testing an s.s.b. exciter or transmitter. An audio oscillator is required to furnish the audio signal, and its output is best controlled by the external control R_1. The audio volume control in the s.s.b. exciter should not be turned on too far, or it should be set at the normal position if you know that position, and all volume controlling should then be done with R_1 and the output attenuator of the audio oscillator. This will reduce the chances of overloading the audio and other amplifier stages in the exciter, a common cause of distortion.

The oscilloscope is coupled to the dummy load through a loop, length of coaxial line, and an L-C circuit tuned to the operating frequency. It is necessary to go directly to the vertical deflection plates of the oscilloscope rather than through the vertical amplifier.

The receiver is coupled to the dummy load through a loop and a length of shielded line. If too much signal is obtained this way, an attenuator, R_2R_3, can be added to the input terminals of the receiver. Small values of R_2 and large values of R_3 give the most attenuation; in some cases R_2 might be merely a few inches of solid wire.

Filter-Type Exciters

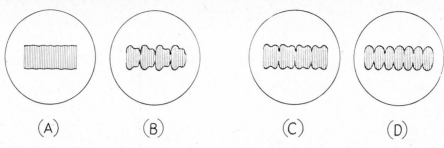

(A) (B) (C) (D)

Fig. 11-8—Sketches of the oscilloscope face showing different conditions of adjustment of the exciter unit. (A) shows the substantially clean carrier obtained when all adjustments are at optimum and a sine-wave signal is fed to the audio input. (B) shows improper r.f. phase and unbalance between the outputs of the two balanced modulators. (C) shows improper r.f. phasing but outputs of the two balanced modulators equal. (D) shows proper r.f. phasing but unbalance between outputs of two balanced modulators.

equal, adjust the 100-ohm audio balance control until they are. Listening to the signal, from the 6AG7, or looking at it on the scope, should give a modulated signal. Try various settings of L_2 until the modulation is minimized, as well as touching up the 500-ohm audio balance control. With the v.t.v.m. check the r.f. voltages at the arms of the 1000-ohm carrier balance potentiometers — they should be about the same. If not, they can be brought into this condition by readjustment of the tuning conditions which, however, must be kept consistent with minimum modulation on the output signal.

The s.s.b. signal with single-tone audio input is a steady unmodulated signal. While it may not be possible to eliminate the modulation entirely, it will be possible to get it down to a satisfactorily low level. Conditions that will prevent this are improper r.f. phasing, lack of carrier balance (suppression), distortion in the audio signal (at the source or through overload in the speech amplifier), and lack of audio balance at the 12AT7 audio amplifier. Of these, the r.f. phasing is perhaps the most critical.

A final check on the signal can be made with the receiver in its most selective condition. The spectrum testing described below cannot be done with a broad receiver. Examining the spectrum near the signal, the side signals other than the main one (carrier, unwanted sidebands, and sidebands from audio harmonics) should be at least 30 db. down from the desired signal. This checking can be done with the S-meter and the a.v.c. on — in the earlier tests the a.v.c. should be off but the r.f. gain reduced low enough to avoid receiver overload.

Examples of the proper and improper scope patterns are shown in Fig. 11-8.

(For an extensive treatment of the alignment of commercial phasing-type s.s.b. exciters, see Ehrlich, "How to Adjust Phasing-Type S.S.B. Exciters," *QST*, November, 1956.)

Filter-Type S.S.B. Exciters

The basic configuration of a filter-type s.s.b. exciter was shown earlier in this chapter (Fig. 11-4). Suitable filters, sharp enough to reject the unwanted sideband above a few hundred cycles, can be built in the range 20 kc. to 5 Mc. The low-frequency filters generally use iron-cored inductors, and the new toroid forms find considerable favor at frequencies up to 50 or 60 kc. These filters are of normal band-pass constant-k and m-derived configuration. In the range 450 to 500 kc., either crystal-lattice or electromechanical filters are used. Low-frequency filters are manufactured by Barker & Williamson and by Burnell & Co., and electromechanical filters are made by the Collins Radio Co. Crystal-lattice filters are available from Hermes Electronics in the megacycle range; homemade filters generally utilize crystals from military surplus.

The frequency of the filter determines how many conversions must be made before the operating frequency is reached. For example, if the filter frequency is 30 kc. or so, it is wise to convert first to 500 or 600 kc. and then convert to the 3.9-Mc. band, to avoid the image that would almost surely result if the conversion from 30 to 3900 kc. were made without the intermediate step. When a filter at 500 kc. is used, only one conversion is necessary to operate in the 3.9-Mc. band, but 14-Mc. and higher-frequency operation would require at least two conversions to hold down the images (and local-oscillator signals if balanced mixers aren't used) and make them easy to eliminate.

The choice of converter circuit depends largely on the frequencies involved and the impedance level. At low frequencies (up to 500 kc.) and low impedances, rectifier-type balanced modulators are often used for mixers, because the balanced modulator does not show the local-oscillator frequency in its output and one source of spurious signal is minimized. At frequencies at high impedance levels, and at the higher frequencies, vacuum tubes are generally used, in straight converter or balanced-modulator circuits, depending upon the need for minimizing the local-oscillator frequency in the output.

Low-frequency sideband filters in the 30- to 50-kc. range are usually low-impedance devices, and rectifier-type balanced modulators are common practice. Sideband filters in the i.f. range

this can be nothing more elaborate than a shielded b.f.o. unit. The signal should be introduced at the balanced modulator, and an output indicator connected to the plate circuit of the vacuum tube following the filter. With the crystals out of the circuit, the transformers can be

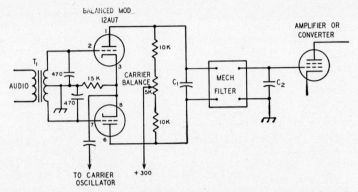

Fig. 11-9—One type of balanced-modulator circuit that can be used with a mechanical filter (Collins F455-31 or F500-31 series) in the i.f. range. The filters are furnished in various types of mountings, and the values of C_1 and C_2 will depend upon the type of filter selected.

T_1—Plate-to-push-pull grids audio transformer.

are higher-impedance circuits and vacuum-tube balanced modulators are the rule in this case. An example of one that can be used with the high-impedance (15,000 ohms) mechanical filter is shown in Fig. 11-10. The filter can be followed by a converter or amplifier tube, depending upon the signal level. Some models of the mechanical filters have a 23-db. insertion loss, while others have only 10.

Crystal-lattice filters are also used to reject the unwanted sideband. These filters can be

brought close to frequency by plugging in small capacitors (10 to 25 $\mu\mu$f.) in one crystal socket in each stage and then tuning the transformers for peak output at one of the two crystal frequencies. The small capacitors can then be removed and the crystals replaced in their sockets.

Tuning the signal source slowly across the pass band of the filter and watching the output indicator will show the selectivity characteristic of the filter. The objective is a fairly flat response for about two kc. and a rapid drop-off outside

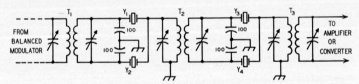

Fig. 11-10—A cascaded half-lattice crystal filter that can be used for sideband selection. The crystals are surplus type of FT-243A holders. Y_1 and Y_3 should be the same frequency and Y_2 and Y_4 should be 1.8 kc. higher. T_1, T_2, T_3—450-kc. i.f. transformers.

made from crystals in the i.f. range — many of these are still available from stores selling military surplus. A popular configuration is the "cascaded half lattice" shown in Fig. 11-10. The crystals used in this filter can be obtained at frequencies in the i.f. range, and ones that are within the ranges of the modified i.f. transformers will be satisfactory. Two 100-$\mu\mu$f. capacitors are connected across the secondary winding of two of the transformers to give push-pull output. The crystals should be obtained in pairs 1.8 kc. apart. The i.f. transformers can be either capacitor-tuned as shown, or they can be slug-tuned.

A variable-frequency signal generator of some kind is required for alignment of the filter, but

this range. It will be found that small changes in the tuning of the transformers will change the shape of the selectivity characteristic, so it is wise to make a small adjustment of one trimmer, swing the frequency across the band, and observe the characteristic. After a little experimenting it will be found which way the trimmers must be moved to compensate for the peaks that will rise when the filter is out of adjustment.

The (suppressed) carrier frequency must be adjusted so that it falls properly on the slope of the filter characteristic. If it is too close to the filter mid-frequency the sideband rejection will be poor; if it is too far away there will be a lack of "lows" in the signal.

Amplification of S.S.B. Signals

● AMPLIFICATION OF S.S.B. SIGNALS

When an s.s.b. signal is generated at some frequency other than the operating frequency, it is necessary to change frequency by heterodyne methods. These are exactly the same as those used in receivers, and any of the normal mixer or converter circuits can be used. One exception to this is the case where the heterodyning oscillator frequency is close to the desired output frequency. In this case, a balanced mixer should be used, to eliminate the heterodyning oscillator frequency in the output.

To increase the power level of an s.s.b. signal, a **linear amplifier** must be used. A linear amplifier is one that operates with low distortion, and the low distortion is obtained by the proper choice of tube and operating conditions. Physically there is little or no difference between a linear amplifier and any other type of r.f. amplifier stage. The circuit diagram of a tetrode r.f. amplifier is shown in Fig. 11-11; it is no different basically than the similar ones in Chapter Six. The practical differences can be found in the supply voltages for the tube and their special requirements. The proper voltages for a number of suitable tubes can be found in Table 11-I; filament-type tubes will require the addition of the filament bypass capacitors C_9 and C_{10} and the completion of the filament circuit by grounding the filament-transformer center tap. The grid bias, E_1, is furnished through an r.f. choke, although a resistor can be used if the tube is operated in Class AB_1 (no grid current). The screen voltage, E_2, must be supplied from a "stiff" source (little or no voltage change with current change) which eliminates the use of a dropping resistor from the plate supply unless a voltage-regulator tube is used to stabilize the screen voltage.

Any r.f. amplifier circuit can be adapted to linear operation through the proper choice of operating conditions. For example, the circuit in Fig. 11-11 can be modified by the use of different input and/or output coupling circuits, or by the use of another neutralizing scheme, and the resultant amplifier will still be linear if the proper operating conditions are observed. A triode or pentode amplifier circuit will differ in detail; typical circuits can be found in Chapter Six.

The simplest form of linear amplifier is the Class A amplifier, which is used almost without exception throughout receivers and low-level speech equipment. (See Chapter Three for an explanation of the classes of amplifier operation.) While its linearity can be made relatively good, it is inefficient. The theoretical limit of efficiency is 50 per cent, and most practical amplifiers run 25-35 per cent efficient at full output. At low levels this is not worth worrying about, but when the 2- to 10-watt level is exceeded something else must be done to improve this efficiency and reduce tube, power-supply and operating costs.

Class AB_1 amplifiers make excellent linear amplifiers if suitable tubes are selected. Primary advantages of Class AB_1 amplifiers are that they give much greater output than straight Class A amplifiers using the same tubes, and they do not require any grid driving power (no grid current drawn at any time). Although triodes can be used for Class AB_1 operation, tetrodes or pentodes are usually to be preferred, since Class AB_1 operation requires high peak plate current without grid current, and this is easier to obtain in tetrodes and pentodes than in most triodes.

To obtain maximum output from tetrodes, pentodes and most triodes, it is necessary to operate them in Class AB_2. Although this produces maximum peak output, it increases the driving-power requirements and, what is more important, requires that the **driver regulation** (ability to maintain wave form under varying load) be good or excellent. The usual method to improve the driver regulation is to connect a fixed resistor, R_1, across the grid circuit of the driven stage, to offer a load to the driver that is modified only slightly by the additional load of the tube when

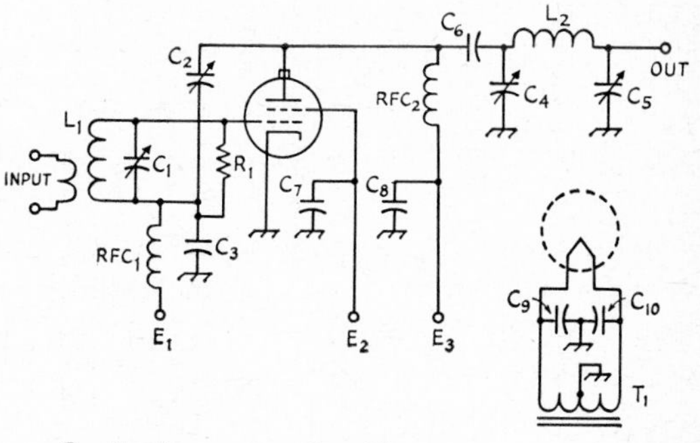

Fig. 11-11—Circuit diagram of a tetrode linear amplifier using link-coupled input tuning and pi network output coupling. The grid, screen and plate voltages (E_1, E_2 and E_3) are given in Table 11-1 for a number of tubes. Although the circuit is shown for an indirectly-heated cathode tube, the only change required when a filament type tube is used is the addition of the filament bypass capacitors C_9 and C_{10}.

Minimum voltage ratings for the capacitors are given in terms of the power supply voltages.

C_1—Grid tuning capacitor, $3E_1$.
C_2—Neutralizing capacitor, $2E_3$.
C_3—Grid-circuit bypass capacitor, part of neutralizing circuit, $3E_1$.
C_4—Plate tuning capacitor, $1.5E_3$.
C_5—Output loading capacitor. 0.015 spacing for kilowatt peak.
C_6—Plate coupling capacitor, $2E_3$.
C_7—Screen bypass capacitor, $2E_2$.

C_8—H.v. bypass capacitor, $2E_3$.
C_9, C_{10}—Filament bypass capacitor.
L_1—Grid inductor.
L_2—Plate inductor.
R_1—Grid circuit swamping resistor, required for AB_2. See text.
RFC_1—Grid-circuit r.f. choke.
RFC_2—Plate r.f. choke.

T_1—Filament transformer.

TABLE 11-I — LINEAR-AMPLIFIER TUBE-OPERATION DATA FOR SINGLE SIDEBAND

Except where otherwise noted, ratings are manufacturers'[1] for audio operation. Values given are for one tube. Driving powers represent tube losses only—circuit losses will increase the figures.

Tube	Class	Plate Voltage	Screen Voltage	D.C. Grid Voltage	Zero-Sig. D.C. Plate Current	Max.-Sig. D.C. Plate Current	Zero-Sig. D.C. Screen Current	Max.-Sig. D.C. Screen Current	Peak R.F. Grid Voltage	Max.-Sig. D.C. Grid Current	Max.-Sig. Driving Power	Max.-Rated Screen Dissipation	Max.-Rated Grid Dissipation	Avg. Plate Dissipation	Max.-Sig. Useful Power Output
2E26	AB₁	500	200	−25	9	45	—	10	25	0	0	2.5	—	—	15
6146	AB₁	600	200	−50	14	115	.5	14	50	0	0	3	—	25	47
6883		750	200	−50	12	110	.5	13	50	0	0	3	—	25	60
807	AB₂	600	300	−30	30	100	.4	6	39	—	.1	3.5	—	25	40
1625		750	300	−32	26	120	.3	8	46	—	.1	3.5	—	30	60
811-A	B	1000	—	0	22	175	—	—	93	13	3.8	—	—	65	124
		1250	—	0	27	175	—	—	88		3.0	—	—	65	155
		1500	—	−4.5	16	157	—	—	85		2.2	—	—	65	170
4-65A	AB₂	1500	300	−55[1]	35	200[2]	—	45[3]	150	15	2.3[3]	10	5	60	150
		2000	400	−80[1]	25	270[2]	—	65[3]	190	20	3.8[3]	10	5	65	300
		2500	500	−105[1]	20	230[2]	—	45[3]	165	8	1.3[3]	10	5	65	325
7094	AB₁	2000	400	−50	30	200	0	35	44	0	.4[8]	20	—	—	250
813	AB₁	2000	750	−90	25	145		27	90	0	0	—	—	—	245
	AB₂	2250	750	−95	23	158	.8	29	115	—	.1	22	—	100	258
		2500	750		18	180	.6	28	118	—	.2	22	—	125	325
4-125A	AB₁	2000	615	−105[1]	40	135 (100)[4]	0	14 (4.0)[4]	105	0	0	20	—	—	150
		2500	555	−100[1]	35	120 (85)[4]	0	10 (3.0)[4]	100	0	0	20	—	—	180
		3000	510	−95[1]	30	105 (75)[4]	0	6.0 (1.5)[4]	95	0	0	20	—	—	200
	AB₂	1500	350	−41[1]	44	200	0	17	141	9	1.25	20	5	125	175
		2000	350	−45[1]	35	150	0	3	105	7	.7	20	5	125	175
		2500	350	−43[1]	47	130	0	3	89	6	.5	20	5	122	200
7034/ 4X150A	AB₁	1000	300	−50	50	225	0	11	50	0	0	12	—	—	115
		1500	300	−50	50	225	0	11	50	0	0	12	—	—	200
		1800	300		50	225						12	—	—	250
4-250A	AB₁	2500	600	−115	65	230 (170)[4]	0	15 (3.5)[4]	115	0	0	35	—	—	335
		3000	600	−110	55	210 (150)[4]	0	12 (2.5)[4]	110	0	0	35	—	—	400
		3500	555	−105	45	185 (130)[4]	0	9.5 (2.0)[4]	105	0	0	35	—	—	425
		4000	510	−100	40	165 (115)[4]	0	7.5 (1.5)[4]	100	0	0	35	—	—	450
	AB₂	1500	300	−48[1]	50	243	0	17	96	11	1.1	35	10	150	214
		2000	300	−48[1]	60	255	0	13	99	12	1.2	35	10	185	325
		2500	300	−51[1]	60	250	0	12	100	11	1.1	35	10	205	420
		3000	300	−53[1]	63	237	0	17	99	10	1	35	10	190	520
304TL	AB₁	1500	—	−118[1]	135	286	0	—	118	0	0	—	—	—	128
		2000	—	−170[1]	100	273	0	—	170	0	0	—	—	—	245
		2500	—	−230[1]	80	242	0	—	230	0	0	—	—	—	305
		3000	—	−290[1]	65	222	0	—	290	0	0	—	—	—	365
PL-6569	B[5]	2500	—	−60[1]	40	300	—	—	180	80	70[6]	—	—	—	550
		3500	—	−90[1]	30	270	—	—	220	68	75[6]	—	—	—	760
		4000	—	−105[1]	24	250	—	—	205	42	60[6]	—	—	—	800
PL-6580	B[5]	2500	—	−50	60	350	—	—	195	95	75[6]	—	—	—	610
		3500	—	−85	45	300	—	—	210	65	68[6]	—	—	—	765
		4000	—	−100	40	300	—	—	230	65	72[6]	—	—	—	910
PL-172	AB₁	2000	500[7]	−110	200	800	9	48	110	0	0	35	—	—	1020
		2500	500[7]	−110	220	800	9	43	110	0	0	35	—	—	1280
		3000	500[7]	−115	220	780	9	41	110	0	0	35	—	—	1540

[1] Adjust to give stated zero-signal plate current.
[2] Single-sideband suppressed-carrier ratings, voice signal.
[3] Approximate value.
[4] Values in parentheses are with two-tone test signal.
[5] Grounded-grid circuit.
[6] Includes bias loss, grid dissipation, and feed-through power.
[7] +75 v. suppressor grid.
[8] 60 Mc.

Amplification of S.S.B. Signals

it is driven into the grid-current region. This increases the driver's output-power requirements. Further, it is desirable to make the grid circuit of the Class AB$_2$ stage a high-C circuit, to improve regulation and simplify coupling to the driver. A "stiff" bias source is also required, since it is important that the bias remain constant, whether or not grid current is drawn.

Class B amplifiers are theoretically capable of 78.5 per cent efficiency at full output, and practical amplifiers run at 60–70 per cent efficiency at full output. Triodes normally designed for Class B audio work can be used in r.f. linear amplifiers and will operate at the same power rating and efficiency provided, of course, that the tube is capable of operation at the radio frequency. The operating conditions for r.f. are substantially the same as for audio work — the only difference is that the input and output transformers are replaced by suitable r.f. tank circuits. Further, in r.f. circuits it is readily possible to operate only one tube if only half the power is wanted — push-pull is not a necessity in Class B r.f. work. However, the r.f. harmonics may be higher in the case of the single-ended amplifier, and this should be taken into consideration if TVI is a problem.

For proper operation of Class AB$_2$ and B amplifiers, and to reduce harmonics and facilitate coupling, the input and output circuits should not have a low C-to-L ratio. A good guide to the proper size of tuning capacitor will be found in Chapter Six; in case of any doubt, it is well to be on the high-capacitance side. When zero-bias tubes are used, it may not be necessary to add much "swamping" resistance across the grid circuit, because the grids of the tubes load the circuit at all times. However, in AB$_2$ operation, the swamping resistor should be such that it dissipates from five to ten times the power required by the grids of the tubes, insuring an almost constant load on the driver stage and good regulation of the r.f. grid voltage. In turn this means that at least five to ten times more driving power will be required than is indicated in Table 11-I. Where an excess of driving power is available, it is generally better to increase the loading (decrease the resistance of the swamping resistor) to the point where the maximum available driver power is utilized on peaks.

Before going into detail on the adjustment and loading of the linear amplifier, a few general considerations should be kept in mind. If proper operation is expected, it is essential that the amplifier be so constructed, wired and neutralized that no trace of regeneration or parasitic instability remains. Needless to say, this also applies to the stages ahead of it.

The bias supply to the Class AB$_2$ or B linear amplifier should be quite stiff, such as batteries or some form of voltage regulator. If nonlinearity is noticed when testing the unit, the bias supply may be checked by means of a large electrolytic capacitor. Simply shunt the supply with 100 μf. or so of capacity and see if the linearity improves. If so, rebuild the bias supply for better regula-

tion. *Do not rely on a large capacitor alone.*

Where tetrodes or pentodes are used, the screen supply should have good regulation and its voltage should remain constant under the varying current demands. If the maximum screen current does not exceed 30 or 35 ma., a string of VR tubes in series can be used to regulate the screen voltage. If the current demand is higher, it may be necessary to use an electronically regulated power supply or a heavily bled power supply with a current capacity of several times the current demand of the screen circuit.

Where VR tubes are used to regulate the screen supply, they should be selected to give a regulated voltage as close as possible to the tube's rated voltage, but it does not have to be exact. Minor differences in idling plate current can be made up by readjusting the grid bias.

The plate voltage applied to the linear amplifier should be held as constant as possible under the varying current-demand conditions. This condition can be met by using low-resistance transformers and inductors and by using a large value of output capacitor in the power-supply filter. An output capacitor value three or four times the minimum required for normal filtering (Chapter Seven) is reasonable. Although some slight improvement can be obtained by using still higher values of output capacitance, the problem of turning on the supply without blowing fuses (from the initial surge) starts to become significant.

One should bear in mind that the same amplifier can be operated in several classes of operation by merely changing the operating conditions (bias, loading, drive, screen voltage, etc.). However, when the power sensitivity of an amplifier is increased, as by changing the operation from Class AB$_2$ to Class AB$_1$, the stability requirements for the amplifier become stringent.

From the standpoint of ease of adjustment and availability of proper operating voltages, a linear amplifier with Class AB$_1$ tetrodes or pentodes or one with zero-bias Class B triodes would be first choice. The Class B amplifier would require more driving power. (For examples of Class AB$_1$ tetrode amplifiers, see Russ, "The 'Little Firecracker' Linear Amplifier," *QST*, Sept., 1953, Eckhardt, "The Single Side-Saddle Linear," *QST*, Nov., 1953, Wolfe and Romander, "A 4X-250B Linear," *QST*, Nov., 1956, Muir, "Grounded-Grid Tetrode Kilowatt," *QST*, April, 1957, and Rinaudo, "Compact AB$_1$ Kilowatt," *QST*, Nov., 1957.)

Table 11-I lists a few of the more popular tubes commonly used for s.s.b. linear-amplifier operation. Except where otherwise noted, these ratings are those given by the manufacturer for audio work and as such are based on a sine-wave signal. These ratings are adequate ones for use in s.s.b. amplifier design, but they are conservative for such work and hence do not necessarily represent the maximum powers that can be obtained from the tubes in voice-signal s.s.b. service. In no case should the *average* plate dissipation be exceeded for any considerable length of time, but the nature of a s.s.b. signal is such that the average plate dissipation of the tube will run well below the peak plate dissipation.

Getting the most out of a linear amplifier is done by increasing the peak power without exceeding the average plate dissipation over any appreciable length of time. This can be done by raising the plate voltage or the peak current (or both), provided the tube can withstand the increase. However, the manufacturers have not released any data on such operation, and any extrapolation of the audio ratings is at the risk of the amateur. A 35- to 50-per cent increase above plate-voltage ratings should be perfectly safe in most cases. In a tetrode or pentode, the peak plate current can be boosted some by raising the screen voltage.

When running a linear amplifier at considerably higher than the audio ratings, the "two-tone test signal" (described later) should never be applied at full amplitude for more than a few seconds at any one time. The above statements about working tubes above ratings apply only when a voice signal is used — a prolonged whistle or two-tone test signal may damage the tube. (For a method of adjusting amplifiers safely at high input, see Goodman, "Linear Amplifiers and Power Ratings," *QST*, August, 1957.)

Grounded-Grid Amplifiers With Filament-Type Tubes

It is not necessary to use indirectly heated cathode type tubes in grounded-grid circuits, and filament-type tubes can be used just as effectively. However, it is necessary to raise the filament above r.f. ground, and one way is shown in Fig. 11-12. Here filament chokes are used between the filament transformers and the tube socket. The inductance of the r.f. chokes does not have to be very high, and 5 to 10 μh. will usually suffice from 80 meters on down. The current-carrying capacities of the r.f. chokes must be adequate for the tube or tubes in use, and if the resistance of the chokes is too high the filament voltage *at the tube socket* may be too low and the tube life will be endangered. In such a case, a higher-voltage filament transformer can be used, with its primary voltage cut down until the voltage at the tube socket is within the proper limits.

Filament chokes can be wound on ceramic or wooden forms, using a wire size large enough to carry the filament current without undue heating. Large cylindrical ceramic antenna insulators can be used for the forms. If enameled wire is used, it should be spaced from half the diameter to the diameter of the wire; heavy string can be used for this purpose. The separate chokes indicated in Fig. 11-12 are not essential; the two windings can be wound in parallel. In this case it is not necessary to space all windings; the two parallel wires can be treated as one wire, winding them together with a single piece of string to space the turns. Enameled wire can be used because the enamel is sufficient insulation to handle the filament voltage.

When considerable power is available for driving the grounded-grid stage, the matching between driver stage and the amplifier is not too important. However, when the driving power is

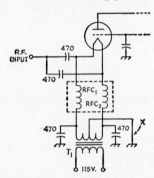

Fig. 11-12—When filament-type tubes are used in a grounded-grid circuit, it is necessary to use filament chokes to keep the filament above r.f. ground. In the portion of a typical circuit shown here, the filament chokes, RFC₁ and RFC₂, can be a manufactured unit (e.g., B&W FC15 or FC30) or homemade as described in the text. Total plate and grid current can be read on a milliammeter inserted at x.

marginal or when the driver and amplifier are to be connected by a long length of coaxial cable, a pi network matching circuit can be used in the input of the grounded-grid amplifier. The input impedance of a grounded-grid amplifier is in the range of 100 to 400 ohms, depending upon the tube or tubes and their operating conditions. When data for grounded-grid operation is available (as for two tubes in Table 11-I), the input impedance can be computed from

$$Z_{in} = \frac{(peak\ r.f.\ driving\ voltage)^2}{2 \times driving\ power}$$

From this and the equations for a pi network, a suitable network can be devised.

Adjustment of Amplifiers

One of the more important features of the linear amplifier is that the ordinary plate and grid meters are at best only a poor indicator of what is going on. As the meters bounce back and forth, even a person who is thoroughly familiar with this kind of amplifier would be hard put to sense whether the input power registered is attributable to (a) overdrive and underload, which yield distortion, splatter, TVI, etc., or (b) underdrive and too-heavy loading, resulting in inefficiency and loss of output.

The simplest and best way to get the whole

Adjustment of Amplifiers

story is to make a linearity test; that is, to send through the amplifier a signal whose amplitude varies from zero up to the peak level in a certain known manner and then observe, by means of an oscilloscope, whether this same waveform comes out of the amplifier at maximum ratings.

Test Equipment

Even the simplest type of cathode-ray oscilloscope can be used for linearity tests, so long as it has the regular internal sweep circuit. If this instrument is not already part of the regular station equipment, it might be well to purchase one of the several inexpensive kits now on the market, so that it will be on hand not only to make initial tests but also as a permanent monitor during all operation. Barring a purchase, it is recommended at least that a scope be borrowed to make the line-up checks, whereupon the regular plate and grid meters can serve thereafter to indicate roughly changes in operating conditions.

All linearity tests require that the vertical plates of the scope be supplied with r.f. from the amplifier output. To avoid interaction within the instrument, it is usually best to connect directly to the cathode-ray tube terminals at the back of the cabinet. A pick-up device and its connections to the oscilloscope are shown in Fig. 11-7. Normally, the pick-up loop should be coupled to the dummy load, antenna tuner, or transmission line; i.e., to a point in the system beyond where any tuning adjustments are to be made.

The only other piece of test equipment will be an audio oscillator. Since only one frequency is needed, the simple circuit of Fig. 11-13 works quite well. Some equipment has a circuit similar to this one built right into the exciter audio system.

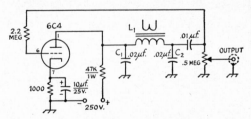

Fig. 11-13—Fixed-frequency audio oscillator having good output waveform. The frequency can be varied by changing the values of C_1 and C_2.

L_1—Small speaker output transformer, secondary not used.

Two-Tone Test

The two-tone test involves sending through the amplifier or the system a pair of r.f. signals of equal amplitude and a thousand cycles or so apart in frequency. The combined envelope of two such signals looks like two sine waves folded on one another. If this waveform comes out of the final, well and good; if not, there is work to do.

There are two commonly used ways to generate

the two-tone signal, and the choice of which to use depends on the particular exciter.

Method A — for Filter or Phasing Exciters:

1) Turn up the carrier insertion until a carrier is obtained at about half the expected output amplitude.

2) Connect an audio oscillator to the microphone input and advance audio gain until (when the carrier and the one sideband are equal) the scope pattern takes on the appearance of full modulation; i.e., the cusps just meet at the center line. See Fig. 11-14, photo No. 1.

3) To change the drive through the system, increase or decrease the carrier and audio settings together, maintaining equality of the two signals.

Method B — for Phasing Exciters:

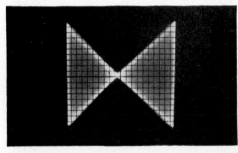

(1)

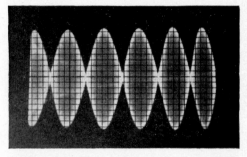

(2)

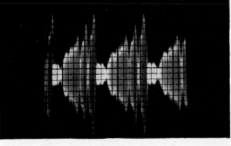

(3)

Fig. 11-14—Correct Patterns. 1—Desired two-tone test pattern. 2—Desired double-trapezoid test pattern. 3—Typical voice pattern in a correctly adjusted amplifier, scope set for 30-cycle sweep. Note that peaks are clean and sharp.

1) Disable the audio input to *one* balanced modulator, by removing a tube or by temporarily short-circuiting an audio transformer.

2) Connect the audio oscillator and advance audio gain to get the desired drive. Note that with one balanced modulator cut out, the resultant signal will be double-sideband with no carrier, hence two equal r.f. signals.

Double-Trapezoid Test

When Method B can be used with phasing exciters, it is possible to derive a somewhat more informative pattern by making a connection from the exciter audio system to the horizontal signal input of the oscilloscope and using this audio signal, instead of the regular internal sweep, to cause the horizontal deflection. Those who are familiar with the regular trapezoid test for a.m. transmitters will recognize this set-up as being the same, except that instead of one trapezoid, this test produces two triangles pointing toward each other.

Each individual triangle is subject to the same analysis as the regular trapezoid pattern; i.e., the sloping sides of the pattern should be straight lines for proper operation. Since it is much easier to tell whether a line is straight or not than to judge the correctness of a sine curve, the double trapezoid has the advantage of being somewhat more positive and sensitive to slight departures from linearity than is the regular two-tone pattern.

If the audio can be picked off at the plate of the audio modulator tube that is still working, the input signal need not be a pure sine wave; merely whistling or talking into the microphone should produce the appropriate pattern. If, because of the exciter layout, it is necessary to pick up the audio signal ahead of the phase-shift network, it will then be necessary to use a good sine-wave audio oscillator as before. Also, with the latter set-up, the pattern will probably have a loopy appearance at first, and phase correction

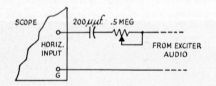

Fig. 11-15—"Phaser" circuit for the oscilloscope.

will be needed to make the figure close up. This can be done either by varying the audio frequency or by putting a phaser in series with the horizontal input to the scope, as shown in Fig. 11-15.

Ratings

Before proceeding with linearity tests, it is well to have in mind the current and power levels to expect. A suppressed-carrier signal is

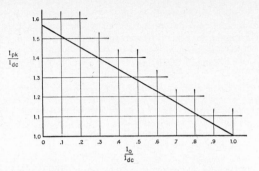

Fig. 11-16—When the two-tone test signal is used for checking the linearity of an amplifier, the peak current is higher than the current indicated by the plate meter. The ratio of these values depends upon the ratio of the idling (no-signal) current to the indicated current. The graph shows the relationship.

I_o = no-signal (idling) current,
I_{dc} = meter reading with two-tone test signal,
I_{pk} = actual peak current.

exactly like an audio signal, except for its frequency, so the audio ratings for any tube are perfectly applicable for linear r.f. service where no carrier is involved. On the other hand, the ratings sometimes shown for Class B r.f. telephony are *not* what is wanted, because they are for conventional a.m. transmission with carrier.

If audio ratings are not given for the desired tube type, it will be safe to assume that the maximum-signal input for Class B or AB_2 service is about 10 per cent less than the key-down Class C c.w. conditions. The input will have to be held somewhat lower in Class AB_1 operation because the average efficiency is lower and, also, the tube can draw only a limited amount of current at zero grid voltage.

The maximum-signal conditions determined from tube data correspond in s.s.b. work to the very peak of the r.f. envelope; when a two-tone test signal (or voice) is used, the plate milliammeter does not indicate the peak plate current. The relationship between peak current and indicated current is variable with voice signals, but with the two-tone test signal applied there is a definite relationship between indicated (d.c.) current and peak current. This relationship is plotted in Fig. 11-16. Knowing the ratio of the idling current to the plate current with the two-tone test signal, I_O/I_{DC}, one can find the factor that can be applied to give the peak current. For example, an amplifier draws 50 ma. with no signal and 250 ma. (before flattening) with the two-tone test signal. $I_O/I_{DC} = 0.2$, and $I_{PK}/I_{DC} = 1.45$, from Fig. 11-16. Thus $I_{PK} = 1.45 \times 250 = 363$ ma.

Should the resulting peak input (0.363 × plate voltage) be different than the design value for the particular amplifier tube, the drive and loading adjustments can be changed in the proper directions (always adjusting the loading so that the peaks of the envelope are on the verge of flattening) and the proper value reached.

Adjustment of Amplifiers

Using the Linearity Tests

The photos (Figs. 11-14, 11-17 and 11-18) have been taken to show many of the typical patterns that may be encountered with either of the test arrangements described previously. They are classified separately as to those representing correct conditions (Fig. 11-14), faulty operation of the r.f. amplifier (Fig. 11-17), and various other patterns that look irregular but which really represent a peculiarity in the test set-up or the exciter but not in the final (Fig. 11-18).

Aside from the problem of parasitics, which may or may not be a difficult one, it should be possible without much difficulty to achieve the correct linearity pattern by taking action as indicated by the captions accompanying the photos. It can then be assumed that the amplifier is not contributing any distortion to the signal so long as the peak power level indicated by the test is not exceeded. It is entirely possible, however, that good linearity will be obtained only by holding the power down to a level considerably below what is expected, or conversely that there will be signs of excessive plate dissipation at a level that the tubes should handle quite easily. In such cases, some attention should be given to the plate loading, as discussed below.

The several patterns of Fig. 11-19 show how loading affects the output and efficiency of a linear amplifier. In the first two, loading is relatively light and limiting takes place in the final plate circuit. Reserve power is still available in the driver, evidenced by the fact that heavier loading on the final allows the peak output to increase up to the optimum level of the third pattern. With still heavier loading the output ceases to increase but in fact drops somewhat; even though the input power goes up all the time, the efficiency goes down rapidly. In the last two patterns, the driver is the limiting element in the system, and the extra power-handling *capability* of the final, due to heavier loading, is wasted by inability of the driver to do it justice.

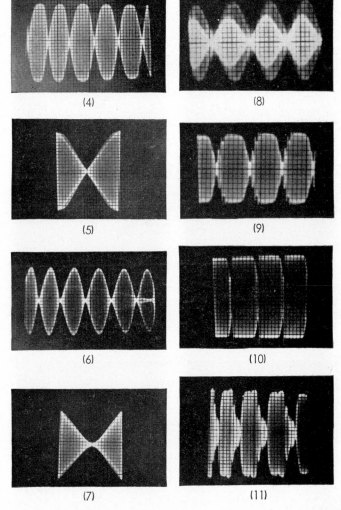

(4)

(8)

(5)

(9)

(6)

(10)

(7)

(11)

Fig. 11-17—*Improper Amplifier Operation.* 4—Overdrive, indicated by flattening of peaks. 5—Same as 4, double-trapezoid test. 6—Too much bias, causing crossover to become pinched together rather than cutting straight across center line. 7—Same as 6, double-trapezoid test. 8—Two-tone test with v.h.f. parasitics. Note fuzzy halo or fringe. In milder cases the fuzziness will appear just at the peaks. 9—Two-tone test with fundamental frequency parasitics, accompanied by overdrive. 10—Severe overdrive and parasitics. 11—Voice pattern showing flattening of peaks due to overdrive. When flattening is apparent on the voice pattern, the case is a severe one.

1) For good efficiency, the final itself must be the limiting element in the power-handling capability of the system.

2) If the final is not being driven to its limit, it should be loaded less heavily until such is the case.

3) If the power level obtained above is less than should be expected, more driving power is needed.

There are several ways to tell whether or not the final is being driven to its limit. One way is to advance the drive until peak limiting is apparent in the output, then move the oscilloscope coupling link over to the driver plate tank and see whether or not the same limiting appears there. Another way is to decrease or increase the final loading slightly and note whether the limiting output level increases or decreases correspondingly. If it does not, the final is not controlling the system. Still another but similar method is to detune the final slightly while limiting is apparent, and if proper drive conditions prevail the pattern will improve when the amplifier plate is detuned.

The intermediate and driver stages will follow the same laws, except that what is called "loading" on a final is often referred to as "impedance matching" when going between tubes. More

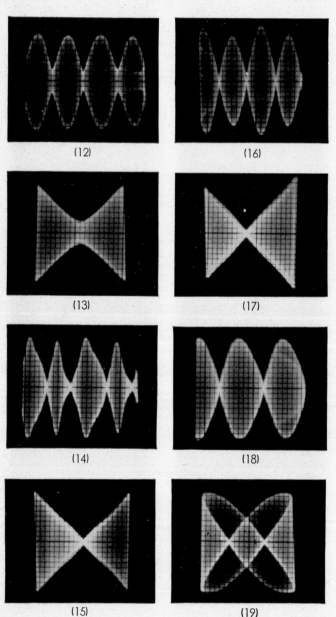

(12)   (16)

(13)   (17)

(14)   (18)

(15)   (19)

Fig. 11-18—*Improper Test Set-up* 12—Two r.f. signals unequal. in Method A, caused by improper settings of either carrier or audio control. Method B, either carrier leakage through disabled modulator or unequal sidebands due to selective action of some high-Q circuit off resonance. 13—Same as 12, double-trapezoid test (Method B). 14—Distorted audio. A clue to this defect is that successive waves are not identical. 15—Same distortion as 14, but switched to double trapezoid test pattern. Note that correct pattern prevails regardless of poor audio signal. 16—Carrier leakage through working modulator (Method B only). 17—Same as 16, double trapezoid. 18 —(Note tilt to left.) Caused by incomplete suppression of unwanted sideband (Method A) or by r.f. leakage into horizontal circuits of scope. 19—Double trapezoid with audio phase shift in test set-up.

Frequency Conversion

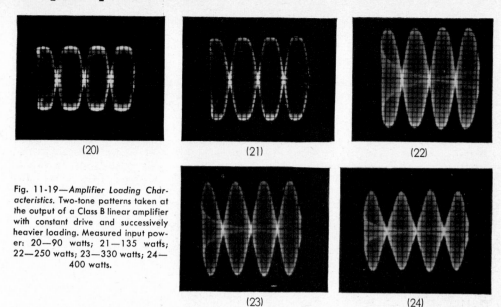

(20)   (21)   (22)

Fig. 11-19—*Amplifier Loading Characteristics.* Two-tone patterns taken at the output of a Class B linear amplifier with constant drive and successively heavier loading. Measured input power: 20—90 watts; 21—135 watts; 22—250 watts; 23—330 watts; 24—400 watts.

(23)   (24)

often than not, an apparent lack of power transfer from a driver to its succeeding stage is due to a poor match. In Class AB$_2$ or B service, a step-down type of coupling is required between power stages, and a person accustomed to the conventional plate-to-grid coupling capacitor technique will be surprised to find how effective it is to tap the driven stage down on its tank — or otherwise to decouple the system. For example, an 807 driving a pair of 811s requires a voltage step-down of about 3 or 4 to 1 from plate to each grid.

Dummy Load

For the sake of everyone concerned, linearity tests should be kept off the air as much as possible. They make quite a racket and spurious signals are plentiful in earlier stages of misadjustment. Ordinary lamp bulbs make a fine dummy load so long as it is recognized that their impedance is not exactly the same as the antenna and that this impedance changes somewhat as the bulbs light up. These factors can be taken into account by making careful note of plate and grid currents after the transmitter has been adjusted and is operating with a linearity test signal at maximum linear output into the lamp load. Then, having reconnected the regular antenna, the same loading conditions for the final will be reproduced by adjusting its tuning and loading until the identical combination of plate and grid currents can be obtained. This process will require only a few moments of on-the-air operation.

When the final on-the-air checks are made, it will be convenient to make a few reference marks on the oscilloscope screen to indicate the peak height of the pattern. The scope will then serve as a permanent output monitor for all operations. For best results the sweep should be set for about 30 cycles, in which case the voice patterns will stand out clearly and can easily be kept just within the reference lines. Incidentally, the pattern is really fascinating to watch.

Don't be a "meter bender." Input power isn't everything. If you have to cut your input in half to avoid overload, the fellow at the other end will hardly notice the difference in level. At the same time, your neighbors, both those on the ham band and those next door trying to watch TV, will appreciate the difference right away.

Frequency Conversion

The preferred s.s.b. transmitter is probably one that generates the s.s.b. signal at some suitable frequency and then heterodynes the signal into the desired amateur bands, although a few designs exist that generate the s.s.b. signal at the operating frequency and consequently eliminate the need for heterodyning. When the heterodyning is done at low level (involving an s.s.b. signal of not more than a few volts), standard receiving techniques are satisfactory. The converter tubes operated at manufacturer's rat- ings leave little to be desired.

When high-level heterodyning is required, as when an exciter delivering from 5 to 20 watts on a single band is available and multiband operation is desired, a high-level converter is used. Since the efficiency of a converter is only about one-fourth that of the same tube or tubes used in Class AB$_2$, using a converter stage as the output stage is not very economical, and the high-level converter is generally used to drive the output stage.

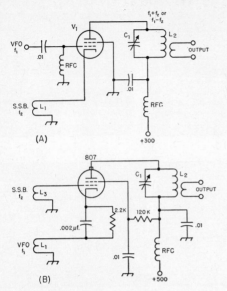

Fig. 11-20—Two examples of "high-level" mixer circuits.
The circuit at A has been used with 6V6, 6L6, 6AQ5 and 6Y6 type tubes. With 300 volts on the plate the idling current is about 15 ma., kicking as high as 30 ma. with the s.s.b. signal.

The circuit in B operates with a positive screen voltage and some cathode bias, and is capable of somewhat more output than the circuit shown in A.

In either case the output circuit, C_1L_2, is tuned to the sum or difference frequency of the oscillator and s.s.b. signal. Coupling coils L_1 and L_3 will usually be three or four turns coupled to their respective driving sources.

Reference to tube manuals will disclose no information of the operation of small transmitting tubes as mixers. However, it has been found that most of the tetrodes in the 15- to 35-watt plate-dissipation class make acceptable mixers, and tubes like the 6V6, 6L6, 807 and 6146 have been used successfully. The usual procedure is to feed one of the signals (oscillator or s.s.b.) to the control grid and the other to the cathode or screen grid. Typical circuits are shown in Fig. 11-20.

(Suggestions for converting to and operating in the 50- and 144-Mc. bands can be found in Tilton, "Single-Sideband Ideas for the V.H.F. Man," *QST*, May, 1957.)

● **VOICE-CONTROLLED BREAK-IN**

Although it is possible for two s.s.b. stations operating on widely different frequencies to work "duplex" if the carrier suppression is great enough (inadequate carrier suppression would be a violation of the FCC rules), most s.s.b. operators prefer to use voice-controlled break-in and operate on the same frequency. This overcomes any possibility of violating the FCC rules and permits "round table" operation.

Many various sytems of voice-controlled break-in are in use, but they are all basically the same. Some of the audio from the speech amplifier

is amplified and rectified, and the resultant d.c. signal is used to key an oscillator and one or more stages in the s.s.b. transmitter and "blank" the receiver at the time that the transmitter is on. Thus the transmitter is on at any and all times that the operator is speaking but is off during the intervals between sentences. The voice-control circuit must have a small amount of "hold" built into it, so that it will hold in between words, but it should be made to turn on rapidly at the slightest voice signal coming through the speech amplifier. Both tube and relay keyers have been used with good success. Some voice-control systems require the use of headphones by the operator, but a loudspeaker can be used with the proper circuit. (See Nowak, "Voice-Controlled Break-In . . . and a Loudspeaker," *QST*, May, 1951, and Hunter, "Simplified Voice Control with a Loudspeaker," *QST*, October, 1953.)

If an antenna relay is used to switch the antenna from the receiver to the transmitter and back again, it is often possible to operate the output linear amplifier stage with some idling current and experience no difficulty with the "diode noise" generated by the amplifier plate current. However, when the receiver, transmitter and antenna are always connected together, as when an electronic transmit-receive switch is used (see Chapter Eight), weak signals will not be heard through the diode noise of the transmitter. To overcome this difficulty, the idling current of the amplifier must be reduced to zero during listening periods. This can be accomplished through the use of the circuit in Fig. 11-21. Here

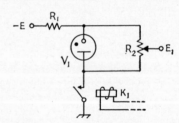

Fig. 11-21—Bias-switching circuit for use with a Class AB$_1$ linear amplifier and an electronic t.r. switch.

R_1—4700 ohms, 1 watt.
R_2—100,000 ohms, 2 watts.
K_1—VOX relay or relay controlled by VOX circuit.
V_1—0A2 or 0B2, depending upon amplifier requirements.

K_1 is a relay controlled by the voice-controlled break-in circuit. When the relay is closed, the operating bias E_1 for the linear amplifier is determined by the setting of the arm on R_2. When the relay is open, the grid bias jumps to the value E, which should be high enough to cut off the amplifier stage. The voltage regulator tube should be one with a nominal voltage drop in excess of the normal bias for the amplifier tube, and the negative supply voltage E should be at least 25 per cent higher than the ignition potential of the VR tube. The circuit in Fig. 11-21 is applicable to Class AB$_1$ amplifiers; it cannot be used when grid current is drawn during operation.

Receiving Suppressed-Carrier Signals

Restriction of Audio Range

In either type of s.s.b. generator, it is good practice to restrict the frequency range of the audio amplifier. In the filter-type exciter, reducing the response below 300 or 400 cycles makes it easier for the filter to eliminate the unwanted side frequencies below this range. In the phasing-type exciter, restricting the range of the audio amplifier to the frequencies at which the network gives its best performance (usually about 300 to 3000 cycles) reduces the possibility of generating unwanted side frequencies outside this range. High-frequency audio cut-off is not as important in the filter-type exciter because the filter takes care of the higher frequencies.

When a restricted audio range is used, it is a good idea to make a number of checks on the system, in an effort to obtain the best compromise between naturalness and intelligibility. Voice characteristics differ from operator to operator, and it is sometimes preferable to accentuate the "highs" slightly to give better intelligibility. No standards can be given here — it is a subject for experimentation and checking under varied conditions.

The simplest means for reducing the low-frequency response in the audio amplifier is to reduce the values of the coupling capacitors. High-frequency response can be reduced by adding capacitance across grid resistors. More elaborate means require the use of filters using inductance and capacitance combinations.

Receiving Suppressed-Carrier Signals

The reception of suppressed-carrier signals requires that the carrier be accurately reinserted at the receiver. In addition, the reception of a double-sideband suppressed-carrier signal requires that one sideband be filterd off in the receiver before demodulation or that a special type of converter be used. Because little or no carrier is transmitted, the usual a.v.c. in the receiver has nothing that indicates the average signal level, and this fact requires either manual variation of the r.f. gain control or the use of a special a.v.c. system. (As, for example, Luick, "Improved A.V.C. for Sideband and C.W.," *QST*, October, 1957.)

A suppressed-carrier signal can be identified by the absence of a strong carrier and by the severe variation of the S meter at a syllabic rate. When such a signal is encountered, it should first be peaked with the main tuning dial. (This centers the signal in the i.f. pass band.) After this operation, do not touch the main tuning dial. Then set the r.f. gain control at a very low level and switch off the a.v.c. Increase the audio volume control to maximum, and bring up the r.f. gain control until the signal can be heard weakly. Switch on the beat oscillator, and carefully adjust the frequency of the beat oscillator until proper speech is heard. If there is a slight amount of carrier present, it is only necessary to *zero-beat* the beat oscillator with this weak carrier. It will be noticed that with incorrect tuning of an s.s.b. signal, the speech will sound high- or low-pitched or even inverted (very garbled), but no trouble will be had in getting the correct setting once a little experience has been obtained. The use of minimum r.f. gain and maximum audio gain will insure that no distortion (overload) occurs in the receiver. It may require a readjustment of your tuning habits to tune the receiver slowly enough during the first few trials.

Once the proper setting of the b.f.o. has been established by the procedure above, all further tuning should be done with the main tuning control. However, it is not unlikely that s.s.b. stations will be encountered that are transmitting the other sideband, and to receive them will require shifting the b.f.o. setting to the other side of the receiver i.f. passband. The initial tuning procedure is exactly the same as outlined above, except that you will end up with a considerably different b.f.o. setting. The two b.f.o. settings should be noted for further reference, and all tuning of s.s.b. signals can then be done with the main tuning dial. With experience, it becomes a simple matter to determine which way to tune to make the signal sound lower- or higher-pitched if receiver (or transmitter) drifts off.

When a double sideband suppressed-carrier signal is received, sufficient selectivity will be required in the receiver to eliminate one sideband and convert the signal into a single-sideband signal before detection, where it can be received by the method outlined above. Receiver bandwidths of 3 kc. or less will be required for this purpose, or the use of a "Signal Slicer," a selectivity device that uses the phasing principle. (See *GE Ham News*, Vol. 6, No. 4, July, 1951.)

Newcomers to single sideband often wonder if there is any device that can be added to a receiver that will make the tuning of sideband signals less critical. At the present time there is no device that will "lock in" automatically. However, if the receiver is lacking in selectivity, an apparent improvement can be obtained by using an adapter that adds selectivity to the receiving system. No improvement in ease of tuning will be noticed on good sideband signals (good suppression of unwanted sideband), but fair or mediocre signals will be easier to tune. The reason is that the adapter makes a better sideband signal out of the incoming signal by removing the vestiges of the unwanted sideband, and a good sideband signal will tune easier than a fair one. The sideband adapters also usually have detectors designed for best detection of sideband signals, a point that was overlooked in some of the older receivers. Good detectors for sideband signals include diodes with *sufficient* b.f.o. injection (5 to 10 times peak signal) and "product detectors" (see Chapter Five). Either detector is capable of low distortion output if the input is held down.

● WHICH SIDEBAND?

It is sometimes confusing to remember how to identify, from the way your receiver tunes, which sideband the other station is using. This is especially awkward with those receivers in which the high-frequency oscillator is on the high-frequency side of the signal in some ranges and on the low side in others. With any receiver having sufficient selectivity to give a stronger signal on one side than on the other of zero beat, when the b.f.o. is offset to one side of the i.f., the chart below will help you identify which sideband is being transmitted. Set the b.f.o. to the side of the i.f. that you find is right for receiving single-sideband signals on a particular band. Then with the main dial tune through a steady carrier (or

the signal from your 100-kc. standard). Note which side of zero beat gives little or no signal.

If tuning through a steady carrier gives little or no signal on the	
High Frequency	*Low Frequency*
side of zero beat, and then if tuning the receiver to a *lower* frequency makes the voice of a single-sideband signal sound *lower* pitched, he is using the	
Lower	*Upper*
sideband.	

CHAPTER 12

Specialized Communication Systems

Frequency and Phase Modulation

It is possible to convey intelligence by modulating any property of a carrier, including its frequency and phase. When the frequency of the carrier is varied in accordance with the variations in a modulating signal, the result is **frequency modulation (f.m.)**. Similarly, varying the phase of the carrier current is called **phase modulation (p.m.)**.

Frequency and phase modulation are not independent, since the frequency cannot be varied without also varying the phase, and vice versa. The difference is largely a matter of definition.

The effectiveness of f.m. and p.m. for communication purposes depends almost entirely on the receiving methods. If the receiver will respond to frequency and phase changes but is insensitive to amplitude changes, it will discriminate against most forms of noise, particularly impulse noise such as is set up by ignition systems and other sparking devices. Special methods of detection are required to accomplish this result.

Modulation methods for f.m. and p.m. are simple and require practically no audio power. There is also the advantage that, since there is no amplitude variation in the signal, interference to broadcast reception resulting from rectification of the transmitted signal in the audio circuits of the BC receiver is substantially eliminated. These two points represent the principal reasons for the use of f.m. and p.m. in amateur work.

Frequency Modulation

Fig. 12-1 is a representation of frequency

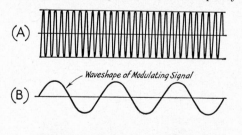

Fig. 12-1—Graphical representation of frequency modulation. In the unmodulated carrier at A, each r.f. cycle occupies the same amount of time. When the modulating signal, B, is applied, the radio frequency is increased and decreased according to the amplitude and polarity of the modulating signal.

modulation. When a modulating signal is applied, the carrier frequency is increased during one half-cycle of the modulating signal and decreased during the half-cycle of opposite polarity. This is indicated in the drawing by the fact that the r.f. cycles occupy less time (higher frequency) when the modulating signal is positive, and more time (lower frequency) when the modulating signal is negative. The change in the carrier frequency **(frequency deviation)** is proportional to the instantaneous amplitude of the modulating signal, so the deviation is small when the instantaneous amplitude of the modulating signal is small, and is greatest when the modulating signal reaches its peak, either positive or negative.

As shown by the drawing, the amplitude of the signal does not change during modulation.

Phase Modulation

If the phase of the current in a circuit is changed there is an instantaneous frequency change during the time that the phase is being shifted. The amount of frequency change, or deviation, depends on how rapidly the phase shift is accomplished. It is also dependent upon the total amount of the phase shift. In a properly operating p.m. system the amount of phase shift is proportional to the instantaneous amplitude of the modulating signal. The rapidity of the phase shift is directly proportional to the frequency of the modulating signal. Consequently, the frequency deviation in p.m. is proportional to both the amplitude and frequency of the modulating signal. The latter represents the outstanding difference between f.m. and p.m., since in f.m. the frequency deviation is proportional only to the amplitude of the modulating signal.

Modulation Depth

Percentage of modulation in f.m. and p.m. has to be defined differently than for a.m. Practically, "100 per cent modulation" is reached when the transmitted signal occupies a channel just equal to the bandwidth for which the *receiver* is designed. If the frequency deviation is greater than the receiver can accept, the receiver distorts the signal. However, on another receiver designed for a different bandwidth the same signal might be equivalent to only 25 per cent modulation.

In amateur work "narrow-band" f.m. or p.m. (frequently abbreviated n.f.m.) is defined as having the same channel width as a properly modulated a.m. signal. That is, the effective channel width does not exceed twice the highest

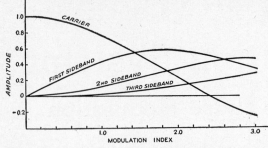

Fig. 12-2—How the amplitude of the pairs of sidebands varies with the modulation index in an f.m. or p.m. signal. If the curves were extended for greater values of modulation index it would be seen that the carrier amplitude goes through zero at several points. The same statement also applies to the sidebands.

audio frequency in the modulating signal. N.f.m. transmissions based on an upper audio limit of 3000 cycles therefore should occupy a channel not significantly wider than 6 kc.

F.M. and P.M. Sidebands

The sidebands set up by f.m. and p.m. differ from those resulting from a.m. in that they occur at integral multiples of the modulating frequency on either side of the carrier rather than, as in a.m., consisting of a single set of side frequencies for each modulating frequency. An f.m. or p.m. signal therefore inherently occupies a wider channel than a.m.

The number of "extra" sidebands that occur in f.m. and p.m. depends on the relationship between the modulating frequency and the frequency deviation. The ratio between the frequency deviation, in cycles per second, and the modulating frequency, also in cycles per second, is called the **modulation index**. That is,

$$Modulation\ index = \frac{Carrier\ frequency\ deviation}{Modulating\ frequency}$$

Example: The maximum frequency deviation in an f.m. transmitter is 3000 cycles either side of the carrier frequency. The modulation index when the modulating frequency is 1000 cycles is

$$Modulation\ index = \frac{3000}{1000} = 3$$

At the same deviation with 3000-cycle modulation the index would be 1; at 100 cycles it would be 30, and so on.

In p.m. the modulation index is constant regardless of the modulating frequency; in f.m. it varies with the modulating frequency, as shown in the above example. In an f.m. system the ratio of the *maximum* carrier-frequency deviation to the *highest* modulating frequency used is called the **deviation ratio**.

Fig. 12-2 shows how the amplitudes of the carrier and the various sidebands vary with the modulation index. This is for single-tone modulation; the first sideband (actually a pair, one above and one below the carrier) is displaced from the carrier by an amount equal to the modulating frequency, the second is twice the modulating frequency away from the carrier, and so on. For example, if the modulating frequency is 2000 cycles and the carrier frequency is 29,500 kc., the first sideband pair is at 29,498 kc. and 29,502 kc., the second pair is at 29,496 kc. and 29,504 kc., the third at 29,494 kc. and 29,506 kc., etc. The amplitudes of these sidebands depend on the

modulation index, not on the frequency deviation.

Note that, as shown by Fig. 12-2, the carrier strength varies with the modulation index. (In amplitude modulation the carrier strength is constant; only the sideband amplitude varies.) At a modulation index of approximately 2.4 the carrier disappears entirely. It then becomes "negative" at a higher index, meaning that its phase is reversed as compared to the phase without modulation. In f.m. and p.m. the energy that goes into the sidebands is taken from the carrier, the *total* power remaining the same regardless of the modulation index.

Frequency Multiplication

Since there is no change in amplitude with modulation, an f.m. or p.m. signal can be amplified without distortion by an ordinary Class C amplifier. The modulation can take place in a very low-level stage and the signal can then be amplified by either frequency multipliers or straight amplifiers.

If the modulated signal is passed through one or more frequency multipliers, the modulation index is multiplied by the same factor that the carrier frequency is multiplied. For example, if modulation is applied on 3.5 Mc. and the final output is on 28 Mc. the total frequency multiplication is 8 times, so if the frequency deviation is 500 cycles at 3.5 Mc. it will be 4000 cycles at 28 Mc. Frequency multiplication offers a means for obtaining practically any desired amount of frequency deviation, whether or not the modulator itself is capable of giving that much deviation without distortion.

Narrow-Band F.M. and P.M.

"Narrow-band" f.m. or p.m., the only type that is authorized by FCC for use on the lower frequencies where the phone bands are crowded, is defined as f.m. or p.m. that does not occupy a wider channel than an a.m. signal having the same audio modulating frequencies.

If the modulation index (with single-tone modulation) does not exceed 0.6 or 0.7, the most important extra sideband, the second, will be at least 20 db. below the unmodulated carrier level, and this should represent an effective channel width about equivalent to that of an a.m. signal. In the case of speech, a somewhat higher modulation index can be used. This is because the energy distribution in a complex wave is such that the modulation index for any one frequency com-

Frequency and Phase Modulation

ponent is reduced, as compared to the index with a sine wave having the same peak amplitude as the voice wave.

The chief advantage of narrow-band f.m. or p.m. for frequencies below 30 Mc. is that it eliminates or reduces certain types of interference to broadcast reception. Also, the modulating equipment is relatively simple and inexpensive. However, assuming the same unmodulated carrier power in all cases, narrow-band f.m. or p.m. is not as effective as a.m. with the methods of reception used by most amateurs. As shown by Fig. 12-2, at an index of 0.6 the amplitude of the first sideband is about 25 per cent of the unmodulated-carrier amplitude; this compares with a sideband amplitude of 50 per cent in the case of a 100 per cent modulated a.m. transmitter. So far as effectiveness is concerned, a narrowband f.m. or p.m. transmitter is about equivalent to a 100 per cent modulated a.m. transmitter operating at one-fourth the carrier power.

Comparison of F.M. and P.M.

Frequency modulation cannot be applied to an amplifier stage, but phase modulation can; p.m. is therefore readily adaptable to transmitters employing oscillators of high stability such as the crystal-controlled type. The amount of phase shift that can be obtained with good linearity is such that the maximum practicable modulation index is about 0.5. Because the phase shift is proportional to the modulating frequency, this index can be used only at the highest frequency present in the modulating signal, assuming that all frequencies will at one time or another have equal amplitudes. Taking 3000 cycles as a suitable upper limit for voice work, and setting the modulation index at 0.5 for 3000 cycles, the frequency response of the speech-amplifier system above 3000 cycles must be sharply attenuated, to prevent sideband splatter. Also, if the "tinny" quality of p.m. as received on an f.m. receiver is to be avoided, the p.m. must be changed to f.m., in which the modulation index decreases in inverse proportion to the modulating frequency. This requires shaping the speech-amplifier frequency-response curve in such a way that the output voltage is inversely proportional to frequency over most of the voice range. When this is done the maximum modulation index can only be used at some relatively low audio frequency, perhaps 300 to 400 cycles in voice transmission, and must decrease in proportion to the increase in frequency. The result is that the maximum linear frequency deviation is only one or two hundred cycles, when p.m. is changed to f.m. To increase the deviation for n.f.m. requires a frequency multiplication of 8 times or more.

It is relatively easy to secure a fairly large frequency deviation when a self-controlled oscillator is frequency-modulated directly. (True frequency modulation of a crystal-controlled oscillator results in only very small deviations and so requires a great deal of frequency multiplication.) The chief problem is to maintain a satisfactory degree of carrier stability, since the greater the inherent stability of the oscillator the more difficult it is to secure a wide frequency swing with linearity.

Methods of Frequency and Phase Modulation

A simple and satisfactory device for producing f.m. in the amateur transmitter is the reactance modulator. This is a vacuum tube connected to the r.f. tank circuit of an oscillator in such a way as to act as a variable inductance or capacitance.

Fig. 12-3 is a representative circuit. The control grid of the modulator tube, V_2, is connected across the oscillator tank circuit, C_1L_1, through resistor R_1 and blocking capacitor C_2. C_8 represents the input capacitance of the modulator tube. The resistance of R_1 is made large compared to the reactance of C_8, so the r.f. current through R_1C_8 will be practically in phase with the r.f. voltage appearing at the terminals of the tank circuit. However, the voltage across C_8 will lag the current by 90 degrees. The r.f. current in the plate circuit of the modulator will be in phase with the grid voltage, and consequently is 90 degrees behind the current through C_8, or 90 degrees behind the r.f. tank voltage. This lagging current is drawn through the oscillator tank, giving the same effect as though an inductance were connected across the tank. The frequency increases in proportion to the amplitude of the lagging plate current of the modulator. The audio voltage, introduced through a radio-frequency choke, RFC_1, varies the transconductance of the tube and thereby varies the r.f. plate current.

The modulated oscillator usually is operated on a relatively low frequency, so that a high order of carrier stability can be secured. Frequency multipliers are used to raise the frequency to the final frequency desired.

A reactance modulator can be connected to a crystal oscillator as well as to the self-controlled type. However, the resulting signal is more phase-modulated than it is frequency-modulated, for the reason that the frequency deviation that can be secured by varying the tuning of a crystal oscillator is quite small.

Design Considerations

The sensitivity of the modulator (frequency change per unit change in grid voltage) depends on the transconductance of the modulator tube. It increases when R_1 is made smaller in comparison with C_8. It also increases with an increase in L/C ratio in the oscillator tank circuit. However, for highest carrier stability it is desirable to use the largest tank capacitance that will permit the desired deviation to be secured while keeping within the limits of linear operation.

A change in any of the voltages on the modu-

325

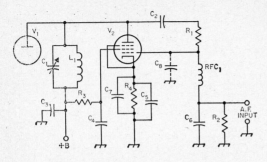

lator tube will cause a change in r.f. plate current, and consequently a frequency change. Therefore it is advisable to use a regulated plate power supply for both modulator and oscillator. At the low voltage used (250 volts or less) the required stabilization can be secured by means of gaseous regulator tubes.

Speech Amplification

The speech amplifier preceding the modulator follows ordinary design, except that no power is taken from it and the a.f. voltage required by the modulator grid usually is small — not more than 10 or 15 volts, even with large modulator tubes. Because of these modest requirements, only a few speech stages are needed; a two-stage amplifier consisting of a pentode followed by a triode, both resistance-coupled, will more than suffice for crystal microphones.

● PHASE MODULATION

The same type of reactance-tube circuit that is used to vary the tuning of the oscillator tank in f.m. can be used to vary the tuning of an amplifier tank and thus vary the phase of the tank current for p.m. Hence the modulator circuit of Fig. 12-3 can be used for p.m. if the reactance tube works on an amplifier tank instead of directly on a self-controlled oscillator.

The phase shift that occurs when a circuit is detuned from resonance depends on the amount of detuning and the Q of the circuit. The higher the Q, the smaller the amount of detuning needed to secure a given number of degrees of phase shift. If the Q is at least 10, the relationship between phase shift and detuning (in kilocycles either side of the resonant frequency) will be sub-

stantially linear over a phase-shift range of about 25 degrees. From the standpoint of modulator sensitivity, the Q of the tuned circuit on which the modulator operates should be as high as possible. On the other hand, the effective Q of the circuit will not be very high if the amplifier is delivering power to a load since the load resistance reduces the Q. There must therefore be a compromise between modulator sensitivity and r.f. power output from the modulated amplifier. An optimum figure for Q appears to be about 20; this allows reasonable loading of the modulated amplifier and the necessary tuning variation can be secured from a reactance modulator without difficulty. It is advisable to modulate at a very low power level — preferably in a stage where receiving-type tubes are used.

Reactance modulation of an amplifier stage usually also results in simultaneous amplitude modulation because the modulated stage is detuned from resonance as the phase is shifted. This must be eliminated by feeding the modulated signal through an amplitude limiter or one or more "saturating" stages — that is, amplifiers that are operated Class C and driven hard enough so that variations in the amplitude of the grid excitation produce no appreciable variations in the final output amplitude.

For the same type of reactance modulator, the speech-amplifier gain required is the same for p.m. as for f.m. However, as pointed out earlier, the fact that the actual frequency deviation increases with the modulating audio frequency in p.m. makes it necessary to cut off the frequencies above about 3000 cycles before modulation takes place. If this is not done, unnecessary sidebands will be generated at frequencies considerably away from the carrier.

Checking F.M. and P.M. Transmitters

Accurate checking of the operation of an f.m. or p.m. transmitter requires different methods than the corresponding checks on an a.m. set. This is because the common forms of measuring devices either indicate amplitude variations only (a d.c. milliammeter, for example), or because their indications are most easily interpreted in terms of amplitude. There is no simple measuring instrument that indicates frequency deviation directly.

However, there is one favorable feature in f.m. or p.m. checking. The modulation takes place at a very low level and the stages following the one that is modulated do not affect the linearity of modulation so long as they are properly tuned. Therefore the modulation may be checked *without putting the transmitter on the air*, or even on a dummy antenna. The power is simply cut off the amplifiers following the modulated stage. This not only avoids unneces-

Frequency and Phase Modulation

sary interference to other stations during testing periods, but also keeps the signal at such a low level that it may be observed quite easily on the station receiver. A good receiver with a crystal filter is an essential part of the checking equipment of an f.m. or p.m. transmitter, particularly for narrow-band f.m. or p.m.

The quantities to be checked in an f.m. or p.m. transmitter are the linearity and frequency deviation. Because of the essential difference between f.m. and p.m. the methods of checking differ in detail.

Reactance-Tube F.M.

It is possible to calibrate a reactance modulator by applying an adjustable d.c. voltage to the modulator grid and noting the change in oscillator frequency as the voltage is varied. A suitable circuit for applying the adjustable voltage is shown in Fig. 12-4. The battery should have a

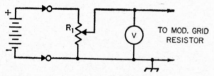

Fig. 12-4—D.c. method of checking frequency deviation of a reactance-tube-modulated oscillator. A 500- or 1000-ohm potentiometer may be used at R_1.

voltage of 3 to 6 volts (two or more dry cells in series). The arrows indicate clip connections so that the battery polarity can be reversed.

The oscillator frequency deviation should be measured by using a receiver in conjunction with an accurately calibrated frequency meter, or by any means that will permit accurate measurement of frequency differences of a few hundred cycles. One simple method is to tune in the oscillator on the receiver (disconnecting the receiving antenna, if necessary, to keep the signal strength well below the overload point) and then set the receiver b.f.o. to zero beat. Then increase the d.c. voltage applied to the modulator grid from zero in steps of about $\frac{1}{2}$ volt and note the beat frequency at each change. Then reverse the battery terminals and repeat. The frequency of the beat note may be measured by comparison with a calibrated audio-frequency oscillator. Note that with the battery polarity positive with respect to ground the radio frequency will move in one direction when the voltage is increased, and in the other direction when the battery terminals are reversed. When several readings have been taken a curve may be plotted to demonstrate the relationship between grid voltage and frequency deviation.

A sample curve is shown in Fig. 12-5. The usable portion of the curve is the center part which is essentially a straight line. The bending at the ends indicates that the modulator is no longer linear; this departure from linearity will cause harmonic distortion and will broaden the channel occupied by the signal. In the example, the characteristic is linear 1.5 kc. on

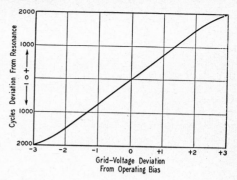

Fig. 12-5—A typical curve of frequency deviation vs. modulator grid voltage.

either side of the center or carrier frequency.

A good modulation indicator is a "magic-eye" tube such as the 6E5. This should be connected across the grid resistor of the reactance modulator as shown in Fig. 12-6. Note its deflection (using the d.c. voltage method as in Fig. 12-4) at the maximum deviation to be used. For narrow-band f.m. the proper deviation is approximately 2000 cycles (this maximum deviation is based on an upper a.f. limit of 3000 cycles and a deviation ratio of 0.7) at the *output* frequency. This deflection represents "100 per cent modulation" and with speech input the gain should be kept at the point where it is just reached on voice peaks. If the transmitter is used on more than one band, the gain control should be marked at the proper setting for

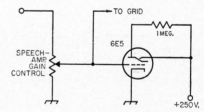

Fig. 12-6—6E5 modulation indicator for f.m. or p.m. modulators. To insure sufficient grid voltage for a good deflection, it may be necessary to connect the gain control in the modulator grid circuit rather than in an earlier speech-amplifier stage.

each band, because the signal amplitude that gives the correct deviation on one band will be either too great or too small on another. For example, if the output frequency is in the 29-Mc. band and the oscillator is on 7 Mc., the deviation at the *oscillator* frequency should not exceed 2000/4, or 500 cycles.

Checking with a Crystal-Filter Receiver

With p.m. the d.c. method of checking just described cannot be used, because the frequency deviation at zero frequency (d.c.) also is zero. For narrow-band p.m. it is necessary to check the actual width of the channel occupied by the transmission. (The same method also can be used to check f.m.) For this purpose it is necessary to have a crystal-filter receiver and an a.f. oscillator that generates a 3000-cycle sine wave.

Keeping the signal intensity in the receiver at a medium level, tune in the carrier at the *output* frequency. Do not use the a.v.c. Switch on the beat oscillator, and set the crystal filter at its sharpest position. Peak the signal on the crystal and adjust the b.f.o. for any convenient beat note. Then apply the 3000-cycle tone to the speech amplifier (through an attenuator, if necessary, to avoid overloading; see chapter on audio amplifiers) and increase the audio gain until there is a small amount of modulation. Tuning the receiver near the carrier frequency will show the presence of sidebands 3 kc. from the carrier on both sides. With low audio input, these two should be the only sidebands detectable.

Now increase the audio gain and tune the receiver over a range of about 10 kc. on both sides of the carrier. When the gain becomes high enough, a second set of sidebands spaced 6 kc. on either side of the carrier will be detected. The signal amplitude at which these sidebands become detectable is the maximum speech amplitude that should be used. If the 6E5 modulation indicator is incorporated in the modulator, its deflection with the 3000-cycle tone will be the "100 per cent modulation" deflection for speech.

When this method of checking is used with a reactance-tube-modulated f.m. (not p.m.) transmitter, the linearity of the system can be checked by observing the *carrier* as the a.f. gain is slowly increased. The beat-note frequency will stay constant so long as the modulator is linear, but nonlinearity will be accompanied by a shift in the average carrier frequency that will cause the beat note to change in frequency. If such a shift occurs at the same time that the 6-kc. sidebands appear, the extra sidebands may be caused by modulator distortion rather than by an excessive modulation

index. This means that the modulator is not capable of shifting the frequency over a wide-enough range. The 6-kc. sidebands should appear *before* there is any shift in the carrier frequency.

R.F. Amplifiers

The r.f. stages in the transmitter that follow the modulated stage may be designed and adjusted as in ordinary operation. In fact, there are no special requirements to be met except that all tank circuits should be carefully tuned to resonance (to prevent unwanted r.f. phase shifts that might interact with the modulation and thereby introduce hum, noise and distortion). In neutralized stages, the neutralization should be as exact as possible, also to minimize unwanted phase shifts. With f.m. and p.m., all r.f. stages in the transmitter can be operated at the manufacturer's maximum c.w.-telegraphy ratings, since the average power input does not vary with modulation as it does in a.m. phone operation.

The output power of the transmitter should be checked for amplitude modulation. It should not change from the unmodulated-carrier value when the transmitter is modulated. If no output indicator is available, a flashlight lamp and loop can be coupled to the final tank coil to serve as a current indicator. If the carrier amplitude is constant, the lamp brilliance will not change with modulation.

Amplitude modulation accompanying f.m. or p.m. is just as much to be avoided as frequency or phase modulation that accompanies a.m. A mixture of a.m. with either of the other two systems results in the generation of spurious sidebands and consequent widening of the channel. If the presence of a.m. is indicated by variation of antenna current with modulation, the cause is almost certain to be nonlinearity in the modulator.

Reception of F.M. and P.M. Signals

Receivers for f.m. and p.m. signals differ from those for a.m. and s.s.b. principally in two features — there is no need for linearity in the amplifier stages preceding detection (in fact, it is advantageous if the amplitude variations in the signal and background noise can be "washed out"), and the detector must be capable of converting the frequency variations in the incoming signal into amplitude variations. These amplitude variations, combined with rectification, produce an audio voltage corresponding to the frequency or phase modulation on the signal.

Frequency- or phase-modulated signals can be received after a fashion on any ordinary receiver that has a selectivity curve with sloping sides. As shown in Fig. 12-7A, the receiver is tuned so that the carrier frequency is placed part-way down on one side of the selectivity curve so that the amplitude is less than the maximum that would be

possible with normal tuning. When the frequency of the signal varies with modulation it swings between some such limits as are indicated in Fig. 12-7A, resulting in an amplitude-modulated output varying between X and Y. After this f.m.-to-a.m. conversion the signal goes to a conventional detector (usually a diode) and is rectified in the same way as an a.m. signal.

With most receivers, particularly those having steep-sided selectivity curves, the method is not very satisfactory because the distortion is quite severe unless the frequency deviation is small, because the relationship between frequency deviation and output amplitude is linear over only a small part of the selectivity curve.

A detector designed expressly for f.m. or p.m. will have a characteristic similar to that shown in Fig. 12-7B. The output is zero when the unmodulated carrier is tuned to the center, O, of

Frequency and Phase Modulation

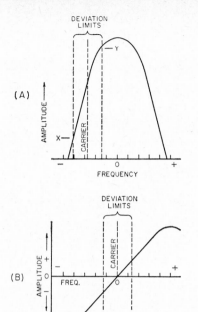

Fig. 12-7—F.m. or p.m. detection characteristics. A—"Slope detection," using the sloping side of the receiver's selectivity curve to convert f.m. or p.m. to a.m. for subsequent rectification. B—Typical discriminator characteristic. The straight portion of this curve between the two peaks is the useful region. The peaks should always lie outside the pass band of the receiver's selectivity curve.

the characteristic. When the frequency swings higher, the rectified output amplitude increases in the positive direction (as chosen in this example), and when the frequency swings lower the output amplitude increases in the negative direction. Over the range in which the characteristic is a straight line the conversion from f.m. to a.m. is linear and there is no distortion. One type of detector that operates in this way is the fre-

quency discriminator, which combines the f.m.-to-a.m. conversion with rectification to give an audio-frequency output from the frequency-modulated r.f. signal.

Limiter and Discriminator

A practical discriminator circuit is shown in Fig. 12-8. The f.m.-to-a.m. conversion takes place in transformer T_1, which operates at the intermediate frequency of a superheterodyne receiver. The voltage induced in the transformer secondary, S, is 90 degrees out of phase with the primary current. The primary voltage is introduced at the center tap on the secondary through C_1 and combines with the secondary voltages on each side of the center tap in such a way that the resultant voltage on one side of the secondary leads the primary voltage and the voltage on the other side lags by the same phase angle, when the circuits are resonated to the unmodulated carrier frequency. When rectified, these two voltages are equal and of opposite polarity. If the frequency changes, there is a shift in the relative phase of the voltage components that results in an increase in output amplitude on one side of the secondary and a corresponding decrease in amplitude on the other side. Thus the voltage applied to one diode of V_2 increases while the voltage applied to the other diode decreases. The difference between these two voltages, after rectification, is the audio-frequency output of the detector.

The output amplitude of a simple discriminator depends on the amplitude of the input r.f. signal, which is undesirable because the noise-reducing benefits of f.m. are not secured if the receiving system is sensitive to amplitude variations. A discriminator is always preceded by some form of amplitude limiting, therefore. The conventional type of limiter also is shown in Fig. 12-8. It is simply a pentode i.f. amplifier, V_1, with its operating conditions chosen so that it "saturates" on a relatively small signal voltage. The limiting action is aided by grid rectification, with grid-leak

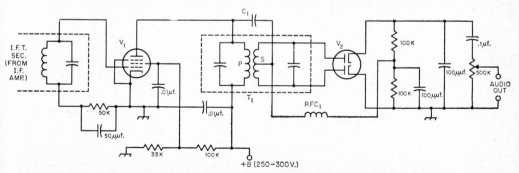

Fig. 12-8—Limiter-discriminator circuit. This type of circuit is frequently used at 455 kc. in the form of an "adapter" for communications receivers, for reception of narrow-band f.m. signals.

C₁—App. 100 μμf. for 455-kc. i.f.; 50 μμf. for higher frequencies.

T₁—Discriminator transformer for intermediate frequency used. Push-pull diode transformer may be substituted.

RFC₁—10 mh. r.f. choke for 455-kc. i.f.; 2.5 mh. satisfactory for frequencies above 3 Mc.

V₁—6AU6 or equivalent.

V₂—6AL5 or equivalent.

bias developed in the 50,000-ohm resistor in the grid circuit. Another contributing factor is low screen voltage, the screen voltage-divider constants being chosen to result in about 50 volts on the screen.

Receiver Tuning with an F.M. Detector

In tuning a signal with a receiver having a discriminator or other type of f.m. detector the tuning controls should be adjusted to center the carrier on the detector characteristic. At this point the noise suppression is most marked, so the proper setting is easily recognized. An amplitude-modulated signal tuned at the same point will have its modulation "washed off" if the signal is completely limited in amplitude and the discriminator alignment is symmetrical. With either f.m. or a.m. signals, there will be a distorted audio-frequency output if the receiver is tuned "off center."

Radioteletype

Radioteletype (abbreviated **RTTY**) is a form of telegraphic communication employing typewriter-like machines for 1) generating a coded set of electrical impulses when a typewriter key corresponding to the desired letter or symbol is pressed, and 2) converting a received set of such impulses into the corresponding printed character. The message to be sent is typed out in much the same way that it would be written on a typewriter, but the printing is done at the distant receiving point. The teletypewriter at the sending point also prints the same material, for checking and reference.

The machines used for RTTY are far too complex mechanically for home construction, and if purchased new would be highly expensive. However, used teletypewriters in good mechanical condition are available at quite reasonable prices. These are machines retired from commercial service but capable of entirely satisfactory operation in amateur work. They may be obtained from a number of sources (latest information on this may be obtained from ARRL, West Hartford, Conn.) on condition that they will be used purely for amateur purposes and will not be re-sold for commercial use.

Types of Machines

There are two general types of machines, the **page printer** and the **tape printer**. The former prints on a paper roll about the same width as a business letterhead. The latter prints on paper tape, usually gummed on the reverse side so it may be cut to letter-size width and pasted on a sheet of paper in a series of lines. The page printer is the more common type in the equipment available to amateurs.

The operating speed of most machines is such that characters are sent at the rate of about 60 words per minute. Ordinary teletypewriters are of the **start-stop** variety, in which the pulse-forming mechanism (motor driven) is at rest until a typewriter key is depressed. At this time it begins operating, forms the proper pulse sequence, and then comes to rest again before the next key is depressed to form the following character. The receiving mechanism operates in similar fashion, being set into operation by the first pulse of the sequence from the transmitter. Thus, although the actual transmission speed cannot exceed about 60 w.p.m. it can be considerably slower, depending on the typing speed of the operator.

It is also possible to transmit by using perforated tape. This has the advantage that the complete message may be typed out in advance of actual transmission, at any convenient speed; when transmitted, however, it is sent at the machine's normal maximum speed. A special transmitting head and tape perforator are required for this process. A **reperforator** is a device that may be connected to the conventional teletypewriter for punching tape when the machine is operated in the regular way. It may thus be used either for an original message or for "taping" an incoming message for retransmission.

Teletype Code

In the special code used for teletype every character has five "elements" sent in sequence. Each element has two possible states, either "mark" or "space," which are indicated by different types of electrical impulses (i.e., mark might be indicated by a negative voltage and space by a positive voltage). In customary practice each element occupies a time of 22 milliseconds. In addition, there is an initial "start" element (space), also 22 milliseconds long, to set the transmitting and receiving mechanisms in operation, and a terminal "stop" element (mark) 31 milliseconds long, to shut down the operation and ready the machine for the next character.

This sequence is illustrated in Fig. 12-9, which

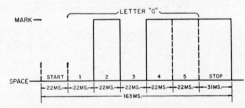

Fig. 12-9—Pulse sequence in the teletype code. Each character begins with a start pulse, always a "space," and ends with a "stop" pulse, always a "mark." The distribution of marks and spaces in the five elements between start and stop determines the particular character transmitted.

shows the letter G with its start and stop elements. The letter code as it would appear on perforated tape is shown in Fig. 12-10, where the black dots indicate marking pulses. Figures and arbitrary signs — punctuation, etc. — use the

Radioteletype

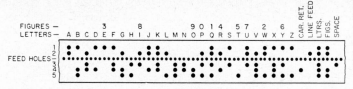

Fig. 12-10—Teletype letter code as it appears on perforated tape. Start and stop elements do not appear on tape. Elements are numbered from top to bottom, and dots indicate marking pulses. Numerals, punctuation signs, and other arbitrary symbols are secured by carriage shift.

There are no lower-case letters on a teletypewriter. Where blanks appear in the above chart in the "FIGS" line, characters may differ on different machines.

same set of code impulses as the alphabet, and are selected by shifting the carriage as in the case of an ordinary typewriter. The carriage shift is accomplished by transmitting either the "LTRS" or "FIGS" code symbol as required. There is also a "carriage return" code character to bring the carriage back to the starting position after the end of the line is reached on a page printer, and a "line feed" character to advance the page to the next line after a line is completed.

Additional System Requirements

To be used in radio communication, the pulses (d.c.) generated by the teletypewriter must be utilized in some way to key a radio transmitter so they may be sent in proper sequence and usable form to a distant point. At the receiving end the incoming signal must be converted into d.c. pulses suitable for operating the printer. These functions, shown in block form in Fig. 12-11, are

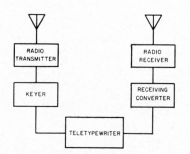

Fig. 12-11—Radioteletype system in block form.

performed by electronic units known respectively as the **keyer** and **receiving converter**.

The radio transmitter and receiver are quite conventional in design. Practically all the special features needed can be incorporated in the keyer and converter, so that any ordinary amateur equipment is suitable for RTTY with little modification.

Transmission Methods

It is quite possible to transmit teletype signals by ordinary "on-off" or "make-break" keying such as is used in regular hand-keyed c.w. transmission. In practice, however, **frequency-shift keying** is preferred because it gives definite pulses on both mark and space, which is an advantage in printer operation. Also, since f.s.k. can be received by methods similar to those used for f.m. reception, there is considerable discrimination against noise, both natural and man-made, distributed uniformly across the receiver's pass band, when the received signal is not too weak. Both factors make for increased reliability in printer operation.

Frequency-Shift Keying

General practice with f.s.k. is to use a frequency shift of 850 cycles per second, although FCC regulations permit the use of any value of frequency shift up to 900 cycles. The smaller values of shift have been shown to have a signal-to-noise-ratio advantage in commercial circuits, and are currently being experimented with by amateurs. At present, however, the major part of amateur RTTY work is done with the 850-cycle shift. This figure also is used in much commercial work. The nominal transmitter frequency is the mark condition and the frequency is shifted 850 cycles (or whatever shift may be chosen) lower for space.

On the v.h.f. bands where A2 transmission is permitted **audio frequency-shift keying (a.f.s.k.)** is generally used. In this case the r.f. carrier is transmitted continuously, the pulses being transmitted by frequency-shifted tone modulation. The audio frequencies used have been more-or-less standardized at 2125 and 2975 cycles per second, the shift being 850 cycles as in the case of straight f.s.k. (These frequencies are the 5th and 7th harmonics, respectively, of 425 cycles, which is half the shift frequency, and thus are convenient for calibration and alignment purposes.) With a.f.s.k. the lower audio frequency is customarily used for mark and the higher for space.

The Receiving Converter

In receiving an f.s.k. teletype signal, the receiver's beat-frequency oscillator is turned on as for ordinary c.w. reception and the receiver tuning is then adjusted so that the mark and space signals produce audio beat tones of 2125 and 2975 cycles. Either frequency can be used for either mark or space, but no matter which may be used at the transmitter, the mark and space frequencies can be reversed at the receiver simply by tuning to the "other side of zero beat." (This cannot be done with a.f.s.k., of course, but the reversal can be accomplished quite simply, if

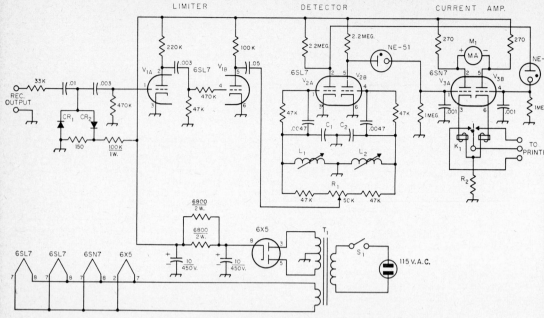

Fig. 12-12—Receiving converter for f.s.k. teletype signals (W2PAT). Unless otherwise indicated, capacitances are in μf. resistances are in ohms, resistors are ½ watt. Capacitors of 0.01 μf. or less may be mica or ceramic; larger values may be paper. Capacitors with polarities indicated are electrolytic.

C_1—0.15-μf. paper.
C_2—0.1-μf. paper.
CR_1, CR_2—1N34 or equivalent.
K_1—Polar relay, to operate on 20 ma.
L_1—36 mh. (TV width control, GE type RLD-019).
L_2—29 mh. (TV width control, GE type RLD-014).
M_1—Zero-center d.c. milliammeter, 20 ma. or more full scale (may be a 100-0-100 microammeter appropriately shunted).

R_1—50,000-ohm volume control, linear taper.
R_3—1000 ohms, 1 watt.
S_1—S.p.s.t. toggle.
T_1—Power transformer, 500 volts c.t., 30 ma; 6.3 volts 3 amp.
V_1, V_2—6SL7 (or 12AX7).
V_3—6SN7GT (or 12AU7).

necessary, by interchanging the outputs from the two frequencies as applied to the printer.) The audio-frequency tones are applied to separate rectifiers to convert them into d.c. impulses, which may then be further amplified to the power level required to operate the printer.

The receiving converter which performs these functions generally will include means for clipping or limiting the signals so they are held at constant amplitude, and may also include provision for some shaping of the pulses to overcome distortion that occurs in transmission. There are many ways by which these results can be accomplished, and the higher the order of performance the more complicated the circuits become. However, satisfactory results under reasonably good receiving conditions can be secured with relatively simple equipment, and the "basic" circuit shown in Fig. 12-12 has proved to be quite successful in practice. It operates as follows:

When audio output from the receiver is applied, the two diodes, CR_1 and CR_2, which are biased with approximately 0.3 volt, limit the peak voltage at the grid of the limiter tube, V_{1A}, to 0.6 volt or less for signal voltages up to 30 volts or more. Additional limiting in V_{1A} further stabilizes the voltage level. V_{1B} is primarily an

amplifier, and delivers approximately 15 volts output, constant to within 1 db. for receiver output voltages varying between about 0.5 volt and more than 30 volts.

The two tones, thus limited in amplitude, are applied to two simple filter circuits, L_1C_1 and L_2C_2, tuned to 2125 and 2975 cycles, respectively. The two tones are thus separated, one being applied to the grid of V_{2A} and the other to the grid of V_{2B}. V_{2A} and V_{2B} operate as grid-leak detectors, and when a signal is applied to, say, V_{2A}, the flow of grid current causes the grid to be driven practically to plate-current cutoff. As a result the plate voltage on V_{2A}, normally 15 volts with no signal, rises to 50 volts. This is sufficient to ignite the neon lamp connected between the plate of V_{2A} and the grid of V_{3B}, and a positive bias of about 25 volts is applied to the grid of V_{3B}. V_{3B} then takes a plate current of about 20 ma. and a bias of 20 volts is developed across the common cathode resistor, R_2. This is sufficient to cut off the plate current of V_{3A}, hence the left-hand magnet of the polarized relay, K_1, is inoperative while the right-hand magnet closes the contacts on its side. A similar action takes place when a signal is applied to the grid of V_{2B} but not to V_{2A}; in this

Radioteletype

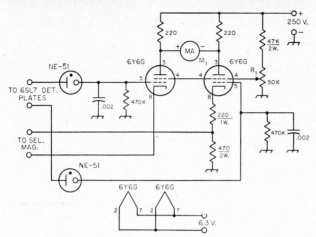

Fig. 12-13—Modification of converter circuit for use with single-magnet printers. Unless otherwise indicated, capacitances are in μf., resistances in ohms, resistors are ½ watt.

M_1—Zero-center d.c. milliammeter, 100 ma. full scale (may be microammeter with appropriate shunt).

R_1—50,000-ohm volume control.

case the relay contacts are pulled to the left. The relay thus keys the mark and space voltages applied to the printer.

Potentiometer R_1 is adjusted so that incoming noise (which will affect both channels equally) is balanced out and does not cause K_1 to operate. The neon lamps improve the operation of the circuit by acting as switches, thus making a sharp demarcation between mark and space pulses.

The zero-center meter, M_1, is not a necessity but is a convenience in making adjustments. R_1 should be adjusted on receiver noise for zero reading. With a 2125-cycle tone the pointer will swing to the left and L_1 should be adjusted for maximum deflection. With a 2975-cycle tone the pointer will swing to the right and L_2 should be adjusted for maximum deflection. Equal deflections should be obtained from both channels.

The keying circuit shown in Fig. 12-12 is for use with the Model 12 machine which requires an external power supply. For machines having a single selector magnet the modification shown in Fig. 12-13 may be used so the printer may be operated directly. These machines usually require a current of 60 ma., which will be furnished by this circuit and may be adjusted to the correct value by means of R_1.

Frequency-Shift Keyers

The keyboard contacts of the teletypewriter actuate a direct-current circuit that operates the printer magnets, and a pair of terminals is provided at which a keyed d.c. signal of the order of 100 volts is available. (Some machines, such as the Model 12, require an external d.c. power supply for this purpose; others have self-contained power supplies.) In the "resting" or non-operating condition the contacts are closed (mark) and the voltage at the terminals, which are in parallel with the contacts, is zero. In operation, the contacts open for "space" and the full voltage appears across the terminals. As normally connected, the spacing signal is of positive polarity.

This keyed d.c. voltage may be used to operate a keyer circuit for the radio transmitter, provided it is not "loaded" to such an extent that it affects the operation of the printer. Alternatively, the keyed current, rather than the voltage, may be used for external keying. This can be done by using an auxiliary keying relay with its coil connected in series with the printer magnet or relay circuit. A fast-acting relay must be used, and the coil must be one that will operate satisfactorily on the current available in the printer circuit. This will usually be either 20 or 60 milliamperes, depending on the type of machine.

F.S.K. with Variable-Frequency Oscillators

Perhaps the simplest satisfactory circuit for frequency-shift keying a v.f.o. is the one shown in Fig. 12-14A. This operates from the voltage available at the keyboard contact terminals and uses a reactance tube to obtain the required frequency shift.

The frequency shift is obtained by changing the plate resistance of the reactance tube, V_2, so that in effect the variable capacitor C_2 is alternately disconnected or connected in parallel with the tuning capacitor in the v.f.o. tank circuit. With no voltage applied to the grid, V_2 is biased so that the plate current is low and the effect of C_2 on the oscillator frequency is small. When a positive voltage from the keyboard contacts is applied to the grid the plate resistance is low and the oscillator frequency becomes lower because of the greater effect of C_2. The amount of frequency shift depends on the capacitance of C_2 and the amplitude of the positive voltage applied to the grid of V_2. The latter can be controlled by R_1.

C_1, the associated 20,000-ohm resistor, and the neon bulb, V_1, constitute a filter for removing clicks generated at the keyboard contacts. The value of C_1 depends somewhat on the machine,

333

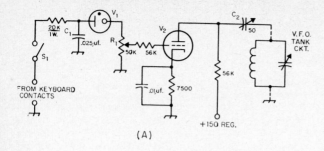

(A)

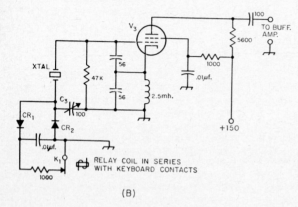

RELAY COIL IN SERIES
WITH KEYBOARD CONTACTS

(B)

Fig. 12-14—Frequency-shift keyer circuits. Unless otherwise indicated, capacitances are in $\mu\mu f.$, resistances are in ohms, resistors are ½ watt. A—Reactance-tube keyer for use with variable-frequency oscillator (W6OWP). B—Crystal oscillator circuit (W2PAT). It is essential that all leads associated with the crystal portion of the circuit be held to a small fraction of an inch in length if maximum shift is desired.

C_1—Paper (see text).
C_2—50-$\mu\mu f.$ midget variable.
C_3—100-$\mu\mu f.$ midget variable.
CR_1, CR_2—1N34 or equivalent.
K_1—Normally closed relay, fast operating, coil current according to printer magnet or relay current
R_1—Volume control.
S_1—S.p.s.t. toggle.
V_1—1-watt neon bulb without base resistor.
V_2—6C4 or equivalent.
V_3—6AK5 or equivalent.

and values up to 0.25 $\mu f.$ can be used, if necessary, without objectionable distortion of the keying pulses. The capacitance should be adjusted for clickless keying.

The frequency-shift circuit should be initially adjusted at the lowest radio frequency to be used, since the shift will be smallest in this case. If C_2 is set so a shift of 850 cycles is obtained at this frequency, further adjustment of the shift may be made by means of R_1. If the transmitter output is on a higher-frequency band than that on which the v.f.o. operates, the shift at the v.f.o. fundamental frequency must be reduced accordingly.

F.S.K. With Crystal Oscillators

Fig. 12-14B is a circuit which has been found to give a frequency shift of 850 cycles or more with crystals of the type ordinarily used for frequencies of the order of 3.5 Mc. and higher. This is an oscillator of the "grid-plate" type discussed in Chapter 6 on transmitters, with the addition of a variable capacitor, C_3, in series with the crystal. C_3 reduces the total capacitance across the crystal and thus raises the oscillation frequency. When it is shorted out the capacitance across the crystal is higher and the resulting frequency is lower.

Although relay contacts could be used for shorting the capacitor, the diode arrangement shown in Fig. 12-14B is more reliable in practice. With the contacts of K_1 open there is no d.c. path through CR_2 and it acts simply as a small capacitance (about 1 $\mu\mu f.$) in parallel with C_3. When the contacts of K_1 are closed there is a d.c. circuit through CR_1, CR_2 and the 1000-ohm resistor. Thus there is a path for direct current

flow as a result of rectification of the r.f. voltage across CR_2. Because of the d.c. bias the resistance of CR_2 drops to a low value and C_3 is effectively shorted out.

Adjustment of the circuit consists simply of determining the setting of C_3 at which the operating frequency is 850 cycles (or the desired shift) higher with the contacts of K_1 open than the frequency when the relay contacts are closed. A normally closed relay is used in order to make the mark frequency lower than the space frequency, in accordance with usual practice.

Frequency Adjustment

The frequency shift, whatever the type of circuit, should be made as nearly exact as available equipment will permit, since the shift must match the frequency difference between the filters in the receiving converter if the signals are to be usable at the receiving end. An accurately calibrated audio oscillator is useful for this purpose. To check, the mark frequency should be tuned in on the station receiver, with the b.f.o. on, and the receiver set to exact zero beat (see Chapter 21 on measurements for identification of exact zero beat). The space frequency should then be adjusted to exactly the desired shift. This may be done by adjusting for an auditory zero beat between the beat tone from the receiver and the tone from the audio oscillator. If an oscilloscope is available, the frequency adjustment may be accomplished by feeding the receiver tone to the vertical plates and the audio-oscillator tone to the horizontal plates, and then adjusting the space frequency for the elliptical pattern that indicates the two frequencies are the same.

CHAPTER 13

Transmission Lines

The place where r.f. power is generated is very frequently not the place where it is to be utilized. A transmitter and its antenna are a good example: The antenna, to radiate well, should be high above the ground and should be kept clear of trees, buildings and other objects that might absorb energy, but the transmitter itself is most conveniently installed indoors where it is readily accessible.

The means by which power is transported from point to point is the r.f. transmission line.

At radio frequencies a transmission line exhibits entirely different characteristics than it does at commercial power frequencies. This is because the speed at which electrical energy travels, while tremendously high as compared with mechanical motion, is not infinite. The peculiarities of r.f. transmission lines result from the fact that a time interval comparable with an r.f. cycle must elapse before energy leaving one point in the circuit can reach another just a short distance away.

Operating Principles

If a source of e.m.f. — a battery, for example — is connected to the ends of a pair of insulated parallel wires that extend outward for an infinite distance, electric currents will immediately become detectable in the wires near the battery terminals. The electric field of the battery will cause free electrons in the wire connected to the positive terminal to be attracted to the battery, and an equal number of free electrons in the wire connected to the negative terminal will be repelled from the battery. These currents do not flow instantaneously throughout the length of the wires; the electric field that causes the electron movement cannot travel faster than the speed of light, so a measurable interval of time elapses before the currents become evident even a relatively short distance away.

For example, the currents would not become detectable 300 meters (nearly 1000 feet) from the battery until at least a microsecond (one millionth of a second) after the connection was made. By ordinary standards this is a very short length of time, but in terms of radio frequency it represents the time of one complete cycle of a 1000-kilocycle current — a frequency considerably lower than those with which amateurs communicate.

The current flows to charge the capacitance between the two wires. However, the conductors of this "linear" capacitor also have appreciable inductance. The line may be thought of as being

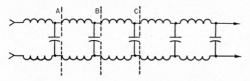

Fig. 13-1—Equivalent of a transmission line in lumped circuit constants.

composed of a whole series of small inductances and capacitances connected as shown in Fig. 13-1, where each coil is the inductance of a very short section of one wire and each capacitor is the capacitance between two such short sections.

Characteristic Impedance

An infinitely long chain of coils and capacitors connected as in Fig. 13-1, where the small inductances and capacitances all have the same values, respectively, has an important property. To an electrical impulse applied at one end, the combination appears to have an impedance — called the **characteristic impedance** or **surge impedance** — approximately equal to $\sqrt{L/C}$, where L and C are the inductance and capacitance per unit length. This impedance is purely resistive.

In defining the characteristic impedance as $\sqrt{L/C}$, it is assumed that the conductors have no inherent resistance — that is, there is no I^2R loss in them — and that there is no power loss in the dielectric surrounding the conductors. There is thus no power loss in or from the line no matter how great its length. This may not seem consistent with calling the characteristic impedance a pure resistance, which implies that the power supplied is all dissipated in the line. But in an infinitely long line the effect, so far as the source of power is concerned, is exactly the same as though the power were dissipated in a resistance, because the power leaves the source and travels outward forever along the line.

The characteristic impedance determines the amount of current that can flow when a given voltage is applied to an infinitely long line, in exactly the same way that a definite value of actual resistance limits current flow when a voltage is applied.

The inductance and capacitance per unit length of line depend upon the size of the conductors and the spacing between them. The closer the two conductors and the greater their diameter, the higher the capacitance and the lower the inductance. A line with large conductors closely spaced will have low impedance, while one with small conductors widely spaced will have relatively high impedance.

"Matched" Lines

Actual transmission lines do not extend to infinity but have a definite length and are connected to, or **terminate in**, a load at the "output" end, or end to which the power is delivered. If the load is a pure resistance of a value equal to the characteristic impedance of the line, the line is said to be **matched.** To current traveling along the line such a load just looks like still more transmission line of the same characteristic impedance.

In other words, a short line terminated in a purely resistive load equal to the characteristic impedance of the line acts just as though it were infinitely long. In a matched transmission line, power travels outward along the line from the source until it reaches the load, where it is completely absorbed.

R.F. on Lines

The principles discussed above, although based on direct-current flow from a battery, also hold when an r.f. voltage is applied to the line. The difference is that the alternating voltage causes the amplitude of the current at the input terminals of the line to vary with the voltage, and the direction of current flow also periodically reverses when the polarity of the applied voltage reverses. The current at a given instant at any point along the line is the result of a voltage that was applied at some *earlier* instant at the input terminals. Since the distance traveled by the electromagnetic fields in the time of one cycle is equal to one wavelength (Chapter 2), the instantaneous amplitude of the current is different at all points in a one-wavelength section of line. In fact, the current flows in opposite directions in the same wire in successive half-wavelength sections. However, at any given point along the line the current goes through similar variations with time that the current at the input terminals did.

Thus the current (and voltage) travels along the wire as a series of waves having a length equal to the speed of travel divided by the frequency of the a.c. voltage. On an infinitely long line, or one properly matched by its load, an ammeter inserted anywhere in the line will show the same current, because the ammeter averages out the variations in current during a cycle. It is only when the line is not properly matched that the wave motion becomes apparent through observations made with ordinary instruments.

● STANDING WAVES

In the infinitely long line (or its matched counterpart) the impedance is the same at any point on the line because the ratio of voltage to current is always the same. However, the impedance at the end of the line in Fig. 13-2 is zero — or at least extremely small — because the line is short-circuited at the end. The outgoing power, on meeting the short-circuit, reverses its direction of flow and goes back along the transmission line toward the input end. There is a large current in the short-circuit, but substantially no voltage across the line at this point. We now have a voltage and current representing the power going outward **(incident power)** toward the short-circuit,

and a second voltage and current representing the **reflected power** traveling back toward the source.

The reflected current travels at the same speed as the outgoing current, so its instantaneous value will be different at every point along the line, in the distance represented by the time of one cycle. At some points along the line the phase of the incident and reflected currents will be such that the currents cancel each other while at others the amplitude will be doubled. At in-between points the amplitude is between these two extremes. The points at which the currents are in and out of phase depend only on the *time* required for them to travel and so depend only on the *distance* along the line from the point of reflection.

In the short-circuit at the end of the line the two current components are in phase and the total current is large. At a distance of one-half wavelength back along the line from the short-circuit the outgoing and reflected components will again be in phase and the resultant current will again have its maximum value. This is also

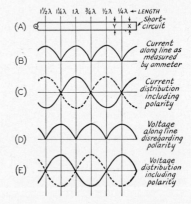

Fig. 13-2—Standing waves of voltage and current along short-circuited transmission line.

true at any point that is a multiple of a half wavelength from the short-circuited end of the line.

The outgoing and reflected currents will cancel at a point one-quarter wavelength, along the line, from the short-circuit. At this point, then, the current will be zero. It will also be zero at all points that are an *odd* multiple of one-quarter wavelength from the short-circuit.

If the current along the line is measured at successive points with an ammeter, it will be found to vary about as shown in Fig. 13-2B. The same result would be obtained by measuring the current in either wire, since the ammeter cannot measure phase. However, if the phase could be checked, it would be found that in each successive half-wavelength section of the line the currents at any given instant are flowing in opposite directions, as indicated by the solid line in Fig. 13-2C. Furthermore, the current in the second wire is flowing in the opposite direction to the current

Standing Waves

in the adjacent section of the first wire. This is indicated by the broken curve in Fig. 13-2C. The variations in current intensity along the transmission line are referred to as **standing waves**. The point of maximum line current is called a **current loop** or **current antinode** and the point of minimum line current is called a **current node**.

Voltage Relationships

Since the end of the line is short-circuited, the voltage at that point has to be zero. This can only be so if the voltage in the outgoing wave is met, at the end of the line, by a reflected voltage of equal amplitude and opposite polarity. In other words, the phase of the voltage wave is *reversed* when reflection takes place from the short-circuit. This reversal is equivalent to an extra half cycle or half wavelength of travel. As a result, the outgoing and returning voltages are in phase a quarter wavelength from the end of the line, and again out of phase a half wavelength from the end. The standing waves of voltage, shown at D in Fig. 13-2, are therefore displaced by one-quarter wavelength from the standing waves of current. The drawing at E shows the voltages on both wires when phase is taken into account. The polarity of the voltage on each wire reverses in each half wavelength section of transmission line. A voltage maximum is called a **voltage loop** or **antinode** and a voltage minimum is called a **voltage node**.

Open-Circuited Line

If the end of the line is open-circuited instead of short-circuited, there can be no current at the end of the line but a large voltage can exist. Again the incident power is reflected back toward the source. The incident and reflected components of current must be equal and opposite in phase at the open circuit in order for the total current at the end of the line to be zero. The incident and reflected components of voltage are in phase and add together. The result is again that there are standing waves, but the conditions are reversed as compared with a short-circuited line. Fig. 13-3 shows the open-circuited line case.

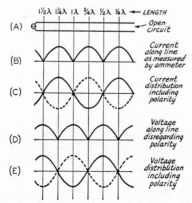

Fig. 13-3—Standing waves of current and voltage along an open-circuited transmission line.

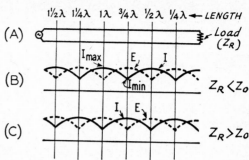

Fig. 13-4—Standing waves on a transmission line terminated in a resistive load.

Lines Terminated in Resistive Load

Fig. 13-4 shows a line terminated in a resistive load. In this case at least part of the incident power is absorbed in the load, and so is not available to be reflected back toward the source. Because only part of the power is reflected, the reflected components of voltage and current do not have the same magnitude as the incident components. Therefore neither voltage nor current cancel completely at any point along the line. However, the *speed* at which the incident and reflected components travel is not affected by their amplitude, so the phase relationships are similar to those in open- or short-circuited lines.

It was pointed out earlier that if the load resistance, Z_R, is equal to the characteristic impedance, Z_0, of the line all the power is absorbed in the load. In such a case there is no reflected power and therefore no standing waves of current and voltage. This is a special case that represents the change-over point between "short-circuited" and "open-circuited" lines. If Z_R is less than Z_0, the current is largest at the load, while if Z_R is greater than Z_0 the voltage is largest at the load. The two conditions are shown at B and C, respectively, in Fig. 13-4.

The resistive termination is an important practical case. The termination is seldom an actual resistor, the most common terminations being resonant circuits or resonant antenna systems, both of which have essentially resistive impedances. If the load is reactive as well as resistive, the operation of the line resembles that shown in Fig. 13-4, but the presence of reactance in the load causes two modifications: The loops and nulls are shifted toward or away from the load; and the amount of power reflected back toward the source is increased, as compared with the amount reflected by a purely resistive load of the same total impedance. Both effects become more pronounced as the ratio of reactance to resistance in the load is made larger.

Standing-Wave Ratio

The ratio of maximum current to minimum current along a line, Fig. 13-5, is called the **standing-wave ratio**. The same ratio holds for maximum voltage and minimum voltage. It is a measure of the mismatch between the load and the line, and is equal to 1 when the line is perfectly matched. (In that case the "maximum" and "minimum" are the same, since the current and voltage do not vary along the line.) When the line is terminated in a purely resistive load, the standing-wave ratio is

$$S.W.R. = \frac{Z_R}{Z_0} \text{ or } \frac{Z_0}{Z_R} \qquad (13\text{-}A)$$

Where $S.W.R.$ = Standing-wave ratio

Z_R = Impedance of load (must be pure resistance)

Z_0 = Characteristic impedance of line

Example: A line having a characteristic impedance of 300 ohms is terminated in a resistive load of 25 ohms. The s.w.r. is

$$S.W.R. = \frac{Z_0}{Z_R} = \frac{300}{25} = 12 \text{ to } 1$$

It is customary to put the larger of the two quantities, Z_R or Z_0, in the numerator of the fraction so that the s.w.r. will be expressed by a number larger than 1.

It is easier to measure the standing-wave ratio than some of the other quantities (such as the

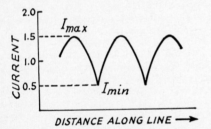

Fig. 13-5—Measurement of standing-wave ratio. In this drawing, I_{max} is 1.5 and I_{min} is 0.5, so the s.w.r. = I_{max}/I_{min} = 1.5/0.5 = 3 to 1.

impedance of an antenna) that enter into transmission-line computations. Consequently, the s.w.r. is a convenient basis for work with lines. The higher the s.w.r., the greater the mismatch between line and load. In practical lines, the power loss in the line itself increases with the s.w.r., as shown later.

● INPUT IMPEDANCE

The input impedance of a transmission line is the impedance seen looking into the sending-end or input terminals; it is the impedance into which the source of power must work when the line is connected. If the load is perfectly matched to the line the line appears to be infinitely long, as stated earlier, and the input impedance is simply the characteristic impedance of the line itself. However, if there are standing waves this is no longer true; the input impedance may have a wide range of values.

This can be understood by referring to Figs. 13-2, 13-3, or 13-4. If the line length is such that standing waves cause the voltage at the input terminals to be high and the current low, then the

input impedance is higher than the Z_0 of the line, since impedance is simply the ratio of voltage to current. Conversely, low voltage and high current at the input terminals mean that the input impedance is lower than the line Z_0. Comparison of the three drawings also shows that the range of input impedance values that may be encountered is greater when the far end of the line is open- or short-circuited than it is when the line has a resistive load. In other words, the higher the s.w.r. the greater the range of input impedance values when the line length is varied.

In addition to the variation in the absolute value of the input impedance with line length, the presence of standing waves also causes the input impedance to contain both reactance and resistance, even though the load itself may be a pure resistance. The only exceptions to this occur at the exact current loops or nodes, at which points the input impedance is a pure resistance. These are the only points at which the outgoing and reflected voltages and currents are exactly in phase: At all other distances along the line the current either leads or lags the voltage and the effect is exactly the same as though a capacitance or inductance were part of the input impedance.

The input impedance can be represented either by a resistance and a capacitance or by a resistance and an inductance, as shown in Fig. 13-6. Whether the impedance is inductive or capacitive depends on the characteristics of the load and the length of the line. It is possible to represent the input impedance by an equivalent circuit having resistance and reactance either in series or parallel, so long as the total impedance and phase angle are the same in either case. For a given impedance and phase angle, different values of resistance and reactance are required in the series circuit as compared with the parallel equivalent circuit.

The magnitude and character of the input impedance is quite important, since it determines the method by which the power source must be coupled to the line. The calculation of input impedance is rather complicated and its measurement is not feasible without special equipment. Fortunately, in amateur work it is unnecessary either to calculate or measure it. The proper coupling can be achieved by relatively simple methods described later in this chapter.

Lines Without Load

The input impedance of a short-circuited or open-circuited line not an exact multiple of one-quarter wavelength long is practically a pure reactance. This is because there is very little power lost in the line. Such lines are frequently used as "linear" inductances and capacitances.

If a shorted line is less than a quarter-wave long, as at X in Fig. 13-2, it will have inductive reactance. The reactance increases with the line length up to the quarter-wave point. Beyond that, as at Y, the reactance is capacitive, high near the quarter-wave point and becoming lower as the half-wave point is approached. It then alternates between inductive and capacitive in successive quarter-wave sections. Just the reverse is true of the open-circuited line.

At exact multiples of a quarter wavelength the impedance is purely resistive. It is apparent, from examination of B and D in Fig. 13-2, that at points that are a multiple of a half wavelength — i.e., $\frac{1}{2}$, 1, $1\frac{1}{2}$ wavelengths, etc. — from the short-circuited end of the line the current and

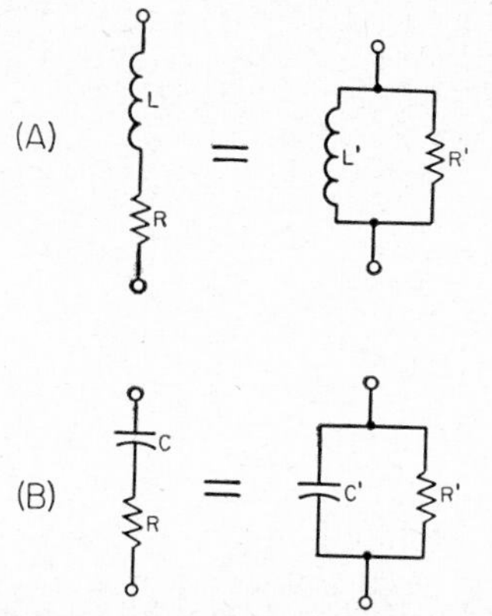

(A)

(B)

Fig. 13-6—Series and parallel equivalents of a line whose input impedance has both reactive and resistive components. The series and parallel equivalents do not have the same values; e.g., in A, L does not equal L' and R does not equal R'.

voltage have the same values that they do at the short circuit. In other words, if the line were an exact multiple of a half wavelength long the generator or source of power would "look into" a short circuit. On the other hand, at points that are an odd multiple of a quarter wavelength — i.e., $\frac{1}{4}$, $\frac{3}{4}$, $1\frac{1}{4}$, etc. — from the short circuit the voltage is maximum and the current is zero. Since $Z = E/I$, the impedance at these points is theoretically infinite. (Actually it is very high, but not infinite. This is because the current does not actually go to zero when there are losses in the line. Losses are always present, but usually are small.)

Impedance Transformation

The fact that the input impedance of a line depends on the s.w.r. and line length can be used to advantage when it is necessary to transform a given impedance into another value.

Study of Fig. 13-4 will show that, just as in the open- and short-circuited cases, if the line is one-half wavelength long the voltage and current are exactly the same at the input terminals as they are at the load. This is also true of lengths that are integral multiples of a half wavelength. It is also true for all values of s.w.r. Hence the input impedance of any line, no matter what its Z_0, that is a multiple of a half wavelength long is exactly the same as the load impedance. Such a line can be used to transfer the impedance to a new location without changing its value.

When the line is a quarter wavelength long, or an odd multiple of a quarter wavelength, the load impedance is "inverted." That is, if the current is low and the voltage is high at the load, the input impedance will be such as to require high

current and low voltage. The relationship between the load impedance and input impedance is given by:

$$Z_S = \frac{Z_0{}^2}{Z_R} \qquad \text{(13-B)}$$

where Z_S = Impedance looking into line (line length an odd multiple of one-quarter wavelength)

Z_R = Impedance of load (must be pure resistance)

Z_0 = Characteristic impedance of line

Example: A quarter-wavelength line having a characteristic impedance of 500 ohms is terminated in a resistive load of 75 ohms. The impedance looking into the input or sending end of the line is

$$Z_S = \frac{Z_0{}^2}{Z_R} = \frac{(500)^2}{75} = \frac{250,000}{75} = 3333 \text{ ohms}$$

If the formula above is rearranged, we have

$$Z_0 = \sqrt{Z_S Z_R} \qquad \text{(13-C)}$$

This means that if we have two values of impedance that we wish to "match," we can do so if we connect them together by a quarter-wave transmission line having a characteristic impedance equal to the square root of their product. A quarter-wave line, in other words, has the characteristics of a transformer.

Resonant and Nonresonant Lines

The input impedance of a line operating with a high s.w.r. is critically dependent on the line length, and resistive only when the length is some integral multiple of one-quarter wavelength. Lines cut to such a length and operated with a high s.w.r. are called "tuned" or "resonant" lines. On the other hand, if the s.w.r. is low the input impedance is close to the Z_0 of the line and does not vary a great deal with the line length. Such lines are called "flat," or "untuned," or "nonresonant."

There is no sharp line of demarcation between tuned and untuned lines. If the s.w.r. is below 1.5 to 1 the line is essentially flat, and the same input coupling method will work with all line lengths. If the s.w.r. is above 3 or 4 to 1 the type of coupling system, and its adjustment, will depend on the line length and such lines fall into the "tuned" category.

It is usually advantageous to make the s.w.r. as low as possible. A resonant line becomes necessary only when a considerable mismatch between the load and the line has to be tolerated. The most important practical example of this is when a single antenna is operated on several harmonically related frequencies, in which case the antenna impedance will have widely different values on different harmonics.

● RADIATION

Whenever a wire carries alternating current the electromagnetic fields travel away into space with the velocity of light. At power-line frequencies the field that "grows" when the current is increasing has plenty of time to return or "collapse" about the conductor when the current is decreasing, because the alternations are so slow. But at radio frequencies fields that travel only a relatively short distance do not have time to get back to the conductor before the next cycle commences. The consequence is that some of the electromagnetic energy is prevented from being restored to the conductor; in other words, energy is radiated into space in the form of electromagnetic waves.

The amount of energy radiated depends, among other things, on the length of the conductor in relation to the frequency or wavelength of the r.f. current. If the conductor is very short compared to the wavelength the energy radiated (for a given current) will be small. However, a transmission line used to feed power to an antenna is not short; in fact, it is almost always an appreciable fraction of a wavelength long and may have a length of several wavelengths.

The lines previously considered have consisted of two parallel conductors of the same diameter. Provided there is nothing in the system to destroy symmetry, at every point along the line the current in one conductor has the same intensity as the current in the other conductor at that point, but the currents flow in opposite directions. This

was shown in Figs. 13-2C and 13-3C. It means that the fields set up about the two wires have the same intensity, but *opposite directions*. The consequence is that the total field set up about such a transmission line is zero; the two fields "cancel out." Hence no energy is radiated.

Practically, the fields do not quite cancel out because for them to do so the two conductors would have to occupy the same space, whereas they are actually slightly separated. However, the cancelation is substantially complete if the distance between the conductors is very small compared to the wavelength. Transmission line radiation will be negligible if the distance between the conductors is 0.01 wavelength or less, provided the currents in the two wires are balanced.

The amount of radiation also is proportional to the current flowing in the line. Because of the way in which the current varies along the line when there are standing waves, the effective current, for purposes of radiation, becomes greater as the s.w.r. is increased. For this reason the radiation is least when the line is flat. However, if the conductor spacing is small and the currents are balanced, the radiation from a line with even a high s.w.r. is inconsequential. A small unbalance in the line currents is far more serious — and is just as serious when the line is flat as when the s.w.r. is high.

Practical Line Characteristics

The foregoing discussion of transmission lines has been based on a line consisting of two parallel conductors. The **parallel-conductor** line is but one of two general types, the other being the **coaxial** or **concentric** line. The coaxial line consists of a conductor placed in the center of a tube. The inside surface of the tube and the outside surface of the smaller inner conductor form the two conducting surfaces of the line.

In the coaxial line the fields are entirely inside the tube, because the tube acts as a shield to prevent them from appearing outside. This reduces radiation to the vanishing point. So far as the electrical behavior of coaxial lines is concerned, all that has previously been said about the operation of parallel-conductor lines applies. There are, however, practical differences in the construction and use of parallel and coaxial lines.

● PARALLEL-CONDUCTOR LINES

A type of parallel-conductor line sometimes used in amateur installations is one in which two wires (ordinarily No. 12 or No. 14) are supported a fixed distance apart by means of insulating rods called "spacers." The spacings used vary from two to six inches, the smaller spacings being necessary at frequencies of the order of 28 Mc. and higher so that radiation will be minimized. The construction is shown in Fig. 13-7. Such a line is said to be **air-insulated.** Typical spacers are shown in Fig. 13-8. The characteristic impedance of such "open-wire" lines is between 400 and 600 ohms, depending on the wire size and spacing.

Parallel-conductor lines also are occasionally constructed of metal tubing of a diameter of ¼ to ½ inch. This reduces the characteristic impedance

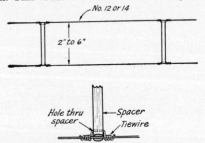

Fig. 13-7—Typical construction of open-wire line. The line conductor fits in a groove in the end of the spacer, and is held in place by a tie-wire anchored in a hole near the groove.

of the line. Such lines are mostly used as quarter-wave transformers, when different values of impedance are to be matched.

Prefabricated parallel-conductor line with air insulation, developed for television reception, can be used in transmitting applications. This line consists of two conductors separated one-half to one inch by molded-on spacers. The characteristic impedance is 300 to 450 ohms, depending on the wire size and spacing.

A convenient type of manufactured line is one in which the parallel conductors are imbedded in low-loss insulating material (polyethylene). It is commonly used as a TV lead-in and has a charac-

Practical Line Characteristics

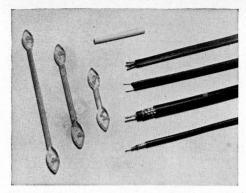

Fig. 13-8—Typical manufactured transmission lines and spacers.

teristic impedance of about 300 ohms. It is sold under various names, the most common of which is "Twin-Lead." This type of line has the advantages of light weight, close and uniform conductor spacing, flexibility and neat appearance. However, the losses in the solid dielectric are higher than in air, and dirt or moisture on the line tends to change the characteristic impedance. Moisture effects can be reduced by coating the line with silicone grease. A special form of 300-ohm Twin-Lead for transmitting uses a polyethylene tube with the conductors molded diametrically opposite; the longer dielectric path in such line reduces moisture troubles.

In addition to 300-ohm line, Twin-Lead is obtainable with a characteristic impedance of 75 ohms for transmitting purposes. Light-weight 75- and 150-ohm Twin-Lead also is available.

Characteristic Impedance

The characteristic impedance of an air-insulated parallel-conductor line is given by:

$$Z_0 = 276 \log \frac{b}{a} \qquad \text{(13-D)}$$

where Z_0 = Characteristic impedance
b = Center-to-center distance between conductors
a = Radius of conductor (in same units as b)

It does not matter what units are used for a and b so long as they are the *same* units. Both quantities may be measured in centimeters, inches, etc. Since it is necessary to have a table of common logarithms to solve practical problems, the solution is given in graphical form in Fig. 13-9 for a number of common conductor sizes.

In solid-dielectric parallel-conductor lines such as Twin-Lead the characteristic impedance cannot be calculated readily, because part of the electric field is in air as well as in the dielectric.

Unbalance in Parallel-Conductor Lines

When installing parallel-conductor lines care should be taken to avoid introducing electrical unbalance into the system. If for some reason the current in one conductor is higher than in the other, or if the currents in the two wires are not exactly out of phase with each other, the electromagnetic fields will not cancel completely and a considerable amount of power may be radiated by the line.

Maintaining good line balance requires, first of all, a balanced load at its end. For this reason the antenna should be fed, whenever possible, at a point where each conductor "sees" exactly the same thing. Usually this means that the antenna system should be fed at its electrical center. However, even though the antenna appears to be symmetrical, physically, it can be unbalanced electrically if the part connected to one of the line conductors is coupled to something (such as house wiring or a metal pole or roof) that is not duplicated on the other part of the antenna. Every effort should be made to keep the antenna as far as possible from other wiring or sizable

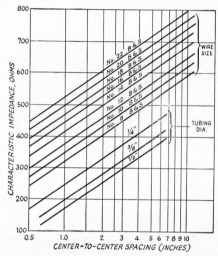

Fig. 13-9—Chart showing the characteristic impedance of spaced-conductor parallel transmission lines with air dielectric. Tubing sizes given are for outside diameters.

metallic objects. The transmission line itself will cause some unbalance if it is not brought away from the antenna at right angles to it for a distance of at least a quarter wavelength.

In installing the line conductors take care to see that they are kept away from metal. The minimum separation between either conductor and all other wiring should be at least four or five times the conductor spacing. The shunt capacitance introduced by close proximity to metallic objects can drain off enough current (to ground) to unbalance the line currents, resulting in increased radiation. A shunt capacitance of this sort also constitutes a reactive load on the line, causing an impedance "bump" that will prevent making the line actually flat.

● COAXIAL LINES

The most common form of coaxial line consists of either a solid or stranded-wire inner conductor surrounded by polyethylene dielectric. Copper braid is woven over the dielectric to form the outer conductor, and a waterproof vinyl covering is placed on top of the braid. This cable is made in a number of different diameters. It is moderately flexible, and so is convenient to install. Some different types are shown in Fig. 13-8. This solid coaxial cable is commonly available in impedances approximating 50 and 70 ohms.

Air-insulated coaxial lines have lower losses than the solid-dielectric type, but are rarely used in amateur work because they are expensive and difficult to install as compared with the flexible cable. The common type of air-insulated coaxial line uses a solid-wire conductor inside a copper tube, with the wire held in the center of the tube by means of insulating "beads" placed at regular intervals.

Characteristic Impedance

The characteristic impedance of an air-insulated coaxial line is given by the formula

$$Z_0 = 138 \log \frac{b}{a} \qquad \text{(13-E)}$$

where Z_0 = Characteristic impedance
b = Inside diameter of outer conductor
a = Outside diameter of inner conductor
(in same units as b)

Curves for typical conductor sizes are given in Fig. 13-10.

The formula for coaxial lines is approximately correct for lines in which bead spacers are used, provided the beads are not too closely spaced. When the line is filled with a solid dielectric, the characteristic impedance as given by the chart should be multiplied by $1/\sqrt{K}$, where K is the dielectric constant of the material.

● ELECTRICAL LENGTH

In the discussion of line operation earlier in this chapter it was assumed that currents traveled along the conductors at the speed of light. Actually, the velocity is somewhat less, the reason being that electromagnetic fields travel more

		TABLE 13-I			
		Transmission-Line Data			
Type	Description or Type Number	Characteristic Impedance	Velocity Factor	Capacitance per foot; $\mu\mu f.$
Coaxial	Air-insulated	50–100	0.85[1]	
	RG-8/U	53	0.66	29.5
	RG-58/U	53	0.66	28.5
	RG-11/U	75	0.66	20.5
	RG-59/U	73	0.66	21.0
Parallel-Conductor	Air-insulated	200–600	0.975[2]	
	214–080[3]	75	0.68	19.0
	214–023[3]	75	0.71	20.0
	214–079[3]	150	0.77	10.0
	214–056[3]	300	0.82	5.8
	214–076[3]	300	0.84	3.9
	214–022[3]	300	0.85	3.0

[1] Average figure for small-diameter lines with ceramic beads.
[2] Average figure for lines insulated with ceramic spacers at intervals of a few feet.
[3] Amphenol type numbers and data. Line similar to 214–056 is made by several manufacturers, but rated loss may differ from that given in Fig. 13-11. Types 214–023, 214–076, and 214–022 are made for transmitting applications.

slowly in material dielectrics than they do in free space. In air the velocity is practically the same as in empty space, but a practical line always has to be supported in some fashion by solid insulating materials. The result is that the fields are slowed down; the currents travel a shorter distance in the time of one cycle than they do in space, and so the wavelength along the line is less than the wavelength would be in free space at the same frequency.

Whenever reference is made to a line as being so many wavelengths (such as a "half wavelength" or "quarter wavelength") long, it is to be understood that the *electrical* length of the line is meant. Its actual physical length as measured by a tape always will be somewhat less. The physical length corresponding to an electrical wavelength is given by

$$Length \ in \ feet = \frac{984V}{f} \qquad \text{(13-F)}$$

where f = Frequency in megacycles
V = Velocity factor

The **velocity factor** is the ratio of the actual velocity along the line to the velocity in free space. Values of V for several common types of lines are given in Table 13-I.

Example: A 75-foot length of 300-ohm Twin-Lead is used to carry power to an antenna at a frequency of 7150 kc. From Table 13-I, V is 0.82. At this frequency (7.15 Mc.) a wavelength is

$$Length \ (\text{feet}) = \frac{984V}{f} = \frac{984}{7.15} \times 0.82$$

$$= 137.6 \times 0.82 = 112.8 \ \text{ft.}$$

The line length is therefore 75/112.8 = 0.665 wavelength.

Because a quarter-wavelength line is frequently used as a linear transformer, it is con-

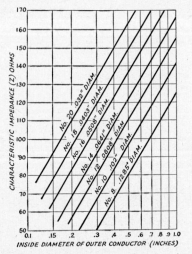

Fig. 13-10—Chart showing characteristic impedance of various air-insulated concentric lines.

CHARACTERISTIC IMPEDANCE (Z) OHMS

INSIDE DIAMETER OF OUTER CONDUCTOR (INCHES)

Losses in Transmission Lines

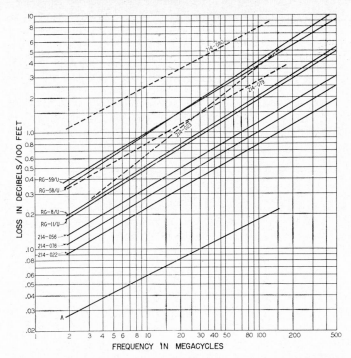

Fig. 13-11—Attenuation data for common types of transmission lines. Curve A is the nominal attenuation of 600-ohm open-wire line with No. 12 conductors, not including dielectric loss in spacers nor possible radiation losses. Additional line data is given in Table 13-I.

venient to calculate the length of a quarter-wave line directly. The formula is

$$Length \text{ (feet)} = \frac{246V}{f} \qquad \textbf{(13-G)}$$

where the symbols have the same meaning as above.

● LOSSES IN TRANSMISSION LINES

There are three ways by which power may be lost in a transmission line: by radiation, by heating of the conductors (I^2R loss), and by heating of the dielectric, if any. Radiation losses are in general the result of "antenna currents" on the line, resulting from undesired coupling to the radiating antenna. They cannot readily be estimated or measured, so the following discusssion is based only on conductor and dielectric losses.

Heat losses in both the conductor and the dielectric increase with frequency. Conductor losses also are greater the lower the characteristic impedance of the line, because a higher current flows in a low-impedance line for a given power input. The converse is true of dielectric losses because these increase with the voltage, which is greater on high-impedance lines. The dielectric loss in air-insulated lines is negligible (the only loss is in the insulating spacers) and such lines operate at high efficiency when radiation losses are low.

It is convenient to express the loss in a transmission line in decibels per unit length, since the loss in db. is directly proportional to the line length. Losses in various types of lines operated without standing waves (that is, terminated in a resistive load equal to the characteristic imped-

ance of the line) are given in graphical form in Fig. 13-11. In these curves the radiation loss is assumed to be negligible.

When there are standing waves on the line the power loss increases as shown in Fig. 13-12. Whether or not the increase in loss is serious depends on what the original loss would have been if the line were perfectly matched. If the loss with perfect matching is very low, a large s.w.r. will not greatly affect the *efficiency* of the line — i.e.,

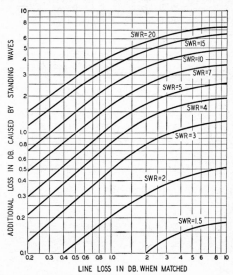

Fig. 13-12—Effect of standing-wave ratio on line loss. The ordinates give the *additional* loss in decibels for the loss, under perfectly matched conditions, shown on the horizontal scale.

the ratio of the power delivered to the load to the power put into the line.

> Example: A 150-foot length of RG-11/U cable is operating at 7 Mc. with a 5-to-1 s.w.r. If perfectly matched, the loss from Fig. 13-11 would be $1.5 \times 0.4 = 0.6$ db. From Fig. 13-12 the additional loss because of the s.w.r. is 0.73 db. The total loss is therefore $0.6 + 0.73 = 1.33$ db.

An appreciable s.w.r. on a solid-dielectric line may result in excessive loss of power at the higher frequencies. Such lines, whether of the parallel-conductor or coaxial type, should be operated as nearly flat as possible, particularly when the line length is more than 50 feet or so. As shown by Fig. 13-12, the increase in line loss is not too serious so long as the s.w.r. is below 2 to 1, but increases rapidly when the s.w.r. rises above 3 to 1. Tuned transmission lines such as are used with multiband antennas always should be air-insulated, in the interests of highest efficiency.

Loads and Balancing Devices

The most important practical load for a transmission line is an antenna which, in most cases, will be "balanced" — that is, symmetrically constructed with respect to the feed point. Aside from considerations of matching the actual impedance of the antenna at the feed point to the characteristic impedance of the line (if such matching is attempted) a balanced antenna should be fed through a balanced transmission line in order to preserve symmetry with respect to ground and thus avoid difficulties with unbalanced currents on the line. Such currents, as pointed out earlier in this chapter, will result in undesirable radiation from the transmission line itself.

If, as is often the case, the antenna is to be fed through coaxial line (which is inherently unbalanced) some method should be used for connecting the line to the antenna without upsetting the symmetry of the antenna itself. This requires a circuit that will isolate the balanced load from the unbalanced line while providing efficient power transfer. Devices for doing this are called **baluns**. The types used between the antenna and transmission line are generally "linear," consisting of transmission-line sections as described in Chapter 14.

The need for baluns also arises in coupling a transmitter to a balanced transmission line, since the output circuits of most transmitters have one side grounded. (This type of output circuit is desirable for a number of reasons, including TVI reduction.) The most flexible type of balun for this purpose is the inductively coupled matching network described in a subsequent section in this chapter. This combines impedance matching with balanced-to-unbalanced operation, but has the disadvantage that it uses resonant circuits and thus can work over only a limited band of frequencies without readjustment. However, if a fixed impedance ratio in the balun can be tolerated, the coil balun described below can be used without adjustment over a frequency range of about 10 to 1 — 3 to 30 Mc., for example. Alternatively, a similarly wide band can be covered by a properly designed transformer (with the same impedance limitation) but the design principles and materials used in such transformers are quite specialized. Their construction is beyond the scope of this *Handbook*.

Coil Baluns

The type of balun known as the "coil balun" is based on the principles of a linear transmission-line balun as shown in the upper drawing of Fig. 13-13. Two transmission lines of equal length having a characteristic impedance Z_0 are connected in series at one end and in parallel at the other. At the series-connected end the lines are balanced to ground and will match an impedance equal to $2Z_0$. At the parallel-connected end the lines will be matched by an impedance equal to $Z_0/2$. One side may be connected to ground at the parallel-connected end, provided the two lines have a length such that, considering each line as a single wire, the balanced end is effectively decoupled from the parallel-connected end. This requires a length that is an odd multiple of $\frac{1}{4}$ wavelength. The impedance transformation from the series-connected end to the parallel-connected end is 4 to 1.

A definite line length is required only for decoupling purposes, and so long as there is adequate decoupling the system will act as a 4-to-1 impedance transformer regardless of line length. If each line is wound into a coil, as in the lower drawing, the inductances so formed will act as choke coils and will tend to isolate the series-connected end from any ground connection that may be placed on the parallel-connected end. Balun coils made in this way will operate over a wide frequency range, since the choke inductance is not critical. The lower frequency limit is where the coils are no longer effective in isolating one end from the other; the length of line in each coil should be about equal to a quarter wavelength at the lowest frequency to be used.

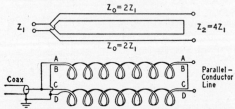

Fig. 13-13—Baluns for matching between push-pull and single-ended circuits. The impedance ratio is 4 to 1 from the push-pull side to the unbalanced side. Coiling the lines as shown in the lower drawing increases the frequency range over which satisfactory operation is obtained.

Loads and Balancing Devices

The principal application of such coils is in going from a 300-ohm balanced line to a 75-ohm coaxial line. This requires that the Z_0 of the lines forming the coils be 150 ohms. Design data for winding the coils is not available; however, Equation 13-D can be used for determining the approximate wire spacing. Allowance should be made for the fact that the effective dielectric constant will be somewhat greater than 1 if the coil is wound on a form. The proximity effect between turns can be reduced by making the turn spacing somewhat larger than the conductor spacing. For operation at 3.5 Mc. and higher frequencies the length of each conductor should be about 60 feet. The conductor spacing can be adjusted to the proper value by terminating each line in a noninductive 150-ohm resistor and adjusting the spacing until an impedance bridge at the input end shows the line to be matched to 150 ohms.

A balun of this type is simply a fixed-ratio transformer, when matched. It cannot compensate for inaccurate matching elsewhere in the system. With a "300-ohm" line on the balanced end, for example, a 75-ohm coax cable will not be matched unless the 300-ohm line actually is terminated in a 300-ohm load.

● **NONRADIATING LOADS**

Typical examples of nonradiating loads for a transmission line are the grid circuit of a power amplifier (considered in the chapter on transmitters), the input circuit of a receiver, and another transmission line. This last case includes the "antenna tuner" — a misnomer because it is actually a device for coupling a transmission line to the transmitter. Because of its importance in amateur installations, the antenna coupler is considered separately in a later part of this chapter.

Coupling to a Receiver

A good match between an antenna and its transmission line does not guarantee a low standing-wave ratio on the line when the antenna system is used for receiving. The s.w.r. is determined wholly by what the line "sees" at the receiver's antenna-input terminals. For minimum s.w.r. the receiver input circuit must be matched to the line. The rated input impedance of a receiver is a nominal value that varies over a considerable range with frequency. Methods for bringing about a proper match are discussed in the chapter on receivers.

It should be noted that *if* the receiver is matched to the line, then it is desirable that the antenna and line also be matched, since this results in maximum signal transfer from the antenna to the line. If the receiver is *not* matched to the line, the input impedance of the line (at the terminals of the antenna itself) in turn cannot match the antenna impedance. In such a case the signal input to the receiver depends on the coupling system used between the line and the receiver. For greatest signal strength the coupling system has to be adjusted to the best compromise between receiver input impedance and load appearing at the input (antenna) end of the line. The proper adjustments must be determined by experiment.

A similar situation exists when the receiver input impedance inherently matches the line Z_0, but the line and antenna are mismatched. Under these conditions perfect matching at the receiver does not result in greatest signal strength; a deliberate mismatch has to be introduced so that the maximum power will be taken from the antenna.

The most desirable condition is that in which the receiver is matched to the line Z_0 and the line in turn is matched to the antenna. This transfers maximum power from the antenna to the receiver with the least loss in the transmission line.

Coupling the Transmitter to the Line

The type of coupling system that will be needed to transfer power adequately from the final r.f. amplifier to the transmission line depends almost entirely on the input impedance of the line. As shown earlier in this chapter, the input impedance is determined by the standing-wave ratio and the line length. The simplest case is that where the line is terminated in its characteristic impedance so that the s.w.r. is 1 to 1 and the input impedance is equal to the Z_0 of the line, regardless of line length.

Coupling systems that will deliver power into a flat line are readily designed. For all practical purposes the line can be considered to be flat if the s.w.r. is no greater than about 1.5 to 1. That is, a coupling system designed to work into a pure resistance equal to the line Z_0 will have enough leeway to take care of the small variations in input impedance that will occur when the line length is changed, if the s.w.r. is higher than 1 to 1 but no greater than 1.5 to 1.

Current practice in transmitter design is to provide an output circuit that will work into such a line, usually a coaxial line of 50 to 75 ohms characteristic impedance. The design of such output circuits is discussed in the chapter on high-frequency transmitters. If the input impedance of the transmission line that is to be connected to the transmitter differs appreciably from the value of impedance into which the transmitter output circuit is designed to operate, an impedance-matching network must be inserted between the transmitter and the line input terminals.

● **IMPEDANCE-MATCHING CIRCUITS FOR PARALLEL CONDUCTOR LINES**

As shown earlier in this chapter, the input impedance of a line that is operating with a high standing-wave ratio can vary over quite wide

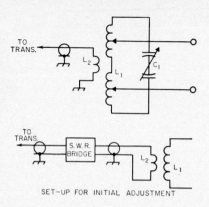

Fig. 13-14—Matching circuits using a coaxial link, for use with parallel-conductor transmission lines. Adjustment setup using an s.w.r. bridge is shown in the lower drawing. Design considerations and method of adjustment are discussed in the text.

limits. The simplest type of circuit that will match such a range of impedances to 50 to 75 ohms is a parallel-tuned circuit approximately resonant at the operating frequency. In its ordinary form, such a circuit will be connected to a short length of coaxial line or "link" by inductive coupling as shown in Fig. 13-14, the other end of the cable being attached to the output terminals of the transmitter. The cable may be any convenient length if the impedance that it "sees" at the matching circuit is equal to its own characteristic impedance. This method has the further advantage that the coaxial link offers an ideal spot for the insertion of a low-pass filter for preventing harmonic interference to television and f.m. reception.

The constants of the tuned circuit C_1L_1 are not particularly critical; the principal requirement is that the circuit must be capable of being tuned to the operating frequency. Constants similar to those used in the plate tank circuit will be satisfactory. The construction of L_1 must be such that it can be tapped at least every turn. L_2 must be tightly coupled to L_1, and the inductance of L_2 should be approximately the value that gives a reactance equal to the Z_0 of the connecting line at the frequency in use. An average reactance of about 60 ohms will suffice for either 52- or 75-ohm coaxial line.

The most satisfactory way to set up the system initially is to connect a coaxial s.w.r. bridge in the link as shown in Fig. 13-14. The "Monimatch" type of bridge, which can handle the full transmitter power and may be left in the line for continuous monitoring, is excellent for this purpose. However, a simple resistance bridge such as is described in the chapter on measurements is perfectly adequate, requiring only that the transmitter output be reduced to a very low value so that the bridge will not be overloaded. To adjust the circuit, take a trial position of the line taps on L_1, keeping them equidistant from the center of the coil, and adjust C_1 for minimum s.w.r. as indicated by the bridge. If the s.w.r. is not close

to 1 to 1, try new tap positions and adjust C_1 again, continuing this procedure until the s.w.r. is practically 1 to 1. The setting of C_1 and the tap positions may then be logged for future reference. At this point, check the link s.w.r. over the frequency range normally used in that band, without changing the setting of C_1. No readjustment will be required if the s.w.r. does not exceed 1.5 to 1 over the range, but if it goes higher it is advisable to note as many settings of C_1 as may be necessary to keep the s.w.r. below 1.5 to 1 at any part of the band. Changes in the link s.w.r. are caused chiefly by changes in the s.w.r. on the main transmission line with frequency, and relatively little by the coupling circuit itself. A single setting of C_1 at mid-frequency will suffice if the antenna itself is broad-tuning.

If it is impossible to get a 1-to-1 s.w.r. at any settings of the taps or C_1, the s.w.r. on the main transmission line is high and the line length is probably unfavorable. Ordinarily there should be no difficulty if the transmission-line s.w.r. is not more than about 3 to 1, but if the line s.w.r. is higher it may not be possible to bring the link s.w.r. down except by using the methods for reactance compensation described in a subsequent section in this chapter.

The matching adjustment can be considerably facilitated by using a variable capacitor in series with the matching-circuit coupling coil as shown in Fig. 13-15. The additional adjustment thus provided makes the tap settings on L_1 much less critical since varying C_2 has the effect of varying the coupling between the two circuits. For optimum control of coupling, L_2 should be somewhat larger than when C_2 is not used — perhaps twice the reactance recommended above — and the reactance of C_2 at maximum capacitance should be the same as that of L_2 at the operating frequency. L_1 and C_1 are the same as before. The method of adjustment is the same, except that for each trial tap position C_1 and C_2 are alternately adjusted, a little at a time, until the s.w.r. is brought to its lowest possible value. In general, the adjustment sought should be the one that keeps C_2 at the largest possible capacitance, since this broadens the frequency response. Also, the taps on L_1 should be kept as far apart as possible, while still permitting a match, since this also broadens the frequency response of the circuit.

Once the matching circuit is properly adjusted, the s.w.r. bridge may be removed, if necessary, and full power applied to the transmitter. The power input should be adjusted by the coupling or loading control built into the transmitter, *not*

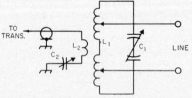

Fig. 13-15—Using a series capacitor for control of coupling between the link and line circuits with the coax-coupled matching circuit.

Coupling the Transmitter to the Line

by making any changes in the matching-circuit adjustments. If an amplifier having a parallel-tuned tank circuit will not load properly, tuned coupling should be used into the coax link.

It is possible to use a circuit of this type without initially setting it up with the s.w.r. bridge. In such a case it is a matter of cut-and-try until adequate power transfer between the amplifier and main transmission line is secured. However, this method frequently results in a high s.w.r. in the link, with consequent power loss, "hot spots" in the coaxial cable, and tuning that is critical with frequency. The bridge method is simple and gives the optimum operating conditions quickly and with certainty.

Untuned Coupling

A simple coil can be used for coupling to a line having a high standing-wave ratio providing the line length is adjusted so there is a current loop near the point where it connects to the pick-up coil. The coupling will be maximum, for a given degree of separation between the pick-up coil and the amplifier tank coil, if the line is pruned to a length such that the input impedance is just sufficiently capacitive to cancel the inductive reactance of the pick-up coil. This can be done by cut-and-try. The higher the s.w.r. on the line the easier it becomes to load the amplifier with loose coupling between the two coils. The sharper the antenna and the higher the line s.w.r. the more difficult it becomes to operate with this system over a band without progressively changing the line length.

Series and Parallel Tuning

Lines classified as "tuned" or "resonant" — i.e., cut to lengths approximately equal to integral multiples of one-quarter wavelength, and operating with a high standing-wave ratio — are characterized by having either very high or very low input impedances. Also, the input impedances of such lines are essentially resistive.

Under these conditions the circuit arrangements shown in Fig. 13-16 will work satisfactorily.

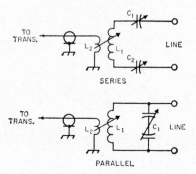

Fig. 13-16—Link-coupled series and parallel tuning.

Their advantage over the circuit of Fig. 13-14 is that it is not necessary to provide for taps on the matching-circuit coil, L_1. "Series" tuning

is used when a current loop occurs at or near the input end of the line; i.e., when the input impedance is low. "Parallel" tuning is used when there is a voltage loop at or near the input end; i.e., when the input impedance is high.

In the series case, the circuit formed by L_1, C_1 and C_2 with the line terminals short-circuited should tune to the operating frequency. C_1 and C_2 should be maintained at equal capacitance. In the parallel case, the circuit formed by L_1 and C_1 should tune to resonance with the line disconnected.

The L/C ratio in either circuit depends on the transmission line Z_0 and the standing-wave ratio. With series tuning, a high L/C ratio must be used if the s.w.r. is relatively low and the line Z_0 is high. With parallel tuning, a low L/C ratio must be used if the s.w.r. is relatively low and the transmission-line Z_0 also is low. With either series or parallel tuning the L/C ratio becomes less critical when the s.w.r. is high. As a first approximation, coil and capacitor values of the same order as those used in the plate tank circuit may be tried. The coupling coil, L_2, should have a reactance about equal to the Z_0 of the coaxial line, just as in the case of the circuit of Fig. 13-14. The coupling between L_1 and L_2 should be continuously adjustable.

Two capacitors are used in the series-tuned circuit in order to keep the line balanced to ground. This is because two identical capacitors, both connected with either their stators or rotors to the line, will have the same capacitance to ground. A single capacitor would be perfectly usable so far as the operation of the coupling circuit is concerned, but will slightly unbalance the circuit because the frame has more capacitance to ground than the stator. The unbalance is not especially serious unless the capacitor is mounted near a large mass of metal, such as a chassis or shield assembly.

A balanced capacitor is used in the parallel circuit, in preference to a single unit, for the same reason. An alternative scheme to maintain balance is to use two single-ended capacitors in parallel, but with the frame of one connected to one side of the line and the frame of the other connected to the other side of the line. The same two capacitors may be switched in series when series tuning is to be used.

As an alternative to adjustable coupling between L_1 and L_2, fixed coupling may be used and a variable capacitor connected in series with L_2 as shown in Fig. 13-15.

These circuits should be set up and adjusted in the same way as the tapped matching circuit, Fig. 13-14. That is, an s.w.r. bridge should be used to indicate the impedance match, which is brought about by alternately adjusting C_1 and the coupling between L_1 and L_2 until the bridge shows a null.

In the event that there is difficulty in bringing the s.w.r. down to 1 to 1 in the coaxial link, the probable cause is that the input impedance of the transmission line is neither very high nor very low. In such a case, if series tuning does not work it may pay to try parallel tuning, and vice versa. If a match cannot be secured with either, the circuit should be changed to that of Fig. 13-14.

Adjustment Without the S.W.R. Bridge

Use of the s.w.r. bridge with the circuits described above is the only certain way of arriving at optimum adjustments. However, if a bridge is not available, the transmitter usually can be made to take the proper load by a cut-and-try method of adjustment. In the case of Fig. 13-14, take a trial position of the taps fairly close to the center of L_1. With loose coupling between L_1 and L_2 (this may be controlled either by adjustment of the mutual inductance or by means of the series capacitor C_2) and with the amplifier plate tank circuit tuned to resonance as indicated by the plate-current dip, vary C_1 until a setting is found that causes the plate current to rise to a peak. This peak should be less than the expected normal loaded plate current. Then increase the coupling between L_1 and L_2, readjust C_1 for maximum plate current, and readjust the amplifier tank for the plate-current dip. Continue until the amplifier is fully loaded at the plate-current dip, increasing the coupling between the transmitter tank and the coax line if necessary to obtain full loading. Then spread the taps on L_1 a little farther apart and go through the same procedure. The object is to use the widest spread between taps that will permit proper loading of the transmitter.

The procedure with series or parallel tuning is similar except that there are no taps to adjust. If full loading cannot be secured with either, the circuit should be changed to Fig. 13-14.

Although this cut-and-try method generally will lead to adequate transmitter loading, the adjustments seldom are optimum from the standpoint of low s.w.r. in the coax link. This may lead to excessive power dissipation in the link, with overheating the result. Also, the loading may change more rapidly with small frequency changes than would be the case with a matching circuit adjusted for optimum performance with the aid of the s.w.r. bridge.

Lines of Random Length

Series or parallel tuning will always work satisfactorily with lines having a high standing-wave ratio so long as either a current loop or node occurs at the input end of the transmission line. This will be the case if the antenna is resonant and the line length is a multiple of one-quarter wavelength. However, it is not always possible to couple satisfactorily when intermediate line lengths are used. This is because at some lengths the input impedance of the line has a considerable reactive component, and because the resistive component is too large to be connected in series with a tuned circuit and too small to be connected in parallel.

The coupling system shown in Fig. 13-14 is capable of handling the resistive component of the input impedance of the transmission lines used in most amateur installations, regardless of

the standing-wave ratio on the line. Consequently, it can generally be used wherever either series or parallel tuning would normally be called for, simply by setting the taps properly on the coil. (A possible exception is where the s.w.r. is considerably higher than 10 to 1 and the line length is such as to bring a current loop at the input end. In such a case the resistance may be only a few ohms, which is difficult to match by means of taps on a coil.)

Within limits, the same circuit is capable of being adjusted to compensate for the reactive component of the input impedance; this merely means that a 1-to-1 s.w.r. in the link will be obtained at a different setting of C_1 than would be the case if the line "looked like" a pure resistance. Sometimes, however, C_1 does not have enough range available to give complete compensation, particularly when (as is the case with some line lengths when the s.w.r. is high) the input impedance is principally reactive.

Under such conditions it is necessary, if the line length cannot be changed to a more satisfactory value, to provide additional means for compensating for or "canceling out" the reactive component of the input impedance. As described earlier in this chapter (Fig. 13-6) the input impedance can be considered to be equivalent to a circuit consisting either of resistance and inductance or resistance and capacitance. It is generally more convenient to consider these elements as a parallel combination, so if the line "looks like" $L'R'$ at A in Fig. 13-6, it is apparent that if we connect a capacitance of the right value across L' the circuit will become resonant and will appear to be a pure resistance of the value R'. Similarly, connecting an inductance of the right value across C' in Fig. 13-6B will resonate the circuit and the impedance will be equal to R'. The resistive impedance that remains can easily be matched to the coax link by means of the circuit of Fig. 13-14.

The practical application of this principle is shown in Fig. 13-17, where L and C are the react-

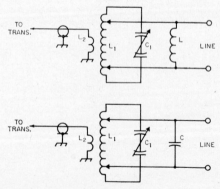

Fig. 13-17—Reactance cancellation on random-length lines having a high standing-wave ratio.

ances required to cancel out the line reactance, L for cases where the line is capacitive, C for lines having inductive reactance. The amount of either

Matching to Coaxial Lines

inductance or capacitance required is easily determined by trial, using the s.w.r. bridge in the coax link. First disconnect the main transmission line from L_1 and connect a noninductive resistor in its place. A 1-watt carbon resistor of about the same resistance as the line Z_0 will do, if a low-power bridge of the resistance type is used. With the "Monimatch" bridge, a suitable load may be made by connecting carbon resistors in parallel; for example, five 1500-ohm 2-watt resistors in parallel will make a 300-ohm load capable of handling 10 watts of r.f. Adjust the coil taps and C_1 for a 1-to-1 standing-wave ratio in the link, as described earlier. This determines the proper setting of C_1 for a purely resistive load. Then take off the resistor and connect the line, again adjusting the taps and C_1 to make the s.w.r. as low as possible, and compare the new setting of C_1 with the original setting. If the capacitance has increased, the line reactance is inductive and a capacitor must be connected at C in Fig. 13-17. The amount of capacitance needed to bring the proper setting of C_1 near the original setting can be determined by trial. On the other hand, if the capacitance of C_1 is less than the original, an inductance must be connected at L. Trial values will show when the proper tuning conditions have been reached.

It is not necessary that C_1 be at exactly the original setting after the compensating reactance has been adjusted; it is sufficient that it be in the same vicinity.

Using this procedure practically any length of line can be coupled properly to the transmitter, even when the line s.w.r. is quite high. Unfortunately, no specific values can be suggested for L and C, since they vary widely with Z_0, line length and s.w.r. Their values usually are comparable with the values used in the regular coupling circuits at the same frequency.

● MATCHING TO COAXIAL LINES

Coaxial transmission lines usually are (or at least should be) operated at a low-enough standing-wave ratio so that no special matching circuits are needed; the line simply may be connected to the transmitter output terminals. A properly designed transmitter output circuit (see chapter on high-frequency transmitters) will be capable of handling variations in s.w.r. that are acceptable from the standpoint of line losses.

However, there are cases where it becomes necessary to provide some frequency selectivity between the transmitter and antenna system in order to prevent undesirable radiation of harmonics. A matching circuit of the same general type as those discussed above can provide a considerable degree of selectivity in addition to matching the input impedance of the transmission line to the Z_0 of the coaxial link. The difference in the circuit arrangement is simply that the secondary or output side need not be balanced with respect to ground.

Fig. 13-18 shows a typical circuit. Except for

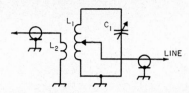

Fig. 13-18—Inductively coupled matching circuit for coupling between coaxial lines. The principles are the same as in Fig. 13-14; the secondary circuit is simply made single-ended for use with a coaxial transmission line.

the fact that there is only one coil tap, the design considerations and adjustment procedure are the same as described for Fig. 13-14. Also, the series capacitor, C_2, shown in Fig. 13-15 may be used with this circuit for fine variation of the effective coupling between L_1 and L_2. Constants for the circuit L_1C_1 are not critical; any convenient values that will tune to the operating frequency may be used. The Q of this circuit, and hence the selectivity, is controlled principally by the position of the line tap. As the tap is moved farther up the coil the Q and selectivity decrease.

The practical matching circuits described in the following section may be used with coaxial line simply by connecting the outer conductor of the line to the center of the coil and tapping the inner conductor along one side. The balanced circuit may still be used, although if the coupler is to be used only with coaxial line the circuit may be made single-ended as shown in Fig. 13-18.

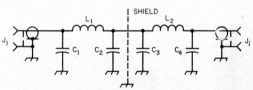

Fig. 13-19—Half-wave filter for harmonic suppression. The two sections of the filter should be shielded from each other as indicated by the dashed line, and the whole filter should be constructed in a shield enclosure to insure effective operation. A separate filter is required for each amateur band. All capacitors have the same value, as do all inductors, for a given band. Suggested constants are as follows:

Band	Capacitance	Inductance
3.5 Mc.	820 $\mu\mu$f.	2.2 μh.
7 Mc.	390 $\mu\mu$f.	1.3 μh.
14 Mc.	220 $\mu\mu$f.	0.57 μh.
21 Mc.	150 $\mu\mu$f.	0.375 μh.
28 Mc.	100 $\mu\mu$f.	0.3 μh.

Design is based on standard values of fixed mica capacitors. Larger capacitances may be made up by using smaller-capacitance units in parallel, if necessary. See text for voltage ratings. Inductances may be adjusted to proper value by resonating to center of band with the capacitance value given in the above table.

"Half-wave" Filters
for Harmonic Suppression

If impedance matching is not a consideration —i.e., the transmission line to the antenna is operating at a low s.w.r. — but harmonic suppression is desirable, the circuit of Fig. 13-19 may be used as an alternative to Fig. 13-18. This is a "half-wave" filter circuit, so called because it has similar properties to a half-wave transmission line. When inserted in a line, the impedance at the input terminals of the filter is the same impedance that the filter "sees" at its output terminals. Thus if the line input impedance is a pure resistance of 50 ohms, the impedance at the filter input terminals also will be 50 ohms.

Just as in the half-wave line case, the characteristic impedance of the filter can be any value without altering its performance with respect to input and output impedance. However, it is desirable in the interests of broad-band operation to make the filter characteristic impedance approximately the same as the Z_0 of the line. The constants given in Fig. 13-19 will serve for either 50- or 75-ohm line. The filter can be used without adjustment at any frequency within the amateur band for which it is designed.

The capacitance values required are fairly large, but under the assumed conditions (low s.w.r. on the line, filter Z_0 approximately equal to line Z_0) the voltages across the capacitors are low. Mica capacitors having a voltage rating suitable for the power level are satisfactory. The peak rating required is equal to $\sqrt{2PZ_0}$, where P is the r.f. power and Z_0 is the characteristic impedance of the line. This value should be doubled for 100 per cent amplitude modulation, and it is advisable to allow a safety factor in addition. A rating of 1500 volts d.c. will be sufficient for a kilowatt a.m. transmitter if the line is well matched by the antenna.

The attenuation of a filter of this type is about 30 db. at the second harmonic and greater at higher harmonics, until limited by self-resonances at high frequencies that occur in the inductors. These usually are not important at harmonics below the fourth.

Coupler or Matching-Circuit Construction

The design of matching or "antenna coupler" circuits has been covered in the preceding section, and the adjustment procedure also has been outlined. Since circuits of this type are most frequently used for transferring power from the transmitter to a parallel-conductor transmission line, a principal point requiring attention is that of maintaining good balance to ground. If the coupler circuit is appreciably unbalanced the currents in the two wires of the transmission line will also be unbalanced, resulting in radiation from the line.

In most cases the matching circuit will be built on a metal chassis, following common practice in the construction of transmitting units. The chassis, because of its relatively large area, will tend to establish a "ground" — even though not actually grounded — particularly if it is assembled with other units of the transmitter in a rack or cabinet. The components used in the coupler, therefore, should be placed so that they are electrically symmetrical with respect to the chassis and to each other.

In general, the construction of a coupler circuit should physically resemble the tank layouts used with push-pull amplifiers. In parallel-tuned circuits a split-stator capacitor should be used. The capacitor frame should be insulated from the chassis because, depending on line length and other factors, harmonic reduction and line balance may be improved in some cases by grounding and in others by not grounding. It is therefore advisable to adopt construction that permits either. Provision also should be made for grounding the center of the coil, for the same reason. The coil in a parallel-tuned circuit should be mounted so that its hot ends are symmetrically placed with respect to the chassis and other components. This equalizes stray capacitances and helps maintain good balance.

When the coupler is of the type that can be shifted to series or parallel tuning as required, two separate single-ended capacitors will be satisfactory. As described earlier, they should be connected so that both frames go to corresponding parts of the circuit — i.e., either to the coil or to the line — for series tuning, and when used in parallel for parallel tuning should be connected frame-to-stator.

A coupler designed and adjusted so that the connecting link acts as a matched transmission line may be placed in any convenient location. Some amateurs prefer to install the coupler at the point where the main transmission line enters the station. This helps maintain a tidy station lay-

Fig. 13-20—Matching circuit for coupling balanced line to a coaxial link. It may also be used between two coaxial lines as described in the text. The coil at the left is simply "stored" on the chassis as a convenience for changing between two favorite bands. A "Monimatch" bridge is mounted under the 7 × 11 × 3 inch chassis.

Coupler Construction

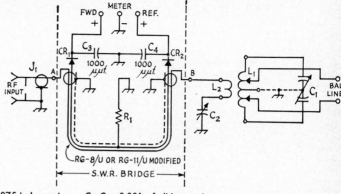

Fig. 13-21—Circuit of the coax-coupled matching circuit of Fig. 13-20. The s.w.r. bridge, a highly useful aid in adjustment, may be omitted if desired, in which case points A and B are simply connected together. See text for data on modified line.

C_1—100 $\mu\mu$f. per section variable, 0.075-inch spacing (Johnson 154-505).
C_2—700 to 800 $\mu\mu$f.; dual-section 365- to 400-$\mu\mu$f. broadcast-receiver type capacitor with sections in parallel.

C_3, C_4—0.001-μf. disk ceramic.
CR_1, CR_2—1N34A or equivalent.
J_1—Coax receptacle, chassis-mounting type.
L_1, L_2—See coil table.
R_1—See text.

out when an air-insulated parallel-conductor transmission line is used. With solid-dielectric lines, which lend themselves well to neat installation indoors, it is probably more desirable to install the coupler where it can be reached easily for adjustment and band-changing.

● COAX-COUPLED MATCHING CIRCUIT

The matching unit shown in Fig. 13-20 is constructed according to the design principles outlined earlier in this chapter. It uses a parallel-tuned circuit with taps for matching a parallel-conductor line through a link coil to a coaxial line to the transmitter. It will handle about 500 watts of r.f. power and will work, without modification, into lines of any length if the s.w.r. is below 3 or 4 to 1. If the s.w.r. is high, it may be necessary to compensate for the reactive part of the input impedance of the line, at certain line lengths, by using an additional coil or capacitor as discussed earlier. The necessity for such compensation can be avoided, on lines having a high s.w.r., by making the electrical length of the line a multiple of a quarter wavelength.

As shown by the circuit diagram, Fig. 13-21, the link circuit is adjusted by means of a variable capacitor, C_2, to facilitate matching between the main transmission line from the antenna and the coax line to the transmitter. The coils are constructed from commercially available coil material, and the link (L_2) inductances are chosen to provide adequate coupling for flat lines. The link

coil, of smaller diameter than the tank coil L_1, is mounted inside the latter at the center. Duco cement is used to hold the coils together at their bottom tie strips. The coils are mounted on Millen type 40305 plugs and require no other support than the stiffness of the short lengths of wire going into the end prongs of the plug from the tank coil. Short lengths of spaghetti tubing are slipped over the leads to the link coil where they go between the tank coil turns to reach the plug.

Taps on the tank coil for connection to a parallel-conductor transmission line are made by means of Johnson type 235-860 clips. If coils are changed frequently it will be convenient, after finding the proper tap points for each band, to bend ordinary soldering lugs around the wire and solder them in place so they project radially from the coil. The clips can then be adjusted to fit snugly over the lugs when pushed on sidewise. Used this way, the clips provide an easy and rapid method of connecting and disconnecting the line.

Monimatch

The circuit as shown in Fig. 13-21 includes a bridge or directional coupler of the Monimatch type to assist in adjusting the circuit to match the coax line. It is constructed from a 24-inch length of either RG-8/U or RG-11/U (depending on the Z_0 of the coax line between the transmitter and the matching circuit) as described in the section on measurements. The pickup line, to

Band, Mc.	L_1				L_2			
	Turns	Wire Size	Dia., In.	Turns/In.	Turns	Wire Size	Dia., In.	Turns/In.
3.5	44	16	2½	10	10	16	2	10
7	18	12	2½	6	6	16	2	10
14	10	12	2½	6	3	16	2	10
21–28	6	12	2½	6	2	16	2	10

Coil Data for Fig. 13-21

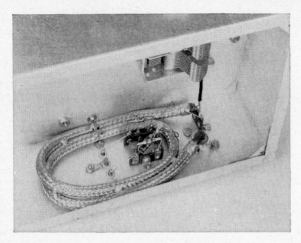

Fig. 13-22—Below-chassis view of the matching circuit, showing Monimatch made from a section of coax cable. The crystal rectifiers are mounted on dual tie-point strips, with R_1 between them.

which R_1 and the crystal rectifiers are connected, is a length of No. 30 enameled wire inserted between the insulation and the shield-braid outer conductor of the coax cable. In constructing this line section be careful not to scrape the enamel from the wire, and after the braid has been smoothed out to its original length check between it and the pickup wire with an ohmmeter to make sure the two are not short-circuited. The cable is formed into a double turn so that the center, where R_1 connects to the pickup wire, is close to the ends. This keeps the ground paths to minimum length and helps in obtaining proper balance in the bridge. The braided outsides of the turns are spot soldered together at several points to reduce the effect of unwanted currents on the surface, and also to improve the assembly mechanically.

Bridge Adjustment

Adjusting the bridge is simply a matter of finding the value of R_1 that gives a good null reading with the indicating meter connected to the "reflected" position when the output end is terminated in a resistive load of either 52 or 75 ohms, depending on whether RG-8/U or RG-11/U is used. If a suitable dummy load is available (see chapter on measurements) the wiring to L_2 should be disconnected at B in Fig. 13-21 and the dummy load connected between B and ground (that is, to the output terminals of the Monimatch). R_1 may be set to the proper value by trying several values of half-watt carbon resistors, or combinations in parallel, to find the resistance that gives the deepest null. A value of about 35 ohms proved to be optimum with RG-8/U in the bridge shown in the photograph.

Alternatively, a dummy load may be connected to the balanced line terminals, and the Monimatch disconnected at B. If a suitable bridge can be borrowed, it can be connected at B and r.f. power fed through it to the matching circuit, which should then be adjusted to match the coax line. This establishes a load of known value which may then be used for adjustment of the built-in Monimatch as described above, after the connection at B has been restored.

A suitable indicator unit, including meter, variable resistor, and forward-reflected switch, is described in the chapter on measurements.

Matching-Circuit Adjustment

The method of adjusting a matching circuit of this type has been described earlier in this chapter in connection with Figs. 13-14 and 13-15. The construction is such that either the center tap of L_1 or the rotor of C_1 may be grounded to the chassis, since C_1 is mounted on small stand-off insulators. Insofar as normal balanced-line operation is concerned, it makes no difference which is grounded (or neither). Grounding will, however, affect any parallel or "antenna" currents on the line. In general, the effect of such currents will be minimized if the ground connection showing the least r.f. current is chosen. This test should also be tried with and without an actual earth connection to the matching-circuit chassis.

The coupler may be used between coaxial lines by grounding the center tap of L_1 and connecting the outer braid of the coax line to the chassis and the inner conductor to a single tap on the coil. The method of adjustment is otherwise the same as for balanced lines.

The matching circuit should be adjusted with the aid of an s.w.r. bridge, as described earlier in this chapter. In general, the tuning will be less critical, and the circuit will work over a wider frequency range without readjustment, if the taps are kept as far toward the ends of the coil as possible and C_2 is set at the largest capacitance that will permit bringing the s.w.r. in the coax link down to 1 to 1.

● ANTENNA MATCHING CIRCUIT FOR HIGH OR LOW IMPEDANCE

The unit shown in Figs. 13-23 and 13-25 can be used to match the coaxial-line output of a transmitter to either a high- or low-impedance load. To facilitate tuning it includes an s.w.r. indicator that can be set for a wide range of power levels. The power-handling ability of a circuit of this type will depend to some extent upon the imped-

Coupler Construction

Fig. 13-23—Antenna coupler out of its case. The large dial controls a 100-$\mu\mu$f. tuning capacitor, and the smaller dial (bottom center) turns a 320-$\mu\mu$f. coupling capacitor. Two knobs control the sensitivity and direction of the s.w.r. bridge. Simple band switches on top of the aluminum arch are made from banana plugs and insulated jacks

ance of the load, but as shown the matching circuit will handle up to 300 or 400 watts under practically any condition. If higher power is involved, the circuit can be "scaled upward" with heavier inductances and greater capacitor spacings.

Referring to the circuit in Fig. 13-24, a series-tuned circuit, L_3C_1, is coupled to a balanced circuit, $C_2L_2L_4$. This latter circuit is series-tuned if the load is connected to terminals A-A and parallel-tuned if a jumper is used between A-A and the load is connected at B-B. Low-impedance loads (high-current) call for series tuning, and high-impedance loads (high voltage) couple better with parallel tuning.

A simple version of the "Monimatch" s.w.r. indicator is included by wrapping the necessary length of RG-58/U around the indicating meter (see Fig. 13-25).

The unit shown here was built on a 7 × 9 × 2-inch aluminum chassis, but dimensions are not critical so long as the inductance is not crowded against the metal parts of the chassis or housing. Capacitor C_2 is insulated from the chassis and panel by using small stand-off insulators for its support and a ceramic insulating shaft coupling.

The switches S_1 and S_2 are made from nylon-insulated banana jacks (Johnson 108-901) mounted on an arch of $\frac{3}{32}$-inch sheet aluminum. In each switch one jack serves as the rotor

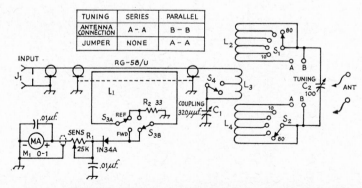

TUNING	SERIES	PARALLEL
ANTENNA CONNECTION	A - A	B - B
JUMPER	NONE	A - A

Fig. 13-24—Circuit diagram of the antenna coupler.

C_1—320-$\mu\mu$f. midget variable (Hammarlund MC-325-M).

C_2—100-$\mu\mu$f. tuning, .077-inch spacing (National TMC-100).

J_1—Coaxial receptacle, type SO-239.

L_1—Wire inside coaxial line. See text.

L_2, L_3, L_4—See Fig. 13-26.

M_1—0-1 milliammeter (Triplett 227-PL).

R_1—25,000-ohm volume control (Mallory U-28).

R_2—33 ohms, ½ watt. Must be composition, not wirewound.

S_1, S_2—See text.

S_3—D.p.d.t. rotary switch (Centralab 1462).

S_4—Tap on L_3, shorted to end of coil by copper test clip (Mueller 45C).

353

Fig. 13-25—Rear view of the coupler shows the coaxial line of the s.w.r. indicator wrapped around the meter. The test clip of S_4 is parked on one of the feedthrough insulators for L_3. Shorting bar in B-B (center) only for photograph; it is used only in A-A.

terminal and the others serve as the contacts. A shorting bar of aluminum with two banana plugs (Johnson 108-750) mounted on it at the proper distance is used as the switch arm. The shorting bar for the A-A connection is made similarly. Two feedthrough insulators at the rear of the cabinet (Bud C-1746) are used as antenna terminals; flexible leads connected to them have banana plugs at the other end to connect to A-A or B-B as required.

The inductors L_2, L_3 and L_4 are made from a length of 2-inch diameter transmitting coil stock, as indicated in Fig. 13-26. While the over-all sizes of the coils will suffice for practically any installation, it is suggested that the taps be made temporarily until the unit can be tested with the antenna to be used. The taps as indicated will be correct for most cases, but variations in antenna systems will account for some discrepancies. The inductors are supported by their leads from the banana jacks. Switch S_4 is merely two solder lugs on the proper wires; they can be shorted together by clipping them with a copper test clip. (It is recommended that screws and hardware be tested with a magnet before using near the coils; iron will get hot in the fields surrounding the coils.)

The s.w.r. bridge is made by first peeling the vinyl outer coating from a 3½-foot length of RG-58/U. Measure 6½ inches out either side of the center and open the shield braid slightly with a pointed tool. Thread a length of insulated wire (No. 22 or 24) in one hole and out the other, being careful not to scratch off the insulation of the wire; test with an ohmeter to make sure. Smooth out the shield braid on the RG-58/U and wrap the coaxial line for two turns around the meter housing. The coaxial line can then be threaded through a rubber grommet in the chassis

and led to J_1 and the feedthrough from L_3, both at the rear of the chassis. The length of insulated wire, L_1, will have its ends conveniently situated for soldering to S_3.

In operation, the antenna feed line can be connected for series tuning if coaxial line is used and for parallel tuning if open-wire line is used. This is not an iron-clad rule, however, particularly when a high s.w.r. exists on the line to the antenna. Capacitors C_1 and C_2 are then adjusted for minimum reflected reading and maximum forward reading of M_1. If the maximum reading tends to send the meter off scale, increase the resistance at R_1. If the reflected reading cannot be brought down to a very low value, it may be necessary to try the opposite series/parallel connection or, as mentioned earlier, to change the location of the taps on L_2 and L_4.

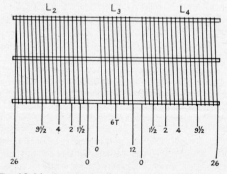

Fig. 13-26—Details of coil tapping. Material is No. 16 wound 10 t.p.i. on 2-inch diameter (B&W 3907-1). Half turns peeled off between L_2-L_3 and L_3-L_4 to give one-turn separation. Tap placement may vary somewhat with antenna system.

CHAPTER 14

Antennas

An *antenna system* can be considered to include the antenna proper (the portion that radiates the r.f. energy), the feed line, and any coupling devices used for transferring power from the transmitter to the line and from the line to the antenna. Some simple systems may omit the transmission line or one or both of the coupling devices. This chapter will describe the antenna proper, and in many cases will show popular types of lines, as well as line-to-antenna couplings where they are required. However, it should be kept in mind that *any* antenna proper can be used with *any* type of feedline if a suitable coupling is used between the antenna and the line. Changing the line does not change the type of antenna.

Selecting an Antenna

In selecting the type of antenna to use, the majority of amateurs are somewhat limited through space and structural limitations to simple antenna systems, except for v.h.f. operation where the small space requirements make the use of multielement beams readily possible. This section will consider antennas for frequencies as high as 30 Mc. — a later chapter will describe the popular types of v.h.f. antennas. However, even though the available space may be limited, it is well to consider the propagation characteristics of the frequency band or bands to be used, to insure that best possible use is made of the available facilities. The propagation characteristics of the amateur-band frequencies are described in Chapter Fifteen. In general, antenna construction and location become more critical and important on the higher frequencies. On the lower frequencies (3.5 and 7 Mc.) the vertical angle of radiation and the plane of polarization may be of relatively little importance; at 28 Mc. they may be all-important.

Definitions

The **polarization** of a straight-wire antenna is determined by its position with respect to the earth. Thus a vertical antenna radiates vertically polarized waves, while a horizontal antenna radiates horizontally polarized waves in a direction broadside to the wire and vertically polarized waves at high vertical angles off the ends of the wire. The wave from an antenna in a slanting position, or from the horizontal antenna in directions other than mentioned above, contains components of both horizontal and vertical polarization.

The **vertical angle of maximum radiation** of an antenna is determined by the free-space pattern of the antenna, its height above ground, and the nature of the ground. The angle is measured in a vertical plane with respect to a tangent to the earth at that point, and it will usually vary with the horizontal angle, except in the case of a simple vertical antenna. The **horizontal angle of maximum radiation** of an antenna is determined by the free-space pattern of the antenna.

The **impedance** of the antenna at any point is the ratio of the voltage to the current at that point. It is important in connection with feeding power to the antenna, since it constitutes the load to the line offered by the antenna. It can be either resistive or complex, depending upon whether or not the antenna is resonant.

The **field strength** produced by an antenna is proportional to the current flowing in it. When there are standing waves on an antenna, the parts of the wire carrying the higher current have the greater radiating effect. All resonant antennas have standing waves — only terminated types, like the terminated rhombic and terminated "V," have substantially uniform current along their lengths.

The ratio of power required to produce a given field strength with a "comparison" antenna to the power required to produce the same field strength with a specified type of antenna is called the **power gain** of the latter antenna. The field is measured in the optimum direction of the antenna under test. The comparison antenna is generally a half-wave antenna at the same height and having the same polarization as the antenna under consideration. Gain usually is expressed in decibels.

In unidirectional beams (antennas with most of the radiation in only one direction) the **front-to-back** ratio is the ratio of power radiated in the maximum direction to power radiated in the opposite direction. It is also a measure of the reduction in received signal when the beam direction is changed from that for maximum response to the opposite direction. Front-to-back ratio is usually expressed in decibels.

The **bandwidth** of an antenna refers to the frequency range over which a property falls within acceptable limits. The **gain bandwidth**, the **front-to-back-ratio bandwidth** and the **standing-wave-ratio bandwidth** are of prime interest in amateur work.

Ground Effects

The radiation pattern of any antenna that is many wavelengths distant from the ground and all other objects is called the **free-space pattern** of that antenna. The free-space pattern of an antenna is almost impossible to obtain in practice, except in the v.h.f. and u.h.f. ranges. Below 30 Mc., the height of the antenna above ground is a major factor in determining the radiation pattern of the antenna.

When any antenna is near the ground the free-space pattern is modified by reflection of radiated waves from the ground, so that the actual pattern is the resultant of the free-space pattern and ground reflections. This resultant is dependent upon the height of the antenna, its position or orientation with respect to the surface of the ground, and the electrical characteristics of the ground. The effect of a perfectly reflecting ground is such that the

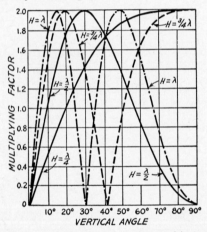

Fig. 14-1—Effect of ground on radiation of horizontal antennas at vertical angles for four antenna heights. This chart is based on perfectly conducting ground.

original free-space field strength may be multiplied by a factor which has a maximum value of 2, for complete reinforcement, and having all intermediate values to zero, for complete cancellation. These reflections only affect the radiation pattern in the vertical plane — that is, in directions upward from the earth's surface — and not in the horizontal plane, or the usual geographical directions.

Fig. 14-1 shows how the multiplying factor varies with the vertical angle for several representative heights for horizontal antennas, As the height is increased the angle at which complete reinforcement takes place is lowered, until for a height equal to one wavelength it occurs at a vertical angle of 15 degrees. At still greater heights, not shown on the chart, the first maximum will occur at still smaller angles.

Radiation Angle

The vertical angle of maximum radiation is of primary importance, especially at the higher

frequencies. It is advantageous, therefore, to erect the antenna at a height that will take advantage of ground reflection in such a way as to reinforce the space radiation at the most desirable angle. Since low angles usually are most effective, this generally means that the antenna should be high — at least one-half wavelength at 14 Mc., and preferably three-quarters or one wavelength, and at least one wavelength, and preferably higher, at 28 Mc. The physical height required for a given height in wavelengths decreases as the frequency is increased, so that good heights are not impracticable; a half wavelength at 14 Mc. is only 35 feet, approximately, while the same height represents a full wavelength at 28 Mc. At 7 Mc. and lower frequencies the higher radiation angles are effective, so that again a useful antenna height is not difficult of attainment. Heights between 35 and 70 feet are suitable for all bands, the higher figures being preferable.

Imperfect Ground

Fig. 14-1 is based on ground having perfect conductivity, whereas the actual earth is not a perfect conductor. The principal effect of actual ground is to make the curves inaccurate at the lowest angles; appreciable high-frequency radiation at angles smaller than a few degrees is practically impossible to obtain over horizontal ground. Above 15 degrees, however, the curves are accurate enough for all practical purposes, and may be taken as indicative of the result to be expected at angles between 5 and 15 degrees.

The effective ground plane — that is, the plane from which ground reflections can be considered to take place — seldom is the actual surface of the ground but is a few feet below it, depending upon the character of the soil.

Impedance

Waves that are reflected directly upward from the ground induce a current in the an-

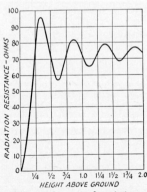

Fig. 14-2—Theoretical curve of variation of radiation resistance for a very thin half-wave horizontal antenna as a function of height in wavelength above perfectly reflecting ground.

Half-Wave Antenna

tenna in passing, and, depending on the antenna height, the phase relationship of this induced current to the original current may be such as either to increase or decrease the total current in the antenna. For the same power input to the antenna, an increase in current is equivalent to a decrease in impedance, and vice versa. Hence, the impedance of the antenna varies with height. The theoretical curve of variation of radiation resistance for a very thin half-wave antenna above perfectly reflecting ground is shown in Fig. 14-2. The impedance approaches the free-space value as the height becomes large, but at low heights may differ considerably from it.

Choice of Polarization

Polarization of the transmitting antenna is generally unimportant on frequencies between 3.5 and 30 Mc. However, the question of whether the antenna should be installed in a horizontal or vertical position deserves consideration for other reasons. A vertical half-wave or quarter-wave antenna will radiate equally well in all *horizontal* directions, so that it is substantially nondirectional, in the usual sense of the word. If installed horizontally, however, the antenna will tend to show directional effects, and will radiate best in the direction at right angles, or broadside, to the wire. The radiation in such a case will be least in the direction toward which the wire points.

The vertical angle of radiation also will be affected by the position of the antenna. If it were not for ground losses at high frequencies, the vertical half-wave antenna would be preferred because it would concentrate the radiation horizontally.

The Half-Wave Antenna

A fundamental form of antenna is a single wire whose length is approximately equal to half the transmitting wavelength. It is the unit from which many more-complex forms of antennas are constructed. It is known as a **dipole antenna.**

The length of a half-wave in space is:

$$Length \text{ (feet)} = \frac{492}{Freq. \text{ (Mc.)}} \quad \textbf{(14-A)}$$

The actual length of a half-wave antenna will not be exactly equal to the half-wave in space, but depends upon the thickness of the conductor in relation to the wavelength as shown in Fig. 14-3, where K is a factor that must be multiplied by the half wavelength in free space to obtain the resonant antenna length. An additional shortening effect occurs with wire antennas supported by insulators at the ends because of the capacitance added to the system by the insulators **(end effect)**. The following formula is sufficiently accurate for wire antennas at frequencies up to 30 Mc.:

$$Length \text{ of half-wave antenna (feet)} =$$
$$\frac{492 \times 0.95}{Freq. \text{ (Mc.)}} = \frac{468}{Freq. \text{ (Mc.)}} \quad \textbf{(14-B)}$$

Example: A half-wave antenna for 7150 kc. (7.15 Mc.) is $\frac{468}{7.15}$ = 65.45 feet, or 65 feet 5 inches.

Above 30 Mc. the following formulas should be used, particularly for antennas constructed from rod or tubing. K is taken from Fig. 14-3.

$$Length \text{ of half-wave antenna (feet)} =$$
$$\frac{492 \times K}{Freq. \text{ (Mc.)}} \quad \textbf{(14-C)}$$

$$or \text{ length (inches)} = \frac{5905 \times K}{Freq. \text{ (Mc.)}} \quad \textbf{(14-D)}$$

Example: Find the length of a half wavelength antenna at 29 Mc., if the antenna is made of 2-inch diameter tubing. At 29 Mc., a half wavelength in space is $\frac{492}{29}$ = 16.97 feet, from Eq. 14-A. Ratio of half wavelength to conductor diameter (changing wavelength to inches) is $\frac{16.97 \times 12}{2}$ = 101.8. From Fig. 14-3, $K = 0.963$ for this ratio. The length of the antenna, from Eq. 14-C, is $\frac{492 \times 0.963}{29}$ = 16.34 feet, or 16 feet 4 inches. The answer is obtained directly in inches by substitution in Eq. 14-D: $\frac{5905 \times 0.963}{29}$ = 196 inches.

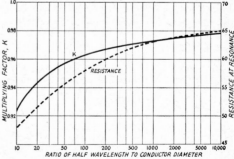

Fig. 14-3—Effect of antenna diameter on length for half-wave resonance, shown as a multiplying factor, K, to be applied to the free-space half wavelength (Equation 14-A). The effect of conductor diameter on the center impedance also is shown.

Current and Voltage Distribution

When power is fed to an antenna, the current and voltage vary along its length. The current is maximum **(loop)** at the center and nearly zero **(node)** at the ends, while the opposite is true of the r.f. voltage. The current does not actually reach zero at the current nodes, because of the end effect; similarly, the voltage is not

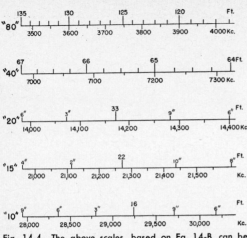

Fig. 14-4—The above scales, based on Eq. 14-B, can be used to determine the length of a half-wave antenna of wire.

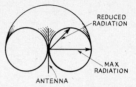

Fig. 14-5—The free-space radiation pattern of a half-wave antenna. The antenna is shown in the vertical position, and the actual "doughnut" pattern is cut in half to show how the line from the center of the antenna to the surface of the pattern varies. In practice this pattern is modified by the height above ground and if the antenna is vertical or horizontal. Fig. 14-1 shows some of the effects of height on the vertical angle of radiation.

uniform in all directions but varies with the angle with respect to the axis of the wire. It is most intense in directions perpendicular to the wire and zero along the direction of the wire, with intermediate values at intermediate angles. This is shown by the sketch of Fig. 14-5, which represents the radiation pattern in free space. The relative intensity of radiation is proportional to the length of a line drawn from the center of the figure to the perimeter. If the antenna is vertical, as shown, then the field strength will be uniform in all horizontal directions; if the

zero at its node because of the resistance of the antenna, which consists of both the r.f. resistance of the wire (*ohmic resistance*) and the **radiation resistance**. The radiation resistance is an *equivalent* resistance, a convenient conception to indicate the radiation properties of an antenna. The radiation resistance is the equivalent resistance that would dissipate the power the antenna radiates, with a current flowing in it equal to the antenna current at a current loop (maximum). The ohmic resistance of a half wavelength antenna is ordinarily small enough, compared with the radiation resistance, to be neglected for all practical purposes.

Impedance

The radiation resistance of an infinitely-thin half-wave antenna in free space is about 73 ohms. The value under practical conditions is commonly taken to be in the neighborhood of 60 to 70 ohms, although it varies with height in the manner of Fig. 14-2. It increases toward the ends. The actual value at the ends will depend on a number of factors, such as the height, the physical construction, the insulators at the ends, and the position with respect to ground.

Conductor Size

The impedance of the antenna also depends upon the diameter of the conductor in relation to the wavelength, as indicated in Fig. 14-3. If the diameter of the conductor is increased the capacitance per unit length increases and the inductance per unit length decreases. Since the radiation resistance is affected relatively little, the decreased L/C ratio causes the Q of the antenna to decrease, so that the resonance curve becomes less sharp. Hence, the antenna is capable of working over a wide frequency range. This effect is greater as the diameter is increased, and is a property of some importance at the very-high frequencies where the wavelength is small.

Radiation Characteristics

The radiation from a dipole antenna is not

Fig. 14-6—Illustrating the importance of vertical angle of radiation in determining antenna directional effects. Off the end, the radiation is greater at higher angles. Ground reflection is neglected in this drawing of the free-space pattern of a horizontal antenna.

antenna is horizontal, the relative field strength will depend upon the direction of the receiving point with respect to the direction of the antenna wire. The variation in radiation at various vertical angles from a half wavelength horizontal antenna is indicated in Figs. 14-16 and 14-7.

● FEEDING A DIPOLE ANTENNA
Direct Feed

If possible, it is advisable to locate the antenna at least a half wavelength from the transmitter and use a transmission line to carry the power from the transmitter to the antenna. However, in many cases this is impossible, particularly on the lower frequencies, and direct feed must be used. Three examples of direct feed are shown in Fig. 14-8. In the method shown at A, C_1 and C_2 should be about 150 $\mu\mu f$. each for the 3.5-Mc. band, 75 $\mu\mu f$. each at 7 Mc., and proportionately smaller at the higher frequencies. The antenna coil connected between them should resonate to 3.5 Mc. with about 60 or 70 $\mu\mu f$., for the 80-meter band, for 40 meters it should resonate with 30 or 35 $\mu\mu f$., and so on. The circuit is adjusted by using loose coupling between the antenna coil and the transmitter tank coil and adjusting C_1 and C_2 until resonance is indi-

Feeding a Dipole Antenna

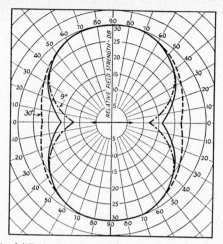

Fig. 14-7—Horizontal pattern of a horizontal half-wave antenna at three vertical radiation angles. The solid line is relative radiation at 15 degrees. Dotted lines show deviation from the 15-degree pattern for angles of 9 and 30 degrees. The patterns are useful for shape only, since the amplitude will depend upon the height of the antenna above ground and the vertical angle considered. The patterns for all three angles have been proportioned to the same scale, but this does not mean that the maximum amplitudes necessarily will be the same. The arrow indicates the direction of the horizontal antenna wire.

cated by an increase in plate current. The coupling between the coils should then be increased until proper plate current is drawn. It may be necessary to re-resonate the transmitter tank circuit as the coupling is increased, but the change should be small.

The circuits in Fig. 14-8B and C are used when only one end of the antenna is accessible. In B, the coupling is adjusted by moving the

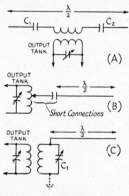

Fig. 14-8—Methods of directly exciting the half-wave antenna. A, current feed, series tuning; B, voltage feed, capacitive coupling; C, voltage feed, with inductively coupled antenna tank. In A, the coupling circuit is not included in the effective electrical length of the antenna system proper. Link coupling can be used in A and C.

tap toward the "hot" or plate end of the tank coil — the series capacitor may be of any convenient value that will stand the voltage, and it doesn't have to be variable. In the circuit at C, the antenna tuned circuit (C_1 and the antenna coil) should be similar to the transmitter tank circuit. The antenna tuned circuit is adjusted to resonance with the antenna connected but with loose coupling to the transmitter. Heavier loading of the tube is

then obtained by tightening the coupling between the antenna coil and the transmitter tank coil.

Of the three systems, that at A is preferable because it is a symmetrical system and generally results in less r.f. power "floating" around the shack. The system of B is undesirable because it provides practically no protection against the radiation of harmonics, and it should only be used in emergencies.

Transmission-Line Feed for Dipoles

Since the impedance at the center of a dipole is in the vicinity of 70 ohms, it offers a good match for 75-ohm two-wire transmission lines. Several types are available on the market, with different power-handling capabilities. They can be connected in the center of the antenna, across a small strain insulator to provide a convenient connection point. Coaxial line of 75 ohms impedance can also be used, but it is heavier and thus not as

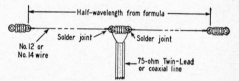

Fig. 14-9—Construction of a dipole fed with 75-ohm line. The length of the antenna is calculated from Equation 14-B or Fig. 14-4.

convenient. In either case, the transmission line should be run away at right angles to the antenna for at least one-quarter wavelength, if possible, to avoid current unbalance in the line caused by pick-up from the antenna. The antenna length is calculated from Equation 14-B, for a half wavelength antenna. When No. 12 or No. 14 enameled wire is used for the antenna, as is generally the case, the length of the wire is the over-all length measured from the loop through the insulator at each end. This is illustrated in Fig. 14-9.

The use of 75-ohm line results in a "flat" line over most of any amateur band. However, by making the half-wave antenna in a special manner, called the two-wire or folded dipole, a good match is offered for a 300-ohm line. Such an antenna is shown in Fig. 14-10. The open-wire line shown in Fig. 14-10 is made of No. 12 or No. 14 enameled wire, separated by

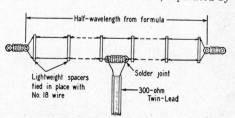

Fig. 14-10—The construction of an open-wire folded dipole fed with 300-ohm line. The length of the antenna is calculated from Equation 14-B or Fig. 14-4.

lightweight spacers of Lucite or other material (it doesn't have to be a *low-loss* insulating material), and the spacing can be on the order of from 4 to 8 inches, depending upon what is convenient and what the operating frequency is. At 14 Mc., 4-inch separation is satisfactory, and 8-inch spacing can be used at 3.5 Mc.

The half wavelength antenna can also be made from the proper length of 300-ohm line, opened on one side in the center and connected to the feedline. After the wires have been soldered together, the joint can be strengthened by molding some of the excess insulating material (polyethylene) around the joint with a hot iron, or a suitable lightweight clamp of two pieces of Lucite can be devised.

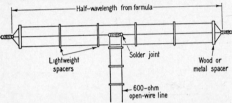

Fig. 14-11—The construction of a 3-wire folded dipole is similar to that of the 2-wire folded dipole. The end spacers may have to be slightly stronger than the others because of the greater compression force on them. The length of the antenna is obtained from Equation 14-B or Fig. 14-4. A suitable line can be made from No. 14 wire spaced 5 inches, or from No. 12 wire spaced 6 inches.

Similar in some respects to the two-wire folded dipole, the three-wire folded dipole of Fig. 14-11 offers a good match for a 600-ohm line. It is favored by amateurs who prefer to use an open-wire line instead of the 300-ohm insulated line. The three wires of the antenna proper should all be of the same diameter.

Another method for offering a match to a 600-ohm open-wire line with a half wavelength antenna is shown in Fig. 14-12. The system is called a **delta match**. The line is "fanned" as it approaches the antenna, to have a gradually increasing impedance that equals the antenna impedance at the point of connection. The dimensions are fairly critical, but careful measurement before installing the antenna and matching section is generally all that is necessary. The length of the antenna, L, is calcu-

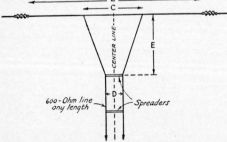

Fig. 14-12—Delta-matched antenna system. The dimensions C, D, and E are found by formulas given in the text. It is important that the matching section, E, come straight away from the antenna without any bends.

lated from Equation **14-B** or Fig. 14-4. The length of section C is computed from:

$$C \text{ (feet)} = \frac{118}{\text{Freq. (Mc.)}} \qquad \textbf{(14-E)}$$

The feeder clearance, E, is found from

$$E \text{ (feet)} = \frac{148}{\text{Freq. (Mc.)}} \qquad \textbf{(14-F)}$$

Example: For a frequency of 7.1 Mc., the length

$$L = \frac{468}{7.1} = 65.91 \text{ feet, or 65 feet 11 inches.}$$

$$C = \frac{118}{7.1} = 16.62 \text{ feet, or 16 feet 7 inches.}$$

$$E = \frac{148}{7.1} = 20.84 \text{ feet, or 20 feet 10 inches.}$$

Since the equations hold only for 600-ohm line, it is important that the line be close to this value. This requires 5-inch spaced No. 14 wire, 6-inch spaced No. 12 wire, or 3¾-inch spaced No. 16 wire.

If a half wavelength antenna is fed at the center with other than 75-ohm line, or if a two-wire dipole is fed with other than 300-ohm line, standing waves will appear on the line and coupling to the transmitter may become awkward for some line lengths, as described in Chapter 13. However, in many cases it is not convenient to feed the half-wave antenna with the correct line (as is the case where multiband operation of the same antenna is desired), and sometimes it is not convenient to feed the antenna at the center. Where multiband operation is desired (to be discussed later) or when the antenna must be fed at one end by a trans-

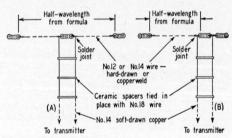

Fig. 14-13—The half-wave antenna can be fed at the center or at the end with an open-wire line. The antenna length is obtained from Equation 14-B or Fig. 14-4.

mission line, an open-wire line of from 450 to 600 ohms impedance is generally used. The impedance at the end of a half wavelength antenna is in the vicinity of several thousand ohms, and hence a standing-wave ratio of 4 or 5 is not unusual when the line is connected to the end of the antenna. It is advisable, therefore, to keep the losses in the line as low as possible. This requires the use of ceramic or Micalex feeder spacers, if any appreciable power is used. For low-power installations in dry climates, dry wood spacers boiled in paraffin are satisfactory. Mechanical details of half wavelength antennas fed with open-wire lines are given in Fig. 14-13. Regardless of the power level, solid-dielectric Twin-Lead is not recommended for this use.

Long-Wire Antennas

An antenna will be resonant so long as an integral number of standing waves of current and voltage can exist along its length; in other words, so long as its length is some integral multiple of a half wavelength. When the antenna is more than a half-wave long it usually is called a long-wire antenna, or a harmonic antenna.

Current and Voltage Distribution

Fig. 14-14 shows the current and voltage distribution along a wire operating at its fundamental frequency (where its length is

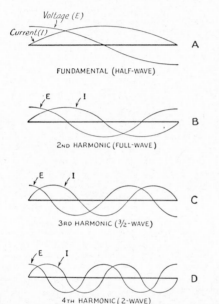

FUNDAMENTAL (HALF-WAVE)

A

2ND HARMONIC (FULL-WAVE)

B

3RD HARMONIC (³⁄₂-WAVE)

C

4TH HARMONIC (2-WAVE)

D

Fig. 14-14—Standing-wave current and voltage distribution along an antenna when it is operated at various harmonics of its fundamental resonant frequency.

equal to a half wavelength) and at its second, third and fourth harmonics. For example, if the fundamental frequency of the antenna is 7 Mc., the current and voltage distribution will be as shown at A. The same antenna excited at 14 Mc. would have current and voltage distribution as shown at B. At 21 Mc., the third harmonic of 7 Mc., the current and voltage distribution would be as in C; and at 28 Mc., the fourth harmonic, as in D. The number of the harmonic is the number of half waves contained in the antenna at the particular operating frequency.

The polarity of current or voltage in each standing wave is opposite to that in the adjacent standing waves. This is shown in the figure by drawing the current and voltage curves successively above and below the antenna (taken as a zero reference line), to indicate that the polarity reverses when the current or voltage goes through zero. Currents

flowing in the same direction are *in phase;* in opposite directions, *out of phase.*

It is evident that one antenna may be used for harmonically-related frequencies, such as the various amateur bands. The long-wire or harmonic antenna is the basis of multiband operation with one antenna.

Physical Lengths

The length of a long-wire antenna is not an exact multiple of that of a half-wave antenna because the end effects operate only on the end sections of the antenna; in other parts of the wire these effects are absent, and the wire length is approximately that of an equivalent portion of the wave in space. The formula for the length of a long-wire antenna, therefore, is

$$Length \text{ (feet)} = \frac{492\,(N-0.05)}{Freq.\text{ (Mc.)}} \qquad \textbf{14-G}$$

where N is the number of *half*-waves on the antenna.

Example: An antenna 4 half-waves long at 14.2
Mc. would be $\dfrac{492\,(4-0.05)}{14.2} = \dfrac{492 \times 3.95}{14.2}$
= 136.7 feet, or 136 feet 8 inches.

It is apparent that an antenna cut as a half-wave for a given frequency will be slightly off resonance at exactly twice that frequency (the second harmonic), because of the decreased influence of the end effects when the antenna is more than one-half wavelength long. The effect is not very important, except for a possible unbalance in the feeder system and consequent

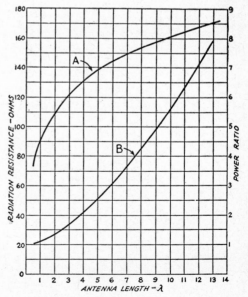

Fig. 14-15—Curve A shows variation in radiation resistance with antenna length. Curve B shows power in lobes of maximum radiation for long-wire antennas as a ratio to the maximum radiation for a half-wave antenna.

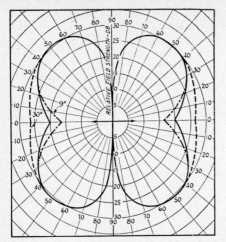

Fig. 14-16—Horizontal patterns of radiation from a full-wave antenna. The solid line shows the pattern for a vertical angle of 15 degrees; dotted lines show deviation from the 15-degree pattern at 9 and 30 degrees. All three patterns are drawn to the same relative scale; actual amplitudes will depend upon the height of the antenna.

radiation from the feedline. If the antenna is fed in the exact center, no unbalance will occur at any frequency, but end-fed systems will show an unbalance on all but one frequency in each harmonic range.

Impedance and Power Gain

The radiation resistance as measured at a current loop becomes higher as the antenna length is increased. Also, a long-wire antenna radiates more power in its most favorable direction than does a half-wave antenna in its most favorable direction. This power gain is secured at the expense of radiation in other

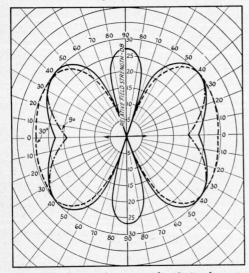

Fig. 14-17—Horizontal patterns of radiation from an antenna three half-waves long. The solid line shows the pattern for a vertical angle of 15 degrees; dotted lines show deviation from the 15-degree pattern at 9 and 30 degrees. Minor lobes coincide for all three angles.

directions. Fig. 14-15 shows how the radiation resistance and the power in the lobe of maximum radiation vary with the antenna length.

Directional Characteristics

As the wire is made longer in terms of the number of half wavelengths, the directional effects change. Instead of the "doughnut" pattern of the half-wave antenna, the directional characteristic splits up into "lobes" which make various angles with the wire. In general, as the length of the wire is increased the direction in which maximum radiation occurs tends to approach the line of the antenna itself.

Directional characteristics for antennas one wavelength, three half-wavelengths, and two wavelengths long are given in Figs. 14-16, 14-17 and 14-18, for three vertical angles of radiation. Note that, as the wire length in-

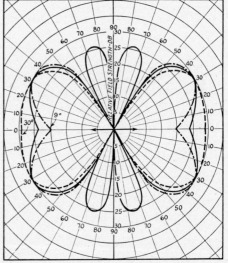

Fig. 14-18—Horizontal patterns of radiation from an antenna two wavelengths long. The solid line shows the pattern for a vertical angle of 15 degrees; dotted lines show deviation from the 15-degree pattern at 9 and 30 degrees. The minor lobes coincide for all three angles.

creases, the radiation along the line of the antenna becomes more pronounced. Still longer antennas can be considered to have practically "end-on" directional characteristics, even at the lower radiation angles.

Methods of Feeding

In a long-wire antenna, the currents in adjacent half-wave sections must be out of phase, as shown in Fig. 14-14. The feeder system must not upset this phase relationship. This is satisfied by feeding the antenna at either end or at any current loop. A two-wire feeder cannot be inserted at a current node, however, because this invariably brings the currents in two adjacent half-wave sections in phase. A long wire antenna is usually made a half wavelength at the lowest frequency and fed at the end.

Multiband Antennas

As suggested in the preceding section, the same antenna may be used for several bands by operating it on harmonics. When this is done it is necessary to use tuned feeders, since the impedance matching for nonresonant feeder operation can be accomplished only at one frequency unless means are provided for changing the length of a matching section and shifting the point at which the feeder is attached to it.

A dipole antenna that is center-fed by a solid-dielectric line is useless for even harmonic operation; on all even harmonics there is a voltage maximum occurring right at the feed point, and the resultant impedance mismatch causes a large standing-wave ratio and consequently high losses arise in the solid dielectric. It is wise not to attempt to use on its even harmonics a half-wave antenna center-fed with coaxial cable. On odd harmonics, as between 7 and 21 Mc., a current loop will appear in the center of the antenna and a fair match can be obtained. High-impedance solid-dielectric lines such as 300-ohm Twin-Lead may be used in an emergency, provided the power does not exceed a few hundred watts, but it is an inefficient feed method.

When the same antenna is used for work in several bands, the directional characteristics will vary with the band in use.

Simple Systems

The most practical simple multiband antenna is one that is a half wavelength long at the lowest frequency and is fed either at the center or one end with an open-wire line. Although the standing wave ratio on the feedline will not approach 1.0 on any band, if the losses in the line are low the system will be efficient. From the standpoint of reduced feedline radiation, a center-fed system is superior to one that is end-fed, but the end-fed arrangement is often more convenient and should not be ignored as a possibility. The center-fed antenna will not have the same radiation pattern as an end-fed one of the same length, except on frequencies where the length of the antenna is a half wavelength. The end-fed antenna acts like a long-wire antenna on all bands (for which it is longer than a half wavelength), but the center-fed one acts like two antennas of half that length fed in phase. For example, if a full-wavelength antenna is fed at one end, it will have a radiation pattern as shown in Fig. 14-16, but if it is fed in the center the pattern will be somewhat similar to Fig. 14-7, with the maximum radiation broadside to the wire. Either antenna is a good radiator, but if the radiation pattern is a factor, the point of feed must be considered.

Since multiband operation of an antenna does not permit matching of the feedline, some attention should be paid to the length of the feedline if convenient transmitter-coupling arrangements are to be obtained. Table 14-I gives some suggested antenna and feeder lengths for multiband operation. In general, the length of the feedline can be other than that indicated, but the type of coupling circuit may change.

Open-wire line feed is recommended for an antenna of this type, since the losses will run too high in solid-dielectric line. For low-power applications up to a few hundred watts, open-wire TV line is convenient and satisfactory to use. However, for high-power installations up to the kilowatt limit, an open-wire line with No. 14 or No. 12 conductors should be used. This can be built from soft-drawn wire and ceramic or other suitable spacers, or it can be bought ready-made.

Antennas for Restricted Space

If the space available for the antenna is not large enough to accommodate the length necessary for a half wave at the lowest frequency to be used, quite satisfactory operation can be secured by using a shorter antenna and making up the missing length in the feeder system. The antenna itself may be as short as a quarter wavelength and will radiate fairly well, although of course it will not be as effective as one a half wave long. Nevertheless, such a system is useful where operation on the desired band otherwise would be impossible.

Tuned feeders are a practical necessity with such an antenna system, and a center-fed antenna will give best all-around performance.

		TABLE 14-I	
	Multiband Tuned-Line-Fed Antennas		
Antenna Length (Ft.)	Feeder Length (Ft.)	Band	Type of Coupling Circuit
With end feed:			
135	45	3.5 – 21 28	Series Parallel
67	45	7 – 21 28	Series Parallel
With center feed:			
135	42	3.5 – 21 28	Parallel Series
135	77½	3.5 – 28	Parallel
67	42½	3.5 7 – 28	Series Parallel
67	65½	3.5, 14, 28 7, 21	Parallel Series

Antenna lengths for end-fed antennas are approximate and should be cut to formula length at favorite operating frequency.

Where parallel tuning is specified, it will be necessary in some cases to tap in from the ends of the coil for proper loading — see Chapter 13 for examples of antenna couplers.

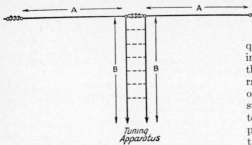

Fig. 14-19—Practical arrangement of a shortened antenna. When the total length, $A + B + B + A$, is the same as the antenna length plus twice the feeder length of the center-fed antennas of Table 14-I, the same type of coupling circuit will be used. When the feeder length or antenna length, or both, makes the sum different, the type of coupling circuit may be different but the effectiveness of the antenna is not changed, unless $A + A$ is less than a quarter wavelength.

With end feed the feeder currents become badly unbalanced.

With center feed, practically any convenient length of antenna can be used. If the total length of antenna plus twice feedline is the same as in Table 14-I, the type of tuning will be the same as stated. This is illustrated in Fig. 14-19. If the total length is not the same, different tuning conditions can be expected on some bands. This should not be interpreted as a fault in the antenna, and any tuning system (series or parallel) that works well without any trace of heating is quite satisfactory. Heating may result when the taps with parallel tuning are made too close to the center of the coil — it can often be corrected by using less total inductance and more capacitance.

Bent Antennas

Since the field strength at a distance is proportional to the current in the antenna, the high-current part of a dipole antenna (the center quarter wave, approximately) does most of the radiating. Advantage can be taken of this fact when the space available does not permit building an antenna a half-wave long. In this case the ends may be bent, either horizontally or vertically, so that the total length equals a half wave, even though the straightaway horizontal length may be as short as a quarter wave. The operation is illustrated in Fig. 14-20. Such an antenna will be a somewhat better radiator than a quarter wavelength antenna on the lowest fre-

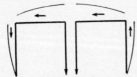

Fig. 14-20—Folded arrangement for shortened antennas. The total length is a half-wave, not including the feeders. The horizontal part is made as long as convenient and the ends dropped down to make up the required length. The ends may be bent back on themselves like feeders to cancel radiation partially. The horizontal section should be at least a quarter wave long.

quency, but is not so desirable for multiband operation because the ends play an increasingly important part as the frequency is raised. The performance of the system in such a case is difficult to predict, especially if the ends are vertical (the most convenient arrangement) because of the complex combination of horizontal and vertical polarization which results as well as the dissimilar directional characteristics. However, the fact that the radiation pattern is incapable of prediction does not detract from the general usefulness of the antenna. For one-band operation, end-loading with coils (5 feet or so in from each end) is practical and efficient.

''Windom'' or Off-Center-Fed Antenna

A multiband antenna that enjoyed considerable popularity in the 1930s is the "off-center feed" or "Windom," named after the amateur who wrote a comprehensive article about it. Shown in Fig. 14-21A, it consists of a half wavelength antenna on the lowest-frequency band to be used, with a *single-wire* feeder connected 14% off center. The antenna will operate satisfactorily

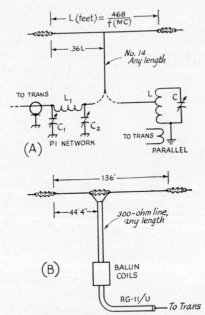

Fig. 14-21—Two versions of the off-center-fed antenna.
(A) Single-wire feed shows approximately 600 ohms impedance to ground and is most conveniently coupled to the transmitter as shown. The pi-network coupling will require more capacity at C_1 than at C_2. L_1 is best found by experiment—an inductance of about the same size as that used in the output stage is a good starting point. The parallel-tuned circuit will be a tuned circuit that resonates at the operating frequency with L and C close to those used in the output stage. The tap is found by experiment, and it should be as near the top of L as it can and still give good loading of the transmitter.
(B) Two-wire off-center feed uses 300-ohm TV line. Although the 300-ohm line can be coupled directly to some transmitters, it is common practice to step down the impedance level to 75 ohms through a pair of "balun" coils.

on the even-harmonic frequencies, and thus a single antenna can be made to serve on the 80-, 40-, 20-, and 10-meter bands. The single-wire feeder shows an impedance of approximately 600 ohms to ground, and consequently the antenna coupling system must be capable of matching this value to the transmitter. A tapped parallel-tuned circuit or a properly-proportioned pi-network coupler is generally used. Where TVI is a problem, the antenna coupler is required, so that a low-pass filter can be used in the connecting link of coaxial line.

Although theoretically the feed line can be of any length, some lengths will tend to give trouble with "too much r.f. in the shack," with the consequence that r.f. sparks can be drawn from the transmitter's metal cabinet and/or v.f.o. notes will develop serious modulation. If such is found to be the case, the feeder length should be changed.

A newer version of the off-center-feed antenna uses 300-ohm TV Twin-Lead to feed the antenna, as shown in Fig. 14-21B. It is claimed that the antenna offers a good match for the 300-ohm line on four bands and, although this is more wishful thinking than actual truth, the system is widely used and does work satisfactorily. It is subject to the same feed line length and "r.f.-in-the-shack" troubles that the single-wire version enjoys. However, in this case a pair of "balun" coils can be used to step down the impedance level to 75 ohms and at the same time alleviate some of the feed line troubles. This antenna system is popular among amateurs using multiband transmitters with pi-network-tuned output stages.

With either of the off-center-fed antenna systems, the feed line should run away from the antenna at right angles for as great a distance as possible before bending. No sharp bends should be allowed anywhere in the line.

Multiband Operation with Coaxial Line Feed

The proper use of coaxial line requires that the standing-wave ratio be held to a low value, preferably below 2:1. Since the impedance of an ordinary antenna changes widely from band to band, it is not possible to feed a simple antenna with coaxial line and use it on a number of bands without tricks of some kind. The single exception to this is the use of 75-ohm coaxial line to feed a 7-Mc. half-wave antenna, as in Fig. 14-19; this antenna can also be used on 21 Mc. and the s.w.r. in the line will not run too high.

One multiband antenna system that can be used by anyone without much trouble is shown in Fig. 14-22. Here separate dipoles are connected to one feedline. The 7-Mc. dipole also serves on 21 Mc. A low s.w.r. will appear on the feedline in each band if the dipoles are of the proper length. The antenna system can be built by suspending one set of elements from the one above, using insulator-terminated wood spreaders about one foot long. An alternative is to let one antenna droop several feet under the other, bring ropes attached to the insulators back to a common sup-

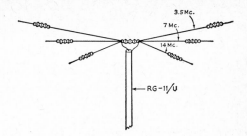

Fig. 14-22—An effective "all-band" antenna fed with a single length of coaxial line can be constructed by joining several half wavelength antennas at their centers and feeding them at the common point. In the example above, a low s.w.r. will be obtained on 80, 40, 20 and 15 meters. (The 7-Mc. antenna also works at 21 Mc.) If a 28-Mc. antenna were added, 10-meter operation could also be included.

The antenna lengths can be computed from formula 14-B. The shorter antennas can be suspended a foot or two below the longest one.

port point. It has been found that a separation of only an inch or two between dipoles is satisfactory. By using a length of the Twin-Lead used for folded dipoles (one Copperweld conductor and one soft-drawn), the strong wire can be used for the low-frequency dipole. The soft-drawn wire is then used on a higher band, supported by the solid dielectric.

A vertical antenna can be operated on several bands and fed with a single length of coaxial line provided the antenna is no longer than 0.6 wavelength at the highest frequency and that a suitable matching network for each band is used at the base. A good radial or ground system is required. The matching sections can be housed in a weatherproof box and changed manually or by stepping relays; their form will vary from parallel-tuned circuits to L sections. (See McCoy, *QST*, December, 1955, for description of L-section coupler.)

Multiband "Trap" Antennas

Another approach to the problem of multiband operation with a single untuned feed line is the use of parallel-tuned circuits installed in the antenna at the right points to "divorce" the remainder of the antenna from the center section (part fed by coaxial line) as the transmitter is changed to a higher-frequency band. This principle of the divorcing circuits is utilized in a commercial "all-band" vertical antenna, and a 5-band kit for horizontal antennas is also available commercially. The divorcing circuits are also used in several commercial multiband beams for the 14-, 21- and 28-Mc. bands.

The multiband antenna system shown in Fig. 14-23 may be of interest to the ham who wishes to work on several bands but doesn't have sufficient space for an 80-meter antenna and consequently is limited to 40 meters and below. (A five-band antenna requires more than a 100-foot span; see Greenberg, *QST*, October, 1956.)

On 40 meters the traps serve as inductors to load the system to 7 Mc. On 20, the traps (resonant to 14.1 Mc.) divorce the B sections from the

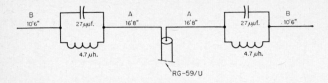

Fig. 14-23—Sketch showing dimensions of a trap dipole covering the 40-, 20- and 10-meter bands. The total span is less than 60 feet.

antenna proper. On 28 Mc. the entire antenna becomes approximately a 5/2-radiator.

As shown in Fig. 14-23, each trap is literally built around an "egg" or "strain" insulator. In this type of insulator, the hole at one end is at right angles to the hole at the other end, and the wires are fastened as in Fig. 14-25. These insulators have greater compressive strength than tensile strength and will not permit the antenna to fall should the insulator break, since the two inter-looped wires prevent it. There is ample space within the inductor for both the insulator and capacitor. The plastic covers are not essential but are considered desirable because they provide mechanical protection and prevent the accumulation of ice or soot and tars which may not wash off the traps when it rains.

Electrically, each trap consists of a 25-μμf. capacitor shunted by 4.7 μh. of inductance. A Centralab ceramic transmitting capacitor 857-25Z, rated at 15,000 volts d.c., is shown and will safely handle a kilowatt. Other ceramic capacitors rated at approximately 6000 volts would be satisfactory, as well as cheaper. The inductors are made of No. 12 wire, 2½ inches in diameter, 6 turns per inch (B & W 3905-1 coil stock).

One may wish to choose a different frequency in the 20-meter band for which optimum results are desired; for example, 14.05 Mc. for c.w. operation, 14.25 Mc. for phone operation, or perhaps 14.175 Mc. for general coverage. In any case, the number of inductor turns is adjusted accordingly.

Trap Adjustment

As a preliminary step, loops of No. 12 wire are fitted to one of the egg insulators in the normal manner (see Fig. 14-25), except that after the wraps are made, the end leads are snipped off close to

the wraps. A capacitor is then placed in position and bridged with short leads across the insulator and soldered sufficiently to provide temporary support. The combination is then slipped inside about 10 turns of the inductor, one end of which should be soldered to an insulator-capacitor lead. Adjustment to the resonant frequency can now proceed, using a grid-dip meter.

Coupling between the g.d.o. and the trap should be very loose. To insure accuracy, the station receiver should be used to check the g.d.o. frequency. The inductance should be reduced ¼ turn at a time. If one is careful, the resonant frequency can easily be set to within a few kilocycles of the chosen figure.

The reason for snipping the end leads close to the wraps and the inclusion of the loops through the egg insulator soon becomes apparent. The resonant frequency of the capacitor and inductor alone is reduced about 20 kc. per inch of end lead length and about 350 kc. by the insulator loops. The latter add approximately 2 μμf. to the fixed capacitor value and account for the total of 27 μμf. shown in Fig. 14-23.

Assembly

Having determined the exact number of inductor turns, the trap is taken apart and reassembled with leads of any convenient length. One may, of course, connect the entire lengths of sections A and B to the trap at this time, if desired. But, if more convenient, a foot or two of wire can be fastened and the remaining lengths soldered on just before the antenna is raised.

The protective covers are most readily formed by wrapping two turns (plus an overlap of ½ inch) of 0.020-inch polystyrene or lucite sheeting around a 3-inch plastic disk held at the center of the cylinder so formed. The length of the cover should be about 4 inches. A very small amount of plastic solvent (a cohesive cement that actually softens the plastic surfaces) should then be applied under the edge of the overlap and the joint held firmly for about

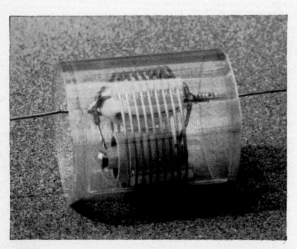

Fig. 14-24—The 14-Mc. trap is enclosed in a weatherproof cover made of plastic sheet. The ceramic capacitor and strain insulator are inside the coil.

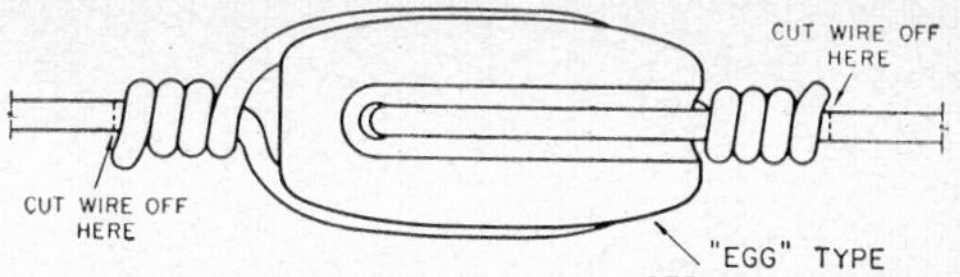

Vertical Antennas

Fig. 14-25—Method of connecting the antenna wire to the strain insulator. The antenna wire is cut off close to the wrap before checking the resonant frequency of the trap.

two minutes to insure a strong, tight seal. The disk is pushed out and the inner seam of the sheeting sealed.

The trap is then placed in the plastic cylinder and the end disks marked where the antenna wires are to pass through. After drilling these holes, the disks are slipped over the leads, pressed into the ends of the cylinder and a small amount of solvent applied to the periphery to obtain a good seal. Some air can flow in and out of the trap through the antenna-wire holes, and this will prevent the accumulation of condensation.

Length Adjustment

Standing-wave ratios are not uniform throughout the band or bands for which an antenna is designed. In a trap antenna, the choice of frequencies for best performance is a compromise. After making the traps resonant at 14.1 Mc., sections A are adjusted for resonance. Sections

B are then adjusted for resonance at approximately 7.2 Mc. For the dimensions shown, with the antenna about 250 ft. above street level and 35 ft. above electrical ground, an s.w.r. of virtually 1 to 1 was obtained at 7.2 Mc., with maximums of 1.3 and 1.1 at 7.0 and 7.3 Mc., respectively. In the 20-meter band, the s.w.r. was also 1 to 1 at 14.1 Mc., 1.1 at 14.0 Mc. and 1.3 at 14.3 Mc. In the 10-meter band, the s.w.r. was 1.3 to 1 at 28.0 Mc., 1.1 at 28.4 Mc., 1.5 at 29 Mc., and only 2.4 at the upper extreme of the band. The s.w.r. on 21 Mc. will be high because the antenna is not resonant in that band.

RG-59/U 73-ohm coaxial cable forms the transmission line and is connected to the antenna through a Continental Electronics & Sound Co. "Dipole Dri-Fit Connector." After connecting the cable and antenna wires, the connector should be coated with several layers of insulating varnish to make certain that the junction is watertight.

Vertical Antennas

A vertical quarter-wavelength antenna is often used in the low-frequency amateur bands to obtain low-angle radiation. It is also used when there isn't enough room for the supports for a horizontal antenna. For maximum effectiveness it should be located free of nearby objects and it should be operated in conjunction with a good ground system, but it is still worth trying where these ideal conditions cannot be obtained.

Four typical examples and suggested methods for feeding a vertical antenna are shown in Fig. 14-26. The antenna may be wire or tubing supported by wood or insulated guy wires. When tubing is used for the antenna, or when guy wires (broken up by insulators) are used to reinforce the structure, the length given by the formula is likely to be long by a few per cent. A check of the standing-wave ratio on the line will indicate the frequency at which the s.w.r. is minimum, and the antenna length can be adjusted accordingly.

A good ground connection is necessary for the most effective operation of a vertical antenna (other than the ground-plane type). In some cases a short connection to the cold-water system of the house will be adequate. But maximum performance usually demands a separate ground system. A single 4- to 6-foot ground rod driven into the earth at the base of the antenna is usually not sufficient, unless the soil has exceptional conductivity. A minimum ground system that can be depended upon is 6 to 12 quarter wavelength radials laid out as the spokes of a wheel from the base of the antenna. These radials can

be made of heavy aluminum wire, of the type used for grounding TV antennas, buried at least

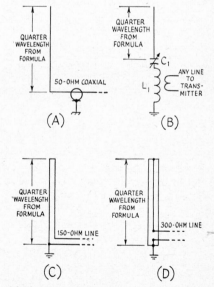

Fig. 14-26—A quarter-wavelength antenna can be fed directly with 50-ohm coaxial line (A) with a low standing-wave ratio, or a coupling network can be used (B) that will permit a line of any impedance to be used. In (B), L_1 and C_1 should resonate to the operating frequency, and L_1 should be larger than is normally used in a plate tank circuit at the same frequency. By using multiwire antennas, the quarter-wave vertical can be fed with (C) 150- or (D) 300-ohm line.

6 inches in the ground. This is normally done by slitting the earth with a spade and pushing the wire into the slot, after which the earth can be tamped down.

The examples shown in Fig. 14-26 all require an antenna insulated from the ground, to provide for the feed point. A *grounded* tower or pipe can be used as a radiator by employing "shunt feed," which consists of tapping the inner conductor of the coaxial-line feed up on the tower until the best match is obtained, in much the same manner as the "gamma match" (described later) is used on a horizontal element. If the antenna is not an electrical quarter wavelength long, it is necessary to tune out the reactance by adding capacity or inductance between the coaxial line and the shunting conductor. A metal tower supporting a TV antenna or rotary beam can be shunt-fed only if all of the wires and leads from the supported antenna run down the center of the tower and underground away from the tower.

● THE GROUND-PLANE ANTENNA

A ground-plane antenna is a vertical quarter-wavelength antenna using an artificial metallic ground, usually consisting of four rods or wires perpendicular to the antenna and extending radially from its base. Unlike the quarter-wavelength vertical antennas without an artificial ground, the ground-plane antenna will give low-angle radiation regardless of the height above actual ground. However, to be a true ground-plane antenna, the plane of the radials should be at least a quarter wavelength above ground. Despite this one limitation, the antenna is useful for DX work in any band below 30 Mc.

The vertical portion of the ground-plane antenna can be made of self-supported aluminum tubing or a top-supported wire depending upon the necessary length and the available supports. The radials are also made of tubing or heavy wire depending upon the available supports and necessary lengths. They need not be exactly symmetrical about the base of the vertical portion.

The radiation resistance of a ground-plane antenna varies with the diameter of the vertical element. Since the radiation resistance is usually in the vicinity of 30 to 32 ohms the antenna can be fed with 75-ohm coaxial line if a quarter wavelength matching section of 50-ohm coaxial line is used between the line and the antenna. (See "Quarter-Wave Transformers" in this chapter.)

For multiband operation, a ground-plane antenna can be fed with tuned open-wire line.

Three-Band Ground-Plane Antenna

A three-band ground-plane antenna using wire elements and fed with coaxial line is shown in Fig. 14-27. The builder (K5AYJ) elected to mount it on top of a 34-foot length of galvanized iron pipe, since a ground-plane antenna close to the ground is not a ground-plane antenna at all. Four 17-foot "drooping radials" form the ground plane and double as guy wires. These four wires are fastened to a pipe flange at the top of the mast. At one point on the mast the pipe sections are joined by a T fitting, which provides a convenient point for bringing out the RG-8/U feed line. If it is more convenient to bring out the coax at the base of the mast, one can eliminate the T fitting and use an ordinary coupling.

A cane fishing pole supports the three separate vertical elements. These elements, made of No. 12 wire, are taped to the pole every three inches with Scotch electrical tape. The bottom end of the pole is jammed tight into the upper end of the support pipe and the coaxial line is brought out of the pipe through a small hole just below the bottom of the flange. The inner conductor of the coaxial line is soldered to the junction of the three vertical elements and the braid of the coaxial line is connected to the pipe flange. Anyone worrying about the insulating ability of a cane pole can forget it; it is being used at a low-impedance point.

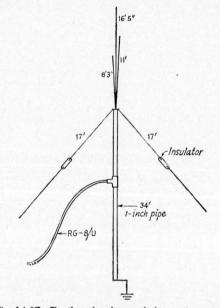

Fig. 14-27—The three-band ground-plane antenna uses wire elements. Vertical elements are taped to a cane pole; the four radials also serve as guy wires. The radials "droop" a little, making a 40-degree angle with the supporting 1-inch pipe.

Antennas for 160 Meters

Results on 1.8 Mc. will depend to a large extent on the antenna system and the time of day or night. Almost any random long wire that can be

tuned to resonance will work during the night but it will generally be found very ineffective during the day. A vertical antenna — or rather an antenna from which the radiation is predominantly vertically polarized — is probably the best for 1.8-Mc. operation. A horizontal antenna (horizontally-polarized radiation) will give better results during the night than the day. The vertically-polarized radiator gives a strong ground wave that is effective day or night, and it is to be preferred on 1.8 Mc.

The low-angle radiation from a horizontal antenna $\frac{1}{8}$ or $\frac{1}{4}$ wavelength above ground is almost insignificant. Any reasonable height is small in terms of wavelength, so that a horizontal antenna on 160 meters is a poor radiator at angles useful for long distances ("long," that is, for this band). Its chief usefulness is over relatively short distances at night.

Bent Antennas

Since ideal vertical antennas are generally out of the question for practical amateur work, the best compromise is to bend the antenna in such a way that the high-current portions of the antenna run vertically. It is advisable to place the antenna so that the highest currents in the antenna occur at the highest points above actual ground. Two antenna systems designed along these lines are shown in Fig. 14-28. The antenna of Fig. 14-28B uses a full half wavelength of wire but is bent so that the high-current portion runs vertically. The horizontal portion running to L_1C_1 should run 8 or 10 feet above ground.

Grounds

A good ground connection is generally important on 160 meters. The ideal system is a number of wire radials buried a foot or two underground and extending 50 to 100 feet from the central connection point. The use of any less than six or eight radials is inadvisable.

If the soil is good (not rocky or sandy) and generally moist, a low-resistance connection to the cold-water pipe system in the house will often serve as an adequate ground system. The connection should be made close to where the pipe enters the ground, and the surface of the pipe should be scraped clean before tightening the ground clamp around the pipe.

A 6- or 8-foot length of 1-inch water pipe, driven into the soil at a point where there is considerable natural moisture, can be used for the ground connection. Three or four pipes driven into the ground 8 or 10 feet apart and all joined

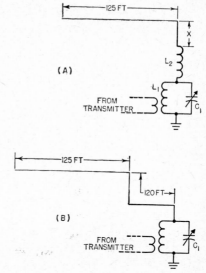

Fig. 14-28—Bent antenna for the 160-meter band. In the system at A, the vertical portion (length X) should be made as long as possible. In either antenna system, L_1C_1 should resonate at 1900 kc., roughly. To adjust L_2 in antenna A, resonate L_1C_1 alone to the operating frequency, then connect it to the antenna system and adjust L_2 for maximum loading. Further loading can be obtained by increasing the coupling between L_1 and the link.

together with heavy wire are more effective than the single pipe.

The use of a counterpoise is recommended where a buried system is not practicable or where a pipe ground cannot be made to have low resistance because of poor soil conditions. A counterpoise consists of a number of wires supported from 6 to 10 feet above the surface of the ground. Generally the wires are spaced 10 to 15 feet apart and located to form a square or polygonal configuration under the vertical portion of the antenna.

Long-Wire Directive Arrays

As the length (in wavelengths) of an antenna is increased, the lobes of maximum radiation make a more acute angle with the wire. Two long wires can be combined in the form of a horizontal "V", in the form of a horizontal rhombus, or in parallel, to provide a long-wire directive array. In the "V" and rhombic antennas the main lobes reinforce along a line bisecting the acute angle between the wires; in the parallel antenna the reinforcement is along the line of the lobe. This reinforcement provides both gain and directivity along the line, since the lobes in other directions tend to cancel out. In general, the power gain

depends upon the length in wavelengths of the wires, assuming that the proper configuration for a given length and height above ground is used.

Rhombic and "V" antennas are normally bidirectional along the bisector line mentioned above. They can be made unidirectional by terminating the ends of the wires away from the feed point in the proper value of resistance. When properly terminated, "V" and rhombic antennas of sufficient length work well over a three-to-one or four-to-one frequency range and hence are useful for multiband operation.

Antenna gains of the order of 10 to 15 db. can

be obtained with properly-constructed long-wire arrays. However, the pattern is rather sharp with gains of this order, and rhombic and "V" beams are not used by amateurs as commonly as

they were, having been displaced by the rotatable multi-element Yagi beam. Further information on these antennas can be found in *The ARRL Antenna Book.*

Beams with Driven Elements

By combining individual half-wave antennas into an **array** with suitable spacing between the antennas (called **elements**) and feeding power to them simultaneously, it is possible to make the radiation from the elements add up along a single direction and form a beam. In other directions the radiation tends to cancel, so a power gain is obtained in one direction at the expense of radiation in other directions. There are several methods of arranging the elements. If they are strung end to end, so that all lie on the same straight line, the elements are said to be **collinear**. If they are parallel and all lying in the same plane, the elements are said to be **broad-side** when the phase of the current is the same in all, and **end-fire** when the currents are not in phase.

Collinear Arrays

Simple forms of collinear arrays, with the current distribution, are shown in Fig. 14-29.

Collinear arrays may be mounted either horizontally or vertically. Horizontal mounting gives increased horizontal directivity, while the vertical directivity remains the same as for a single element at the same height. Vertical mounting gives the same horizontal pattern as a single element, but concentrates the radiation at low angles.

Broadside Arrays

Parallel antenna elements with currents in phase may be combined as shown in Fig. 14-30 to form a **broadside** array, so named because the direction of maximum radiation is broadside to the plane containing the antennas. Again the gain and directivity depend upon the spacing of the elements.

Broadside arrays may be suspended either with the elements all vertical or with them horizontal and one above the other (**stacked**). In the former case the horizontal pattern becomes quite sharp,

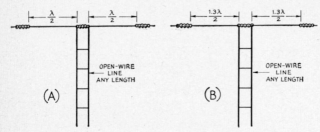

Fig. 14-29—Collinear antennas in phase. The system at A is known as "two half waves in phase" and has a gain of 1.8 db. over a half-wave antenna. By lengthening the antenna slightly, as in B, the gain can be increased to 3 db. Maximum radiation is at right angles to the antenna. The antenna at A is sometimes called a "double Zepp" antenna, and that at B is known as an "extended double Zepp."

The two-element array at A is popularly known as "two half-waves in phase" or a **double Zepp** antenna. It will be recognized as simply a center-fed dipole operated at its second harmonic.

By extending the antenna, as at B, the additional gain of an **extended double Zepp** antenna can be obtained. Carrying the length beyond that shown will result in an "X"-shaped pattern that no longer has the maximum radiation at right angles to the wire.

while the vertical pattern is the same as that of one element alone. If the array is suspended horizontally, the horizontal pattern is equivalent to that of one element while the vertical pattern is sharpened, giving low-angle radiation.

Broadside arrays may be fed either by tuned open-wire lines or through quarter-wave matching sections and flat lines. In Fig. 14-30B, note the "crossing over" of the phasing section, which is necessary to bring the elements into proper

Fig. 14-30—Simple broadside array using horizontal elements. By making the spacing S equal to ⅜ wavelength, the antenna at A can be used at the corresponding frequency and up to twice that frequency. Thus when designed for 14 Mc. it can also be used on 21 and 28 Mc. The antenna at B can be used on only the design band. This array is bidirectional, with maximum radiation "broadside" or perpendicular to the antenna plane (perpendicularly through this page). Gain varies with the spacing S, running from 2½ to almost 5 db. (See Fig. 14-32).

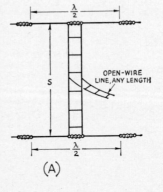

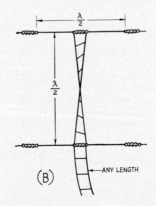

Beams with Driven Elements

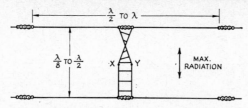

Fig. 14-31—Top view of a horizontal end-fire array. The system is fed with an open-wire line at x and y; the line can be of any length. Feed points x and y are equidistant from the two insulators, and the feed line should drop down vertically from the antenna. The gain of the system will vary with the spacing, as shown in Fig. 14-32, and is a maximum at ⅛ wavelength. By using a length of 33 feet and a spacing of 8 feet, the antenna will work on 20, 15 and 10 meters.

phase relationship.

End-Fire Arrays

Fig. 14-31 shows a pair of parallel half-wave elements with currents out of phase. This is known as an **end-fire** array because it radiates best along the plane of the antennas, as shown.

The end-fire array may be used either vertically or horizontally (elements at the same height), and is well adapted to amateur work because it gives maximum gain with relatively close element spacing. Fig. 14-32 shows how the gain varies with spacing. End-fire elements may be combined with additional collinear and broadside elements to give a further increase in gain and directivity.

Either tuned or untuned lines may be used with this type of array. Untuned lines preferably are matched to the antenna through a quarter-wave

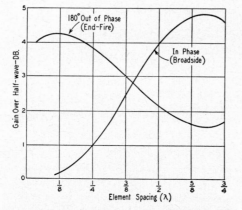

Fig. 14-32—Gain vs. spacing for two parallel half-wave elements combined as either broadside or end-fire arrays.

matching section or phasing stub.

Combined Arrays

Broadside, collinear and end-fire arrays may be combined to give both horizontal and vertical directivity, as well as additional gain. The lower angle of radiation resulting from stacking elements in the vertical plane is desirable at the higher frequencies. In general, doubling the number of elements in an array by stacking will raise the gain from 2 to 4 db.

Although arrays can be fed at one end as in Fig. 14-30B, it is not especially desirable in the case of large arrays. Better distribution of energy between elements, and hence better over-all performance will result when the feeders are attached as nearly as possible to the center of the array.

A four-element array, known as the "lazy-H" antenna, has been quite frequently used. This arrangement is shown, with the feed point indicated, in Fig. 14-33. (Compare with Fig. 14-30B). For best results, the bottom section should be at least a half wavelength above ground.

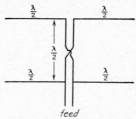

Fig. 14-33—A four-element combination broadside-collinear array, popularly known as the "lazy-H" antenna. A closed quarter-wave stub may be used at the feed point to match into an untuned transmission line, or tuned feeders may be attached at the point indicated. The gain over a half-wave antenna is 5 to 6 db.

It will usually suffice to make the length of each element that given by Equations **14-B** or **14-C**. The phasing line between the parallel elements should be of open-wire construction, and its length can be calculated from:

Length of half-wave line (feet) =

$$\frac{480}{Freq. \ (Mc.)} \qquad \textbf{(14-H)}$$

Example: A half-wavelength phasing line for 28.8 Mc. would be $\frac{480}{28.8}$ = 16.66 feet = 16 feet 8 inches.

The spacing between elements can be made equal to the length of the phasing line. No special adjustments of line or element length or spacing are needed, provided the formulas are followed closely.

Directive Arrays with Parasitic Elements

Parasitic Excitation

The antenna arrays previously described are bidirectional; that is, they will radiate in directions both to the "front" and to the "back" of the antenna system. If radiation is wanted in only one direction, it is necessary to use different element arrangements. In most of these arrangements the additional elements receive power by induction or radiation from the driven element generally called the "antenna," and reradiate it

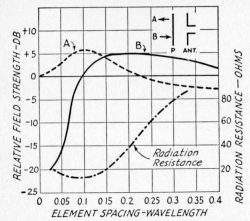

Fig. 14-34—Gain *vs.* element spacing for an antenna and one parasitic element. The reference point, 0 db., is the field strength from a half-wave antenna alone. The greatest gain is in direction A at spacings of less than 0.14 wavelength, and in direction B at greater spacings. The front-to-back ratio is the difference in db. between curves A and B. Variation in radiation resistance of the driven element also is shown. These curves are for a self resonant parasitic element. At most spacings the gain as a reflector can be increased by slight lengthening of the parasitic element; the gain as a director can be increased by shortening. This also improves the front-to-back ratio.

in the proper phase relationship to achieve the desired effect. These elements are called *parasitic* elements, as contrasted to the driven elements which receive power directly from the transmitter through the transmission line.

The parasitic element is called a **director** when it reinforces radiation on a line pointing to it from the antenna, and a **reflector** when the reverse is the case. Whether the parasitic element is a director or reflector depends upon the parasitic-element tuning, which usually is adjusted by changing its length.

Gain vs. Spacing

The gain of an antenna with parasitic elements varies with the spacing and tuning of the elements and thus for any given spacing there is a tuning condition that will give maximum gain at this spacing. The maximum front-to-back ratio seldom if ever, occurs at the same condition that gives maximum forward gain. The impedance of the driven element also varies with the tuning and spacing, and thus the antenna system must be tuned to its final condition before the match between the line and the antenna can be completed. However, the tuning and matching may interlock to some extent, and it is usually necessary to run through the adjustments several times to insure that the best possible tuning has been obtained.

Two-Element Beams

A 2-element beam is useful where space or other considerations prevent the use of the larger structure required for a 3-element beam. The general practice is to tune the parasitic element as a reflector and space it about 0.15 wave-

length from the driven element, although some successful antennas have been built with 0.1-wavelength spacing and director tuning. Gain *vs.* element spacing for a 2-element antenna is given in Fig. 14-34, for the special case where the parasitic element is resonant. It is indicative of the performance to be expected under maximum-gain tuning conditions.

Three-Element Beams

Where room is available for an over-all length greater than 0.2 wavelength, a 3-element beam is preferable to one with only 2 elements. Once the over-all length has been decided upon, the curves of Fig. 14-35 can be used to determine the proper spacing of director and reflector. If, for example, the distance between director and reflector can be made 0.4 wavelength, Fig. 14-35 shows that a spacing of 0.15D-0.25R gives a gain of 7.8 db., and a spacing of 0.25D-0.15R gives a gain of 8.2 db. Obviously the latter is the better choice, although the practical difference might be difficult to measure, and practical (mechanical) considerations might call for using the more balanced 0.2D-0.2R construction and a gain of 8.1 db.

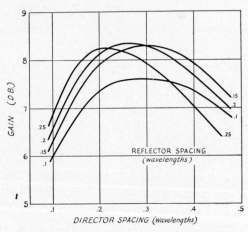

Fig. 14-35—Gain *vs.* element spacing for 3-element beams using a driven element and a director and a reflector. The 0-db. reference level is the field strength from a half-wavelength antenna alone. These curves are for the system tuned for maximum forward gain.

The element spacing shown is the fraction of wavelength determined by $\frac{984}{f (Mc.)}$. Thus a wavelength at 14.2 Mc. = 984/14.2 = 69.3 feet. A spacing of 0.15 wavelength at 14.2 Mc. would be 0.15 × 69.3 = 10.4 feet = 10 feet 5 inches.

When the over-all length has been decided upon, and the element spacing has been determined, the element lengths can be found by referring to Fig. 14-36. It must be remembered that the lengths determined by these charts will vary slightly in actual practice with the element diameter and the method of supporting the elements, and the tuning of a beam should always be checked after installation. However, the lengths obtained by the use of the charts will be

Rotary Beams

close to correct in practically all cases, and they can be used without checking if the beam is difficult of access.

The preferable method for checking the beam is by means of a field-strength meter or the

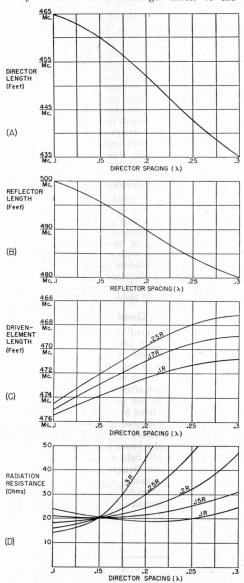

(A) DIRECTOR LENGTH (Feet)

(B) REFLECTOR LENGTH (Feet)

(C) DRIVEN-ELEMENT LENGTH (Feet)

(D) RADIATION RESISTANCE (Ohms)

Fig. 14-36—Element lengths for a 3-element beam. These lengths will hold closely for tubing elements supported at or near the center. The radiation resistance (D) is useful information in planning for a matching system, but it is subject to variation with height above ground and must be considered an approximation.

The driven-element length (C) may require modification for tuning out reactance if a T- or gamma-match feed system is used, as mentioned in the text.

A 0.2D-0.2R beam cut for 28.6 Mc. would have a director length of 452/28.6 = 15.8 = 15 feet 10 inches, a reflector length of 490/28.6 = 17.1 = 17 feet 1 inch, and a driven-element length of 470.5/28.6 = 16.45 = 16 feet 5 inches.

S-meter of a communications receiver, used in conjunction with a dipole antenna located at least 10 wavelengths away and as high as or higher than the beam that is being checked. A few watts of power fed into the antenna will give a useful signal at the observation point, and the power input to the transmitter (and hence the antenna) should be held constant for all of the readings. Beams tuned on the ground and then lifted into place are subject to tuning errors and cannot be depended upon. The impedance of the driven element will vary with the height above ground, and good practice dictates that all final matching between antenna and line be done with the antenna in place at its normal height above ground.

Simple Systems: the Rotary Beam

Two- and 3-element systems are popular for rotary-beam antennas, where the entire antenna system is rotated, to permit its gain and directivity to be utilized for any compass direction. They may be mounted either horizontally (with the plane containing the elements parallel to the earth) or vertically.

A 4-element beam will give still more gain than a 3-element one, provided the support is sufficient for about 0.2 wavelength spacing between elements. The tuning for maximum gain involves many variables, and complete gain and tuning data are not available.

The elements in close-spaced (less than one-quarter wavelength element spacing) arrays preferably should be made of tubing of one-half to one-inch diameter. A conductor of large diameter not only has less ohmic resistance but also has lower Q; both these factors are important in close-spaced arrays because the impedance of the driven element usually is quite low compared to that of a simple dipole antenna. With 3- and 4-element close-spaced arrays the radiation resistance of the driven element may be so low that ohmic losses in the conductor can consume an appreciable fraction of the power.

Feeding the Rotary Beam

Any of the usual methods of feed (described later under "Matching the Antenna to the Line") can be applied to the driven element of a rotary beam. Tuned feeders are not recommended for lengths greater than a half wavelength unless open lines of copper-tubing conductors are used. The popular choices for feeding a beam are the gamma match with series capacitor and the T match with series capacitors and a half-wavelength phasing section, as shown in Fig. 14-37. These methods are preferred over any others because they permit adjustment of the matching and the use of coaxial line feed. The variable capacitors can be housed in small plastic cups for weatherproofing; receiving types with close spacing can be used at powers up to a few hundred watts. Maximum capacity required is usually 140 μμf. at 14 Mc. and proportionately less at the higher frequencies.

373

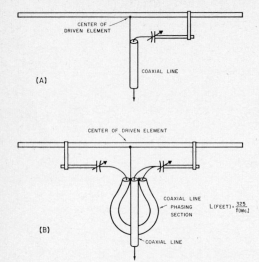

Fig. 14-37—The most popular methods of feeding the driven element of a beam antenna are (A) the gamma match and (B) the T match. The aluminum tubing or rod used for the matching section is usually of smaller diameter than the antenna element; its length will vary somewhat with the spacing and number of elements in the beam. The coaxial line in the phasing section can be coiled in a 2- or 3-foot diameter coil instead of hanging as shown.

$$L\ (\text{FEET}) = \frac{325}{f(\text{Mc.})}$$

If physically possible, it is better to adjust the matching device after the antenna has been installed at its ultimate height, since a match made with the antenna near the ground may not hold for the same antenna in the air.

Sharpness of Resonance

Peak performance of a multielement parasitic array depends upon proper phasing or tuning of the elements, which can be exact for one frequency only. In the case of close-spaced arrays, which because of the low radiation resistance usually are quite sharp-tuning, the frequency range over which optimum results can be secured is only of the order of 1 or 2 per cent of the resonant frequency, or up to about 500 kc. at 28 Mc. However, the antenna can be made to work satisfactorily over a wider frequency range by adjusting the director or directors to give maximum gain at the *highest* frequency to be covered, and by adjusting the reflector to give optimum gain at the *lowest* frequency. This sacrifices some gain at all frequencies, but maintains more uniform gain over a wider frequency range.

The use of large-diameter conductors will broaden the response curve of an array because the larger diameter lowers the Q. This causes the reactances of the elements to change rather slowly with frequency, with the result that the tuning stays near the optimum over a considerably wider frequency range than is the case with wire conductors.

Combination Arrays

It is possible to combine parasitic elements with driven elements to form arrays composed of collinear driven and parasitic elements and combination broadside-collinear-parasitic elements. Thus two or more collinear elements might be provided with a collinear reflector or director set, one parasitic element to each driven element. Or both directors and reflectors might be used. A broadside-collinear array can be treated in the same fashion.

The Quad Antenna

The "cubical quad" antenna shown in Fig. 14-38 uses a square loop driven element and a square loop parasitic reflector. The spacing is usually between .15 and .20 wavelength and it is not critical, since the reflector element is tuned for maximum gain after installation.

Quad antennas are popular because they are lightweight and have low wind resistance. Their gain has been measured at 8 db. or more. A 14-Mc. quad will have approximately a 17-foot "wing span" and a boom length of about 12 feet, and it can be built light enough to be turned by a good TV rotator. Suggestions for the construction of a quad antenna are given in Fig. 14-39. The design was intended to be as light as possible and while the antenna will whip some in the wind, this should not cause any noticeable change in

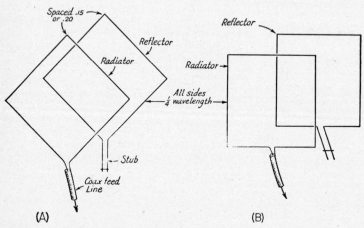

Fig. 14-38—Two different arrangements of cubical quad antennas.

Quad Antenna

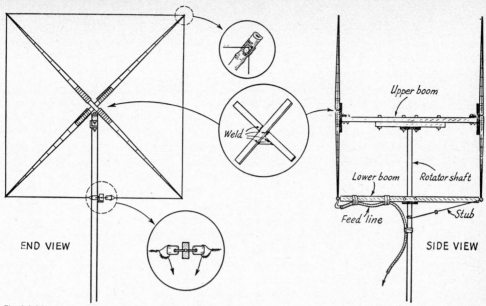

Fig. 14-39—End and side views of a quad. Upper insert shows method of fastening antenna wire to support arms. Center insert shows construction of support-arm mounting bracket. Lower insert shows method of attaching feed line and stub to the center insulators. Two small egg insulators are used, fastened to end of lower boom as shown with a small nail.

$$\text{The length of one side is found from } L \text{ (feet)} = \frac{251}{f \text{ (Mc.)}}$$

loading or on received signals. There is nothing critical in the construction except the length of the wire elements. One quad used 1×2-inch pine for the support arms but this beam was much too heavy and blew down in the first light wind. The support arms shown in the drawing are ordinary bamboo fishing poles about 16 feet long, with the butt ends wrapped with friction tape to prevent the metal mounting bracket and wire from biting into the bamboo. These arms are fastened to the mounting brackets with several turns of No. 14 galvanized wire, and the far ends are not trimmed until the antenna wire has been fastened in place. Two mounting brackets and eight bamboo support arms are required. The mounting brackets serve to hold the arms in place and to fasten them to the end of the boom. These brackets are made by welding two 24-inch lengths of 1-inch angle iron together back to back to form a large "X" 90 degrees between legs, and welding a 5-inch length of $1\frac{1}{2}$-inch strap iron between two of the legs to fasten the "X" to the boom end. The arms are assembled and the antenna wire is fastened in place before attaching the brackets to the boom.

If the fishing poles are well treated with a weatherproofing compound they will last several years. Weatherproofing compounds are available at all lumber dealers. Get straight poles with no splits in them. No insulators are necessary, the poles themselves acting as long insulators. The

easiest way to mount the antenna wire on the arms is to lay a long length of wire on the ground and mark it at the approximate quarter-wave intervals, and use these marks to indicate where the wire fastens to the pole.

Dual and triple quads can be built for the bands 20 through 10 meters. One such antenna is shown in Fig. 14-40, a dual quad for 15 and 10 meters. The same supporting structure is used for the two antennas, making the boom length equal to 0.15 to 0.2 wavelengths at the lower-frequency band. Separate coaxial cable feed lines are brought down from the two driven elements. In a two-band quad (20/15 or 15/10) the length of one side is obtained from

$$L \text{ (feet)} = 250 \div \text{ (Mc.)}$$

In the case of any quad or combination of

Fig. 14-40—A 15/10-meter quad. Tuning stubs for the reflectors are looped back along the tie bars. Total weight of this assembly, not including the mast, is 13 pounds.

quads, each quad should be tuned up separately for maximum forward gain by adjusting the stub length on the reflector element and checking the field strength with a nearby ham. If accessible, the reflector element can be resonated with a grid-dip meter to a frequency just below the lowest to be used; this is a good starting place for further adjustment. The resonance of the antenna

system can be checked by finding the frequency that gives the lowest s.w.r. on the feed line; this lowest s.w.r. is not necessarily 1.0. If the resonant frequency is higher than the desired frequency, lengthen the driven element; shorten the element if the resonant frequency is too low. In the dual antennas that have been constructed, there has been little or no evidence of interaction of tuning.

Matching the Antenna to the Line

The load for a transmission line may be any device capable of dissipating r.f. power. When lines are used for transmitting applications the most common type of load is an antenna. When a transmission line is connected between an antenna and a receiver, the receiver input circuit (not the antenna) is the load, because the power taken from a passing wave is delivered to the receiver.

Whatever the application, the conditions existing at the load, and *only* the load, determine the standing-wave ratio on the line. If the load is purely resistive and equal in value to the characteristic impedance of the line, there will be no standing waves. If the load is not purely resistive, and/or is not equal to the line Z_0, there will be standing waves. No adjustments that can be made at the input end of the line can change the s.w.r., nor is it affected by changing the line length.

Only in a few special cases is the load inherently of the proper value to match a practicable transmission line. In all other cases it is necessary either to operate with a mismatch and accept the s.w.r. that results, or else to take steps to bring about a proper match between the line and load by means of transformers or similar devices. Impedance-matching transformers may take a variety of physical forms, depending on the circumstances.

Note that it is essential, if the s.w.r. is to be made as low as possible, that the load at the point of connection to the transmission line be purely resistive. In general, this requires that the load be tuned to resonance. If the load itself is not resonant at the operating frequency the tuning sometimes can be accomplished in the matching system.

● THE ANTENNA AS A LOAD

Every antenna system, no matter what its physical form, will have a definite value of impedance at the point where the line is to be connected. The problem is to transform this **antenna input impedance** to the proper value to match the line. In this respect there is no one "best" type of line for a particular antenna system, because it is possible to transform impedances in any desired ratio. Consequently, any type of line may be used with any type of antenna. There are frequently reasons other than impedance matching that dictate the use of one type of line in preference to another, such as ease of installation, inherent loss in the line, and so on, but these are not considered in this section.

Although the input impedance of an antenna system is seldom known very accurately, it is often possible to make a reasonably close estimate of its value. The information earlier in this chapter can be used as a guide.

Matching circuits may be constructed using ordinary coils and capacitors, but are not used very extensively because they must be supported at the antenna and must be weatherproofed. The systems to be described use **linear transformers.**

The Quarter-Wave Transformer or "Q" Section

As described earlier in this chapter, a quarter-wave transmission line may be used as an impedance transformer. Knowing the antenna impedance and the characteristic impedance of the

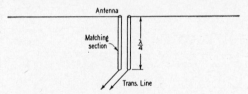

Fig. 14-41—"Q" matching section, a quarter-wave impedance transformer.

transmission line to be matched, the required characteristic impedance of a matching section such as is shown in Fig. 13-13 is

$$Z = \sqrt{Z_1 Z_0} \qquad \text{(14-I)}$$

where Z_1 is the antenna impedance and Z_0 is the characteristic impedance of the line to which it is to be matched.

> Example: To match a 600-ohm line to an antenna presenting a 72-ohm load, the quarter-wave matching section would require a characteristic impedance of $\sqrt{72 \times 600} = \sqrt{43,200}$ = 208 ohms.

The spacings between conductors of various sizes of tubing and wire for different surge impedances are given in graphical form in the chapter on "Transmission Lines." (With ½-inch tubing, the spacing in the example above should be 1.5 inches for an impedance of 208 ohms.)

The length of the quarter-wave matching section may be calculated from

$$Length \text{ (feet)} = \frac{246V}{f} \qquad \text{(14-J)}$$

where V = Velocity factor
f = Frequency in Mc.

> Example: A quarter-wave transformer of RG-11/U is to be used at 28.7 Mc. From the table in Chapter

Folded Dipoles

Thirteen, $V = 0.66$.

$$\text{Length} = \frac{246 \times 0.66}{28.7} = 5.67 \text{ feet}$$
$$= 5 \text{ feet } 8 \text{ inches}$$

The antenna must be resonant at the operating frequency. Setting the antenna length by formula is amply accurate with single-wire antennas, but in other systems, particularly close-spaced arrays, the antenna should be adjusted to resonance before the matching section is connected.

When the antenna input impedance is not known accurately, it is advisable to construct the matching section so that the spacing between conductors can be changed. The spacing then may be adjusted to give the lowest possible s.w.r. on the transmission line.

Folded Dipoles

A half-wave antenna element can be made to match various line impedances if it is split into two or more parallel conductors with the transmission line attached at the center of only one of them. Various forms of such "folded dipoles" are shown in Fig. 14-42. Currents in all conductors are in phase in a folded dipole, and since the conductor spacing is small the folded dipole is equivalent in radiating properties to an ordinary single-conductor dipole. However, the current flowing into the input terminals of the antenna from the line is the current in one conductor only, and the entire power from the line is delivered at this value of current. This is equivalent to saying that the input impedance of the antenna has been raised by splitting it up into two or more conductors.

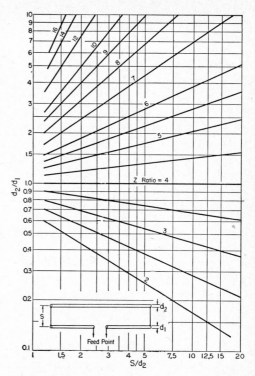

Fig. 14-43—Impedance transformation ratio, two-conductor folded dipole. The dimensions d_1, d_2 and s are shown on the inset drawing. Curves show the ratio of the impedance (resistive) seen by the transmission line to the radiation resistance of the resonant antenna system.

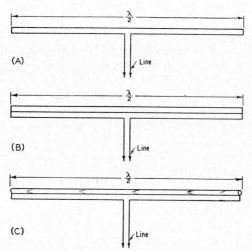

Fig. 14-42—The folded dipole, a method for using the antenna element itself to provide an impedance transformation.

The ratio by which the input impedance of the antenna is stepped up depends not only on the number of conductors in the folded dipole but also on their relative diameters, since the distribution of current between conductors is a function of their diameters. (When one conductor is larger than the other, as in Fig. 14-42C, the larger one carries the greater current.) The ratio also depends, in general, on the spacing between the conductors, as shown by the graphs of Figs. 14-43 and 14-44. An important special case is the 2-conductor dipole with conductors of equal diameter; as a simple antenna, not a part of a directive array, it has an input resistance close enough to 300 ohms to afford a good match to 300-ohm Twin-Lead.

The required ratio of conductor diameters to give a desired impedance ratio using two conductors may be obtained from Fig. 14-43. Similar information for a 3-conductor dipole is given in Fig. 14-44. This graph applies where all three conductors are in the same plane. The two conductors not connected to the transmission line must be equally spaced from the fed conductor, and must have equal diameters. The fed conductor may have a different diameter, however. The unequal-conductor method has been found particularly useful in matching to low-impedance antennas such as directive arrays using close-spaced parasitic elements.

The length of the antenna element should be such as to be approximately self-resonant at the median operating frequency. The length is usually not highly critical, because a folded dipole tends to have the characteristics of a "thick" antenna and thus has a relatively broad frequency-response curve.

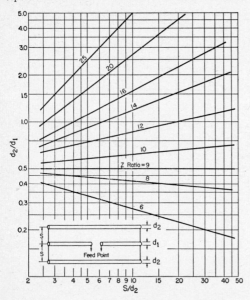

Fig. 14-44—Impedance transformation ratio, three-conductor folded dipole. The dimensions d_1, d_2 and s are shown on the inset drawing. Curves show the ratio of the impedance (resistive) seen by the transmission line to the radiation resistance of the resonant antenna system.

"T" and "Gamma" Matching Sections

The method of matching shown in Fig. 14-45A is based on the fact that the impedance between any two points along a resonant antenna is resistive, and has a value which depends on the spacing between the two points. It is therefore possible to choose a pair of points between which the impedance will have the right value to match a transmission line. In practice, the line cannot be connected directly at these points because the distance between them is much greater than the conductor spacing of a practicable transmission line. The "T" arrangement in Fig. 14-45A overcomes this difficulty by using a second conductor paralleling the antenna to form a matching section

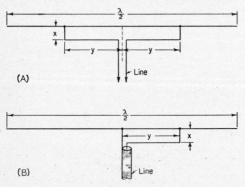

Fig. 14-45—The "T" match and "gamma" match.

to which the line may be connected.

The "T" is particularly suited to use with a parallel-conductor line, in which case the two points along the antenna should be equidistant from the center so that electrical balance is maintained.

The operation of this system is somewhat complex. Each "T" conductor (y in the drawing) forms with the antenna conductor opposite it a short section of transmission line. Each of these transmission-line sections can be considered to be terminated in the impedance that exists at the point of connection to the antenna. Thus the part of the antenna between the two points carries a transmission-line current in addition to the normal antenna current. The two transmission-line matching sections are in series, as seen by the main transmission line.

If the antenna by itself is resonant at the operating frequency its impedance will be purely resistive, and in such case the matching-section lines are terminated in a resistive load. However, since these sections are shorter than a quarter wavelength their input impedance — i.e., the impedance seen by the main transmission line looking into the matching-section terminals — will be reactive as well as resistive. This prevents a perfect match to the main transmission line, since its load must be a pure resistance for perfect matching. The reactive component of the input impedance must be tuned out before a proper match can be secured.

One way to do this is to detune the antenna just enough, by changing its length, to cause reactance of the opposite kind to be reflected to the input terminals of the matching section, thus cancelling the reactance introduced by the latter. Another method, which is considerably easier to adjust, is to insert a variable capacitor in series with the matching section where it connects to the transmission line, as shown in Fig. 14-37. The capacitor must be protected from the weather.

The method of adjustment commonly used is to cut the antenna for approximate resonance and then make the spacing x some value that is convenient constructionally. The distance y is then adjusted, while maintaining symmetry with respect to the center, until the s.w.r. on the transmission line is as low as possible. If the s.w.r. is not below 2 to 1 after this adjustment, the antenna length should be changed slightly and the matching-section taps adjusted again. This process may be continued until the s.w.r. is as close to 1 to 1 as possible.

When the series-capacitor method of reactance compensation is used (Fig. 14-37) the antenna should be the proper length to be resonant at the operating frequency. Trial positions of the matching-section taps are taken, each time adjusting the capacitor for minimum s.w.r., until the standing waves on the transmission line are brought down to the lowest possible value.

The unbalanced ("gamma") arrangement in Fig. 14-45B is similar in principle to the "T," but is adapted for use with single coax line. The method of adjustment is the same.

Balancing Devices

● BALANCING DEVICES

An antenna with open ends, of which the half-wave type is an example, is inherently a balanced radiator. When opened at the center and fed with a parallel-conductor line this balance is maintained throughout the system, so long as the causes of unbalance discussed in the transmission-line chapter are avoided.

If the antenna is fed at the center through a coaxial line, as indicated in Fig. 14-46A, this balance is upset because one side of the radiator is connected to the shield while the other is connected to the inner conductor. On the side connected to the shield, a current can flow down over the *outside* of the coaxial line, and the fields thus set up cannot be canceled by the fields from the inner conductor because the fields *inside* the line cannot escape through the shielding afforded by the outer conductor. Hence these "antenna" currents flowing on the outside of the line will be responsible for radiation.

Linear Baluns

Line radiation can be prevented by a number of devices whose purpose is to detune or decouple the line for "antenna" currents and thus greatly reduce their amplitude. Such devices generally are known as **baluns** (a contraction for "balanced to unbalanced"). Fig. 14-46B shows one such arrangement, known as a **bazooka**, which uses a sleeve over the transmission line to form, with the outside of the outer line conductor, a shorted quarter-wave line section. As described earlier in this chapter, the impedance looking into the open end of such a section is very high, so that the end of the outer conductor of the coaxial line is effectively insulated from the part of the line below the sleeve. The length is an *electrical* quarter wave, and may be physically shorter if the insulation between the sleeve and the line is other than air. The bazooka has no effect on the impedance relationships between the antenna and the coaxial line.

Another method that gives an equivalent effect is shown at C. Since the voltages at the antenna terminals are equal and opposite (with reference to ground), equal and opposite currents flow on the surfaces of the line and second conductor. Beyond the shorting point, in the direction of the transmitter, these currents combine to cancel out. The balancing section "looks like" an open circuit to the antenna, since it is a quarter-wave parallel-conductor line shorted at the far end, and thus has no effect on the normal antenna operation. However, this is not essential to the line-balancing function of the device, and baluns of this type are sometimes made shorter than a quarter wavelength in order to provide the shunt inductive reactance required in certain types of matching systems.

Fig. 14-46D shows a third balun, in which equal and opposite voltages, balanced to ground, are taken from the inner conductors of the main transmission line and half-wave phasing section. Since the voltages at the balanced end are in series while the voltages at the unbalanced end are in

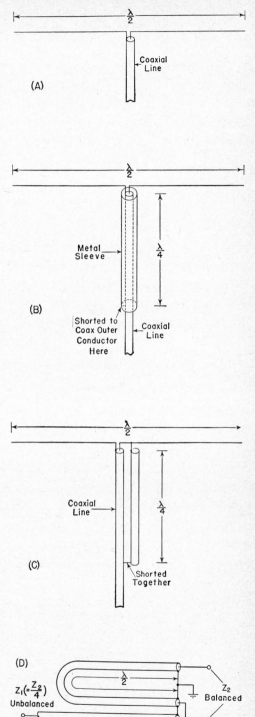

Fig. 14-46—Radiator with coaxial feed (A) and methods of preventing unbalance currents from flowing on the outside of the transmission line (B and C). The half-wave phasing section shown at D is used for coupling between an unbalanced and a balanced circuit when a 4-to-1 impedance ratio is desired or can be accepted.

parallel, there is a 4-to-1 step-down in impedance from the balanced to the unbalanced side. This arrangement is useful for coupling between a balanced 300-ohm line and a 75-ohm coaxial line, for example.

● RECEIVING ANTENNAS

Nearly all of the properties possessed by an antenna as a radiator also apply when it is used for reception. Current and voltage distribution, impedance, resistance and directional characteristics are the same in a receiving antenna as if it were used as a transmitting antenna. This reciprocal behavior makes possible the design of a receiving antenna of optimum performance based on the same considerations that have been discussed for transmitting antennas.

The simplest receiving antenna is a wire of random length. The longer and higher the wire, the more energy it abstracts from the wave. Because of the high sensitivity of modern receivers, sometimes only a short length of wire strung around the room is used for a receiving antenna, but such an antenna cannot be expected to give good performance, although it is adequate for loud signals on the 3.5- and 7-Mc. bands. It will serve in emergencies, but a longer wire outdoors is always better.

The use of a tuned antenna improves the operation of the receiver, because the signal strength is greater than with a wire of random length. Where local electrical noise is a problem, as from an electrical appliance, a measure of relief can often be obtained by locating the antenna as high above and as far as possible from the noise source and power lines. The lead-in wire, from the center of the antenna, should be a coaxial line or shielded twin-conductor cable (RG-62/U). If the twin-conductor cable is used, the conductors connect to the antenna binding posts and the shield to the ground binding post of the receiver.

Antenna Switching

Switching of the antenna from receiver to

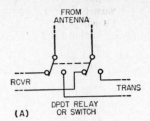

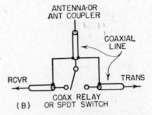

Fig. 14-47—Antenna changeover for receiving and transmitting in two-wire line (A) and coaxial line (B). The low-pass filter for TVI reduction should be connected between switch or relay and the transmitter.

transmitter is commonly done with a changeover relay, connected in the antenna leads or the coupling link from the antenna tuner. If the relay is one with a 115-volt a.c. coil, the switch or relay that controls the transmitter plate power will also control the antenna relay. If the convenience of a relay is not desired, porcelain knife switches can be used and thrown by hand.

Typical arrangements are shown in Fig. 14-47. If coaxial line is used, a coaxial relay is recommended, although on the lower-frequency bands a regular switch or change-over relay will work almost as well. The relay or switch contacts should be rated to handle at least the maximum power of the transmitter.

An additional refinement is the use of an electronic transit-receive switch, which permits full break-in operation even when using the transmitting antenna for receiving. For details and circuitry on t.r. switches, see Chapter Eight.

Antenna Construction

The use of good materials in the antenna system is important, since the antenna is exposed to wind and weather. To keep electrical losses low, the wires in the antenna and feeder system must have good conductivity and the insulators must have low dielectric loss and surface leakage, particularly when wet.

For short antennas, No. 14 gauge hard-drawn enameled copper wire is a satisfactory conductor. For long antennas and directive arrays, No. 14 or No. 12 enameled copper-clad steel wire should be used. It is best to make feeders and matching stubs of ordinary soft-drawn No. 14 or No. 12 enameled copper wire, since hard-drawn or copper-clad steel wire is difficult to

handle unless it is under considerable tension at all times. The wires should be all in one piece; where a joint cannot be avoided, it should be carefully soldered. Open-wire TV line is excellent up to several hundred watts.

In building a two-wire open line, the spacer insulation should be of as good quality as in the antenna insulators proper. For this reason, good ceramic spacers are advisable. Wooden dowels boiled in paraffin may be used with untuned lines, but their use is not recommended for tuned lines. The wooden dowels can be attached to the feeder wires by drilling small holes and binding them to the feeders.

At points of maximum voltage, insulation is

Antenna Construction

most important, and Pyrex glass or ceramic insulators with long leakage paths are recommended for the antenna. Insulators should be cleaned once or twice a year, especially if they are subjected to much smoke and soot.

In most cases poles or masts are desirable to lift the antenna clear of surrounding buildings, although in some locations the antenna will be sufficiently in the clear when strung from one chimney to another or from a housetop to a tree. Small trees usually are not satisfactory as points of suspension for the antenna because of their movement in windy weather. If the antenna is strung from a point near the center of the trunk of a large tree, this difficulty is not so serious. Where the antenna wire must be strung from one of the smaller branches, it is best to tie a pulley firmly to the branch and run a rope through the pulley to the antenna, with the other end of the rope attached to a counterweight near the ground. The counterweight will keep the tension on the antenna wire reasonably constant even when the branches sway or the rope tightens and stretches with varying climatic conditions.

Telephone poles, if they can be purchased and installed economically, make excellent supports because they do not ordinarily require guying in heights up to 40 feet or so. Many low-cost television-antenna supports are now available, and they should not be overlooked as possible antenna aids.

● "A"-FRAME MAST

The simple and inexpensive mast shown in Fig. 14-48 is satisfactory for heights up to 35 or 40 feet. Clear, sound lumber should be selected. The completed mast may be protected by two or three coats of house paint.

If the mast is to be erected on the ground, a couple of stakes should be driven to keep the bottom from slipping and it may then be "walked up" by a pair of helpers. If it is to go on a roof, first stand it up against the side of the building and then hoist it from the roof, keeping it vertical. The whole assembly is light enough for two men to perform the complete operation — lifting the mast, carrying it to its permanent berth, and fastening the guys — with the mast vertical all the while. It is entirely practicable, therefore, to erect this type of mast on any small, flat area of roof.

By using 2 × 3s or 2 × 4s, the height may be extended up to about 50 feet. The 2 × 2 is too flexible to be satisfactory at such heights.

● SIMPLE 40-FOOT MAST

The mast shown in Fig. 14-49 is relatively strong, easy to construct, readily dismantled, and costs very little. Like the "A"-frame, it is suitable for heights of the order of 40 feet.

The top section is a single 2 × 3, bolted at the bottom between a pair of 2 × 3s with an

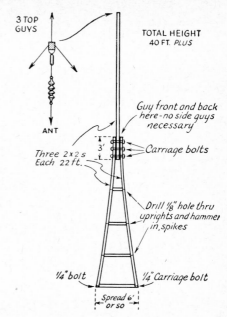

Fig. 14-48—Details of a simple 40-foot "A"-frame mast suitable for erection in locations where space is limited.

overlap of about two feet. The lower section thus has two legs spaced the width of the narrow side of a 2 × 3. At the bottom the two legs are bolted to a length of 2 × 4 which is set in the ground. A short length of 2 × 3 is placed between the two legs about halfway up

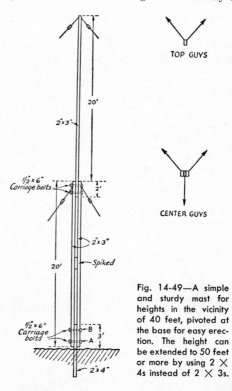

Fig. 14-49—A simple and sturdy mast for heights in the vicinity of 40 feet, pivoted at the base for easy erection. The height can be extended to 50 feet or more by using 2 × 4s instead of 2 × 3s.

the bottom section, to maintain the spacing.

The two back guys at the top pull against the antenna, while the three lower guys prevent buckling at the center of the pole.

The 2 × 4 section should be set in the ground so that it faces the proper direction, and then made vertical by lining it up with a plumb bob. The holes for the bolts should be drilled beforehand. With the lower section laid on the ground, bolt A should be slipped in place through the three pieces of wood and tightened just enough so that the section can turn freely on the bolt. Then the top section may be bolted in place and the mast pushed up, using a ladder or another 20-foot 2 × 3 for the job. As the mast goes up, the slack in the guys can be taken up so that the whole structure is in some measure continually supported. When the mast is vertical, bolt B should be slipped in place and both A and B tightened. The lower guys can then be given a final tightening, leaving those at the top a little slack until the antenna is pulled up, when they should be adjusted to pull the top section into line.

● GUYS AND GUY ANCHORS

For masts or poles up to about 50 feet, No. 12 iron wire is a satisfactory guy-wire material. Heavier wire or stranded cable may be used for taller poles or poles installed in locations where the wind velocity is likely to be high.

More than three guy wires in any one set usually are unnecessary. If a horizontal antenna is to be supported, two guy wires in the top set will be sufficient in most cases. These should run to the rear of the mast about 100 degrees apart to offset the pull of the antenna. Intermediate guys should be used in sets of three, one running in a direction opposite to that of the antenna, while the other two are spaced 120 degrees either side. This leaves a clear space under the antenna. The guy wires should be adjusted to pull the pole slightly back from vertical before the antenna is hoisted so that when the antenna is pulled up tight the mast will be straight.

When raising a mast that is big enough to tax the available facilities, it is some advantage to know nearly exactly the length of the guys. Those on the side on which the pole is lying can then be fastened temporarily to the anchors beforehand, which assures that when the pole is raised, those holding opposite guys will be able to pull it into nearly vertical position with no danger of its getting out of control. The guy lengths can be figured by the right-angled-triangle rule that "the sum of the squares of the two sides is equal to the square of the hypotenuse." In other words, the distance from the base of the pole to the anchor should be measured and squared. To this should be added the square of the pole length to the point where the guy is fastened. The square root of this sum will be the length of the guy.

Guy wires should be broken up by strain insulators, to avoid the possibility of resonance at the transmitting frequency. Common practice is to insert an insulator near the top of each guy, within a few feet of the pole, and then cut each section of wire between the insulators to a length which will not be resonant either on the fundamental or harmonics. An insulator every 25 feet will be satisfactory for frequencies up to 30 Mc. The insulators should be of the "egg" type with the insulating material under compression, so that the guy will not part if the insulator breaks.

Twisting guy wires onto "egg" insulators may be a tedious job if the guy wires are long and of large gauge. A simple time- and finger-saving

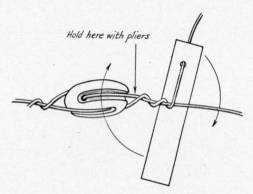

Fig. 14-50—Using a lever for twisting heavy guy wires.

device (piece of heavy iron or steel) can be made by drilling a hole about twice the diameter of the guy wire about a half inch from one end of the piece. The wire is passed through the insulator, given a single turn by hand, and then held with a pair of pliers at the point shown in Fig. 14-50. By passing the wire through the hole in the iron and rotating the iron as shown, the wire may be quickly and neatly twisted.

Guy wires may be anchored to a tree or building when they happen to be in convenient spots. For small poles, a 6-foot length of 1-inch pipe driven into the ground at an angle will suffice.

● HALYARDS AND PULLEYS

Halyards or ropes and pulleys are important items in the antenna-supporting system. Particular attention should be directed toward the choice of a pulley and halyards for a high mast since replacement, once the mast is in position, may be a major undertaking if not entirely impossible.

Galvanized-iron pulleys will have a life of only a year or so. Especially for coastal-area installations, marine-type pulleys with hardwood blocks and bronze wheels and bearings should be used.

For short antennas and temporary installations, heavy clothesline or window-sash cord may be used. However, for more permanent jobs, 3/8-inch or 1/2-inch waterproof hemp rope should be used. Even this should be replaced about once a year to insure against breakage.

Rotary Beam Construction

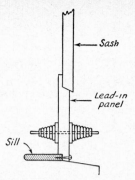

Fig. 14-51—An antenna lead-in panel may be placed over the top sash or under the lower sash of a window. Substituting a smaller height sash in half the window will simplify the weatherproofing problem where the sash overlaps.

It is advisable to carry the pulley rope back up to the top in "endless" fashion in the manner of a flag hoist so that if the antenna breaks close to the pole, there will be a means for pulling the hoisting rope back down.

● BRINGING THE ANTENNA OR FEED LINE INTO THE STATION

The antenna or transmission line should be anchored to the outside wall of the building, as shown in Fig. 14-52, to remove strain from the lead-in insulators. Holes cut through the walls of the building and fitted with feed-through insulators are undoubtedly the best means of

bringing the line into the station. The holes should have plenty of air clearance about the conducting rod, especially when using tuned lines that develop high voltages. Probably the best place to go through the walls is the trimming board at the top or bottom of a window frame which provides flat surfaces for lead-in insulators. Cement or rubber gaskets may be used to waterproof the exposed joints.

Where such a procedure is not permissible, the window itself usually offers the best opportunity. One satisfactory method is to drill holes in the glass near the top of the upper sash. If the glass is replaced by plate glass, a stronger job will result. Plate glass may be obtained from automobile junk yards and drilled before placing in the frame. The glass itself provides insulation and the transmission line may be fastened to bolts fitting the holes. Rubber gaskets will render the holes waterproof. The lower sash should be provided with stops to prevent damage when it is raised. If the window has a full-length screen, the scheme shown in Fig. 14-52B may be used.

As a less permanent method, the window may be raised from the bottom or lowered from the top to permit insertion of a board which carries the feed-through insulators. This lead-in arrangement can be made weatherproof by making an overlapping joint between the board and window sash, as shown in Fig. 14-51, or by using weatherstrip material where necessary.

Coaxial line can be brought through clearance holes without additional insulation.

Fig. 14-52—A—Anchoring feeders takes the strain from feed-through insulators or window glass. B—Going through a full-length screen, a cleat is fastened to the frame of the screen on the inside. Clearance holes are cut in the cleat and also in the screen.

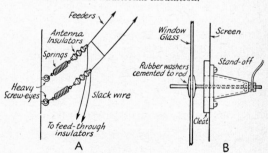

Rotary-Beam Construction

It is a distinct advantage to be able to shift the direction of a beam antenna at will, thus securing the benefits of power gain and directivity in any desired compass direction. A favorite method of doing this is to construct the antenna so that it can be rotated in the horizontal plane. The use of such rotatable antennas is usually limited to the higher frequencies — 14 Mc. and above — and to the simpler antenna-element combinations if the structure size is to be kept within practicable bounds. For the 14-, 21- and 28-Mc. bands such antennas usually consist of two to four elements and are of the parasitic-array type described earlier in this chapter. At 50 Mc. and

higher it becomes possible to use more elaborate arrays because of the shorter wavelength and thus obtain still higher gain. Antennas for these bands are described in another chapter.

The problems in rotary-beam construction are those of providing a suitable mechanical support for the antenna elements, furnishing a means of rotation, and attaching the transmission line so that it does not interfere with the rotation of the system.

Elements

The antenna elements usually are made of metal tubing so that they will be at least partially self-supporting, thus simplifying the

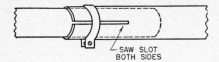

Fig. 14-53—Details of telescoping tubing for beam elements.

—SAW SLOT BOTH SIDES

supporting structure. The large diameter of the conductor is beneficial also in reducing resistance, which becomes an important consideration when close-spaced elements are used.

Aluminum alloy tubes are generally used for the elements. The elements frequently are constructed of sections of telescoping tubing making length adjustments for tuning quite easy. Electrician's thin-walled conduit also is suitable for rotary-beam elements. Regardless of the tubing used, the ends should be plugged up with corks sealed with glyptal varnish.

The element lengths are made adjustable by sawing a 6- to 12-inch slot in the ends of the larger-diameter tubing and clamping the smaller tubing inside. Homemade clamps of aluminum can be built, or hose clamps of suitable size can

be used. An example of this construction is shown in Fig. 14-53. If steel clamps are used, they should be cadmium- or zinc-plated before installation.

Supports

Metal is commonly used to support the elements of the rotary beam. For 28 Mc., a piece of 2-inch diameter duraluminum tubing makes a good "boom" for supporting the elements. The elements can be made to slide through suitable holes in the boom, or special clamps and brackets can be fashioned to support the elements. Fittings for TV antennas can often be used on 21- and 28-Mc. beams. "Irrigation pipe" is a good source of aluminum tubing up to diameters of 6 inches and lengths of 20 feet. Muffler clamps can be used to hold beam elements to a boom.

Most of the TV antenna rotators are satisfactory for turning the smaller beams.

With all-metal construction, delta, "gamma" or "T"-match are the only practical matching methods to use to the line, since anything else requires opening the driven element at the center, and this complicates the support problem for that element.

"Plumber's-Delight" Construction

The lightest beam to build is the so-called "plumber's delight", an array constructed entirely of metal, with no insulating members between the elements and the supporting structure. Some suggestions for the constructional details are given in Figs. 14-54, 14-55 and 14-56. These show portions of a 4-element 10-meter beam, but the same principles hold for 15- and 20-meter beams.

Boom material can be the irrigation pipe suggested earlier (available from Sears Roebuck). Muffler clamps and homemade brackets (aluminum or cadmium-plated steel) can be used to hold the parasitic elements to the boom, as

shown in Fig. 14-54. The muffler clamps and all hardware should be cadmium-plated to forestall corrosion; the plating can be done at a plating shop and will not be very expensive if it is all done at the same time.

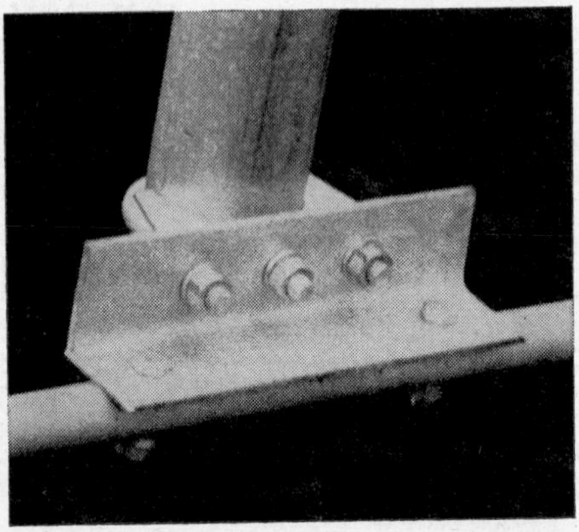

Fig. 14-55—The boom can be tied to the mast with muffler clamps and a steel plate. The coaxial line from the driven element is taped to the boom and mast.

Muffler clamps and a steel plate can be used to hold the boom to the supporting mast, as shown in Fig. 14-55. For maximum strength, the mast section should be a length of galvanized iron pipe. The plate thickness should run from $3/16$ inch for a 10-meter beam to $1/2$ inch or more for a 20-meter beam. Steel plates of this thickness are best cut in a welding shop, where it can be done quickly for a nominal fee. After the plate has been cut and the muffler-clamp holes drilled, the plate, clamps and hardware should be plated.

The photograph in Fig. 14-56 shows one way

Fig. 14-54—Muffler clamps can be used to hold beam elements to the boom. The angle can be aluminum angle or angle iron; if iron is used it should be cadmium plated. This example shows a ¾-inch-diameter element held to a 2-inch diameter boom.

Rotary Beam Construction

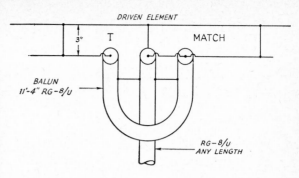

Fig. 14-56—Details of a coaxial-line termination board and T-match support for a 10-meter beam. The balun of a half-wavelength of coaxial line is coiled and then fastened to the boom with tape.

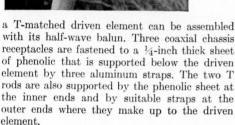

a T-matched driven element can be assembled with its half-wave balun. Three coaxial chassis receptacles are fastened to a ¼-inch thick sheet of phenolic that is supported below the driven element by three aluminum straps. The two T rods are also supported by the phenolic sheet at the inner ends and by suitable straps at the outer ends where they make up to the driven element.

Rotation

It is convenient but not essential to use a motor to rotate the beam. If a rope-and-pulley arrangement can be brought into the operating room or if the pole can be mounted near a window in the operating room, hand rotation will work.

If the use of a rope and pulleys is impracticable, motor drive is about the only alternative. There are several complete motor driven rotators on the market, and they are easy to mount, convenient to use, and require little or no maintenance. Generally speaking, light-weight units are better because they reduce the tower load.

The speed of rotation should not be too great — one or 1½ r.p.m. is about right. This requires a considerable gear reduction from the usual 1750-r.p.m. speed of small induction motors; a large reduction is advantageous because the gear train will prevent the beam from turning in weather-vane fashion in a wind. The usual beam does not require a great deal of power for rotation at slow speed, and a ⅛-hp. motor will be ample. A reversible motor should be used. War-surplus "prop pitch" motors have found wide application for rotating 14-Mc. beams, while TV rotators can be used with many 28-Mc. lightweight beams.

Driving motors and gear housings will stand the weather better if given a coat of aluminum paint followed by two coats of enamel and a coat of glyptal varnish. Even commercial units will last longer if treated with glyptal varnish. Be sure that the surfaces are clean and free from grease before painting. Grease can be removed by brushing with kerosene and then squirting the surface with a solid stream of water. The work can then be wiped dry with a rag.

The power and control leads to the rotator should be run in electrical conduit or in lead covering, and the metal should be grounded.

A Compact 14-Mc. 3-Element Beam

A 20-meter beam no larger than the usual 10-meter beam can be made by using center-loaded elements and close spacing. Such an antenna will show good directivity and can be rotated with a TV-antenna rotator.

Constructional details of the elements are shown in Figs. 14-57 and 14-58. The loading coils are space-wound by interwinding plumb line (sometimes known as chalk line) with the No. 12 wire coils. The coil ends are secured by drilling small holes through the polystyrene bar, as shown in Fig. 14-60. The coils should be sprayed or painted with Krylon before installing the protective Lucite tubes.

The beam will require 4-foot lengths of the tubings indicated in Fig. 14-57A. For good telescoping, element wall thickness of 0.058 inch is recommended. The ends of the tubing sections should be slotted to permit adjustment, and secured with clamps, so that the joints will not work loose in the wind. Perforated ground clamps can be used for this purpose. The boom is a 12-foot length of 1½-inch o.d. 61ST aluminum tubing, with 0.125-inch wall.

The line is coupled and matched at the center of the driven element through adjustment of the link wound on the outside of the Lucite tubing. To check the adjustment of the elements, first resonate the driven element to the desired frequency in the 14-Mc. band with a grid-dip oscil-

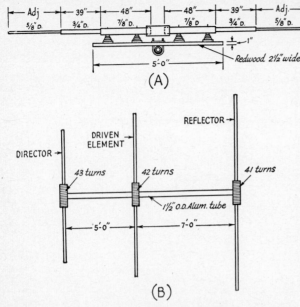

Fig. 14-57—Dimensions of a compact 14-Mc. beam. A—Side view of a typical element. TV-antenna "U" clamps hold the support arms to the boom. Birnbach 4176 insulators support the elements. B—Top plan of the beam showing element spacing and loading-coil dimensions. Elements are made of aluminum tubing. Construction of the loading coils and adjustment of the elements are discussed in the text. End-section lengths of 41 inches for the reflector, 40 inches for the driven element, and 10 inches for the director will be close to optimum.

lator. Then resonate the director to approximately 14.8 Mc., and the reflector to approximately 13.6 Mc. This is not critical and only serves as a rough point for the final tuning, which is done by use of a conventional field-strength indicator. Check the transmitter loading and readjust if necessary. Adjust the director for maximum forward gain, and then adjust the reflector for maximum forward gain. At this point, check the driven element for resonance and readjust if necessary. Turn the reflector toward the field-strength indicator and adjust for back cut-off.

This must be done in small steps. Do not expect the attenuation off the sides of a short beam to be as high as that obtained with full-length elements. The s.w.r. of the line feeding the antenna can be checked with a bridge, and after the elements have been tuned, a final adjustment of the s.w.r. can be made by adjusting the coupling at the antenna loading coil turns and spacing. As in any beam, the s.w.r. will depend upon this adjustment and not on any that can be made at the transmitter. Transmitter coupling is the usual for any coaxial line. (From *QST*, May, 1954.)

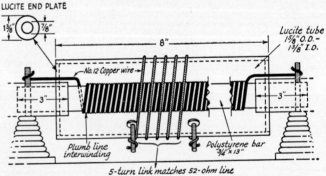

Fig. 14-58—Detailed sketch of the loading and coupling coils at the center of the driven element, and its mounting. Similar loading coils (see text) are used at the centers of the director and reflector.

A "One-Element Rotary" for 21 Mc.

The directional properties of a simple half-wavelength antenna become more apparent at higher frequencies, and it is possible to take advantage of this fact to build a "one-element rotary" for 21 or 28 Mc. To take advantage of the directional properties of the antenna, it is only necessary to rotate it 180 degrees. It can be rotated by hand, as will be described, or by a small TV antenna rotator. A 28-Mc. antenna should be made full size (14-C) and fed at the center with RG-11/U.

The 21-Mc. antenna is made from two pieces of ½-inch diameter electrical thin-wall steel tubing or conduit. This tubing is readily available at any electric supply shop. It comes in 10-foot lengths and, while 20 feet is short for a half-wave antenna

Rotary Beam Construction

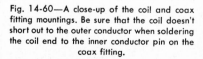

Fig. 14-59—(A) Diagram of the 21-Mc. antenna and mounting. The U-bolts that hold the 2 by 2 to the floor flange are standard 2-inch TV mast type bolts. (B) A more detailed drawing of the coil and coax-fitting mountings. The ¼-inch spacing between turns is not critical, and they can vary as much as ⅟₁₆ inch without any apparent harm to the match.

at 21-Mc., with loading the length is just about right for 52-ohm line feed. (A half-wavelength antenna would normally be fed with 72-ohm cable, since the antenna offers a good match for this impedance value. In this antenna system, the shorter elements, plus the small coil, offer a good match for 52-ohm cable.) If aluminum tubing is available, it can be used in place of the conduit, and the antenna will be lighter in weight. As shown in Figs. 14-59 and 14-60, the two pieces of tubing are supported by four stand-off insulators on a four foot long 2 by 2. The coax fitting for the feed line is mounted on the end of one of the lengths of tubing. A mounting point is made by flattening the end of the tubing for a length of about 1½ inches. The tubing can be flattened by squeezing it in a vise or by laying the end of the tubing on a hard surface and then hammering it flat. This will provide enough space to accommodate the coax fitting (Amphenol type 83-1R). A ⅝-inch hole will be needed in the flat section to clear the shell of the coax fitting.

The coil, L_1, is made from ⅛-inch diameter copper tubing. It consists of 5 turns spaced ¼ inch apart and is 1 inch inside diameter. The coil is connected in series with the inner conductor pin on the coax fitting and the other half of the antenna. To secure a good connection at the coax fitting, the coil lead should be wound around the inner-conductor pin and soldered. The other end of the coil can be connected with a screw and nut.

Mounting

The antenna can be mounted on a 1-inch floor flange and held in place by two 2-inch bolts, as shown in Fig. 14-61. The floor flange can be connected to a 12-foot length of 1-inch pipe which will serve as a mast. Television antenna wall mounts can be used to support the mast.

In the installation shown in Fig. 14-61, 19-inch wall mounts were used in order to clear the eaves of the house. A 2-inch long piece of 1¼-inch pipe was used as a sleeve, and it was clamped in the U bolt on the bottom wall mount. A ¼-inch hole

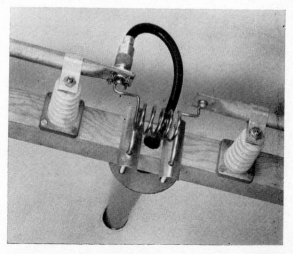

Fig. 14-60—A close-up of the coil and coax fitting mountings. Be sure that the coil doesn't short out to the outer conductor when soldering the coil end to the inner conductor pin on the coax fitting.

Fig. 14-61—Over-all view of the antenna and mounting. The feed line comes out of the bottom of the mast and through the wall into the shack.

so that the rod projected on each side of the mast. To turn the mast, a piece of rope was attached to each end of the rod and the rope was brought into the shack, so that the antenna could be rotated by the "arm-strong" method. Obviously, one could spend more money for a "de luxe" version and use a TV antenna rotator and mast.

RG-8/U 52-ohm coax cable is recommended to feed the antenna. For power inputs up to 100 watts, the smaller and less expensive RG-58/U can be used. However, when you buy RG-58/U, be sure that the line is made by a reputable manufacturer (such as Amphenol or Belden). Some of the line made for TV installations is of inferior quality and is likely to have higher losses. The feedline was fed up through the mast pipe and through a ¾-inch hole in the 2 by 2. An Amphenol 83-1SP fitting on the end of the coax line connects to the female fitting on the antenna.

Coupling to the Transmitter

It may be found that, when the feed line is coupled to the transmitter, the antenna won't take power. Since the line is terminated at the antenna in its characteristic impedance of 52 ohms, the output of the final r.f. amplifier must be adjusted to couple into a 52-ohm load. Where the output coupling device is a variable link, all that may be needed is the correct setting of the link. If the link is fixed, one end of the link can be grounded to the transmitter chassis and the other end of the link connected in series with a small variable capacitor to the inner conductor of the feed line. The outer conductor of the coax is grounded to the transmitter chassis. The capacitor is tuned to the point where the final amplifier is properly loaded. For transmitters having a pi-network output circuit, it is merely a matter of adjusting the network to the point where the amplifier is properly loaded.

(From *QST*, January, 1955.)

was drilled through the mast pipe approximately 6 inches from the bottom. Then a 1½-inch bolt was slipped through the hole and the mast was then mounted in the sleeve on the bottom wall mount. The bolt acted as a bearing point against the top of the sleeve. Another ¼-inch hole was drilled through the mast about three feet above the bottom wall mount. A piece of ¼-inch metal rod, six inches long, was forced through the hole

CHAPTER 15

Wave Propagation

Much of the appeal of amateur communication lies in the fact that the results are not always predictable. Transmission conditions on the same frequency vary with the year, season and with the time of day. Although these variations usually follow certain established patterns, many peculiar effects can be observed from time to time. Every radio amateur should have some understanding of the known facts about radio wave propagation so that he will stand some chance of interpreting the unusual conditions when they occur. The observant amateur is in an excellent position to make worthwhile contributions to the science, provided he has sufficient background to understand his results. He may discover new facts about propagation at the very-high frequencies or in the microwave region, as amateurs have in the past. In fact, it is through amateur efforts that most of the extended-range possibilities of various radio frequencies have been discovered, both by accident and by long and careful investigation.

Characteristics of Radio Waves

Radio waves, like other forms of electromagnetic radiation such as light, travel at a speed of 300,000,000 meters per second in free space, and can be reflected, refracted, and diffracted.

An electromagnetic wave is composed of moving fields of electric and magnetic force. The lines of force in the electric and magnetic fields are at right angles, and are mutually perpendicular to the direction of travel. A simple representation of a wave is shown in Fig. 15-1. In this drawing the electric lines are perpendicular to the earth and the magnetic lines are horizontal. They could, however, have any position with respect to earth so long as they remain perpendicular to each other.

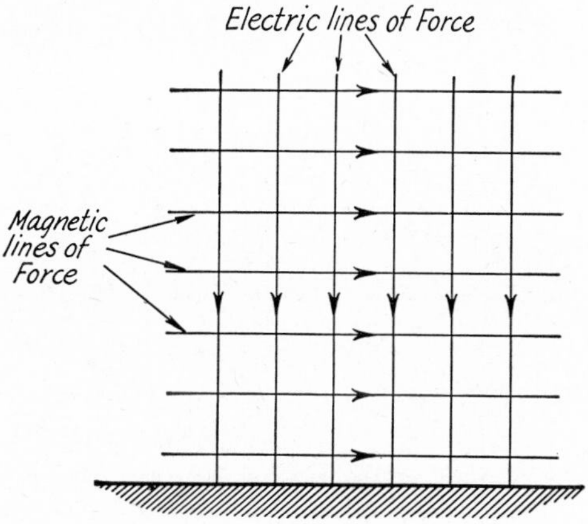

The plane containing the continuous lines of electric and magnetic force shown by the grid- or mesh-like drawing in Fig. 15-1 is called the wave front.

The **medium** in which electromagnetic waves travel has a marked influence on the speed with which they move. When the medium is empty space the speed, as stated above, is 300,000,000 meters per second. It is almost, but not quite, that great in air, and is much less in some other substances. In dielectrics, for example, the speed is inversely proportional to the square root of the dielectric constant of the material.

When a wave meets a good **conductor** it cannot penetrate it to any extent (although it will travel through a dielectric with ease) because the electric lines of force are practically short-circuited.

Polarization

The **polarization** of a radio wave is taken as the direction of the lines of force in the electric field. If the electric lines are perpendicular to the earth, the wave is said to be **vertically polarized**; if parallel with the earth, the wave is **horizontally polarized**. The longer waves, when traveling along the ground, usually maintain their polarization in the same plane as was generated at the antenna. The polarization of shorter waves may be altered during travel, however, and sometimes will vary quite rapidly.

Spreading

The field intensity of a wave is inversely proportional to the distance from the source. Thus if in a uniform medium one receiving point is twice as far from the transmitter as another, the field strength at the more distant point will be just half the field strength at the nearer point. This results from the fact that the energy in the wave front must be distributed over a greater area as the wave moves away from the source. This **inverse-distance law** is based on the assumption that there is nothing in the medium to absorb energy from the wave as it travels. This is not the case in practical communication along the ground and through the atmosphere.

Types of Propagation

According to the altitudes of the paths along which they are propagated, radio waves may

Fig. 15-1—Representation of electric and magnetic lines of force in a radio wave. Arrows indicate instantaneous directions of the fields for a wave traveling toward the reader. Reversing the direction of one set of lines would reverse the direction of travel.

be classified as **ionospheric waves, tropospheric waves** or **ground waves.**

The ionospheric wave or **sky wave** is that part of the total radiation that is directed toward the ionosphere. Depending upon variable conditions in that region, as well as upon transmitting wave length, the ionospheric wave may or may not be returned to earth by the effects of refraction and reflection.

The tropospheric wave is that part of the total radiation that undergoes refraction and reflection in regions of abrupt change of dielectric constant in the troposphere, such as may occur at the boundaries between air masses of differing temperature and moisture content.

The ground wave is that part of the total radia-

Fig. 15-2—Showing how both direct and reflected waves may be received simultaneously.

tion that is directly affected by the presence of the earth and its surface features. The ground wave has two components. One is the **surface wave,** which is an earth-guided wave, and the other is the **space wave** (not to be confused with the ionospheric or sky wave). The space wave is itself the resultant of two components — the **direct wave** and the **ground-reflected wave,** as shown in Fig. 15-2.

Ionospheric Propagation

● PROPERTIES OF THE IONOSPHERE

Except for distances of a few miles, nearly all amateur communication on frequencies below 30 Mc. is by means of the sky wave. Upon leaving the transmitting antenna, this wave travels upward from the earth's surface at such an angle that it would continue out into space were its path not bent sufficiently to bring it back to earth. The medium that causes such bending is the **ionosphere,** a region in the upper atmosphere, above a height of about 60 miles, where free ions and electrons exist in sufficient quantity to have an appreciable effect on wave travel.

The ionization in the upper atmosphere is believed to be caused by ultraviolet radiation from the sun. The ionosphere is not a single region but is composed of a series of layers of varying densities of ionization occurring at different heights. Each layer consists of a central region of relatively dense ionization that tapers off in intensity both above and below.

Refraction

The greater the intensity of ionization in a layer, the more the path of the wave is bent. The bending, or refraction (often also called reflection), also depends on the wavelength; the longer the wave, the more the path is bent for a given degree of ionization. Thus low-frequency waves are more readily bent than those of high frequency. For this reason the lower frequencies — 3.5 and 7 Mc. — are more "reliable" than the higher frequencies — 14 to 28 Mc.; there are times when the ionization is of such low value that waves of the latter frequency range are not bent enough to return to earth.

Absorption

In traveling through the ionosphere the wave gives up some of its energy by setting the ionized particles into motion. When the moving ionized particles collide with others this energy is lost. The **absorption** from this cause is greater at lower frequencies. It also increases with the intensity of

ionization, and with the density of the atmosphere in the ionized region.

Virtual Height

Although an ionospheric layer is a region of considerable depth it is convenient to assign to it a definite height, called the **virtual height.** This is the height from which a simple reflection would give the same effect as the gradual bend-

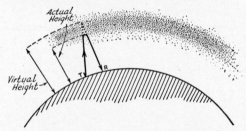

Fig. 15-3—Bending in the ionosphere, and the echo or reflection method of determining virtual height.

ing that actually takes place, as illustrated in Fig. 15-3. The wave traveling upward is bent back over a path having an appreciable radius of turning, and a measurable interval of time is consumed in the turning process. The virtual height is the height of a triangle having equal sides of a total length proportional to the time taken for the wave to travel from T to R.

Normal Structure of the Ionosphere

The lowest useful ionized layer is called the **E layer.** The average height of the region of maximum ionization is about 70 miles. The air at this height is sufficiently dense so that the ions and electrons set free by the sun's radiation do not travel far before they meet and recombine to form neutral particles, so the layer can maintain its normal intensity of ionization only in the presence of continuing radiation from the sun. Hence the ionization is greatest around local noon and practically disappears after sundown.

In the daytime there is a still lower ionized

area, the **D region.** D-region ionization is proportional to the height of the sun and is greatest at noon. The lower amateur-band frequencies (1.8 and 3.5 Mc.) are almost completely absorbed by this layer, and only the high-angle radiation is reflected by the *E* layer. (Lower-angle radiation travels farther through the *D* region and is absorbed.)

The second principal layer is the **F layer** which has a height of about 175 miles high. At this altitude the air is so thin that recombination of ions and electrons takes place very slowly. The ionization decreases after sundown, reaching a minimum just before sunrise. In the daytime the *F* layer splits into two parts, the F_1 and F_2 **layers**, with average virtual heights of, respectively, 140 miles and 200 miles. These layers are most highly ionized at about local noon, and merge again at sunset into the *F* layer.

● SKY-WAVE PROPAGATION

Wave Angle

The smaller the angle at which a wave leaves the earth, the less the bending required in the ionosphere to bring it back. Also, the smaller the angle the greater the distance between the point where the wave leaves the earth and that at which it returns. This is shown in Fig. 15-4. The vertical angle that the wave makes with a tangent to the earth is called the **wave angle** or **angle of radiation.**

Skip Distance

More bending is required to return the wave to earth when the wave angle is high, and at times the bending will not be sufficient unless the wave angle is smaller than some critical value. This is illustrated in Fig. 15-4, where *A* and smaller angles give useful signals while waves sent at higher angles penetrate the layer and are not returned. The distance between *T* and R_1 is, therefore, the shortest possible distance, at that particular frequency, over which communication by ionospheric refraction can be accomplished.

The area between the end of the useful ground wave and the beginning of ionospheric-wave reception is called the **skip zone,** and the distance from the transmitter to the nearest point where the sky wave returns to earth is called the **skip distance.** The extent of the skip zone depends upon the frequency and the state of the ionosphere, and also upon the height of the layer in which the refraction takes place. The higher layers give longer skip distances for the same wave angle. Wave angles at the transmitting and receiving points are usually, although not always, approximately the same for any given wave path.

Critical and Maximum Usable Frequencies

If the frequency is low enough, a wave sent vertically to the iono-

sphere will be reflected back down to the transmitting point. If the frequency is then gradually increased, eventually a frequency will be reached where this vertical reflection just fails to occur. This is the **critical frequency** for the layer under consideration. When the operating frequency is below the critical value there is no skip zone.

The critical frequency is a useful index to the highest frequency that can be used to transmit over a specified distance — the **maximum usable frequency (m.u.f.).** If the wave leaving the transmitting point at angle *A* in Fig. 15-4 is, for example, at a frequency of 14 Mc., and if a higher frequency would skip over the receiving point R_1, then 14 Mc. is the m.u.f. for the distance from *T* to R_1.

The greatest possible distance is covered when the wave leaves along the tangent to the earth; that is, at zero wave angle. Under average conditions this distance is about 4000 kilometers or 2500 miles for the F_2 layer, and 2000 km. or 1250 miles for the *E* layer. The distances vary with the layer height. Frequencies above these limiting m.u.f.'s will not be returned to earth at any distance. The 4000-km. m.u.f. for the F_2 layer is approximately 3 times the critical frequency for that layer, and for the *E* layer the 2000-km. m.u.f. is about 5 times the critical frequency.

Absorption in the ionosphere is least at the maximum usable frequency, and increases very rapidly as the frequency is lowered below the m.u.f. Consequently, best results with low power always are secured when the frequency is as close to the m.u.f. as possible.

It is readily possible for the ionospheric wave to pass through the *E* layer and be refracted back to earth from the *F*, F_1 or F_2 layers. This is because the critical frequencies are higher in the latter layers, so that a signal too high in frequency to be returned by the *E* layer can still come back from one of the others, depending upon the time of day and the existing conditions.

Multihop Transmission

On returning to the earth the wave can be reflected upward and travel again to the ionosphere. There it may once more be refracted, and

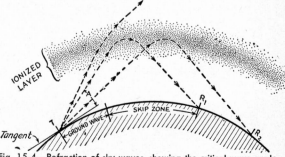

Fig. 15-4—Refraction of sky waves, showing the critical wave angle and the skip zone. Waves leaving the transmitter at angles above the critical (greater than A) are not bent enough to be returned to earth. As the angle is decreased, the waves return to earth at increasingly greater distances.

again bent back to earth. This process may be repeated several times. **Multihop** propagation of this nature is necessary for transmission over great distances because of the limited heights of the layers and the curvature of the earth, which restrict the maximum one-hop distance to the values mentioned in the preceding section. However, ground losses absorb some of the energy from the wave on each reflection (the amount of the loss varying with the type of ground and being least for reflection from sea water), and there is also absorption in the ionosphere at each reflection. Hence the smaller the number of hops the greater the signal strength at the receiver, other things being equal.

Fading

Two or more parts of the wave may follow slightly different paths in traveling to the receiving point, in which case the difference in path lengths will cause a phase difference to exist between the wave components at the receiving antenna. The total field strength will be the sum of the components and may be larger or smaller than one component alone, since the phases may be such as either to aid or oppose. Since the paths change from time to time, this causes a variation in signal strength called **fading**. Fading can also result from the combination of single-hop and multihop waves, or the combination of a ground wave with an ionospheric or tropospheric wave.

Fading may be either rapid or slow, the former type usually resulting from rapidly-changing conditions in the ionosphere, the latter occurring when transmission conditions are relatively stable.

It frequently happens that transmission conditions are different for waves of slightly different frequencies, so that in the case of voice-modulated transmission, involving sidebands differing slightly from the carrier in frequency, the carrier and various side band components may not be propagated in the same relative amplitudes and phases they had at the transmitter. This effect, known as **selective fading**, causes severe distortion of the signal.

Back Scatter

Even though the operating frequency is above the m.u.f. for a given distance, it is usually possible to hear signals from within the skip zone. This phenomenon, called **back scatter**, is caused by reflections from distances beyond the skip zone. Such reflections can occur when the transmitted energy strikes the earth at a distance and some of it is reflected back into the skip zone to the receiver. Such scatter signals are weaker than those normally propagated, and also have a rapid fade or "flutter" that makes them easily recognizable.

A certain amount of scattering of the wave also takes place in the ionosphere because the ionized region is not completely uniform. Scattering in the normal propagation direction is called **forward scatter**, and is responsible for extending the range of transmission beyond the distance of a regular hop, and for making communication possible on frequencies greater than the actual m.u.f.

● OTHER FEATURES OF IONOSPHERIC PROPAGATION

Cyclic Variations in the Ionosphere

Since ionization depends upon ultraviolet radiation, conditions in the ionosphere vary with changes in the sun's radiation. In addition to the daily variation, seasonal changes result in higher critical frequencies in the E layer in summer, averaging about 4 Mc. as against a winter average of 3 Mc. The F layer critical frequency is of the order of 4 to 5 Mc. in the evening. The F_1 layer, which has a critical frequency near 5 Mc. in summer, usually disappears entirely in winter. The daytime maximum critical frequencies for the F_2 are highest in winter (10 to 12 Mc.) and lowest in summer (around 7 Mc.). The virtual height of the F_2 layer, which is about 185 miles in winter, averages 250 miles in summer. These values are representative of latitude 40 deg. North in the Western hemisphere, and are subject to considerable variation in other parts of the world.

Very marked changes in ionization also occur in step with the **11-year sunspot cycle**. Although there is no apparent direct correlation between sunspot activity and critical frequencies on a given day, there is a definite correlation between *average* sunspot activity and critical frequencies. The critical frequencies are highest during sunspot maxima and lowest during sunspot minima. During the period of minimum sunspot activity the lower frequencies — 7 and 3.5 Mc. — frequently are the only usable bands at night. At such times the 28-Mc. band is seldom useful for long-distance work, while the 14-Mc. band performs well in the daytime but is not ordinarily useful at night.

Ionosphere Storms

Certain types of sunspot activity cause considerable disturbances in the ionosphere (**ionosphere storms**) and are accompanied by disturbances in the earth's magnetic field (**magnetic storms**). Ionosphere storms are characterized by a marked increase in absorption, so that radio conditions become poor. The critical frequencies also drop to relatively low values during a storm, so that only the lower frequencies are useful for communication. Ionosphere storms may last from a few hours to several days. Since the sun rotates on its axis once every 28 days, disturbances tend to recur at such intervals, if the sunspots responsible do not become inactive in the meantime. Absorption is usually low, and radio conditions therefore good, just preceding a storm.

Sporadic-E Ionization

Scattered patches or clouds of relatively dense ionization occasionally appear at heights approximately the same as that of the E layer, for reasons not yet known. This **sporadic-***E* ionization is most prevalent in the equatorial regions, where it is substantially continuous. In northern latitudes it is most frequent in the spring and early summer, but is present in some degree a fair percentage of the time the year 'round. It accounts for a good deal of the night-time short distance work on the lower frequencies (3.5 and 7 Mc.) and, when more intense, for similar work on 14 to 28 Mc. Exceptionally intense sporadic-*E* ionization is responsible for work over distances exceeding 400 or 500 miles on the 50-Mc. band.

There are indications of a relationship between sporadic-*E* ionization and average sunspot activity, but it does not appear to be directly related to daylight and darkness since it may occur at any time of the day. However, there is an apparent tendency for the ionization to peak at mid-morning and in the early evening.

Tropospheric Propagation

Changes in temperature and humidity of air masses in the lower atmosphere often permit work over greater than normal ground-wave distances on 28 Mc. and higher frequencies. The effect can be observed on 28 Mc., but it is generally more marked on 50 and 144 Mc. The subject is treated in detail later.

● **PREDICTION CHARTS**

The Central Radio Propagation Laboratory of National Bureau of Standards offers prediction charts three months in advance, by means of which it is possible to predict with considerable accuracy the maximum usable frequency that will hold over any path on the earth during a monthly period. The charts can be obtained from the Superintendent of Documents, U. S. Government Printing Office, Washington 25, D. C. for 10 cents a copy or $1.00 per year. They are called *"CRPL-D Basic Radio Propagation Predictions."* The use of the charts is explained in Circular 462, *"Ionospheric Radio Propagation,"* available for $1.00 from the same address. This publication also contains much information of value to those who wish to pursue the subject of ionospheric propagation in more detail.

● **PROPAGATION IN THE 3.5 TO 30-MC. BANDS**

The 1.8-Mc., or "160-meter," band offers reliable working over ranges up to 25 miles or so during daylight. On winter nights, ranges up to several thousand miles are not impossible. Only small sections of the band are currently available to amateurs, because of the presence of the loran service in that part of the spectrum.

The 3.5-Mc., or "80-meter," band is a more useful band during the night than during the daylight hours. In the daytime, one can seldom hear signals from a distance of greater than 200 miles or so, but during the darkness hours distances up to several thousand miles are not unusual, and transoceanic contacts are regularly made during the winter months. During the summer, the static level is high.

The 7-Mc., or "40-meter," band has many of the same characteristics as 3.5, except that the distances that can be covered during the day and night hours are increased. During daylight, distances up to a thousand miles can be covered under good conditions, and during the dawn and dusk periods in winter it is possible to work stations as far as the other side of the world, the signals following the darkness path. The winter months are somewhat better than the summer ones. In general, summer static is much less of a problem than on 80 meters, although it can be serious in the semitropical zones.

The 14-Mc., or "20-meter," band is probably the best one for long-distance work. During the high portion of the sunspot cycle it is open to some part of the world during practically all of the 24 hours, while during a sunspot minimum it is generally useful only during daylight hours and the dawn and dusk periods. There is practically always a skip zone on this band.

The 21-Mc., or "15-meter," band shows highly variable characteristics depending on the sunspot cycle. During sunspot maxima it is useful for long-distance work during a large part of the 24 hours, but in years of low sunspot activity it is almost wholly a daytime band, and sometimes unusable even in daytime. However, it is often possible to maintain communication over distances up to 1500 miles or more by sporadic-*E* ionization which may occur either day or night at any time in the sunspot cycle.

The 28-Mc. ("10-meter") band is generally considered to be a DX band during the daylight hours (except in summer) and good for local work during the hours of darkness, for about half the sunspot cycle. At the very peak of the sunspot cycle, it may be "open" into the late evening hours for DX communication. At the sunspot minimum the band is usually "dead" for long-distance communication, by means of the F_2 layer, in the northern latitudes. Nevertheless, sporadic-*E* propagation is likely to occur at any time, just as in the case of the 21-Mc. band.

Propagation Above 50 Mc.

The importance to the amateur of having some knowledge of wave propagation was stressed at the beginning of this chapter. An understanding of the means by which his signals reach their destination is an even greater aid to the v.h.f. worker. Each of his bands shows different characteristics, and knowledge of their peculiarities is as yet far from complete. The observant user of the amateur v.h.f. assignments has a good opportunity to contribute to that knowledge, and his enjoyment of his work will be greatly enhanced if he knows when to expect unusual propagation conditions.

● CHARACTERISTICS OF THE V.H.F. BANDS

An outstanding feature of our bands from 50 Mc. up is their ability to provide consistent and interference-free communication within a limited range. All lower frequencies are subject to varying conditions that impair their effectiveness for work over distances of 100 miles or less at least part of the time, and the heavy occupancy they support results in severe interference problems in areas of dense population. The v.h.f. bands, being much wider, can handle many times the amateur population without crowding, and their characteristics for local work are more stable. It is thus to the advantage of amateur radio as a whole to make use of 50 Mc. and higher bands for short-range communication wherever possible.

In addition to reliable local coverage, the v.h.f. bands also exhibit several forms of long-distance propagation at times, and use of 50 and 144 Mc. has been taken up in recent years by many isolated amateurs who must depend on these propagation peculiarities for all or most of their contacts. It is particularly important to these operators that they understand common propagation phenomena. The material to follow supplements information presented earlier in this chapter, but deals with wave propagation only as it affects the occupants of the world above 50 Mc. First let us consider the bands individually.

50 to 54 Mc.: This band is borderline territory between the DX frequencies and those normally employed for local work. Thus just about every form of wave propagation found throughout the radio spectrum appears, on occasion, in the 50-Mc. region. This has contributed greatly to the popularity of the 50-Mc. band.

During the peak years of a sunspot cycle it is occasionally possible to work 50-Mc. DX of world-wide proportions, by reflection of signals from the F_2 layer. Sporadic-E skip provides contacts over distances from 400 to 2500 miles or so during the early summer months, regardless of the solar cycle. Reflection from the aurora regions allows 100- to 1000-mile work during pronounced ionospheric disturbances. The ever-changing weather pattern offers extension of the normal coverage to as much as 300 to 500 miles. This develops most often during the warmer months, but may occur at any season. In the absence of any favorable propagation, the average well-equipped 50-Mc. station should be able to work regularly over a radius of 75 to 100 miles or more, depending on local terrain.

144 to 148 Mc.: Ionospheric effects are greatly reduced at 144 Mc. F_2-layer reflection is unlikely, and sporadic-E skip is rare. Aurora DX is fairly common, but signals are generally weaker than on 50 Mc. Tropospheric effects are more pro-

nounced than on 50 Mc., and distances covered during favorable weather conditions are greater than on lower bands. Air-mass boundary bending has been responsible for communication on 144 Mc. over distances in excess of 2500 miles, and 500-mile work is fairly common in the warmer months. The reliable range under normal conditions is slightly less than on 50 Mc., with comparable equipment.

220 Mc. and Higher: Ionospheric propagation is unlikely at 220 Mc. and up, but tropospheric bending is more prevalent than on lower bands. Amateur experience on 220 and 420 Mc. is showing that they can be as useful as 144 Mc., when comparable equipment is used. Under minimum conditions the range may be slightly shorter, but when signals are good on 144 Mc., they may be better on 220 or 420. Even above 1000 Mc. there is evidence of tropospheric DX.

● PROPAGATION PHENOMENA

The various known means by which v.h.f. signals may be propagated over unusual distances are discussed below.

F_2-Layer Reflection: Most contacts made on 28 Mc. and lower frequencies are the result of reflection of the wave by the F_2 layer, the ionization density of which varies with solar activity, the highest frequencies being reflected at the peak of the 11-year solar cycle. The maximum usable frequency (m.u.f.) for F_2 reflection also follows other well-defined cycles, daily, monthly, and seasonal, all related to conditions on the sun and its position with respect to the earth.

At the low point of the 11-year cycle, such as in the early '50s, the m.u.f. may reach 28 Mc. only during a short period each spring and fall, whereas it may go to 60 Mc. or higher at the peak of the cycle. The fall of 1946 saw the first authentic instances of long-distance work on 50 Mc. by F_2-layer reflection, and as late as 1950 contacts were made in the more favorable areas of the world by this medium. The rising curve of the current solar cycle again made F_2 DX on 50 Mc. possible in the low latitudes in the winter of 1955-6. DX was worked over much of the earth in 1956-8 and may be expected through 1959. Loss of the 50-Mc. band to television in some countries will limit the scope of 50-Mc. DX in years to come.

The F_2 m.u.f. is readily determined by observation, and it may be estimated quite accurately for any path at any time. It is predictable for months in advance, enabling the v.h.f. worker to arrange test schedules with distant stations at propitious times. As there are numerous commercial signals, both harmonics and fundamental transmissions, on the air in the range between 28 and 50 Mc., it is possible to determine the approximate m.u.f. by careful listening in this range. Daily observations will show if the m.u.f. is rising or falling, and once the peak for a given month is determined it can be assumed that another will occur about 27 days later, this cycle coinciding with the turning of

Miscellaneous Phenomena

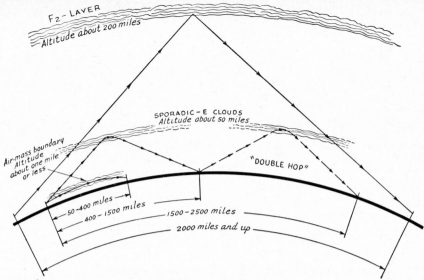

Fig. 15-5—The principal means by which v.h.f. signals may be returned to earth, showing the approximate distances over which they are effective. The F_2 layer, highest of the reflecting layers, may provide 50-Mc. DX at the peak of the 11-year sunspot cycle. Such communication may be world-wide in scope. Sporadic ionization of the E region produces the familiar "short skip" on 28 and 50 Mc. It is most common in early summer and in late December, but may occur at any time, regardless of the sunspot cycle. Refraction of v.h.f. waves also takes place at air-mass boundaries, making possible communication over distances of several hundred miles on all v.h.f. bands. Normally it exhibits no skip zone.

the sun on its axis. The working range, via F_2 skip, is roughly comparable to that on 28 Mc., though the *minimum* distance is somewhat longer. Two-way work on 50 Mc. by reflection from the F_2 layer has been accomplished over distances from 2200 to 12,000 miles. The maximum frequency for F_2 reflection is believed to be about 70 Mc.

Sporadic-E Skip: Patchy concentrations of ionization in the E-layer region are often responsible for reflection of signals on 28 and 50 Mc. This is the popular "short skip" that provides fine contacts on both bands in the range between 400 and 1300 miles. It is most common in May, June and July, during morning and early evening hours, but it may occur at any time or season. Multiple-hop effects may appear, when ionization develops simultaneously over large areas, making possible work over distances of more than 2500 miles.

The upper limit of frequency for sporadic-E skip is not positively known, but scattered instances of 144-Mc. propagation over distances in excess of 1000 miles indicate that E-layer reflection, possibly aided by tropospheric effects, may be responsible.

Aurora Effect: Low-frequency communication is occasionally wiped out by absorption in the ionosphere, when ionospheric storms, associated with variations in the earth's magnetic field, occur. During such disturbances, however, v.h.f. signals may be reflected back to earth, making communication possible over distances not normally workable in the v.h.f. range. Magnetic storms may be accompanied by an aurora-borealis display, if the disturbance occurs at night and visibility is good. Aiming a directional array at

the auroral curtain will bring in signals strongest, regardless of the true direction to the transmitting station.

Aurora-reflected signals are characterized by a rapid flutter, which lends a "dribbling" sound to 28-Mc. carriers and may render modulation on 50- and 144-Mc. signals completely unreadable. The only satisfactory means of communication then becomes straight c.w. The effect may be noticeable on signals from any distance other than purely local, and stations up to about 1000 miles in any direction may be worked at the peak of the disturbance. Unlike the two methods of propagation previously described, aurora effect exhibits no skip zone. It is observed frequently on 50 and 144 Mc. in northeastern U. S. A., usually in the early evening hours or after midnight. The highest frequency for auroral reflection is not yet known, but pronounced disturbances have permitted work by this medium in the 220-Mc. band.

Tropospheric Bending: The most common form of v.h.f. DX is the extension of the normal operating range associated with easily observed weather phenomena. It is the result of the change in refractive index of the atmosphere at the boundary between air masses of differing temperature and humidity characteristics. Such air-mass boundaries usually lie along the western or southern edges of a stable slow-moving area of high barometric pressure (fair, calm weather) in the period prior to the arrival of a storm.

A typical upper-air sounding showing temperature and water-vapor gradients favorable to v.h.f. DX is shown in Fig. 15-6. An increase in temperature and a sharp drop in water-vapor gradient are seen at about 4000 feet, in comparison to the U. S. Standard Atmosphere curves at the left.

Such a favorable condition develops most often in the late summer or early fall, along the junction between air masses that may have come together from such widely separated points as the Gulf of Mexico and Northern Canada. Under stable weather conditions the two air masses may retain their original character for several

wave range, and there is good evidence to indicate that our assignments in the u.h.f. and s.h.f. portions of the frequency spectrum may someday support communication over distances far in excess of the optical range.

Scatter: Forward scatter, both ionospheric and tropospheric, may be used for marginal communication in the v.h.f. bands. Both provide very weak but consistent signals over distances that were once thought impossible on frequencies

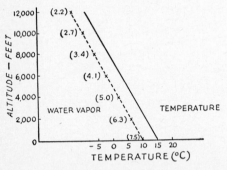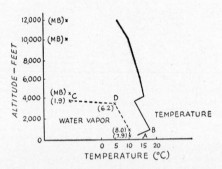

Fig. 15-5—Upper-air conditions that produce extended-range communication on the v.h.f. bands. At the left is shown the U. S. Standard Atmosphere temperature curve. The humidity curve (dotted) is that which would result if the relative humidity were 70 per cent from the ground level to 12,000 feet elevation. There is only slight refraction under this standard condition. At the right is shown a sounding that is typical of marked refraction of v.h.f. waves. Figures in parentheses are the "mixing ratio"—grams of water vapor per kilogram of dry air. Note the sharp break in both curves at about 4000 feet. (From Collier, "Upper-Air Conditions for 2-Meter DX," QST, September, 1955.)

days at a time, usually moving slowly eastward across the country. When the path between two v.h.f. stations separated by fifty to several hundred miles lies along such a boundary, signal levels run far above the average value.

Many factors other than air-mass movement of a continental character provide increased v.h.f. operating range. The convection along coastal areas in warm weather is a good example. The rapid cooling of the earth after a hot day in summer, with the air aloft cooling more slowly, is another, producing a rise in signal strength in the period around sundown. The early morning hours, when the sun heats the air aloft, before the temperature of the earth's surface begins to rise, may be the best of the day for extended v.h.f. range, particularly in clear, calm weather, when the barometer is high and the humidity low.

The v.h.f. enthusiast soon learns to correlate various weather manifestations with radio-propagation phenomena. By watching temperature, barometric pressure, changing cloud formations, wind direction, visibility, and other easily-observed weather signs, he can tell with a reasonable degree of accuracy what is in prospect on the v.h.f. bands.

The responsiveness of radio waves to varying weather conditions increases with frequency. The 50-Mc. band is more sensitive to weather variations than is the 28-Mc. band, and the 144-Mc. band may show strong signals from far beyond visual distances when lower frequencies are relatively inactive. It is probable that this tendency continues on up through the micro-

higher than about 30 Mc.

Tropospheric scatter is prevalent all through the v.h.f. and microwave regions, and is usable over distances up to about 400 miles. Ionospheric scatter, augmented by meteor bursts, brings in signals over 600 to 1300 miles, on frequencies up to about 100 Mc. Either form of scatter requires high power, large antennas and c.w. technique to provide effective communication.

Back scatter, of the type heard on lower bands, is also heard occasionally on 50 Mc., when F_2 or sporadic-E skip is present.

Reflections from Meteor Trails: Probably the least-known means of v.h.f. wave propagation is that resulting from the passage of meteors across the signal path. Reflections from the ionized meteor trails may be noted as a Doppler-effect whistle on the carrier of a signal already being received, or they may cause bursts of reception from stations not normally receivable. Ordinarily such reflections are of little value in communication, since the increases in signal strength are of short duration, but meteor showers of considerable magnitude and duration may provide fluttery signals from distances up to 1500 miles or more on both 50 and 144 Mc.

As meteor-burst signals are relatively weak, their detection is greatly aided if high power and high-gain antennas are used. Two-way communication of sorts has been carried on by this medium on 50 and 144 Mc. over distances of 600 to 1300 miles, through the use of short c.w. transmissions and frequent repetition.

CHAPTER 16

V.H.F. Receivers

Good receiving facilities are all-important in v.h.f. work. High sensitivity, adequate stability and good signal-to-noise ratio, necessary attributes in a receiving system for 50 Mc. and higher frequencies, are most readily attained through the use of a converter working into a communications receiver designed for lower frequencies. Though receivers and converters for the v.h.f. bands are available on the amateur market, the amateur worker can build his own with fully as good results, usually at a considerable saving in cost.

Basically, modern v.h.f. receiving equipment is little different from that employed on lower frequencies. The same order of selectivity may be used on all amateur frequencies up to at least 450 Mc. The greatest practical selectivity should be employed in v.h.f. reception, as it not only allows more stations to operate in a given band, but is an important factor in improving the signal-to-noise ratio. The effective sensitivity of a receiver having "communication" selectivity can be made much better than is possible with broadband systems.

This rules out converted radar-type receivers and others using high intermediate frequencies. The superregenerative receiver, a simple but broadband device that was popular in the early days of v.h.f. work, is now used principally for portable operation, or for other applications where high sensitivity and selectivity are not of prime importance. It is capable of surprising performance, for a given number of tubes and components, but its lack of selectivity, its poor signal-to-noise ratio, and its tendency to radiate a strong interfering signal have eliminated the superregenerator as a fixed-station receiver in areas where there is appreciable v.h.f. activity.

● R. F. AMPLIFIER DESIGN

The noise generated within the receiver itself is an important factor in the effectiveness of v.h.f. receiving gear. At lower frequencies, and to a considerable extent on 50 Mc., external noise is a limiting factor. At 144 Mc. and higher the receiver noise figure, gain and selectivity determine the ability of the system to respond to weak signals. Proper selection of r.f. amplifier tubes and appropriate circuit design aimed at low noise figure are more important in the v.h.f. receiver "front end" than mere gain.

Triode or Pentode?

Certain triode tubes have been developed with this end in view. Their superiority over pentode types is more pronounced as we go higher in frequency. Because of the limitation on sensitivity imposed by external noise at that frequency, triode or pentode r.f. amplifiers give about the same results at 50 Mc. Thus the pentode types, which offer the advantages of better selectivity and simpler circuitry, are often used for 50-Mc. work. But at 144 Mc., the newer triodes designed for r.f. amplifier service give fully as much gain as the pentodes, and with lower internal noise. With the exception of the simplest unit, the equipment described in the following pages incorporates low-noise r.f. amplifier techniques.

Neutralizing Methods

When triodes are used as r.f. amplifiers some form of neutralization of the grid-plate capacitance is required. This can be capacitive, as is commonly used in transmitting applications, or inductive. The alternative to neutralization is the use of grounded-grid technique. Circuits for v.h.f. triode r.f. amplifier stages are given in Figs. 16-1 through 16-4.

A dual triode operated as a neutralized push-pull amplifier is shown at 16-1. This ar-

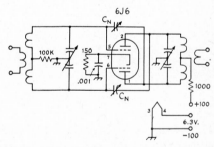

Fig. 16-1—Schematic diagram of a push-pull r.f. amplifier for v.h.f. applications. This circuit is well-suited to use with antenna systems having balanced lines. Coil and capacitor values not given depend on the frequency at which the amplifier is to be used. Neutralizing capacitance, C_N, may be built up by twisting ends of insulated leads together.

rangement is well adapted to v.h.f. preamplifier applications, or as the first stage in a converter, particularly when a balanced transmission line such as the popular 300-ohm Twin-Lead is used. It is relatively selective and may require resistive loading of the plate circuit, when used as a preamplifier. The loading effect of the following circuit may be sufficient to give the required band width, when the push-pull stage is inductively coupled to the mixer.

A triode amplifier having excellent noise figure and broadband characteristics is shown in Fig.

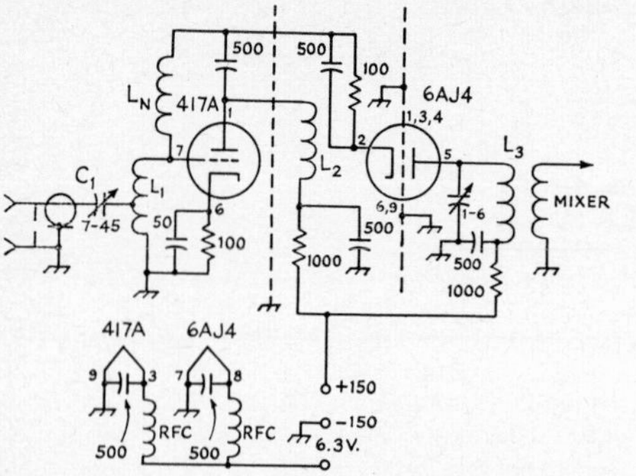

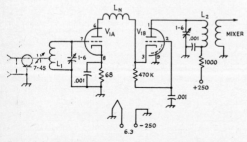

Fig. 16-2—Circuit of the cascode r.f. amplifier. Coupling capacitor, C_1, may be omitted if spurious receiver responses are not a problem. Neutralizing winding, L_N should resonate at the signal frequency with the grid-plate capacitance of the first tube. Base connections are for 417A and 6AJ4, but other small triodes may be used.

it requires higher voltage than the other circuits shown.

The neutralization process for the cascode and neutralized-triode amplifiers is somewhat similar. With the circuit operating normally the neutralizing adjustments (capacitance of C_N in Fig. 16-1; inductance of L_N in Figs. 16-2 and 16-3) can be set for best signal-to-noise ratio. The best results are obtained using a noise generator, adjusting for lowest noise figure, but careful adjustment on a weak signal provides a fair approximation. Noise generators and their use in v.h.f. receiver adjustment are treated in July, 1953, *QST*, p. 10, and in this *Handbook*, Chapter 21.

Grounded-grid r.f. amplifier technique is illustrated in Figs. 16-4 and 16-14. Here the input is in the cathode lead, with the grid of the tube grounded, to act as a shield between cathode and plate. The grounded-grid circuit is stable and easily adjusted, and is well adapted to broadband applications. The gain per stage is low, so that two or more stages may be required.

Tubes well-suited to grounded-grid amplifier service include the 6J4, 6AN4, 6AJ4, 6AM4, 6BC4, 417A and 416B. Disk-seal tubes such as the "lighthouse" and "pencil tube" types are often used as r.f. amplifiers above 500 Mc., and the new ceramic tubes show great possibilities for r.f. amplifier service in the u.h.f. range.

Great care should be used in adjusting the r.f. portion of a v.h.f. receiver, whatever circuit is used. If it is working properly it will control the noise figure of the entire system.

16-2. Commonly called the cascode, it uses a triode or triode-connected pentode followed by a triode grounded-grid stage. This circuit is extremely stable and uncritical in adjustment. At 50 Mc. and higher its over-all gain is at least equal to the best single-stage pentode amplifier and its noise figure is far lower.

Neutralization is accomplished by the coil L_N, whose value is such that it resonates at the signal frequency with the grid-plate capacitance of the tube. Its inductance is not critical; it may be omitted from the circuit without the stage going into oscillation, but neutralization results in a lower noise figure than is possible without it. Any of several v.h.f. tubes may be used in the cascode circuit. The example shown in Fig. 16-2 uses the 417A, followed by a 6AJ4. Two 6AJ4s would work almost equally well, as would the 6AM4, 6AN4 and 6BC4. Pin connections in Fig. 16-2 should be changed to suit the tubes selected.

A simplified version of the cascode, using a dual triode tube designed especially for this application, is shown in Fig. 16-3. By reducing stray capacitance, through direct coupling between the two triode sections, this circuit makes for improved performance at the frequencies above 100 Mc. The two sections of the tube are in series, as far as plate voltage is concerned, so

Reducing Spurious Responses

In areas where there is a high level of v.h.f. activity or extensive use of other frequencies in the v.h.f. range, the ability of the receiver to operate properly in the presence of strong signals may be an important consideration. Special tube types, otherwise similar to older numbers, have been developed for low overload and cross-modulation susceptibility. The 6BC8, which may be used as a replacement for the 6BQ7A or 6BZ7, is one of these.

Modification of the converter design can also improve performance in these respects. In general, the gain ahead of the mixer stage should be made no more than is necessary to achieve good noise figure characteristics. The plate voltage on the r.f. amplifier should be kept as high as practical, to prevent easy overloading.

Rejection of signals outside the desired frequency range can be improved by the use of high-Q tuned circuits ahead of the first r.f. amplifier stage. Television transmitters are particularly troublesome in this respect, and one or more coaxial-type circuits inserted in the lead from the antenna to the converter may be necessary to keep such signals from interfering with normal reception.

A common cause of unwanted signals appearing in the tuning range is the presence of oscillator harmonics in the energy being fed to the mixer of a crystal-controlled converter. This may be pre-

Fig. 16-3—Simplified cascode circuit for use with dual triodes having separate cathodes. Coil and capacitance values not given depend on frequency. Bifilar r.f. chokes are occasionally used in heater leads.

Mixer Circuits

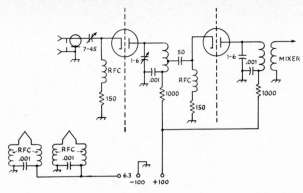

Fig. 16-4—Grounded-grid amplifier. Position of tap on plate coil should be adjusted for lowest noise figure. Low gain with this circuit makes two stages necessary for most applications. R.f. choke and coil values depend on frequency.

voltage. When a good r.f. amplifier is used the mixer plate current may be run higher, for better operation with strong signals.

Occasionally oscillation near the signal frequency may be encountered in v.h.f. mixers. This usually results from stray lead inductance in the mixer plate circuit, and is most common with triode mixers. It may be corrected by connecting a small capacitance from plate to cathode, *directly* at the tube socket. Ten to 25 $\mu\mu$f. will be sufficient, depending on the signal frequency.

● OSCILLATOR STABILITY

When a high-selectivity i.f. system is employed in v.h.f. reception, the stability of the oscillator is extremely important. Slight variations in oscillator frequency that would not be noticed when a broadband i.f. amplifier is used become intolerable when the passband is reduced to crystal-filter proportions.

One satisfactory solution to this problem is the use of a crystal-controlled oscillator, with frequency multipliers if needed, to supply the injection voltage. Such a converter usually employs one or more broadband r.f. amplifier stages, and tuning is done by tuning the receiver with which the converter is used to cover the desired intermediate frequency range.

vented by using a high oscillator frequency, to keep down the number of multiplications, and by shielding the oscillator and multiplier stages from the rest of the converter.

Signals at the intermediate frequency may ride through a converter. This can be prevented by keeping down capacitive interstage coupling in the r.f. circuitry, and by shielding the converter and the receiver antenna terminals. The problem of receiver responses is dealt with in *QST* for April, 1955, p. 56, and February, 1958, p. 27.

● MIXER CIRCUITS

The mixer in a v.h.f. converter may be either a pentode or a triode tube. Pentodes give generally higher output, and may require less injection. When used without a preceding r.f. amplifier stage, the triode mixer may provide a better noise figure. With either tube, the grid circuit is tuned to the signal frequency, and the plate circuit to the intermediate frequency.

A simple triode mixer is shown in Fig. 16-5A, with a pentode mixer at B. A dual-triode version (push-push mixer) is shown at C. The push-push mixer is well adapted to use at 420 Mc., and may, of course, be used at any lower frequency. Dual tubes may be used as both mixer and oscillator, combining the circuits of Figs. 16-5 and 16-6. A 6U8 could use its pentode as a mixer (16-5B) and the oscillator portion (16-6A) would be a triode. Dual-triode tubes (6J6, 12AT7 and many others) would combine 16-5A and 16-6A. In dual triodes having separate cathodes some external coupling may be required, but the common cathode of the 6J6 will provide sufficient injection in most cases. If the injection is more than necessary it can be reduced by dropping the oscillator plate voltage, either directly or by increasing the value of the dropping resistor.

A pentode mixer is less subject to oscillator pulling than a triode, and it will probably require less injection voltage. In a pentode mixer with no r.f. amplifier, plate current should be held to the lowest usable value, to reduce tube noise. This may be controlled by varying the mixer screen

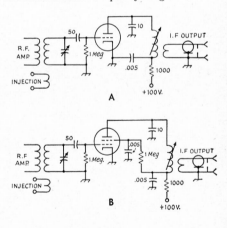

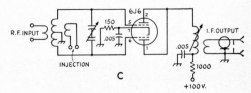

Fig. 16-5—Typical v.h.f. mixer circuits for triode (A), pentode (B) and push-push triode (C). Circuits A and B may be used with one portion of various dual-purpose tubes. Plate current of pentode (B) should be held at lowest usable value if no r.f. stage is used.

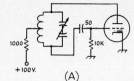

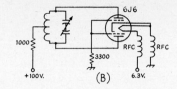

(A)   (B)

When a tunable oscillator and a fixed intermediate frequency are used, special attention must be paid to the oscillator design, to be sure that it is mechanically and electrically stable. The tuning capacitor should be solidly built, preferably of the double-bearing type. Split-stator capacitors specifically designed for v.h.f. service, usually having ball-bearing end plates and special construction to insure short leads, are well worth their extra cost. Leads should be made with stiff wire, to reduce vibration effects. Mechanical stability of air-wound coils can be improved by tying the turns together with narrow strips of household cement at several points.

Recommended oscillator circuits for v.h.f. work are shown in Fig. 16-6. The single-ended oscillator may be used for 50 or 144 Mc. with good results. The push-pull version is recommended for higher frequencies and may also be used on the two lower bands, as well. Circuit A works well with almost any small triode, or one half of a 6J6 or 12AT7. The 6J6 is well suited to push-pull applications, as shown in circuit 16-6B.

● THE I.F. AMPLIFIER

Superheterodyne receivers for 50 Mc. and up should have fairly high intermediate frequencies, to reduce both oscillator pulling and image response. Approximately 10 per cent of the signal frequency is commonly used, with 10.7 Mc. being set up as the standard i.f. for commercially-built f.m. receivers. This particular frequency has a disadvantage for 50-Mc. work, in that it makes the receiver subject to image response from 28-Mc. signals, if the oscillator is on the low side of the signal frequency. A spot around 7 Mc. is favored for amateur converter service, as practically all communications receivers are capable of tuning this range.

For selectivity with a reasonable number of i.f. stages, double conversion is usually employed in complete receivers for the v.h.f. range. A 7-Mc. intermediate frequency, for instance, is changed to 455 kc., by the addition of a second mixer-oscillator. This procedure is, of course, inherent in the use of a v.h.f. converter ahead of a communications receiver.

If the receiver so used is lacking in sensitivity, the over-all gain of the converter-receiver combination may be inadequate. This can be corrected by building an i.f. amplifier stage into the converter itself. Such a stage is useful even when the gain of the system is adequate without it, as the gain control can be used to permit operation of the converter with receivers of

widely different performance. If the receiver has an S-meter, its adjustment may be left in the position used for lower frequencies and the converter gain set so as to make the meter read normally on v.h.f. signals.

Where reception of wide-band f.m. or unstable signals of modulated oscillators is desired, a converter may be used ahead of an f.m. broadcast receiver. A superregenerative detector operating at the intermediate frequency, with or without additional i.f. amplifier stages, also may serve as an i.f. and detector system for reception of wide-band signals. By using a high i.f. (10 to 30 Mc. or so) and by resistive loading of the i.f. transformers, almost any desired degree of bandwidth can be secured, providing good voice quality on all but the most unstable signals. Any of these methods may be used for reception in the microwave region, where stabilized transmission is extremely difficult at the current state of the art.

● THE SUPERREGENERATIVE RECEIVER

The simplest type of v.h.f. receiver is the superregenerator. It affords fair sensitivity with few tubes and elementary circuits, but its weaknesses, listed earlier, have relegated it to applications where small size and low power consumption are important considerations.

Its sensitivity results from the use of an alternating quenching voltage, usually in the range between 20 and 200 kc., to interrupt the normal oscillation of a regenerative detector. The regeneration can thus be increased far beyond the amount usable in a straight regenerative circuit.

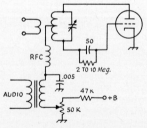

Fig. 16-7—Superregenerative detector circuit for self-quenched detector. Pentode tube may be used, varying screen voltage by means of the potentiometer to control regeneration.

The detector itself can be made to furnish the quenching voltage, or a separate oscillator tube can be used. Regeneration is usually controlled by varying the plate voltage in triode detectors, or the screen voltage in the case of pentodes. A typical circuit is shown in Fig. 16-7.

Crystal-Controlled Converters for 50, 144 and 220 Mc.

The three converters and their power supply, shown below, were designed to meet the special requirements of each of the v.h.f. bands, insofar as possible. They offer high stability and reasonably low noise figure, and special attention was paid to the reduction of spurious responses, particularly in the converters for 50 and 220 Mc. Each unit plugs into the power supply, which also includes the i.f. output circuitry. Anyone interested in one or two of the bands can thus build for his own purposes and omit the other band or bands. The i.f. tuning range is 7 to 11 Mc. for 50- and 144-Mc. coverage, and 7-12 Mc. for the 220-Mc. band.

● THE 50-MC. CONVERTER

A pentode r.f. amplifier stage is used in the 50-Mc. converter, Figs. 16-9 and 16-10. With proper design and adjustment such a stage will have a noise figure sufficiently low that it will respond to the weakest signals that can be heard with other and more complex stages. The tube shown is a 6CB6, but other pentodes such as the 6AK5 may be substituted.

A gain control is included in the cathode circuit. Normally this is run all-out, for optimum noise figure and gain, but in the presence of strong local signals it can be cut in to reduce overloading. This causes some impairment of the noise figure, but may still make possible reception of distant signals through the locals.

Note the double-tuned coupling circuits in the r.f. input and between the r.f. amplifier and the mixer. The capacitors C_1 and C_2 are kept as small as possible, and the coils are not coupled together otherwise. A value of 1 to 2 $\mu\mu$f. gives sufficient coupling at the desired frequency, but the system responds only very slightly to lower frequencies. This helps to prevent interference from signals on the intermediate frequency.

The mixer is also a 6CB6. Its operating conditions are set up for resistance to overloading and cross-modulation from strong signals, rather than for optimum noise figure, as the latter is taken care of by the r.f. amplifier. Note that the plate circuit of the mixer is omitted from the converters. It is built into the power unit, and thus only one coil need be made for all the converters.

The oscillator is a 6AF4 triode. Any other small triode could be substituted. Input is held to a low level (note 47,000-ohm resistor in series with L_7) in the interest of stability. The oscillator circuitry is isolated from the rest of the converter, so that injection can be controlled readily. Energy from the oscillator is carried to the mixer grid circuit through a shielded link.

Mechanical Features

Each converter is built on a flat plate, which screws onto a standard aluminum chassis. Connection to the power unit is made through a 4-pin plug mounted on the side of the case. This carries the heater voltage, the plate voltage, the mixer plate lead and the common chassis connection. The plug on the converter is the male type. It may be fastened to the chassis conveniently by soldering 4-40 nuts to the back of the flanges used for mounting the plug. Flat-head machine screws in countersunk holes, in both the converter and the power supply unit, allow the two to fit snugly together. This is important in preventing pickup of signals in the i.f. range.

In the bottom view, Fig. 16-9, the antenna connector is seen at the lower right. Just to the left, separated by a small shield, are the two r.f. coils, L_1 and L_2. The coupling capacitor, C_1, made of two wires twisted together, is on the low side of the shield, its lead to L_2 running through a hole in the shield.

The lead from L_2 to the amplifier grid pin runs through the main lengthwise shield. This lead was made of shielded wire, with the shielding removed from the part of the lead that is in the coil compartment. The portion of the wire in the tube compartment must be shielded to prevent feedback between the plate coil, L_3, and the grid circuit. The coupling capacitor, C_2, the gain control, the plate coil and all other amplifier components are in this section, upper right.

Mixer components are at the upper left, with the oscillator section below. The coupling link between L_5 and L_6 is made of shielded wire, running through the main shield partition.

The leads from the mixer to the plug, J_2, and all power leads, are made with shielded wire. The common connection for ground and heater lead is the shielding over the other three wires. These leads should be long enough so that the converter can be lifted from the box without removing the plug. A length of vinyl sleeving slipped over the leads will help to prevent shorts. Transparent sleeving was used, so it does not show in the

Fig. 16-8—Converters for the three v.h.f. bands, with their power supply and i.f. output unit. The 220-Mc. converter is shown plugged into the power unit. At the left is the 50-Mc. converter. The one for 144 Mc. is at the right.

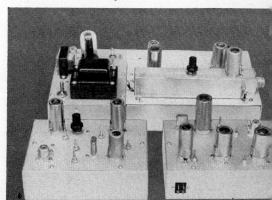

Fig. 16-9—Bottom view of the 50-Mc. converter. R.f. input circuit is at the lower right, with the amplifier itself above. Crystal oscillator components at lower left; mixer and output cable above.

photographs.

The main shield is 6 by $1^{15}/_{16}$ inches in size, with a $\frac{1}{4}$-inch lip folded over for mounting to the plate. The two shields perpendicular to it are $1\frac{7}{8}$ by $1^{15}/_{16}$ inches, with lips folded over on the bottom and one end. The isolation shield between the r.f. coils is $1\frac{3}{4}$ by $1^{15}/_{16}$ inches, and is mounted $\frac{3}{4}$ inch in from the lower edge of the cross shield.

The placing of the parts otherwise is not particularly critical, except that bypass capacitors should be connected with the shortest possible leads. Use of the smallest size disk ceramic type is recommended.

Adjustment

Tuning up the converter is a simple matter. Check the wiring to be sure that no errors have been made. Apply a.c. and see if all heaters come on. Then apply plate voltage by closing S_2 on the power supply unit. If the converter output is

connected to a communications receiver tuned to the 7-Mc. range there should be a considerable increase in noise as plate voltage is applied, even with circuits out of tune.

First check the oscillator. This can be done by listening in the 43-Mc. range, if a receiver is available for that frequency, or a grid-dip meter may be used as a wavemeter. Output should appear on 43 Mc., and on that frequency only. Adjust L_7 for maximum output indication, with the grid-dip coil coupled to L_7. Check around 14.3 and 28.6 Mc. to be sure that no output is in evidence on these frequencies. Should there be energy on these frequencies it means that the crystal is oscillating on its fundamental frequency and showing output on its various harmonics. Oscillation on the fundamental indicates that the plate circuit is not properly tuned.

If the converter is wired correctly it should now be possible to receive strong signals, even before the circuits have been resonated. A calibrated signal generator is helpful, but it is by no means necessary. A test signal should be fed into the antenna connector and the core screws in all coils adjusted for maximum signal strength.

The response of the converter will not be flat across the entire 4000 kc. of the 50-Mc. band, but it will work over a wider frequency range than most directive antenna systems. The setting of the cores in L_3 and L_4 can be varied to give uniform response across the desired pass band. The input circuit should be adjusted for best signal-to-noise ratio at the middle of the desired frequency range.

The value of the small coupling capacitors, C_1 and C_2, will have some effect on the bandwidth of the r.f. portion of the converter. Few directive antennas will work over more than about 1500

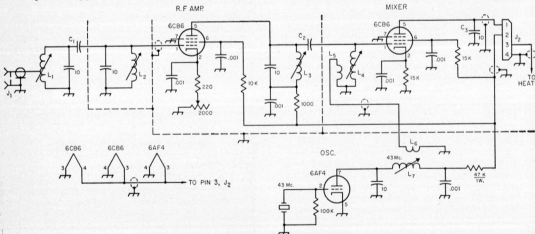

Fig. 16-10—Schematic diagram of the 50-Mc. converter. Capacitors are ceramic; values .001 and up are in μf. Resistors $\frac{1}{2}$-watt unless specified.

C_1, C_2—Approx. 1 to 2 $\mu\mu$f. Make from two pieces of plastic-covered No. 18 wire twisted together about 1 inch.

C_3—10-$\mu\mu$f. ceramic. Connect at plate terminal.

L_1, L_3, L_4—11 turns No. 24 enam. at top end of $\frac{1}{4}$-inch iron-slug form (North Hills Type F-1000). L_1 tapped at 3 turns.

L_2—Same as L_3, but 9 turns.

L_5—2 turns insulated hookup wire at low end of L_4.

L_6—Same as L_5, but at low end of L_7.

L_7—Same as L_3, but 16 turns.

J_1—Coaxial connector, female.

J_2—4-pin power connector, male. Must mount flush with chassis surface.

144-Mc. Converter

kc. of the band, so there is seldom much point in making the front end of the converter broader than this. If optimum performance is needed at the opposite end of the band it is merely necessary to repeak the core studs for best results at the desired frequency. Adjustment of the i.f. coil in the power unit also affects the bandwidth. It can be peaked somewhat above the middle of the tuning range if it is desired to extend the coverage of the converter-antenna combination.

When the converter is tuned for best results it may be desirable to check the oscillator injection. This is best done with the aid of a noise generator, though a signal generator or weak signals may be used if care is taken to observe optimum signal-to-noise ratio, rather than mere gain. The value of the dropping resistor in series with L_7 can be varied, the idea being to use the highest value that will not affect the signal-to-noise ratio adversely.

A simple check on performance that can be made in a location free of manmade noise is as follows: Connect a 50-ohm resistor in place of the antenna coax. Observe the noise level, either by ear or as indicated on an output meter or the receiver S-meter. Now put the antenna back on. If the r.f. stage is free of regeneration, a rise in noise level when the antenna is connected shows that external noise can be heard. This noise is the limiting factor in weak-signal reception, and further reduction in receiver noise figure will serve no useful purpose.

● THE 144-MC. CONVERTER

In the converter for 144 Mc., Figs. 16-11 and 16-12, triode r.f. amplifiers are used, as they give better noise figure than pentodes at this frequency and higher. The tubes shown are 6BC4s, but comparable results can be achieved with the 6AJ4, 6AM4 or 6AN4, with the necessary revision of the pin connections. Noise figure obtainable with any of these tubes is about 5 db., which is about the level at which external noise begins to limit receiver sensitivity. A noise figure of 3 db. or lower can be had with 417As, or even one 417A and one less expensive tube, but there may be no observable difference in weak-signal performance.

The cascode circuit (see beginning of chapter) is used, with the circuit of Fig. 16-2 in preference to that of 16-3. The latter, operating at lower plate voltage per stage, may be slightly more susceptible to overloading. The 6CB6 mixer is also operated under conditions designed to keep down overloading and cross-modulation troubles.

The crystal oscillator is operated at the highest frequency that is possible with simple circuitry. This holds down the number of unwanted frequencies appearing in the multiplier output, which could beat in signals from outside the intended frequency range. The crystal oscillates on 45.667 Mc., using the triode portion of a 6U8. The pentode portion is a tripler to 137 Mc.

The oscillator-tripler portion is isolated from the rest of the converter by a copper shield running down the middle of the 5 by 5-inch plate.

The grid circuit of the first r.f. amplifier stage is adjacent to the tripler, but is as far away from it as possible, and the coils are positioned for minimum coupling. The lower section of the converter, as shown in Fig. 16-11, is the portion in question, the antenna connection and grid coil being at the lower right.

Above the shield may be seen the first r.f. stage, right, the second stage, with a shield down through the middle of its socket, center, and the mixer at the far left. To provide effective isolation and bypassing, feed-through capacitors are mounted in the copper shield to carry power leads from one compartment to the other. Three are used for the B-plus line and two for the heater leads.

R.f. circuits and the tripler plate circuit are tuned by means of small TV-type trimmers. Four of these are shown in the photograph, but the one that is connected to the first r.f. plate coil, L_3, may be omitted, as the circuit tunes very broadly. The r.f. plate coil, L_4, and the mixer grid coil, L_5, are ¾ inch apart, center to center. Coupling between the two stages is mainly through the twisted-wire capacitor, C_{10}. The r.f. input coil, L_1, is connected to the grid pin of the V_1 by a lead that runs through a ¼-inch hole in the shield.

Both shields are made of flashing copper. The larger is 5¾ by 1¾ inches, with folded-over edges for mounting, and for rigidity. The smaller is 1½ by 1¾ inches. It is held in place by soldering to lugs under the mounting screws of the 6BC4 socket. This shield turned out to be required to prevent oscillation in the grounded-grid stage. It crosses the middle of the tube socket.

Connections for the power are made in the same manner as for the 50-Mc. converter, and leads should be long enough to permit removal of the converter from the box without unsoldering any leads. The shields are bonded together and anchored to a lug bolted to the main shield, near the left end.

Note that wafer-type sockets are used. This is

Fig. 16-11—Bottom view of the 144-Mc. converter. Crystal oscillator and tripler occupy lower left side of the assembly. Antenna input circuit is at the right. Above the partition, right to left, are the cathode trimmer, the first r.f. amplifier socket, the r.f. plate coil, the second amplifier socket, with shield across its center, the plate coil, mixer grid coil and mixer tube socket.

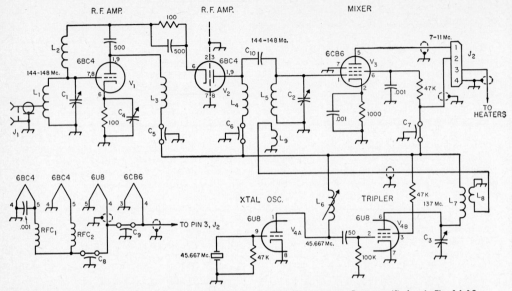

Fig. 16-12—Wiring diagram and parts information for the 144-Mc. converter. Parts specified as in Fig. 16-10.

C_1, C_2, C_3—8-$\mu\mu$f. plastic trimmer (Erie No. 532-10).
C_4—3-30-$\mu\mu$f. mica trimmer. Set at tight position initially.
C_5, C_6, C_7, C_8, C_9—500-$\mu\mu$f. feed-through bypass (Centralab MFT-500).
L_1—4½ turns No. 18 tinned, ¼-inch inside diam., ½ inch long, tapped at 1½ turns.
L_2—14 turns No. 24 enam., ³⁄₁₆-inch diam., ½ inch long.
L_3—5 turns No. 18 tinned, ¼-inch diam., ¼ inch long.
L_4—5½ turns like L_3.
L_5—3½ turns like L_3.

L_6—13 turns No. 24 enam. closewound on ¼-inch diam. iron-slug form (North Hills F-1000).
L_7—8 turns like L_3, ¾ inch long.
L_8—1 turn insulated hookup wire between first two turns of L_7.
L_9—Same as L_8, inserted in L_5.
J_1—Coaxial connector, female.
J_2—4-pin power connector, male. Must mount flush with surface of chassis.
RFC$_1$, RFC$_2$—1.8 μh. solenoid r.f. choke (Ohmite Z-144).

more than an economy measure; shorter ground leads are possible with this type of socket. Where socket terminals are to be grounded, they are bent down flush with the bottom of the plate. Then a hole is drilled adjacent to the lug and it can then be secured to the plate under a washer and nut. This method of grounding is superior, at these frequencies, to the more commonly used lead-and-lug arrangement.

Adjustment

The first step in putting the 144-Mc. converter into service is to be sure that the oscillator is working correctly, as described in connection with the 50-Mc. converter. This may be done with the plate and screen voltages disconnected from the pentode portion of the 6U8, if desired, by lifting tripler plate coil and the screen resistor from the B-plus line temporarily. Be sure that the oscillator is on the right frequency, and no other, as described earlier.

Now connect the tripler plate coil and screen resistor to the B-plus line and check the tuning of the tripler capacitor, C_3. Set it for maximum output on 137 Mc., as indicated by a grid-dip meter coupled to L_7. The output required from the tripler may be checked after the r.f. section is tuned properly. It may be controlled by varying the value of the screen dropping resistor, which is 47,000 ohms in the original. The tripler may be run at the lowest input that will give

satisfactory signal-to-noise ratio. Above that point the injection is not critical.

The r.f. circuits may now be adjusted. Set the trimmer, C_4, across the r.f. cathode resistor, at maximum at first. Then on a test signal tune C_1 and C_2 for maximum response. The spacing between the turns of the r.f. plate coils, L_3 and L_4, should also be adjusted for highest signal level.

If a noise generator is available, it should be used to set up the r.f. input circuit, the inductance of the neutralizing coil, and the value of the cathode bypass, C_4. If signals or a signal generator are used, the criterion should be greatest rise over noise for a given signal, rather than maximum S-meter reading or loudest volume. Adjustment of the neutralizing coil, and setting of the cathode bypass value are all but impossible without a noise generator. Lacking one, it is best to use a fixed bypass of about 100 $\mu\mu$f. for C_4, and leave the neutralizing winding at the specification given in the cut label. Changes in the neutralizing coil affect the tuning of the grid circuit. Recheck the setting of C_1 after altering L_2.

The coupling capacitor, C_{10}, is not critical, but for best rejection of i.f. signals it should be as low as will give satisfactory performance on 144-Mc. signals. Insulated wires twisted together provide a convenient adjustment method.

As the band is nearly three times as high in frequency as the 50-Mc. band, there will be less

220-Mc. Converter

difficulty in getting uniform response across the entire band. Tuning of the second r.f. and mixer circuits can be staggered to develop the desired bandwidth, and the value of C_{10} will have some effect on it as well.

● THE 220-MC. CONVERTER

In the converter for 220 Mc., Figs. 16-13 and 16-14, an additional r.f. amplifier stage is used ahead of the cascode-and-mixer combination. This is required because the gain per stage is lower at this frequency. It is also desirable because of the added selectivity it affords. This may be very helpful in areas where interference from other services adjacent to the band may be bothersome.

The additional stage is a grounded-grid amplifier, using a modified coaxial-line plate circuit for high "Q" and selectivity. It is not a broadband device and must be retuned in covering the band. The tube shown is a 6AM4. Similar results were achieved with the 6BC4, and nearly identical performance is possible with other u.h.f. triodes. The 417A and 416B should be superior. Noise figure is about 6 db.

A series cascode using a 6BC8 dual triode follows. This type of amplifier is easily adjusted and tends to deliver superior results as the upper limit of frequency is approached. The mixer is a 6AK5. Its output circuit is, of course, the coil assembly in the power unit.

The r.f. amplifier is similar to the one described separately later in the chapter, except that the output is taken off through the bottom of the assembly, with a tuned link, instead of through a coaxial fitting on the side. In the diagram, Fig. 16-14, the plate line and coupling loop are shown as if they were coils, it being cumbersome to express a trough-line circuit schematically.

Mechanical Details

A somewhat different method of construction is employed in the 220-Mc. converter, in order to insure the most effective grounding and bypassing. A plate of aluminum is used, as in the other converters, but only for appearance and rigidity. The plate used for actual electrical grounding is a sheet of flashing copper. Wafer sockets are used, and wherever a terminal is grounded it is bent down flat and soldered directly to the copper plate. This makes for less lead and more effective grounding than where socket mounting screws and lugs are used ground connections. It also allows shield partitions of copper to be soldered directly to the base plate.

The 220-Mc. converter requires more space than the others, so a 7 by 9-inch chassis and plate are used. The lengthwise partition $1\frac{1}{8}$ by 7 inches in size, after folding over $\frac{1}{8}$ inch on each side for mounting and rigidity. The smaller is $1\frac{1}{8}$ by 4 inches. The large shield is centered on the plate $2\frac{3}{8}$ inches in from the long edge. The smaller is $4\frac{1}{4}$ inches in from the left edge.

The oscillator is similar to the 144-Mc. unit, except that an air-wound coil and a variable capacitor are used instead of a slug-tuned coil. The pentode section of the 6U8 is a quadrupler to 213 Mc. from a crystal frequency of 53.25 Mc. A series-tuned link feeds energy to the mixer grid circuit through a shielded-wire line. Oscillator-multiplier components are in the left portion of Fig. 16-13.

At the right are the mixer (upper socket) and the series cascode r.f. amplifier, below. Note that power wiring is made with shielded wire, laid close to the shields. Plate voltage is fed into the oscillator-multiplier and r.f.-mixer compartments on feed-through bypasses. Heater voltage for the r.f. amplifier goes through the plate on shielded wire at the lower left, and plate voltage at the

Fig. 16-13—Interior of the 220-Mc. converter. Bottom plate and partitions are of flashing copper, for effective grounding. Oscillator-multiplier circuitry is at the left; mixer and cascode r.f. amplifier at the right. Grounded-grid amplifier is above the chassis.

lower right. The mica trimmer at the lower right is C_2, in series with the low side of the coupling loop, L_2. The other end of the loop comes out on a feed-through bushing, National Type TPB. Its lead to L_3 is shielded wire, running through the partition.

In working with flashing copper parts the metal work should be completed, up to the point where the parts are ready to assemble. The copper parts may then be polished with steel wool and given a fine spray coat of clear lacquer. This will help to keep them clean and bright, and it will not affect the soldering operations to be done later.

Adjustment

The oscillator and multiplier stages should be adjusted as outlined for the other converters, making sure that the

«

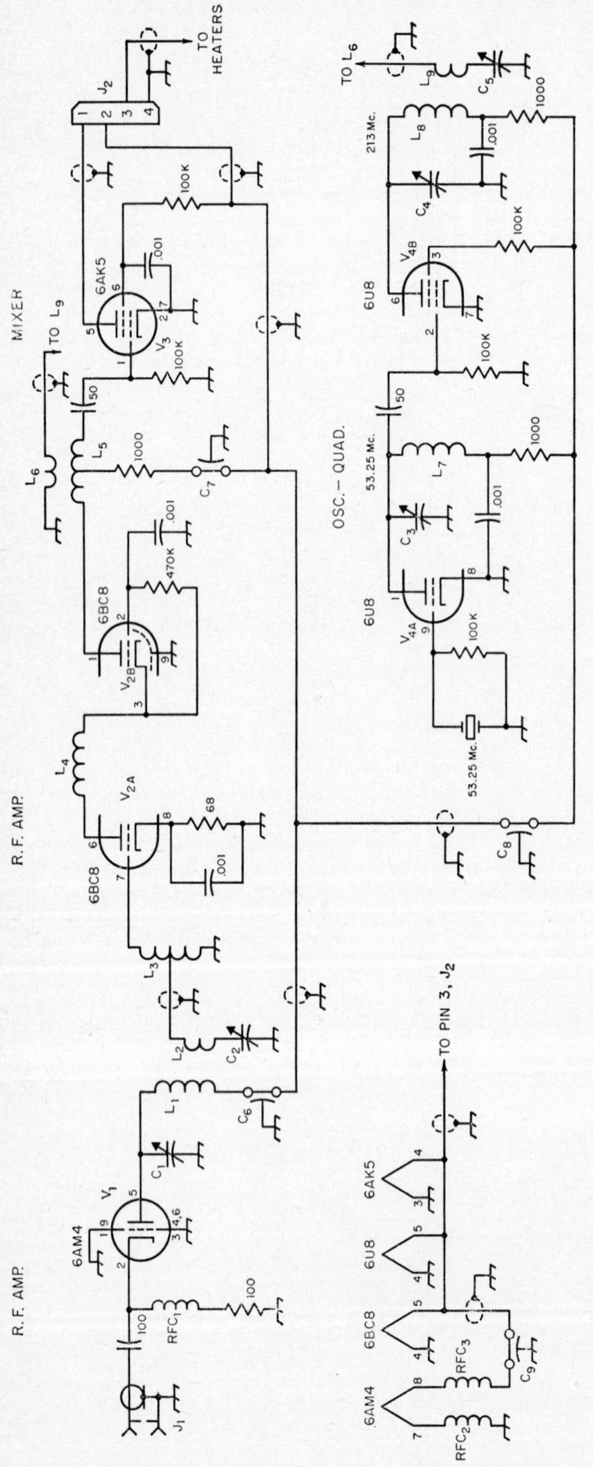

C_1—5-$\mu\mu$f. miniature variable (Hammarlund MAC-5).
C_2—3-30-$\mu\mu$f. mica trimmer.
C_3—20-$\mu\mu$f. miniature variable (Hammarlund MAC-20).
C_4—10-$\mu\mu$f. miniature variable (Hammarlund MAC-10).
C_5—7-45-$\mu\mu$f. ceramic trimmer (Centralab 822-BN).
C_6, C_7, C_8, C_9—500-$\mu\mu$f. feed-through bypass (Centralab MFT 500).
L_1—Inner conductor of trough line—$\frac{1}{4}$-inch copper tubing, $6\frac{1}{4}$ inches long, $\frac{1}{4}$-inch diam. C_1 connects $1\frac{3}{4}$ inches from plate end. See Fig. 16-22 and text.
L_2—Coupling loop—insulated hookup wire 3 inches long. Loop portion lays close to cold end of L_1 for 2 inches. Hot end comes through chassis on National Type TPB feed-through bushing.
L_3—3 turns No. 18 tinned, $\frac{1}{4}$-inch diam., $\frac{1}{4}$ inch long, center-tapped.
L_4—4 turns like L_3, $\frac{3}{8}$ inch long.
L_5—$8\frac{1}{2}$ turns like L_3, $\frac{5}{8}$ inch long, center-tapped.
L_6—2 turns insulated hookup wire at center of L_5.
L_7—6 turns No. 20 tinned $\frac{1}{2}$-inch diam., $\frac{1}{2}$ inch long. (B & W No. 3003).
L_8—2 turns No. 18 tinned, $\frac{3}{8}$-inch diam., spaced $\frac{1}{8}$ inch.
L_9—2 turns insulated hookup wire between turns of L_8.
J_1—Coaxial fitting, female.
J_2—4-pin power connector, male. Must mount flush with surface of chassis.
RFC_1, RFC_2, RFC_3—18 turns No. 24 enam. close-wound, $\frac{1}{8}$-inch diam.

Fig. 16-14—Schematic diagram and parts information for the 220-Mc. converter.

correct frequencies are obtained. Next a signal may be fed into the 6BC8 stage through the shielded line to L_3. This may be disconnected from L_2 temporarily and coax-fed antenna or a 50-ohm signal generator termination may be connected across it. Now adjust the spacing of the turns in L_3 and L_5 for best performance. Maximum gain will be a good-enough indication here, so a noise generator is not needed.

Now the 6AM4 amplifier may be hooked up and tuned. It will be quite selective and will have to be retuned several times across the band. With the plate tuning capacitor tapped down the line as it is, the tuning range in megacycles is not great. Be sure, therefore, that it actually does tune the entire way, and does not hit maximum or minimum capacitance inside the band.

Adjustments may be made all along the line using maximum signal level as the basis for achieving the optimum setting, but only a noise generator will show if the converter is delivering the best sensitivity of which it is capable. It should be possible to get the noise figure down to about 6 db. using the 6AM4, if everything is working properly.

If any doubt exists that the coils L_3 and L_5 are tuning properly, small twisted-wire capacitors may be connected from the grid end of L_3 and the plate end of L_5 to ground, and gradually increased in value. If the gain drops when the capacitor is connected, the coil is too large. If a small amount of added capacitance increases the gain, squeeze the coil turns closer together and try again. The inductance of L_4 should not be particularly critical. It should be as large as can be used without causing instability.

Injection from the quadrupler may be controlled by varying the position of either link winding, L_6 or L_9, with respect to its coil, and by adjusting C_5. Coupling should be increased until

Fig. 16–15—Bottom view of the power supply and i.f. output circuitry for the v.h.f. converters. A.c. switch is above power transformer, right. Next are the filter capacitor and the rectifier socket. The switch at the lower left cuts off the high voltage. The i.f. plate coil and the output fitting are in the upper left of the picture.

there is no improvement in signal to noise ratio. Injection beyond that point is not critical, though it will affect the overall gain somewhat. Fairly low injection is desirable as it will keep down the level of spurious responses.

● POWER SUPPLY AND I.F. OUTPUT

Though it may be possible to run a v.h.f. converter from the power supply of the receiver with which it is to be used, a supply for the converters is desirable. The one shown in Fig. 16-15 and 16-16 is inexpensive and convenient. It delivers the heater and plate power required by the converters, and in addition carries the mixer plate circuit and the provision for coupling into the receiver.

Construction is not critical. Parts are assembled on a 5 by 7-inch plate and this fastens to a similarly sized chassis that matches the converters. The 50- and 144-Mc. units plug into the

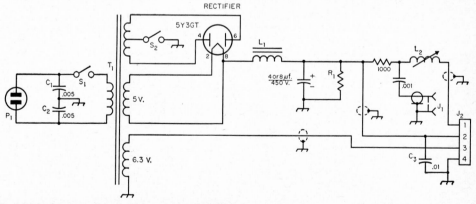

Fig. 16-16—Schematic diagram of the converter power supply and i.f. output unit. Capacitors with polarity marked are electrolytic; others ceramic.

C_1, C_2—Dual .005-μf., 125 volts a.c. disk ceramic (Sprague 125L-2D50).
C_3—.01-μf. disk ceramic. Mount at plug end of cable.
R_1—50,000 ohms, 2 watts (2 100,000-ohm 1-watt resistors in parallel).
L_1—10-hy. 50-ma. filter choke.
L_2—No. 28 enam. closewound ½ inch long on ⅜-inch iron-slug form. Wind near upper end.

J_1—Coaxial fitting, female.
J_2—4-pin power connector, female. Must mount flush with surface of chassis.
S_1, S_2—S.p.s.t. toggle switch.
T_1—Power transformer, 480 v. a.c., c.t., 40 ma., 5 v. 2 amp., 6.3 v. 2 amp. (Thordarson TS-24R00).
P_1—A.c. plug on cord.

power unit through matching fittings on the sides. The larger 220-Mc. converter has the plug mounted on the end wall of the chassis, so that its 7-inch dimension is aligned with that of the supply.

Arrangement of parts should be clear from the photographs, and parts location is in no way critical. Note that the a.c. connection is bypassed on both sides of the line. The capacitors C_1 and C_2 are a dual unit designed for this purpose. The bypass on the B-plus line, C_3, should be at the plug end of the cable, with as short leads as possible. It is important in preventing pickup of signals in the i.f. tuning range, as are C_1 and C_2.

Switches are provided for turning on the a.c., and for breaking the flow of plate current. This feature is helpful during adjustment when it may be desirable to remove the converter from its case. Plate voltage may be cut off for safety in handling, and then turned on again without loss of the time needed to warm up the tubes.

Contact between the converter case and the power supply case may be important in preventing signal pickup at 7 Mc. If i.f. signals are bothersome, try putting a spring clip under one of the screws that holds the power supply plate down. Place this so that it will make contact with the converter case or top plate when the two units are plugged together. It also may be necessary to bond the converter and power supply combination to the frame of the communications receiver with which they are to be used. This should be done with a short heavy copper strap or braid.

Connection between the i.f. unit and the receiver should be with coaxial line, and it is highly desirable to install a coaxial fitting on the receiver in place of the usual terminal strip. The connections should be removed from the back of the strip, or the terminals may still allow some i.f. pickup.

Using Other Intermediate Frequencies

The i.f. tuning range beginning at 7 Mc. was selected as the most desirable for most receivers. Other ranges may be preferred, and the i.f. can be altered easily enough. The injection frequency is lower than the signal frequency by whatever i.f. you intend to use. For example, a 50-Mc. converter with a 14-Mc. i.f. would have a crystal and injection frequency of 50–14, or 36 Mc. The 144-Mc. converter would have a 130-Mc. injection frequency, and the crystal would be one-third of this, or 43.33 Mc.

Generally speaking, single-conversion communications receivers (most inexpensive types, and all older receivers) work best with low intermediate frequencies, such as 7 Mc. or lower. Double-conversion receivers will be satisfactory in the 14-Mc. range in almost every case, and some are stable enough to do well around 30 Mc. At least one communications receiver, the NC-300, has a range designed especially for v.h.f. converter use, starting at 30.5 Mc.

Preamplifier for 220 Mc.

The amplifier shown in Figs. 16-17 to 16-19 will improve the gain and noise figure of a 220-Mc. converter that is not operating at maximum effectiveness. It also provides some additional selectivity, which may be helpful in areas where signals from outside the band are troublesome. The plate circuit has high Q, so it must be retuned in covering the band.

The schematic diagram is the same as the first stage of the 220-Mc. converter, Fig. 16-14. The signal is fed into the cathode of the grounded-grid amplifier. The plate circuit is a trough line. Any of the small u.h.f. triodes may be used, though a 6AM4 is shown. Check pin connections and cathode resistor values for other types.

Construction

The outer conductor of the line, which also serves as the chassis, is made of flashing copper. If the details of Fig. 16-18 are followed, it may be made from a single piece. A small copper shield is placed across the tube socket to isolate the input and plate circuits. Just where this shield is located depends on the tube used, as various

Fig. 16-17—220-Mc. trough-line preamplifier. Construction is similar to that used with the 220-Mc. converter, Fig. 16-8, except that provision is made for cable connection to a remote receiver or converter.

420-Mc. Receiver

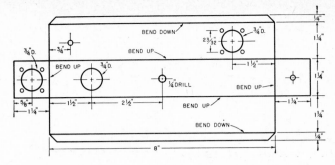

Fig. 16-18—Details of the outer conductor and chassis for the 220-Mc. preamplifier.

tubes have different grid pin arrangements. All grid terminals are bent flat against the copper case, and soldered in place.

The left end (bottom view, Fig. 16-19) contains the coaxial fitting for the antenna connection, the r.f. chokes and other components of the input circuit. The plate line, tuning capacitor, output coupling loop and coax fitting, and the B-plus feed-through capacitor mount in the large portion. A bottom cover for the line can be made of copper 8 inches long and $2\frac{1}{4}$ inches wide. Bend over a quarter inch on each side, and slip the cover over the edges of the case.

The inner conductor is $\frac{1}{4}$-inch copper tubing. Start with a piece $6\frac{1}{4}$ inches long. Saw the ends lengthwise to depths of $\frac{1}{4}$ and $\frac{1}{2}$ inch. Cut off one half at each end. The remaining portions are used to make connections. The half-inch end is bent down to solder to the plate lugs of the socket. The quarter-inch end solders to the feed-through capacitor.

The tuning capacitor, C_1, is mounted with its stator bars toward the tube end of the line. The inner conductor will rest between these bars and they can be soldered to it readily. Plate voltage

is fed through C_6, heater voltage through C_9. Output is taken off through the coupling loop, L_2, visible in Fig. 16-19. The series capacitor, C_2, was omitted from the preamplifier, though it might be useful if the amplifier works into a converter with an untuned input circuit.

Adjustment

The preamplifier may be connected to the converter through a coaxial line of any convenient length, but the converter input should be a coaxial fitting. To put the preamplifier into service, adjust the plate line for maximum signal strength. Then check the position of the coupling loop, adjusting for maximum response. Readjust the tuning of the line as the coupling is changed.

The tuning range of C_1 is not wide, so be sure that it actually tunes the line at both ends of the band. Some adjustment of tuning range can be had by rotating the mounting of the capacitor 180 degrees. If this does not bring the tuning within range, the mounting hole can be elongated and the position of the trimmer adjusted as required.

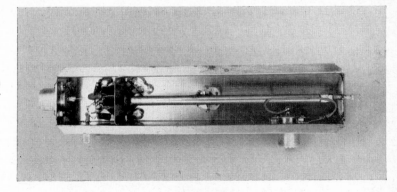

Fig. 16-19—Bottom view of the preamplifier

Receivers for 420 Mc.

For best signal-to-noise ratio, receivers for any frequency should have the highest degree of selectivity that can be used successfully at the frequency in question. With crystal control or its equivalent in stability accepted as standard practice on all bands up through 148 Mc., there is little point in using more bandwidth in receivers for these frequencies than is necessary for satisfac-

tory voice reception, a maximum of about 10 kc. Such communication selectivity is now being used successfully by most workers on 220 and 420 Mc., too, but it imposes several problems not encountered on lower bands.

First is the matter of oscillator instability in the converter. Even the best tunable oscillator at 420 Mc. suffers from vibration and hand-capacity

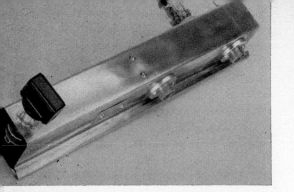

Fig. 16-20—A highly effective r.f. amplifier for 420 Mc. The tank circuit is a half-wave line made of flashing copper. Coaxial fittings are for input and output connections. Heater and plate voltages are brought in on feed-through bypass capacitors just visible on either side of the 6AJ4 tube.

effects sufficiently to make it difficult to hold the signal in a 10-kc. i.f. band width.

Then, there are still some unstable transmitters being used in work on 220 and 420 Mc. It is out of the question to copy these on a selective receiver.

Last, searching a band 30 megacycles wide is excessively time-consuming when communications-receiver selectivity is used in the i.f. system.

There is no single solution to these problems, but the best approach appears to be that of breaking up of the band into segments for different types of operation. This is being done by mutual agreement among 420-Mc. operators at present, as follows: 420 to 432 Mc. — modulated oscillators and wide-band f.m., 432 to 436 Mc. — crystal-controlled c.w., a.m. and narrow-band f.m.; 436 to 450 — television.

The first segment can be covered with a superregenerative receiver, a superheterodyne having a wideband i.f. system, or a converter used ahead of an f.m. broadcast receiver. The high selectivity required for best use of the middle portion makes a crystal-controlled or otherwise highly stable converter and communications receiver combination almost mandatory. Amateur TV is usually received with a converter ahead of a standard TV receiver, tuned to some channel that is not in use locally.

Many of the tubes used on the v.h.f. bands are useless at 420 Mc., and the performance of even the best u.h.f. tubes is down compared to lower bands. Only the lighthouse or pencil-triode tubes and a few of the miniatures are usable, and these require modifications of conventional circuit technique to produce satisfactory results.

Crystal diodes are often used as mixers in 420-Mc. receivers, as in this frequency range they work nearly as well as vacuum tubes. The over-all gain of a converter having a crystal mixer is about 10 db. lower than one using a tube, so this difference must be made up in the i.f. amplifier. The noise figure of a receiver having a crystal mixer and no r.f. stage includes the noise figure of the i.f. amplifier following the mixer, so best results require that the i.f. amplifier employ low-noise techniques discussed earlier in this chapter. If the i.f. is 50 Mc. or higher it is particularly important that a low-noise triode be used for the first i.f. stage.

Crystal diodes of the type used in radar mixers, such as the 1N21 series, are well suited to 420-Mc. mixer service, though care must be taken to avoid damage from transmitter r.f. energy. Other types of crystal diodes such as the 1N72 and CK710

will stand higher values of crystal current, and their use is recommended.

Few conventional vacuum tubes work well as mixers at 420 Mc. and higher. The 6J6 is useful where a balanced input circuit is desired, as in Fig. 16-5C. For single-ended circuitry the 6AM4 and 6AN4 are recommended. They may be used in grounded-grid or grounded-cathode circuits.

For high-selectivity coverage of the 432- to 436-Mc. segment of the band, a common practice is to use a crystal-controlled converter working into another converter for either the 50- or 144-Mc. band, tuning the latter for the four-megacycle tuning range.

● A 420-MC. R.F. AMPLIFIER

The r.f. amplifier shown in Figs. 16-20 through 16-22 is capable of a gain or more than 15 db. and its noise figure can be as low as 6 db. with careful adjustment. It will make a large improvement in the sensitivity of any converter or receiver that has no r.f. stage, or one that is working poorly.

The design shown is for either the 6AJ4 or 6AM4, but with suitable socket and pin-connection changes the 417A, 6BC4 or 6AN4 will work equally well. It is a grounded-grid amplifier with

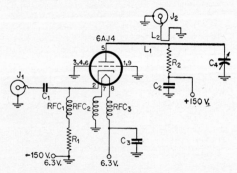

Fig. 16-21—Schematic diagram of the 420-Mc. r.f. amplifier.

C$_1$—500-$\mu\mu$f. ceramic.
C$_2$, C$_3$—1000-$\mu\mu$f. ceramic feedthrough (Erie style 2404).
C$_4$—Copper tabs, $\frac{7}{8}$-inch diam.; see text and photographs.
R$_1$—150 ohms, $\frac{1}{2}$ watt.
R$_2$—470 ohms, $\frac{1}{2}$ watt.
L$_1$—$\frac{1}{4}$-inch copper tubing, $7\frac{3}{8}$ inches long, tapped $2\frac{3}{8}$ inches from plate end.
L$_2$—Loop of insulated wire adjacent to L$_1$ for $\frac{3}{4}$ inch.
J$_1$, J$_2$—Coaxial fitting.
RFC$_1$, RFC$_2$, RFC$_3$—9 turns No. 22, $\frac{3}{8}$-inch diam., spaced one diam.

420-Mc. R.F. Amplifier

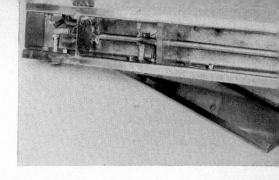

Fig. 16-22—Bottom view of the 420-Mc. r.f. amplifier, with the slip-on cover removed. The inner conductor of the tank circuit is held in place by a block of polystyrene, mounted near the low-voltage point on the line. The plate-voltage feedthrough and output coupling loop may be seen at the left of this support. Heater, cathode and antenna-circuit components are in a separate compartment at the tube end of the assembly. The line is tuned at the opposite end by a handmade copper-tab capacitor.

a half-wave line in the plate circuit. The antenna is connected to the cathode of the tube through a coupling capacitor. As the input impedance of the grounded-grid stage is low, nothing is gained by the use of a tuned circuit in the cathode lead. Output is taken off through a coupling loop at the point of lowest r.f. voltage along the line.

The amplifier is built in a frame of flashing copper that serves as the outer conductor of the tank circuit. The whole assembly is 10 inches long and $1\frac{1}{4}$ inches square, except for the bottom, which is about $1\frac{3}{4}$ inches wide. Edges are folded over with lips $\frac{1}{4}$ inch wide which slide into a bottom cover made from copper sheet $2\frac{1}{4}$ by 10 inches in size, with its edges bent up $\frac{1}{4}$ inch wide on each side.

The plate circuit is made of $\frac{1}{4}$-inch copper tubing tuned by a copper-tab capacitor at the far end from the tube. Plate voltage is fed in at the point of minimum r.f. voltage, which in this instance is about 5 inches from the open end. The antenna is connected to the cathode through a coupling capacitor. The input impedance of the grounded-grid amplifier is so low that nothing is gained by using a tuned circuit at this point. The cathode and heater are maintained above ground potential by small air-wound r.f. chokes.

The tube socket is two inches in from the end of the trough, and is so oriented that its plate connection, Pin 5, is in the proper position to connect to the line with the shortest possible lead. A copper shielding fin is mounted across the interior of the trough $2\frac{1}{8}$ inches from the end, dividing the socket so that Pins 3, 4, 5 and 6 are on the plate side of the partition.

Minimum grid-lead inductance is important. This was insured by bending all the grid prongs down against the ceramic body of the socket, and then making the mounting hole just big enough to pass this part of the socket and the prongs. They were soldered to the wall of the trough.

Input and output connections are coaxial fittings mounted on the side wall of the trough. B-plus and heater voltage are brought into the assembly on feed-through capacitors mounted on the same side of the trough as the tube. Connection to the inner conductor of the line is made with a grid clip, so that the point of connection can be adjusted for optimum results.

The copper tubing is slotted at the plate end with a hack saw to a depth of about $\frac{1}{4}$ inch, and a strip of flashing copper soldered into this slot to make the plate connection. A copper tab about the size of a one-cent piece is soldered to the other

end of the tubing to provide the stationary plate of C_4. The line is supported near the low-voltage point by a $\frac{1}{4}$-inch-thick block of polystyrene. This is centered at a point $5\frac{1}{4}$ inches in from the tube end of the trough assembly. The hole for the B-plus feedthrough is $4\frac{1}{4}$ inches from the same end.

The movable plate of C_4 is soldered to a screw running through a nut soldered on the upper surface of the trough at a point $\frac{3}{8}$ inch in from the open end. If a fine-thread screw is available for this purpose it will make for easier tuning, though a 6-32 thread was used in this model. This made a wobbly contact, so a coil spring was installed between the top of the trough and the knob to keep some tension on the adjusting screw.

Adjustment of the 420-Mc. amplifier is made easier if a noise generator is used, though it is not as important as in the case amplifiers with tuned input circuits. If the amplifier is working properly there will be an appreciable rise in noise as the plate circuit is tuned through resonance, and it may break into oscillation if operated without load. When connected to a following stage, with a reasonably matched antenna plugged into J_1, the amplifier should not oscillate unless the coupling loop, L_2, is much too far from the inner conductor.

When the amplifier is operating stably and tuned to a test signal (or to a peak of response to a noise generator), the next step is to locate the optimum position for feeding the plate voltage into the line. This may be done by running a pencil lead slowly up and down the inner conductor, until a spot is found where touching the lead to the line has little or no effect on the operation of the amplifier. The plate voltage clip should be placed at this point and the process repeated, moving the clip slightly until it is at the minimum-voltage point precisely. This adjustment should be made at the midpoint of the tuning range over which the amplifier is to be used.

The position of the coupling loop should then be adjusted for best signal-to-noise ratio. This will probably turn out to be with the insulated wire lying against the inner conductor for a distance of about $\frac{3}{4}$ to 1 inch, starting at the minimum-voltage point just located.

● A CRYSTAL-CONTROLLED CONVERTER FOR 432 MC.

The converter shown in Figs. 16-23 through 16-26 is designed to provide high sensitivity and

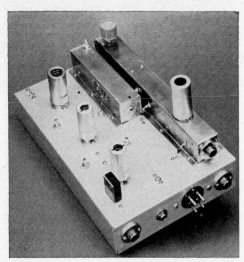

Fig. 16-23—A crystal-controlled converter for 432 to 436 Mc. R.f. and mixer stages are in copper subassemblies at the right. Oscillator, multiplier and i.f. amplifier are on the left side.

signal-to-noise ratio in reception of signals in the 432- to 436-Mc. range. It uses a grounded-grid r.f. amplifier stage similar to the one shown in Fig. 16-20, working into a crystal-diode mixer. The intermediate frequency, with the design constants given, is 50 to 54 Mc., though lower frequencies could be used by suitable modification of the injection chain.

Crystal-controlled injection on 382 Mc. is provided by two 6J6s operating as overtone oscillator-tripler and tripler-doubler, respectively. As only a small amount of r.f. is required at 382 Mc., this line-up is not difficult to build or adjust. An inexpensive 7-Mc. crystal is used. An i.f. preamplifier stage follows the crystal mixer. This may or may not be needed, depending on the performance of the receiver or converter that will serve as the tunable i.f. Low-noise amplification in the i.f. stage is a factor in the over-all performance of the system, so use of the built-in i.f. stage is recommended.

Construction

The converter is built on a 7 × 11 × 2-inch aluminum chassis, with the r.f. and mixer portions in a copper subassembly that mounts on the top of the chassis, at the right side as seen in Fig. 16-23. The oscillator-tripler and tripler-doubler 6J6s are at the left front, with the 6BQ7A i.f. amplifier at the rear. The mixer line is the short portion of the copper assembly, with the r.f. amplifier line at the right. In the bottom view, Fig. 16-25, the injection-chain and i.f. amplifier components are visible.

Fig. 16-24 is an interior view of the r.f. and mixer lines. These are made as two separate assemblies, joined by short length of copper tubing that is visible in the top view. Both tank circuits are $1\frac{1}{4}$ inches square, with $\frac{1}{4}$-inch copper tubing inner conductors. They are made from sheets of flashing copper $4\frac{1}{4}$ inches wide. The mixer compartment is $5\frac{1}{2}$ inches long and the r.f. portion is 10 inches long.

The r.f. amplifier is similar structurally to the one described previously, except for the method of coupling between it and the crystal mixer. This is done with a grid clip on each line and a ceramic coupling capacitor. The lead from the capacitor, inside the amplifier line, is brought through a half-inch length of copper tubing that is soldered into the walls of both lines. The lead is insulated with spaghetti sleeving.

The B-plus feed to the r.f. stage should be at the point of minimum r.f. voltage, $1\frac{7}{8}$ inches from the plate end of the copper tubing. The coupling tap is one inch out from the B-plus feedpoint. The coupling point on the mixer line is 1 inch from the ground end. The crystal diode is inserted in a small hole in the mixer inner conductor, $1\frac{3}{4}$ inches from the ground end. The inner conductors of the r.f. and mixer lines are 7 3/16 and 5 inches long, respectively. Mixer tuning is done with a small plastic trimmer, C_{10}, while the r.f. plate circuit is tuned with a hand-made tab capacitor, C_9, similar to C_4 in Fig. 16-21.

Note the r.f. bypass, C_8, on the outside of the mixer line. This is made from a piece of copper $\frac{7}{8}$ inch in diameter, insulated from the line housing by a piece of vinyl plastic. Two thicknesses of the material commonly used for small parts envelopes are satisfactory. The crystal, which may be any of the u.h.f. diodes, is slipped through a close-fit hole and is held in place by the wire soldered to its outside terminal.

Plate and filament voltages are fed into the assembly on feed-through bypass capacitors, visible in the top-view photograph. Antenna connection is made through a coaxial fitting on the end of the r.f. assembly. A crystal-current jack, a 4-pin power fitting and two i.f. connectors are on the end wall of the chassis. The second coaxial connector was installed so that tests could be made with and without the i.f. amplifier stage.

Wiring in the power circuits is done with shielded wire, in case that TVI might result from the oscillator or multiplier stages. The addition of a bottom plate and power-lead filtering would then be effective. Injection and i.f. coupling leads are also made of shielded wire, this serving in place of coax line that is harder to handle.

The output of the injection chain is coupled into the mixer line by means of a loop, L_8, that

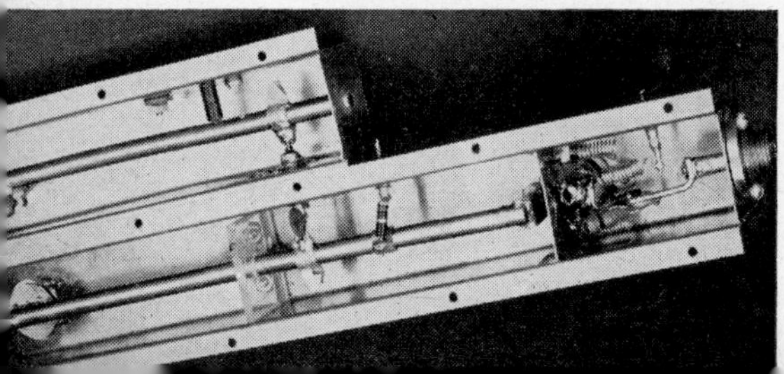

Fig. 16-24—Interior view of the r.f. amplifier and mixer assemblies. The r.f. circuit is a half-wave line. The shorter assembly is the quarter-wave line using a crystal diode mixer.

Crystal-Controlled Converter for 432 Mc.

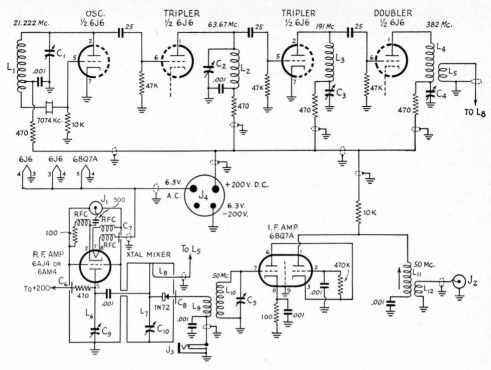

Fig. 16-26—Wiring diagram and parts list for the 432-Mc. crystal-controlled converter. Values given are for an i.f. of 50 to 54 Mc.

C₁—75-μμf. miniature trimmer (Hammarlund MAPC-75).

C₂, C₃, C₄—20-μμf. miniature trimmer (Johnson 20M11).

C₅—25-μμf. miniature trimmer (Hammarlund MAPC-25).

C₆, C₇—500-μμf. feed-through ceramic (Centralab MFT-500).

C₈—Handmade copper-tab bypass; see text.

C₉—Handmade copper-tab variable; see text.

C₁₀—0.5- to 5-μμf. plastic trimmer (Erie style 532-08-OR5).

L₁—13½ turns No. 20 tinned, ⅝-inch diam., ⅞ inch long, tapped at 4½ turns (B & W Miniductor No. 3007).

L₂—5 turns No. 20 tinned, ½-inch diam., ⅜ inch long (B & W Miniductor No. 3003).

L₃—2¾ turns similar to L₂.

L₄—2 turns No. 12 tinned, ¼-inch diam., ¼ inch long.

L₅—1 turns ins. wire between turns of L₄ May be inner conductor of shielded wire, with braid removed.

L₆—Half-wave line, ¼-inch copper tubing, 7³⁄₁₆ inches long.

L₇—Quarter-wave line, ¼-inch copper tubing, 5 inches long.

L₈—Loop of insulated wire 1 inch long and ½ inch high projecting through base plate on which line assemblies are mounted. May be made from inner conductor of shielded wire, with braid removed from last two inches.

L₉—2 turns No. 22 enam. around cold end of L₁₀.

L₁₀—6 turns similar to L₂.

L₁₁—11 turns No. 22 enam. close-wound on ⅜-inch slug-tuned form (National XR-91).

L₁₂—4 turns No. 28 silk or enamel wound over cold end of L₁₁.

J₁, J₂—Coaxial fitting.

J₃—Closed-circuit jack.

J₄—4-pin male chassis fitting.

RFC—10 turns No. 22 tinned, ⅛-inch diam. Space turns diam. of wire.

is not visible in the photographs. This loop is mounted on the copper base plate that is under the mixer and r.f. assembly. Its size and proximity to the mixer inner conductor are not particularly critical, as there is a surplus of injection under ordinary conditions of operation.

Adjustment

The first step in putting the converter into operation is to tune up the oscillator and multiplier stages. This process is similar to the adjustment of a transmitter and will not be detailed here. Check to see that the proper frequencies appear as indicated on the schematic diagram. Only enough power at 382 Mc. is needed to develop

about 0.5 ma. of crystal current. Anything from 0.2 to 1.0 ma. is satisfactory. Adjustments should be made with no plate voltage on the r.f. stage.

Now connect the converter to a 50-Mc. receiver or converter and peak the i.f. amplifier circuits at about 52 Mc. on noise. Next apply plate voltage and feed a signal into the r.f. stage. Peak the r.f. and mixer capacitors for maximum response at about 434 Mc. These adjustments can be made on noise also, if the circuits were close to resonance originally. If a noise generator is not available, the margin of signal over receiver noise that is obtained on a received signal is also usable, if adjustments are made with care.

The points of connection for the B-plus and the

Fig. 16-25—Bottom view of the 432-Mc. converter, showing the oscillator, multiplier and i.f. amplifier circuits.

coupling taps on the r.f. and mixer lines are critical adjustments, but if the dimensions given above are followed carefully the points should be close to optimum. Adjustments can be made and checked readily if the r.f.-mixer assembly is mounted in place temporarily with a few self-tapping screws. (Originally described in January, 1954, *QST*, p. 24.)

A Crystal-Controlled Converter for 1296 Mc.

For simplicity, no r.f. amplifier stage is used ahead of the crystal mixer in the converter shown in Fig. 16-27. While a good amplifier may have advantages over a straight crystal-mixer type of superheterodyne at this frequency, much interesting work can be done with the simpler arrangement. By following certain design principles, to be discussed later, the performance of a crystal mixer can be made very nearly as good as that of the best r.f. amplifier stages.

The converter uses a 1N21E crystal diode in a radial cavity. Injection at 1280 Mc. is furnished by an oscillator-multiplier chain consisting of a 6U8, two 6J6s, and a 446A lighthouse tube. The converter layout leaves plenty of space for changes, and the various units can be modified readily. R.f. connections between stages are made with coaxial connectors and RG-58/U or RG-59/U cable.

The Cavity Mixer

Most mixer cavities described are the coaxial type, but this converter employs the radial variety. In a coaxial cavity the length is the primary frequency-determining dimension. (The diameter has a small effect.) A radial cavity resonates at a frequency almost totally dependent on its diameter. Center loading the radial cavity capacitively lowers its resonant frequency, just as does end loading a coaxial line.

The physical details of the mixer are shown in Figs. 16-28 and 16-29. The dimensions given are not critical. A first model was made by sawing a ¾-inch length off a 4½-inch diameter aluminum pipe for the main body. The ¾-inch length was chosen to accommodate the physical length of the 1N21-series crystals.

The antenna input, the local oscillator injection and the mixing crystal are all on one face of the mixer, spaced 120 degrees apart. The crystal was mounted somewhat closer to the middle of the cavity than the antenna input connector. This was because the antenna connection on an earlier model was a wire ¾ inch long, from the center conductor of the connector to the opposite end plate of the cavity. Assuming the r.f. input impedance of the crystal to be about 100 to 150 ohms, the crystal would have to be closer to the center than the input tap, for the latter to provide a good match for 50-ohm input. Laboratory

Fig. 16-27—Rear view of the 1296-Mc. crystal-controlled converter. At the back of the chassis is the injection string assembly, except for the 1280-Mc. doubler, which is at the far right. The small assembly adjacent to the doubler is the 16-Mc. i.f. preamplifier. The radial mixer cavity is fastened to the front panel. Power-supply components are at the left.

Crystal-Controlled Converter for 1296 Mc.

tests showed that this arrangement worked out quite well, but the loop coupling gives just as good match. The cavity is loaded quite heavily, as image rejection is no problem. So long as the image rejection is 10 db. or more the over-all noise figure will not be adversely affected. The lower Q reduces insertion loss and lessens the mechanical rigidity requirements of the mixer.

Tuning the mixer is done with a ¼-inch brass shaft passing through the end plate opposite to that containing the mixer crystal and coaxial connectors. A penny-sized copper disk is soldered to the shaft for a capacitor plate, and the shaft runs through a locking-type panel bushing adjusted to provide the necessary friction. In practice the mixer rarely requires tuning, but the red-blooded experimenter would rightfully feel cheated if something were not available for adjusting occasionally.

Spring copper wipers, shown in the drawing, were a refinement that was found to be unnecessary, but it may be just as well to add them anyway. Erratic mixer tuning was at first thought to be due to poor contact between the shaft and its bushing. Later it was found that the end plates were "oil-canning." This was cured by mounting the mixer against a heavy panel, as seen in the rear-view photograph, and changing the end plate to a heavier stock. A further refinement to reduce mixer loss and improve tuning stability was to improve contact between the main body and the end plates by undercutting the end faces of the main body,[1] as shown in Fig. 16-29A.

The mixing crystal protrudes through one end plate and contacts the opposite one. The large end is insulated by a tight-fitting piece of spaghetti sleeving. The i.f. output is brought off by a copper tab that presses down on the end of the crystal. The tab also serves as a mixer bypass capacitor. It is fastened to the end plate with two

[1] Cavities are available in the form shown in Fig. 16-29 from Mooradian Machine Works, 1752 E. 23rd St., Los Angeles. Price, $1.50 each.

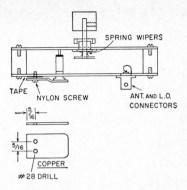

Fig. 16-28—Cut-away view of the radial cavity mixer assembly in the 1296-Mc. converter.

nylon screws, and is insulated from the plate by a strip of plastic electrical tape. (Metal screws, suitably insulated, may be used if the nylon screws are not available.) Because of 40 μμf. of capacitance to ground so provided, and the relatively low impedance of the circuit, about 400 ohms, there is negligible pickup at the intermediate frequency.

I.F. Preamplifier

As no communications receiver has enough gain to accommodate the low signal level from the mixer, a preamplifier is necessary. Other arrangements might give more gain and lower noise figure than the one shown in Fig. 16-30, but none would be more simple or readily adjusted. Like the injection string, the i.f. preamplifier is built as a subassembly. Experimentation with other circuits is thus made easy, but in the meantime the builder of the converter is able to receive signals.

The i.f. amplifier is a 12AT7. The first stage is grounded-grid, and has an input impedance, neglecting input capacitance, of nominally 400 ohms. This happens to be the optimum i.f. im-

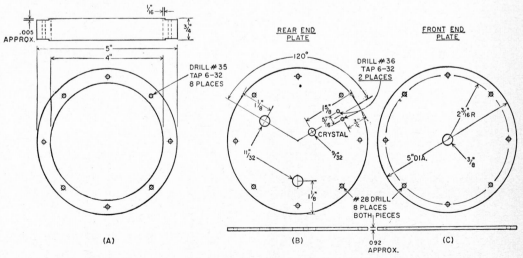

Fig. 16-29—Dimensions of the principal parts of the radial cavity. Material may be aluminum or brass.

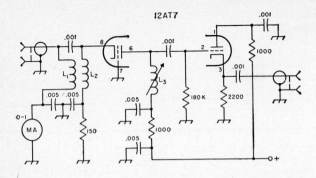

Fig. 16–30—Schematic diagram of the i.f. preamplifier stage.
L_1, L_2—Bifilar-wound choke resonating at 16 Mc. 23 double turns No. 26 enamel, ¼ diam., close-wound.
L_3—25 turns No. 22 enamel, ½-inch slug-tuned form.

pedance for the 1N21-series mixing crystal. The d.c. return for the crystal is through one half of a bifilar r.f. choke winding, the cathode return being the other half. This choke is resonated at the intermediate frequency by the combined effect of the mixer bypass, the coaxial cable and the tube input capacitances. Resonance is checked with a grid-dip meter, removing or adding turns as required. It is not at all critical, as the operating Q is low and the bandwidth consequently is large. Be sure to remove the crystal from the mixer before using the grid-dip meter; otherwise the dip may be questionable.

For maximum gain in the first stage it should be loaded with as low-capacitance and high-impedance a second stage as possible. There should be no tuning capacitance, so a slug-tuned coil is used. The second stage is a cathode follower. This has virtually infinite input resistance, and no Miller-effect capacitance, making the slug-tuned coil the sole frequency-determining element of the preamp. The pass band of the amplifier is very narrow; no more than a few hundred kilocycles. This is not a disadvantage as the coil is quickly adjusted by turning the slug and listening to the noise peak when the receiver is tuned to the desired frequency.

The casual observer may suggest at this point that the cathode follower is useless, as it has no gain and could be replaced by link coupling from the interstage coil. Nothing could be further from correct. A low-impedance link coupled to the interstage coil would load it, and the gain from the grounded-grid stage would drop rapidly. While having a *voltage* gain of only about 0.9, the cathode follower definitely provides gain compared to the conventional grounded-cathode amplifier. Furthermore, its output impedance is very nearly that of the input of most low- and medium-priced communications receivers.

Oscillator-Multiplier Chain

One problem in crystal-controlled converters operating in the higher bands is instability. Having gone to crystal control to achieve stability, one should get as much as crystals will provide. Expensive crystals and ovens can be used, but only as a last resort. Overtone oscillators are ruled out. Possibly their use would save one stage, but at some sacrifice in sta-

bility and only a slight reduction in circuit complexity. Crystal-diode multipliers have merit, but their peculiarities may not be familiar to the v.h.f. man already experienced in vacuum-tube multipliers.

As seen in Fig. 16-31, the injection chain starts with a 10.0-Mc. crystal oscillator using the pentode section of a 6U8. Check the frequency before construction progresses too far; if the oscillator is only 8 kc. off, the final injection frequency will be off by more than a megacycle. The 4th harmonic, 40 Mc., is taken from the plate circuit and fed to the triode section of the 6U8, where it is doubled to 80 Mc. Two halves of a 6J6 double twice to 320 Mc. The 320-Mc. circuit is balanced, for optimum coupling to the balanced input of the 6J6 push-push doubler to 640 Mc. The 640-Mc. plate circuit of this stage is a small loop, parallel-resonant with the 6J6 output capacitance, and tuned by a small variable series capacitor.

The final doubler is a 2C40 or 446A lighthouse tube, available at most surplus houses for 25 to 50 cents. It uses a modified ASB-5 mixer cavity, also a surplus item. Little use has been found for this unit in the past, though its companion unit, the r.f. amplifier in the ASB-5, is much in demand. Its input circuit will not quite reach 640 Mc. in its original form, so it was shortened about ¾ inch by installing a false bottom in the cathode cavity. This was made by punching a 1⅜-inch hole in the middle of the plate cover of the mixer, and slotting the rim in numerous places with a jeweler's saw or coping saw. The cavity is heated *on one end only* over a gas stove, and the original bottom and cathode conductor temporarily removed. The modified mixer plate cover is slipped over the cathode connector and soldered in place. The works is then reassembled.

The original input hole will then be covered by the false bottom. However, what was originally the ASB local oscillator injection hole is now in the exact position for the 640-Mc. drive. Under operating conditions the s.w.r. looking into this doubler was found to be 1.19. A BNC fitting is attached to take the 640-Mc. drive.

The 1280-Mc. plate circuit is quite simple, and details are more readily conveyed by drawings than by description. The inner conductor is made

Crystal-Controlled Converter for 1296 Mc.

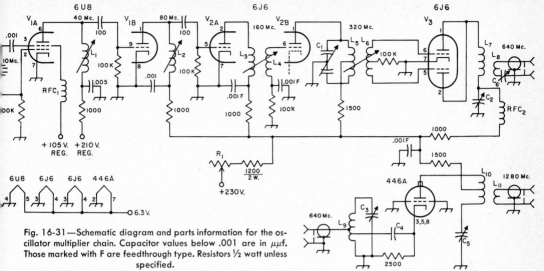

Fig. 16-31—Schematic diagram and parts information for the oscillator multiplier chain. Capacitor values below .001 are in μμf. Those marked with F are feedthrough type. Resistors ½ watt unless specified.

C₁—1.8 to 5.1 μμf.-per-section split-stator variable. (Johnson 160-205).
C₂, C₆—1.8-μμf. plastic trimmer (Erie 532).
C₃, C₄—Part of ASB cavity.
C₅—Piston from trimmer capacitor; slides inside end of L₁₀. See Fig. 5.
L₁—18 t. No. 22 on 9/32-inch diam. iron-slug form.
L₂—8 t. No. 22 on 9/32-inch diam. iron-slug form, spaced to ⅝ inch.
L₃—9 t. No. 22, ¼-inch diam., ¾ inch long.
L₄—8 t. like L₃. L₃ and L₄ are side by side ½ inch apart, c. to c.
L₅—3 t. No. 14, 5/16-inch diam., 7/16 inch long, center tapped. Leads ⅜ inch long.
L₆—2 t. No. 22, ½-inch diam., 7/16 inch long.
L₇—2 t. No. 14, ¼-inch diam., 7/16 inch long. One ⅜-inch lead.
L₈—2-inch length of No. 16 bent into U shape, ¾ inch wide at open end, ¼ inch at bent end.
L₉—Part of ASB cavity.
L₁₀—Final doubler plate circuit; see Fig. 5.
RFC₁—1-mh r.f. choke.
RFC₂—5 t. No. 24 enam. on 1-watt resistor.

from 5/16-inch copper fuel line, slotted at the end to receive the plate cap of the 446A. (See Fig. 16-32.) The insulating bushing, preferably of Teflon, is installed at the other end. The plunger and spring-loaded bearing were taken from a precision piston trimmer found in many pieces of surplus gear. (The ARR-26 has 30 of them.)

The ring attaching the outer conductor to the ASB cavity was cut from flat copper sheet with tin snips. It is held on the end of the ASB cavity and holes are drilled through both it and the cavity. The holes in the cavity are then tapped for 6-32 screws. The outer conductor (brass plumbing pipe) was soldered to the copper ring, and allowed to protrude through it. This makes the outer conductor press firmly against the grid ring of the ASB cavity, giving a good r.f. joint.

The output link enters through a ⅜-inch hole, about ½ inch above the plate cap, as seen in Fig. 16-32. The B-plus feed resistor enters through a 3/16-inch hole. Its cold side is connected to a feedthrough bypass, mounted on a small angle bracket, as close to the hole as possible.

Power Supply

The d.c. output voltage of the power supply is about 230. Two 0B2 regulator tubes in series pro-

vide regulated 210 volts for the oscillator plate and 105 for the oscillator screen. Other stages of the injection chain are run from the unregulated output of the supply, through a 2000-ohm wirewound potentiometer. This is useful for varying the injection electrically. It will be found that crystal currents from 50 to 500 microamperes have very little effect on the mixer operation.

The i.f. preamplifier is also operated from the unregulated supply. It will be seen from Fig. 16-31 that the oscillator voltage is left on continuously during transmit or standby periods. This keep-alive voltage eliminates the last few cycles of drift when going from transmit to receive. Stability, both long and short term, was found to be worth the effort when making straight c.w. contacts on 1296 Mc. Stability and c.w. notes were like 80 meters — a vast improvement over several previous converters used on this band. Being able to set up the receiver on a frequency precisely, and then just wait for the signal to come through, is an important factor in DX attempts on 1296 Mc.

Improvements

After the first signal is copied on the converter, ideas will come along for possible improvements.

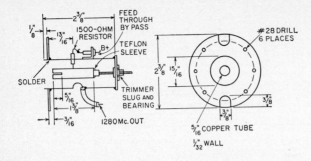

Fig. 16-32—Details of the 1280-Mc. doubler plate circuit. Circular plate fits top of an ASB cavity. See text and Fig. 16-27. The inner conductor of the line fits over the plate cap of the 2C40 or 446A tube. Output coupling loop can be made from the inner conductor of the coaxial line. Tuning capacitor is made from a piston-type trimmer and its bearing assembly.

With the subassembly construction employed ideas can be tried one at a time, with the assurance that unchanged other units will continue to operate properly. A pi-network input to the i.f. preamplifier may aid materially in matching the crystal to the grounded-grid amplifier input. This can be done by adjusting different combinations while listening to a fairly weak signal. The ninth harmonic of a 144-Mc. transmitter can be used as a signal source, though a silicon diode or vacuum-tube noise generator may give better results.

Cascode and pentode preamplifier circuits can be explored. Two problems to be expected will be instability and matching the input imedance of the amplifier. Keep in mind that mere absence of oscillation in an amplifier does not guarantee that it is free of regeneration.

Adequate injection was obtained with the setup described, but some experimenters may experience trouble due to variation in lighthouse tube condition. Many 446A and 2C40 tubes obtained on the surplus market are inferior in one way or another. Nearly all have been removed from equipment, even when they are advertised as "new."

While the ⅜-inch signal injection loop seems to work well there is no assurance at this point that some other size loop or different coupling method would not be better. Untuned mixers deserve consideration. Some experimenters report poor results with these, possibly because of mismatched antenna or feedline impedances. Poor mixer performance may also result from much of the signal being shunted into the local oscillator chain, where it is dissipated. High-Q tank circuit design for the injection chain output stage may be helpful here, a point that is often overlooked in 420-Mc. crystal-mixer converters, as well. The untuned mixer has the advantage that the signal may be injected at 640 or 427 Mc. with only slightly degraded performance.

In spite of the fact that most u.h.f. triodes are not supposed to work well at 1300 Mc., several experimenters have used 446As, pencil triodes and the 416B with gratifying results. The *apparent* improved performance may be due to a poorly constructed or improperly adjusted mixer, benefiting greatly from the gain of the r.f. amplifier. The 416B, particularly, was designed for commercial applications at 4000 Mc., so it should be good at 1300 Mc. when properly handled. Poor noise figures quoted for this tube are from data intended for wide-band applications. By proper cavity design the bandwidth can be kept low in amateur applications, and improved noise figures might result.

A good ready-made r.f. amplifier is the ASB-5 (CPR-46-ACJ) r.f. cavity. This was originally intended for use in the 500-Mc. region. Both input and output cavities will tune to 1300 Mc. as three-quarter wave lines. This cavity uses the 446A tube, but adapter rings have been constructed to permit the use of the 416B. The ASB-7 cavity is also useful. In many ways, this unit is more flexible than the former, and more circuit adaptations become apparent during its use. Fairly successful attempts have been made in other directions also. One such amplifier used a 6BY4 ceramic u.h.f. receiving triode on 1200 Mc. As nearly as could be determined, this tube performed as well as a 416B known to be operating properly.

Crystal mixer diodes come in a variety of types. The most common ones are 1N21 and 1N23 series. These have been made in suffixes ranging through the letter "E." The 1N21 series is intended for use from 1000 to 3000 Mc. It will work higher. The 1N23 is intended for use from 3000 to 10,000 Mc., and will work lower. As long as a mixer is operating poorly, or only fairly well, there is virtually no difference in the performance of any of these crystals. It is when a really effective mixer is coupled with an i.f. preamp of 1 to 3 db. noise figure that the amazing difference between 1N21A and the 1N21E becomes evident.

Newer crystals such as the MA421 give noise figures of 6 db. and better in standard test setups. Individually-tailored amateur circuits can be expected to perform even better. Because of semiconductor progress, both in mixers and amplifiers, the vacuum-tube r.f. amplifier at 1200 Mc. appears less desirable than ever.

The rectified crystal current flowing as a result of the local oscillator injection should be measured with a milliammeter having as low a d.c. resistance as possible. Degraded performance may result from the d.c. bias developed across this resistance. The experimenter is invited to try the use of small amounts of back bias on the crystal to improve performance.

(From *QST*, September, 1959.)

V.H.F. Transmitters

Transmitter stability regulations for the 50-Mc. band are the same as for lower bands, and proper design may make it possible to use the same rig for 50, 28, 21, and even 14 Mc., but incorporation of 144 Mc. and higher in the usual multiband transmitter is generally not feasible. Rather, it is usually more satisfactory to combine 50 and 144 Mc., since the two bands are close to a third-harmonic relationship. At least the exciter portion of the transmitter may be made to cover both bands very readily.

Though no stability restrictions are imposed by law on amateur operation at 144 Mc. and higher, the use of stabilized narrow-band systems pays off in improved effectiveness in both transmitter and receiver. It is this factor, more than the interference potentialities of the wide-band systems, which makes it desirable to employ advanced techniques at 144, 220 and 420 Mc.

The low-power stages of a transmitter for the v.h.f. bands need not be greatly different in design from those used for lower bands, and the techniques of Chapter Six can be used. The constructor has the choice of starting at some lower frequency, usually around 6, 8 or 12 Mc., multiplying to the operating frequency in one or more additional stages, or he can use a high initial frequency and thus reduce the number of multiplier stages. The first approach has the virtue of using low-cost crystals, but h.f. crystals may effect an economy in power consumption, an important factor in portable or emergency-powered gear.

● CRYSTAL OSCILLATORS

Crystal oscillator stages for v.h.f. transmitters may make use of any of the circuits shown in Chapter Six when crystals up to 12 Mc. are used, but certain variations are helpful for higher frequencies. Crystals for 12 Mc. or higher are usually of the overtone variety. Their frequency of oscillation is an approximate odd multiple of some lower frequency, for which the crystal is actually ground. Thus 24-Mc. crystals commonly used in 144-Mc. work are 8-Mc. cuts, specially treated for overtone characteristics. The overtone crystals currently being supplied are nearly as stable as those designed for fundamental operation, and they are easy to handle in properly designed circuits.

Best results are usually obtained with overtone crystals if some regeneration is added. This makes for easy starting under load and greater output than would be obtainable in a simple triode or tetrode circuit. Regenerative circuits, with constants for 8- or 24-Mc. crystals, are shown in Figs. 17-20 and 17-24. Triodes are shown, but the same arrangement may be used with tetrode or pentolde tubes. The important point in either case is the amount of regeneration, controlled by the

number of turns below the tap in L_1 of Fig. 17-20 or 17-24. There should be only enough feedback to assure easy crystal starting and satisfactory operation under load; too much will result in oscillation not under the control of the crystal.

Overtone operation is possible with standard fundamental-type crystals, using these circuits. Practically all will oscillate on their third overtones, and fifth and higher odd overtones may be possible. Adjustment of regeneration is more critical, however, if the crystals are not ground for overtone characteristics. The frequency may not be an exact multiple of that marked on the crystal holder, so care should be used in working with crystals that are near a band edge.

Crystals ground for overtone service can be made to oscillate on other overtones than the one marked on the holder. For more discussion of overtone oscillator techniques, see *QST* for April, 1951, page 56, and March, 1955, page 16.

Crystals are now available for frequencies up to around 100 Mc. They are somewhat more expensive and more critical in operation than those for 30 Mc. and lower, however. Use of 50-Mc. crystals is made occasionally as a means of preventing radiation of the harmonics from lower frequency crystals that might cause TVI.

● FREQUENCY MULTIPLIERS

Frequency multiplying stages in a v.h.f. transmitter follow standard practice, the principal precaution being arrangement of components for short lead length and minimum stray capacitance. This is particularly important at 144 Mc. and higher. To reduce the possibility of radiation of oscillator harmonics on frequencies that might interfere with television orother services, the lowest satisfactory power level should be used. Low-powered stages are easier to shield or filter, in case such steps become necessary.

Common practice in v.h.f. exciter design is to make the tuned circuits capable of operation over the whole range from 48 to 54 Mc., so that the output stage can drive either an amplifier at 50 to 54 Mc. or a tripler from 48 to 144 Mc. Tripling is often done with push-pull stages, particularly when the output frequency is to be 144 Mc. or higher.

● AMPLIFIERS

Most transmitting tubes now used by amateurs will work on 50 Mc., but for 144 Mc. and higher the tube types are limited to those having low input and output capacitances and compact physical structure. Leads must be as short as possible, and soldered connections should be avoided in high-powered circuits, where heating may be great enough to melt the solder.

Plug-in coils and their associated sockets or

jack bars are generally unsatisfactory for use at 144 Mc. and higher because of the stray inductance and capacitance they introduce. One way around this trouble is the use of a dual tank circuit in which the inductor for 144 Mc. is a conventional tuned line, with its shorting bar made as a removable plug. When the stage is to be used on another band the short is removed and a coil is plugged into the jack, the line then serving as a pair of plate leads. Such an arrangement will operate as efficiently on 144 Mc. as if it were designed for that band alone.

At 220 Mc. and higher it may be necessary to employ half-wave lines as tuned circuits, as shown in Fig. 17-28 (P_1 in place).

Neutralization of triode amplifiers for 50 and 144 Mc. can follow standard practice, but the stray inductance and capacitance introduced by the neutralizing circuits may be excessive for 220 Mc. and higher. In such instances grounded-grid amplifiers may be used. Driving power is applied to the cathode circuit, with the grid acting as a shield. Some of the drive appears in the output, so both the driver and amplifier must be modulated when a.m. is used. For this reason the grounded-grid amplifier is used mainly for f.m.

Instability shows up frequently in tetrode amplifiers as the result of ineffective screen by-passing. The solution lies in series-resonating the screen circuits to ground, as shown in Figs. 17-13 and 17-24. The r.f. choke and capacitor values vary with frequency, so screen neutralization is essentially a one-band device.

● FREQUENCY MODULATION

Though f.m. has not enjoyed great popularity in v.h.f. operation, probably because of lack of suitable receivers in most v.h.f. stations, its possibilities should not be overlooked, particularly for the higher bands. At 420 Mc., for instance, the efficiency of most amplifiers is so low that it is often difficult to develop sufficient grid drive for proper a.m. service. With f.m. any amount of grid drive may be used without affecting the audio quality of the signal, and the modulation process adds nothing to the plate dissipation. Thus considerably higher power can be run with f.m. than with a.m. before damage to the tubes develops or the signal is of poor quality.

Frequency modulation also simplifies transmitter design. The principal obstacle to greater use of f.m. in v.h.f. work is the wide variation in selectivity of v.h.f. receivers, making it difficult for the operator to set up his deviation so that it will be satisfactory for all listeners.

● V.H.F. TVI PREVENTION AND CURE

The principal causes of TVI from v.h.f. transmitters are as follows:

1) Adjacent-channel interference in Channel 2 from 50 Mc.

2) Fourth harmonic of 50 Mc. in Channels 11, 12 or 13, depending on the operating frequency.

3) Radiation of unused harmonics of the oscillator or multiplier stages. Examples are 9th harmonic of 6 Mc., and 7th harmonic of 8 Mc. in Channel 2; 10th harmonic of 8 Mc. in Channel 6; 7th harmonic of 25-Mc. stages in Channel 7; 4th harmonic of 48-Mc. stages in Channel 9 or 10; and many other combinations. This may include i.f. pickup, as in the cases of 24-Mc. interference in receivers having 21-Mc. i.f. systems, and 48-Mc. trouble in 45-Mc. i.f.'s.

4) Fundamental blocking effects, including modulation bars, usually found only in the lower channels, from 50-Mc. equipment.

5) Image interference in Channel 2 from 144 Mc., in receivers having a 45-Mc. i.f.

6) Sound interference (picture clear in some cases) resulting from r.f. pickup by the audio circuits of the TV receiver.

There are many other possibilities, and u.h.f. TV in general use will add to the list, but nearly all can be corrected completely, and the rest can be substantially reduced.

Items 1, 4 and 5 are receiver faults, and nothing can be done at the transmitter to reduce them, except to lower the power or increase separation between the transmitting and TV antenna systems. Item 6 is also a receiver fault, but it can be alleviated at the transmitter by using f.m. or c.w. instead of a.m. phone.

Treatment of the various harmonic troubles, Items 2 and 3, follows the standard methods detailed elsewhere in this *Handbook*. It is suggested that the prospective builder of new v.h.f. equipment familiarize himself with TVI prevention techniques, and incorporate them in new construction projects.

Use as high a starting frequency as possible, to reduce the number of harmonics that might cause trouble. Select crystal frequencies that do not have harmonics in TV channels in use locally. Example: The 10th harmonic of 8-Mc. crystals used for operation in the low part of the 50-Mc. band falls in Channel 6, but 6-Mc. crystals for the same band have no harmonic in that channel.

If TVI is a serious problem, use the lowest transmitter power that will do the job at hand. Much interesting work can be done on the v.h.f. bands with but a few watts output, particularly if a good antenna system is used.

Keep the power in the multiplier and driver stages at the lowest practical level, and use link coupling in preference to capacitive coupling.

Plan for complete shielding and filtering of the r.f. sections of the transmitter, should these steps become necessary.

Use coaxial line to feed the antenna system, and locate the radiating portion as far as possible from TV receivers and antenna systems.

Some v.h.f. TV tuners have removable strips that can be replaced with double-conversion inserts for u.h.f. reception. For a number of channels the first conversion frequency may then fall in or near the 144-Mc. band. Where this method is employed for u.h.f. reception the receiver is very sensitive to 144-Mc. interference. The cure is to replace the strips with others having a different conversion frequency, or use a conventional u.h.f. converter for reception of the channels from 14 up.

A High-Power Transmitter

High-Power Transmitter for 50 and 144 Mc.

The gear described in the next several pages shows how transmitting equipment for two v.h.f. bands can be coordinated in design so as to work from a single exciter. If the builder so desires, the station may be operated from one set of power supplies and speech equipment, with a single set of meters measuring the important currents in both transmitters. Each item can be used by itself, or they combine readily to cover both 50 and 144 Mc., at a power level approaching the legal limit.

In order of their description they are an exciter capable of delivering up to 40 watts output at 48 to 54 Mc., a companion amplifier for the 50-Mc. band, a tripler-driver-amplifier for 144 Mc., and a dual antenna coupler for feeding 50- and 144-Mc. antennas having balanced lines. Their physical appearance is such that they combine neatly for rack mounting, as seen in Fig. 17-1.

● **THE EXCITER**

Though it is shown mounted on the same panel as the 50-Mc. amplifier in Fig. 17-2, the exciter unit might well be used alone, as a versatile 50-Mc. transmitter capable of running up to about

65 watts input. Provision is made for taking off 48-Mc. output at two power levels, through J_3 or J_2, the latter being used for driving the 144-Mc. tripler to be described later.

The exciter is completely shielded, and its power leads are filtered to prevent radiation of harmonics by the power cable. In addition, there are built-in traps to absorb unwanted oscillator harmonics that might otherwise be passed on to the amplifier, or to the antenna. Harmonics of this kind are particularly troublesome when they fall in Channel 2, which is so close to the operating frequency that a filter in the antenna line is relatively ineffective against them.

The interstage coupling circuits are of band-pass design. Once they are properly adjusted they require no further tuning, when the frequency is changed over a 4-Mc. range. Thus only the crystal switch and the output plate circuit need be adjusted when changing frequency.

Circuit Details

The oscillator is a 5763, using crystals above 6, 8, 12, or 24 Mc. for 144-Mc. operation, or 6.25, 8.34, 12.5 or 25 Mc. for 50 Mc. Its plate circuit tunes 24 to 27 Mc., quadrupling, tripling or doubling the crystal frequency. (Crystals at 24 to 27 Mc. are overtone cuts that oscillate at one-third the marked frequency in this circuit.) A series-tuned trap, L_1C_1, in the oscillator plate circuit absorbs the third harmonic of 6-Mc. crystals. This 18-Mc. energy otherwise would pass on to the next stage, where it would be tripled to a frequency in Channel 2. This harmonic has been found to be a common cause of 50-Mc. TVI in Channel 2 areas.

The doubler is also a 5763. A second trap, C_4L_4, in the grid circuit, is tuned to the 7th harmonic of 8-Mc. crystals. The two traps thus prevent radiation of energy in Channel 2, the most critical transmitter problem a 6-meter man is likely to encounter in correcting TVI. They can be modified for other fre-

Fig. 17-1—A high-power r.f. section for a 50- and 144-Mc. station. Equipment includes a band-pass exciter for both bands, a 50-Mc. r.f. amplifier built on the same panel, a tripler-driver-amplifier for 144 Mc., and a dual antenna coupler for both frequencies. Units can be operated with a single set of power supplies, and with common speech equipment and meters.

Fig. 17-2—The 50-Mc. r.f. unit. Exciter, left portion on the assembly, also serves on 144 Mc. Amplifier utilizes a 4-125A, 4-250A or 4-400A.

quencies to suit local problems. An example is the 10th harmonic of 8-Mc. crystals, that falls in Channel 6. A trap for the 5th harmonic of the crystal frequency should take care of this.

The 6146 amplifier stage has a shunt-fed pi-network plate circuit. For best stability over the entire operating range the stage is neutralized. The choke, RFC_4, is provided to short out the d.c. voltage that would appear on the output circuit if C_9 should break down. The choke in the plate lead, RFC_5, is for parasitic oscillation suppression. Note that each of the three cathode leads is bypassed separately at the socket. The exciter may be keyed in the 6146 cathode jack, J_4.

Double-tuned band-pass circuits between the oscillator and doubler, and between the doubler and final, provide essentially flat response from 48 to 52 Mc., or 50 to 54 Mc. A potentiometer in the doubler screen circuit provides excitation control for the 6146, and may be used to compensate for variations in drive that may appear at some spots in the band.

The link winding on the doubler plate circuit, L_6, is for the purpose of taking off low-level 48-Mc. output to drive the tripler in the 144-Mc. r.f. unit. Note that the keying jack in the 6146 cathode circuit is the open-circuit type. Removing the key thus disables the 6146 stage, when the first two stages are being used in this way. Separate heater and filament switches on all units allow them to be operated separately. High-voltage supplies may be left connected to all r.f. units, energizing only the filaments and heaters in the ones being used.

Construction

The exciter is built on a $5 \times 10 \times 3$-inch aluminum chassis, with a bottom plate and a perforated aluminum cage to complete the shielding. The small knobs at the lower left of the front view are for the crystal switch and the excitation control. The crystal switch has 12 positions. Ten are for the crystals on the multiple crystal socket

(Johnson No. 126–120–1). One more crystal position is provided on the front panel (a convenience if you want to use a frequency not covered by the 10 crystals in the multiple socket), and the 12th switch position is for an external v.f.o. It connects the 5763 grid to the coaxial v.f.o. input fitting, and shorts out RFC_1 and its parallel capacitor. The stage then functions as a frequency multiplier. The output frequency of the v.f.o. could thus be in the 6-, 8- or 12-Mc. range. Above the excitation control may be seen the knobs for the 6146 plate and output coupling capacitors.

Three coaxial connectors are on the rear wall of the exciter. The one at the outside edge is for v.f.o. input. The others are the doubler and 6146 output fittings. Two 4-terminal steatite strips handle the various power and metering leads. Adjacent to each terminal except the ground connection is a feed-through bypass capacitor to take the power lead through the chassis.

TVI that might result from radiation of harmonics by the power leads is prevented by filtering of each lead. The feed-through bypasses are connected to the exciter circuits through r.f. chokes, the inner ends of which are again bypassed with small disk ceramic capacitors. All power leads are made with shielded wire, bonded at intervals to the chassis.

The side view shows the multiple crystal socket at the front of the chassis. Separate crystal sockets may be used if desired. The oscillator and doubler tubes are in the foreground. The trap capacitors, C_1 and C_4, are adjacent to these tubes, while C_2 and C_3 are between them, a bit off their center line. To the rear of the 5763 doubler are C_5 and C_7. The grid tuning capacitor for the 6146, C_6, is just visible inside the amplifier compartment.

A separate lead is provided for each power circuit. Fixed bias for the 6146 is brought in from the bias supply that is part of the high-power amplifier assembly. This bias is desirable to prevent the plate current from rising too high when

Exciter Construction

the excitation is backed off. If the exciter is used alone, fixed bias is unnecessary. External meters can be connected in any of the circuits at the terminal strips.

The sides, back and top of the amplifier cage are Reynolds "Do-It-Yourself" perforated aluminum sheet, now available in many hardware stores. The pieces are joined together at the corners with lengths of $3/8$-inch aluminum angle which can be bought or bent up from sheet stock. The tuning and loading capacitors are mounted on the front of the cage, so this part should be a piece of solid sheet stock rather than the perforated material. The dimensions of the cage are not critical. The original is $5\frac{3}{4}$ inches deep, $2\frac{5}{8}$ inches across, and $4\frac{1}{4}$ inches high. Make provision for removing the top and outside sheets of perforated stock for convenience in servicing, when the exciter is mounted against the amplifier unit. Extension shafts and couplings bring out the amplifier controls to the panel.

Inside the cage, the 6146 can be seen with its socket mounted above the chassis on $1/2$-inch metal sleeves. The cathode and screen bypasses should connect to separate ground lugs on the top of the chassis, with the shortest possible leads. This wiring can be done conveniently before the socket is mounted on the chassis if nuts are used temporarily to hold the ground lugs in place over the socket mounting screws. The neutralizing adjustment, C_8, is mounted on the rear wall of the cage, and wired to the 6146 plate clip and the feed-through bushing with $3/8$-inch wide strips of thin copper. A ceramic insulator mounted on the wall near the 6146 plate cap supports the junction of RFC_5, RFC_3, and C_9. An ordinary tie point supports the other end of RFC_3 and the shielded power lead. The plate coil, L_8, can be seen in back of the 5763 doubler tube, wired between the stators of C_{10} and C_{11}. C_{12} and RFC_4 are mounted near C_{11}, and hooked between its stator bar and a ground lug. A short length of RG-58/U coax runs down through a hole in the chassis from C_{11} over to J_3.

Most of the parts visible in the chassis view can be identified from our description of the panel, rear, and topside layouts. The oscillator cathode choke, RFC_1, can be seen mounted upright near the oscillator tube and crystal sockets. Both 5763 sockets should be oriented so that Pins 4 and 5 are adjacent to the outside chassis wall. L_1 is visible between C_1 and the oscillator tube socket. L_2 and L_3 run between this socket and that of the doubler. These

coils are made from a single length of Miniductor stock with the specified number of turns removed to provide spacing between them. The same applies to L_5 and L_7. These are to the left of the 6146 socket. L_4 is between the doubler socket and C_4. The trap coils are mounted with their axes vertical, to minimize coupling to the band-pass coils. L_6 is wound around and cemented to the by-passed end of L_5.

The power lead r.f. chokes are mounted between single-terminal tie points on the rear lip of the chassis and the feed-through capacitors. The disk ceramic bypasses are then applied to the tie points. A single-terminal tie point mounted under RFC_1 holds one end of the 3300-ohm doubler screen resistor and the lead over to the terminal strip at the rear. A double tie point is mounted between the two 5763 sockets to support the by-passed ends of L_2 and L_3. Another over nearer the rear of the chassis supports the cold end of L_5 and the bottom of the doubler grid resistor.

Wiring will be simplified by the following procedure. Before mounting the crystal switch, ground one terminal of each crystal socket through a bus wire. Connect short lengths of tinned wire to the other terminal of each socket that will be under the switch. Then when the latter is installed, the wires can be run to the proper contacts and soldered in place. Note that the front wafer of the switch is used for shorting out RFC_1, while the crystal socket connections are made to the rear wafer, which is more accessible. The v.f.o. input socket is connected to the proper switch contact with a length of RG-58/U coax.

In assembling the power lead filtering compo-

Fig. 17-3—Side view of the exciter, with cover removed. Band-pass coupling circuits eliminate front-panel tuning controls except for crystal switch and output stage tuning.

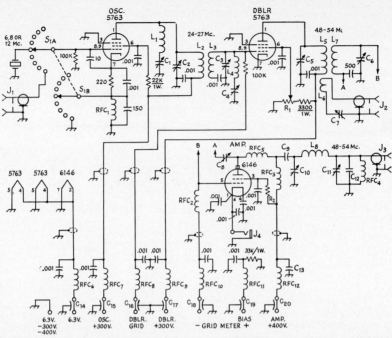

Fig. 17-4—Schematic diagram of 48–54-Mc. exciter. All capacitances less than .001 μf. are in $\mu\mu$f. All .001-μf. capacitors are disk ceramic. All resistors are ½ watt unless otherwise specified.

C₁, C₂, C₃—35-$\mu\mu$f. miniature trimmer (Hammarlund MAPC-35).
C₄—10-$\mu\mu$f. miniature variable (Hammarlund MAC-10).
C₅, C₆—20-$\mu\mu$f. miniature variable (Hammarlund MAC-20).
C₇—50-$\mu\mu$f. miniature trimmer (Hammarlund MAPC-50).
C₈—15-$\mu\mu$f. miniature trimmer (Hammarlund MAPC-15).
C₉, C₁₃—.001-μf. 3000-volt disk ceramic.
C₁₀—35-$\mu\mu$f. miniature variable (Hammarlund HF-35).
C₁₁—100-$\mu\mu$f. miniature variable (Hammarlund MAPC-100B).
C₁₂—100-$\mu\mu$f. 1000-volt mica.
C₁₄–C₂₀—.001-$\mu\mu$f. feedthrough-type ceramic (Centralab FT-1000).
L₁—16 turns No. 24, ⅝-inch diam., 32 t.p.i. (B & W Miniductor No. 3008).
L₂, L₃—12 turns each No. 20, ⅝-inch diam., 16 t.p.i (B & W Miniductor No. 3007). Make from one piece of Miniductor with 5 turns removed between coils. Cold ends are adjacent.
L₄—10 turns No. 20, ½-inch diam., 16 t.p.i. (B & W Miniductor No. 3003).

L₅, L₇—6 turns No. 20, ½-inch diam., 16 t.p.i. (B & W Miniductor No. 3003). Make from one piece of Miniductor with 3 turns removed between coils.
L₆—2 turns hookup wire wound around cold end of L₅ and cemented in place.
L₈—4 turns No. 18, ¾-inch diam., 8 t.p.i. (B & W Miniductor No. 3010).
J₁, J₂, J₃—Coaxial chassis fitting (Amphenol 83-1R).
J₄—Open-circuit phone jack.
R₁—25,000-ohm 4-watt pot.
R₂—33,000-ohm 3-watt (3 100,000-ohm 1-watt in parallel).
RFC₁—2.5-mh. r.f. choke (National R-100S).
RFC₂, RFC₃, RFC₄—7-μh. solenoid v.h.f. choke (Ohmite Z-50).
RFC₅—6 turns No. 22 tinned wire, ¼-inch diam., spaced one-wire diam.
RFC₆–RFC₁₂—15 turns No. 24 enam. close-wound on high value 1-watt resistor.
S₁—2-pole 12-position miniature ceramic rotary (Centralab PA-2005).

nents at the rear of the chassis, the disk ceramic bypasses can most easily be mounted on the tie points before the latter are fastened inside the chassis. Wiring up the power leads should be done before the r.f. chokes are mounted in place.

● THE 50-MC. AMPLIFIER

Though the exciter and amplifier are pictured on a single panel, the possibility of using either by itself should not be overlooked. The exciter will make a fine low-powered transmitter, and the final amplifier may be used with any exciter delivering 15 watts or more.

It will take up to the legal limit of power with a 4–400A tube, 750 watts with a 4–250A, or 400 watts with a 4–125A.

The plate circuit is a larger version of the one used in the 6146 stage of the exciter, a shunt-fed pi-network. Operation is completely stable without neutralization, probably because the natural neutralized frequency of the tubes is close to 50 Mc. Provision was originally made for neutralization, but it was found to be unnecessary. Parasitic suppression devices were not required, but if the layout is varied appreciably from that shown, the builder should check for both types of instability with great care.

The jack in the filament center-tap lead is for keying, or for insertion of a grid-bias modulator. A bias supply that delivers about 50 volts negative for the 6146 and 150 for the final amplifier is included in the final stage assembly. Filament transformers for the exciter and final are also part

50-Mc. Amplifier

of this unit. Separate filament switches are included; one for the exciter and the other for the final tube and the blower motor. Power leads except the high voltage, are brought in on an 8-pin plug.

Building the Amplifier

A $12 \times 10 \times 3$-inch aluminum chassis is used for the amplifier unit. Thus, it may be combined with the exciter on a $10\frac{1}{2}$-inch rack panel, if desired. The amplifier controls mounted near the panel bottom are, left to right, the input link reactance capacitor, C_1; the grid tuning capacitor, C_2; and S_1 and S_2. S_1 applies a.c. to the transformer for the exciter heaters and to the bias supplies. S_2 applies a.c. to the filament transformer of the amplifier and starts the cooling fan. Above the switches on the panel are the amplifier plate tuning and loading controls.

On the rear of the chassis, coaxial connectors for r.f. input and output are mounted at either end. Between them are the high-voltage connector for the plate supply, the cathode circuit jack, and a fitting for the remaining power and meter leads.

Above the chassis, the 4–250A tube is seen near the front of the chassis. Note that its socket is mounted on $\frac{1}{2}$-inch sleeves. Holes $\frac{3}{8}$ inch in diameter are drilled in the chassis directly underneath those provided in the socket for the passage of cooling air. Holes are also drilled adjacent to the cathode, grid, and screen pins to pass their leads. Bypassing of cathode and screen is done above the chassis. The heat radiating plate connector for the 4-250A was cut down to four fins to reduce the over-all height requirement. The filament transformer, T_3, and the screen modulation choke, L_4, are also topside.

The amplifier plate circuit components are to the left of the tube. The tuning capacitor, C_7, originally a neutralizing capacitor, is mounted on the side wall of the shielding assembly. Two modifications should be made to the neutralizing unit before mounting. The circular plates supplied should be replaced with larger ones, 3 inches in diameter, to increase the available tuning range. The bearing assembly of the rotor disk must be temporarily removed, and a strap of copper run between the screw holding the bearing in place and the opposite (grounded) end of the square ceramic

insulating pillar, grounding the capacitor rotor. Two copper straps must be inserted between the stator disk and its insulator, to connect the stator with the blocking capacitor, C_5, and with L_3.

The blocking capacitor, the shunt-feed r.f. choke, RFC_2, and the high-voltage bypass, C_6, are assembled into one unit before mounting in the amplifier. This is done with the aid of the hardware supplied with the TV-type high voltage capacitors. The bypass capacitor, on the bottom of the stack, is equipped with one terminal threaded and one tapped. The latter is on the bottom end, for fastening the assembly to the chassis. The threaded terminal screws into the $2\frac{1}{2}$-inch ceramic insulator upon which RFC_2 is wound. The ends of the choke winding are secured by lugs at each end of the insulator. C_5 should be fitted with a threaded terminal at the lower end for screwing into the top of the insulator. This also serves to fasten the $\frac{3}{4}$-inch wide strip of copper which runs up to the 4–250A plate cap. Finally, the longer of the two copper strips coming from the stator of C_7 is screwed to the top of C_5. A $\frac{1}{2}$-inch feedthrough bushing brings the high-voltage up to the hot side of C_6. The loading capacitor, C_8, is mounted on the chassis directly underneath C_7. The plate coil, L_3, gets rather warm when the rig is operated at high power level, so both of its ends must be bolted in place rather than soldered. One end is bent around and fastened under a

Fig. 17-5—Bottom view of the 50-Mc. exciter, showing band-pass circuits and TVI protective measures.

Fig. 17-6—Interior of the 50-Mc. final amplifier. Plate tuning capacitor is modified neutralizing unit, left.

nut provided on the stator of C_8. The other is bolted to the short length of copper strap previously fastened to the stator of C_7. A length of RG-8/U coaxial cable is run between C_8 and J_2. At the capacitor end, this cable is connected to lugs under the stator and frame mounting screws.

Solid sheet aluminum is used for the enclosure of this unit, as it must be reasonably airtight except for holes directly above the tube itself. The side that supports C_7 must be of fairly heavy stock for rigidity. Home-bent ¾-inch angle stock was used to hold the assembly together. If the over-all height of the unit is kept to just about that of the 10½-inch rack panel, there will be enough clearance above the tube plate connector.

Most of the under-chassis components are visible in the bottom view. The grid circuit is near the front edge of the chassis. Copper strap connects the tube socket grid pin with the stator of C_2. L_2 then is soldered between this strap and a tie point. L_1 is slid inside the cold end of L_2, and cemented lightly in place.

The cooling fan sucks air in from the side of the amplifier near the back corner. The motor is mounted on an aluminum bracket. The fan as supplied will blow, rather than suck, so the blades must be bent back to reverse their pitch. A small piece of aluminum window screening shields the hole cut in the chassis side for the fan.

Bias supply components occupy the lower left quarter of the bottom view. Layout and wiring of this portion of the rig is anything but critical. Shielded wire was used for all power leads. By-passing at the power connector should be done with very short leads, and C_{14} should be mounted as close as possible to the high-voltage connector.

Adjustment and Operation

An initial setting of the exciter controls can be made before power is applied, if a grid-dip meter is available. The series traps, L_1C_1 and L_4C_4, introduce varying amounts of reactance across the tuned circuits when they are adjusted, so some further adjustment will be needed after these are set up finally, but the following procedure will result in a close approximation.

Disconnect one end of L_3, Fig. 17-4. Couple the grid-dip meter to L_2 and tune it with C_2 to about 24.5 Mc. Leaving the setting of C_2 at that position, lift one end of L_2. Reconnect L_3 and resonate C_3L_3 to about 25.5 Mc. Reconnect L_2, and the circuits should be set for operation on 48 to 52 Mc. For 50 to 54 Mc., the frequencies should be 25.5 and 26.5 Mc.

Procedure for the second band-pass circuit is similar except for the frequencies involved. For 48 to 52 Mc., disconnect L_7 and tune C_5L_5 to 49 Mc. Reconnect L_7 and disconnect L_5, tuning L_7C_6 to 51 Mc. Reconnect L_5. For the 50- to 54-Mc. range these frequencies would be about 51 and 53 Mc.

50-Mc. Amplifier

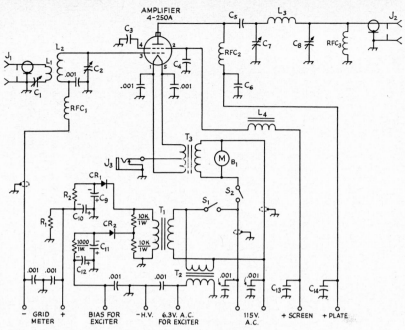

Fig. 17-7—Schematic diagram and parts list for the 4-250A amplifier. All capacitors marked .001 μf. are 600-volt disk ceramic.

C_1—50-$\mu\mu$f. miniature variable (Hammarlund HF-50).

C_2—15-$\mu\mu$f. miniature variable, double-spaced (Hammarlund HF-15X).

C_3, C_4, C_{13}—.001-μf. 1000-volt disk ceramic.

C_5, C_6, C_{14}—500-$\mu\mu$f. 20,000-volt ceramic (Cornell-Dubilier MM120T5).

C_7—Disk-type capacitor with 3-inch diam. plates (made from Millen 15011).

C_8—250-$\mu\mu$f. variable, double-spaced (Johnson 250-F20).

C_9, C_{10}, C_{11}, C_{12}—12-μf. 250-volt electrolytic.

J_1, J_2—Coaxial chassis fitting (Amphenol 83-1R).

J_3—Closed-circuit phone jack.

CR_1—65-ma. selenium rectifier (Federal 1002A).

CR_2—20-ma. selenium rectifier (Federal 1159).

L_1—5 turns No. 24, 1/2-inch diam., 32 t.p.i. (B & W Miniductor No. 3004).

L_2—4 turns No. 18, 3/4-inch diam., 8 t.p.i. (B & W Miniductor No. 3010).

L_3—6 turns No. 12 tinned wire, 1-inch diam., spaced twice wire diam.

L_4—Filter choke, about 10-hy. 100-ma. (Triad C-10X).

B_1—Blower motor and fan (Allied cat. No. 72P715).

R_1—20,000 ohms 10 watts.

R_2—500 ohms 2 watts (2 1000-ohm 1-watt resistors in parallel).

RFC_1, RFC_3—7-μh. solenoid choke (Ohmite Z-50).

RFC_2—Solenoid choke, 42 turns No. 24 d.c.c. close-wound on 1/2-inch diam., 2 1/2-inch long insulator (National GS-2).

S_1, S_3—Single-pole single-throw toggle switch.

T_1—Power transformer, 135 volts at 50 ma. (Triad R-30X).

T_2—Filament transformer, 6.3 volts at 3 amp. (Triad F-16X).

T_3—Filament transformer, 5.2 volts c.t. at 15 am. (Triad F-11U).

Connect a source of 6.3 volts a.c. at 2.5 amperes or more between the ground and heater terminals, and a low-range meter from the doubler grid return terminal to ground. Insert crystals for the desired frequency range. Apply about 200 volts d.c. to the oscillator plate-screen terminal through a 50- or 100-ma. meter. Current should be 20 to 30 ma., and grid current in the following stage should be about 0.5 ma., when the voltage is increased to the normal 300 volts. Touch up the tuning of the band-pass circuit, if necessary, to get uniform response across the desired range.

The trap circuits can be adjusted at this point, tuning for minimum signal at the frequency to be attenuated in each case. A receiver tuning to the harmonic frequencies is helpful. These will be about 18 to 20.25 Mc. for the first trap and 56 to 60 Mc. for the second, if they are for Channel 2. A TV receiver on the channels to be protected may also be used, merely tuning the traps for minimum TVI. Some slight readjustment of the

band-pass circuit may be needed after the final trap tuning is done.

Now remove the grid current meter and ground the metering terminal in the doubler grid circuit. Connect a meter (0 to 5 ma. or more) between the terminals provided for measuring the 6146 grid current. Set the screen potentiometer, R_1, to about the middle of its range and apply about 200 volts to the doubler plate-screen input terminal. Adjust the band-pass circuit, L_5C_5, L_7C_6 for nearly uniform response across the desired range, using the 6146 grid current as the output indication. There should be at least 2 ma. across a 4-Mc. range when the doubler plate voltage is raised to 300. Note that the screen potentiometer controls the input to the doubler, and through it the excitation to the 6146.

The 48-Mc. output coupling adjustment, L_6C_7, may be checked at this time. The line to a 144-Mc. tripler stage should be connected to J_2, and the series capacitor, C_7, adjusted for maximum grid current in the driven stage. Recheck the adjustment of the band-pass circuit after this is done.

The 6146 amplifier stage had to be neutralized for stable operation. Its adjustment was not critical, however, and C_8 could be set anywhere near minimum capacitance with good results. Start out with its plates meshed about $\frac{1}{8}$ inch. With grid drive applied but no plate or screen voltage, tune the 6146 plate circuit through resonance, trying various settings of C_8 until there is no grid current dip at resonance.

A load for the 6146 output circuit is now required. This can be a 40- or 60-watt lamp, with a 50-$\mu\mu$f. capacitor in series to tune out its reactance. Adjust it for minimum reflected power, as indicated on an s.w.r. bridge. With the load connected and grid drive on, apply 300 to 400 volts to the amplifier plate and screen terminal. Tune C_{10} for maximum indicated output. Loading can be adjusted by varying C_{11}, retuning C_{10} after each movement of C_{11}.

Recheck for neutralization at this point, working for a setting of C_8 at which minimum plate current, maximum grid current, and maximum output all occur at the same setting of the plate tuning capacitor, C_{10}. The input can be run up to about 65 watts with plate modulation and 35–40 watts output should be obtained. Higher input can be run on c.w. Plate voltage should not exceed about 400 with plate modulation, though it can be somewhat more for c.w.

Now make a final check on the trap circuits, if necessary. In case TVI is experienced, adjust the traps while someone watches the TV screen, and see whether any improvement is possible. Remember that the traps shown were designed primarily to reduce Channel 2 interference. Where the trouble is with other channels, the traps can be modified to reduce the offending harmonic as required. A low-pass filter or a 4th harmonic trap will be needed if there is harmonic interference in Channels 11–13.

The amplifier as shown furnishes heater voltage and protective bias for the exciter. Hook together the 6.3-volt and ground terminals of the two units, and connect the bias output pin on the amplifier to the 6146 grid return in the exciter.

Apply 115 volts a.c. to the appropriate pins on the amplifier power plug. When S_1, Fig. 17-7, is closed, the exciter heaters and the bias supplies are energized. The bias voltages are about 50 and 150 negative for the driver and amplifier, respectively. Closing S_2 lights the amplifier filament and starts the fan motor.

For the initial testing of the amplifier disconnect its fixed bias supply, by lifting the connection between R_1 and R_2, so that instability will be more evident. Connect the output of the exciter through a length of coaxial cable to J_1. Hook a 0-25- or 0-50-ma. meter to the terminals provided for measuring grid current. Turn on the exciter and adjust the driver output and amplifier input for maximum grid current. Set this current between 10 and 15 ma. with the excitation control, R_1, in the exciter. To insure proper adjustment of the amplifier grid circuit, insert an s.w.r. bridge unit such as a Micromatch in the coax connecting the driver and amplifier, and tune C_1 and C_2 in the amplifier alternately for minimum reflected power. Adjust the driver tuning for maximum forward power.

Never apply screen voltage without having the plate voltage on also, and do not operate the amplifier without load. Either will result in excessive screen dissipation, and almost certain tube failure if continued for any length of time. A usable dummy load for testing can be made by connecting two or more 100-watt lamps in parallel. A variable series capacitor, 50 $\mu\mu$f. or more, will be helpful in making the lamp load something like 50 ohms, resistive, at this frequency.

It is well to start with something less than maximum voltages in testing. If the plate voltage is under 1000 and the screen voltage about 200 to 300 volts, little harm can result if something is not quite right. With the dummy load connected, apply plate and screen voltages. Set C_8 near the middle of its range and tune C_7 for maximum output. If this occurs at or close to the end of the tuning range of C_7, adjust the spacing of the turns in the plate coil accordingly. Adjust C_8 for maximum output, returning C_7 as required. If the grid current dropped below 10 ma. under load,

Fig. 17-8—Bottom view of 50-Mc. exciter and amplifier. Note that the two units are built separately, though they mount together on a single panel. Amplifier unit includes bias and filament supplies for both.

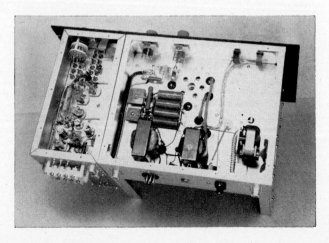

144-Mc. Driver-Amplifier

increase the drive with the doubler screen potentiometer in the exciter.

Check now for stability. Briefly cut off the drive and see if the amplifier grid current drops to zero. If it doesn't, the amplifier either needs neutralization, or it has a parasitic oscillation. If no grid current shows with drive removed, note whether, when drive is applied and the amplifier is tuned properly, maximum output, minimum plate current and maximum grid current all occur at the same plate tuning. If they do, the amplifier is operating satisfactorily.

If oscillation does show up, check its frequency. If it is much higher than the operating frequency (probably over 150 Mc.) v.h.f. parasitic suppression measures are in order. If it is in the 50-Mc. region, neutralization will be required. These troubles are most common in multiband designs, and unlikely in a layout of this sort. Neutralization of the capacity-bridge type, like that in the exciter, can be incorporated readily, and parasitic suppression is covered in detail elsewhere in this *Handbook*. Neutralization may require *additional* grid-plate capacitance in some layouts. Provision was made for neutralization in the original layout (explaining the plugged hole in the front panel), but it was found to be unnecessary.

When the amplifier is operating stably, the plate and screen voltages may be increased in accordance with the tube manufacturer's ratings, for the type of operation intended. Operating conditions are different for the three tubes which can be used and they should follow the manufacturer's recommendations. This is not to say that variations from the published data are unsafe or undesirable. Any of the values can be varied over quite a range if the maximum rating for each tube element concerned is not exceeded. In this connection, it is highly desirable to provide continuous metering for the grid, screen, and plate currents. This, with a knowledge of the applied voltages, will help insure proper operation and make correct adjustment a simple matter.

● A 144-MC. DRIVER-AMPLIFIER

The unit shown in Figs. 17-9 through 17-14 is a three-stage tripler-driver-amplifier that may be used with the exciter just described. Driving power at 48 Mc. may be taken from the doubler stage (by connecting to J_2 in Fig. 17-4) or from the output stage, running at low power. Almost any 50-Mc. transmitter of 3 to 5 watts output could be used by substituting a suitable crystal and retuning the stages for operation at 48 to 49.3 Mc. If a small 144-Mc. transmitter is available, the tripler stage may be dispensed with, in which case about 5 watts drive on 144 Mc. is required.

This section of the station is built in two parts. The tripler and driver stages are in the small portion at the right of Fig. 17-9, with the final stage at the left. All are push-pull stages, the tripler and driver using dual tetrodes. The tripler is an Amperex 6360, followed by an RCA 6524 straight-through amplifier. This drives a pair of 4-125As in the final stage.

Input to the 4-125As can be up to 600 watts on a.m. phone, or 800 watts on c.w. or f.m. By suitable adjustment of screen and plate voltages the power can be dropped as low as 150 watts input and still maintain good efficiency. Some means of reducing power is highly desirable, as most operation on 144 Mc. can be carried on satisfactorily with low power.

The Driver Portion

The tripler and driver stages, Figs. 17-11 and 17-12, both operate well below their maximum ratings. Self-tuned grid circuits are used in each stage. This simplifies construction, and in the case of the driver stage, reduces the possibility of self-oscillation. With a surplus of drive available, the grid circuit of the 6524 may be resonated as low as 130 Mc. There is little tendency to tuned-plate tuned-grid oscillation, therefor, and neutralization is not required.

Tripler and driver are built on a standard 5 × 10 × 3-inch aluminum chassis, with the tripler at the back. Its plate circuit is tuned from the front panel by an extension shaft. Omission of the screen bypass on the tripler is intentional as the stage works satisfactorily without screen bypassing.

The 6524 is easily over driven. This may be corrected by squeezing the driver grid coil turns

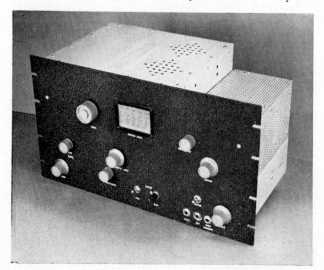

Fig. 17-9—The high-power 2-meter rig, with shielding enclosures in place. The small unit at the right houses the tripler and driver stages.

closer together, lowering the resonant frequency until the desired 2.5 to 3.5 ma. is obtained across the band. The farther it can be resonated below 144 Mc. the less likelihood there is of self-oscillation in the driver stage.

The 6524 is mounted horizontally, and holes are drilled in the chassis under the tube to allow for air circulation. Plate leads are made of thin phosphor bronze or copper, bent into a semicircle, connecting the butterfly capacitor and the heat-dissipating connectors. This allows the latter to be removed for changing tubes, without putting undue strain on the plate pins. The connectors have to be sawed or filed down on the insides to fit on the 6524 pins. The coupling link at the driver plate circuit is tuned, to provide efficient transfer of energy to the amplifier grids.

Small feedthrough bypasses are used in the driver screen circuit. C_5 is mounted in the aluminum plate that supports the 6524 socket, and C_6 is in the chassis surface.

Amplifier Features

Design of the 4-125A grid circuit is important in achieving efficient transfer of energy from the driver stage. The input capacitance of the large tetrodes is so high that a tuned grid circuit of conventional design cannot be used at 144 Mc., so a half-wave line is substituted, as shown in Figs. 17-13 and 17-14. The input coupling link is series tuned, permitting adjustment for minimum standing wave ratio on the coaxial line connecting it to the driver stage output link. The grid line, L_1L_2, is made of $\frac{1}{4}$-inch copper tubing, to reduce heat losses.

Maintaining the 4-125A screens and filament leads at ground potential for r.f. is necessary for stability. To this end, the tube sockets are mounted above the chassis, rather than below. They are elevated only enough to allow the socket contacts to clear the chassis, and are mounted corner to corner, with the inner corners almost touching. The grid line is brought up through $\frac{1}{2}$-inch chassis holes and soldered directly to the grid contacts. This determines the line spacing, about $1\frac{1}{2}$-inches center to center.

The inner filament terminals on each socket are grounded to the chassis. The others connect to feedthrough bypasses with the shortest possible leads. These are joined under the chassis with a shielded wire and tied to the filament transformer. The r.f. chokes in the screen leads are under the chassis, their wire leads coming up through Millen type 32150 feedthrough bushings inserted in chassis holes under the screen terminals. The two screen terminals on each socket are strapped together with a $\frac{3}{8}$-inch wide strip of flashing copper. The screen neutralizing capacitor is mounted as close to the sockets as possible and still leave room for the shaft coupling on its rotor. Leads to its stators are about one half inch long.

More compact and symmetrical design is possible if a modified single-section capacitor is used for C_6. It should be the type having supports at both ends of the rotor shaft. The Millen 19140 and Hammarlund MC-140 are suitable units for the purpose. The stator bars are sawed at each side of the center stator plate. The front rotor plate is removed, making a split-stator variable with 4 plates on each stator and 8 on the rotor. This procedure may not be applicable to all 140-$\mu\mu$f. capacitors, but any method that results in a balanced unit having about 50 $\mu\mu$f. per section should do.

Construction of the final plate circuit should be clear from Fig. 17-10. Tuning is done with parts of a disk-type neutralizing capacitor (Millen 15011) mounted on ceramic stand-offs $3\frac{1}{2}$ inches high. These are made of one 1-inch and one $2\frac{1}{2}$-inch stand off each, fastened together with a threaded insert. Connection to the lines is made with copper or silver strap, $4\frac{1}{2}$ inches from the plate end. Silver plating of all tank circuit parts is a worth-while investment, though it should not be considered a necessity. A shaft coupling designed for high-voltage service is attached to the threaded shaft of the movable plate, and this is rotated with a shaft of insulating material brought out to the front panel.

A word about the extension shafts is in order at this point. If they are of metal they may have a serious detuning effect in some circuits, even though they are connected through insulating couplings. Bakelite rod is fine, but since the insulating qualities are of no importance, $\frac{1}{4}$-inch wooden doweling will do the job just as well. Lucite or polystyrene rod will

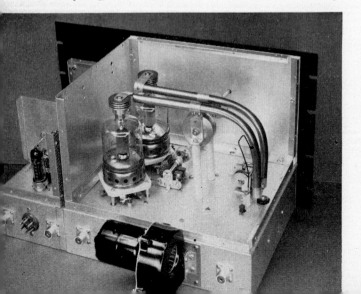

Fig. 17-10—Rear view of the 4-125A final stage. The split-stator capacitor near the middle of the picture is the screen neutralizing adjustment. The plate line is tuned with a capacitor made from parts of a neutralizing unit, mounted on ceramic stand offs.

144-Mc. Driver-Amplifier

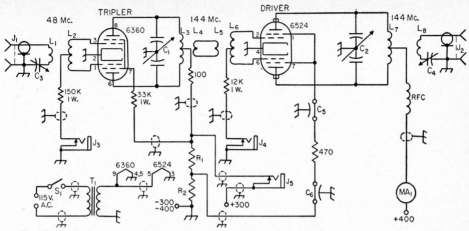

Fig. 17-11—Schematic diagram of the tripler and driver stages of the high-powered 2-meter transmitter.

C_1, C_2—10.5 $\mu\mu f.$-per-section butterfly variable (Johnson 10LB15).

C_3—25-$\mu\mu f.$ screwdriver-adjustment variable (Hammarlund APC-25).

C_4—25-$\mu\mu f.$ miniature variable (Bud LC-1642).

C_5, C_6—500-$\mu\mu f.$ feed-through bypass (Centralab FT-500).

R_1—11,000 ohms 2 watts (two 22,000-ohm 1-watt resistors in parallel.)

R_2—50,000 ohms 2 watts (two 100,000-ohm 1-watt resistors in parallel).

L_1—2 turn insulated wire around center of L_2. Twist leads to J_1 and C_3.

L_2—13 turns No. 20, 5/8-inch diam., 7/8-inch long, center tapped (B & W Miniductor No. 3007).

L_3—3 turns No. 14 enamel, 3/4-inch diam., spaced 1/16 inch center-tapped.

L_4—2 turns No. 18 enamel, same as L_3, inserted at center.

L_5—2 turns No. 18 enamel, same as L_6, inserted at center.

L_6—4 turns No. 14 enamel, 1/2-inch diam., turns spaced wire diameter.

L_7—2 turns No. 14 enamel, 1-inch diam., spaced 1/4 inch.

L_8—1 turn No. 14 enamel between turns of L_7.

J_1, J_2—Coaxial fitting, female (Amphenol 83-1R).

J_3, J_4, J_5—Closed-circuit jack. Insulate J_5 from panel and chassis.

MA_1—External meter not shown in photo, 200 ma.

S_1—Toggle switch.

T_1—Filament transformer, 6.3 volts, 3 amp. (UTC S-55).

not stand the heat and should not be used.

The final chassis is aluminum, 10 by 12 by 3 inches, matching up with the driver chassis to fit into a standard 10½-inch rack panel. Complete enclosure is a must for TVI prevention, and it pays dividends in improved stability by providing effective isolation of circuits that tend to give trouble in open layouts.

The enclosures were made by mounting ½-inch aluminum angle stock around the edges of the chassis of both units and cutting the sides and covers to fit. It was not intended to cool the driver unit originally, so the enclosure was made of perforated aluminum. The blower for the final provided plenty of air, however, so three holes are made

in the walls of the two chassis to allow some of the air flow to go through the driver enclosure as well. The chassis are bolted together where the vent holes are drilled. The main flow is up through the amplifier chassis, around the 4-125As, and out through the ¼-inch holes drilled in the top cover above the tubes. Holes in the amplifier chassis are drilled to line up with the ventilating holes in the 4-125A sockets. All other holes and cracks are sealed with household cement to confine the air to the desired paths, and bottom covers are fitted tightly to both units.

Fig. 17-12—Side view of the tripler and driver stages. Coil adjacent to the 6360 tripler tube is the grid coil for the 6524 driver. Plate leads for the driver tube are flexible copper straps, to permit removal of the tube from its socket. Screwdriver adjustment at the lower right is the reactance tuning capacitor for the tripler input link.

The somewhat random appearance of the front panel is the result of the development of the unit in experimental form. A slight rearrangement of some of the noncritical components could be made to achieve a symmetrical panel layout readily enough.

Operation

The two units have their own filament transformers. Plate supply requirements are 300 volts at 50 ma. for the tripler, 400 volts at 100 ma. for the driver, 300 to 400 volts at 75 ma. for the final screens and 1000 to 2500 volts at 400 ma. for the final plates. The driver plates and final screens may be run from the same supply, but more flexibility is possible if they are supplied separately. A variable-voltage supply for the final screens is a fine way to control the power level.

In putting the rig on the air the stages are fired up separately, beginning with the tripler. A jack (J_3, in Fig. 17-11) is provided on the front panel for measuring the 6360 grid current. About 1 ma. through the 150,000-ohm grid resistor is plenty of drive. The series capacitor, C_3, in the link can be used as a drive adjustment, if more than necessary is available.

Next plug the grid meter into the 6524 grid current jack, J_4, and tune the 6360 plate circuit for maximum grid current. If it is higher than 3 to 4 ma. increase the inductance of the grid coil, L_6, by squeezing its turns closer together. Now apply plate and screen voltage to the 6524, and check for signs of self-oscillation. If the plate circuit is tuned down to the same frequency as that at which the grid coil resonates with the tube capacitance, the stage may oscillate, but if it is stable across the intended tuning range there should be no operating difficulty resulting from a tendency to oscillate lower in frequency, and no neutralization should be needed.

Connect a coaxial line between the driver output and the final grid input preferably with a standing-wave bridge connected to indicate the standing-wave ratio on this line. Tune the driver plate circuit and its series-tuned link for maximum grid current in the final amplifier. Adjust the final grid tuning, C_1, for maximum grid current, and the series capacitor, C_3, in the link for minimum reflected power on the s.w.r. bridge. Adjust the coupling loop position for maximum transfer of power, using the least coupling that will achieve this end.

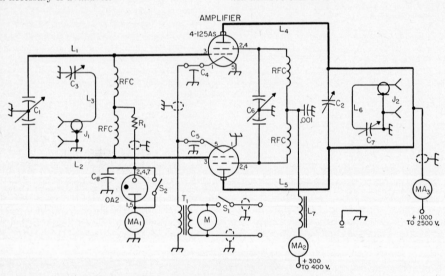

Fig. 17-13—Schematic diagram of the 4-125A amplifier for 144 Mc.

C_1—30-$\mu\mu$f.-per-section split-stator variable (Hammarlund HFD-30X).

C_2—Plate tuning capacitor made from Millen 15011 neutralizing unit; see text and photo.

C_3—25-$\mu\mu$f. miniature variable (Bud LC-1642).

C_4, C_5—500-$\mu\mu$f. feedthrough bypass Centralab FT-500).

C_6—Approx. 50-$\mu\mu$f.-per-section split-stator variable. Make from Millen 19140 or Hammarlund MC-140; see text.

C_7—25-$\mu\mu$f. variable (Johnson 25L15).

C_8—0.25-μf. tubular.

R_1—5000 ohms, 10 watts.

L_1, L_2—¼-inch copper tubing, 12 inches long, spaced 1½ inches center to center. Bend around 1½-inch radius, 1 inch from grid end.

L_3—Loop made from 5 inches No. 14 enamel. Portion coupled to line is 1 inch long each side, about ⅜ inch from line.

L_4, L_5—½-inch copper tubing 12 inches long, spaced 1½ inches center to center. Bend around 2-inch radius to make line 4 inches high. Attach C_2 4½ inches from plate end.

L_6—Loop made from 7 inches No. 14 enamel. Sides spaced 1¼ inches.

L_7—5-h. (min.) 100-ma. rating filter choke.

J_1, J_2—Coaxial fitting, female (Amphenol 83-1R).

MA_1, MA_2, MA_3—External meters, not shown; 100, 200 and 500 ma.

M—Motor-blower assembly, 17 c.f.m. (Ripley Inc., Middletown, Conn., Type 8433).

RFC—V.h.f. solenoid choke (Ohmite Z-144). Four required.

S_1—Toggle switch.

S_2—Rotary jack-type switch (Mallory 720).

T_1 — Filament transformer, 5-volt 13-amp. (Chicago FO-513).

144-Mc. Amplifier

Adjust the screen neutralizing capacitor, C_6, for maximum final grid current, with the plate and screen voltages off. Do not attempt to run the final stage without load. With a fixed screen supply the screen dissipation goes very high when the plate load is removed or made too light. It is important to meter the screen current at all times. With 4-125As danger to the plates can be detected by their color, but the screen current is the only indication of possible damage to that element.

There is no suitable inexpensive dummy load for testing a v.h.f. rig of this power level. The best load is probably an antenna. This can be an indoor gamma-matched dipole, fed with coax. Its series capacitor should be adjusted for a standing-wave ratio close to 1:1. The Micromatch can be used in this operation, but adjustments should be made at less than full power. Watch for any sign of heating in the bridge unit.

The position of the coupling loop, L_6, should be adjusted for maximum transfer of energy to the antenna, keeping the coupling as loose as possible. The series capacitor, C_7, can be used as a loading adjustment thereafter. If the screen voltage is continuously variable it will be found that there is an optimum value around 325 to 350 volts.

Below are some conditions under which the rig has been operated experimentally:

Stage	E_p	I_p	E_{sc}	I_{so}	I_g
Tripler	300 v.	35 ma.	—	—	1.5 ma.
Driver	400 v.	92 ma.	—	8 ma.	3–4 ma.
Final	1000 v.	300 ma.	400 v.	60 ma.	22 ma.
Final	2000 v.	350 ma.	350 v.	45 ma.	20 ma.
Final	2500 v.	400 ma.	320 v.	40 ma.	18 ma.

The first and third conditions given for the final stage represent extremes, both exceeding the tubes' ratings in some way, so they are not recommended. At low plate voltages the screen has to be run above recommended ratings to make the tubes draw their full rated plate current and operate efficiently. At high plate voltages the screen dissipation drops markedly. The use of 4-125As at a full kilowatt input exceeds the manufacturer's maximum ratings, and is done at the user's risk. To operate safely, the maximum plate voltage for voice work at 144 Mc. should probably not go over 2000. At this level the tubes will handle 600 watts input on voice, and 750 watts on c.w. easily.

Modulation and Keying

Keying is done in the screen circuit of the driver stage, and in the screen and plate circuits of the tripler. Cathode keying of the driver was attempted, but it caused instability troubles, so was abandoned. The screen method makes the key hot, so an insulated key or a keying relay must be used in the interest of safety. The keying jack must be insulated from the panel.

Fixed bias for the final amplifier is provided by the VR-tube method. When the tube ignites at the application of drive, the capacitor C_8 charges. Removing excitation stops the flow through the VR tube and leaves the negative charge in the capacitor applied to the amplifier grids. The effectiveness of this system requires a low-leakage capacitor for C_8.

Modulation is applied to the plates only. A choke of about 10 henrys is connected in the screen lead, or the modulation can be supplied through a screen winding on the modulation transformer. The bypass value in the screen circuit should be low enough to avoid affecting the higher audio frequencies. Occasionally audio resonance in the screen choke may cause a singing effect on the modulation. If this develops, the choke may be shunted with a resistor. Use the highest value that will stop the singing.

In neutralizing the 4-125As it may be found that what appears to be the best setting of the screen capacitor will result in a very large drop in grid current when plate voltage is applied. The setting may be altered slightly, raising the full-load grid current, without adversely affecting the stability of the amplifier. The final check for neutralization is twofold. There should be no oscillation when drive is removed; and maximum grid current, minimum plate current and maximum output should all show at one setting of the plate tuning capacitor. The latter condition

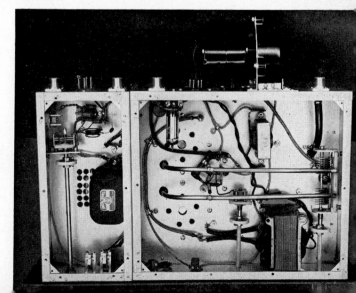

Fig. 17-14—Under-chassis view of the 2-meter transmitter. Tripler grid and plate circuits are at the upper left. Only two of the three jacks on the front panel show in the lower left. The half-wave line used in the 4-125A grid circuit is the main item of interest in the amplifier section. Both units are fitted with bottom covers, to provide shielding and confine the flow of cooling air to the desired areas.

Fig. 17-15—Antenna couplers for 50 and 144 Mc. designed for use with the high-power transmitters on the previous pages.

may be observed only when the amplifier is operated without fixed bias.

● ANTENNA COUPLERS FOR 50 AND 144 MC.

The antenna couplers shown in Figs. 17-15, and at the top of Fig. 17-1, can be used with 52-ohm or 75-ohm coaxial line, and with balanced lines of any impedance from 200 to 600 ohms or more. They were designed for use with the high-power transmitters described previously, but may be used at any power level.

Construction

The two couplers are identical circuitwise. They are built inside a standard 3 by 4 by 17-inch aluminum chassis, with a bottom plate to complate the shielding. The panel is $3\frac{1}{2}$ inches high. If only one coupler is required, a 3 by 4 by 6-inch utility box can be used. Terminals on the back of the chassis include a coaxial input fitting and a two-post output fitting for each coupler. The circuit diagram, Fig. 17-16, serves for both.

The 50-Mc. coils are cut from commercially available stock, though they can be made by hand if desired. The coupling winding, L_1, is inserted inside the tuned circuit. The polyethylene strips on which the coils are wound keep the two coils from making electrical contact, so no support other than the wire leads is needed.

Leads to L_1 are brought out between the turns of L_2, and are insulated from them by two sleeves of spaghetti, one inside the other. Do not use the soft vinyl type of sleeving, as it will melt too readily if, through an accident to the antenna system, the coil should run hot. In the 144-Mc. coupler the positions of the coils are reversed, with the tuned circuit, L_2, at the center, and the coupling coil outside it.

Similar tuning capacitors are used in both couplers, but some of the plates are removed from the one in the 144-Mc. circuit. This provides easier tuning, though it has little effect on the minimum capacitance, and therefor on the size of the coil.

Adjusting the Couplers

An antenna coupler can be adjusted properly only if some form of standing-wave bridge is connected in the line between the transmitter and the coupler. If it is a power-indicating type, so much the better, as it then can be used for adjusting the transmitter loading, and the work can be done at normal transmitter power.

With the bridge set to read forward power, adjust the coupler capacitors and the transmitter tuning roughly for maximum indication. Now set the bridge to read reflected power, and adjust the antenna coupler capacitors, first one and then the other, until minimum reflected power is

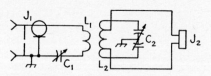

Fig. 17-16—Circuit and parts information for the v.h.f. antenna couplers.

C_1—100-$\mu\mu$f. variable for 50 Mc., 50-$\mu\mu$f. for 144 Mc. (Hammarlund MC-100 and MC-50).

C_2—35-$\mu\mu$f. per-section split-stator variable, 0.07-inch spacing (Hammarlund MCD-35SX). Reduce to 4 stator and 4 rotor plates in each section in 144-Mc. coupler for easier tuning; see text.

J_1—Coaxial fitting, female.

J_2—Two-post terminal assembly (National FWH).

L_1—50 Mc.: 4 turns No. 18 tinned, 1 inch diameter, $\frac{1}{8}$-inch spacing (Air-Dux No. 808T).

    114 Mc.: 2 turns No. 14 enam., 1 inch diameter, $\frac{1}{8}$-inch spacing. Slip over L_2 before mounting.

L_2—50 Mc.: 7 turns No. 14 tinned, $1\frac{1}{2}$ inch diameter, $\frac{1}{4}$ inch spacing (Air Dux No. 1204). Tap $1\frac{1}{2}$ turns from each end.

    144 Mc.: 5 turns No. 12 tinned, $\frac{1}{2}$ inch diameter, $\frac{7}{8}$ inch long. Tap $1\frac{1}{2}$ turns from each end.

achieved. Unless the line input impedance is very highly reactive, it should be possible to get the reflected power down to zero, or very close to it. Adjustment of the coupler is now complete. Tuning for maximum transfer of power from the transmitter is done *entirely* at the transmitter.

Simple Transmitters

Simple Transmitters for 50 and 144 Mc.

The two transmitters shown in Fig. 17-17 are designed to fill several needs. They can be used as complete r.f. sections for 50 and 144 Mc., or they serve well as exciters for higher-powered amplifiers. Depending on the final amplifier tubes chosen, the power level can be anything from under 10 to as much as 50 watts input. At low power they are well suited to mobile and portable applications. Provision is included for c.w. operation. Modulation equipment for the transmitters can be found elsewhere in this *Handbook*.

The designs are as similar as possible, mechanically and electrically, the tubes and many of the parts being interchangeable. They are built on standard 5 by 10 by 3-inch aluminum chassis, with shield covers of perforated aluminum over their output stages. These shields are an aid to TVI prevention, and they provide protection for the tuned circuits mounted topside.

Circuitry

Both transmitters employ third-overtone crystal oscillators of simple design. Crystals should be in the range between 8.34 and 9 Mc. or 25 and 27 Mc. for 50-Mc. operation. For 144-Mc. work the crystals are 8 to 8.22 Mc. or 24- to 24.66 Mc. If the feedback in the oscillator circuit is adjusted to make conventional 8-Mc. crystals oscillate on their third overtone, crystals in the 24-to-27-Mc. range will also work. If only the latter (third overtone) type crystals are used, the feedback can be set at a lower level. This is controlled by the position of the tap on the coil, L_1. Crystals in the 8-Mc. range that multiply out close to a band edge should be checked carefully under actual operating conditions in the equipment, as the oscillation frequency may not be exactly three times that marked on the holder.

The oscillator is the triode portion of a 6U8 triode-pentode. The pentode section is a frequency multiplier, doubling to 50 Mc. in the 6-meter transmitter and tripling to 72 Mc. in the 144-Mc. one. The doubler section drives the output stage in the 50-Mc. rig. An extra stage is required to reach 144 Mc. This is a 12AT7 dual triode with its corresponding triode elements connected in parallel, doubling from 72 to 144 Mc. The output stage is a 2E26, where the input power is to be under 25 watts. A 6146 may be used at higher power levels. There is substantially no difference in the driving power required by these tubes, and they can be interchanged with only slight readjustment of the tuned circuits.

When the exciters are to drive an amplifier using an 829B or a 5894, the output tube should be a 2E26. The plate supply voltage need be no more than 300 volts, and as little as 200 may suffice. When the units are used alone the final plate voltage should be 300 for a 2E26, or 400 to 500 for the 6146. If the latter tube is used in exciter service the output will be sufficient to drive tetrode amplifiers of up to 1 kilowatt input.

Construction

Arrangement of parts is not particularly critical, though it would be well for the inexperienced constructor to follow the layouts shown closely in all principal details. Layout drawings, Figs. 17-21 and 17-25 are provided for those who may wish to make exact duplicates. The dimensions given apply only when identical parts to those of the original are purchased. Check sockets, particularly, for mounting dimensions before following the layouts in complete detail.

The shield covers of the two transmitters were made in slightly different ways, to illustrate differing techniques. The method used in the 50-Mc. unit may be the easier of the two for amateurs not well equipped with metal working tools. The front and back plates are 5 inches wide and 4½ inches high. The bottom half inch of each plate overlaps the main chassis, and is fastened

Fig. 17-17—Transmitters for 50 (right) and 144 Mc. Designs are similar and many parts are interchangeable. Power ratings may be varied from under to more than 50 watts input, depending on tube used in the output stage.

to it with self-tapping screws. The cover is made of perforated aluminum, available in many hardware stores. This can be cut and bent with simple tools. The box thus made is 4 inches high, 5 inches wide and 5 inches deep. The perforated cover is made larger than these dimensions by about $\frac{3}{8}$ inch on all sides. The extra material is bent over so that the front and back plates can be fastened to it with self-tapping screws.

In the 144-Mc. transmitter the edges of the front and back plates are bent over, so that the cover need be only a plate bent into an inverted U. The enclosure is 4 by 4 by 5 inches in size. The bent-over edges of the front and back walls show plainly in the top view, Fig. 17-22.

Building the 50-Mc. Transmitter

Looking at the bottom view of the 50-Mc. transmitter, Fig. 17-19, we see the oscillator tuning capacitor, C_1, and the plate coil, L_1, at the right. Next to the left is the 6U8 socket. The doubler plate coil, L_2, and the amplifier grid coil, L_3, are between the tube sockets. Note that these coils are mounted side by side, with their axes vertical. Their position with respect to each other is adjusted for maximum grid drive, with the optimum spacing being about one coil diameter. The amplifier screen-dropping resistor (4 1-watt resistors in parallel) is just above the 2E26 socket. Jacks for cathode keying and grid-current measurement occupy the left side of the front wall, as seen in Fig. 17-19.

Arrangement of parts inside the shield compartment can be seen in Fig. 17-18. The amplifier tube, a 6146 in this instance, is at the left side of the box. The plate tuning capacitor, C_4, is near the middle of the front wall. The antenna loading capacitor, C_5, and the coaxial output fitting, J_1, are on the rear wall. The power connector strip is centered on the rear wall of the chassis. Note the parasitic choke, L_4, between the tube and the plate coil. This is wound on the resistor in parallel with it. The plate coil, L_5, is mounted with its axis vertical. The output coupling coil, L_6, is close against the bottom of L_5, and insulated from it by spaghetti sleeving.

The type of socket used for the amplifier tube is important. Do not use the common moulded socket with an elevated grounding ring having 4 lugs spaced around its circumference. These lugs may introduce coupling between the circuits grounded or bypassed thereto, causing instability that cannot be neutralized out. A Millen ceramic socket was used in the original, but any type that does not have the separate grounding lugs and ring is suitable. Grounding should be done to lugs under the nuts used for mounting the socket. It is imperative that bypass capacitor connections be made with virtually no leads at all, particularly in the amplifier circuits. Note that each cathode lead is bypassed separately. This is important where the cathode is keyed, as in this instance.

The neutralizing capacitor, C_3, is a type intended for mounting with one side grounded, so another mounting method must be provided in this application. A small tab of copper about $\frac{3}{8}$ by 1 inch in size supports the capacitor, the end of the tab being soldered to a lug on the 3-lug tie-point strip nearest the socket. The 150-$\mu\mu$f. bypass at the low end of L_3 connects from that point to the ground lug at the middle of the terminal strip. The lead from the sleeve of C_3 is a stiff wire that passes up through a $\frac{3}{8}$-inch hole in the chassis to the lower stator terminal of the plate tuning capacitor, C_4. The latter is mounted with its stator terminals one above the other.

Adjustment and Operation

For initial tests a power supply capable of delivering 200 to 300 volts d.c. at about 100 ma., and 6.3 volts a.c. or d.c. at 1.7 amperes may be used. (Only 1.25 amp. will be needed if a 2E26 is used.) The negative side of the plate supply and one side of the heater supply are connected together. The oscillator is tested first. This is done by feeding plate power to the 4700-ohm resistor in the oscillator plate lead only, disconnecting the doubler plate-screen lead temporarily.

Apply heater voltage only, and allow the tubes to warm up for 30 seconds or more. Connect a 100-milliampere meter in the lead to the plate sup-

Fig. 17-18—Looking down inside the amplifier shield. The plate tuning capacitor, C_4, is on the front wall, with the loading adjustment, C_5, on the rear wall. Parasitic suppressor and plate coil connect to top stator bar of C_4. Black lead, lower left, runs through a rubber grommet to the neutralizing capacitor, below the chassis.

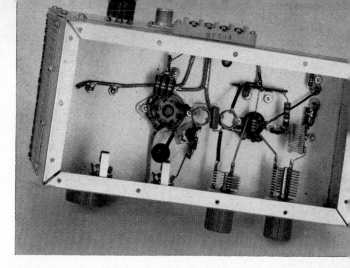

Fig. 17-19—Bottom view of the 50-Mc. transmitter. Note positions of the various coils, particularly those in the doubler plate and amplifier grid circuits, near the middle of the assembly.

ply, and apply power. Swing the oscillator tuning capacitor, C_1, through its range. There will be a sharp dip in current to about 10 ma. as the crystal starts oscillating.

Check the frequency of oscillator with a grid-dip meter or wavemeter. If you have a receiver that tunes the 25- or 50-Mc. region, listen for the oscillator to determine if it is crystal controlled. The frequency will change only slightly, if at all, when the circuit is tuned through resonance. Listen to the note with the receiver beat oscillator on, and place a screwdriver or other metal object near the tuned circuit. There should be very little change in frequency. Should the frequency change more than a few hundred cycles under these tests the oscillator may not be controlled by the crystal.

Self-oscillation is the result of too much feedback. This can be corrected by moving the tap

lower on the coil. Too little feedback may prevent the oscillator from working at all, or it may drop out of oscillation when loaded appreciably by the following stage. The cure is to raise the tap position on the coil.

When the oscillator is working correctly, remove the milliammeter from its power lead and connect it between the high-voltage source and the junction of the screen resistor and 1000-ohm resistor at the low end of the plate coil. Plug a low-range milliammeter, preferably 5 or 10 ma., into the grid current jack, J_2, of the amplifier. Apply plate voltage to the first two stages and tune the doubler plate circuit for maximum grid current, as read on the meter in J_2. This should be at least 2 ma., with a 250-volt plate supply. Try varying the separation between L_2 and L_3, leaving spacing at the point that yields greatest grid current. Retune the doubler plate circuit as the

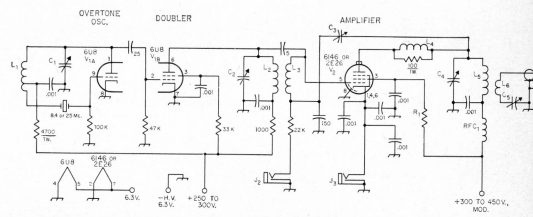

Fig. 17-20—Schematic diagram and parts information for the 50-Mc. transmitter. Capacitors are ceramic unless specified. Values under .001 are in $\mu\mu f$. Resistors ½ watt unless specified.

C_1—50-$\mu\mu f$. variable (Johnson 157-4).
C_2—25-$\mu\mu f$. variable (Johnson 157-3).
C_3—0.5 to 3 $\mu\mu f$. ceramic trimmer (Erie 3139D).
C_4—25-$\mu\mu f$. variable (Johnson 167-2).
J_1—Coaxial chassis fitting.
J_2, J_3—Closed-circuit jack.
L_1—14 t. No. 20 tinned, ½-inch diam., ⅞ inch long, tapped at 4½ t. from crystal end (B & W No. 3003).
L_2—6½ t., ⁷⁄₁₆ inch long, similar to L_1.

L_3—7¼ t., ½-inch long, similar to L_2.
L_4—5 t. No. 20 wound on and spaced to fill 100-ohm 1-watt resistor.
L_5—3½ t. No. 14 tinned, ¾-inch i.d., ½-inch long.
L_6—2 t. No. 14, similar to and at cold end of L_5. Cover with spaghetti sleeving.
R_1—37,500 ohms, 4 watts (4 150,000-ohm 1-watt resistors in parallel).
RFC_1—Single-layer v.h.f. choke, 2 to 7 μh. (Ohmite Z-50 or National R-60).

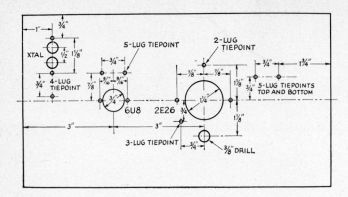

Fig. 17-21—Layout drawing of the 50-Mc. chassis top. Precise duplication is not important, though the general parts layout should be followed. Hole sizes may vary with different types of sockets.

spacing is changed.

Next comes neutralization of the amplifier. With drive on, but no plate or screen voltage, tune the amplifier plate circuit through its range, watching the grid current meter. There may be a downward dip in grid current when the plate circuit is resonated. Adjust the neutralizing capacitor, C_3, a turn or two and check the grid current dip again. If there is less change than before, the adjustment was in the right direction. Continue in this way until no downward movement can be seen in the grid current as the plate circuit is tuned through resonance.

If neutralization cannot be achieved, a different value of bypass will be required at the low end of L_3. If the neutralizing capacitor is at minimum setting when neutralization is approached, a larger value of bypass will be needed. Try 220 $\mu\mu$f. as a next step.

Power may now be applied to the final amplifier. This can be from the same source as has been used for the earlier tests, for the time being. The meter may be removed from the doubler power lead and connected between the junction of the r.f. choke, RFC_1, and screen resistor and the terminal on the back of the transmitter. This will measure the combined plate and screen current drawn by the amplifier. The meter may also be plugged into the cathode jack, where it will read combined plate, screen and grid current.

A light bulb of about 25 watts or more can be connected to a coaxial fitting and used as a dummy load in place of an antenna. This will not represent a 50-ohm load, so the tuning of the stage will not be the same as when a matched antenna system is used, but it will do for initial tests, and it will give a rough indication of power output.

Apply plate-screen power to all stages, and tune the plate circuit of the amplifier to the point where plate current dips the lowest. Now adjust the series capacitor, retuning the plate capacitor, until maximum brilliance is seen in the load lamp. Check carefully for any sign of oscillation in the amplifier. Remove the crystal from its socket briefly, while watching the amplifier grid current. This current and the amplifier output should drop to zero, and remain there regardless of the tuning of any of the transmitter circuits. Should grid current appear with the oscillator inoperative,

recheck neutralization. The grid-current dip may be only an approximate indication of neutralization, so the adjustment may have to be touched up after power is applied to the amplifier. Turn off power as a safety measure when this is done. With perfect neutralization, maximum grid current, minimum plate current and maximum output will all occur at the same setting of the amplifier plate circuit tuning. Perfection in this respect may not be possible, but there should be no sign of oscillation (grid current in the amplifier when the drive is removed) at any setting of the tuning controls.

When the rig is operated with a properly designed antenna the settings of the amplifier plate and antenna loading adjustments may be somewhat different from those obtained with a lamp load. Both should be adjusted for maximum power delivered to the antenna. This can be recorded on a field-strength meter, giving a relative indication of the power radiated by the antenna. Better than this is a power-indicating standing-wave bridge, which may be left connected in the line to the antenna at all times.

Final operating conditions for the transmitter will depend on the supply voltage and final tube used. With a 300-volt supply the oscillator plate current will run about 10 ma. with the oscillator operating properly, and 17 ma. with the crystal out of oscillation. The doubler plate-screen current is about 12 ma. Amplifier grid current will be at least 3 ma. without plate and screen voltage, and around 2.5 ma. with the amplifier operating under load. These values will be slightly lower with a 250-volt supply. Plate-screen current to the amplifier will depend on the power level and tube. With a 2E26 at 300 volts the current will be about 20 ma. at resonance, with no load, and 95 ma. off resonance. Loaded for maximum efficiency the 2E26 plate and screen current will be about 60 ma. With a 6146 at 450 volts the loaded plate and screen current will be about 120 ma.

The 50-Mc. transmitter was described originally in *QST* for October, 1958.

The 144-Mc. Transmitter

Layout and testing of the 144-Mc. unit are very similar to the 50-Mc. model already described, so only the points of difference will be covered in this part of the text. Looking at the bottom view,

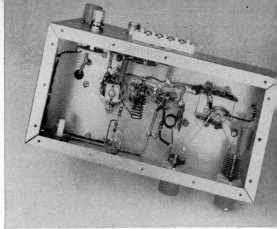

Fig. 17-22—Top view of the 144-Mc. transmitter with shield cover removed. A 2E26 is shown in the amplifier socket.

Fig. 17-23—Bottom of the 144-Mc. transmitter, with oscillator-tripler at the right. Doubler stage is near the middle of the chassis and amplifier at the left.

Fig. 17-23, the oscillator tuned circuit is at the far right. The tripler plate capacitor, C_2, is next on the front wall. The 6U8 socket is between these two capacitors, on the center line of the chassis. The 12AT7 parallel doubler socket is approximately in the middle of the chassis. The coil mounted vertically at the right and slightly below the 12AT7 socket is the tripler plate coil, L_2.

The doubler plate coil, L_3, and the amplifier grid coil, L_4, are mounted on a common center line and close together, making them appear as one coil in the photograph. The top end of L_3, as seen in the schematic diagram, Fig. 17-24, is toward the back of the chassis. The grid end of L_4 is toward the front. Capacitors C_3 and C_4 are cylindrical plastic trimmers. They are at either side of and just above the upper end of L_3.

The amplifier socket is at the left. The screen tuning capacitor, C_7, is mounted across the socket. Screen voltage is fed through the r.f. choke just above the socket. The switch for shorting out the grid leak when c.w. is used is in the upper left corner of the photograph. The two jacks on the front wall are for keying (far left) and grid current measurement.

Circuit differences between the two units, aside from the inclusion of the extra multiplier stage in the 144-Mc. model, arise mainly from the effects of tube and circuit capacitances at the higher frequency. Tube capacitances load the tuned circuits heavily, so series-tuned circuits are used in the amplifier stage. It will be seen that the keying jack is connected in the cathode of the doubler stage instead of in the amplifier cathode lead. It is difficult to bypass the amplifier cathode completely at 144 Mc., and the insertion of the keying jack in that position would cause oscilla-

Fig. 17-24—Schematic diagram and parts information for the 144-Mc. transmitter.

C_1, C_6—50-$\mu\mu$f. variable (Johnson 157-4).
C_2, C_5—15-$\mu\mu$f. variable (Johnson 157-2).
C_3, C_4—1-8-$\mu\mu$f. plastic trimmer (Erie 532-10).
J_1, J_2—Closed-circuit jack.
J_3—Coaxial chassis fitting.
L_1—14 turns No. 20 tinned, $\frac{1}{2}$-inch diam., $\frac{7}{8}$ inch long, tapped at 4 turns from crystal end (B & W No. 3003).
L_2—5$\frac{3}{4}$ turns No. 18 enam., $\frac{7}{16}$-inch diam., $\frac{5}{8}$ inch long.
L_3—2$\frac{3}{4}$ turns No. 18 enam., $\frac{7}{16}$-inch diam., $\frac{1}{4}$ inch long.
L_4—6 turns No. 18 enam., $\frac{7}{16}$-inch diam., $\frac{5}{8}$ inch long, center tapped.
L_5—4 turns No. 14 tinned, $\frac{3}{4}$-inch diam., turns spaced 2 diameters. Make extra space at center for L_6; see Fig. 17-22.
L_6—1 turn No. 14 enamel, $\frac{3}{4}$-inch diam. Cover with insulating sleeving and insert at center of L_5.
R_1—33,000 ohms, 3 watts (3 100,000-ohm 1-watt resistors in parallel).
RFC$_1$—7-μh. solenoid choke (Ohmite Z-50).
RFC$_2$—1.8-μh. solenoid choke (Ohmite Z-144).
S_1—S.p.s.t. switch, any type.

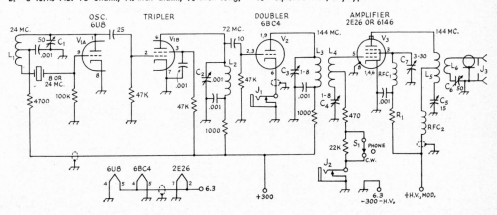

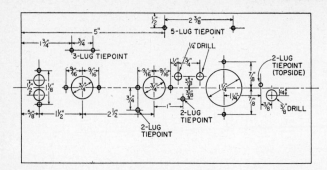

Fig. 17-25—Layout drawing of the 144-Mc. chassis.

tion. Screen bypassing is a similar problem, as conventional bypassing methods are ineffective at this and higher frequencies. Bringing the screen to ground potential requires a critical value of capacitance, so a trimmer (C_7) is connected from screen to ground.

Adjustment Procedure

The power supply for testing the 144-Mc. transmitter should deliver 6.3 volts at 1.6 amperes if a 2E26 amplifier tube is used. With a 6146 it should be capable of supplying 2 amperes. Initially 250 to 300 volts at 150 ma. will do for the plate supply. Final plate voltage for a 6146 may be as high as 500 volts.

Testing the first two stages is similar to that outlined for the 50-Mc. transmitter, except for the frequencies involved. Make sure that the oscillator is between 24 and 24.66 Mc., and that the pentode section of the 6U8 multiplies this frequency by 3. Tune the tripler plate circuit, L_2-C_2, for maximum output, as indicated by a 2-volt 60-ma. pilot lamp coupled to the cold end of L_2 with a single-turn loop of insulated wire about the diameter of the coil.

Next apply plate voltage to the 12AT7 doubler, and tune it for maximum amplifier grid current. Adjustment of C_3 and C_4 will interlock to some extent, but be sure that each is tuned for maximum grid current, as read in J_2. The switch S_1 can be in either position for this adjustment, though the grid current will be much higher if it is in the closed position.

Neutralization is done similarly to the manner outlined for the 50-Mc. transmitter, except that the setting of the screen capacitor, C_7, is the means by which it is achieved. If stability is approached as C_7 reaches maximum capacitance, a larger trimmer will be needed. Experimentation with the value of the r.f. choke in the screen lead may also be helpful. A variation of the neutralization system shown is the use of a critical value of inductance in the screen lead, and the elimination of C_7. Grid current, when neutralization is completed, should be at least 1.5 ma. with S_1 in the open position. Go over all adjustments carefully, and experiment with the spacing between L_3 and L_4 if the grid drive is low.

The balance of the testing is similar to the 50-Mc. procedure. Plate current for the 12AT7 doubler will be about 25 ma. Amplifier grid current should be all that can be obtained, but preferably not below 1.5 ma. under full load. Should it be less than 1.5 ma. running the amplifier at slightly less than full loading may make it possible to get satisfactory output and still retain good modulation characteristics.

Amplifier plate current at resonance with no load will be higher than on 50 Mc., and the output will be lower. Efficiency will be lower with a 6146 than with a 2E26, but the higher plate dissipation rating of the 6146 may make its use desirable if more output is needed than can be obtained with the 2E26. Either transmitter can be used in mobile service. For 6-volt cars the tubes can be as shown. Twelve-volt equivalents of all the tube types are now available for cars with 12-volt systems.

Modulation and Keying

For voice work a modulator is required. This should have a power output of approximately half the input to the final amplifier. Several suitable modulators are shown in other chapters of this *Handbook*. The plate and screen current of the amplifier are run through the secondary of the modulator output transformer. If the transmitter is to run at low power, a single 300-volt supply can be used for all stages, including the modulator, if it has a sufficiently high current rating.

Keying methods differ for the two r.f. units. The 50-Mc. transmitter is keyed for c.w. by breaking the cathode lead. This would cause instability if applied to the 144-Mc. transmitter, so the latter is keyed in the cathode of the doubler stage. Fixed bias must be applied to the final amplifier grid, to keep the plate current to a safe value. The voltage required will depend on the plate voltage applied to the final. The plate current need not be cut completely off, but merely held to less than the plate dissipation rating for the tube used. A 22½ volt battery is sufficient for plate voltages up to 400. The simplest way to apply bias, for occasional c.w. use, is to plug it into the grid current jack. The positive terminal of the bias battery should connect to the ground side of the plug.

The switch S_1 cuts out the 27,000-ohm grid resistor, so that the grid bias will not be excessive when fixed bias is applied. The rig can be operated in this manner (fixed bias plus the smaller of the two grid resistors) on voice, if it is desirable or convenient to do this. The grid current is so low that the bias battery will last almost indefinitely, and a small hearing aid size is suitable. It can be mounted inside the chassis and wired into the circuit permanently, where more frequent c.w. operation is expected.

A Simple Transmitter

Simple Transmitter for 220 and 420 Mc.

The transmitter in Figs. 17-26–17-29 is for the newcomer who wants to start with simple gear, going on to something better when he has gained construction and operating experience. It is built in two units, with the idea that the modulator can be retained when the r.f. portion is discarded.

The r.f. section is a simple oscillator with two 6AF4 or 6AT4 tubes in push-pull. Its plate

pending on the plate voltage and whether a 6V6 or 6L6 tube is used. It may be considered as a long-term investment that will be suitable for use with any r.f. section of up to 20 watts input that may be constructed at a later date.

Construction

The two units are built on identical 5 by 7 by 2-inch aluminum chassis, connecting by

Fig. 17-26—The simple transmitter for 220 and 420 Mc. is made in two parts. The modulator, left, may be retained for use with more advanced r.f. sections than the simple oscillator shown at the right. The two units may be plugged together or connected by a cable.

circuit is changed from a quarter-wave line at 220 Mc. to a half-wave line at 420 Mc. by plugging in suitable terminations at the end of the tuned circuit.

Because the oscillator is modulated directly it will have considerable frequency modulation, and the signal will not be readable on selective receivers unless the modulation is kept at a very low level. Where a broader receiver is in use at the other end of the path a higher modulation level can be employed.

The modulator is designed for a crystal microphone. It delivers 3 to 10 watts output, de-

means of a plug on the oscillator and a socket on the modulator. Power is fed through a similar plug on the back of the modulator. Arrangement of parts in the modulator is not critical, but the oscillator should be exactly as shown.

Sockets for the tubes are one inch apart center to center, $2\frac{3}{16}$ inch in from the end of the chassis. C_1 is at the exact center of the chassis, with J_2 $1\frac{1}{2}$ inches to its left, as seen in Fig. 17-27. At the far left is a crystal socket, used for the antenna terminal, J_1. One-inch ceramic standoffs are mounted on the screws that hold J_2 in place. These support the antenna coupling loop, L_2.

Testing and Use

A power supply delivering about 200

Fig. 17-27—Bottom view of the oscillator unit, showing the two-band tank circuit. The line terminations, with their protecting caps removed, are in the foreground. At the left is the 220-Mc. plug, with the 420-Mc. one at the right.

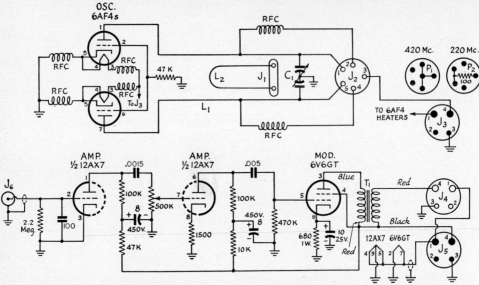

Fig. 17-28—Schematic diagram and parts information for the two-band oscillator and modulator.

C₁—10.5-μμf.-per-section butterfly variable (Johnson 10LB15).

L₁—2 3½ inch pieces No. 12 tinned, spaced ½ inch. Bend down ¾ inch at tube end and ½ inch at socket end. R.f. chokes connect ⅝ inch from bend at tube end. Connect C₁ at 1 inch from bend at socket end.

L₂—Hairpin loop 2¼ inches long and ½ inch wide, No. 16, covered with insulating sleeving.

J₁—Crystal socket used for antenna terminal.

J₂—5-contact ceramic socket (Amphenol 49–RSS5).

J₃, J₅—4-contact male fitting (Amphenol 86–RCP4).

J₄—4 contact female chassis fitting (Amphenol 78–S4 or RS4).

J₆—Microphone connector (Amphenol 75–PC1M).

P₁—5-contact male cable connector (Amphenol 86–PM5) with Pins 2, 3 and 4 joined together.

P₂—Same as P₁, but with Pins 1 and 5 joined. Connect 100-ohm resistor between these and Pin 3.

RFC (6 required)—12 turns No. 28 enamel close-wound on high-value 1-watt resistor.

T₁—10-watt modulation trans. (Merit A-3008).

volts d.c. at 50 ma. or more and 6.3 volts at 1 amp. or more is needed. Plug the units together or connect them by a cable. With a cable, a milliammeter may be connected between the No. 4 pins to measure the oscillator plate current. Otherwise the meter should be connected temporarily between Pin 4 of J_3 and Pin 3 of J_2, in place of the wire shown in Fig. 17-28.

Plate current should be about 25 to 30 ma. If the stage is oscillating there will be a fluctuation in current as the plate line is touched with an *insulated* metal object. Do not hold the metal in the hands for this test! The frequency is best checked by means of Lecher wires, a technique that is covered in the chapter on measurements.

With the dimensions given the range with P_1 plugged in should be about 405 to 450 Mc. With P_2 plugged in the frequency should fall within the 220-Mc. band with C_1 set in the same position

as it was for the middle of the 420-Mc. band. Some alteration of the connection point for C on L_1 may be necessary to achieve this.

In using the transmitter it is well to stay between 221 and 224 Mc. to avoid out-of band operation. On 420, keep the transmitter below 432 Mc. to avoid interference with the high-selectivity work that is done between 432 and 436 Mc. (Further details on this transmitter in *QST* for December, 1954.)

Fig. 17-29—Looking at the underside of the modulator.

A 40-Watt Transmitter for 220 Mc.

The crystal-controlled transmitter shown in Figs. 17-30 and 17-32 will run 30 to 40 watts at 220 Mc. Referring to Fig. 17-31, a simple overtone oscillator circuit uses one half of a 12AT7 dual triode. The crystal may be between 8.15 and 8.33 Mc. or 24.45 and 25 Mc. In either case, the frequency of oscillation is in the latter range, as the crystal works on its third overtone. The second half of the 12AT7 is a tripler to 73 to 75 Mc. This stage has a balanced plate circuit, so that its output may be capacitively coupled to the grids of a second 12AT7, working as a push-pull tripler to 220 Mc. The low side of the first tripler plate circuit has a balancing capacitor, C_3, so that a capacitance equal to the output capacitance of the 12AT7 can be added to that side of the circuit. Without this the two halves of the push-pull tripler may receive unequal drive, and one half of the tube will run hotter than the other.

The plate circuit of the push-pull tripler is inductively coupled to the grid circuit of an Amperex 6360 dual tetrode amplifier that runs straight through on 220 Mc. Similar inductive coupling transfers the drive to the grid circuit of the final amplifier stage, an Amperex 6252 dual tetrode. This tube is a somewhat more efficient outgrowth of the 832A, which may also be used, though with lower efficiency and output. Base connections are the same for both tubes.

The grid return of the 6252 is brought out to the terminal strip on the back of the unit, to allow for connection of a grid meter. Both this point and the tip jack in the 6360 grid return have 1000-ohm resistors completing the grid returns to ground, so that operation of the stages is unaffected if the meters are removed.

Instability in tetrode amplifiers for v.h.f. service may develop as a result of the ineffective bypassing of the screen. In the case of the 6360 stage stable operation was obtained with no bypassing at all, while on the 6252 a small mica trimmer was connected directly from the screen terminal to ground. It is operated near the minimum setting.

Construction

The transmitter is built on an aluminum plate 6 by 17 inches in size. This screws to a standard chassis of the same dimensions, which serves as both shield and case. Cut-outs about three inches square are made in the chassis and base plate, above and below the tube, to allow for ventilation. These openings are fitted with perforated aluminum or screening to preserve shielding. The case should be equipped with rubber feet, to avoid marring the surface it rests on, and to allow air circulation around the tube.

The tube sockets and all the controls except the tuning capacitor of the oscillator are mounted along the center line of the cover plate. The 220-Mc. stages are inductively coupled, using hairpin loop tank circuits the dimensions of which are given in Fig. 17-33. The tuning range of these circuits is affected by the widths of the loops as well as their length, so some variation can be had by squeezing the sides together or spreading them apart.

It is important that the method of mounting the 6252 socket be followed closely. An aluminum bracket about $2\frac{7}{8}$ inches high and 4 inches wide supports the socket. Note that the socket and tube are on the *same* side of the plate. Holes are drilled in the plate in line with the control grid terminals to pass the grid leads. These holes are $\frac{3}{8}$-inch diameter, and are equipped with rubber grommets to prevent accidental shorting of the grid leads to ground. The shape of the grid inductance should be such that its leads pass through the centers of the holes. The socket is supported on $\frac{5}{16}$-inch metal pillars. It may be necessary to bend the socket lugs slightly to keep them from shorting to the mounting plate. The heater lead comes to the top of the plate, and the cathode lead bends around the bottom of it.

Power leads are made with shielded wire, and are brought out to a terminal strip on the back of the chassis. These leads and the coax to the output connector should be long enough so that the plate on which the transmitter is built can be lifted off the chassis and inverted as shown in the photograph.

Adjustment

Initial tests should be made with a power supply that delivers no more than 250 volts, and as little as 150 to 200 volts can be used. If the voltage is more than 250, insert a 5000-ohm 10-watt resistor in series with the power lead

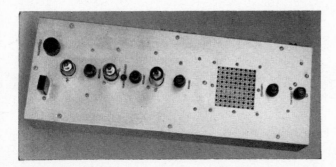

Fig. 17-30—Top view of the 220-Mc. transmitter. Final amplifier tube is inside the chassis, below the screened ventilation hole. Power connections, keying jack and output terminal are on the back of the chassis.

443

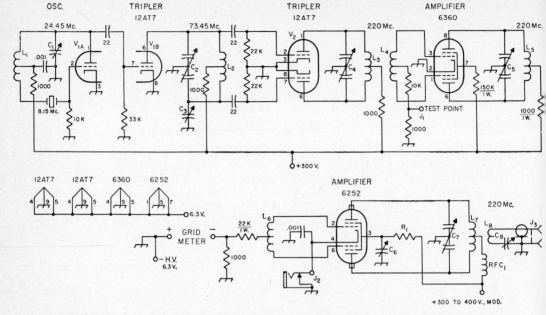

Fig. 17-31—Schematic diagram and parts information for the 220-Mc. transmitter. Capacitor values below 0.001 μf. are in μμf. Resistors ½ watt unless specified.

C₁—50-μμf. miniature variable (Hammarlund MAPC-50-B).

C₂, C₄, C₅—8-μ μf. miniature butterfly variable (Johnson 160–208).

C₃, C₆—3-30-μμf. mica trimmer.

C₇—Butterfly variable, 1 stator and 1 rotor (Johnson 167–21, with plates removed).

C₈—15-μμf. miniature variable (Hammarlund MAPC-15-B).

J₁—Tip jack, insulated.

J₂—Closed-circuit phone jack.

J₃—Coaxial chassis fitting, SO-239.

L₁—15 t. No. 20 tinned, ½-inch diam., 1 inch long (B & W Miniductor No. 3003). Tap at 4 turns from crystal end; see text.

L₂—12 t. No. 18 tinned, ½-inch diam., 1 inch long, center-tapped.

L₃, L₄, L₅, L₆—U-shaped loops No. 18 enam., center-tapped. Dimensions given in Fig. 17-33.

L₇—2 t. No. 14 enam., 1-inch, 1-inch diam., leads ⅝ inch long. Center-tapped, space turns ½ inch apart.

L₈—1 t. No. 18 enam., inserted between turns of L₇. Cover with insulating sleeving.

R₁—23,500 ohms, 2 watts. (Two 47,000-ohm 1-watt resistors in parallel.)

RFC₁—25 t. No. 28 enam. on 1-watt high-value resistor.

temporarily. Plate voltage should be applied to the various stages separately, starting with the oscillator, making sure that each stage is working correctly before proceeding to the next.

A milliammeter of 50- to 100-ma. range should be connected temporarily in series with the 1000-ohm resistor in the oscillator plate lead. When power is applied the current should be not more than about 10 ma. Rotate C₁ and note if an upward kick occurs, probably near the middle of the range of C₁. At this point the stage is oscillating. Lack of oscillation indicates too low feedback, or a defective crystal. Listen for the note on a communications receiver tuned near 24 Mc., if one is available. There should be no more than a slight change in frequency when a metallic tool is held near the tuned circuit, or when the circuit is tuned through its range. The note should be of pure crystal quality. If there is a rough sound, or if the frequency changes with mechanical vibration, the oscillator is not controlled by the crystal. This indicates too much feedback, and the tap on the coil, L₁, should be moved near the crystal end.

The proper amount of feedback is the lowest tap position that allows the oscillator to start readily under load. If 24-Mc. crystals are used the tap can be lower on the coil than with 8-Mc. crystals. When 8-Mc. crystals are operated on the third overtone, as in this case, the frequency of oscillation may not be exactly three times that marked on the crystal holder.

Now apply plate voltage to the second half of the 12AT7, again using a temporary plate meter connected in series with the 100-ohm decoupling resistor that feeds plate power to L₂. Current will be about 10 ma., as with the oscillator. Tune C₂ for maximum output. This can be determined by brilliance indication in a 2-volt 60-ma. pilot lamp connected to a 1-turn loop of insulated wire coupled to L₂. Check the frequency of this stage with a wavemeter.

Now connect a low-range milliammeter (not more than 10 ma.) between the test point, J₁, and ground. Apply power to the push-pull tripler, again using a temporary milliammeter connected in the lead to the plate coil, L₃. Tune the plate circuit for maximum indication on the grid meter. Plate current will be about 20 ma. Adjust the position of L₃ with respect to L₄ for maximum grid current. Now go back over all previous adjustments and set them carefully for maximum

220-Mc. Transmitter

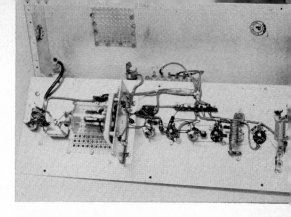

Fig. 17-32—Interior view of the 220-Mc. transmitter. All r.f. components are mounted on an aluminum plate, which is screwed to the top of a standard 6 × 17-inch chassis. Screen trimmer capacitor C_6 mounts on the tube socket mounting plate.

The crystal socket and the oscillator coil and capacitor are at the far right. Next is the first 12AT7 socket. Next to the left is the first tripler plate coil, mounted over its trimmer, with the mica balancing padder, C_3, above. The 12AT7 tripler, the test point, J_1, the tuning capacitor C_4, the tripler plate and amplifier grid loops, L_3 and L_4, the 6360 socket, the 6360 plate and amplifier grid loops, the 6252, and its tuned circuits follow in that order. The series capacitor, C_8, and the coaxial lead to the output connector, J_3, are at the far left.

grid current. Adjust the balancing padder, C_3, retuning C_2 each time this is done, until the combination of C_2 and C_3 that gives the highest grid current is found. Check the frequency to be sure that the stage is tripling to 220 Mc.

Now apply power to the 6360 plate circuit, again using the temporary meter to check the current. Connect the low-range milliammeter between the grid-metering terminal on the connector strip and ground. Set the screen trimmer, C_6, near minimum, and tune the 6360 plate circuit for maximum grid current. With 300 volts on the preceding stages, it should be possible to get at least 4 ma. Adjust the spacing between L_5 and L_6 carefully for maximum grid current, retuning C_5 each time this is done. Plate current should not exceed 55 ma.

Check for neutralization of the final amplifier by tuning C_7 through resonance while watching the grid-current meter. If there is no change, or only a slight rise as the circuit goes through resonance, the stage is near enough to neutralization to apply plate power. The 6252 has built-in cross-over capacitance, intended to provide neutralization in the v.h.f. range, so it is likely to be stable at this frequency. If there is a downward kick in the grid current at resonance, adjust the screen trimmer until it disappears. If best neutralization shows at minimum setting of the screen trimmer it may be desirable to eliminate the trimmer.

With an antenna or dummy load connected at J_3, final plate voltage can be applied. Tune the final plate circuit for maximum output, with a meter of 100 ma. or higher range connected to read the combined plate and screen current. This meter may be connected in the power lead, or it can be plugged into the cathode jack. In the latter position it will read the combined plate, screen and grid currents. Tune for maximum output and note the plate current. If it is much over 100 ma., loosen the coupling between L_7 and L_8. The input should not be over 50 watts at this frequency.

A final check for neutralization should now be made. Pull out the crystal or otherwise disable the early stages of the transmitter. The grid current and output should drop to zero. If they do not, adjust the screen trimmer until they do. Make this test only very briefly, as the tubes will draw excessive current when drive is removed. When perfect neutralization is achieved, maximum output will be found at a setting of C_7 at which plate current is at a minimum and grid current at maximum.

Operation

All stages should be run as lightly as possible, for stable operation and long tube life. No more than 300 volts should be run on the exciter stages, and if sufficient grid drive can be obtained, lower voltage is desirable. The 6360 stage runs with rather low drive, and its efficiency is consequently poor, but it delivers enough power to drive the 6252, even when run as low as 250 volts, if all stages are operating as they should.

Observe the plates of the tubes when the transmitter is operated in a darkened room. There should be no reddening of the plates. If one side of any of the last three stages shows red and the other does not it is evidence of unbalance. This can usually be corrected by adjustment of the balancing trimmer, C_3, in the first tripler plate circuit. Lack of symmetry in lead lengths or unbalanced capacitance to ground in any of the r.f. circuits may also lead to lopsided operation.

Though the 6252 is rated for up to 600 volts on the plates, it is recommended that no more than 400 be used in this application, particularly if the stage is to be modulated for voice work.

For voice work the plate-screen current of the 6252 is run through the secondary of the output transformer on the modulator. The latter should have an output of 20 watts or so.

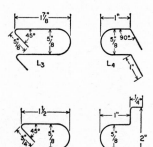

Fig. 17-33—Details of the hairpin loops used in the 220-Mc. transmitter.

A Tripler-Amplifier for 432 Mc.

Only tubes designed especially for u.h.f. service will work satisfactorily at 420 Mc. and higher. The various small receiving triodes made for u.h.f. TV use will work well in low-powered frequency multipliers and r.f. amplifiers for transmitting, but the trend is to tetrodes. Several of the latter are now available.

The tripler-amplifier shown in Figs. 17-34 to 17-37 delivers up to 20 watts output on 432 Mc.

holes in the top cover. Holes are drilled in the chassis under the amplifier tube, and in the cover over it. With a bottom plate fitted to the chassis there should be enough air flowing through both top vents to lift a paper briskly when the fan is started.

Half-wave lines are used in all 432-Mc. circuits. The grid circuit of the amplifier is capacitively coupled to the tripler plate line, the two over-

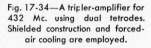

Fig. 17-34—A tripler-amplifier for 432 Mc. using dual tetrodes. Shielded construction and forced-air cooling are employed.

when driven on 144 Mc. by any 2-meter unit delivering 10 watts output or more. In plate-modulated service the output is 12 watts. Tubes are RCA 6524 dual tetrodes, but with slight modification Amperex 6252s or 5894s may be used. With 6252s the output will be about the same as with the 6524. The 5894 will deliver up to 40 watts with higher plate voltages. The 832A may also be used, but the output will be no more than 4 or 5 watts. Forced-air cooling and shielding are recommended.

The tripler tube is mounted vertically, at the left, with its socket $1\frac{1}{2}$ inches below the chassis. There is just room under the socket for the self-resonant input circuit, L_2. The amplifier is horizontal, with its socket mounted in back of a plate that is 8 inches from the left edge of the $3 \times 4 \times 17$-inch aluminum chassis. The shielding enclosure is $3\frac{1}{4}$ inches wide by $3\frac{1}{2}$ inches high. A cooling fan is mounted on the rear wall of the chassis. Air circulates around the tripler tube through its 2-inch hole, flowing out through

lapping about $1\frac{1}{4}$ inches. The spacing between them must be adjusted carefully for maximum grid drive. Plate voltage is fed to the lines through small resistors. These should be connected at the point of lowest r.f. voltage on the lines. The amplifier grid r.f. chokes are connected at the tube socket.

Note that the plate line capacitors, C_1 and C_2, have their rotors floating. This is important. Grounding the rotors, or use of capacitors having metal end plates, may introduce multiple r.f. paths and circuit unbalance. The capacitors have small metal mounting brackets that are not connected directly to the rotors, but even so it was necessary to resort to polystyrene mounting plates for best circuit balance and efficiency. Holes $\frac{3}{4}$ inch in diameter are punched in the front wall to pass the rotor shafts.

Testing

The tripler-amplifier is designed to operate in conjunction with a 144-Mc. transmitter such as

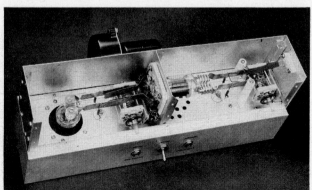

Fig. 17-35—Looking into the tripler-amplifier with the top cover and front plate removed.

A Tripler-Amplifier

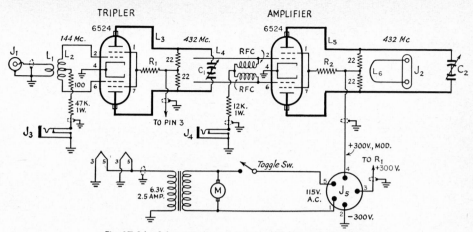

Fig. 17-36—Schematic diagram for the 432-Mc. tripler-amplifier.

C_1, C_2—10-$\mu\mu$f.-per-section split stator, double spaced (Bud LC-1664). Do not use metal end-plate or grounded-rotor types.

R_1, R_2—23,500 ohms, 2 watts (two 47,000 ohm 1-watt resistors in parallel).

L_1—2 turns No. 20 enam., $\frac{1}{2}$-inch diam. Insert between turns of L_2.

L_2—4 turns No. 16 enam., $\frac{1}{2}$-inch diam., $\frac{1}{2}$-inch long, center-tapped.

L_3—Copper strap on heat-dissipating connectors, $3\frac{1}{2}$ inches long. Twist 90 degrees $\frac{1}{2}$ inch from plate end. Space $\frac{3}{4}$ inch.

L_4—Copper strap $2\frac{7}{8}$ inches long, soldered to grid termi-

nals. Space about $\frac{1}{2}$ inch.

L_5—Copper strap $3\frac{7}{8}$ inches long, fastened to heat-dissipating connectors. Space $\frac{3}{4}$ inch. All tank circuits of flashing copper $\frac{1}{2}$ inch wide.

L_6—Coupling loop, No. 20 enam. U-shaped portion is 1 inch long and $\frac{5}{8}$ inch wide. Mount on 3-inch ceramic stand-offs.

J_1—Coaxial input fitting (Amphenol 83-1R).

J_2—Crystal socket used for antenna terminal.

J_3, J_4—Closed-circuit jack.

J_5—5-pin male chassis connector (Amphenol 86-RCP5).

M—Motor-blower assembly, 17 c.f.m. (Ripley Inc., Middletown, Conn., Type 8433).

the 2E26 rig shown in Fig. 17-17. A plate supply of 300 volts at 200 ma. is needed (400 volts may be used with 5894s). Apply power to the 144-Mc. driver stage and adjust the spacing of the turns in L_2 and the degree of coupling between L_1 and L_2 for maximum tripler grid current. This should be about 3 ma.

Next apply plate and screen voltage to the tripler and tune C_1 for maximum grid current in the amplifier, with no plate or screen voltage to the latter. Adjust the position of the grid lines with respect to the plate circuit, readjusting C_1 whenever a change is made, until at least 4 ma. grid current is obtained.

Now connect a lamp load across the output terminal, J_2. Ordinary house lamps are not suitable. A fair load can be made by connecting 6 or more blue-bead pilot lamps in parallel. This can be done by wrapping a $\frac{1}{4}$-inch copper strap

around the brass bases and soldering them all together. Then another strap should be soldered to the lead terminals. Apply plate and screen voltage and tune C_2 for maximum lamp brilliance. It should be possible to develop a very bright glow in the 6-lamp load with a plate current of about 100 ma. at 300 volts.

Cut drive very briefly to check for oscillation in the final stage. Grid current should drop to zero. The screen and grid resistors shown are for operation with plate modulation. More input can be run if the screen or grid resistance is decreased, but this should be done only when the rig is to be used for f.m. or c.w. service.

Operating conditions are about as follows: tripler grid current — 2 to 3 ma.; amplifier grid current — 3 to 4 ma.; tripler plate and screen current — 90 ma.; amplifier plate and screen current — 110 ma.; output — 12 watts.

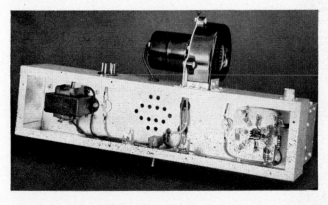

Fig. 17-37—Bottom view of the 432-Mc. transmitter.

CHAPTER 18

V.H.F. Antennas

While the basic principles of antenna design remain the same at all frequencies where conventional elements and transmission lines are used, certain aspects of v.h.f. work call for changes in antenna techniques above 50 Mc. Here the physical size of arrays is reduced to the point where some form of antenna having gain over a simple halfwave dipole can be used in almost any location, and the rotatable high-gain directional array has become a standard feature of all well-equipped v.h.f. stations. The importance of antenna gain in v.h.f. work cannot be over-emphasized. By no other means can so large a return be obtained from a small investment as results from the erection of a good directional array.

● DESIGN CONSIDERATIONS

At 50 Mc. and higher it is usually important to have the antenna work well over all or most of the band in question, and as the bands are wider than at lower frequencies the attention of the designer must be focused on broad frequency response. This may be attained in some instances through sacrificing other qualities such as high front-to-back ratio.

The loss in a given length of transmission line rises with frequency. V.h.f. feedlines should be kept as short as possible, therefor. Matching of the impedances of the antenna and transmission line should be done with care, and in open locations a high-gain antenna at relatively low height may be preferable to a low-gain system at great height. Wherever possible, however, the v.h.f.

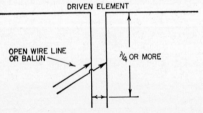

DRIVEN ELEMENT

OPEN WIRE LINE OR BALUN

λ/4 OR MORE

Fig. 18-1—Combination tuning and matching stub for v.h.f. arrays. Sliding short is used to tune out reactance of the driven element or phasing system. Transmission line, either balanced or coax, is connected at the point of lowest standing-wave ratio. Adjustment procedure is outlined in text.

array should be well above heavy foliage, buildings, power lines or other obstructions.

The physical size of a v.h.f. array is usually more important than the number of elements. A 4-element array for 432 Mc. may have as much gain over a dipole as a similarly designed array for 144 Mc., but it will intercept only one-third as much energy in receiving. Thus to be equal in communication, the 432-Mc. array must equal the 144-Mc. antenna in *capture area*, requiring three times as many elements, if similar element configurations are used in both.

Polarization

Early v.h.f. work was done with simple antennas, and since the vertical dipole gave as good results in all directions as its horizontal counterpart offered in only two directions, vertical polarization became the accepted standard. Later when high-gain antennas came into use it was only natural that these, too, were put up vertical in areas where v.h.f. activity was already well established.

When the discovery of various forms of long-distance propagation stirred interest in v.h.f. operation in areas where there was no previous experience, many newcomers started in with horizontal arrays, these having been more or less standard practice on frequencies with which these operators were familiar. As use of the same polarization at both ends of the path is necessary for best results, this lack of standardization resulted in a conflict that, even now, has not been completely resolved.

Tests have shown no large difference in results over long paths though evidence points to a slight superiority for horizontal in certain kinds of terrain, but vertical has other factors in its favor. Horizontal arrays are generally easier to build and rotate. Where ignition noise and other forms of man-made interference are present, horizontal systems usually provide better signal-to-noise ratio. Simple 3- or 4-element arrays are more effective horizontal than vertical, as their radiation patterns are broad in the plane of the elements and sharp in a plane perpendicular to them.

Vertical systems can provide uniform coverage in all directions, a feature that is possible only with fairly complex horizontal arrays. Gain can be built up without introducing directivity, an important feature in net operation, or in locations where the installation of rotatable systems is not possible. Mobile operation is simpler with vertical antennas. Fear of increased TVI has kept v.h.f. men in densely populated areas from adopting horizontal as a standard.

The factors favoring horizontal have been predominant on 50 Mc., and today we find it the standard for that band, except for emergency net operation involving mobile units. The slight advantage it offers in DX work has accelerated the trend to horizontal on 144 Mc. and higher bands, though vertical polarization is still widely used. The picture on 144, 220 and 420 Mc. is still confused, the tendency being to follow the local

Impedance Matching

trend. The newcomer should check with local amateurs to see which polarization is in general use in the area he expects to cover. Eventual standardization should be a major objective, and to this end it is recommended that horizontal polarization be established in areas where activity is developing for the first time.

● IMPEDANCE MATCHING

Because line losses increase with frequency it is important that v.h.f. antenna systems be matched to their transmission lines carefully. Lines commonly used in v.h.f. work include open-wire, usually 300 to 500 ohms impedance, spaced ½ to two inches; polyethylene-insulated flexible lines, available in 300, 150 and 72 ohms impedance; and coaxial lines of 50 to 90 ohms impedance.

The various methods of matching antenna and line impedance are described in detail in Chapter 14. Matching devices commonly used in v.h.f. arrays fed with balanced lines include the folded dipole in its various forms, Fig. 14-42, the "T" Match, Fig. 14-45, the "Q" section, Fig. 14-41, and the adjustable stub, Fig. 18-1. The gamma match, useful for feeding the driven element of a parasitic array with coaxial line, is shown in schematic form in Fig. 14-45. Balanced loads such as a split dipole or a folded dipole can be fed with coax through a balun, as shown in Fig. 14-46. Practical examples of the use of these devices are shown in the following pages. The principles upon which their operation depends are explained in Chapter 14, with the exception of the adjustable stub of Fig. 18-1.

The Corrective Stub

The adjustable stub shown in Fig. 18-1 provides a means of matching the antenna to the transmission line and also tuning out reactance in the driven element. It is, in effect, a tuning device to which the transmission line may be connected at the point where impedances match. Both the shorting stub and the point of connection are made adjustable, though once the proper points are found the connections may be made permanent.

For antenna experiments the stub may be made of tubing, and the connections made with sliding clips. In a permanent installation a stub of open-wire line, with all connections soldered, may be more satisfactory mechanically. The transmission line may be open-wire or Twin-Lead, connected directly to the stub, or coaxial line of any impedance, which should be connected through a balun.

To adjust the stub start with the short at a point about a half wavelength below the antenna, moving the point of connection of the transmission line up and down the stub until the lowest standing-wave ratio is achieved. Then move the shorting stub a small amount and readjust the line connection for lowest s.w.r. again. If the minimum s.w.r. is lower than at the first point checked the short

was moved in the right direction. Continue in that direction, readjusting the line connection each time, until the s.w.r. is as close to 1:1 as possible. When adjustments are completed the portion of the stub below the short can be cut off, if this is desirable mechanically.

● TYPES OF V.H.F. ARRAYS

Directional antenna systems commonly used in amateur v.h.f. work are of three general types, the collinear, the Yagi, and the plane reflector

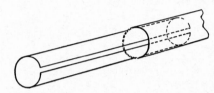

Fig. 18-2—Inserts for the ends of the elements in a v.h.f. array provide a means of adjustment of length for optimum performance. Short pieces of the element material are sawed lengthwise and compressed to fit inside the element ends.

array. Collinear systems have two or more driven elements end to end, fed in phase, usually backed up by parasitic reflectors. The Yagi has a single driven element, with one or more parasitic elements in front and in back of the driven element, all in the same plane. The plane-reflector array has a large reflecting surface in back of its driven element or elements. This may be a sheet of metal, a metal screen, or closely spaced rods or wires. The reflector may be a flat plane, or it can be bent into several forms, such as the corner and the parabola.

Examples of all three types are described, and each has points in its favor. The collinear systems such as the 12- and 16-element arrays of Figs. 18-14 and 18-15 require little or no adjustment and they present few feed problems. They work well over a wide band of frequencies. Yagi, or parasitic arrays, Figs. 18-5 to 18-10, depend on fairly precise tuning of their elements for gain, and thus work over a narrower frequency range. They are simple mechanically, however, and usually offer more gain for a given number of elements than do the collinear systems. Plane- and corner-reflector arrays are broadband devices, having broad forward lobes and high front-to-back ratio. They are easily adjusted, but somewhat cumbersome mechanically.

● ELEMENT LENGTHS AND SPACINGS

Designing a v.h.f. array presents both mechanical and electrical problems. The electrical problems are basic, and their solution involves choosing the type of performance most desired. Mechanical design, on the other hand, can be subject to almost endless variations, and the form that the array will take can usually be decided by the materials and tools available. One common

TABLE 18-I

Dimensions for V.H.F. Arrays in Inches

Freq. (Mc.)	52*	146*	222.5*	435*
Driven Element	106.5	38	24⅞	12¾
Change per Mc.*	2	0.25	0.12	0.03
Reflector	111½	40	26⅛	13⅜
1st Director	101½	36	23⅝	12⅛
2nd Director	99½	35¾	23⅜	12
3rd Director	97½	35	23	11⅞
1.0 Wavelength	234	81	53	27
0.625 Wavelength	147	50½	33⅛	16¾
0.5 Wavelength	117	40½	26½	13.5
0.25 Wavelength	58½	20¼	13¼	6¾
0.2 Wavelength	47	16	10⅝	5⅜
0.15 Wavelength	35	12	8	4
Balun loop (coax)	76	26.5	17¼	8¾

* Dimensions given for element lengths are for the middle of each band. For other frequencies adjust lengths as shown in the third line of table. Example: A dipole for 50.0 Mc. would be 106.5 + 4 = 110.5 inches.

Apply change figure to parasitic elements as well.

For phasing lines or matching sections, and for spacing between elements, the midband figures are sufficiently accurate. They apply only to open-wire lines.

Parasitic-element lengths are optimum for 0.2 wavelength spacing.

source of materials for amateur arrays is commercially built TV antennas. They can often be revamped for the amateur v.h.f. bands with a minimum of effort and expense.

Dimensions for Yagi or collinear arrays and their matching devices can be taken from Table 18-I. The driven element is usually cut to the formula:

$$Length \text{ (in inches)} = \frac{5540}{Freq. \text{ (Mc.)}}.$$

This is the basis of the lengths in Table 18-I, which are suitable for the tubing or rod sizes commonly used. Arrays for 50 Mc. usually have ½ to 1-inch elements. For 144 Mc. ¼ to ½-inch stock is common. Rod or tubing ⅛ to ⅜ inch in diameter is suitable for 220 and 420 Mc. Note that the element lengths in the table are for the middle of the band concerned. For peaked performance at other frequencies the element lengths

should be altered according to the figures in the third line of the table.

Reflector elements are usually about 5 per cent longer than the driven element. The director nearest the driven element is 5 per cent shorter, and others are progressively shorter, as shown in the table. Parasitic elements should also be adjusted according to Line 3 of the table, if peak performance is desired at some frequency other than midband.

Parasitic element lengths of Table 18-I are based on element spacings of 0.2 wavelength. This is most often used in v.h.f. arrays, and is suitable for up to 4 or 5 elements. Other spacings can be used, however. If the element lengths are adjusted properly there is little difference in gain with reflector spacings of 0.15 to 0.25 wavelength. The closer the reflector is to the driven element,

Fig. 18-3—Omnidirectional vertical array for 144 Mc. Elements of aluminum clothesline wire are mounted on ceramic standoff insulators screwed to a wooden pole. Feedline shown is 52-ohm coax, with a balun at the feedpoint. Twin-Lead or other 300-ohm balanced line may also be used, but it should be brought away horizontally from the supporting pole and elements for at least a quarter wavelength. Coax may be taped to the support.

the shorter it must be for optimum forward gain, and the greater will be its effect on the driven element impedance.

Directors may also be spaced over a similar range. Closer spacing than 0.2 wavelength for arrays of two or three elements will require a longer director than shown in Table 18-I. Thus it can be seen that close-spaced arrays tend to work over a narrower frequency range than wide-spaced ones, when they are tuned for best performance. They also result in lower driven-element impedance, making them more difficult to feed properly. Spacings less than 0.15 wavelength are not commonly used in v.h.f. arrays for these reasons.

Practical Designs for V.H.F. Arrays

The antenna systems pictured and described herewith are examples of ways in which the information in Table 18-I can be used in arrays of proven performance. Dimensions can be taken from the table, except where otherwise noted. If

the builder wishes to experiment with element adjustment, a simple method is shown in Fig. 18-2. With elements ½-inch or larger diameter a piece of the element material can be used. It is sawed lengthwise and then compressed to make

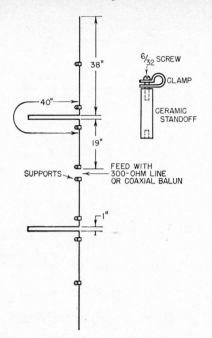

Fig. 18-4—Dimensions and supporting method for the 144-Mc. vertical array.

a tight fit inside the end of the element.

A readily available material often used for elements in arrays for 144 Mc. and higher is aluminum clothesline wire. This is a stiff hard-drawn wire about $\frac{1}{8}$ inch in diameter. It should be used in preference to a similar-appearing wire commonly sold for TV grounding purposes. The latter is too soft to make satisfactory elements if the length is more than about two feet.

A Collinear Array for 144 Mc.

Where a vertically-polarized array having some gain over a dipole is needed, yet directivity is undesirable, collinear halfwave elements may be mounted vertically and fed in phase, as shown in Figs. 18-3 and 18-4. Such an array may have 3 elements, as shown, or 5. The impedance at the center is approximately 300 ohms, permitting it to be fed directly with TV-type line, or through a coaxial balun, as in the model shown. Either 52- or 72-ohm line may be employed without serious mismatch.

The array is made from two pieces of aluminum clothesline wire about 97 inches long overall. These are bent to provide a 38-inch top section, a folded-back 40-inch phasing loop, and a 19-inch center section. These elements are mounted on ceramic pillars, which are fastened to a round wooden pole. Small clamps of sheet aluminum are wrapped around the elements and screwed to the stand-offs. A cheaper but somewhat less desirable method of mounting is to use TV screw-eye insulators to hold the elements in place.

Feeding the array at the center with a coaxial balun makes a neat arrangement. The balun loop may be taped to the vertical support, and the

coaxial line likewise taped at intervals down the mast. The same type of construction can be applied to a 220-Mc. vertical collinear array, using the lengths for that band given in Table 18-I.

● PARASITIC ARRAYS

Single-bay arrays of 2 to 5 elements are widely used in 50-Mc. work. These may be built in many different ways, using the dimensions given in the table. Probably the strongest and lightest structure results from use of aluminum or dural tubing (usually $1\frac{1}{4}$ to $1\frac{1}{2}$ inches in diameter) for the boom, though wood is also usable. If the elements are mounted at their midpoints there is no need to use insulating supports. Usually the elements are run through the boom and clamped in place in a manner similar to that shown in Fig. 18-12. Where a metal boom is used the joints between it and the elements must be tight, as any movement at this point will result in noisy reception.

2-Element 50-Mc. Array

The 2-element antenna of Fig. 18-5 was designed for portable use, but it is also suitable for fixed-station work with minor modification. The 2-meter array above it is described later. The elements are made in three sections, for portability, using inserts similar to that shown in Fig. 18-2. The driven element is gamma matched for coax feed, and the parasitic element is a 0.15-wavelength spaced director. Details of

Fig. 18-5—Two-element 50-Mc. and four-element 144-Mc. arrays designed for portable use. Support is sectional TV masting clamped to car door handle. Elements of 50-Mc. array are made in three sections, for stowing in back of car. Antenna for 144 Mc. is cut-down TV array. Both use gamma match, as shown in Fig. 18-6.

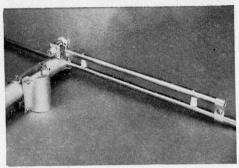

Fig. 18-6—Details of the gamma match for the 50-Mc. portable array. In a permanent installation the variable capacitor should be mounted in an inverted plastic cup or other device to protect it from the weather. The gamma arm is about 12 inches long for 50 Mc., 5 inches for 144 Mc.

the gamma section, the boom and its supporting clamp are shown in Fig. 18-6. The arm is about 12 inches long, and the capacitor is a 50-μμf. variable. Clean, tight connections between the arm and element are important. Where the array is to be mounted permanently outdoors the capacitor may be protected from the weather by mounting it in an inverted plastic cup. More details on this array are given in August, 1955, *QST*.

3-Element Lightweight Array

The 3-element 50-Mc. array of Fig. 18-7 weighs only 5 pounds. It uses the closest spacing that is practical for v.h.f. applications, in order to make an antenna that could be used individually or stacked in pairs without requiring a cumbersome support. The elements are half-inch aluminum tubing of 1/16-inch wall thickness, attached to the 1¼-inch dural boom with aluminum castings made for the purpose. (Dick's, RR1, Tiffin, Ohio, Type HASL.) By limiting the element spacing to 0.15 wavelength the boom is only 6 feet long. Two booms for a stacked array (Fig. 18-11) can thus be cut from a single 12-foot length of tubing.

The folded-dipole driven element has No. 12 wire for the fed portions. These are mounted on ¾-inch cone standoff insulators and joined to the outer ends of the main portion by means of metal pillars and 6-32 screws and nuts. When the wires are pulled up tightly and wrapped around the screw, solder should be sweated over the nuts and screw ends to seal the whole against weather corrosion. The same treatment should be used at each standoff. Mount a soldering lug on the ceramic cone and wrap the end of the lug around the wire and solder the whole assembly together. These joints and other portions of the array may be sprayed with clear lacquer as an additional protection.

The inner ends of the folded dipole are 1½ inches apart. Slip the dipole into its aluminum casting, and then

drill through both element and casting with a No. 36 drill, and tap with 6-32 thread. Suitable inserts for mounting the stand-offs can be made by cutting the heads off 6-32 screws. Taper the cut end of the screw slightly with a file and it will screw into the standoff readily.

Cut the dipole length according to Table 18-I, for the middle of the frequency range you expect to use most. The reflector and director will be approximately 4 per cent longer and shorter, respectively. The closer spacing of the parasitic elements (0.15 wavelength) makes this deviation from the dimensions of the table desirable.

The single 3-element array has a feed impedance of about 200 ohms at its resonant frequency. Thus it may be fed with 52-ohm coax and a balun. A gamma-matched dipole may also be used, as in the 2-element array. If the gamma match and 72-ohm coax are used, a balun will convert to 300-ohm balanced feed, if Twin-Lead or 300-ohm open-wire TV line feed is desired. If the dimensions are selected for optimum performance at 50.5 Mc. the array will show good performance and fairly low standing-wave ratio over the range from 50 to 51.5 Mc.

A closeup of a mounting method for this or any other array using a round boom is shown in Fig. 18-8. Four TV-type U bolts clamp the horizontal and vertical members together. The metal plate is about 6 inches square. If ¼-inch sheet aluminum is available it may be used alone, though the photograph shows a sheet of 1/16-inch stock backed up by a piece of wood of the same size for stiffening.

High-Performance 4-Element Array

The 4-element array of Fig. 18-9 was designed for maximum forward gain, and for direct feed with 300-ohm balanced transmission line. The parasitic elements may be any diameter from ½ to 1 inch, but the driven element should be made as shown in the sketch. The same general arrangement may be used for a 3-element array, except that the solid portion of the dipole should

Fig. 18-7—Lightweight 3-element 50-Mc. array. Feedline is 52-ohm coax, with a balun for connection to the folded-dipole driven element. Balun may be coiled as shown or taped to supporting pipe.

Parasitic Arrays

be ¾-inch tubing instead of 1-inch. With the element lengths given the array will give nearly uniform response from 50 to 51.5 Mc., and usable gain to above 52 Mc. It may be peaked for any portion of the band by using the information in Table 18-I.

If a shorter boom is desired, the reflector spacing can be reduced to 0.15 wavelength and both

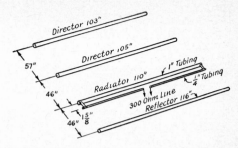

Fig. 18-9—Details of a 4-element 50-Mc. array designed for 300-ohm balanced feed. Element lengths and spacings were derived experimentally for optimum performance over the first 1.5 megacycles of the band.

Fig. 18-8—Closeup photograph of the boom mounting for the 50-Mc. array. A sheet of aluminum 6 inches square is backed up by a piece of wood of the same size. TV-type U clamps hold the boom and vertical support together at right angles. At the left of the mounting assembly is one of the aluminum castings for holding the beam elements.

directors spaced 0.2 or even 0.15 wavelength, with only a slight reduction in forward gain and bandwidth.

5-Element 50-Mc. Array

As aluminum or dural tubing is usually sold in 12-foot lengths this dimension imposes a practical limitation on the construction of a 50-Mc. beam. A 5-element array that makes optimum use of a 12-foot boom may be built according to Table 18-I. If the aluminum casting method of mounting elements shown for the 3-element array is employed the weight of a 5-element beam can be held to under 10 pounds. The gamma match and coaxial line are recommended for feeding such an array, though a balun and 72-ohm coax can be used for the rotating portion of the line, converting to balanced feed at the anchor point.

Elements should be spaced 0.15 wavelength, or about 36 inches. With 5 or more elements, good bandwidth can be secured by tapering the element lengths properly. A dipole 110 inches long, with a 116-inch reflector, and directors of 105, 103 and 101 inches respectively will work well over the first two megacycles of the band, provided that the s.w.r. is adjusted for optimum at 51 Mc.

Long Yagis for 50 Mc.

With boom lengths greater than about 12 feet and with more elements than 4, somewhat

better performance can be obtained by using gradually increasing spacing between the directors. The 6-element array in Fig. 18-10 is an example of this approach. It also employs a variation of the gamma match that has mechanical advantages. The long boom and wide-spaced elements give a sharpness of horizontal pattern that is not obtainable with the same number of elements in a stacked array.

The long Yagi is not a broadband device. This one works well over the first megacycle of the band with the following dimensions. Subtract 2 inches from each element for each megacycle

Fig. 18-10—A 6-element long Yagi for 50 Mc. and a 16-element collinear array for 144 Mc. Both are all-metal construction. Each has its own vertical member, which is clamped to the rotating vertical pipe that runs down through the tower bearing.

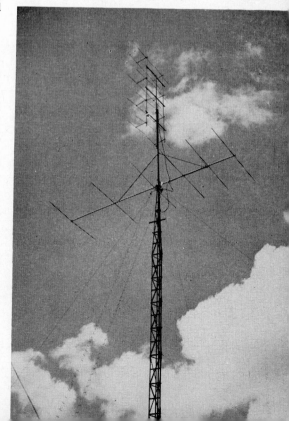

higher. Reflector — 116 inches. Driven element — 110.5. First director — 105.5. Second director — 104. Third director — 102.75. Fourth director — 101.5. Spacings are, from back forward: 36, 36, 42, 59 and 70 inches. If a longer array is to be built each additional director should be 70 inches from the last.

Construction

The long Yagi is built similar to the 3-element array of Fig. 18-7 and 18-8, using those same castings for mounting the elements. The gusset plate for fastening the boom to the vertical support is made larger, and four U bolts are used on each member instead of two. The array is mounted at its center of gravity, rather than at its physical center. The boom is braced to prevent drooping, at points about 5 feet out from the mounting point. Braces are aluminum tubing, flattened at the ends, and clamped to the boom and the vertical member. Suspension bracing, as shown in Fig. 18-10, provides strength with lightweight supports.

The dimensions given require a boom slightly more than 20 feet long. This was made up by splicing, but if a 20-foot length is available in one piece the spacings of the two forward directors can be made slightly less, in order to avoid splicing. Element spacing is not particularly critical, but lengths are fairly so.

The Gamma Match

The gamma match is ideal for matching arrays fed with coax. The arrangement shown in Fig. 18-11 combines the adjustable arm with the series capacitor, and provides a rugged assembly that can be weather-proofed readily. The main arm is cut from the same material as the elements, 15 inches long. It is supported parallel to the driven element by means of two 1-inch ceramic standoffs and sheet-aluminum clips. Its inner end is connected to the inner conductor of a coaxial fitting, mounted on a small bracket screwed to the boom.

The series capacitor, for tuning out the reactance of the matching arm and making connection to the driven element, is ¼-inch rod or tubing 14 inches long. It is maintained coaxial with the main arm by two polystyrene bushings. One is force-fitted to the end of the rod and the other is fitted tightly inside the main arm to act as a bearing. These can be made from ⅜-inch rod stock, or National Type PRC-1 forms can be adapted readily to the purpose. A clip of sheet aluminum connects the rod and the driven element. Be sure that a clean tight contact is made at this point.

Adjustment

Matching requires an s.w.r. bridge. It can be done properly in no other way. Mount the beam at least a half wavelength above ground and clear of trees and wires by at least the same distance. Set the transmitter at a frequency in the middle of the range you want to work (50.3 is a good spot for low-end operation) and adjust the position of the clip and the length of the rod outside the main arm for minimum s.w.r. Move first one variable and then the other until zero reflected power is indicated. Tighten the clip solidly, tape over the junction between the arm and the rod with waterproof tape, and the array is ready for use.

● 144-MC. PARASITIC ARRAYS

The main features of the arrays described above can be adapted to 144-Mc. antennas, but the small physical size of arrays for this frequency makes it possible to use larger numbers of elements with ease. Few 2-meter antennas have less than 4 or 5 elements, and most stations use more, either in a single bay or in stacked systems.

Parasitic arrays for 144 Mc. can be made readily from TV antennas for Channels 4, 5 or 6. The relatively close spacing normally used in TV arrays makes it possible to approximate the recommended 0.2 wavelength at 144 Mc., though the element spacing is not a critical factor. A 4-element array for 144 Mc. made from a Channel 6 TV Yagi is shown in Fig. 18-5. It is fed with a gamma match and 52-ohm coax, and was designed primarily for portable work. As most TV antennas are designed for 300-ohm feed the same feed system can be employed for the 2-meter array that is made from them.

If one wishes to build his own Yagi antennas from available tubing sizes, the boom of a 2-meter antenna should be ¾ to 1 inch aluminum

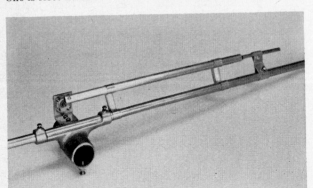

Fig. 18-11—Details of the gamma match used on the 6-element 50-Mc. array. Series capacitor is formed by sliding a rod or tube inside the main arm.

or dural. Elements can be ¼ to ½-inch stock, fastened to the boom as shown in Fig. 18-12. Recommended spacing for up to 6 elements is 0.2 wavelength, though this is not too critical. Gamma match feed is recommended for coax, or a folded dipole and balun may be used. If balanced line is to be used the folded dipole is

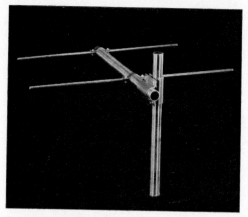

Fig. 18-12—Model showing method of assembling all-metal arrays for 144 Mc. and higher frequencies. Dimensions of clamps are given in Fig. 18-16.

recommended, the 4 to 1 ratio of conductor sizes being about right for most designs.

Very high gain can be obtained with long Yagi-type arrays for 144 Mc. and higher frequencies, though the bandwidth of such antennas is considerably narrower than for those having up to 4 or 5 elements. The first two directors in long Yagis are usually spaced about 0.1 wavelength. The third is spaced about 0.2, increasing to 0.4 wavelength or so for the forward directors. Highest gain is obtained when all directors are made the same length, but better front-to-back ratio and lower side lobe content results if the director lengths are tapered ⅛ to ¼ inch per director. Tapering the element lengths also widens the effective bandwidth. There is more on long Yagis in *QST* for January and September, 1956.

● STACKED YAGI ARRAYS

The gain (in power) obtainable from a single Yagi array can be more than doubled by stacking two or more of them vertically and feeding them in phase. This refers to horizontal systems, of course. Vertically-polarized bays are usually stacked side by side. The principles to follow apply in either case.

The spacing between bays should be at least one-half wavelength, and more is desirable. For dipoles or Yagis of up to three elements optimum spacing between bays is about ⅝ wavelength, but with longer Yagis the spacing can be increased to one wavelength or more. Bays of 5 elements or more, spaced one wavelength, are commonly used in antennas for 144 Mc. and higher frequencies. Optimum spacing for long Yagis is about two wavelengths.

Where half-wave stacking is to be employed, the phasing line between bays can be treated as a double "Q" section. If two bays, each designed for 300-ohm feed, are to be stacked a half wavelength apart and fed at the midpoint between them, the phasing line should have an impedance of about 380 ohms. No. 12 wire spaced one inch will do for this purpose. The midpoint then can be fed either with 300-ohm line, or with 72-ohm coax and a balun.

When a spacing of ⅝ wavelength between bays is employed, the phasing lines can be coax. (The velocity factor of coax makes a full wavelength of line actually about ⅝ wavelength physically.) The impedance at the midpoint between two bays is slightly less than half the impedance of either bay alone, due to the coupling between bays. This effect decreases with increased spacing.

When two bays are spaced a full wavelength the coupling is relatively slight. The phasing line can be any open-wire line, and the impedance at the midpoint will be approximately half that of the individual bays. Predicting what it will be with a given set of dimensions is difficult, as many factors come into play. It will usually be of a value that can be fed through the combination of a "Q" section and a transmission line of 300 to 450 ohms impedance. An adjustable "Q" section, or an adjustable stub like the one shown in Fig. 18-1, may be used when the antenna impedance is not known.

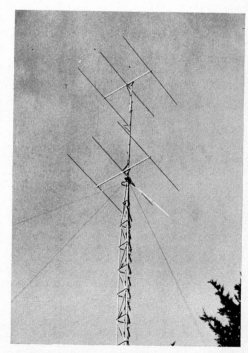

Fig. 18-13—Stacked array for 50 Mc. using two of the 3-element bays of Fig. 18-7. Phasing system and flexible section for rotation are of coaxial line. A "Q" section matches this to 450-ohm open-wire line for run to the station.

The stacked 3-over-3 for 50 Mc., Fig. 18-13, uses a coaxial phasing line and an additional section of coax to provide for the flexible portion of the feedline. Each bay is fed with a balun and halfwave section of RG-8/U cable. These are joined at the center between bays with a Tee fitting. As each bay has an impedance of 200 ohms, two 50-ohm leads are paralleled at the center, resulting in an impedance of about 20 ohms, when the coupling effect between bays is included. A flexible section of 50-ohm coax one wavelength long, with a balun at the end, steps this up to about 80 ohms. A "Q" section of ¼-inch tubing ¾ inch center to center steps this up to the point where it can be fed with 450-ohm open-wire TV line.

The "Twin-Five" for 144 Mc.

A popular stacked array for 144-Mc. work is the Twin-Five, originally developed by W2PAU [1]. In this design two 5-element arrays of standard design are stacked a full wavelength apart. If the folded-dipole driven elements are constructed so that the individual bays have a feed impedance of about 400 ohms the midpoint of the open-wire phasing line can be fed with 52-ohm coax and a balun. Where open-wire line is desired, the impedances can be matched through a "Q" section of about 300 ohms impedance. If the constructor is in doubt as to the actual feed impedance to be matched, the stub arrangement of Fig. 18-1 will take care of a wide range of impedances and lines to be matched. Dimensions can be taken from Table 18-I.

An effective 20-element array can be made by using two of these arrays side by side, with full-wave spacing horizontally also. The impedance at the midpoint of the horizontal phasing line will then be about 100 ohms, which is still well within the range of "Q" sections of practical dimensions.

● LARGE COLLINEAR ARRAYS FOR 144 MC. AND HIGHER

High gain and very broad frequency response are desirable characteristics found in curtains of half-wave elements fed in phase and backed up by reflectors. The reflector can be made up of parasitic elements, or it can be a screen extending approximately a quarter wavelength beyond the ends of the driven elements. There is not a large difference between the two types of reflectors, except that higher front-to-back ratio and somewhat broader frequency response are achieved with the plane reflector.

12- and 16-Element Arrays

Two collinear systems that may be used on 144, 220 or 420 Mc. are shown in Figs. 18-14 and 18-15. Either may be fed directly with 300-ohm transmission line, or through coaxial line and a balun. In the 12-element array, Fig. 18-14, the reflectors are spaced 0.15 wavelength in back of

[1] Brown — "The Wide-Spread Twin-Five" *CQ*, March, 1950.

the driven elements, while the 16-element array, Figs. 18-15 and 18-10, uses 0.2 wavelength spacing. Dimensions may be taken from Table 18-I, and figures for the middle of the band will give good performance across either band.

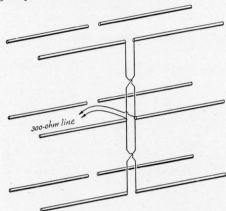

Fig. 18-14—Element arrangement and feed system of the 12-element array. Reflectors are spaced 0.15 wavelength behind the driven elements.

The supporting frame for either array may be made of wood or metal. Details of a metal support for the 12-element array are shown in Figs. 18-16 and 18-17. Note that all elements are mounted at their midpoints, and that no insulators are used. The elements are mounted in front of the supporting frame, to keep metal out of the field of the array. This method is preferable to that wherein mechanical balance is maintained

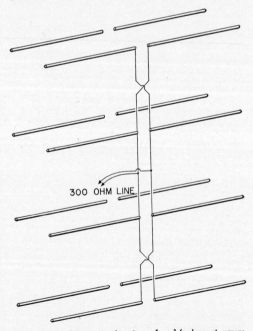

Fig. 18-15—Schematic drawing of a 16-element array. A variable "Q" section may be inserted at the feed point if accurate matching is desired. Reflector spacing is 0.2 wavelength.

Large Collinear Arrays

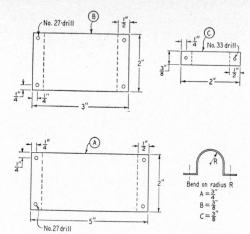

Fig. 18-16—Detail drawings of the clamps used to assemble the all-metal 2-meter array. A, B and C are before bending into "U" shape. The right-angle bends should be made first, along the dotted lines as shown, then the plates may be bent around a piece of pipe of the proper diameter. Sheet stock should be ¹⁄₁₆-inch or heavier aluminum.

through mounting the driven elements in front and the reflectors in back of the supporting structure.

Two 12-element arrays may be mounted one above the other and fed in phase, to form a 24-element array. This is done in the 420-Mc. array of Fig. 18-18. The two midpoints are connected

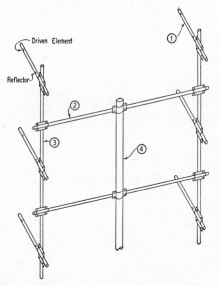

Fig. 18-17—Supporting framework for a 12-element 144-Mc. array of all-metal design. Dimensions are as follows: element supports (1) ¾ by 16 inches; horizontal members (2) ¾ by 46 inches; vertical members (3) ¾ by 86 inches; vertical support (4) 1½-inch diameter, length as required; reflector-to-driven-element spacing 12 inches. Parts not shown in sketch: driven elements ¼ by 38 inches; reflectors ¼ by 40 inches; phasing lines No. 18 spaced 1 inch, 80 inches long, fanned out to 3½ inches at driven elements (transpose each half-wave section).

through a phasing line one wavelength long, and the center of this phasing line fed through a "Q" section. The impedance at the midpoint is about 150 ohms, requiring a 255-ohm "Q" section for feeding with 450-ohm open-wire line.

Combination of collinear arrays may be carried further. Pairs of 16-element systems fed in phase are common, and even 64-element arrays (4 16-element beams fed in phase) are used in some leading stations on 144 Mc. Configurations of 32 to 64 elements are not difficult to build and support at 220 or 420 Mc. Examples of 16- and 24-element arrays for 220 and 420 Mc. are shown mounted back to back in Fig. 18-18.

● ARRAYS FOR 220 AND 420 MC.

The use of high-gain antenna systems is almost a necessity if work is to be done over any great distance on 220 and 420 Mc. Experimentation with antenna arrays for these frequencies is fascinating indeed, as their size is so small as to permit trying various element arrangements and feed systems with ease. Arrays for 420 Mc., particularly, are convenient for study and demon-

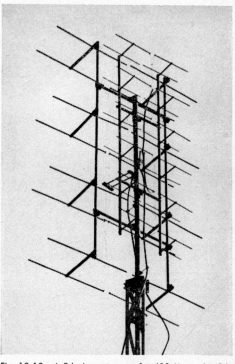

Fig. 18-18—A 24-element array for 420 Mc. and a 16-element for 220 mounted back-to-back on a single support.

stration of antenna principles, as even high-gain systems may be of table-top proportions.

Any of the arrays described previously may be used on these bands, but those having large numbers of driven elements in phase are more readily adjusted for maximum effectiveness.

A 16-element array for 220 Mc. and a 24-

element array for 420 Mc. are shown mounted back-to-back in Fig. 18-18. The 220-Mc. portion follows the 16-element design already described. It is fed at the center of the system with 300-ohm tubular Twin-Lead, matched to the center impedance of the array through a "Q" section of $\frac{7}{16}$-inch tubing, spaced about $1\frac{1}{2}$ inches center to center. This spacing was adjusted for minimum standing-wave ratio on the line.

Elements in the array shown are of $\frac{7}{16}$-inch aluminum fuel-line tubing, which is very light in weight and easily worked. The supporting structure is dural tubing, using the clamp assembly methods of Fig. 18-16.

The 420-Mc. array uses two 12-element assemblies similar to Fig. 18-14, mounted one above the other, about one half wavelength separating the bottom of one from the top of the other. The two sets of phasing lines are joined by one-wavelength sections of Twin-Lead at the middle of the array. This junction, which has an impedance of around 150 ohms, is fed with 300-ohm tubular Twin-Lead through an adjustable "Q" section.

Elements in the 420-Mc. array are cut from thin-walled $\frac{1}{4}$-inch tubing. Their supports are the $\frac{7}{16}$-inch stock used for the 220-Mc. elements. Slots were cut in the ends of these supports to take the elements, and a 4–40 screw was run through both pieces and drawn up tightly with a nut. The horizontal supports were fastened in holes drilled in the vertical members, and were also held in place with a 6-32 screw and nut. The small size and light weight of the 420-Mc. array require no clamps to make a strong assembly.

The two one-wavelength sections of 300-ohm line are $21\frac{3}{4}$ inches long, taking the propagation factor into account. The "Q" section may be any convenient size tubing, $\frac{1}{4}$ to $\frac{1}{2}$ inch diameter. It should be made adjustable, as matching is important at this frequency. Dimensions for both arrays can be taken from Table 18-I.

(For an example of stacking several commercial 220-Mc. beams, see Tilton, "A 66-Element Stacked-Yagi Array for 220 Mc.," *QST*, January, 1959.)

● MISCELLANEOUS ANTENNA SYSTEMS

Coaxial Antennas

At v.h.f. the lowest possible radiation angle is essential, and the coaxial antenna shown in Fig. 18-19 was developed to eliminate feeder radiation. The center conductor of a 70-ohm concentric (coaxial) line is extended one-quarter wave beyond the end of the line, to act as the upper half of a half-wave antenna. The lower half is provided by the quarter-wave sleeve, the upper end of which is connected to the outer conductor of the concentric line. The sleeve acts as a shield about the transmission line and very little current is induced on the outside of the line by the antenna field. The line is non-resonant, since its characteristic impedance is the same as the center impedance of the half-wave antenna. The sleeve may be made of copper or brass tub-

ing of suitable diameter to clear the transmission line. The coaxial antenna is somewhat difficult to construct, but is superior to simpler systems in its performance at low radiation angles.

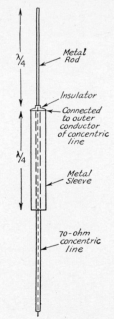

Fig. 18-19—Coaxial antenna. The insulated inner conductor of the 70-ohm concentric line is connected to the quarter-wave metal rod which forms the upper half of the antenna.

Broadband Antennas

Certain types of antennas used in television are of interest because they work across a wide band of frequencies with relatively uniform response. At very-high frequencies an antenna made of small wire is purely resistive only over a very small frequency range. Its Q, and therefore its selectivity, is sufficient to limit is optimum performance to a narrow frequency range, and readjustment of the length or tuning is required for each narrow slice of the spectrum. With tuned transmission lines, the effective length of the antenna can be shifted by retuning the whole system. However, in the case of antennas fed by matched-impedance lines, any appreciable frequency change requires an actual mechanical adjustment of the system. Otherwise, the resulting mismatch with the line will be sufficient to cause significant reduction in power input to the antenna.

A properly designed and constructed wideband antenna, on the other hand, will exhibit very nearly constant input impedance over several megacycles.

The simplest method of obtaining a broadband characteristic is the use of what is termed a "cylindrical" antenna. This is no more than a conventional doublet in which large-diameter tubing is used for the elements. The use of a relatively large diameter-to-length ratio lowers the Q of the antenna, thus broadening the resonance characteristic.

As the diameter-to-length ratio is increased, end effects also increase, with the result that the antenna must be made shorter than thin-

Miscellaneous Antenna Systems

wire antenna resonating at the same frequency. The reduction factor may be as much as 20 per cent with the tubing sizes commonly used for amateur antennas at v.h.f.

Plane-Reflector Arrays

At 220 Mc. and higher, where their dimensions become practicable, plane-reflector arrays are widely used. Except as it affects the impedance of the system, as shown in Fig. 18-20, the spacing between the driven elements and the reflecting plane is not particularly critical. Maximum gain occurs around 0.1 to 0.15 wavelength, which is also the region of lowest impedance. Highest impedance appears at about 0.3 wavelength. A plane reflector spaced 0.22 wavelength in back of the driven elements has no effect on their feed impedance. As the gain of a plane-reflector array is nearly constant at spacings from 0.1 to 0.25 wavelength, it may be seen that the spacing may be varied to achieve an impedance match.

An advantage of the plane reflector is that it may be used with two driven element systems, one on each side of the plane, providing for two-band operation, or the incorporation of horizontal and vertical polarization in a single structure. The gain of a plane-reflector array is slightly higher than that of a similar number of driven elements backed up by parasitic reflectors. It also has a broader frequency response and higher front-to-back ratio. To achieve these ends, the reflecting plane must be larger than the area of the driven elements, extending at least a quarter wavelength on all sides. Chicken wire on a wood or metal frame makes a good plane reflector. Closely spaced wires or rods may be substituted, with the spacing between them running up to 0.1 wavelength without appreciable reduction in effectiveness.

Cone Antennas

From the cylindrical antenna various specialized forms of broadly resonant radiators have been evolved, including the ellipsoid, spheroid, cone, diamond and double diamond. Of these, the conical antenna is perhaps the most interesting. With large angles of revolution, the variation in the characteristic impedance with changes in frequency can be reduced to a very low value, making such an antenna suitable for extremely wide-band operation. The cone may be made up either of sheet metal or of multiple wire spines. A variation of this form of conical antenna is widely used in TV reception.

Corner Reflectors

In the corner reflector two plane surfaces are set at an angle, usually between 45 and 90 degrees, with the antenna on a line bisecting this angle. Maximum gain is obtained with the antenna 0.5 wavelength from the vertex, but compromise designs can be built with closer spacings. There is no focal point, as would be the case for a parabolic reflector. Corner angles greater than 90 degrees can be used at some sacrifice in gain. At

less than 90 degrees the gain increases, but the size of the reflecting sheets must be increased to realize this gain.

At a spacing of 0.5 wavelength from the vertex, the impedance of the driven element is approximately twice that of the same dipole in free space. The impedance decreases with smaller spacings and corner angles, as shown in Fig. 18-20. The gain of a corner-reflector array with a 90-degree angle, 0.5 wavelength spacing and sides one wavelength long is approximately 10 db. Principal advantages of the corner reflector are broad frequency response and high front-to-back ratio.

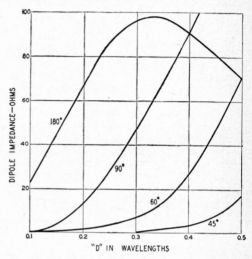

Fig. 18-20—Feed impedance of the driven element in a corner-reflector array for corner angles of 180 (flat sheet), 90, 60 and 45 degrees. "D" is the dipole-to-vertex spacing.

Parabolic Reflectors

A plane sheet may be formed into the shape of a parabolic curve and used with a driven radiator situated at its focus, to provide a highly directive antenna system. If the parabolic reflector is sufficiently large so that the distance to the focal point is a number of wavelengths, optical conditions are approached and the wave across the mouth of the reflector is a plane wave. However, if the reflector is of the same order of dimensions as the operating wavelength, or less, the driven radiator is appreciably coupled to the reflecting sheet and minor lobes occur in the pattern. With an aperture of the order of 10 or 20 wavelengths, sizes that may be practical for microwave work, a beam width of approximately 5 degrees may be achieved.

A reflecting paraboloid must be carefully designed and constructed to obtain ideal performance. The antenna must be located at the focal point. The most desirable focal length of the parabola is that which places the radiator along the plane of the mouth; this length is equal to one-half the mouth radius. At other focal distances interference fields may deform the pattern or cancel a sizable portion of the radiation.

CHAPTER 19

Mobile and Portable-Emergency Equipment

The amateur who goes in for mobile operation will find plenty of room for exercising his individuality and developing original ideas in equipment. Each installation has its special problems to be solved.

Most mobile receiving systems are designed around the use of a h.f. converter working into a standard car broadcast receiver tuned to 1500 kc. which serves as the i.f. and audio amplifiers. The car receiver is modified to take a noise limiter and provide power for the converter.

While a few mobile transmitters may run an input to the final amplifier as high as 100 watts or more, an input of about 30 watts normally is considered the practical limit unless the car is equipped with a special battery-charging system. The majority of mobile operators use phone.

In contemplating a mobile installation, the car should be studied carefully to determine the most suitable spots for mounting the equipment. Then the various units should be built in a form that will make best use of that space. The location of the converter should have first consideration. It should be placed where the controls can be operated conveniently without distracting attention from the wheel. The following list suggests spots that may be found suitable, depending upon the individual car.

On top of the instrument panel
Attached to the steering post
Under the instrument panel
In a unit made to fit between the lower lip of the instrument panel and the floor at the center of the car

The transmitter power control can be placed close to the receiver position, or included in the converter unit. This control normally operates relays, rather than to switch the power circuit directly. This permits a minimum length of heavy-current battery circuit. Frequency within any of the phone bands sometimes is changed remotely by means of a stepping-switch system that switches crystals. In most cases, however, it is necessary to stop the car to make the several changes required in changing bands.

Depending upon the size of the transmitter unit, one of the following places may be found convenient for mounting the transmitter:

In the glove compartment
Under the instrument panel
In a unit in combination with or without the converter, built to fit between the lower edge of the instrument panel and the floor at the center
On the ledge above the rear seat
In the trunk

Most mobile antennas consist of a vertical whip with some system of adjustable loading for the lower frequencies. Power supplies are of the vibrator, motor-generator, or transistor type operating from the car storage battery.

Units intended for use in mobile installations should be assembled with greater than ordinary care, since they will be subject to considerable vibration. Soldered joints should be well made and wire wrap-arounds should be used to avoid dependence upon the solder for mechanical strength. Self-tapping screws should be used wherever feasible, otherwise lock-washers should be provided. Any shafts that are normally operated at a permanent or semi-permanent setting should be provided with shaft locks so they cannot jar out of adjustment. Where wires pass through metal, the holes should be fitted with rubber grommets to prevent chafing. Any cabling or wiring between units should be securely clamped in place where it cannot work loose to interfere with the operation of the car.

Noise Elimination

Electrical-noise interference to reception in a car may arise from several different sources. As examples, trouble may be experienced with ignition noise, generator and voltage-regulator hash, or wheel and tire static.

A noise limiter added to the car broadcast receiver will go far in reducing some types, especially ignition noise from passing cars as well as your own. But for the satisfactory reception of weaker signals, some investigation and treatment of the car's electrical system will be necessary.

Ignition Interference

Fig. 19-1 indicates the measures that may be taken to suppress ignition interference. The capacitor at the primary of the ignition coil should be of the coaxial type; ordinary types are not effective. It should be placed as close to the coil terminal as possible. In stubborn cases, two

Noise Elimination

of these capacitors with an r.f. choke between them may provide additional suppression. The size of the choke must be determined experimentally. The winding should be made with wire heavy enough to carry the coil primary current. A 10,000-ohm suppressor resistor should be inserted at the center tower of the distributor, a 5000-ohm suppressor at each spark-plug tower on the distributor, and a 10,000 ohm suppressor at each spark plug. The latter may be built-in or external. A good suppressor element should be molded of material having low capacitance. Several concerns manufacture satisfactory suppressors. In extreme cases, it may be necessary to use shielded ignition wire. Suppressor ignition wire kits having the resistance distributed throughout the length of the wire are available from some automobile supply dealers. Distributed resistance of this type is somewhat superior to lumped resistance and may be used if the lead lengths are right to fit your car. They should not be cut, but used as they are sold.

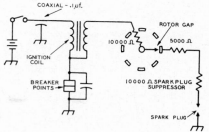

Fig. 19-1—Ignition system with recommended suppression methods.

Generator Noise

Generator hash is caused by sparking at the commutator. The pitch of the noise varies with the speed of the motor. This type of noise may be eliminated by using a 0.1- to 0.25-μf. coaxial capacitor in the generator armature circuit. This capacitor should be mounted as near the armature terminal as possible and directly on the frame of the generator.

To reduce the noise at 28 Mc., it may be necessary to insert a parallel trap, tuned to the middle of the band, in series with the generator output lead. The coil should have about 8 turns of No. 10 wire, space-wound on a 1-inch diameter and should be shunted with a 30-μμf. mica trimmer. It can be pretuned by putting it in the antenna lead to the home-station receiver tuned to the middle of the band, and adjusting the trap to the point of minimum noise. The tuning may need to be peaked up after installing in the car, since it is fairly critical.

Voltage-Regulator Interference

In eliminating voltage-regulator noise, the use of two coaxial capacitors, and a resistor-mica-capacitor combination, as shown in Fig. 19-2, are effective. A 0.1- to 0.25-μf. coaxial capacitor should be placed between the battery terminal of the regulator and the battery, with its case well

grounded. Another capacitor of the same size and type should be placed between the generator terminal of the regulator and the generator. A 0.002-μf. mica capacitor with a 4-ohm carbon resistor in series should be connected between the field terminal of the regulator and ground. Never use a capacitor across the field contacts or between field and ground without the resistor in series, since this greatly reduces the life of the

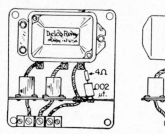

Fig. 19-2—The right way to install bypasses to reduce interference from the regulator. A capacitor should never be connected across the generator field lead without the small series resistor indicated.

regulator. In some cases, it may be necessary to pull double-braid shielding over the leads between the generator and regulator. It will be advisable to run new wires, grounding the shielding well at both ends. If regulator noise persists, it may be necessary to insulate the regulator from the car body. The wire shielding is then connected to the regulator case at one end and the generator frame at the other.

Wheel Static

Wheel static shows up as a steady popping in the receiver at speeds over about 15 m.p.h. on smooth dry streets. Front-wheel static collectors are available on the market to eliminate this variety of interference. They fit inside the dust cap and bear on the end of the axle, effectively grounding the wheel at all times. Those designated particularly for your car are preferable, since the universal type does not always fit well. They are designed to operate without lubrication and the end of the axle and dust cap should be cleaned of grease before the installation is made. These collectors require replacement about every 10,000 miles.

Rear-wheel collectors have a brush that bears against the inside of the brake drum. It may be necessary to order these from the factory through your dealer.

Tire Static

This sometimes sounds like a leaky power line and can be very troublesome even on the broadcast band. It can be remedied by injecting an antistatic powder into the inner tubes through the valve stem. The powder is marketed by General Cement and possibly others. General Cement dealers can also supply a convenient injector for inserting the powder.

Tracing Noise

To determine if the receiving antenna is picking up all of the noise, the shielded lead-in should be disconnected at the point where it connects to the antenna. The motor should be started with the receiver gain control wide open. If no noise is heard, all noise is being picked up via the antenna. If the noise is still heard with the antenna disconnected, even though it may be reduced in strength, it indicates that some signal from the ignition system is being picked up by the antenna transmission

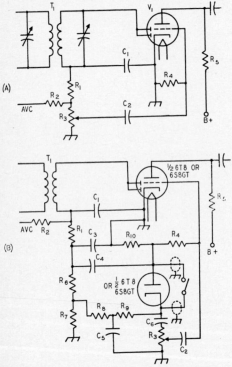

Fig. 19-3—Diagrams showing addition of noise limiter to car receiver. A—Usual circuit. B—Modification.

C_1, C_3—100-$\mu\mu$f. mica.
C_2, C_4, C_6—0.01-μf. paper.
C_5—0.1-μf. paper.
R_1—47,000 ohms.
R_2, R_{10}—1 megohm.
R_3—$\frac{1}{2}$ megohm.
R_7, R_8, R_9—0.47 megohm.
R_4—10 megohms.
R_5—$\frac{1}{4}$ megohm.
R_6—0.1 megohm.
T_1—I.f. transformer.
V_1—Second detector.

line. The lead-in may not be sufficiently-well shielded, or the shield not properly grounded. Noise may also be picked up through the battery circuit, although this does not normally happen if the receiver is provided with the usual r.f.-choke-and-bypass capacitor filter.

In case of noise from this source, a direct wire from the "hot" battery terminal to the receiver is recommended.

Ignition noise varies in repetition rate with engine speed and usually can be recognized by that characteristic in the early stages. Later, however, it may resolve itself into a popping noise that does not always correspond with engine speed. In such a case, it is a good idea to remove all leads from the generator so that the only source left is the ignition system.

Regulator and generator noise may be detected by racing the engine and cutting the ignition switch. This eliminates the ignition noise. Generator noise is characterized by its musical whine contrasted with the ragged raspy irregular noise from the regulator.

With the motor running at idling speed, or slightly faster, checks should be made to try to determine what is bringing the noise into the field of the antenna. It should be assumed that any control rod, metal tube, steering post, etc., passing from the motor compartment through an insulated bushing in the firewall will carry noise to a point where it can be radiated to the antenna. All of these should be bonded to the firewall with heavy wire or braid. Insulated wires can be stripped of r.f. by bypassing them to ground with 0.5-μf. metal-case capacitors. The following should not be overlooked: battery lead at the ammeter, gasoline gauge, ignition switch, headlight, backup and taillight leads and the wiring of any accessories running from the motor compartment to the instrument panel or outside the car.

The firewall should be bonded to the frame of the car and also to the motor block with heavy braid. If the exhaust pipe and muffler are insulated from the frame by rubber mountings, they should likewise be grounded to the frame with flexible copper braid.

Noise Limiting

Fig. 19-3 shows the alterations that may be made in the existing car-receiver circuit to provide for a noise limiter. The usual diode-triode second detector is replaced with a type having an extra independent diode. If the car receiver uses octal-base tubes, a 6S8GT may be substituted. The 7X7 is a suitable replacement in receivers using loktal-type tubes, while the 6T8 may be used with miniatures.

The switch that cuts the limiter in and out of the circuit may be located for convenience on or near the converter panel. Regardless of its placement, however, the leads to the switch should be shielded to prevent hum pick-up.

Several other noise limiter circuits are described in ARRL's publication, *The Mobile Manual For Radio Amateurs*. The *Mobile Manual* also describes an audio squelch system. The latter is a simple circuit designed to suppress receiver background noise in the absence of a signal. It does not, however, function as a noise limiter when the receiver is tuned to a signal.

At least one manufacturer (Gonset) produces a complete noise limiter unit. The unit is mounted external to the main chassis and takes operating voltages from the receiver.

A Converter

A Mobile Converter for 3.5 through 28 Mc.

Figures 19-4 through 19-7 show a crystal-controlled converter covering 3.5 through 28 Mc. without complex band switching or gang-tuned circuits. Plug-in coil assemblies provide rapid band changing and allow construction for either single-band or multiband operation. The converter uses the car broadcast receiver as a tunable i.f. amplifier.

Plate power requirements for the converter are approximately 20 milliamperes at 200 to 250 volts. This means that the unit can be supplied from the car-receiver power pack without overloading it.

The Circuit

The circuit diagram of the converter is shown in Fig. 19-5. A 6BZ6 is used in the r.f. amplifier, and a 12AT7 operates as a mixer-oscillator. The oscillator is crystal-controlled and works on the low-frequency side of the signal frequency. J_1, J_2, and J_3 are the antenna-input, mixer-output and power jacks, respectively. S_1 performs the switching in changing over from ham-band to broadcast input. S_{1A} and S_{1B} shift the antenna from the car receiver input circuit to the car receiver, and S_{1C} is the heater on-off switch.

Since the tuning of the converter is fixed, the circuits of the r.f. amplifier and the mixer must be broadbanded to pass all frequencies in any ham band. A slug-tuned coil, L_3, is used in the amplifier plate circuit, and RFC_1 provides a broad-band plate load for the mixer tube V_{2A}. The grid circuit of the amplifier also uses a slug-tuned coil and includes a trimmer capacitor, C_1, that permits peaking the input for the antenna in use, or in tuning completely across a band. A slug-cored coil is used at L_4 to facilitate resonating the circuit near the crystal frequency.

The frequency of the oscillator must differ from the frequency of the received signal by the frequency of the tunable i.f. amplifier. With the car broadcast receiver following the converter, the i.f. range will be from approximately 550 to 1550 kc. Since the tunable i.f. range is thus limited to a band 1000 kc. wide, the tuning range of the system with any single crystal will be restricted to 1 Mc. This is sufficient for all except the 28-Mc. band. Two crystals are required to cover the entire 10-meter band. The first of these gives a tuning range of 28 to 28.9 Mc. and the second permits tuning 28.8 to 29.7 Mc. An accompanying frequency chart lists the crystal frequencies and the ranges over which the broadcast receiver must be tuned to cover the amateur bands.

Construction

The input-tuning capacitor, C_1, the pilot lamp and the switch are in line across the panel of the converter as shown in Fig. 19-4. Each of these components is centered $\frac{3}{4}$ inch down from the top of the case and each is separated from the other in horizontal plane by $1\frac{3}{4}$ inches. The male jacks for the grid, plate and oscillator coils are below C_1, I_1 and S_1 in that order. Each jack is centered $1\frac{1}{8}$ inches up from the bottom of the cabinet.

The chassis, shown in Fig. 19-7, may be made of thin aluminum sheet and should be fastened to the side walls of the cabinet with homemade brackets, or angle stock. The sockets for V_1 (at the right as seen in the rear view) and V_2 are centered $1\frac{5}{8}$ inches in from the right and left edges of the chassis, respectively. J_3 is centered on the rear wall of the chassis with J_1 and J_2 to the right and left.

A bottom view of the converter clearly shows the components mounted below deck.

The exterior and the interior of the coil box are shown in Figs. 19-4 and 19-7. Wind the antenna coupling coils, L_1 in Fig. 19-5, around the ground ends of the grid coils before the latter are soldered in place. Wind the coupling coils rather snugly but not so tightly as to prevent adjustment of the coupling to L_2 during testing of the converter.

Fig. 19-4—The aluminum case for the converter measures 3 × 4 × 5 inches (Bud CU-3005 or Premier AMC-1005). Amphenol type 86-CP4 male jacks mounted on the front of the box mate with MIP 4-prong sockets mounted on the rear of the coil compartment shown in the foreground. Knobs for C_1 and S_1 are to the left and right, respectively, of the pilot lamp. The coil box measures 2¼ × 2¼ × 5 inches (Bud CU-3004 or Premier AMC-1004). Slug-adjustment screws for L_2, L_3 and L_4 protrude through rubber grommets mounted on the front wall of the plug-in coil assembly.

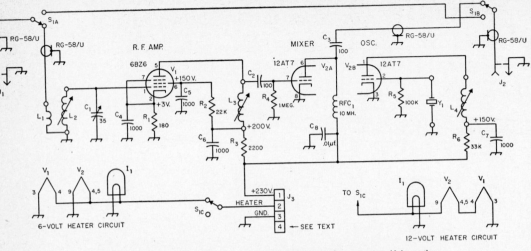

Fig. 19-5—Circuit diagram of the crystal-controlled mobile converter. Unless otherwise indicated, capacitances are in $\mu\mu$f., resistances are in ohms, resistors are ½ watt.

C_1—35-$\mu\mu$f. midget variable (Hammarlund MAPC-35-B).
C_2, C_3—100-$\mu\mu$f. ceramic tubular.
C_4, C_5, C_6, C_7—1000-$\mu\mu$f. disk ceramic.
C_8—0.01-μf. disk ceramic.
I_1—Pilot-light assembly [Johnson 147–503 with No. 44 (6-volt) or No. 1815 (12-volt) lamp].
J_1, J_2—Motorola-type shielded jack (ICA 2378).
J_3—4-prong male chassis connector (Cinch-Jones P-304-AB).
L_1, L_2, L_3, L_4—See coil chart.

R_1—180 ohms, ½ watt.
R_2—22,000 ohms, ½ watt.
R_3—2200 ohms, ½ watt.
R_4—1 megohm, ½ watt.
R_5—0.1 megohm, ½ watt.
R_6—33,000 ohms, ½ watt.
RFC_1—10-mh. r.f. choke (National R-100S).
S_1—3-pole 3-position (used as 3 p.d.t.) selector switch (Centralab PA-1007).
Y_1—See text and frequency chart (International Crystal type FA-9).

An a.c. transformer may be used for the filaments while testing the converter. The plate supply should deliver 20 milliamperes at 200 to 250 volts. A modulated-signal generator covering the bands for which the converter has been constructed is extremely helpful. To be most effective, the generator should have a 50-ohm output termination. A grid-dip meter for preliminary adjustment of the slug-tuned coils is useful, but not essential to alignment. If at all possible, the car receiver that is to be used as the tunable i.f. should be used during the testing.

Using coaxial-cable leads, connect the signal generator and the broadcast receiver to J_1 and J_2, respectively. Switch S_1 to the ham-band position, and apply heater power. The receiver need not be turned on at this time, and plate power for the converter does not have to be applied. Now, rotate C_1 to approximately half capacitance and then adjust L_2 to resonance (use the grid-dip meter as the indicator) at the low end of the band. Move the grid-dipper over to the plate circuit of the amplifier and peak L_3 at the center of the band. Next, couple the meter to L_4 of the oscillator and tune the coil to the frequency of the crystal in use.

After these initial adjustments, plate power may be applied to the converter and a frequency-indicating device used to detect oscillation of V_{2B}. If the grid-dip meter is the self-rectifying type it may be used for the check. An absorption-type wavemeter with indicator or a receiver tuned to the crystal frequency (with the b.f.o. on) may also be used for the purpose. In any

Fig. 19-6—A bottom view of the mobile converter. The amplifier tube socket at the right is mounted with Pin 7 facing toward the rear wall of the chassis. R_1 and R_2 are to the right and left of the socket, respectively. The socket for V_2 is mounted with Pins 4 and 5 facing toward the rear of the unit. C_2 is to the lower left of R_2, and RFC_1 is mounted on the front wall of the housing. C_7 and R_6 are to the left of the base of the choke. C_6, C_8 and R_3 are to the right of RFC_1. The output coupling capacitor C_3 is supported between Terminal 4 of J_3 and Pin 6 of the socket for V_2. R_4 and R_5 are partially visible to the right and left, respectively, of the V_2 socket.

A Converter

Band	Turns	Ind. Range, μh.			Type No.		
Mc.	L_1	L_2	L_3	L_4	L_2	L_3	L_4
3.5–4	14	36–64	64–105	105–200	120-F	120-G	120-H
7–7.3	7	9–18	18–36	36–64	120-D	120-E	120-F
14–14.35	4	3–5	5–9	9–18	120-B	120-C	120-D
21–21.45	3	2–3	3–5	3–5	120-A	120-B	120-B
28–28.9	3	1–1.6	1.6–2.7	2.7–4.5	1000-A	1000-B	1000-C
28.8–29.7	3	1–1.6	1.6–2.7	2.7–4.5	1000-A	1000-B	1000-C

COIL CHART FOR THE MOBILE CONVERTER

Note: L_1 is wound with No. 28 d.c.c. wire at grounded end of L_2. L_2, L_3 and L_4 are slug-tuned coils manufactured by North Hills Electric Co., Inc. (Mineola, L.I.)

event, L_4 should be tuned through resonance to the *high*-frequency side of the crystal frequency until the crystal oscillates reliably as indicated by rapid starting when plate power is turned on.

With the converter and the i.f. amplifier both turned on, and with the signal generator tuned to the center of the band, tune the receiver until the test signal is heard. Peak L_3 and L_4 for best response and then peak L_2 with C_1 set at half capacitance. The coupling between L_1 and L_2 may now be adjusted for optimum performance.

If the aforementioned test equipment is not available, the converter may be aligned while using a strong local of known frequency as the signal source. Of course, the signal frequency must be in the band for which the converter is to be aligned. In using this system, first set the broadcast receiver as closely as possible to the proper i.f. frequency (see the frequency chart) and then tune L_4 until the crystal oscillates. It is advisable to tune the receiver through a narrow range as the oscillator coil is being adjusted to assure that the test signal will be heard as soon as the crystal breaks into oscillation. After the signal is detected, the grid, plate and oscillator circuits may be adjusted for maximum over-all gain.

The mobile antenna should be resonant and tightly coupled to the converter. Traps for suppressing interference cause by strong local broadcast signals that feed in through the converter to the tunable i.f. have not been included in the converter because the need for them will be entirely dependent on local broadcast-station power and frequency assignments.

(Originally described in *QST*, Nov. 1957).

Band Mc.	Crystal Freq., Mc.	I.F. Range Kc.
3.5–4	2.9	650–1100
7–7.3	6.4	600–900
14–14.35	13.4	600–950
21–21.45	20.4	600–1050
28–28.9	27.4	600–1500
28.8–29.7	28.2	600–1500

FREQUENCY CHART FOR THE MOBILE CONVERTER

Note: I.f. range indicates broadcast receiver tuning range necessary for covering the associated amateur frequencies.

(For a description of a bandswitching crystal-controlled converter, see *QST*, January, 1955, or *The Mobile Manual for Radio Amateurs*.)

Fig. 19-7—Homemade L-shaped chassis, mounted on small brackets fastened to the side walls of the converter housing, is 4¹³⁄₁₆ inches long, 2 inches wide and 1½ inches deep. V_1 is mounted on the chassis to the right of V_2 as seen in this rear view. J_1, J_3 and J_2 are in line in that order from right to left across the rear wall of the chassis. An interior view of a coil compartment is shown in the foreground. Terminals of the coils are soldered directly to the socket terminals. Notice that the crystal for the oscillator is mounted adjacent to L_4.

Transistor Mobile Converter

The crystal-controlled converter shown in Fig. 19-8 is a compact, fixed-tuned converter which exhibits excellent performance when used with the automobile receiver. It is designed for one-band operation but may be constructed for any amateur band between 80 and 10 meters.

All of the components, including the power supply for the converter, are housed in a $5\frac{1}{4} \times 3 \times 2\frac{1}{8}$-inch Minibox that can be mounted under the dashboard of the car. The unit is built in one half of the box so that it may be "dropped" for servicing or adjustment while the other half remains mounted to the dash.

Only two external connections to the converter are necessary. A coax lead from the antenna must go to the antenna input of the unit, and an output coax connection to the car radio.

The circuit for the converter is shown in Fig. 19-9. The oscillator circuit is a transistorized version of the triode Pierce. Injection for the mixer is taken from a small link wound over the cold end of the collector tank coil. The emitter of the mixer transistor is returned to ground through this link. The mixer circuit corresponds to a triode vacuum-tube mixer utilizing cathode injection from the oscillator, the major difference being the low input impedance of the transistor base as compared with the relatively high input impedance of a vacuum-tube grid.

The crystal frequency used in the oscillator portion of the converter is given in the tuned circuit data table. On 30 and 21 Mc., the crystal is operated at its third overtone and on the lower bands the fundamental mode is used.

The inductances are wound on slug-tuned forms and shunted with the capacitances shown in the tuned circuit data table.

The circuit shows a crystal diode connected from the high impedance end of L_1 to cell B_2. This gives a measure of protection for the mixer transistor in the event that an excessive amount of r.f. energy is introduced into the converter. When a signal greater in voltage than B_2 appears across L_1, the diode will conduct and short the excess r.f. to ground.

Power Supply

The converter requires about 8 volts d.c. for operation and takes on the order of 3 ma. of current. A built-in battery supply serves two important purposes. First, it eliminates one of the prime sources of ignition interference, since various noises from the electrical system of the car can be carried into the converter via the leads from the car battery. Also, with a self-

TUNED CIRCUIT DATA FOR THE TRANSISTOR CONVERTER

Band	Coil	C_1 μμf.	C_2 μμf.	Crystal Freq.	I.F. Range
28 Mc.*	L_1, 12 turns No. 20 enam. Tap at 4th turn. L_2, 2 turns No. 20 enam. L_3, 12 turns No. 20 enam. L_4, 2 turns No. 24 enam.	15	15	27.85 Mc.	650–1600 kc.
21 Mc.	L_1, 15 turns No. 20 enam. Tap at 5th turn. L_2, 3 turns No. 20 enam. L_3, 15 turns No. 20 enam. L_4, 2 turns No. 24 enam.	15	15	20.35 Mc.	650–1100 kc.
14 Mc.	L_1, 23 turns No. 24 enam. Tap at 6th turn. L_2, 5 turns No. 24 enam. L_3, 26 turns No. 24 enam. L_4, 3 turns No. 24 enam.	15	15	13.35 Mc.	650–1000 kc.
7 Mc.	L_1, 35 turns No. 28 enam. Tap at 10th turn. L_2, 6 turns No. 28 enam. L_3, 40 turns No. 28 enam. L_4, 4 turns No. 28 enam.	33	33	6350 kc.	650–950 kc.
4 Mc.	L_1, 52 turns No. 34 enam. Tap at 13th turn. L_2, 8 turns No. 34 enam. L_3, 72 turns No. 34 enam. L_4, 5 turns No. 34 enam.	40	40	2850 kc.	650–1150 kc.

* 28.5 to 29.45 Mc.
All coils close-wound on ½-inch diam. slug-tuned (iron slug) forms. Tap on L_1 to be made near cold end of coil. L_2 wound over cold end of L_1.

Fig. 19-8—View of the transistorized converter. The variable output capacitor C_4 is mounted on the right front panel. Directly behind C_4 is the 8.4 volt mercury battery B_1 held in place by a bracket which is sold in most hardware stores as a broom holder. The two transistors are the round black objects in the center. They are supported by their own leads which are soldered to tie points. The converter shown here operates on 10 meters.

Transistor Mobile Converter

Fig. 19-9—Circuit of the transistorized converter.

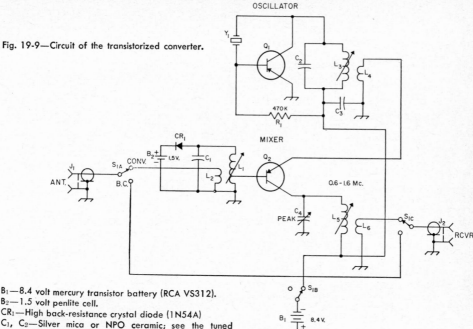

B₁—8.4 volt mercury transistor battery (RCA VS312).
B₂—1.5 volt penlite cell.
CR₁—High back-resistance crystal diode (1N54A).
C₁, C₂—Silver mica or NPO ceramic; see the tuned circuit data table for values.
C₃—.005 µf. ceramic.
C₄—365 µµf. variable capacitor (Allied Radio Co. 61-H-009).
J₁, J₂—Automobile type antenna connectors.
L₁, L₄, inc.—See coil table.
L₅—320-500 µh. slug tuned coil (Miller 4514).
L₆—10 turns No. 30 enam. close-wound over L₅.
Q₁, Q₂—2N247 transistors.

R₁—0.47 megohms, ½ watt (value may require slight adjustment for individual transistors).
S₁—Three pole two position rotary switch (Centralab PA-2007).
Y₁—Crystal (International Crystal Co. type FA-5 for miniature socket, FA-9 for standard socket). See table for frequencies.

contained battery it is unnecessary to make any power-supply connections either to the car receiver or car battery. This saves considerable time during installation and makes the unit readily adaptable to portable operation.

Wiring

No. 30 wire is adequate for wiring because of the small current and voltage requirements of the converter. Spaghetti should be used over exposed leads that might come in contact with other parts because of the vibration that occurs in mobile operation. For the same reason, it is essential that good soldered connections be made.

The information given in the tuned-circuit data table applies to ½-inch coil forms. Ready-wound slug-tuned coils, such as the Miller 4500 series or the CTC LS3 series, can also be used with the links shown in the chart. L_1 is tapped about ⅓ up from the cold end. C_1 and C_2 should be chosen to resonate, in a given amateur band, with the inductance of the particular coil used; the L/C ratio is not critical.

Construction

The converter is assembled in one half of a 5¼ × 3 × 2⅛-inch Minibox. The box-cover (with the lips) is mounted permanently under the automobile dash. The only front-panel con-

trols are the converter-broadcast switch S_1 and the output peaking control C_4. Mount S_1 so that the leads coming from the antenna connectors will line up with the proper switch terminals. Two 5-terminal tie points are mounted in the center of the chassis for supporting the crystal socket, transistors and other small components. The three slug-tuned inductances are supported on the rear wall of the chassis, as are the two antenna connectors.

After the major components have been installed, only a few wiring connections remain. Be sure to leave long leads on the inductances after winding them so that the leads may be directly connected to their proper points.

In the circuit, cell B_2 has its negative terminal grounded. A lug soldered to the cell case and bolted to the chassis will make a sturdy support for the cell.

Adjustment and Testing

After the unit is wired, the first test should be to make certain that the oscillator is functioning. Turn on the converter. Tune a communications receiver to the crystal frequency and adjust the slug in L_3 until the signal is heard. The oscillator will not function unless the collector tank (C_2L_3) is resonant.

After the oscillator is operating properly, install the unit in the car and turn it on. With the broadcast radio turned on, adjust the slug in L_3 for maximum background noise. Next, adjust the slug in L_1 for maximum noise, or select a weak signal and peak it up for maximum gain. Then set the car radio at the high end of the i.f. band and adjust the slug in L_5 for maximum gain with C_4 at minimum capacity. The low end of the i.f. band should peak when C_4 is set near maximum. If only one segment of a particular band is going to be used, additional gain can be had by peaking the coils for that portion of the band. If, for example, 75-meter phone operation is desired, peak the converter for 3800 to 4000 kc. rather than 3500 to 4000 kc.

Crystal-Controlled Converters for 50 and 144 Mc.

The mobile converters shown in Figs. 19-10 through 19-13 combine simplicity with good v.h.f. design practice. Although only two tubes are used in each, the converters include a stage of r.f. amplification plus crystal-controlled oscillators. Ten meters was chosen as the i.f. because when the broadcast receiver is used as the tunable i.f. for v.h.f. converters images are a problem, and only 1 Mc. at a time could be tuned. The converters described here, therefore, are designed to work into a 10-meter converter or receiver. This can be a tunable converter which in turn works into the broadcast receiver, or a complete self-contained 10-meter receiver.

The 50 Mc. Unit

The circuit diagram for the 50-Mc. unit is shown in Fig. 19-11. A 6AK5 is used as an r.f. amplifier. The same gain with lower noise can be obtained with a cascode-type dual-triode amplifier, but the performance of this pentode stage is satisfactory and its design is considerably simpler than the triode amplifier.

The crystal oscillator makes use of a 22-Mc. overtone crystal. A crystal on the required injection frequency eliminates the need for multiplier stages, and makes possible the use of a simple oscillator circuit. The 10-meter receiver or converter is tuned from 28 to 30 Mc. in covering 50 to 52 Mc. If a general coverage receiver covering 26 to 30 Mc. is used, a 24-Mc. crystal in the oscillator will allow tuning 50 to 54 Mc. However, any injection frequency may be used to cover a desired portion of the band.

The pentode half of the 6U8 tube is used as a mixer. The oscillator and mixer sections are in the same tube envelope so there is enough stray coupling between the two for adequate oscillator injection.

The diagram shows the heaters connected for 12 volts. If 6-volt operation is desired, the heaters are connected in parallel and R_1 is disregarded.

The converters are built in a $5\frac{1}{4} \times 3 \times 2\frac{1}{8}$-inch Minibox. All of the parts are mounted on the bottom half of the box while the upper half (the one with lips) is fastened under the car dash. The bottom half containing all the components can be slid in and out for easy servicing.

Fig. 19-10 shows the placement of most of the components. The output peaking control C_1 and switch S_1 are mounted on one side of the chassis to form the front panel. The tubes, slug-tuned inductances, crystal socket and antenna connectors are mounted directly opposite on the back wall. Two tie-points are bolted to the base of the box for connecting and supporting leads and components. When wiring, make the r.f. leads as short and direct as possible.

The 144-Mc. Unit

The circuit diagram for the 144-Mc. converter is shown in Fig. 19-13. Two 6U8 tubes are used with the pentode section of one tube acting as the r.f. amplifier followed by the triode-section mixer. The other 6U8 is used as an overtone crystal oscillator and pentode frequency multiplier. By combining all the features of a 4-tube crystal-controlled converter in a two-tube model space-saving simplicity is achieved.

The same basic circuit used in the 50-Mc.

Fig. 19-10—View of the 50-Mc. converter. The inductances are from left to right: (bottom) L_7, (top) L_5L_6, L_3L_4, L_1L_2. The top of crystal Y_1 can be seen between the tubes. The 22-ohm 2-watt resistor in the center of the chassis is the heater current compensating resistor, used for 12-volt operation. Input and output antenna connectors are mounted on opposite ends of the back wall. Power is fed to the unit through the twisted power cable running in from the left side of the photograph.

Crystal-Controlled Converters

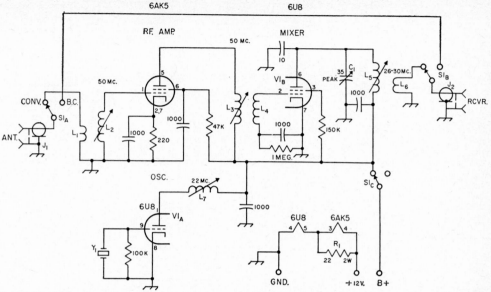

Fig. 19-11—Schematic diagram for the 50-Mc. mobile converter. All resistors ½ watt unless otherwise specified. Capacitor values below 0.001 μf. are in μμf. All 0.001 μf. capacitors are disk ceramic. Other fixed capacitors are tubular ceramic.

C_1—35-μμf. midget variable capacitor (Hammarlund MAPC-35-B).

J_1, J_2—Automobile type antenna connectors.

L_1—3 turns No. 20 insulated wire, close-wound over cold end of L_2.

L_2—9 turns No. 20 enam. wire, close-wound on ½ inch slug tuned coil.

L_3—16 turns No. 20 enam. wire, close-wound on ½ inch slug tuned coil form.

L_4—6 turns No. 20 insulated wire, close-wound over cold end of L_3.

L_5—14 turns No. 20 enam. wire, close-wound on ½ inch

slug tuned coil form.

L_6—2 turns No. 20 insulated wire, close-wound over cold end of L_2.

L_7—28 turns No. 30 enam. wire, close-wound on ½ inch slug tuned coil.

R_1—22-ohm 2-watt resistor (used for 12-volt heater operation only).

S_1—Three-pole two-position rotary switch (Centralab PA-2007).

Y_1—22 Mc. overtone crystal. (International Crystal type FA-5 for miniature socket, FA-9 for standard socket).

model is followed in the 144-Mc. unit except for the addition of a multiplier stage following the crystal oscillator. The oscillator operates at 38.666 Mc. and is multiplied to 116 Mc. in the tripler stage. As in the 50-Mc. converter, this unit is designed to work into a 10-meter receiver or converter. If the i.f. tunes from 27 to 30 Mc., the converter will tune from 144 to 147 Mc. However, any segment of the band may be

tuned by choosing the proper crystal frequency.

Unlike the 50-Mc. converter, the oscillator-multiplier stages of the 144-Mc. converter are physically separated from the mixer stage. It is necessary, therefore, to couple the 116-Mc. energy from the multiplier stage to the grid of the mixer. Capacitor C_2 is used for this purpose. It consists of a pair of twisted hook-up wires with one end of one lead connected to the mixer

Fig. 19-12—View of the 144-Mc. converter. The inductances from left to right are: (top) L_1L_2, L_3L_4, L_5L_6, (bottom) L_7 and L_8. All components except S_1 and C_1 are mounted on the back wall of the chassis. A single tie point in the bottom of the channel supports various leads and provides junctions for sundry connections. The input and output antenna connectors are placed near the bottom right and left of the back panel. The crystal Y_1 is between the two tubes. Converter power is fed through the twisted cable which passes through a hole and grommet in the back wall of the chassis.

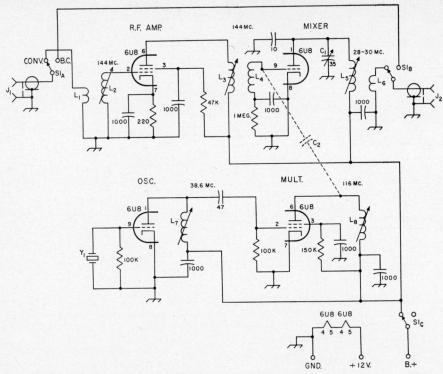

Fig. 19-13—Schematic diagram for the 144-Mc. converter. All resistors ½ watt unless otherwise specified. Capacitor values below 0.001 μf. are in μμf. All 1000-μμf. capacitors are disk ceramic. Other fixed capacitors are tubular ceramic.

C₁—35-μμf. midget variable capacitor (Hammarlund MAPC-35-B).

C₂—Oscillator injection capacitor (see text).

J₁, J₂—Automobile type antenna connectors.

L₁—2 turns No. 18 enam., ⅜ inches long, on ½ inch slug tuned coil form.

L₂—2 turns No. 20 insulated wire, close wound over cold end of L₁.

L₃—2 turns No. 18 enam., ⅜ inches long, on ½ inch slug tuned coil form.

L₄—2 turns No. 20 insulated wire, close wound over cold end of L₁.

L₅—9 turns No. 24 enam., close wound on ½ inch slug tuned coil form.

L₆—2 turns No. 20 insulated wire, close wound over cold end of L₅.

L₇—10 turns No. 24 enam., close wound on ½ inch slug tuned coil form.

L₈—5 turns No. 18 enam., ½ inches long, on ½ inch slug tuned coil form.

S₁—Three-pole two-position rotary switch (Centralab PA-2007).

Y₁—38.666 Mc. overtone crystal (International Crystal Co. type FA-5 for miniature socket, FA-9 for standard socket).

grid and the end of the other lead connected to the multiplier plate.

The circuit diagram shows the heaters connected for 12-volt operation. For 6 volts, the heaters should be connected in parallel.

The same basic outline of construction used in the 50-Mc. converter is followed in the 144-Mc. unit. Fig. 19-12 shows how output peaking control C_1 and the control switch S_1 are mounted on the front wall of the chassis while most of the remaining parts are secured to the rear surface. A single tie point is mounted on the bottom of the chassis for connecting and supporting various leads. The input and output antenna connectors are mounted at opposite ends of the back wall of the chassis.

Testing the Converters

The 50-Mc. converter requires 0.625 ampere at 6 volts (or 0.45 ampere at 12 volts) for the heaters, and approximately 17 ma. at 150 volts for the plate supply. If the car radio delivers in excess of 180 volts, the plate voltage on the converter should be limited by a dropping resistor.

The 144-Mc. converter requires 0.9 ampere at 6 volts (or 0.45 ampere at 12 volts) for the heaters. A plate voltage of 150 volts is required at about 30 ma.

All tuned circuits should be checked for resonance with a grid-dipper. The proper frequency for each circuit is given in Figs. 19-11 and 19-13. Apply power to the converter under test, and adjust the oscillator circuit until it goes into oscillation. This can be confirmed by tuning the home receiver to the oscillator frequency. Tune the oscillator inductance until the maximum oscillator signal is obtained. Now feed a 50 or 144-Mc. signal into the converter under test. This signal may come from a signal generator or a grid-dip meter, or may be an actual signal from the antenna. Go through the converter stage by stage, adjusting the inductances for peak output. After the first run of peaking is completed the converter should be spot-checked through the entire band to make sure the over-all response is fairly flat. Output capacitor C_1 is used to peak the output circuit. L_5 is adjusted so that C_1 peaks at mid-capacitance in the center of the i.f. tuning range.

A 20-Watt High-Frequency Mobile Transmitter

Figures 19-14 through 19-17 illustrate a complete 20-watt transmitter that may be operated on any band from 80 to 10 meters. The design avoids the complication, expense and difficult construction associated with the average multi-band transmitter, but does not confine its application to any one band. Changing from one band to another as operating interest varies is a simple matter of unsoldering a pair of readily-accessible coils and replacing them with others for the new band.

Circuits

The circuit of the transmitter is shown in Fig. 19-15. A 5763 crystal oscillator drives a 2E26 final amplifier. Quadrupling frequency in the output of the grid-plate oscillator from a 7-Mc. crystal will provide adequate drive for the final on 10 meters. Sufficient capacitance is provided in the plate tank of the 2E26 for a Q of 10 or more on all bands except 80 meters. On 80 meters, the tank Q will drop to about 6, but there is little danger of appreciable harmonic output when feeding a high-Q antenna such as the usual loaded whip. Adequate output coupling on this band is assured by tuning the output link line. Parallel plate feed is used in both stages.

The audio circuit is equally simple. One triode unit of a 12AU7 is used as a grounded-grid amplifier. This provides low-impedance input for a carbon microphone without the need for a microphone transformer. The second triode unit of the 12AU7 is used in conventional fashion to drive a 1635 Class B modulator. This tube operates at zero bias with an idling current of only 10 ma. D. c. voltage for operating the carbon microphone is obtained by connecting the microphone in series with the two speech-amplifier cathodes and ground.

The 1-ma. meter M_1 may be switched across appropriate multiplier shunts to read amplifier grid or plate current, or modulator plate current. A d.p.d.t. change-over relay, K_1, actuated by the

microphone push-to-talk switch, is also provided. One pole shifts the antenna from receiver to transmitter, while the other mutes the receiver by shorting the voice coil of the speaker. S_1 removes screen voltage from the 2E26 and disables the relay so that the oscillator may be tuned up before the amplifier is put on the air.

Construction

A $5 \times 6 \times 9$-inch steel utility box (Middletown Mfg. Co., Middletown, Conn.) is used as the cabinet for the transmitter. The chassis is bent up from aluminum sheet approximately $\frac{1}{16}$ inch thick. The chassis is $8\frac{3}{4}$ inches wide, 6 inches deep and has 2-inch lips along the front and rear edges.

C_3 and C_4 are mounted on the front wall of the partition with their shaft centers $1\frac{3}{8}$ inches above the chassis. The shaft of C_4 is centered $1\frac{1}{4}$ inches from the open edge of the shield, while the shaft of C_3 is centered 3 inches in. The shafts of these capacitors are connected to panel-bearing units by rigid metal shaft couplers.

The socket for the 2E26 is submounted on $\frac{3}{4}$-inch spacers, beneath a $1\frac{1}{4}$-inch clearance hole centered 1 inch from the rear edge of the chassis and 2 inches in from the side. RFC_4 is mounted horizontally from the front wall of the partition, below and between C_3 and C_4.

The output tank coil, L_2, is cemented to a 1-inch cone insulator and soldered between a rear stator terminal of C_3 and a grounding lug on the chassis. The bottom end of L_3 is connected to a rear stator terminal of C_4, while the other end goes through a small feed-through point in the chassis to a relay terminal immediately below. The 5763 is centered between the partition and the front panel, and between the shafts of C_3 and C_4.

Fig. 19-17 shows the modulation transformer in the upper right-hand corner of the chassis. The secondary taps of T_2 should be set for 7500 ohms. The 12AU7 and 1635 sockets are centered

Fig. 19-14—A panel-illuminating lamp is mounted to the right of the meter, along with the amplifier-tank and antenna-link tuning controls. Along the bottom, from left to right, are the microphone jack, meter switch, filament switch, tune-operate switch, oscillator tuning control and the crystal.

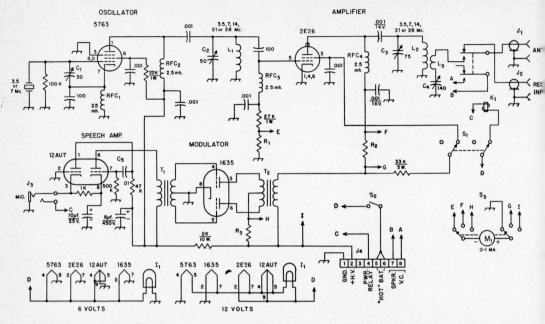

Fig. 19-15—Circuit of the single-band mobile transmitter. All resistors are ½ watt unless otherwise specified. All capacitances less than 0.001 μf. are in $\mu\mu f$. All 0.001-μf. capacitors are disk ceramic. Fixed capacitors of smaller value may be mica or NPO ceramic. Capacitors marked with polarity are electrolytic.

C_1—Mica or ceramic trimmer.
C_2—Air variable (Hammarlund HF-50).
C_3—Air variable (Johnson 167-4).
C_4—Air variable (Hammarlund HF-140).
C_5—Paper ceramic.
I_1—6.3-volt 250-ma. dial lamp.
J_1, J_2—Coaxial connector (SO-239).
J_3—Push-to-talk microphone jack.
J_4—Power connector (octal tube socket).
K_1—D.p.d.t. 6-volt or 12-volt d.c. relay (Guardian Series 200).
L_1, L_2, L_3—See coil table.

M_1—0-1 d.c. milliammeter, 2⅜-in. (Triplett 227-T).
R_1—10-times shunt for M_1 (6.1 ohms for 55-ohm meter.)
R_2, R_3—100-times shunt for M_1. (0.5 ohm for 55-ohm meter.)
S_1—D.p.d.t. rotary switch (Centralab PA-1002).
S_2—S.p.s.t. toggle switch.
S_3—2-pole 3-position rotary switch (Centralab PA-1003).
T_1—Driver transformer, 2.5:1 primary to ½ secondary (Merit A-2920).
T_2—10-watt modulation transformer (Merit A-3008).

on a line about halfway between the rear of the meter and the modulation transformer. The socket for the 12AU7 is centered ⅞ inch from the end of the chassis. Then the socket for the 1635 is spaced sufficiently from the 12AU7 socket so that the driver transformer, T_1, can be mounted between the two sockets, underneath the chassis.

The two coaxial connectors, J_1 and J_2, are mounted on the rear lip of the chassis, spaced to avoid the 2E26 socket. An octal socket serves as the power-supply connector J_4, and the change-over relay is centered between this socket and the nearest coaxial connector.

Testing

The unit will operate from any supply delivering 300 to 400 volts at 125 ma. or more.

While the 2E26 might be used as a doubler if necessary, straight-through operation is recommended. Crystals in the 80-meter band will provide adequate drive for the final on all bands up to and including the 14-Mc. band. Crystals in the 7-Mc. band are needed for 21- and 28-Mc. output. Coils should be selected from the coil

table to suit the band desired.

The oscillator is adjusted with S_1 in the tune position, and the meter switch turned to read amplifier grid current. With power supplied, C_2

			Table of Coil Dimensions				
			L_1				
Band	$L\mu h$.	Turns	Diam. In.	Length In.	Wire Size	B&W No.	Airdux No.
80	29	44	1	1⅜	24	3016	832
40	6.3	28	⅝	⅞	24	3008	532
20	2.8	16	⅝	1	20	3007	516
15	0.9	9	⅝	9⁄16	20	3007	516
10	0.5	6	⅝	⅜	20	3007	516
			L_2				
80	32	80	¾	2½	24	3012	632
40	8	41	¾	2½	20	3011	616
20	3.5	20	¾	1¼	20	3011	616
15	1.6	16	¾	2	18	3010	608
10	1.1	12	¾	1½	18	3010	608

L_3—3 turns No. 20, 1-inch diam., 3⁄16 inch long, over ground end of L_2 (B&W 3015, Airdux 816) for 80, 40 and 20 meters; 2 similar turns for 15 and 10 meters.

20-Watt Mobile Transmitter

Fig. 19-16—Bottom view of the 20-watt mobile transmitter. The driver transformer is placed between the two audio-tube sockets. Along the front lip of the chassis, from left to right, are the microphone jack, meter switch, filament switch S_2, tune-up switch S_1, oscillator tank capacitor C_2 and the crystal socket. C_2 is spaced back of the panel, and mounted behind the 5763 socket. L_1 is soldered across the terminals of the capacitor. All power and control wiring is done with shielded wire.

should be adjusted for maximum grid current. The tuning should be checked with a wave-meter to make sure that the oscillator output circuit is tuned to the desired frequency. Then C_1 should be adjusted for maximum grid current. The reading should be at least 3 or 4 ma.

A pair of G.E. type 1820, 28-volt, 1-amp, miniature lamps connected in series makes a good dummy load for testing the final. With S_1 thrown to the operate position, the meter switched to read 2E26 plate current, and power applied, adjust C_3 for a dip in plate current. Check the frequency with a wavemeter coupled to the output tank. Then adjust C_4 until the meter reads 50 ma. Retune C_3 for the plate-current dip. It may take a little juggling back and forth between C_3 and C_4 before an adjustment is reached where the meter reads 50 ma. at the plate-current dip. The load lamps will not light to full brilliance, but it should be possible to determine the adjustment that gives maximum output. With the amplifier fully loaded, the grid current should still remain at 3 to 4 ma.

The meter should now be turned to read modulator plate current. Without voice, the meter should read about 10 ma. When speaking into the microphone, a kick of the meter reading up to 40 or 50 ma. on peaks should indicate 100 per cent modulation. The r.f. amplifier plate current should remain essentially steady under modulation, but the lamps in the dummy load should show some increase in brilliance.

Adjustment when an antenna is substituted for the dummy load should be done in a similar manner. The antenna must, of course, be checked for resonance in advance with a g.d.o. or by other means. (Originally described in *QST*, Jan., 1957). (For a description of a bandswitching mobile transmitter with v.f.o., see *QST*, August and Sept., 1957).

Fig. 19-17—Interior view of the single-band mobile transmitter. The output components are separated from the other components by an L-shaped aluminum partition which measures 4½ inches along the front and 4 inches along the side. It is 2¼ inches high with ½-inch lips along the bottom edges for fastening to the chassis.

Mobile Transmitters for 50 and 144 Mc.

Figs. 19-18 through 19-23 show circuits and constructional details of compact transmitters covering the 6- and 2-meter bands. The units are only 3 inches deep and therefore are suitable for under-the-dash mounting.

Output on 50-Mc. is obtained by using crystals in the 50-Mc. range. This eliminates any necessity for multiplier stages and greatly simplifies the circuit. In the two-meter unit, a 48-Mc. crystal is used which is multiplied to 144 Mc. by a tripler stage.

Although the r.f. amplifier used in the transmitters will operate at higher voltages, the units are designed primarily to work from a 300-volt, 100-ma. supply. A transistor modulator can be used with the units with a saving in total current drain.

The 50-Mc. Unit

The circuit of the 50-Mc. transmitter is shown in Fig. 19-20. A 5763 (6417 when using 12-volt heaters) is triode-connected in an overtone-type crystal oscillator. Feedback winding L_2 helps to sustain 3rd-overtone oscillation and may require some slight adjustment for optimum output in its placement with respect to L_1. The 50-Mc. signal from the oscillator is capacitively coupled to the grid of the 2E26 (6893 when using 12-volt heaters) amplifier. A jack J_1 on the rear of the transmitter allows the grid current to be measured.

Fig. 19-19—The 50 Mc. mobile transmitter is built into a 7 × 5 × 3-inch aluminum Minibox (Bud CU-3008). Oscillator coil L_1L_2 is near the top left. The jack on the right rear panel is the grid-current meter jack. One-inch holes are punched in both halves of the Minibox for ventilation. Perforated hole plugs can be used for neater appearance. In actual use, the transmitter would sit with the tubes horizontal. The half of the box at left is mounted under the car dash so that the transmitter half can be easily pulled in and out of position for servicing or adjustment.

The amplifier plate tank circuit, C_2L_3, is tuned to resonance by variable capacitor C_2.

The 144-Mc. Unit

The 144-Mc. circuit is shown in Fig. 19-22. The oscillator is similar to the one used in the 50-Mc. transmitter. The 48-Mc. signal from the oscillator is capacitively coupled to the pentode multiplier which is operated as a frequency tripler. From the tripler, the signal is inductively coupled to the grid of the r.f. amplifier. Since this stage contains a fixed capacitor, it is tuned by "pinching" or "spreading" the turns of L_4. As in the 50-Mc. unit, provision is made for measuring grid current (jack J_1).

The amplifier tank circuit in the 144-Mc. model is series tuned. Output coupling is through a single-turn link, L_6. Neutralization is required in this unit; the neutralizing capacitor consists of a 2½-inch length of No. 12 wire with one end connected to pin 5 (control grid) of the amplifier tube, and with the other end run up beside the amplifier tube after passing through the chassis (see the photograph in Fig. 19-21). A piece of spaghetti is used to insulate the neutralizing wire from the chassis.

Construction

A 7 × 5 × 3-inch Minibox is used as the

Fig. 19-18—View of the 50-Mc. transmitter showing the r.f. amplifier tank circuits and output loading control. C_3 is on the top right of the panel with C_2 just below it. Output indicator I_1 is below C_2. This view also shows the two antenna connectors, power plug and grid current jack which are mounted on the rear surface.

6- and 2-Meter Mobile Transmitters

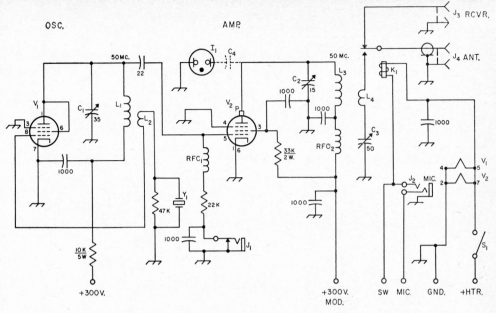

Fig. 19-20—Schematic diagram of the 50-Mc. mobile transmitter. Unless otherwise indicated, capacitances are in $\mu\mu$f., resistances are in ohms, resistors are $\frac{1}{2}$ watt unless specified otherwise.

C_1—35-$\mu\mu$f. midget variable capacitor (Hammarlund MAPC-35-B).

C_2—15-$\mu\mu$f. midget variable capacitor (Hammarlund HF-15).

C_3—50-$\mu\mu$f. midget variable capacitor (Hammarlund MAPC-50-B).

C_4—Coupling capacitor for output indicator (see text).

K_1—Midget antenna relay s.p.d.t. (Advance AM/2C/-12VD. Note: the last four figures in the number indicate the coil voltage. For 6 volts d.c. it should read /6VD).

L_1—3 turns No. 20, $\frac{5}{8}$-inch dia., $\frac{5}{16}$ inches long (B & W 3006).

L_2—2 turn link No. 20 insulated wire, close wound over cold end of L_1.

L_3—4 turns No. 16, 1-inch dia., 1-inch long (B & W 3013)

L_4—2 turn link No. 20 insulated wire, close-wound over cold end of L_3.

I_1—Neon bulb (NE-2).

J_1—Circuit closing jack.

J_2—3 conductor mike jack.

J_3, J_4—Automobile type antenna connectors.

RFC_1, RFC_2—Single-layer v.h.f. choke, 2 to 7 μh. (Ohmite Z-50 or National R-60).

S_1—S.p.s.t. slide switch.

V_1—5763 for 6 volts, 6417 for 12 volts.

V_2—2E26 for 6 volts, 5893 for 12 volts.

Y_1—50-Mc. 3rd overtone crystal (International Crystal Co. type FA-9).

chassis for the transmitters. A single bracket supports the tubes and associated parts. The bracket has a single bend and is fastened to the Minibox with machine screws.

The 6- and 2-meter transmitters are almost identical mechanically. The only real difference between the two is that the 2-meter model has an additional multiplier tube, mounted in line with the oscillator tube on the bracket.

All parts should be mounted before wiring is begun. Since both ends of the chassis are open, wiring and mounting of parts is a simple job. The photographs show the relative position of most of the components. Try to keep r.f. leads as short as possible. The relay, antenna connectors, power plug and grid current jack are all mounted on the rear panel.

The output indicator I_1 is coupled to the final tank circuit through capacitor C_4. This capac-

itor is actually a few turns of hook-up wire wound over a piece of insulated wire that is

Fig. 19-21—The 144 Mc. transmitter with the r.f. amplifier tube removed to show the neutralizing lead C_N. Except for the 6BJ6 multiplier tube in the foreground, the same basic layout is used here as in the 50-Mc. unit.

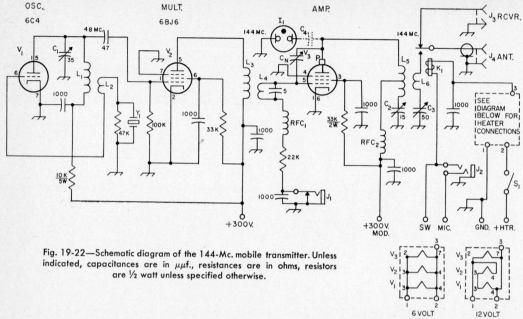

Fig. 19-22—Schematic diagram of the 144-Mc. mobile transmitter. Unless indicated, capacitances are in μμf., resistances are in ohms, resistors are ½ watt unless specified otherwise.

C₁—35-μμf. midget variable capacitor (Hammarlund MAPC-35-B).

C₂—15-μμf. midget variable capacitor (Hammarlund HF-15).

C₃—50-μμf. midget variable capacitor (Hammarlund MAPC-50-B).

C₄—Coupling capacitor for output indicator (see text).

Cₙ—Neutralizing capacitor (see text)

K₁—Midget antenna relay s.p.d.t. (Advance AM/2C/-12VD. Note: the last four figures in the number indicate the coil voltage. For 6 volts it should read 6VD.)

L₁—4 turns No. 20, ⅝ inch diam., ⁵⁄₁₆ inches long (B & W 3006).

L₂—2 turn link No. 20 insulated wire, close wound over cold end of L₁.

L₃—1 turn No. 20 insulated wire ½-inch diam.

L₄—2 turns No. 20 insulated wire ½-inch diam.

L₅—3 turns No. 16, 1-inch diam., ¾ inches long, center tapped (B & W 3013).

L₆—1 turn link No. 20 insulated wire wound in the center of L₅.

I₁—Neon bulb (NE-2).

J₁—Circuit closing jack.

J₂—3 conductor mike jack.

J₃, J₄—Automobile type antenna connector.

RFC₁, RFC₂—Single-layer v.h.f. choke, 2 to 7 μh. (Ohmite Z-50 or National R-60).

S₁—S.p.s.t. slide switch.

V₁—6C4.

V₂—6BJ6.

V₃—2E26 for 6 volts, 5893 for 12 volts.

Y₁—48 Mc. 3rd overtone crystal. Crystal frequency found by dividing desired output frequency by 3 (International Crystal Co. type FA-9).

connected to the final tank circuit. If the lamp fails to ignite, a few more turns may be needed.

Testing Notes

An a.c. power supply delivering 300 volts at 100 ma. can be used during testing of the transmitter. Heater-current requirements for the 50-Mc. unit are 1.55 ampere for 6-volt operation and 0.775 ampere for 12 volts. The 144-Mc. unit requires 1.1 ampere at 6 volts and 0.55 ampere at 12 volts. Do not connect the plate supply to the r.f. amplifier power terminal (marked "300 mod." in the circuit diagram) at this time. The correct crystal and a dummy load should be kept on hand for the test.

To test the driver stage, plug a grid-current meter (0-5 ma.) in J_1, and apply heater voltage. Plug in the proper crystal and turn on the plate voltage (exciter stages only). As quickly as possible adjust capacitor C_1 until the oscillator goes into oscillation. This will be indicated by a downward kick in the plate current. Grid current should begin to show when oscillation occurs.

In the 144-Mc. unit, adjust for maximum grid current by "pinch-tuning" L_3, L_4 once oscillation has begun. Adjust C_1 for maximum grid current. If there is difficulty in obtaining grid drive, try adjusting the position of L_2 with respect to L_1. In the 2-meter model, some rearrangement of L_3 and L_4 may be needed in order to achieve maximum grid drive.

Before testing the 144-Mc. amplifier it will be necessary to neutralize it. With power applied to the exciter portion, slowly rotate the output tuning control C_2 through its full range. If the amplifier is neutralized, there will be no fluctuation in the grid current. If there is such a fluctuation, adjust the neutralizing wire to a new position with respect to the amplifier tube and swing the plate-tuning control again. Repeat until the grid current remains steady, showing that the amplifier is neutralized.

Connect a dummy load to the output antenna connector, close the antenna relay and apply plate power to the entire transmitter. As quickly as possible, tune C_2 for minimum plate current.

Mobile Modulators

Fig. 19-23—View of the 144-Mc. transmitter. The coil and link near the top left rear are L_1L_2. In the foreground are coils L_3L_4.

It is necessary to perform this operation rapidly because the amplifier may draw excessive plate current when not tuned to resonance. When tuned to resonance, the output indicator bulb I_1 will light. This r.f. indicator is not only a tuning aid in the car but also acts as a continuous monitor to show that the transmitter is in operation. Capacitor C_3 is the loading control and should be adjusted for maximum plate current after the amplifier is resonated.

A microphone jack J_2 is included on the transmitter chassis to simplify the control circuits. Leads from the microphone (marked "sw" and "mic" in the diagram) go to the power connector at the rear of the transmitter.

Mobile Modulators

Vacuum-tube modulators for mobile operation are in general similar to those used in fixed-station installations. Equipment shown in the section on modulators may be modified for use with almost any mobile transmitter. As in fixed station work, the mobile modulator must be capable of supplying to the plate modulated r.f. stage sine-wave audio power equal to 50 per cent of the d.c. plate input for 100 percent modulation.

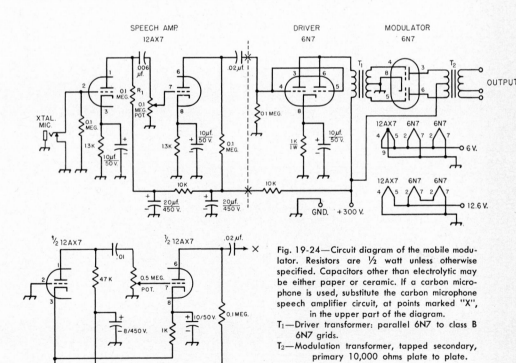

Fig. 19-24—Circuit diagram of the mobile modulator. Resistors are ½ watt unless otherwise specified. Capacitors other than electrolytic may be either paper or ceramic. If a carbon microphone is used, substitute the carbon microphone speech amplifier circuit, at points marked "X", in the upper part of the diagram.

T_1—Driver transformer: parallel 6N7 to class B 6N7 grids.

T_2—Modulation transformer, tapped secondary, primary 10,000 ohms plate to plate.

● A 10-WATT MOBILE MODULATOR

Fig. 19-24 shows a modulator that can be used with any mobile a.m. transmitter whose input does not exceed 20 to 25 watts. A resistance-coupled speech amplifier using a single 12AX7 drives a Class A 6N7 which in turn drives a Class B 6N7. The 6N7 uses the two triode sections in parallel, to obtain sufficient driving power.

Also shown in Fig. 19-24 are the changes in the speech-amplifier circuit necessary to adapt it for use with a carbon microphone. D.c. voltage for the carbon microphone is obtained by connecting the microphone in series with the speech-amplifier cathodes.

The modulator requires 300 volts at about 90 ma. for plate power, and 6 volts at 1.9 amperes or 12 volts at .95 amperes for the heaters. Heater connections are given for both voltages. The plate supply should use a large capacitance (100 μf. or more) in the output, to serve as a reservoir for the heavy peak-current demands.

The main constructional precaution to be observed when building the modulator is that the output transformer T_2 should not be mounted too close to the speech amplifier circuits. Separation will reduce the chance of feedback through stray coupling. A tube shield over the 12AX7 will serve to hold it in the socket over bumpy roads; good octal sockets will normally need no tube clamps to retain the 6N7s.

In any mobile installation, the modulator may be separated from the r.f. assembly by any convenient distance. The cable connecting the modulator to the r.f. section should be made with individually shielded leads.

● A 25-WATT TRANSISTOR MODULATOR

Figs. 19-25 through 19-27 show a complete transistor modulator that obtains its power directly from the automobile's 12-volt storage battery. It requires only a fraction of the space required by a comparable vacuum-tube unit, and it allows full use of the high-voltage power supply for the r.f. section.

The unit is based on a design orignally published by Delco Radio [1]; it is a 12-volt 25-watt Class B modulator. Among the advantages of a modulator of this type are the compactness (25 watts of audio in approximately 90 cubic inches), high over-all efficiency, no warm-up time, and low idling current when not modulating. It will modulate an r.f. stage input of between 45 and 50 watts, at an impedance level of 4000 ohms with the output transformer listed (about 450 volts and 110 ma.). Suitable 12-volt heater tubes for the modulated output stage include the 1625

---

[1] *Transistor Application Note 6-B*, Delco Radio Division, General Motors Corp, Kokomo, Indiana.

Fig. 19-25—A 3 × 4 × 5-inch utility box is sufficient to house the modulation transformer and all of the smaller components of the 25-watt transistor modulator.

Transistor Modulator

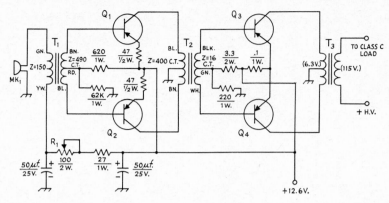

Fig. 19-26—Circuit of the 25-watt transistor modulator. Resistances are in ohms. Capacitors are electrolytic.

MK₁—Single-button carbon microphone.
Q₁, Q₂—2N190 (GE) or 2N109 (RCA).
Q₃, Q₄—DS-501 (Delco).
R₁—100-ohm 2-watt potentiometer.
T₁—150 ohms c.t. (c.t. not used) to 490 ohms c.t. (Thordarson TR-5).

T₂—400 ohms c.t. to 16 ohms, c.t. (see text), Stancor TA-41).
T₃—6.3-volt c.t., 3-amp, filament transformer used as modulation transformer (see text) (Stancor P-5014).

(similar to 807) and the 6883 (similar to the 6146). The exciter portion of the transmitter can be made up of 6417s (similar to the 5763) or of 12V6-GTs or 12L6-GTs (12-volt-heater versions of the 6V6 and 6L6). Maximum economy will be obtained with a transistorized power supply, similar to the unit described later in this chapter.

Construction

The unit is constructed on a 4 × 5 × 3-inch utility box on which a ⅛-inch aluminum cover 5 × 6 inches is substituted. This provides a 2-inch overhang on one edge for mounting the power transistors, and it also serves as a heat sink. Two transformers, plus gain control and mike jack, are also mounted on the cover (see Fig. 19-27).

For a modulation transformer the unit uses a 6.3-volt filament transformer turned backwards; that is, with the 6.3-volt 3-ampere winding toward the collectors. This transformer is mounted inside the utility box. Ample room is left for the input transformers, resistors and capacitors. It was found necessary to add an input filter on the 12-volt line to prevent hash from getting into the microphone circuit and adding noise.

To obtain a true center tap for the driver transformer, a transformer having taps at 4 and 16 ohms is used. Since the impedance varies as the square of the turns ratio, the 4-ohm tap provides a center tap.

Transistor Mounting

Because the collector connection is common with the case of the transistor, mica spacers must be used between the transistor cases and ground. (Insulator package No. 1221264). These can be obtained in a special mounting kit from Delco distributors.

A four-lug terminal box is located on top of the utility box to provide for the 12-volt and output connections of the modulator. Although wiring of the unit may appear difficult, it becomes a relatively simple job if the internal wiring is done separately, before putting on the front cover.

Be careful to apply as little heat as possible when soldering any transistor connections. Either G.E. 2N190 or RCA 2N109 can be used for the input transistors. Although several other types could be used for the output transistors, the specified DS-501 should be easier to obtain than some since it is sold as a replacement in car-radio service.

It is not likely that a 0.1-ohm 1-watt resistor (see Fig. 19-26) can be purchased at any radio store. A satisfactory substitute is to wind a suitable length of resistance wire over a 2-watt resistor used as a form, or three 0.33-ohm ½-watt resistors can be wired in parallel to obtain a value sufficiently close.

Testing

After wiring and construction of the unit is completed, testing for proper operation can be done in several ways. One method is simply to connect a 4000-ohm 10-watt resistor across the modulation transformer output connections and then place a d.c. ammeter in series with the 12-volt line, and watch the current variation while talking into the microphone. The idling current should be around 700 ma., kicking up to above 2 amperes on peaks. Do not, under any circumstances, try to operate the unit without a load of some sort on the output terminals as this may damage the output transistors.

Another method of testing is to place another

Fig. 19-27—The front cover of the modulator unit serves as a heat sink. The driver transformer and microphone jack are at the bottom, the microphone transformer and potentiometer control at the center, and the two power transistors at the top.

6.3-volt filament transformer back-to-back with the modulation transformer, to bring the impedance down to a low level, and then connect a p.m. speaker to the 6.3-volt winding.

A 'scope test can be made after the unit is connected to the transmitter. The Class C load level can be adjusted for impedance matching.

An F1 carbon microphone is suitable for use with this unit. Although not shown in Fig. 19-26, the unit should be connected so that it is turned on only while the transmit-receive switch is in the transmit position. An inexpenisve 12-volt automobile-horn relay (e.g., Echlin HR 101), available at most filling stations or automobile parts distributors, should be used to close and open the circuit. The relay arm and contact should be connected in the +12.6-volt lead from the battery and fuse. If excessive sparking is noted at the relay contacts it may be reduced by moving the 50-μf. 25-volt capacitor to the fuse side of the relay contacting circuit.

Concerning placement of the unit in the car: Try to find a location away from high-temperature spots and in a well-ventilated area. The trunk is not recommended since there is little ventilation; this area can become quite hot in the summertime and damage to the transistors could result. The engine compartment makes a convenient place to mount the unit but this space is not adequately ventilated except possibly while the car is in motion. The most favorable spot is on the fire wall in the passenger compartment, or under the front seat. These areas are usually well ventilated, or at least cooler than any other enclosed section of the car. As in any mobile installation where the modulator is some distance from the r.f. section, the audio leads from the secondary of the modulation transformer to the modulated r.f. stage should be made with individually-shielded leads.

(Original description appeared in *QST* for November, 1959.)

The Mobile Antenna

For mobile operation in the range between 1.8 and 30 Mc., the vertical whip antenna is almost universally used. Since longer whips present mechanical difficulties, the length is usually limited to a dimension that will resonate as a quarter-wave antenna in the 10-meter band. The car body serves as the ground connection. This antenna length is approximately 8 feet.

With the whip length adjusted to resonance in the 10-meter band, the impedance at the feed point, *X*, Fig. 19-28, will appear as a pure resistance at the resonant frequency. This resistance will be composed almost entirely of radiation resistance (see index), and the efficiency will be high. However, at frequencies lower than the resonant frequency, the antenna will show an increasingly large capacitive reactance and a decreasingly small radiation resistance.

The equivalent circuit is shown in Fig. 19-29. For the average 8-ft. whip, the reactance of the

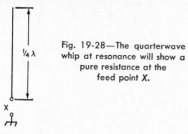

Fig. 19-28—The quarterwave whip at resonance will show a pure resistance at the feed point X.

capacitance, C_A, may range from about 150 ohms at 21 Mc. to as high as 8000 ohms at 1.8 Mc., while the radiation resistance, R_R, varies from about 15 ohms at 21 Mc. to as low as 0.1 ohm at 1.8 Mc. Since the resistance is low, considerable current must flow in the circuit if any appreciable power is to be dissipated as radiation in the resistance. Yet it is apparent that little current can be made to flow in the circuit so long as the comparatively high series reactance remains.

Fig. 19-29—At frequencies below the resonant frequency, the whip antenna will show capacitive reactance as well as resistance. R_R is the radiation resistance, and C_A represents the capacitive reactance.

Eliminating Reactance

The capacitive reactance can be canceled out by connecting an equivalent inductive reactance, L_L, in series, as shown in Fig. 19-30, thus tuning the system to resonance.

Fig. 19-30—The capacitive reactance at frequencies lower than the resonant frequency of the whip can be canceled out by adding an equivalent inductive reactance in the form of a loading coil in series with the antenna.

Unfortunately, all coils have resistance, and this resistance will be added in series, as indicated at R_C in Fig. 19-31. While a large coil may radiate some energy, thus adding to the radiation resistance, the latter will usually be negligible

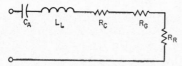

Fig. 19-31—Equivalent circuit of a loaded whip antenna. C_A represents the capacitive reactance of the antenna, L_L an equivalent inductive reactance. R_C is the loading-coil resistance, R_G the ground-loss resistance, and R_R the radiation resistance.

compared to the loss resistance introduced. However, adding the coil makes it possible to feed power to the circuit.

Ground Loss

Another element in the circuit dissipating power is the ground-loss resistance. Fundamentally, this is related to the nature of the soil in the area under the antenna. Little information is available on the values of resistance to be expected in practice, but some measurements have shown that it may amount to as much as 10 or 12 ohms at 4 Mc. At the lower frequencies, it may constitute the major resistance in the circuit.

Fig. 19-31 shows the circuit including all of the elements mentioned above. Assuming C_A lossless

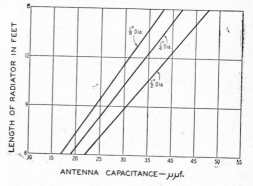

Fig. 19-32—Graph showing the approximate capacitance of short vertical antennas for various diameters and lengths, at 3.9 Mc. These values should be approximately halved for a center-loaded antenna.

and the loss resistance of the coil to be represented by R_C, it is seen that the power output of the transmitter is divided among three resistances — R_C, the coil resistance; R_G, the ground-loss resistance; and R_R, the radiation resistance. Only the power dissipated in R_R is radiated. The power developed in R_C and R_G is dissipated in heat. Therefore, it is important that the latter two resistances be minimized.

● MINIMIZING LOSSES

There is little that can be done about the nature of the soil. However, poor electrical contact between large surfaces of the car body, and especially between the point where the feed line is grounded and the rest of the body, can add materially to the ground-loss resistance. For example, the feed line, which should be grounded as close to the base of the antenna as possible, may be connected to the bumper, while the bumper may have poor contact with the rest of the body because of rust or paint.

Loading Coils

The accompanying tables show the approximate loading-coil inductance required for the various bands. The graph of Fig. 19-32 shows the approximate capacitance of whip antennas of

TABLE 19-I

	Approximate Values for 8-ft. Mobile Whip					
	Base Loading					
$f_{kc.}$	Loading $L_{\mu h.}$	R_C (Q50) Ohms	R_C (Q300) Ohms	R_R Ohms	Feed R* Ohms	Matching $L_{\mu h.}$ *
1800	345	77	13	0.1	23	3
3800	77	37	6.1	0.35	16	1.2
7200	20	18	3	1.35	15	0.6
14,200	4.5	7.7	1.3	5.7	12	0.28
21,250	1.25	3.4	0.5	14.8	16	0.28
29,000	....	....	....	....	36	0.23
	Center Loading					
1800	700	158	23	0.2	34	3.7
3800	150	72	12	0.8	22	1.4
7200	40	36	6	3	19	0.7
14,200	8.6	15	2.5	11	19	0.35
21,250	2.5	6.6	1.1	27	29	0.29

R_C = Loading-coil resistance; R_R = Radiation resistance.
* Assuming loading coil Q = 300, and including estimated ground-loss resistance.
Suggested coil dimensions for the required loading inductances are shown in a following table.

various average diameters and lengths. For 1.8, 4 and 7 Mc., the loading-coil inductance required (when the loading coil is at the base) will be approximately the inductance required to resonate in the desired band with the whip capacitance taken from the graph. For 14 and 21 Mc., this rough calculation will give more than the required inductance, but it will serve as a starting point for final experimental adjustment that must always be made.

Also shown in table 19-I are approximate values of radiation resistance to be expected with an 8-ft. whip, and the resistances of loading coils — one group having a Q of 50, the other a Q of 300. A comparison of radiation and coil resistances will show the importance of reducing the coil resistance to a minimum, especially on the three lower-frequency bands.

To minimize loading-coil loss, the coil should have a high ratio of reactance to resistance, i.e., high Q. A 4-Mc. loading coil wound with small wire on a small-diameter solid form of poor quality, and enclosed in a metal protector, may have a Q as low as 50, with a resistance of 50 ohms or more. High-Q coils require a large conductor, "air-wound" construction, turns spaced, the best insulating material available, a diameter not less than half the length of the coil (not always mechanically feasible), and a minimum of metal in the field. Such a coil for 4 Mc. may show a Q of 300 or more, with a resistance of 12 ohms or less. This reduction in loading-coil resistance may be equivalent to increasing the

transmitter power by 3 times or more. Most low-loss transmitter plug-in coils of the 100-watt size or larger, commercially produced, show a Q of this order. Where larger inductance values are required, lengths of low-loss space-wound coils are available.

TABLE 19-II

Suggested Loading-Coil Dimensions					
Req'd $L_{\mu h.}$	Turns	Wire Size	Diam. In.	Length In.	Form or B & W Type
700	190	22	3	10	Polystyrene
345	135	18	3	10	Polystyrene
150	100	16	2½	10	Polystyrene
77	75	14	2½	10	Polystyrene
77	29	12	5	4¼	160T
40	28	16	2½	2	80B less 7 t.
40	34	12	2½	4¼	80T
20	17	16	2½	1¼	80B less 18 t.
20	22	12	2½	2¾	80T less 12 t.
8.6	16	14	2	2	40B less 4 t.
8.6	15	12	2½	3	40T less 5 t.
4.5	10	14	2	1¼	40B less 10 t.
4.5	12	12	2½	4	40T
2.5	8	12	2	2	15B
2.5	8	6	2⅜	4½	15T
1.25	6	12	1¾	2	10B
1.25	6	6	2⅜	4½	10T

Mobile Antennas

Center Loading

The radiation resistance of the whip can be approximately doubled by placing the loading coil at the center of the whip, rather than at the base, as shown in Fig. 19-33. (The optimum position varies with ground resistance. The center is optimum for average ground resistance.) However, the inductance of the loading coil must be

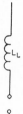

Fig. 19-33—Placing the loading coil at the center of the whip antenna, instead of at the base, increases the radiation resistance, although a larger coil must be used.

approximately doubled over the value required at the base to tune the system to resonance. For a coil of the same Q, the coil resistance will also be doubled. But, even if this is the case, center loading represents a gain in antenna efficiency, especially at the lower frequencies. This is because the ground-loss resistance remains the same, and the increased radiation resistance becomes a larger portion of the total circuit resistance, even though the coil resistance also increases. However, as turns are added to a loading coil (other factors being equal) the inductance (and therefore the reactance) increases at a greater rate than the resistance, and the larger coil will usually have a higher Q.

Top Loading Capacitance

Since the coil resistance varies with the inductance of the loading coil, the coil resistance can be reduced by reducing the number of turns. This can be done, while still maintaining resonance, by adding capacitance to the portion of the antenna above the coil. This capacitance can be provided by attaching a capacitive surface as high up on the antenna as is mechanically feasible. Capacitive "hats," as they are usually called, may consist of a light-weight metal ball, cylinder, disk, or wheel structure as shown in Fig. 19-34. This should be added to the capacitance of the whip above the loading coil (from Fig. 19-32) in determining the approximate inductance of the loading coil.

When center loading is used, the amount of capacitance to be added to permit the use of the same loading inductance required for base loading is not great, and should be seriously considered, since the total gain made by moving the coil to the center of the antenna may be quite marked.

Tuning the Band

Especially at the lower frequencies, where the resistance in the circuit is low compared to the coil reactance, the antenna will represent a very

Fig. 19-34—The top-loaded 4-Mc. antenna designed by W6SCX. The loading coil is a B & W transmitting coil. The coil can be tuned by the variable link which is connected in series with the two halves of the coil.

high-Q circuit, making it necessary to retune for relatively small changes in frequency. While many methods have been devised for tuning the whip over a band, one of the simplest is shown in Fig. 19-35. In this case, a standard B & W plug-in coil is used as the loading coil. A length of large-diameter polystyrene rod is drilled and tapped to fit between the upper and lower sections of the antenna. The assembly also serves to clamp a pair of metal brackets on each side

Fig. 19-35—W8AUN's adjustable capacity hat for tuning the whip antenna over a band. The coil is a B & W type B 160-meter coil, with a turn or two removed. Spreading the rods apart increases the capacitance. This simple top loader has sufficient capacitance to permit the use of approximately the same loading-coil inductance at the center of the antenna as would normally be required for base loading.

of the polystyrene block that serve both as support and connections to the loading-coil jack bar.

A $\frac{1}{8}$-inch steel rod, about 15 inches long, is brazed to each of two large-diameter washers with holes to pass the threaded end of the upper section. The rods form a loading capacitance that varies as the upper rod is swung away from the lower one, the latter being stationary. Enough variation in tuning can be obtained to cover the 80-meter band. (Original description appeared in *QST*, September, 1953.)

● REMOTE ANTENNA RESONATING

Fig. 19-36 shows circuits of two remote-control resonating systems for mobile antennas. As shown, they make use of surplus d.c. motors driving a loading coil removed from a surplus ARC-5 transmitter. A standard coil and motor may be used in either installation at increased expense.

The control circuit shown in Fig. 19-36-A is a three-wire system (the car frame is the fourth conductor) with a double-pole double-throw switch and a momentary (normally off) single-pole single-throw switch. S_2 is the motor reversing switch. The motor runs so long as S_1 is closed.

The circuit shown in Fig. 19-36B uses a latching relay, in conjunction with microswitches, to automatically reverse the motor when the roller reaches the end of the coil. S_3 and S_5 operate the relay, K_1, which reverses the motor. S_4 is the motor on-off switch. When the tuning coil roller

reaches one end or the other of the coil, it closes S_6 or S_7, as the case may be, operating the relay and reversing the motor.

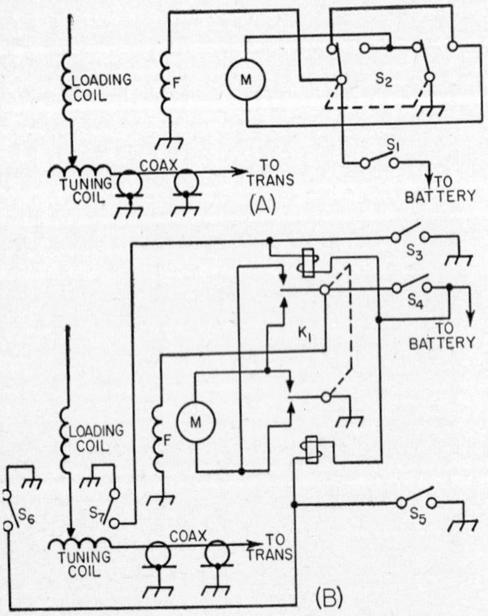

The procedure in setting up the system is to prune the center loading coil to resonate the antenna on the highest frequency used without the base loading coil. Then, the base loading coil is used to resonate at the lower frequencies. When the circuit shown in Fig. 19-36A is used for control, S_1 is used to start and stop the motor, and S_2, set at the "up" or "down" position, will determine whether the resonant frequency is raised or lowered. In the circuit shown in Fig. 19-36B, S_4 is used to control the motor. S_3 or S_5 is momentarily closed (to activate the latching relay) for raising or lowering the resonant frequency. The broadcast antenna is used with a wavemeter to indicate resonance.

(Originally described in *QST*, Dec., 1953.)

Several companies offer motor tuning for getting optimum performance over a low-frequency band. (For a complete description of the commercially available remotely-tuned systems, see Goodman, "Frequency Changing and Mobile Antennas," *QST*, Dec., 1957.)

Automatic Mobile Antenna Tuning

A somewhat more complex antenna tuning system for 75 and 40 meters is one that automatically tunes the antenna as the transmitter frequency is shifted. After initial adjustments, the radiator is kept in resonance without attention from the operator. (For a description of the automatic system, see Hargrave, "Automatic Mobile Antenna Tuning, *QST*, May, 1955.)

● FEEDING THE ANTENNA

It is usually found most convenient to feed the whip antenna with coax line. Unless very low-Q loading coils are used, the feed-point impedance will always be appreciably lower than 52 ohms — the characteristic impedance of the commonly-used coax line, RG-8/U or RG-58/U. Since the length of the transmission line will seldom exceed 10 ft., the losses involved will be negligible, even at 29 Mc., with a fairly-high s.w.r. However, unless a line of this length is made reasonably flat, difficulty may be encountered in obtaining sufficient coupling with a link to load the transmitter output stage.

One method of obtaining a match is shown in Fig. 19-37. A small inductance, L_M, is inserted at the base of the antenna, the loading-coil inductance being reduced correspondingly to maintain resonance. The line is then tapped on the coil at a point where the desired loading is obtained. Table 19-I shows the approximate inductance to be used between the line tap and ground. It is advisable to make the experimental matching coil larger than the value shown, so that there will be provision for varying either side of the proper position. The matching coil can also be of the plug-in type for changing bands.

Fig. 19-36—Circuits of the remote mobile-whip tuning systems.

K_1—D.p.d.t. latching relay.

S_1, S_3, S_4, S_5—Momentary-contact s.p.s.t., normally open.

S_2—D.p.d.t. toggle.

S_6, S_7—S.p.s.t. momentary-contact microswitch, normally open.

Adjustment

For operation in the bands from 29 to 1.8 Mc.,

Mobile Antennas

485

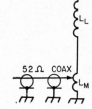

Fig. 19-37—A method of matching the loaded whip to 52-ohm coax cable. L_L is the loading coil and L_M the matching coil.

the whip should first be resonated at 29 Mc. with the matching coil inserted, but the line disconnected, using a grid-dip oscillator coupled to the matching coil. Then the line should be attached, and the tap varied to give proper loading, using a link at the transmitter end of the line whose reactance is approximately 52 ohms at the operating frequency, tightly coupled to the output tank circuit. After the proper position for the tap has been found, it may be necessary to readjust the antenna length slightly for resonance. This can be checked on a field-strength meter several feet away from the car.

The same procedure should be followed for each of the other bands, first resonating, with the g.d.o. coupled to the matching coil, by adjusting the loading coil.

After the position of the matching tap has been found, the size of the matching coil can be reduced to only that portion between the tap and ground, if desired. If turns are removed here, it will be necessary to reresonate with the loading coil.

If an entirely flat line is desired, a s.w.r. indicator should be used while adjusting the line tap. With a good match, it should not be necessary to readjust for resonance after the line tap has been set.

It should be emphasized that the figures shown in the table are only approximate and may be altered considerably depending on the type of car on which the antenna is mounted and the spot at which the antenna is placed.

● ANTENNAS FOR 50 AND 144 MC.

A Simple Vertical Antenna

The most convenient type of antenna for mobile v.h.f. work is the quarter-wave vertical radiator, fed with 50-ohm coaxial line. The antenna, which may be a flexible telescoping "fish pole," can be mounted in any of several places on the car. An ideal mounting spot is on top of the car, though rear-deck mounting presents a better spot for esthetic reasons. Tests have shown that with the car in motion there is no observable difference in average performance of the antennas, regardless of their mounting positions. There may be more in the way of directional effects with the rear-deck mount, but the over-all advantage of the roof mount is slight.

A good match may be obtained by feeding

the simple vertical with 50-ohm line. However, it is well to provide some means for tuning the system, so that all variables can be taken care of. The simplest tuning arrangement consists of a variable capacitor connected between the low side of the transmitter coupling coil and ground, as shown in Fig. 19-38. This capacitor should

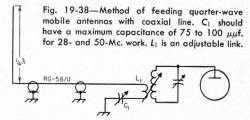

Fig. 19-38—Method of feeding quarter-wave mobile antennas with coaxial line. C_1 should have a maximum capacitance of 75 to 100 $\mu\mu$f. for 28- and 50-Mc. work. L_1 is an adjustable link.

have a maximum capacitance of 75 to 100 $\mu\mu$f. for 50 Mc., and should be adjusted for maximum loading with the least coupling to the transmitter. Some method of varying the coupling to the transmitter should be provided.

Horizontal Polarization

Horizontally polarized antennas have a considerable advantage over the vertical whip under usual conditions of mobile operation. This is particularly true when horizontal polarization is used at both ends of a line-of-sight circuit, or on a longer circuit over reasonably flat terrain. An additional advantage, especially on 6 meters, is a marked reduction in ignition noise from neighboring cars as well as from the station car.

A Horizontally Polarized Two-Band Antenna for V.H.F.

One type of horizontally-polarized antenna, called the "halo," is shown in Fig. 19-39. It is a dipole bent into a circle, with the ends capacitively loaded to reduce the circumference. Since the 50- and 144-Mc. bands are almost in third harmonic relationship, it is possible to build a single halo that will work on both bands. The antenna is changed from one band to another by changing the spacing between the end loading plates and adjusting the matching mechanism.

Mechanical Details

The halo is made of $7/16$-inch aluminum fuel-line tubing. This material is both strong and very light, but any tubing of about $1/2$-inch diameter could be used equally well. The loop is 67 inches in circumference and the capacitor plates are $2\frac{1}{4}$ inches square, with the corners rounded off.

To fasten the capacitor plates to the ends of the tubing, aluminum rod stock is turned down on a lathe to make a tight fit into the ends. This is tapped for 6-32 thread, and then forced into the tubing ends. Holes are drilled through tubing and inserts, at each end of the halo, and a screw run through each to keep the inserts from turning around or slipping out. The binding-head screws that hold the plates to the inserts are equipped

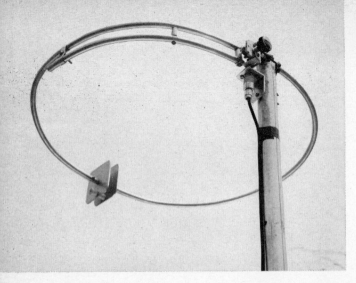

Fig. 19-39—The 2-band halo as it appears when set up for 50-Mc. operation. Changing to 144 Mc. involves decreasing the plate spacing by swapping cone insulators, and resetting the gamma matching clip and series capacitor.

with lock washers. The holes for mounting the ceramic cone spacer are drilled directly below the center, midway between the center and the edge of the capacitor plates.

The halo is set into a slot cut in the vertical support. This slot should be just big enough to permit the halo to be forced into it. The halo has to be stiffened, so cut it at the center and insert about 2 inches of aluminum rod, again turned down on a lathe to fit tightly inside the tubing. The two pieces of tubing are then pushed together, over the insert, and drilled each side of center to pass 6–32 screws. The halo and insert are also drilled at the midpoint, to pass the mounting screw. This is an 8–32 screw, $1\frac{1}{4}$ inches long. If lathe facilities are not available, the mounting of the capacitor plates and the securing of the halo to the vertical support can be handled with angle brackets.

Mechanical stability is important so straps of aluminum $\frac{1}{2}$ inch wide are wrapped around the halo either side of the mounting post. These are bent at right angles and the ends pulled together with a bolt.

The matching arm is $14\frac{1}{2}$ inches long, of the same material as the halo itself. It is mounted below the halo on two $\frac{3}{4}$-inch cone standoffs. For convenience in detaching the feed line a coaxial fitting is mounted on an L bracket bolted to the vertical support. The stator bar of the 25-$\mu\mu$f. variable capacitor (Johnson 167-2) is soldered directly to the coaxial fitting. The rotor of the capacitor is connected to the gamma arm through a piece of stiff wire. For further stiffening an aluminum angle bracket is screwed to the lower mounting stud of the capacitor and the other end mounted under the screw that holds the first cone standoff in place. Contact between the arm and the halo proper is made through a strap of $\frac{1}{2}$-inch wide aluminum bent to form a sliding clip. Be sure that a clean tight contact is made between the tubing and the clip, as high current flows at this point. A poor or varying contact will ruin the effectiveness of the antenna.

Adjustment

The capacity-loaded halo is a high-Q device so

it must be tuned on-the-nose, or it will not work properly. The only reliable method for adjusting a halo is to use a standing-wave bridge, making tuning and matching adjustments for minimum reflected power. Using a field-strength meter and attempting to adjust for maximum radiated power can give confusing indications, and is almost certain to result in something less than maximum effectiveness.

The adjustment process with this design can be simplified if the halo is first resonated approximately to the desired frequency ranges with the aid of a grid-dip meter. Set the clip at about one inch in from the end of the arm, and the series capacitor at the middle of its range. Check the resonant frequency of the loop with the grid-dip meter, with the $\frac{3}{4}$-inch spacer between the capacitor plates. It should be close to 50 Mc. If the frequency is too low, trimming the corners of the plates or putting shims under the ceramic spacer will raise it somewhat. If the frequency is too high already, make new and slightly larger capacitor plates.

Next, insert an s.w.r. bridge between the antenna and the transmission line. Apply power and swing the capacitor through its range, noting whether there is a dip in reflected power at any point. If the reflected power will not drop to zero, slide the clip along the gamma arm and retune the capacitor, until the lowest reading possible is obtained. If this is still not zero, the halo is not resonant. If the halo capacitance is on the low side, moving the hands near the plates will cause the reflected power to drop. Closer spacing of the plates, larger plates or a longer halo loop are possible solutions.

These adjustments should be made on a frequency near the middle of the range you expect to use. Adjusting for optimum at 50.25 Mc., for example, will result in usable operation over the first 500 kc. of the band, and a good match (below 1.5 to 1) from 50.1 to 50.4. The s.w.r. will rise rapidly either side of this range.

To tune up on 144 Mc., insert the $\frac{1}{2}$-inch cone between the capacitor plates. Slide the clip back on the gamma arm about 3 to 4 inches and repeat the adjustment for minimum reflected power,

Field-Strength Meter

using a frequency at the middle of a 2-Mc. range. Tuning up at 145 Mc., for example, will give quite satisfactory operation from the low end to 146 Mc., the halo being much broader in frequency response when it is operated on its third harmonic. In this model the series capacitor in the gamma arm was at about the middle of its range for 50 Mc., and near minimum for 144 Mc. Slight differences in mechanical construction may change the value of capacitance required, so these settings should not be taken as important.

The photograph, Fig. 19-39, shows a method used to avoid running the chance that the second ceramic cone would be missing when a band change was to be made. The head was cut from a 6–32 screw, leaving a threaded stud about ½ inch long. This is screwed into one of the ceramic cones. The other cone then serves as a nut, to tighten down the capacitor plate. In changing bands merely swap cones. (Original description appeared in *QST*, Sept., 1958.)

Bibliography

Swafford, "Improved Coax Feed for Low-Frequency Mobile Antennas," *QST*, December, 1951.

Roberge McConnell, "Let's Go High Hat!," *QST*, January, 1952.

Belrose, "Short Antennas for Mobile Operation," *QST*, September, 1953.

Dinsmore, "The 'Hot-Rod' Mobile Antenna," *QST*, September, 1953.

Picken & Wambsganss, "Remote Mobile-Antenna Resonating," *QST*, December, 1953.

Webster, "Mobile Loop Antennas," *QST*, June, 1954.

Tilton, "Have You Tried V.H.F. Mobile?" *QST*, September, 1954.

Hargrave, "Automatic Mobile Antenna Tuning," *QST*, May, 1955.

Morgan, "Tuning the Mobile Antenna from the Driver's Seat," *QST*, October, 1955.

Braschwitz, "Directional Antenna for the Transmitter Hunter," *QST*, April, 1956.

Tilton, "Polarization Effects in V.H.F. Mobile," *QST*, December, 1956.

Breetz, "A Simple Halo for 2-Meter Mobile Use," *QST*, August, 1957.

Harris, "Continuously Loaded Whip Antennas," *QST*, May, 1958.

A Field-Strength Meter for Portable-Mobile Use

The field-strength meter of Figs. 19-40 through 19-42 can be used in a mobile station as an antenna-resonance indicator or as a continuous output indicator showing that the transmitting system is actually radiating. It is designed to be inserted between the automobile broadcast receiving antenna, which acts as the r.f. pick-up,

Fig. 19-42—Inside view of the meter. The back plate shown in the photograph is used as a cover for the box.

Fig. 19-40—A front view of the field-strength meter. Sensitivity control R_1 is to the right of the 0–1 indicating meter. Antenna input and output connectors are mounted on the right end of the box.

and the broadcast receiver. Small magnets or rubber suction cups on the back plate will hold the meter securely on top of the car dash. Although in this position the meter will be face up in most cases, it can nevertheless usually be read from the driver position.

Fig. 19-41—Circuit of the field-strength meter.
CR_1—Crystal diode (1N34A).
J_1, J_2—Automobile type antenna connectors.
RFC_1—2.5 mh. r.f. choke.
R_1—500 ohm potentiometer (Mallory U-2).
S_1—S.p.d.t. switch for above potentiometer.

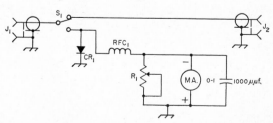

A handle can be mounted on the meter box so that the meter can easily be carried about for portable measurements. The same basic layout less the handle can be used if the box is to be mounted under the dash or in the glove compartment.

The circuit for the field-strength meter is shown in Fig. 19-41. The values shown are not critical. Nearly any type of crystal detector can be used and the meter movement can be anything from 100 μa. to 2 ma. or more, depending upon the size and placement of the antenna and the power output of the transmitter. All components, including the 3-inch indicating meter, are housed in a $2 \times 6 \times 4$-inch aluminum chassis.

If a smaller meter is used, the box could be reduced in size accordingly. However, in mobile operation a large meter is more convenient to read while in motion. An illuminated meter could be substituted for the one shown in the photograph for use at night. A switch, S_1, is used in the circuit to switch the antenna to the field-strength meter position or straight through to the broadcast set. For portable or temporary mobile operation, a short pick-up wire can be used instead of the automobile receiving antenna. The pick-up antenna lead comes into a connector mounted on one end of the box. There is a second connector for attaching the lead to the broadcast receiver.

Conelrad Monitoring

The conelrad rules discussed in the chapters on high-frequency receivers and operating a station must be observed by amateurs who operate mobile. One convenient form of compliance is by means of a separate tunable converter covering the broadcast band, and converting to the same i.f. as the i.f. used by the ham-band converter. This type of converter may also be used when the car radio is used as the tunable i.f. for a broad-band converter, providing that the receiver is tuned to the converter i.f. at ten-minute intervals. This can be accomplished most conveniently by setting one of the push buttons to tune the receiver to the monitor output frequency.

The circuit of a broadcast-band converter is shown in Fig. 19-43. The input circuit $C_{1A}L_2$ covers the broadcast band. The oscillator circuit $C_{1B}L_3$ tunes the range of 2050 to 3000 kc. to produce an i.f. of 1500 kc. A type 6SA7 may be used in the circuit and, of course, either a 12BE6 or a 12SA7 should be used for 12-volt operation.

Plates must be removed from C_{1B} to provide the required tuning range. The oscillator section of the dual unit is the one having the smaller number of plates. Starting at the rear, all rotor plates except five should be removed. It isn't necessary to remove the unused stators. Be very careful to make sure that there are no shorted plates after the modification is complete.

L_2 is a ferrite-core loopstick. This coil usually comes with a length of wire attached to the ungrounded end and wound around the loopstick. When unwound, the short length of wire is intended to provide additional pickup if needed. Disconnect this wire from L_2 and, without unwinding it, use it for L_1.

L_3 is close-wound with 60 turns No. 30 enameled, and either tapped at about one third of the way up from the ground end, or with a separate cathode coil consisting of about one third the number of turns on L_3, wound over the ground end of L_3, and wound in the same direction. The bottom end of this winding should be grounded.

Power for the converter may be taken from the car radio supply since the current requirement is negligible. With 150 volts at the positive B terminal of the converter, the converter draws approximately 4 ma. and the drop across R_2 is about 100 volts. The converter will work well at supply voltages up to 350 or more without change in the resistance value of R_2. The current drain will, of course, be higher at the higher supply voltages, and the wattage rating of the resistor may have to be increased. If current drain is an important consideration, the resistance value of R_2 can be increased in proportion to the increase in supply voltage.

Fig. 19-43—Circuit of the conelrad converter for mobile use.

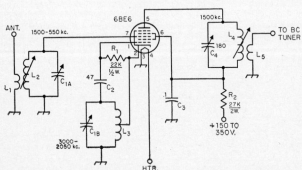

C$_1$—Dual variable capacitor, broadcast-replacement type for superhet receivers, C$_{1B}$ altered as described in the text (approx. 90 $\mu\mu$f.).

C$_2$—47-$\mu\mu$f. mica.

C$_3$—0.1-μf. 400-volt paper.

C$_4$—180-$\mu\mu$f. mica trimmer (Arco type 463).

L$_1$—See text.

L$_2$—BC ferrite core loopstick (approx. 230 μh.).

L$_3$—See text (approx. 65 μh.).

L$_4$—National XR-50 iron-slug form wound full with No. 32 enam. wire (approx. 85 μh.).

L$_5$—15 turns No. 28 wound over cold end of L$_4$.

Conelrad

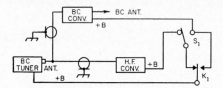

Fig. 19-44—Block diagram showing a switching system for the conelrad converter. K_1 represents a spare set of contacts on the change-over relay. S_1 is a s.p.d.t. toggle. With K_1 in the receiving position as shown, power from the broadcast receiver may be applied to either the b.c. converter or the ham-band converter. With K_1 in the transmitting position, power is applied to the broadcast converter for conelrad monitoring during transmitting periods.

The oscillator can be checked for proper frequency range by the use of a grid-dip meter before power is applied or, after power has been turned on, by listening on a communications receiver covering the 2-to-3 Mc. range.

Now connect an antenna to the input of the converter and connect the converter to the broadcast receiver. Set the broadcast receiver at 1500 kc. (or to the frequency normally used with the ham-band converter). Turn on the power and adjust C_4 and the slug of L_4 for a peak in noise (if you can't find a signal). Then adjust the slug of L_2 for maximum response.

Fig. 19-44 shows how the converter can be connected into a convenient switch system. (Originally described in *QST*, June, 1957).

Mobile Power Supply

By far the majority of amateur mobile installations depend upon the car storage battery as the source of power. The tube types used in equipment are chosen so that the filaments or heaters may be operated directly from the battery. High voltage may be obtained from a supply of the vibrator-transformer-rectifier type, a small motor generator or a transistor-transformer-rectifier system operating from the car battery.

Filaments

Because tubes with directly heated cathodes (filament-type tubes) have the advantage that they can be turned off during receiving periods and thereby reduce the average load on the battery, they are preferred by some for transmitter applications. However, the choice of types with direct heating is limited and the saving may not always be as great as anticipated, because directly heated tubes may require greater filament power than those of equivalent rating with indirectly heated cathodes. In most cases, the power required for transmitter filaments will be quite small compared to the total power consumed.

Plate Power

Under steady running conditions, the vibrator-transformer-rectifier system and the motor-generator-type plate supply operate with approximately the same efficiency. However, for the same power, the motor-generator's over-all efficiency may be somewhat lower because it draws a heavier starting current. On the other hand, the output of the generator requires less filtering and sometimes trouble is experienced in eliminating interference from the vibrator.

Transistor-transformer-rectifier plate supplies currently available operate with an efficiency of approximately 80 per cent. These compact, light-weight supplies use no moving parts (vibrator or armature) or vacuum tubes, and draw no starting surge current. Most transistorized supplies are designed to operate at 12 volts d.c.

and some units deliver 125 watts or more.

Converter units, both in the vibrator and rotating types, are also available. These operate at 6 or 12 volts d.c. and deliver 115 volts a.c. This permits operating standard a.c.-powered equipment in the car. Although these systems have the advantage of flexibility, they are less efficient than the previously mentioned systems because of the additional losses introduced by the transformers used in the equipment.

Mobile Power Considerations

Since the car storage battery is a low-voltage source, this means that the current drawn from the battery for even a moderate amount of power will be large. Therefore, it is important that the resistance of the battery circuit be held to a minimum by the use of heavy conductors and good solid connections. A heavy-duty relay should be used in the line between the battery and the plate-power unit. An ordinary toggle switch, located in any convenient position, may then be used for the power control. A second relay may sometimes be advisable for switching the filaments. If the power unit must be located at some distance from the battery (in the trunk, for instance) the 6- or 12-volt cable should be of the heavy military type.

A complete mobile installation may draw 30 to 40 amperes or more from the 6-volt battery or better than 20 amperes from a 12-volt battery. This requires a considerably increased demand from the car's battery-charging generator. The voltage-regulator systems on cars of recent years will take care of a moderate increase in demand if the car is driven fair distances regularly at a speed great enough to insure maximum charging rate. However, if much of the driving is in urban areas at slow speed, or at night, it may be necessary to modify the charging system. Special communications-type generators, such as those used in police-car installations, are designed to charge at a high rate at slow engine speeds. The charging rate of the standard system can be increased within limits by tightening up slightly on the voltage-regulator and current-regulator springs. This should be done with caution, however, checking for excessive generator temperature or abnormal sparking at the commutator. The average 6-volt car generator has a rating of 35 amperes, but it may be possible to adjust the regulator so that the generator will at least hold even with the transmitter, receiver, lights, etc., all operating at the same time.

If higher transmitter power is used, it may be necessary to install an a.c. charging system. In this system, the generator delivers a.c. and works into a rectifier. A charging rate of 75 amperes is easily obtained. Commutator trouble often experienced with d.c. generators at high current is avoided, but the cost of such a system is rather high.

Some mobile operators prefer to use a separate battery for the radio equipment. Such a system can be arranged with a switch that cuts the auxiliary battery in parallel with the car battery for charging at times when the car battery is lightly loaded. The auxiliary battery can also be charged at home when not in use.

A tip: many mobile operators make a habit of carrying a pair of heavy cables five or six feet long, fitted with clips to make a connection to the battery of another car in case the operator's battery has been allowed to run too far down for starting.

The Automobile Storage Battery

The success of any mobile installation depends to a large extent upon intelligent use and maintenance of the car's battery.

The storage battery is made up of units consisting of a pair of coated lead plates immersed in a solution of sulphuric acid and water. Cells, each of which delivers about 2 volts, can be connected in series to obtain the desired battery voltage. A 6-volt battery therefore has three cells, and a 12-volt battery has 6 cells. The average stock car battery has a rated capacity of 600 to 800 watt-hours, regardless of whether it is a 6-volt or 12-volt battery.

Specific Gravity and the Hydrometer

As power is drawn from the battery, the acid content of the electrolyte is reduced. The acid content is restored to the electrolyte (meaning that the battery is recharged) by passing a current through the battery in a direction opposite to the direction of the discharge current.

Since the acid content of the electrolyte varies with the charge and discharge of the battery, it is possible to determine the state of charge by measuring the *specific gravity* of the electrolyte.

An inexpensive device for checking the s.g. is the hydrometer which can be obtained at any automobile supply store. In checking the s.g., enough electrolyte is drawn out of the cell and into the hydrometer so that the calibrated bulb floats freely without leaning against the wall of the glass tube.

While the readings will vary slightly with batteries of different manufacture, a reading of 1.275 should indicate full charge or nearly full charge, while a reading below 1.150 should indicate a battery that is close to the discharge point. More specific values can be obtained from the car or battery dealer.

Readings taken immediately after adding water, or shortly after a heavy discharge period will not be reliable, because the electrolyte will not be uniform throughout the cell. Charging will speed up the equalizing, and some mixing can be done by using the hydrometer to withdraw and return some of the electrolyte to the cell several times.

A battery should not be left in a discharged condition for any appreciable length of time. This is especially important in low temperatures when there is danger of the electrolyte freezing and ruining the battery. A battery discharged to an s.g. of 1.100 will start to freeze at about 20 degrees F., at about 5 degrees when the s.g. is 1.150 and at 16 below when the s.g. is 1.200.

If a battery has been run down to the point where it is nearly discharged, it can usually be fast-charged at a battery station. Fast-charging rates may be as high as 80 to 100 amperes for a 6-volt battery. Any 6-volt battery that will accept a charge of 75 amperes at 7.75 volts during the first 3 minutes of charging, or any 12-volt battery that will accept a charge of 40 to 45 amperes at 15.5 volts, may be safely fast-charged up to the point where the gassing becomes so excessive that electrolyte is lost or the temperature rises above 125 degrees.

A normal battery showing an s.g. of 1.150 or less may be fast-charged for 1 hour. One showing an s.g. of 1.150 to 1.175 may be fast-charged for 45 minutes. If the s.g. is 1.175 to 1.200, fast-charging should be limited to 30 minutes.

Care of the Battery

The battery terminals and mounting frame should be kept free from corrosion. Any corrosive accumulation may be removed by the use of water to which some household ammonia or baking soda has been added, and a stiff-bristle brush. Care should be taken to prevent any of the corrosive material from falling into the cells. Cell caps should be rinsed out in the same solution to keep the vent holes free from obstructing dirt. Battery terminals and their cable clamps should be polished bright with a wire brush, and coated with mineral grease.

The hold-down clamps and the battery holder should be checked occasionally to make sure that they are tight so the battery will not be damaged by pounding when the car is in motion.

Voltage Checks

Although the readings of s.g. are quite reliable as a measure of the state of charge of a normal battery, the necessity for frequent use of the hydrometer is an inconvenience and will not always serve as a conclusive check on a defective battery. Cells may show normal or almost normal s.g. and yet have high internal resistance that ruins the usefulness of the battery under load.

When all cells show satisfactory s.g. readings and yet the battery output is low, service stations check each cell by an instrument that measures the voltage of each cell under a heavy load. Under a heavy load the cell voltages should not differ by more than 0.15 volt.

A load-voltage test can also be made by measuring the voltage of each cell while closing the starter switch with the ignition turned off. In many cars it is necessary to pull the central distributor wire out to prevent the motor starting.

Electrolyte Level

Water is evaporated from the electrolyte, but the acid is not. Therefore water must be added to each cell from time to time so that the plates are always completely covered. The level should be checked at least once per week, especially during hot weather and constant operation.

Distilled water is preferred for replenishing, but clear drinking water is an acceptable substitute. Too much water should not be added, since the gassing that accompanies charging may force electrolyte out through the vent holes in the caps of the cells. The electrolyte expands with temperature. (From QST, August, 1955.)

Emergency and Independent Power Sources

Emergency power supply which operates independently of a.c. lines is available, or can be built in a number of different forms, depending upon the requirements of the service for which it is intended.

The most practical supply for the average individual amateur is one that operates from a car storage battery. Such a supply may take the form of a small motor generator (often called a dynamotor), a rotary converter, a vibrator-transformer-rectifier combination, or transistor supply.

Dynamotors

A dynamotor differs from a motor generator in that it is a single unit having a double armature winding. One winding serves for the driving motor, while the output voltage is taken from the other. Dynamotors usually are operated from 6-, 12-, 28- or 32-volt storage batteries and deliver from 300 to 1000 volts or more at various current ratings.

Successful operation of dynamotors requires heavy direct leads, mechanical isolation to reduce vibration, and thorough r.f. and ripple filtration. The shafts and bearings should be thoroughly "run in" before regular operation is attempted, and thereafter the tension of the bearings should be checked occasionally to make certain that no looseness has developed.

In mounting the dynamotor, the support should be in the form of rubber mounting blocks, or equivalent, to prevent the transmission of vibration mechanically. The frame of the dynamotor should be grounded through a heavy flexible connector. The brushes on the high-voltage end of the shaft should be bypassed with 0.002-μf. mica capacitors to a common point on the dynamotor frame, preferably to a point inside the end cover close to the brush holders. Short leads are essential. It may prove desirable to shield the entire unit, or even to remove the unit to a distance of three or four feet from the receiver and antenna lead.

When the dynamotor is used for receiving, a filter should be used similar to that described for vibrator supplies. A 0.01-μf. 600-volt (d.c.) paper capacitor should be connected in shunt across the output of the dynamotor, followed by a 2.5-mh. r.f. choke in the positive high-voltage lead. From this point the output should be run to the receiver power terminals through a smoothing filter using 4- to 8-μf. capacitors and a 15- or 30-henry choke having low d.c. resistance.

Vibrator Power Supplies

The vibrator type of power supply consists of a special step-up transformer combined with a vibrating interrupter (vibrator). When the unit is connected to a storage battery, plate power is obtained by passing current from the battery through the primary of the transformer. The circuit is made and reversed rapidly by the vibrator contacts, interrupting the current at regular intervals to give a changing magnetic field which induces a voltage in the secondary. The resulting square-wave d.c. pulses in the primary of the transformer cause an alternating voltage to be developed in the secondary. This high-voltage a.c. in turn is rectified, either by a vacuum-tube rectifier or by an additional synchronized pair of vibrator contacts. The rectified output is pulsating d.c., which may be filtered by ordinary means. The smoothing filter can be a single-section affair, but the output capacitance should be fairly large — 16 to 32 μf.

Fig. 19-45 shows the two types of circuits. At A is shown the nonsynchronous type of vibrator. When the battery is disconnected the reed is midway between the two contacts, touching neither. On closing the battery circuit the magnet coil pulls the reed into contact with one contact point, causing current to flow through the lower half of the transformer primary winding. Simultaneously, the magnet coil is short-circuited, deënergizing it, and the reed swings back. Inertia carries the reed into contact with the upper point, causing current to flow through the upper half of the transformer primary. The magnet coil again is energized, and the cycle repeats itself.

491

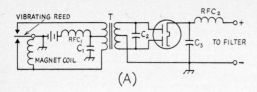

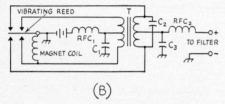

Fig. 19-45—Basic types of vibrator power-supply circuits. A—Nonsynchronous. B—Synchronous.

The synchronous circuit of Fig. 19-45B is provided with an extra pair of contacts which rectify the secondary output of the transformer, thus eliminating the need for a separate rectifier tube. The secondary center-tap furnishes the positive output terminal when the relative polarities of primary and secondary windings are correct. The proper connections may be determined by experiment.

The buffer capacitor, C_2, across the transformer secondary, absorbs the surges that occur on breaking the current, when the magnetic field collapses practically instantaneously and hence causes very high voltages to be induced in the secondary. Without this capacitor excessive sparking occurs at the vibrator contacts, shortening the vibrator life. Correct values usually lie between 0.005 and 0.03 $\mu f.$, and for 250-300-volt supplies the capacitor should be rated at 1500 to 2000 volts d.c. The exact capacitance is critical, and should be determined experimentally. The optimum value is that which results in least battery current for a given rectified d.c. output from the supply. In practice the value can be determined by observing the degree of vibrator sparking as the capacitance is changed. When the system is operating properly there should be practically no sparking at the vibrator contacts. A 5000-ohm resistor in series with C_2 will limit the secondary current to a safe value should the capacitor fail.

Vibrator-transformer units are available in a variety of power and voltage ratings. Representative units vary from one delivering 125 to 200 volts at 100 ma. to others that have a 400-volt output rating at 150 ma. Most units come supplied with "hash" filters, but not all of them have built-in ripple filters. The requirements for ripple filters are similar to those for a.c. supplies. The usual efficiency of vibrator packs is in the vicinity of 70 per cent, so a 300-volt 200-ma. unit will draw approximately 15 amperes from a 6-volt storage battery. Special vibrator transformers are also available from transformer manufacturers so

that the amateur may build his own supply if he so desires. These have d.c. output ratings varying from 150 volts at 40 ma. to 330 volts at 135 ma.

Vibrator-type supplies are also available for operating standard a.c. equipment from a 6- or 12-volt storage battery in power ratings up to 100 watts continuous or 125 watts intermittent.

"Hash" Elimination

Sparking at the vibrator contacts causes r.f. interference ("hash," which can be distinguished from hum by its harsh, sharper pitch) when used with a receiver. To minimize this, r.f. filters are incorporated, consisting of RFC_1 and C_1 in the battery circuit, and RFC_2 with C_3 in the d.c. output circuit.

Equally as important as the hash filter is thorough shielding of the power supply and its connecting leads, since even a small piece of wire or metal will radiate enough r.f. to cause interference in a sensitive amateur receiver.

The power supply should be built on a metal chassis, with all unshielded parts underneath. A bottom plate to complete the shielding is advisable. The transformer case, vibrator cover and the metal shell of the tube all should be grounded to the chassis. If a glass tube is used it should be enclosed in a tube shield. The battery leads should be evenly twisted, since these leads are more likely to radiate hash than any other part of a well-shielded supply. Experimenting with different values in the hash filters should come *after* radiation from the battery leads has been reduced to a minimum. Shielding the leads is not often found to be particularly helpful.

● UNIVERSAL VIBRATOR POWER SUPPLY

A vibrator-type power supply may be designed to operate from a storage battery only, or from either a battery or 115 volts a.c. Most late-model cars use 12-volt batteries, but there are still many cars with 6-volt systems in operation — a point that should be given due consideration where emergency operation is an objective.

The circuit of a universal power supply for emergency, mobile, or home-station use is shown in Fig. 19-46. The unit furnishes a d.c. output of 300 volts at 160 ma. and can be operated from any of the above-mentioned sources. Shifting from one power source to another is accomplished by plugging P_1 or P_2, connected to the selected source, into one of the two chassis connectors J_1 or J_2. The vibrator-primary current is 11.6 amperes with 6-volt input under loaded conditions, and 6.8 amperes with 12-volt input.

Heater Connections

To adapt equipment for optional 6- or 12-volt operation, 6-volt tubes must be used with their heaters in series-parallel. Fig. 19-47 shows a typical example of connections. The tubes in the

492

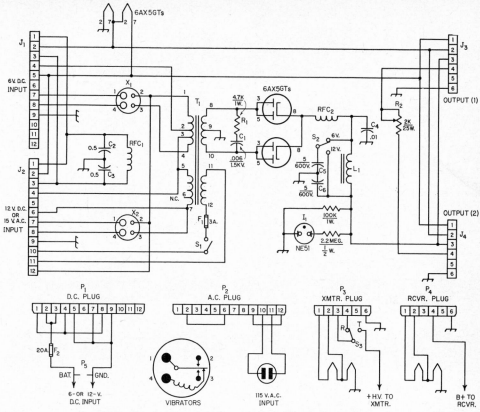

Fig. 19-46—Circuit of the universal power supply. All capacitances are in μf.

C_1—Buffer capacitor, tubular plastic.

C_2, C_3—Hash-filter capacitor, paper.

C_4—Hash-filter capacitor, disk ceramic.

C_5, C_6—Ripple-filter capacitor, 5 μf. or more, 600-volt oil-filled or electrolytic.

F_1—3-amp. cartridge fuse (Littlefuse type 3AG) in extractor-post mounting (Littlefuse 341001).

F_2—20-amp. cartridge fuse (Littlefuse type SFE) in in-line fuse retainer (Littlefuse 155020).

I_1—Neon pilot lamp.

J_1, J_2—12-contact male chassis connector (Cinch-Jones P-312-AB).

J_3, J_4—6-contact female chassis connector (Cinch-Jones S-306-AB).

L_1—5-h. 200-ma. 80-ohm filter choke (Merit C-1396, Stancor C-1411).

P_1, P_2—12-contact female cable connector (Cinch-Jones S-312-CCT).

P_3, P_4—6-contact male cable connector (Cinch-Jones P-306-CCT).

P_5—Cigar-lighter plug (Mallory R-675).

R_1—Buffer resistor.

R_2—Series voltage-dropping resistor for receiver, slider adjustable.

RFC$_1$—30 turns No. 14 enam., ½-inch diam., close-wound.

RFC$_2$—1-mh. r.f. choke (National R-300-U, Millen 34106).

S_1—S.p.s.t. toggle switch.

S_2—S.p.d.t. toggle switch.

S_3—S.p.d.t. toggle, or other, at transmitter.

T_1—Combination power transformer: 6-volt d.c. vibrator or 115 v. a.c. input; 300 volts, 160 ma.; 6.3 volts 3 amp.; 6.3-volt 4.5-amp. tap on vibrator primary (Merit P-3176). Numbered terminals are color-coded as follows: 1—heavy green; 2—yellow; 3—light green; 4—black; 5—brown; 6—blue; 7—white; 8—red; 9—red-yellow; 10—red; 11 and 12—black.

X_1—4-prong tube socket for 6-volt vibrator (Mallory 4501 vibrator).

X_2—4-prong tube socket for 12-volt vibrator (Mallory G4501 vibrator).

equipment should be divided into two groups whose heater-current ratings total as closely as possible the same value. The heaters in each group should be connected in parallel, and the two groups then connected in series. If it is impossible to arrive at a grouping that will have exactly the same total current, a resistor may be connected in parallel with the group drawing the smaller current as shown. The value of this resistor should be such that it will draw enough current at 6 volts to make up the difference between the two totals. One side of one group may be grounded to chassis but the other side of this group and both sides of the second group must be insulated.

Switching Circuits

Battery input connections are made through P_5 which plugs into a cigar-lighter socket in mobile service, F_2 is a fuse which is inserted in the

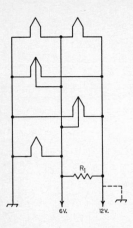

Fig. 19-47—Circuit showing typical series-parallel heater connections for 6-volt and 6/12-volt tubes. Resistor R_1 is used when necessary to balance the currents in the two branches as described in the text. The dashed line shows how the switching system connects all tubes in parallel for 6-volt operation by grounding.

cord between P_5 and P_1.

For 6-volt operation P_1 is plugged into J_1. For 12-volt operation P_1 is plugged into J_2. For 115-volt a.c. operation P_2 is plugged into J_2.

Positive high-voltage output from the supply is fed to Pins 3 on output connectors J_3 and J_4. The three heater connections are made through Pins 1, 2 and 6. The cable for transmitter plug P_3 has provision for connecting to a transmit-receive switch (S_3) at the transmitter. In the transmit position the plate voltage is fed to the transmitter. In the receive position the switch feeds the plate voltage, via Pin 4, through series voltage-dropping resistor R_2 to Pin 4 on the other output jack and thence to the receiver. It will be noticed that the same circuit results with P_3 and P_4 in either output jack.

Construction

The unit is constructed on a $7 \times 12 \times 3$-inch chassis, with only the transformer and output connectors J_3 and J_4 above deck. The two recti-fier tubes and both vibrators are mounted below deck for compactness and shielding. This leaves a clear area on top of the chassis for mounting a receiver or small transmitter. Adequate ventilation is provided by patterns of $\frac{1}{4}$-inch holes in the top of the chassis, directly over the rectifier tubes, and along the bottom edge of the chassis on both sides.

The pilot lamp, a.c. power switch and filter switch S_2 can be mounted on the front end of the chassis, with fuse F_1 and the input jacks at the other end. Shielding should be completed with a chassis bottom plate.

Operation

Although the circuit is arranged so that no damage will occur if a mistake is made, the input connectors should be plainly marked to avoid plugging a cable into the wrong socket.

Original description appeared in *QST*, Oct., 1957.)

● TRANSISTOR POWER SUPPLIES

A mobile or portable power supply using transistors has high over-all efficiency at its rated power output. Since there are no moving parts there are few maintenance problems. Capacitors and resistors may occasionally need replacement, but if the transistors are operated within their electrical and thermal ratings, their life expectancy is in terms of years rather than hours.

In a transistor power supply, the transistors operate as electronic switches to interrupt the d.c. through the primary of the power transformer much like the mechanical vibrator does in a vibrator supply.

When voltage is applied to the power supply circuit, current will flow through the transistors; however, since no two transistors are precisely alike electrically, initially one will conduct a little more current than the other. This difference current or "starting" current will cause a small voltage to be induced in the transformer winding connected to the bases of the transistors. The polarity is such that the conducting transistor is biased to conduct even more heavily while the base of the other transistor is biased to cutoff. This process continues until the increasing current causes magnetic saturation of the transformer core, at which time the induced voltage drops to zero and there is no longer enough base bias to maintain the collector current. When this happens the current decreases, causing an induced voltage of opposite polarity. The process then reverses so that the previously nonconducting transistor starts to conduct and the previously conducting transistor becomes cut off. The result is an alternating current of square-wave form through the transformer primary. This in turn induces a stepped-up voltage in the h.v. secondary of the transformer.

The transistor supply is self-protecting against overload because if a short circuit or heavy overload occurs oscillations cease and the input current drops to a low value. The output voltage regulation is extremely good making the transistor supply especially useful as a source of plate or screen power for a single-sideband mobile or portable rig.

Transistor power transformers are available in both conventional and toroidal construction, with outputs ranging up to 150 watts. The circuit shown in Fig. 19-48, a typical transistor power supply, has an output of about 350 volts at 190 ma. It uses eight selenium rectifiers in a bridge circuit but four silicon-type power diodes having an inverse peak voltage rating of 800 volts or more could be substituted with a substantial saving in space. The center-tapped secondary of T_1 provides a half-voltage source that may be used simultaneously with the high voltage.

In a transistor power supply circuit that has not been properly designed, small spikes may appear on the leading edges of the square wave generated in the transistor power oscillator. Even though the spikes are of short duration they can cause punch-through of the transistor junction if the total voltage exceeds the transistor collector-to-emitter rating. The amplitudes

Mobile Power

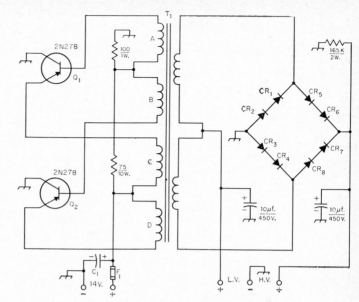

Fig. 19-48 — Circuit of the transistor power supply. Resistances are in ohms.

C_1—2000 μf., 15 volts (2 paralleled 1000 μf. electrolytics, Sprague TVA 1163).

CR_1 through CR_8—150 ma. selenium rectifier (Radio Receptor 5P1).

F_1—10- amp. fuse.

Q_1, Q_2—2N278 transistors.

T_1—Transistor power transformer (Sunair Electronics type 14-450-1).

of these spikes can be held to a safe value if the primary and secondary coils on the power transformer are tightly coupled (bifilar wound) and a large capacitor (C_1 in Fig. 19-48) is connected across the low voltage supply.

It is very important to provide good heat transfer from the mounting bases of the transistors to the chassis. The transistor junction temperature must not be allowed to exceed the manufacturer's ratings and thermal runaway will occur and the transistors will become useless. Layout of the parts is not critical. A conventional box type chassis may be used; the larger the surface area the better, since that means more rapid heat transfer from the transistors.

Since heat is the prime limiting factor in transistor power supply operation, placement of the unit in the car should have special consideration. Try to find a location away from high-temperature spots and in a well-ventilated area.

● GASOLINE-ENGINE DRIVEN GENERATORS

For higher-power installations, such as for communications control centers during emergencies, the most practical form of independent power supply is the gasoline-engine driven generator which provides standard 115-volt 60-cycle supply.

Such generators are ordinarily rated at a minimum of 250 or 300 watts. They are available up to ten kilowatts, or big enough to handle the highest-power amateur rig. Most are arranged to charge automatically an auxiliary 6- or 12-volt battery used in starting. Fitted with self-starters and adequate mufflers and filters, they represent a high order of performance and efficiency. Many of the larger models are liquid-cooled, and they will operate continuously at full load.

The output frequency of an engine-driven generator must fall between the relatively narrow limits of 50 to 60 cycles if standard 60-cycle transformers are to operate efficiently from this source. A 60-cycle electric clock provides a means of checking the output frequency with a fair degree of accuracy. The clock is connected across the output of the generator and the second hand is checked closely against the second hand of a watch. The speed of the engine is adjusted until the two second hands are in synchronism.

Output voltage should be checked with a voltmeter since a standard 115-volt lamp bulb, which is sometimes used for this purpose, is very inaccurate.

Noise Elimination

Electrical noise which may interfere with receivers operating from engine-driven a.c. generators may be reduced or eliminated by taking proper precautions. The most important point is that of grounding the frame of the generator *and* one side of the output. The ground lead should be short to be effective, otherwise grounding may actually increase the noise. A water pipe may be used if a short connection can be made near the point where the pipe enters the ground, otherwise a good separate ground should be provided.

The next step is to loosen the brush-holder locks and slowly shift the position of the brushes while checking for noise with the receiver. Usually a point will be found (almost always different from the factory setting) where there is a marked decrease in noise.

From this point on, if necessary, bypass capacitors from various brush holders to the frame, as shown in Fig. 19-49, will bring the hash down to within 10 to 15 per cent of its

TABLE 19-III

Service life of some typical zinc-carbon cells and batteries

Cell or Battery	ASA Cell Size	Continuous service		4 hours per day service	
		ma.	hrs.	ma.	hrs.
1.5 v. pen light cell	AA	30	14	20	33
1.5 v. flash light cell	D	160	9	130	21
1.5 v. ignition cell	#6	500	43	500	80
45 v., 67.5 v., 90 v. B-battery	F30	18	9	16	14
	F40	19	15	17	24
	F70	20	35	24	47

original intensity, if not entirely eliminating it. Most of the remaining noise will be reduced still further if the high-power audio stages are cut out and a pair of headphones is connected into the second detector.

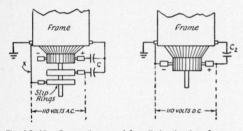

Fig. 19-49—Connections used for eliminating interference from gas-driven generator plants. C should be 1 μf., 300 volts, paper, while C_2 may be 1 μf. with a voltage rating of twice the d.c. output voltage delivered by the generator. X indicates an added connection between the slip ring on the grounded side of the line and the generator frame.

● **POWER FOR PORTABLES**

Dry Cell Batteries

Dry-cell batteries are a practical source of power for supplying portables or equipment which must be transported on foot. However, they are costly and have limited current capa-bility. The zinc-carbon cells lose their power even when not in use, if allowed to stand idle for periods of a year or more. This makes them uneconomical if not used more or less continuously.

The mercury cell has a much higher ratio of ampere-hour capacity to volume at higher current densities than are obtainable from the conventional dry cell. Mercury batteries are well suited for emergency portable operation even after many months of storage.

Typical service life data for several types of zinc-carbon cells and batteries is given in Table 19-III. The figures show length of service time before the cell terminal voltage drops to 1.0 volt (in B-batteries, when individual cells reach 1.0 volt).

Mercury batteries and cells are available in several sizes and shapes. Some may be operated at current drains up in the ampere range and others are available in potentials in the hundreds of volts. A typical 1.35-volt mercury cell measuring only $2\frac{1}{4} \times 2\frac{1}{4} \times 2\frac{3}{4}$ inches, has a capacity of 43 ampere hours (maximum current 3 amperes). Cells of this type would be useful for filament or heater applications. A representative mercury B-battery has a voltage of 67.5 volts and a capacity of 3.6 ampere hours (maximum current 250 ma.). It measures about $3\frac{3}{8} \times 1\frac{1}{2} \times 10\frac{1}{6}$ inches.

CHAPTER 20

Construction Practices

● TOOLS AND MATERIALS

While an easier, and perhaps a better, job can be done with a greater variety of tools available, by taking a little thought and care it is possible to turn out a fine piece of equipment with only a few of the common hand tools. A list of tools which will be indispensable in the construction of radio equipment will be found on this page. With these tools it should be possible to perform any of the required operations in preparing panels and metal chassis for assembly and wiring. It is an excellent idea for the amateur who does constructional work to add to his supply of tools from time to time as finances permit.

Several of the pieces of light woodworking machinery, often sold in hardware stores and mail-order retail stores, are ideal for amateur radio work, especially the drill press, grinding head, band and circular saws, and joiner. Although not essential, they are desirable should you be in a position to acquire them.

Twist Drills

Twist drills are made of either high-speed steel or carbon steel. The latter type is more common and will usually be supplied unless specific request is made for high-speed drills. The carbon drill will suffice for most ordinary equipment construction work and costs less than the high-speed type.

While twist drills are available in a number of sizes those listed in bold-faced type in Table 20-I will be most commonly used in construction of amateur equipment. It is usually desirable to purchase several of each of the commonly used sizes rather than a standard set, most of which will be used infrequently if at all.

Care of Tools

The proper care of tools is not alone a matter of pride to a good workman. He also realizes the energy which may be saved and the annoyance which may be avoided by the possession of a full kit of well-kept sharp-edged tools.

Drills should be sharpened at frequent intervals so that grinding is kept at a minimum each time. This makes it easier to maintain the rather critical surface angles required for best cutting with least wear. Occasional oilstoning of the cutting edges of a drill or reamer will extend the time between grindings.

The soldering iron can be kept in good condition by keeping the tip well tinned with solder and not allowing it to run at full voltage for long periods when it is not being used. After each period of use, the tip should be removed and cleaned of any scale which may have accumulated. An oxidized tip may be cleaned by dipping it in sal ammoniac while

---

INDISPENSABLE TOOLS

Long-nose pliers, 6-inch.
Diagonal cutting pliers, 6-inch.
Wire stripper.
Screwdriver, 6- to 7-inch, ¼-inch blade.
Screwdriver, 4- to 5-inch, ⅛-inch blade.
Scratch awl or scriber for marking lines.
Combination square, 12-inch, for laying out work.
Hand drill, ¼-inch chuck or larger, 2-speed type preferable.
Electric soldering iron, 100 watts, ¼-in. tip.
Hack saw, 12-inch blades.
Center punch for marking hole centers.
Hammer, ball-peen, 1-lb. head.
Heavy knife.
Yardstick or other straightedge.
Carpenter's brace with adjustable hole cutter or socket-hole punches (see text).
Large, coarse, flat file.
Large round or rat-tail file, ½-inch diameter.
Three or four small and medium files—flat, round, half-round, triangular.
Drills, particularly ¼-inch and Nos. 18, 28, 33, 42 and 50.
Combination oil stone for sharpening tools.
Solder and soldering paste (noncorroding).
Medium-weight machine oil.

ADDITIONAL TOOLS

Bench vise, 4-inch jaws.
Tin shears, 10-inch, for cutting thin sheet metal.
Taper reamer, ½-inch, for enlarging small holes.
Taper reamer, 1-inch, for enlarging holes.
Countersink for brace.
Carpenter's plane, 8- to 12-inch, for woodworking.
Carpenter's saw, crosscut.
Motor-driven emery wheel for grinding.
Long-shank screwdriver with screw-holding clip for tight places.
Set of "Spintite" socket wrenches for hex nuts.
Set of small, flat, open-end wrenches for hex nuts.
Wood chisel, ½-inch.
Cold chisel, ½-inch.
Wing dividers, 8-inch, for scribing circles.
Set of machine-screw taps and dies.
Dusting brush.
Socket punches, esp. ⅝", ¾", 1⅛" and 1¼".

---

hot and then wiping it clean with a rag. If the tip becomes pitted it should be filed until smooth and bright, and then tinned immediately by dipping it in solder.

Useful Materials

Small stocks of various miscellaneous materials will be required in constructing radio apparatus, most of which are available from hardware or radio-supply stores. A representative list follows:

Sheet aluminum, solid and perforated, 16 or 18 gauge, for brackets and shielding.
½ × ½-inch aluminum angle stock.
¼-inch diameter round brass or aluminum rod for shaft extensions.
Machine screws: Round-head and flat-head, with nuts to fit. Most useful sizes: 4–36, 6–32 and 8–32, in lengths from ¼ inch to 1½ inches. (Nickel-plated iron will be found satisfactory except in strong r.f. fields, where brass should be used.)
Bakelite, lucite and polystyrene scraps.
Soldering lugs, panel bearings, rubber grommets, terminal-lug wiring strips, varnished-cambric insulating tubing.
Shielded and unshielded wire.
Tinned bare wire, Nos. 22, 14 and 12.

Machine screws, nuts, washers, soldering lugs, etc., are most reasonably purchased in quantities of a gross.

● CHASSIS WORKING

With a few essential tools and proper procedure, it will be found that building radio gear on a metal chassis is no more of a chore than building with wood, and a more satisfactory job results. Aluminum is to be preferred to steel, not only because it is a superior shielding material, but because it is much easier to work and to provide good chassis contacts.

The placing of components on the chassis is shown quite clearly in the photographs in this *Handbook*. Aside from certain essential dimensions, which usually are given in the text, exact duplication is not necessary.

Much trouble and energy can be saved by spending sufficient time in planning the job. When all details are worked out beforehand

TABLE 20-I

Numbered Drill Sizes

Number	Diameter (mils)	Will Clear Screw	Drilled for Tapping Iron, Steel or Brass*
1	228.0	—	—
2	221.0	12–24	—
3	213.0	—	14–24
4	209.0	12–20	—
5	205.0	—	—
6	204.0	—	—
7	201.0	—	—
8	199.0	—	—
9	196.0	—	—
10	193.5	10–32	—
11	191.0	10–24	—
12	189.0	—	—
13	185.0	—	—
14	182.0	—	—
15	180.0	—	—
16	177.0	—	12–24
17	173.0	—	—
18	169.5	8–32	—
19	166.0	—	12–20
20	161.0	—	—
21	159.0	—	10–32
22	157.0	—	—
23	154.0	—	—
24	152.0	—	—
25	149.5	—	10–24
26	147.0	—	—
27	144.0	—	—
28	140.0	6–32	—
29	136.0	—	8–32
30	128.5	—	—
31	120.0	—	—
32	116.0	—	—
33	113.0	4–36, 4–40	—
34	111.0	—	—
35	110.0	—	6–32
36	106.5	—	—
37	104.0	—	—
38	101.5	—	—
39	099.5	3–48	—
40	098.0	—	—
41	096.0	—	—
42	093.5	—	4–36, 4–40
43	089.0	2–56	—
44	086.0	—	—
45	082.0	—	3–48
46	081.0	—	—
47	078.5	—	—
48	076.0	—	—
49	073.0	—	2–56
50	070.0	—	—
51	067.0	—	—
52	063.5	—	—
53	059.5	—	—
54	055.0	—	—

*Use one size larger for tapping bakelite and hard rubber.

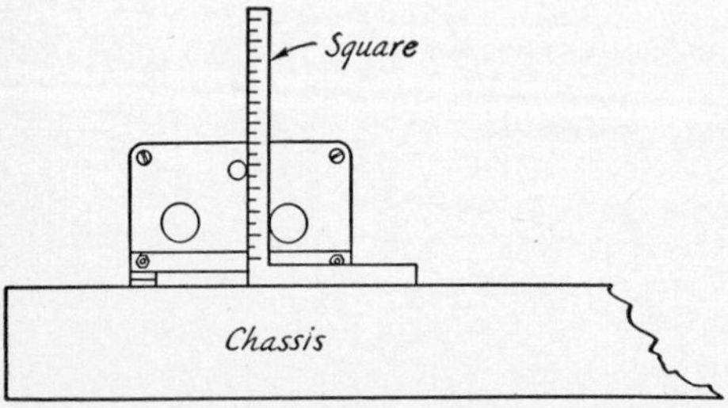

the actual construction is greatly simplified.

Cover the top of the chassis with a piece of wrapping paper or, preferably, cross-section paper, folding the edges down over the sides of the chassis and fastening with adhesive tape. Then assemble the parts to be mounted on top of the chassis and move them about until a satisfactory arrangement has been found, keeping in mind any parts which are to be mounted underneath, so that interferences in mounting may be avoided. Place capacitors and other parts with shafts extending through the panel first, and arrange them so that the controls will

Fig. 20-1—Method of measuring the heights of capacitor shafts, etc. If the square is adjustable, the end of the scale should be set flush with the face of the head.

Metal Work

form the desired pattern on the panel. Be sure to line up the shafts squarely with the chassis front. Locate any partition shields and panel brackets next, and then the tube sockets and any other parts, marking the mounting-hole centers of each accurately on the paper. Watch out for capacitors whose shafts are off center and do not line up with the mounting holes. Do not forget to mark the centers of socket holes and holes for leads under i.f. transformers, etc., as well as holes for wiring leads. The small holes for socket-mounting screws are best located and center-punched, using the socket itself as a template, after the main center hole has been cut.

By means of the square, lines indicating accurately the centers of shafts should be extended to the front of the chassis and marked on the panel at the chassis line, the panel being fastened on temporarily. The hole centers may then be punched in the chassis with the center punch. After drilling, the parts which require mounting underneath may be located and the mounting holes drilled, making sure by trial that no interferences exist with parts mounted on top. Mounting holes along the front edge

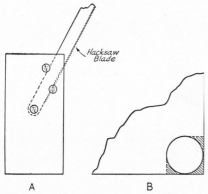

A   B

Fig. 20-2—To cut rectangular holes in a chassis corner, holes may be filed out as shown in the shaded portion of B, making it possible to start the hack-saw blade along the cutting line. A shows how a single-ended handle may be constructed for a hack-saw blade.

of the chassis should be transferred to the panel, by once again fastening the panel to the chassis and marking it from the rear.

Next, mount on the chassis the capacitors and any other parts with shafts extending to the panel, and measure accurately the height of the center of each shaft above the chassis, as illustrated in Fig. 20-1. The horizontal displacement of shafts having already been marked on the chassis line on the panel, the vertical displacement can be measured from this line. The shaft centers may now be marked on the back of the panel, and the holes drilled. Holes for any other panel equipment coming above the chassis line may then be marked and drilled, and the remainder of the apparatus mounted. Holes for terminals etc., in the rear edge of the chassis should be marked and drilled at the same time that they are done for the top.

Drilling and Cutting Holes

When drilling holes in metal with a hand drill it is important that the centers first be located with a center punch, so that the drill point will not "walk" away from the center when starting the hole. When the drill starts to break through, special care must be used. Often it is an advantage to shift a two-speed drill to low gear at this point. Holes more than ¼ inch in diameter may be started with a smaller drill and reamed out with the larger drill.

The chuck on the usual type of hand drill is limited to ¼-inch drills. Although it is rather tedious, the ¼-inch hole may be filed out to larger diameters with round files. Another method possible with limited tools is to drill a series of small holes with the hand drill along the inside of the diameter of the large hole, placing the holes as close together as possible. The center may then be knocked out with a cold chisel and the edges smoothed up with a file. Taper reamers which fit into the carpenter's brace will make the job easier. A large rat-tail file clamped in the brace makes a very good reamer for holes up to the diameter of the file, if the file is revolved counterclockwise.

For socket holes and other large round holes, an adjustable cutter designed for the purpose may be used in the brace. Occasional application of machine oil in the cutting groove will help. The cutter first should be tried out on a block of wood, to make sure that it is set for the correct diameter. The most convenient device for cutting socket holes is the socket-hole punch. The best type is that which works by turning a take-up screw with a wrench.

The burrs or rough edges which usually result after drilling or cutting holes may be removed with a file, or sometimes more conveniently with a sharp knife or chisel. It is a good idea to keep an old wood chisel sharpened and available for this purpose.

Rectangular Holes

Square or rectangular holes may be cut out by making a row of small holes as previously described, but is more easily done by drilling a ½-inch hole inside each corner, as illustrated in Fig. 20-2, and using these holes for starting and turning the hack saw. The socket-hole punch and the square punches which are now available also may be of considerable assistance in cutting out large rectangular openings.

● CONSTRUCTION NOTES

If a control shaft must be extended or insulated, a flexible shaft coupling with adequate insulation should be used. Satisfactory support for the shaft extension can be provided by means of a *metal* panel bearing made for the purpose. Never use panel bearings of the non-metal type unless the capacitor shaft is grounded. *The metal bearing should be connected to the chassis with a wire or grounding strip.*

This prevents any possible danger of shock.

The use of fiber washers between ceramic insulation and metal brackets, screws or nuts will prevent the ceramic parts from breaking.

STANDARD METAL GAUGES

Gauge No.	American or B. & S.[1]	U. S. Standard[2]	Birmingham or Stubs[3]
1	.2893	.28125	.300
2	.2576	.265625	.284
3	.2294	.25	.259
4	.2043	.234375	.238
5	.1819	.21875	.220
6	.1620	.203125	.203
7	.1443	.1875	.180
8	.1285	.171875	.165
9	.1144	.15625	.148
10	.1019	.140625	.134
11	.09074	.125	.120
12	.08081	.109375	.109
13	.07196	.09375	.095
14	.06408	.078125	.083
15	.05707	.0703125	.072
16	.05082	.0625	.065
17	.04526	.05625	.058
18	.04030	.05	.049
19	.03589	.04375	.042
20	.03196	.0375	.035
21	.02846	.034375	.032
22	.02535	.03125	.028
23	.02257	.028125	.025
24	.02010	.025	.022
25	.01790	.021875	.020
26	.01594	.01875	.018
27	.01420	.0171875	.016
28	.01264	.015625	.014
29	.01126	.0140625	.013
30	.01003	.0125	.012
31	.008928	.0109375	.010
32	.007950	.01015625	.009
33	.007080	.009375	.008
34	.006350	.00859375	.007
35	.005615	.0078125	.005
36	.005000	.00703125	.004
37	.004453	.006640626	....
38	.003965	.00625	....
39	.003531	....	....
40	.003145	....	....

[1] Used for aluminum, copper, brass and nonferrous alloy sheets, wire and rods.

[2] Used for iron, steel, nickel and ferrous alloy sheets, wire and rods.

[3] Used for seamless tubes; also by some manufacturers for copper and brass.

Cutting and Bending Sheet Metal

If a sheet of metal is too large to be cut conveniently with a hack saw, it may be marked with scratches as deep as possible along the line of the cut on both sides of the sheet and then clamped in a vise and worked back and forth until the sheet breaks at the line. Do not carry the bending too far until the break begins to weaken; otherwise the edge of the sheet may become bent. A pair of iron bars or pieces of heavy angle stock, as long or longer than the width of the sheet, to hold it in the vise will make the job easier. "C"-clamps may be used to keep the bars from spreading at the ends. The rough edges may be smoothed up with a file or by placing a large piece of emery cloth or sandpaper on a flat surface and running the edge of the metal back and forth over the sheet.

Bends may be made similarly. The sheet should be scratched on both sides, but not so deeply as to cause it to break.

Finishing Aluminum

Aluminum chassis, panels and parts may be given a sheen finish by treating them in a caustic bath. An enamelled container, such as a dishpan or infant's bathtub, should be used for the solution. Dissolve ordinary household lye in cold water in a proportion of ¼ to ½ can of lye per gallon of water. The stronger solution will do the job more rapidly. Stir the solution with a stick of wood until the lye crystals are complete dissolved. Be very careful to avoid any skin contact with the solution. It is also harmful to clothing. Sufficient solution should be prepared to cover the piece completely. When the aluminum is immersed, a very pronounced bubbling takes place and ventilation should be provided to disperse the escaping gas. A half hour to two hours in the solution should be sufficient, depending upon the strength of the solution and the desired surface.

Remove the aluminum from the solution with sticks and rinse thoroughly in cold water while swabbing with a rag to remove the black deposit. Then wipe off with a rag soaked in vinegar to remove any stubborn stains or fingerprints. (See May, 1950, *QST*, for a method of coloring and anodizing aluminum.)

Soldering

The secret of good soldering is in allowing time for the *joint*, as well as the solder, to attain sufficient temperature. Enough heat should be applied so that the solder will melt when it comes in contact with the wires being joined, without touching the solder to the iron. Always use rosin-core solder, never acid-core. Except where absolutely necessary, solder should never be depended upon for the mechanical strength of the joint; the wire should be wrapped around the terminals or clamped with soldering terminals.

When soldering crystal diodes or carbon re-

DECIMAL EQUIVALENTS OF FRACTIONS

1/32	.03125	17/32	.53125
1/16	.0625	9/16	.5625
3/32	.09375	19/32	.59375
1/8	.125	5/8	.625
5/32	.15625	21/32	.65625
3/16	.1875	11/16	.6875
7/32	.21875	23/32	.71875
1/4	.25	3/4	.75
9/32	.28125	25/32	.78125
5/16	.3125	13/16	.8125
11/32	.34375	27/32	.84375
3/8	.375	7/8	.875
13/32	.40625	29/32	.90625
7/16	.4375	15/16	.9375
15/32	.46875	31/32	.96875
1/2	.5	1	1.0

Soldering

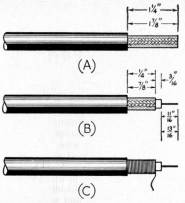

(A)

(B)

(C)

Fig. 20-3—Cable-stripping dimensions for Jones Type P-101 plugs. Smaller dimensions are for ¼-inch plugs, the larger dimensions for ½-inch plugs. As indicated in C, the remaining copper braid is wound with bare or tinned wire and then tinned, to make a snug fit in the sleeve of the plug. Hold a hot iron to the sleeve after the cable is inserted to solder the sleeve to the braid.

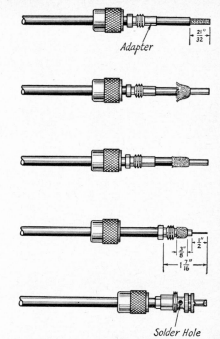

Adapter

Solder Hole

Fig. 20-5—Method of assembling ¼-inch cable, Amphenol Type 83-1SP (PL-259) plug and adapter.

sistors in place, especially if the leads have been cut short and the resistor is of the small ½-watt size, the resistor lead should be gripped with a pair of pliers up close to the resistor so that the heat will be conducted away from the resistor. Overheating of the resistor while soldering can cause a permanent resistance change of as much as 20 per cent. Also, mechanical stress will have a similar effect, so that a small resistor should be mounted so that there is no appreciable mechanical strain on the leads.

Trouble is sometimes experienced in soldering to the pins of coil-forms or male cable plugs. It helps first to tin the inside of the pins by applying soldering paste to the hole, and then flowing solder into the pin. Then immediately clear the solder from the hot pin by a whipping motion or by blowing through the pin from the inside of the form or plug. Before inserting the wire in the pin, file the nickel plate from the tip. After soldering, round the solder tip off with a file.

When soldering to sockets, it is a good idea to have the tube or coil form inserted to prevent solder running down into the socket prongs. It

also helps to conduct the heat away when soldering to polystyrene sockets, which often soften under the heat of the iron.

Wiring

The wire used in connecting up amateur equipment should be selected considering both the maximum current it will be called upon to handle and the voltage its insulation must stand without breakdown. Also, from the consideration of TVI, the power wiring of all transmitters should be done with wire that has a braided shielding cover. Receiver and audio circuits may also require the use of shielded wire at some points for stability, or the elimination of hum.

No. 20 stranded wire is commonly used for most receiver wiring (except for the high-

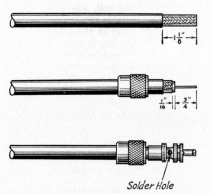

Solder Hole

Fig. 20-4—Dimensions for stripping ½-inch cable to fit Amphenol Type 83-1SP (PL-259) plug.

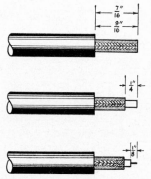

Fig. 20-6—Stripping dimensions for Amphenol 82-830 and 82-832 plug-in connectors. The longer exposed braid is for the first type.

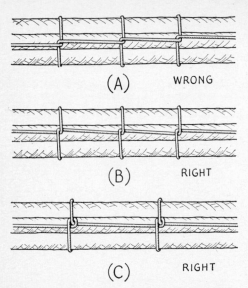

(A)   WRONG

(B)   RIGHT

(C)   RIGHT

Fig. 20-7—Methods of lacing cables. The method shown at C is more secure, but takes more time than the method of B. The latter is usually adequate for most amateur requirements.

frequency circuits) where the current does not exceed 2 or 3 amperes. For higher-current heater circuits, No. 18 is available. Wire with cellulose acetate insulation is good for voltages up to about 500. For higher voltages, thermoplastic-insulated wire should be used. Inexpensive wire strippers that make the removal of insulation from hook-up wire an easy job are available on the market.

In cases where power leads have several branches in the chassis, it is convenient to use fiber-insulated tie points or "lug strips" as anchorages or junction points. Strips of this type are also useful as insulated supports for resistors, r.f. chokes and capacitors. High-voltage wiring should have exposed points held to a minimum, and those which cannot be avoided should be rendered as inaccessible as possible to accidental contact or short-circuit.

Where shielded wire is called for and capacitance to ground is not a factor, Belden type 8885 shielded grid wire may be used. If capacitance must be minimized, it may be necessary to use a piece of car-radio low-capacitance lead-in wire, or coaxial cable.

For wiring high-frequency circuits, rigid wire is often used. Bare soft-drawn tinned wire, sizes 22 to 12 (depending on mechanical requirements), is suitable. Kinks can be removed by stretching a piece 10 or 15 feet long and then cutting into short lengths that can be handled conveniently. R.f. wiring should be run directly from point to point with a minimum of sharp bends and the wire kept well spaced from the chassis or other grounded metal surfaces. Where the wiring must pass through the chassis or a partition, a clearance hole should be cut and lined with a rubber grommet. In case insulation becomes necessary, varnished cambric tubing (spaghetti) can be slipped over the wire.

In transmitters where the peak voltage does not exceed 2500 volts, the shielded grid wire mentioned above should be satisfactory for power circuits. For higher voltages, Belden type 8656, Birnbach type 1820, or shielded ignition cable can be used. In the case of filament circuits carrying heavy current, it may be necessary to use No. 10 or 12 bare or enameled wire, slipped through spaghetti, and then covered with copper braid pulled tightly over the spaghetti. The chapter on TVI shows the manner in which shielded wire should be applied. If the shielding is simply slid back over the insulation and solder flowed into the end of the braid, the braid usually will stay in place without the necessity for cutting it back or binding it in place. The braid should be burnished with sandpaper or a knife so that solder will take with a minimum of heat to protect the insulation underneath.

R.f. wiring in transmitters usually follows the method described above for receivers with due respect to the voltages involved.

Power and control wiring external to the transmitter chassis preferably should be of shielded wire bound into a cable. Fig. 20-7 shows the correct methods of lacing cables.

To give a "commercial look" to the wiring of any unit, run any cabled leads along the edge of the chassis. If this isn't possible, the cabled leads should then run parallel to an edge of the chassis. Further, the generous use of bakelite tie points (mounted parallel to an edge of the chassis), for the support of one or both ends of a resistor or fixed capacitor, will add to the appearance of the finished unit. In a similar manner, "dress" the small components so that they are parallel to the panel or sides of the chassis.

Winding Coils

Close-wound coils are readily wound on the specified form by anchoring one end of a length of wire (in a vise or to a doorknob) and the other end to the coil form. Straighten any kinks in the wire and then pull to keep the wire under slight tension. Wind the coil to the required number of turns while walking toward the anchor, always maintaining the slight tension on the wire.

To space-wind the coil, wind the coil simultaneously with a suitable spacing medium (heavy thread, string or wire) in the manner described above. When the winding is complete, secure the end of the coil to the coil-form terminal and then carefully unwind the spacing material. If the coil is wound under suitable tension, the spacing material can be easily removed without disturbing the winding. Finish the space-wound coil by judicious applications of Duco cement, to hold the turns in place.

● COMPONENT VALUES

Values of composition resistors and small capacitors (mica and ceramic) are specified throughout this *Handbook* in terms of "preferred values." In the preferred-number sys-

Color Codes

TABLE 20-II
Standard Component Values

20% Tolerance	10% Tolerance	5% Tolerance
10	10	10
		11
	12	12
		13
15	15	15
		16
	18	18
		20
22	22	22
		24
	27	27
		30
33	33	33
		36
	39	39
		43
47	47	47
		51
	56	56
		62
68	68	68
		75
	82	82
		91
100	100	100

tem, all values represent (approximately) a constant-percentage increase over the next lower value. The base of the system is the number 10. Only two significant figures are used. Table 20-II shows the preferred values based on tolerance steps of 20, 10 and 5 per cent. All other values are expressed by multiplying or dividing the base figures given in the table by the appropriate power of 10. (For example, resistor values of 33,000 ohms, 6800 ohms, and 150 ohms are obtained by multiplying the base figures by 1000, 100, and 10, respectively.)

"Tolerance" means that a variation of plus or minus the percentage given is considered satisfactory. For example, the actual resistance of a "4700-ohm" 20-per-cent resistor can lie anywhere between 3700 and 5600 ohms, approximately. The permissible variation in the same resistance value with 5-per-cent tolerance would be in the range from 4500 to 4900 ohms, approximately.

Only those values shown in the first column of Table 20-II are available in 20-per-cent tolerance. Additional values, as shown in the second column, are available in 10-per-cent tolerance; still more values can be obtained in 5-per-cent tolerance.

In the component specifications in this *Handbook*, it is to be understood that when no tolerance is specified the *largest* tolerance available in that value will be satisfactory.

Values that do not fit into the preferred-number system (such as 500, 25,000, etc.) easily can be substituted. It is obvious, for example, that a 5000-ohm resistor falls well within the tolerance range of the 4700-ohm 20-per-cent resistor used in the example above.

It would not, however, be usable if the tolerance were specified as 5 per cent.

● COLOR CODES

Standardized color codes are used to mark values on small components such as composition resistors and mica capacitors, and to identify leads from transformers, etc. The resistor-capacitor number color code is given in Table 20-III.

Fixed Capacitors

The methods of marking "postage-stamp" mica capacitors, molded paper capacitors, and tubular ceramic capacitors are shown in Fig. 20-8. Capacitors made to American War Standards or Joint Army-Navy specifications

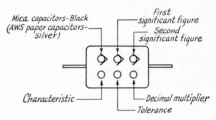

AWS and JAN fixed capacitors

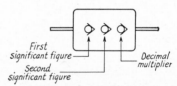

EIA 3-dot 500-volt, ±20% tolerance only

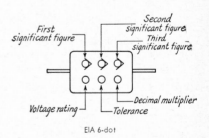

EIA 6-dot

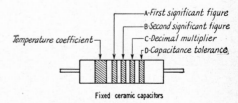

Fixed ceramic capacitors

Fig. 20-8—Color coding of fixed mica, molded paper and tubular ceramic capacitors. The color code for mica and molded paper capacitors is given in Table 20-III. Table 20-IV gives the color code for tubular ceramic capacitors.

are marked with the 6-dot code shown at the top. Practically all surplus capacitors are in this category. The 3-dot EIA code is used for capacitors having a rating of 500 volts and ±20% tolerance only; other ratings and tolerances are covered by the 6-dot EIA code.

> Examples: A capacitor with a 6-dot code has the following markings: Top row, left to right, black, yellow, violet; bottom row, right to left, brown, silver, red. Since the first color in the top row is black (significant figure zero) this is the AWS code and the capacitor has mica dielectric. The significant figures are 4 and 7, the decimal multiplier 10 (brown, at right of second row), so the capacitance is 470 μμf. The tolerance is ± 10%. The final color, the characteristic, deals with temperature coefficients and methods of testing (see Table 20-V on page 505).
>
> A capacitor with a 3-dot code has the following colors, left to right: brown, black, red. The significant figures are 1, 0 (10) and the multiplier is 100. The capacitance is therefore 1000 μμf.
>
> A capacitor with a 6-dot code has the following markings: Top row, left to right, brown, black, black; bottom row, right to left, black, gold, blue. Since the first color in the top row is neither black nor silver, this is the EIA code. The significant figures are 1, 0, 0 (100) and the decimal multiplier is 1 (black). The capacitance is therefore 100 μμf. The gold dot shows that the tolerance is ± 5% and the blue dot indicates 600-volt rating.

Ceramic Capacitors

Conventional markings for ceramic capacitors are shown in the lower drawing of Fig. 20-8. The colors have the meanings indicated in Table 20-IV. In practice, dots may be used instead of the *narrow* bands indicated in Fig. 20-8.

> Example: A ceramic capacitor has the following markings: Broad band, violet; narrow bands or dots, green, brown, black, green. The significant figures are 5, 1 (51) and the decimal multiplier is 1, so the capacitance is 51 μμf. The temperature coefficient is − 750 parts per million per degree C., as given by the broad band, and the capacitance tolerance is ± 5%.

Fixed Composition Resistors

Composition resistors (including small wirewound units molded in cases identical with the composition type) are color-coded as shown in Fig. 20-9. Colored bands are used on resistors having axial leads; on radial-lead resistors the

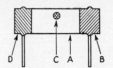

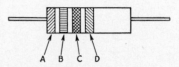

Fixed composition resistors

Fig. 20-9—Color coding of fixed composition resistors The color code is given in Table 20-III. The colored areas have the following significance:

A—First significant figure of resistance in ohms.
B—Second significant figure.
C—Decimal multiplier.
D—Resistance tolerance in per cent. If no color is shown the tolerance is ±20%.

colors are placed as shown in the drawing. When bands are used for color coding the body color has no significance.

> Examples: A resistor of the type shown in the lower drawing of Fig. 20-9 has the following color bands: A, red; B, red; C, orange; D, no color. The significant figures are 2, 2 (22) and the decimal multiplier is 1000. The value of resistance is therefore 22,000 ohms and the tolerance is ±20%.
>
> A resistor of the type shown in the upper drawing has the following colors: body (A), blue; end (B), gray; dot, red; end (D), gold. The significant figures are 6, 8 (68) and the decimal multiplier is 100, so the resistance is 6800 ohms. The tolerance is ±5%.

I.F. Transformers

Blue — plate lead.
Red — "B" + lead.
Green — grid (or diode) lead.
Black — grid (or diode) return.

NOTE: If the secondary of the i.f.t. is center-tapped, the second diode plate lead is green-and-black striped, and black is used for the center-tap lead.

TABLE 20-III

Resistor-Capacitor Color Code

Color	Significant Figure	Decimal Multiplier	Tolerance (%)	Voltage Rating*
Black	0	1	–	—
Brown	1	10	1*	100
Red	2	100	2*	200
Orange	3	1000	3*	300
Yellow	4	10,000	4*	400
Green	5	100,000	5*	500
Blue	6	1,000,000	6*	600
Violet	7	10,000,000	7*	700
Gray	8	100,000,000	8*	800
White	9	1,000,000,000	9*	900
Gold	–	0.1	5	1000
Silver	–	0.01	10	2000
No color	–	—	20	500

* Applies to capacitors only.

TABLE 20-IV

Color Code for Ceramic Capacitors

Color	Significant Figure	Decimal Multiplier	Capacitance Tolerance		Temp. Coeff. p.p.m./deg C.
			More than 10 μμf. (in %)	Less than 10 μμf. (in μμf.)	
Black	0	1	± 20	2.0	0
Brown	1	10	± 1		− 30
Red	2	100	± 2		− 80
Orange	3	1000			− 150
Yellow	4				− 220
Green	5		± 5	0.5	− 330
Blue	6				− 470
Violet	7				− 750
Gray	8	0.01		0.25	30
White	9	0.1	± 10	1.0	500

Color Codes

PILOT-LAMP DATA

Lamp No.	Bead Color	Base (Miniature)	Bulb Type	RATING Volts	RATING Amp.
40	Brown	Screw	T-3¼	6–8	0.15
40A[1]	Brown	Bayonet	T-3¼	6–8	0.15
41	White	Screw	T-3¼	2.5	0.5
42	Green	Screw	T-3¼	3.2	**
43	White	Bayonet	T-3¼	2.5	0.5
44	Blue	Bayonet	T-3¼	6–8	0.25
45	*	Bayonet	T-3¼	3.2	**
46[2]	Blue	Screw	T-3¼	6–8	0.25
47[1]	Brown	Bayonet	T-3¼	6–9	0.15
48	Pink	Screw	T-3¼	2.0	0.06
49[3]	Pink	Bayonet	T-3¼	2.0	0.06
[4]	White	Screw	T-3¼	2.1	0.12
49A[3]	White	Bayonet	T-3¼	2.1	0.12
50	White	Screw	G-3½	6–8	0.2
51[2]	White	Bayonet	G-3½	6–8	0.2
—	White	Screw	G-4½	6–8	0.4
55	White	Bayonet	G-4½	6–8	0.4
292[5]	White	Screw	T-3¼	2.9	0.17
292A[5]	White	Bayonet	T-3¼	2.9	0.17
1455	Brown	Screw	G-5	18.0	0.25
1455A	Brown	Bayonet	G-5	18.0	0.25

[1] 40A and 47 are interchangeable.
[2] Have frosted bulb.
[3] 49 and 49A are interchangeable.
[4] Replace with No. 48.
[5] Use in 2.5-volt sets where regular bulb burns out too frequently.
* White in G.E. and Sylvania; green in National Union, Raytheon and Tung-Sol.
** 0.35 in G.E. and Sylvania; 0.5 in National Union, Raytheon and Tung-Sol.

TABLE 20-V
Capacitor Characteristic Code

Color Sixth Dot	Temperature Coefficient p.p.m./deg. C.	Capacitance Drift
Black	± 1000	±5% + 1 μμf.
Brown	± 500	± 3% + 1 μμf.
Red	+ 200	± 0.5%
Orange	+ 100	± 0.3%
Yellow	− 20 to + 100	± 0.1% + 0.1 μμf.
Green	0 to + 70	± 0.05% + 0.1 μμf.

A.F. Transformers

Blue — plate (finish) lead of primary.
Red — "B" + lead (this applies whether the primary is plain or center-tapped).
Brown — plate (start) lead on center-tapped primaries. (Blue may be used for this lead if polarity is not important.)
Green — grid (finish) lead to secondary.
Black — grid return (this applies whether the secondary is plain or center-tapped).
Yellow — grid (start) lead on center-tapped secondaries. (Green may be used for this lead if polarity is not important.)

NOTE: These markings apply also to line-to-grid and tube-to-line transformers.

Loudspeaker Voice Coils

Green — finish.
Black — start.

Loudspeaker Field Coils

Black and Red — start.
Yellow and Red — finish.
Slate and Red — tap (if any).

Power Transformers

1) Primary Leads...................*Black*
   If tapped:
      Common....................*Black*
      Tap........*Black and Yellow Striped*
      Finish........*Black and Red Striped*
2) High-Voltage Plate Winding.........*Red*
      Center-Tap...*Red and Yellow Striped*
3) Rectifier Filament Winding.......*Yellow*
      Center-Tap..*Yellow and Blue Striped*
4) Filament Winding No. 1...... ....*Green*
      Center-Tap..*Green and Yellow Striped*
5) Filament Winding No. 2..........*Brown*
      Center-Tap.*Brown and Yellow Striped*
6) Filament Winding No. 3........ ...*Slate*
      Center-Tap...*Slate and Yellow Striped*

COPPER-WIRE TABLE

Wire Size A.W.G. (B & S)	Diam. in Mils [1]	Circular Mil Area	Turns per Linear Inch [2] — Enamel	— S.S.C. [4]	— D.S.C. [5] or S.C.C. [6]	— D.C.C. [7]	Turns per Square Inch [2] — S.C.C.	— Enamel S.C.C.	— D.C.C.	Feet per Lb. — Bare	— D.C.C.	Ohms per 1000 ft. 25° C.	Current Carrying Capacity [3] at 700 C.M. per Amp.	Diam. in mm.	Nearest British S.W.G. No.
1	289.3	83690	—	—	—	—	—	—	—	3.947	—	.1264	119.6	7.348	1
2	257.6	66370	—	—	—	—	—	—	—	4.977	—	.1593	94.8	6.544	3
3	229.4	52640	—	—	—	—	—	—	—	6.276	—	.2009	75.2	5.827	4
4	204.3	41740	—	—	—	—	—	—	—	7.914	—	.2533	59.6	5.189	5
5	181.9	33100	—	—	—	—	—	—	—	9.980	—	.3195	47.3	4.621	7
6	162.0	26250	—	—	—	—	—	—	—	12.58	—	.4028	37.5	4.115	8
7	144.3	20820	—	—	—	—	—	—	—	15.87	—	.5080	29.7	3.665	9
8	128.5	16510	7.6	—	7.4	7.1	—	—	—	20.01	19.6	.6405	23.6	3.264	10
9	114.4	13090	8.6	—	8.2	7.8	—	—	—	25.23	24.6	.8077	18.7	2.906	11
10	101.9	10380	9.6	—	9.3	8.9	87.5	84.8	80.0	31.82	30.9	1.018	14.8	2.588	12
11	90.74	8234	10.7	—	10.3	9.8	110	105	97.5	40.12	38.8	1.284	11.8	2.305	13
12	80.81	6530	12.0	—	11.5	10.9	136	131	121	50.59	48.9	1.619	9.33	2.053	14
13	71.96	5178	13.5	—	12.8	12.0	170	162	150	63.80	61.5	2.042	7.40	1.828	15
14	64.08	4107	15.0	—	14.2	13.8	211	198	183	80.44	77.3	2.575	5.87	1.628	16
15	57.07	3257	16.8	—	15.8	14.7	262	250	223	101.4	97.3	3.247	4.65	1.450	17
16	50.82	2583	18.9	18.9	17.9	16.4	321	306	271	127.9	119	4.094	3.69	1.291	18
17	45.26	2048	21.2	21.2	19.9	18.1	397	372	329	161.3	150	5.163	2.93	1.150	18
18	40.30	1624	23.6	23.6	22.0	19.8	493	454	399	203.4	188	6.510	2.32	1.024	19
19	35.89	1288	26.4	26.4	24.4	21.8	592	553	479	256.5	237	8.210	1.84	.9116	20
20	31.96	1022	29.4	29.4	27.0	23.8	775	725	625	323.4	298	10.35	1.46	.8118	21
21	28.46	810.1	33.1	32.7	29.8	26.0	940	895	754	407.8	370	13.05	1.16	.7230	22
22	25.35	642.4	37.0	36.5	34.1	30.0	1150	1070	910	514.2	461	16.46	.918	.6438	23
23	22.57	509.5	41.3	40.5	37.6	31.6	1400	1300	1080	648.4	584	20.76	.728	.5733	24
24	20.10	404.0	46.3	45.3	41.5	35.6	1700	1570	1260	817.7	745	26.17	.577	.5106	25
25	17.90	320.4	51.7	50.4	45.6	38.6	2060	1910	1510	1031	903	33.00	.458	.4547	26
26	15.94	254.1	58.0	55.6	50.2	41.8	2500	2300	1750	1300	1118	41.62	.363	.4049	27
27	14.20	201.5	64.9	61.5	55.0	45.0	3030	2780	2020	1639	1422	52.48	.288	.3606	29
28	12.64	159.8	72.7	68.6	60.2	48.5	3670	3350	2310	2067	1759	66.17	.228	.3211	30
29	11.26	126.7	81.6	74.8	65.4	51.8	4300	3900	2700	2607	2207	83.44	.181	.2859	31
30	10.03	100.5	90.5	83.3	71.5	55.5	5040	4660	3020	3287	2534	105.2	.144	.2546	33
31	8.928	79.70	101	92.0	77.5	59.2	5920	5280	—	4145	2768	132.7	.114	.2268	34
32	7.950	63.21	113	101	83.6	62.6	7060	6250	—	5227	3137	167.3	.090	.2019	36
33	7.080	50.13	127	110	90.3	66.3	8120	7360	—	6591	4697	211.0	.072	.1798	37
34	6.305	39.75	143	120	97.0	70.0	9600	8310	—	8310	6168	266.0	.057	.1601	38
35	5.615	31.52	158	132	104	73.5	10900	8700	—	10480	6737	335.0	.045	.1426	38–39
36	5.000	25.00	175	143	111	77.0	12200	10700	—	13210	7877	423.0	.036	.1270	39–40
37	4.453	19.83	198	154	118	80.3	—	—	—	16660	9309	533.4	.028	.1131	41
38	3.965	15.72	224	166	126	83.6	—	—	—	21010	10666	672.6	.022	.1007	42
39	3.531	12.47	248	181	133	86.6	—	—	—	26500	11907	848.1	.018	.0897	43
40	3.145	9.88	282	194	140	89.7	—	—	—	33410	14222	1069	.014	.0799	44

[1] A mil is 1/1000 (one-thousandth) of an inch. [2] The figures given are approximate only, since the thickness of the insulation varies with different manufacturers. [3] 700 circular mils per ampere is a satisfactory design figure for small transformers, but values from 500 to 1000 C.M. are commonly used. For 1000 C.M./amp. divide the circular mil area (third column) by 1000; for 500 C.M./amp. divide circular mil area by 500. [4] Single cotton-covered. [5] Single silk-covered. [6] Double silk-covered. [7] Double cotton-covered.

CHAPTER 21

Measurements

It is practically impossible to operate an amateur station without making measurements at one time or another. Although quite crude measurements often will suffice, more refined equipment and methods will yield more and better information. With adequate information at hand it becomes possible to adjust a piece of equipment for optimum performance quickly and surely, and to design circuits along established principles rather than depending on cut-and-try.

Measuring and test equipment is valuable during construction, for testing components before installation. It is practically indispensable in the initial adjustment of radio gear, not only for establishing operating values but also for tracing possible errors in wiring. It is likewise needed for locating breakdowns and defective components in existing equipment.

The basic measurements are those of current, voltage, and frequency. Determination of the values of circuit elements — resistance, inductance and capacitance — are almost equally im-

portant. The inspection of waveform in audio-frequency circuits is highly useful. For these purposes there is available a wide assortment of instruments, both complete and in kit form; the latter, particularly, compare very favorably in cost with strictly home-built instruments and are frequently more satisfactory both in appearance and calibration. The home-built instruments described in this chapter are ones having features of particular usefulness in amateur applications, and not ordinarily available commercially.

In using any instrument it should always be kept in mind that the accuracy depends not only on the inherent accuracy of the instrument itself (which, in the case of commercially built units is usually within a few per cent, and in any event should be specified by the manufacturer) but also the conditions under which the measurement is made. Large errors can be introduced by failing to recognize the existence of conditions that affect the instrument readings. This is particularly true in certain types of r.f. measurements, where stray effects are hard to eliminate.

Voltage, Current, and Resistance

● D.C. MEASUREMENTS

A direct-current instrument — voltmeter, ammeter, milliammeter or microammeter — is a device using electromagnetic means to deflect a pointer over a calibrated scale in proportion to the current flowing. In the **D'Arsonval** type a coil of wire, to which the pointer is attached, is pivoted between the poles of a permanent magnet, and when current flows through the coil it causes a magnetic field that interacts with that of the magnet to cause the coil to turn. The design of the instrument is usually such as to make the pointer deflection directly proportional to the current.

A less expensive type of instrument is the **moving-vane** type, in which a pivoted soft-iron vane is pulled into a coil of wire by the magnetic field set up when current flows through the coil. The farther the vane extends into the coil the greater the magnetic pull on it, for a given change in current, so this type of instrument does not have "linear" deflection — that is, the scale is cramped at the low-current end and spread out at the high-current end.

The same basic instrument is used for measuring either current or voltage. Good-quality instruments are made with fairly high **sensitivity** —

that is, they give full-scale pointer deflection with very small currents — when intended to be used as voltmeters. The sensitivity of instruments intended for measuring large currents can be lower, but a highly sensitive instrument can be, and frequently is, used for measurement of currents much greater than needed for full-scale deflection.

Panel-mounting instruments of the D'Arsonval type will give a smaller deflection when mounted on iron or steel panels than when mounted on nonmagnetic material. Readings may be as much as ten per cent low. Specially calibrated meters should be obtained for mounting on such panels.

● VOLTMETERS

Only a fraction of a volt is required for full-scale deflection of a sensitive instrument (1 milliampere or less full scale) so for measuring voltage a high resistance is connected in series with it, Fig. 21-1. Knowing the current and the resistance, the voltage can easily be calculated from Ohm's Law. The meter is calibrated in terms of the voltage drop across the series resistor or **multiplier.** Practically any desired full-scale

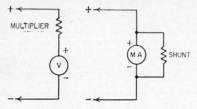

Fig. 21-1—How voltmeter multipliers and milliammeter shunts are connected to extend the range of a d.c. meter.

voltage range can be obtained by proper choice of multiplier resistance, and voltmeters frequently have several ranges selected by a switch.

The sensitivity of the voltmeter is usually expressed in "ohms per volt." A sensitivity of 1000 ohms per volt means that the resistance of the voltmeter is 1000 times the full-scale voltage, and by Ohm's Law the current required for full-scale deflection is 1 milliampere. A sensitivity of 20,000 ohms per volt, another commonly used value, means that the instrument is a 50-microampere meter. The higher the resistance of the voltmeter the more accurate the measurements

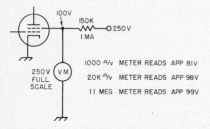

Fig. 21-2—Effect of voltmeter resistance on accuracy of readings. It is assumed that the d.c. resistance of the screen circuit is constant at 100 kilohms. The actual current and voltage without the voltmeter connected are 1 ma. and 100 volts. The voltmeter readings will differ because the different types of meters draw different amounts of current through the 150-kilohm resistor.

in high-resistance circuits. This is because the current flowing through the voltmeter will cause a change in the voltage between the points across which the meter is connected, compared with the voltage with the meter absent, as shown in Fig. 21-2.

Multipliers

The required multiplier resistance is found by dividing the desired full-scale voltage by the current, in amperes, required for full-scale deflection of the meter alone. Strictly, the internal resistance of the meter should be subtracted from the value so found, but this is seldom necessary (except perhaps for very low ranges) because the meter resistance will be negligibly small compared with the multiplier resistance. An exception is when the instrument is already provided with an internal multiplier, in which case the multiplier resistance required to extend the range is

$$R = R_m(n - 1)$$

where R is the multiplier resistance, R_m is the total resistance of the instrument itself, and n is the factor by which the scale is to be multiplied. For example, if a 1000-ohms-per-volt voltmeter having a calibrated range of 0–10 volts is to be extended to 1000 volts, R_m is $1000 \times 10 = 10,000$ ohms, n is $1000/10 = 100$, and $R = 10,000(100 - 1) = 990,000$ ohms.

If a milliammeter is to be used as a voltmeter, the value of series resistance can be found by Ohm's Law:

$$R = \frac{1000E}{I}$$

where E is the desired full-scale voltage and I the full-scale reading of the instrument in milliamperes.

Accuracy

The accuracy of a voltmeter depends on the calibration accuracy of the instrument itself and the accuracy of the multiplier resistors. Good-quality instruments are generally rated for an accuracy within plus or minus 2 per cent. This is also the usual accuracy rating of the basic meter movement.

When extending the range of a voltmeter or converting a low-range milliammeter into a voltmeter the rated accuracy of the instrument is retained only when the multiplier resistance is precise. Precision wire-wound resistors are used in the multipliers of high-quality instruments. These are relatively expensive, but the home constructor can do quite well with 1% tolerance composition resistors. They should be "derated" when used for this purpose — that is, the actual power dissipated in the resistor should not be more than ¼ to ½ the rated dissipation — and care should be used to avoid overheating the body of the resistor when soldering to the leads. These precautions will help prevent permanent change in the resistance of the unit.

Ordinary composition resistors are generally furnished in 10% or 5% tolerance ratings. If possible errors of this order can be accepted, resistors of this type may be used as multipliers. They should be operated below the rated power dissipation figure, in the interests of long-time stability.

● MILLIAMMETERS AND AMMETERS

A microammeter or milliammeter can be used to measure currents larger than its full-scale reading by connecting a resistance **shunt** across its terminals as shown in Fig. 21-1. Part of the current flows through the shunt and part through the meter. Knowing the meter resistance and the shunt resistance, the relative currents can easily be calculated.

The value of shunt resistance required for a given full-scale current range is given by

$$R = \frac{R_m}{n - 1}$$

where R is the shunt, R_m is the internal resistance of the meter, and n is the factor by which the

Milliammeters and Ammeters

original meter scale is to be multiplied. The internal resistance of a milliammeter is preferably determined from the manufacturer's catalog, but if this information is not available it can be measured by the method shown in Fig. 21-3. Do not attempt to use an ohmmeter to measure the internal resistance of a milliammeter; the instrument may be ruined by doing so.

Homemade milliammeter shunts can be constructed from any of the various special kinds of resistance wire, or from ordinary copper wire if no resistance wire is available. The Copper Wire Table in this *Handbook* gives the resistance per 1000 feet for various sizes of copper wire. After computing the resistance required, determine the smallest wire size that will carry the full-scale current (250 circular mils per ampere is a satisfactory figure for this purpose).

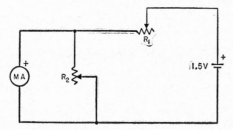

Fig. 21-3—Determining the internal resistance of a milliammeter or microammeter. R_1 is an adjustable resistor having a maximum value about twice that necessary for limiting the current to full scale with R_2 disconnected; adjust it for exactly full-scale reading. Then connect R_2 and adjust it for exactly half-scale reading. The resistance of R_2 is then equal to the internal resistance of the meter, and the resistor may be removed from the circuit and measured separately. Internal resistances vary from a few ohms to several hundred ohms, depending on the sensitivity of the instrument.

Measure off enough wire to provide the required resistance. Accuracy can be checked by causing enough current to flow through the meter to make it read full scale without the shunt; connecting the shunt should then give the correct reading on the new range.

Current Measurement with a Voltmeter

A current-measuring instrument should have very low resistance compared with the resistance of the circuit being measured; otherwise, inserting the instrument will cause the current to differ from its value with the instrument out of the circuit. (This may not matter if the instrument is left permanently in the circuit.) However, the resistance of many circuits in radio equipment is quite high and the circuit operation is affected little, if at all, by adding as much as a few hundred ohms in series. In such cases the voltmeter method of measuring current, shown in Fig. 21-4, is frequently convenient. A voltmeter — or low-range milliammeter provided with a multiplier and operating as a voltmeter — having a full-scale voltage range of a few volts, is used to measure the voltage drop across a compara-

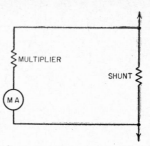

Fig. 21-4—Voltmeter method of measuring current. This method permits using relatively large values of resistance in the shunt, standard values of fixed resistors frequently being usable. If the multiplier resistance is 20 (or more) times the shunt resistance, the error in assuming that all the current flows through the shunt will not be of consequence in most practical applications.

tively high resistance acting as a shunt. The formula previously given is used for finding the proper value of shunt resistance for a given scale-multiplying factor, R_m in this case being the multiplier resistance.

D.C. Power

Power in direct-current circuits is determined by measuring the current and voltage. When these are known, the power is equal to the voltage in volts multiplied by the current in amperes. If the current is measured with a milliammeter, the reading of the instrument must be divided by 1000 to convert it to amperes.

● RESISTANCE MEASUREMENTS

Measurement of d.c. resistance is based on measuring the current through the resistance when a known voltage is applied, then using Ohm's Law. A simple circuit is shown in Fig. 21-5.

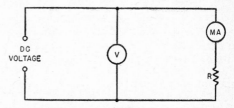

Fig. 21-5—Measuring resistance with a voltmeter and milliammeter. If the approximate resistance is known the voltage can be selected to cause the milliammeter, MA, to read about half scale. If not, additional resistance should be first connected in series with R to limit the current to a safe value for the milliammeter. The set-up then measures the total resistance, and the value of R can be found by subtracting the known additional resistance from the total.

The internal resistance of the ammeter or milliammeter, MA, should be low compared with the resistance, R, being measured, since the voltage read by the voltmeter, V, is the voltage across MA and R in series. The instruments and the d.c. voltage should be chosen so that the readings are in the upper half of the scale, if possible, since the percentage error is less in this region.

An **ohmmeter** is an instrument consisting

fundamentally of a voltmeter (or milliammeter, depending on the circuit used) and a small dry battery as a source of d.c. voltage, calibrated so the value of an unknown resistance can be read directly from the scale. Typical ohmmeter circuits are shown in Fig. 21-6. In the simplest type, shown in Fig. 21-6A, the meter and battery are connected in series with the unknown resistance. If a given deflection is obtained with terminals A-B shorted, inserting the resistance to be measured will cause the meter reading to decrease. When the resistance of the voltmeter is known, the following formula can be applied:

$$R = \frac{eR_m}{E} - R_m$$

where R is the resistance under measurement,

e is the voltage applied (A-B shorted),

E is the voltmeter reading with R connected, and

R_m is the resistance of the voltmeter.

The circuit of Fig. 21-6A is not suited to measuring low values of resistance (below a hundred ohms or so) with a high-resistance voltmeter. For such measurements the circuit of Fig. 21-6B can be used. The milliammeter should be a 0–1 ma. instrument, and R_1 should be equal to the battery voltage, e, multiplied by 1000. The unknown resistance is

$$R = \frac{I_2 R_m}{I_1 - I_2}$$

where R is the unknown,

R_m is the internal resistance of the milliammeter,

I_1 is the current in ma. with R disconnected from terminals A-B, and

I_2 is the current in ma. with R connected.

The formula is approximate, but the error will be negligible if e is at least 3 volts so that R_1 is at least 3000 ohms.

A third circuit for measuring resistance is shown in Fig. 21-6C. In this case a high-resistance voltmeter is used to measure the voltage drop across a reference resistor, R_2, when the unknown resistor is connected so that current flows through it, R_2 and the battery in series. By suitable choice of R_2 (low values for low resistance, high values for high-resistance unknowns) this circuit will give equally good results on all resistance values in the range from one ohm to several megohms, provided that the voltmeter resistance, R_m, is always very high (50 times or more) compared with the resistance of R_2. A 20,000-ohms-per-volt instrument (50-μamp. movement) is generally used. Assuming that the current through the voltmeter is negligible compared with the current through R_2, the formula for the unknown is

$$R = \frac{eR_2}{E} - R_2$$

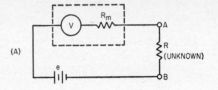
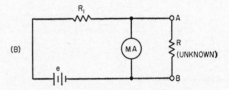
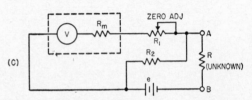

Fig. 21-6—Ohmmeter circuits. Values are discussed in the text.

where R and R_2 are as shown in Fig. 21-6C,

e is the voltmeter reading with A-B shorted, and

E is the voltmeter reading with R connected.

The "zero adjuster," R_1, is used to set the voltmeter reading exactly to full scale when the meter is calibrated in ohms. A 10,000-ohm variable resistor is suitable with a 20,000-ohms-per-volt meter. The battery voltage is usually 3 volts for ranges up to 100,000 ohms or so and 6 volts for higher ranges.

A. C. Measurements

Several types of instruments are available for measurement of low-frequency alternating currents and voltages. The better-grade panel instruments for power-line frequencies are of the **dynamometer** type. This compares with the D'Arsonval movement used for d.c. measurements, but instead of a permanent magnet the dynamometer movement has a field coil which, together with the moving coil, is connected to the a.c. source. Thus the moving coil is urged to turn in the same direction on both halves of the a.c. cycle.

Moving-vane type instruments, described earlier, also are used for a.c. measurements. This is possible because the pull exerted on the vane is in the same direction regardless of the direction of current through the coil. The calibration of a moving-vane instrument on a.c. will, in general, differ from its d.c. calibration.

For measurements in the audio-frequency range, and in applications where high impedance is required, the **rectifier-type** a.c. instrument is

Resistance Measurements

generally used. This is essentially a sensitive d.c. meter, of the type previously described, provided with a rectifier for converting the a.c. to d.c. A typical rectifier-type voltmeter circuit is shown in Fig. 21-7. The half-wave meter rectifier, CR_1, is frequently of the copper-oxide type, but crystal diodes can be used. Such a rectifier is not "perfect" — that is, the application of a voltage of reversed polarity will result in a small current flow — and so CR_2 is used for eliminating the effect of reverse current in the meter circuit. It does this by providing a low-resistance path across CR_1 and the meter during the a.c. alternations when CR_1 is not conducting.

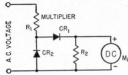

Fig. 21-7—Rectifier-type a.c. voltmeter circuit, with "linearizing" resistor and diode for back-current correction.

Resistor R_2 shunted across M_1 is used for improving the linearity of the circuit. The effective resistance of the rectifier decreases with increasing current, leading to a calibration scale with nonuniform divisions. This is overcome to a considerable extent by "bleeding" several times as much current through R_2 as flows through M_1 so the rectifier is always carrying a fairly large current.

Because of these expedients and the fact that with half-wave rectification the average current is only 0.45 times the r.m.s. value of a sine wave producing it, the impedance of a rectifier-type voltmeter is rather low compared with the resistance of a d.c. voltmeter using the same meter. Values of 1000 ohms per volt are representative, when the d.c. instrument is a 0–200 microammeter.

The d.c. instrument responds to the average value of the rectified alternating current. This average current will vary with the shape of the a.c. wave applied to the rectifier, and so the meter reading will not be the same for different wave forms having the same maximum values or

the same r.m.s. values. Hence a "wave-form error" is always present unless the a.c. wave is very closely sinusoidal. The actual calibration of the instrument usually is in terms of the r.m.s. value of a sine wave.

Modern rectifier-type a.c. voltmeters are capable of good accuracy, within the wave-form limitations mentioned above, throughout the audio-frequency range.

● COMBINATION INSTRUMENTS — THE V.O.M.

Since the same basic instrument is used for measuring current, voltage and resistance, the three functions can readily be combined in one unit using a single meter. Various models of the "v.o.m." (volt-ohm-milliammeter) are available commercially, both completely assembled and in kit form. The less expensive ones use a 0-1 milliammeter as the basic instrument, providing voltmeter ranges at 1000 ohms per volt. The more elaborate meters of this type use a microammeter — 0-50 microamperes, frequently — with voltmeter resistances of 20,000 ohms per volt. With the more sensitive instruments it is possible to make resistance measurements in the megohms range. A.c. voltmeter scales also are frequently included.

The v.o.m., even a very simple one, is among the most useful instruments for the amateur. Besides current and voltage measurements, it can be used for checking continuity in circuits, for finding defective components before installation — shorted capacitors, open or otherwise defective resistors, etc. — shorts or opens in wiring, and many other checks that, if applied during the construction of a piece of equipment, save much time and trouble. It is equally useful for servicing, when a component fails during operation.

● THE VACUUM-TUBE VOLTMETER

The usefulness of the **vacuum-tube voltmeter** (v.t.v.m.) is based on the fact that a vacuum tube can amplify without taking power from the source of voltage applied to its grid. It is therefore possible to have a voltmeter of extremely high resist-

C_1, C_3—0.002- to 0.005-μf. mica.
C_2—0.01 μf., 1000 to 2000 volts, paper or mica.
R_1—1 megohm, $\frac{1}{2}$ watt.
R_2 to R_5, inc.—To give desired voltage ranges, totaling 10 megohms.
R_6, R_7—2 to 3 megohms.
R_8—10,000-ohm variable.
R_9, R_{10}—2000 to 3000 ohms.
R_{11}—5000- to 10,000-ohm control.
R_{12}—10,000 to 50,000 ohms.
R_{13}, R_{14}—App. 25,000 ohms. A 50,000-ohm slider-type wire-wound can be used.
R_{15}—10 megohms.
R_{16}—3 megohms.
R_{17}—10-megohm variable.
M—0-200 μamp. to 0-1 ma. range.
V_1—Dual triode, 6SN7 or 12AU7.
V_2—Dual diode, 6H6 or 6AL5.

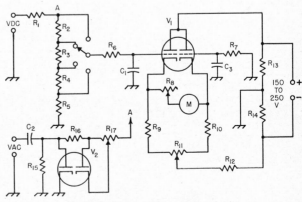

Fig. 21-8—Vacuum-tube voltmeter circuit.

ance, and thus take negligible current from the circuit under measurement, without using a d.c. instrument of exceptional sensitivity.

The v.t.v.m. has the disadvantage that it requires a source of power for its operation, as compared with a regular d.c. instrument. Also, it is susceptible to r.f. pick-up when working around an operating transmitter, unless well shielded and filtered. The fact that one of its terminals is grounded is also disadvantageous in some cases, since a.c. readings in particular may be inaccurate if an attempt is made to measure a circuit having both sides "hot" with respect to ground. Nevertheless, the high resistance of the v.t.v.m. more than compensates for these disadvantages, especially since in the majority of measurements they do not apply.

While there are several possible circuits, the one commonly used is shown in Fig. 21-8. A dual triode, V_1, is arranged so that, with no voltage applied to the left-hand grid, equal currents flow through both sections. Under this condition the two cathodes are at the same potential and no current flows through M. The currents can be adjusted to balance by potentiometer R_{11}, which takes care of variations in the tube sections and in the values of cathode resistors R_9 and R_{10}. When a positive d.c. voltage is applied to the left-hand grid the current through that tube section increases, so the current balance is upset and the meter indicates. The sensitivity of the meter is regulated by R_8, which serves to adjust the calibration. R_{12}, common to the cathodes of both tube sections, is a feed back resistor that stabilizes the system and makes the readings linear. R_6 and C_1 form a filter for any a.c. component that may be present, and R_6 is balanced by R_7 connected to the grid of the second tube section.

To stay well within the linear range of operation the scale is limited to 3 volts or less in the average commercial instrument. Higher ranges are obtained by means of the voltage divider formed by R_1 to R_5, inclusive. As many ranges as desired can be used. Common practice is to use 1 megohm at R_1, and to make the sum of R_2 to R_5, inclusive, 10 megohms, thus giving a total resistance of 11 megohms, constant for all voltage ranges. R_1 should be at the probe end of the d.c. lead to minimize capacitive loading effects when measuring d.c. voltages in r.f. circuits.

Values to be used in the circuit depend considerably on the supply voltage and the sensitivity of the meter, M. R_{12}, and R_{13}–R_{14}, should be adjusted by trial so that the voltmeter circuit can be brought to balance, and to give full-scale deflection on M with about 3 volts applied to the left-hand grid. The meter connections can be reversed to read voltages that are negative with respect to ground.

A.C. Voltage

For measuring a.c. voltages the rectifier circuit shown at the lower left of Fig. 21-8 is used. One section of the double diode, V_2, is a half-wave rectifier and the second half acts as a balancing device, adjustable by R_{17}, to eliminate contact potential effects that would cause a residual d.c. voltage to appear at the v.t.v.m. grid.

The rectifier output voltage is proportional to the peak amplitude of the a.c. wave, rather than to the average or r.m.s. values. Since the positive and negative peaks of a complex wave may not have equal amplitudes, a different reading may be obtained on such wave forms when the voltmeter probe terminals are reversed. This "turnover" effect is inherent in any peak-indicating device, but is not necessarily a disadvantage. The fact that the readings are not the same when the voltmeter connections are reversed is an indication that the wave form under measurement is unsymmetrical. In some measurements, as in audio amplifiers, a peak measurement is more useful than an r.m.s. or average-value measurement because amplifier capabilities are based on the peak amplitudes.

The scale calibration usually is based on the r.m.s. value of a sine wave, R_8 being set so that the same scale can be used either for a.c. or d.c. The r.m.s. reading can easily be converted to a peak reading by multiplying by 1.41.

● INSTRUMENT CALIBRATION

When extending the range of a d.c. instrument, calibration usually is necessary — although resistors for voltmeter multipliers often can be purchased to close-enough tolerances so that the new range will be accurately known. However, in calibrating an instrument such as a v.t.v.m. a known voltage must be available to provide a starting point. Fresh dry cells have an open-circuit terminal voltage of approximately 1.6 volts, and one or more of them may be connected in series to provide several calibration points on the low range. Gas regulator tubes in a power supply, such as the 0C3, 0D3, etc., also provide a stable source of voltage whose value is known within a few per cent. Once a few such points are determined the voltmeter ranges may be extended readily by adding multipliers or a voltage divider as appropriate.

Shunts for a milliammeter may be adjusted by first using the meter alone in series with a source of voltage and a resistor selected to limit the current to full scale. For example, a 0-1 milliammeter may be connected in series with a dry cell and a 2000-ohm variable resistor, the latter being adjusted to allow exactly 1 milliampere to flow. Then the shunt is added across the meter and its resistance adjusted to reduce the meter reading by exactly the scale factor, n. If n is 5, the shunt would be adjusted to make the meter read 0.2 milliampere, so the full-scale current will be 5 ma. Using the new scale, the second shunt is added to give the next range, the same procedure being followed. This can be carried on for several ranges, but it is advisable to check the meter on the highest range against a separate meter used as a standard, since the errors in this process tend to be cumulative.

Measurement of Frequency

● ABSORPTION FREQUENCY METERS

The simplest possible frequency-measuring device is a resonant circuit, tunable over the desired frequency range and having its tuning dial calibrated in terms of frequency. It operates by extracting a small amount of energy from the oscillating circuit to be measured, the frequency being determined by the tuning setting at which the energy absorption is maximum (Fig. 21-9).

Such an instrument is not capable of very high

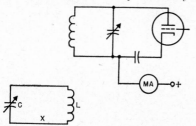

Fig. 21-9—Absorption frequency meter and a typical application. The meter consists simply of a calibrated resonant circuit LC. When coupled to an amplifier or oscillator the tube plate current will rise when the frequency meter is tuned to resonance. A flashlight lamp may be connected in series at X to give a visual indication, but it decreases the selectivity of the instrument and makes it necessary to use rather close coupling to the circuit being measured.

accuracy, because the Q of the tuned circuit cannot be high enough to avoid uncertainty as to the exact dial setting and because any two coupled circuits interact to some extent and change each others' tuning. Nevertheless, the **absorption frequency meter** or "wavemeter" is a highly useful instrument. It is compact, inexpensive, and requires no power supply. There is no ambiguity in its indications, as is frequently the case with the heterodyne-type instruments described later.

When an absorption meter is used for checking a transmitter, the plate current of the tube connected to the circuit being checked can provide the necessary resonance indication. When the frequency meter is loosely coupled to the tank circuit the plate current will give a slight upward flicker as the meter is tuned through resonance. The accuracy is greatest when the loosest possible coupling is used.

A receiver oscillator may be checked by tuning in a steady signal and heterodyning it to give a beat note as in ordinary c.w. reception. When the frequency meter is coupled to the oscillator coil and tuned through resonance the beat note will change. Again, the coupling should be made loose enough so that a just-perceptible change in beat note is observed.

An approximate calibration for the meter, adequate for most purposes, may be obtained by comparison with a calibrated receiver. The usual receiver dial calibration is sufficiently

accurate. A simple oscillator circuit covering the same range as the frequency meter will be useful in calibration. Set the receiver to a given frequency, tune the oscillator to zero beat at the same frequency, and adjust the frequency meter to resonance with the oscillator as described above. This gives one calibration point. When a sufficient number of such points has been obtained a graph may be drawn to show frequency *vs.* dial settings on the frequency meter.

● INDICATING FREQUENCY METERS

The plain absorption meter requires fairly close coupling to the oscillating circuit in order to affect the plate current of a tube sufficiently to give a visual indication. However, by adding a rectifier and d.c. microammeter or milliammeter, the sensitivity of the instrument can be increased to the point where very loose coupling will suffice for a good reading. A typical circuit for this purpose is given in Fig. 21-10, and Figs. 21-11 and 21-12 show how such an instrument can be constructed.

The rectifier, a crystal diode, is coupled to the tuned circuit L_1C_1 through a coupling coil, L_2, having a relatively small number of turns. The step-down transformer action from L_1 to L_2 provides for efficient energy transfer from the high-impedance tuned circuit to the low-impedance rectifier circuit. The number of turns on L_2 can be adjusted for maximum reading on the d.c.

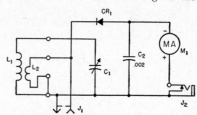

Fig. 21-10—Circuit diagram of indicating frequency meter.

C_1—50-μμf. variable (Johnson 50R12).
C_2—0.002-μf. disk ceramic.
CR_1—General purpose germanium diode (1N34, etc.).
J_1—Phono jack.
J_2—Closed-circuit phone jack.
M_1—D.c. microammeter or 0-1 milliammeter.

| Freq. Range | Coil Data | | Coil |
	Turns, L_1	Turns, L_2	Length, In.
3-6 Mc.	60	5	close-wound
6-12 Mc.	29	5	1¼
12-25 Mc.	13	2	1
23-50 Mc.	5¼	1	½
50-100 Mc.	1½	½	¼
90-225 Mc.	See below		

All except 90-225-Mc. coil wound with No. 24 enam. wire on 1-inch diameter 4-prong forms (Millen 45004). L_2 interwound at bottom of L_1, using smaller wire where necessary. The 90-225-Mc. coil consists of a hairpin loop of No. 14 tinned wire just clearing the bottom of the coil form, which is cut to ⅝-inch length. L_2 is a similar hairpin of No. 16 wire bent over so it almost touches L_1.

Fig. 21-11—The indicating frequency meter, plug-in coils, and pick-up cables. The meter is built in a bakelite meter case measuring 6¼ × 3¾ × 2 inches. The 3-inch dial is cut from a piece of aluminum and has a paper hand-calibrated scale cemented on. Hairline indicators are clear plastic mounted on small metal pillars. A 2-inch d.c. instrument is used. Pick-up loops are one turn of No. 14, spaghetti covered, soldered to the ends of the cables. The longer cable (5 feet) is useful to 30 Mc.; the shorter (13 inches) can be used for the full frequency range. Both are RG-58/U.

milliammeter; when doing this, use a fixed value of coupling between L_1 and the source of energy. The proper number of turns for this purpose will depend on the sensitivity of M_1. The coil dimensions given in Fig. 21-10 are for a 0-500 microammeter but will also be satisfactory for a 0-1 milliammeter. Less than optimum coupling is preferable, in most cases, since heavy loading lowers the Q of the tuned circuit L_1C_1 and makes it less selective. The coupling is reduced by reducing the number of turns on L_2.

The meter can be used with a pick-up loop and coaxial line connected to J_1. Energy picked up by the loop is fed through the cable to L_2 and thence coupled to L_1C_1. This is a convenient method of coupling to circuits where it would be physically difficult to secure inductive coupling to L_1. The pick-up cable should not be self-resonant, as a transmission-line section, at any frequency within the range in which it is to be used, so two cable lengths are provided. The longer one is useful up to 30 Mc. and the shorter at all frequencies up to the maximum useful frequency of the instrument (225 Mc.).

By plugging a headset into the output jack (phones having 2000 ohms or greater resistance should be used for greatest sensitivity) the frequency meter can be used as a monitor for modulated transmissions.

The bakelite case is a desirable feature since the instrument can be brought close to circuits being checked without the danger of short-circuiting any of their wiring. This could occur with a metal-cased unit.

In addition to the uses mentioned earlier, a meter of this type may be used for final adjustment of neutralization in r.f. amplifiers. For this purpose the pick-up loop may be loosely coupled to the plate tank coil. In this case L_1 may be removed from its socket and the meter used as an untuned rectifier. This reduces the sensitivity and insures that the r.f. pickup is only from the tank coil to which the loop is closely coupled.

● THE SECONDARY FREQUENCY STANDARD

The **secondary frequency standard** is a highly stable low-power oscillator generating a fixed frequency, usually 100 kc. It is nearly always crystal-controlled, and inexpensive 100-kc. crystals are available for the purpose. Since the harmonics are multiples of 100 kc. throughout the spectrum, some of them can be compared di-

Fig. 21-12—Inside the wavemeter. Only the milliammeter and phone jack are mounted on the removable panel. The tuning capacitor is mounted vertically on an aluminum bracket fastened to the bottom of the case. The crystal diode is mounted between a coil-socket prong and a tie point. The phono jack for the pick-up cables is at the lower right.

Frequency Standards

rectly with the standard frequencies transmitted by WWV.

The edges of most amateur bands also are exact multiples of 100 kc., so it becomes possible to determine the band edges very accurately. This is an important consideration in amateur frequency measurement, since the only regulatory requirement is that an amateur transmission be inside the assigned band, not on a specific frequency.

Manufacturers of 100-kc. crystals usually supply circuit information for their particular crystals. The circuit given in Fig. 21-13 is representative, and will generate usable harmonics up to 30 Mc. or so. The variable capacitor, C_1, provides a means for adjusting the frequency to exactly 100 kc. Harmonic output is taken from the circuit through a small capacitor, C_5. There are no special constructional points to be observed in building such a unit.

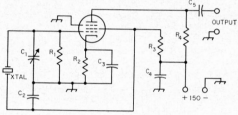

Fig. 21-13—Circuit for crystal-controlled frequency standard. Tubes such as the 6SK7, 6SH7, 6AU6, etc., are suitable.

C_1—50-$\mu\mu$f. variable.
C_2—150-$\mu\mu$f. mica.
C_3, C_4—0.01-μf. ceramic.
C_5—22-$\mu\mu$f. mica.
R_1—0.47 megohm, $\frac{1}{2}$ watt.
R_2—1000 ohms, $\frac{1}{2}$ watt.
R_3—0.1 megohm, $\frac{1}{2}$ watt.
R_4—0.15 megohm, $\frac{1}{2}$ watt.

Power for the tube heater and plate may be taken from the supply in the receiver with which the unit is to be used. The plate voltage is not critical, but it is recommended that it be taken from a VR-150 regulator if the receiver is equipped with one.

Sufficient signal strength from the standard usually will be secured if a wire is run between the output terminal connected to C_5 and the antenna post on the receiver. At the lower frequencies a metallic connection may not be necessary.

Adjusting to Frequency

The frequency can be adjusted exactly to 100 kc. by making use of the WWV transmissions tabulated later in this chapter. Select the WWV frequency that gives a good signal at your location at the time of day most convenient. Tune it in with the receiver b.f.o. off and wait for the period during which the modulation is absent. Then switch on the 100-kc. oscillator and adjust its frequency, by means of C_1, until its harmonic is in zero beat with WWV. The exact setting is easily found by observing the slow pulsation in

background noise as the harmonic comes close to zero beat, and adjusting to where the pulsation disappears or occurs at a very slow rate. The pulsation can be observed even more readily by switching on the receiver's b.f.o., after approximate zero beat has been secured, and observing the rise and fall in intensity (not frequency) of the beat tone. For best results the WWV signal and the signal from the 100-kc. oscillator should be about the same strength. It is advisable not to try to set the 100-kc. oscillator during the periods when the WWV signal is tone-modulated, since it is difficult to tell whether the harmonic is being adjusted to zero beat with the carrier or with a sideband.

Using the Standard

Basically, the 100-kc. standard provides a means for indicating the exact receiver dial settings at which frequencies that are multiples of 100 kc. are to be found. The harmonics of the standard can thus be used to check the dial calibration of a receiver, and many of the better-grade communications receivers either include a 100-kc. oscillator for this purpose or have provision for installing one as an accessory. The actual frequency of at least one 100-kc. point in a given amateur band must be known, of course, but this is generally an easy matter since the activity in amateur bands usually makes identification of the band-edge "marker signal" quite simple. After one frequency is known, the consecutive 100-kc. harmonic signals are simply counted off from it.

Although the 100-kc. standard does not make possible the exact measurement of a frequency, it is readily possible to determine whether or not the signal is in a particular 100-kc. segment. If the unknown signal tunes in between, say, 21,200 and 21,300 kc., as indicated by the marker signals in the receiver, its frequency obviously lies between those two figures. For purposes of complying with the amateur regulations it is usually sufficient to know that the signal is above, or below, some specified 100-kc. point, since the edges of the amateur bands or subbands usually are at such points. If a close measurement is desired a fairly good estimate usually can be made by counting the number of dial divisions between two 100-kc. points and dividing the number into 100 to find how many kilocycles there are per dial division.

In using the receiver to check one's own transmitting frequency it is necessary to take special precautions to reduce the strength of the signal from the transmitter to the point where it does not overload the receiver nor create spurious responses that could be taken for the actual signal. This invariably means that the receiving antenna must be disconnected from the receiver, and it may be necessary, in addition, to short-circuit the receiver's antenna input terminals. Try to reduce stray pickup to such an extent that the transmitter's signal is no stronger than normal incoming signals at the regular gain-control settings. With some receivers this may

Fig. 21-14—A 100-kc. frequency standard and harmonic amplifier. The crystal in this unit is in the metal-tube type envelope. Power and r.f. output connections are taken through the rear chassis lip.

require additional shielding around the signal-frequency circuits, and perhaps filtering of the a.c. and speaker leads where they leave the chassis, to prevent energy picked up on these leads from getting into the front end of the receiver.

Frequency Standard with Harmonic Amplifier

The frequency standard shown in Figs. 21-14 through 21-16 includes a tuned amplifier to increase the strength of the higher harmonics, and incorporates a crystal-diode sawtooth generator to make the harmonic strength reasonably uniform throughout the usable frequency spectrum of the

instrument. It will produce useful calibration signals at 100-kc. intervals up to about 60 Mc. The strength of a particular harmonic may be peaked up by selecting the proper amplifier tuning range with S_2 and adjusting C_4 for maximum output. A gain control, R_2, is included for adjusting the output signal to the desired level.

The 100-kc. oscillator uses the triode section of a 6AN8, while the amplifier uses the pentode section of the same tube. Power required for the unit is 150 volts at 10 ma. and 6.3 volts at 0.45 amp. This may be taken from the accessory socket of a receiver, or a special supply easily can be made using a TV "booster" transformer (such as the Merit P-3046 or equivalent).

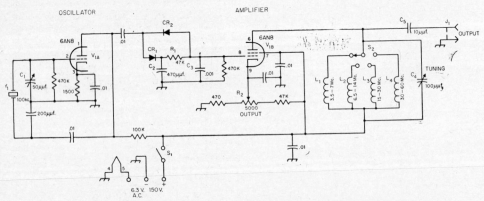

Fig. 21-15—Circuit of the 100-kc. crystal calibrator. Unless otherwise indicated, capacitances are in $\mu f.$, resistances are in ohms, resistors are 1/2 watt.

C_1—50-$\mu\mu f.$ midget variable (Hammarlund MAPC-50).
C_4—100-$\mu\mu f.$ variable (Hammarlund HF-100).
CR_1, CR_2—1N34A.
J_1—Phono jack.
L_1—3.5-7 Mc., 10 $\mu h.$ (National R-33 r.f. choke).
L_2—6.5-14 Mc., 4.7 $\mu h.$ (IRC type CL-1 r.f. choke).
L_3—15-30 Mc., 1.0 $\mu h.$ (IRC type CL-1 r.f. choke).

L_4—30-60 Mc., 0.22 $\mu h.$; 4 turns No. 20 plastic-insulated wire, 3/8-inch diam.
R_2—5000-ohm potentiometer (Mallory U-14).
S_1—S.p.s.t., mounted on R_2 (Mallory US-26).
S_2—1-section, 1-pole, 4-position miniature phenolic rotary switch (Centralab PA-1000).
Y_1—100-kc. crystal.

A Frequency Meter

The standard is built in a $4 \times 5 \times 6$ inch chassis-type box. R_2 and S_2 are mounted on the panel, with the amplifier plate coils mounted on S_2. The remaining components are mounted on the chassis, C_4 being insulated from it because its plates are above ground for d.c. For the same reason, an insulated shaft extension is used for front-panel control of C_4.

Connection between the standard and the receiver can be made through a wire from the hot terminal of J_1 to the antenna input post on the receiver. Depending on how well the receiver is shielded, such a wire may not be needed at the lower-frequency end of the range.

The Heterodyne Frequency Meter

The heterodyne frequency meter is a variable-frequency oscillator designed to be as stable as possible and to be capable of being accurately calibrated. Solid mechanical construction and a good dial are particularly important. In general, the design of such an instrument will be similar to that of the v.f.o.'s described in Chapter 6 on transmitters. Usually, the oscillator will cover a frequency range of approximately 1750 to 2000 kc. so that its harmonics will fall in the various amateur bands. It is used with the receiver in much the same way as the 100-kc. standard, except that in making a measurement the frequency-meter tuning is adjusted until the signal from it is in zero beat with the signal to be measured. The two signals are then on exactly the same frequency, which can be read from the calibration of the frequency meter.

The best method of calibrating a heterodyne frequency meter is to note the dial points at which its signal is in zero beat with consecutive 100-kc. points from a secondary standard. These points may then be plotted on graph paper and a smooth curve drawn through them to give the calibration at frequencies inside the 100-kc. intervals. The calibration preferably should be made on a high range. Points at 100-kc. intervals on 28 Mc., for example, are equivalent to 50-kc. intervals on 14 Mc., 25-kc. intervals on 7 Mc., and so on, since the meter is operating on lower-order harmonics on the lower bands.

More Precise Methods

The methods described above are quite adequate for the primary purpose of amateur frequency measurements — that is, determining whether or not a transmitter is operating inside the limits of an amateur band, and the approximate frequency inside the band. For measurement of an unknown frequency to a high degree of accuracy more advanced methods can be used. Accurate signals at closer intervals can be obtained by using a multivibrator in conjunction with the 100-kc. standard, and thus obtaining signals at intervals of, say, 10 kc. or some other integral divisor of 100. Temperature control is frequently used on the 100-kc. oscillator to give a high order of stability (Collier, "What Price Precision?", *QST*, September and October, 1952). Also, the secondary standard can be used in conjunction with a variable-frequency interpolation oscillator to fill in the standard intervals (Woodward, "A Linear Beat-Frequency Oscillator for Frequency Measurement," *QST*, May, 1951). An interpolation oscillator and standard can be combined in one instrument. One application of this type was described in *QST* for May, 1949 (Grammer, "The Additive Frequency Meter").

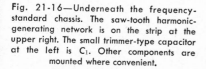

Fig. 21-16—Underneath the frequency-standard chassis. The saw-tooth harmonic-generating network is on the strip at the upper right. The small trimmer-type capacitor at the left is C_1. Other components are mounted where convenient.

STANDARD FREQUENCIES AND TIME SIGNALS

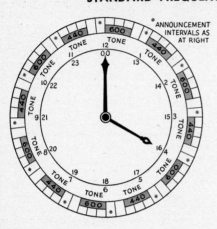

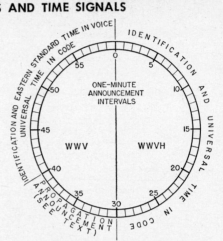

The Central Radio Propagation Laboratory of the National Bureau of Standards maintains two radio transmitting stations, WWV near Washington, D.C., and WWVH at Puunene, T.H., for broadcasting standard radio frequencies of high accuracy. WWV broadcasts are on 2.5, 5, 10, 15, 20 and 25 megacycles per second, and those from WWVH are on 5, 10, and 15 Mc. The radio-frequency signals are modulated by pulses at 1 cycle per second, and also by standard audio frequencies alternating between 440 and 600 cycles per second as shown by the accompanying chart.

Transmissions are continuous, with the following exceptions: The WWV transmissions are interrupted for a 4-minute period beginning at approximately 45 minutes after the hour; the WWVH transmissions are interrupted for a 3-minute period beginning approximately 10 seconds after the hour and each 15 minute interval thereafter. WWVH is also silent each day for a 34-minute period beginning at 1900 Universal Time.

Accuracy

Transmitted frequencies are accurate within 1 part in 100 million. The WWV transmissions are generally stable to 1 part in a billion in any given day, although this is not guaranteed. Frequencies are based on an atomic standard, and daily corrections to the transmitted frequencies are subsequently published each month in the *Proceedings of the Institute of Radio Engineers*.

Time Signals

The 1-c.p.s. modulation is a 5-millisecond pulse at intervals of precisely one second, and is heard as a tick. The pulse transmitted by WWV consists of 5 cycles of 1000 cycle tone; that transmitted by WWVH consists of 6 cycles of 1200-cycle tone. On the WWV transmissions, the 440- or 600-cycle tone is blanked out beginning 10 milliseconds before and ending 25 milliseconds after the pulse. On the WWVH transmissions, the pulse is superimposed on the tone. The pulse on the 59th second is omitted, and for additional identification the zero-second pulse is followed by another 100 milliseconds later.

Propagation Notices

During the announcement intervals at 19½ and 49½ minutes after the hour, propagation notices applying to transmission paths over the North Atlantic are transmitted from WWV on 2.5, 5, 10, 15, 20, and 25 Mc. Similar forecasts for the North Pacific are transmitted from WWVH during the announcement intervals at 9 and 39 minutes after the hour.

These notices, in telegraphic code, consist of the letter N, W, or U followed by a number. The letter designations apply to propagation conditions as of the time of the broadcast, and have the following significance:

W — Ionospheric disturbance in progress or expected.

U — Unstable conditions, but communication possible with high power.

N — No warning.

The number designations apply to expected propagation conditions during the subsequent 12 hours and have the following significance:

Digit	Forecast
1	Impossible
2	Very Poor
3	Poor
4	Fair to Poor
5	Fair
6	Fair to Good
7	Good
8	Very Good
9	Excellent

Special Transmissions During the International Geophysical Year

The special broadcasts instituted during the International Geophysical Year may be continued through part or all of 1960. These broadcasts include information on IGY "Alerts" and "Special World Intervals." The broadcasts from WWV are at 4½ and 34½ minutes past the hour and those from WWVH are at 14 and 44 minutes past the hour. Each such transmission is preceded by the letters "AGI" in International Morse

Code. The code used for the information is as follows:

5 A's — State of alert.

5 E's — No state of alert.

5 S's — Special World Interval begins at 0001Z the following day.

5 T's — Special World Interval terminates at 2359Z.

3 long dashes — Special World Interval in progress.

Grid-Dip Meter
Test Oscillators and Signal Generators

● THE GRID-DIP METER

The **grid-dip meter** is a simple vacuum-tube oscillator to which a microammeter or low-range milliammeter has been added for reading the oscillator grid current. A 0-1 milliammeter is sensitive enough in most cases. The grid-dip meter is so called because if the oscillator is coupled to a tuned circuit the grid current will show a decrease or "dip" when the oscillator is tuned through resonance with the unknown circuit. The reason for this is that the external circuit will absorb energy from the oscillator when both are tuned to the same frequency; the loss of energy from the oscillator circuit causes the feedback to decrease and this in turn is accompanied by a decrease in grid current. The dip in grid current is quite sharp when the circuit to which the oscillator is coupled has reasonably high Q.

The grid-dip meter is most useful when it covers a wide frequency range and is compactly constructed so that it can be coupled to circuits in hard-to-reach places such as in a transmitter or receiver chassis. It can thus be used to check tuning ranges and to find unwanted resonances of the type described in the chapter on TVI. Since it is its own source of r.f. energy it does not require the circuit being checked to be energized. In addition to resonance checks, the grid-dip meter also can be used as a signal source for receiver alignment and, as described later in this chapter, is useful in measurement of inductance and capacitance in the range of values used in r.f. circuits.

The circuit of Fig. 21-17 is representative, although practically any oscillator circuit that will operate over the desired frequency range may be used. An instrument to cover both low and very high frequencies must be constructed with short, direct r.f. leads. With ordinary care in this respect there should be little difficulty in getting satisfactory operation up to 150 Mc.

The power supply for the grid-dip meter may be included with the oscillator, but since this increases the bulk and weight a separate supply is often desirable. The power supply shown in Fig. 21-18 uses a miniature power transformer with a selenium rectifier and a simple filter to give approximately 120 volts for the oscillator plate. The potentiometer R_2 is for adjustment of plate voltage. This is desirable because in any grid-dip meter the grid current may vary over wide limits in different parts of the frequency range, with fixed plate voltage.

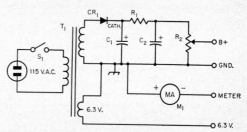

Fig. 21-18—Circuit diagram of the power supply for the grid-dip meter.

C_1, C_2—16-μf. electrolytic, 150 volts.
R_1—1000 ohms, $\frac{1}{2}$ watt.
R_2—0.1-megohm potentiometer.
T_1—Power transformer, 6.3 volts and 125 to 150 volts. (Merit P-3046 or equivalent.)
CR_1—20-ma. selenium rectifier.
M_1—0-1 d.c. milliammeter.

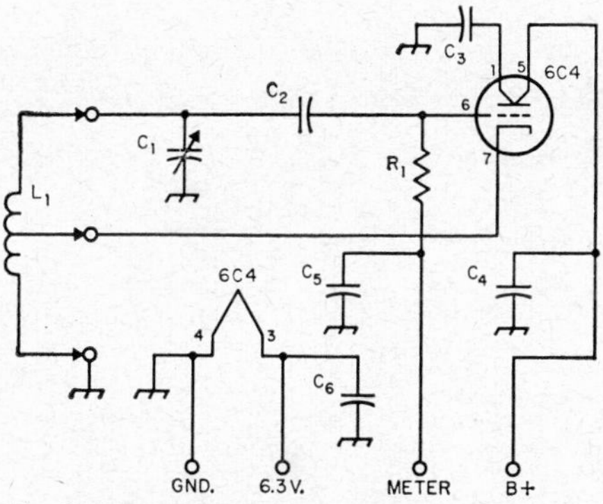

The instrument may be calibrated by listening to its output with a calibrated receiver. The calibration should be as accurate as possible, although "frequency-meter accuracy" is not required in the applications for which a grid-dip meter is useful.

The grid-dip meter may be used as an indicating-type absorption wavemeter by shutting off the plate voltage and using the grid and cathode of the tube as a diode. However, this type of circuit is not as sensitive as the crystal-detector type shown earlier in this chapter, because of the high-resistance grid leak in series with the meter.

In using the grid-dip meter for checking the resonant frequency of a circuit the coupling should be set to the point where the dip in grid current is just perceptible. This reduces interaction between the two circuits to a minimum and gives the highest accuracy. With too-close

Fig. 21-17—Circuit diagram of the grid-dip meter.

C_1—50-$\mu\mu$f. midget variable (Hammarlund HF-50).
C_2—100-$\mu\mu$f. ceramic.
C_3, C_4, C_6—0.001-μf. disk ceramic.
C_5—0.01-μf. disk ceramic.
R_1—22,000 ohms, $\frac{1}{2}$ watt.

Coil Data, L_1

Freq. Range	Turns	Wire	Diameter	Turns/inch	Tap*
1.59– 3.5 Mc.	139	32 enam.	$\frac{3}{4}$ in.	Close-wound	32
3.45– 7.8 Mc.	40	32 enam.	$\frac{3}{4}$ in.	Close-wound	12
7.55–17.5 Mc.	40	24 tinned	$\frac{1}{2}$ in. ‡	32	14
17.2–40 Mc.	15	20 tinned	$\frac{1}{2}$ in. ‡	16	5
37 –85 Mc.	4	20 tinned	$\frac{1}{2}$ in. ‡	16	$1\frac{1}{2}$
78 –160 Mc.	Hairpin of No. 14 wire, $\frac{3}{8}$ in. spacing, 2 inches long including coil form pins. Tapped $1\frac{1}{2}$ in. from ground end.				

Coil forms are $\frac{3}{4}$-in. diameter.
* Turns from ground end.
‡ B. & W. Miniductor or equivalent mounted inside coil form.

Fig. 21-19—Transistor circuit-checker or "grid-dip meter" covering 3 to 40 Mc. in five ranges. The circuit and battery power supply are contained in the 2¼ × 2¼ × 5-inch aluminum box (Bud CU-3004) so the instrument is completely independent of the a.c. line. The dial is white cardboard with an inked-on calibration; the hairline indicator is on a Lucite disk cemented to the tuning knob. The d.c. meter is a miniature type, but the box is large enough to take a standard 2-inch instrument. The control on the near edge is R_2, for setting the d.c. meter reading to a suitable on-scale value.

coupling the oscillator frequency may be "pulled" by the circuit being checked, in which case different readings will be obtained when resonance is approached from the high side as compared with approaching from the low side.

Transistor "Grid-Dip" Oscillator

The transistor oscillator is particularly con-

venient in the applications for which the grid-dip meter is useful, since it lends itself to very compact construction with freedom from dependence on the a.c. line for power. The principal drawback at the present time is that there are no low-cost transistors that will oscillate well in the v.h.f. range. However, it is possible to build an oscillator that will operate at least through the ordinary communication frequencies, as shown by Figs. 21-19 to 21-21, inclusive.

The oscillator circuit in Fig. 21-20 is basically of the Colpitts type. Since there is no d.c. current in the transistor oscillator that compares with grid current in the tube oscillator, an equivalent effect is obtained by using CR_1 to rectify some of the r.f. energy, and then measuring the rectified current. To enable the use of a relatively inexpensive d.c. instrument, a second transistor is used as a d.c. amplifier following the rectifier. Omitting Q_2 would require M_1 to be a sensitive microammeter, since the power in the r.f. oscillator is extremely low. R_2 provides a means for setting the meter reading to the desired point on the scale.

The optimum value of bias resistor, R_1, varies with frequency, so the proper resistor is mounted in the coil form for each range. Any convenient pin arrangement can be used for the coil and resistor terminals. Mount the coils near the open ends of the forms so they can be tightly coupled to the circuit being checked. The resistors should be placed near the bottom so they will be as far as possible from the coils.

The instrument is used in the same way as a tube grid-dip meter in checking unknown circuits, and may be calibrated by the same method.

● AUDIO-FREQUENCY OSCILLATORS

A useful accessory for testing audio-frequency

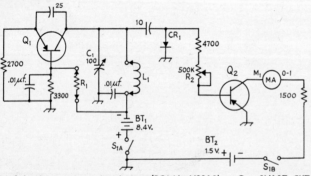

Fig. 21-20—Circuit of the transistorized grid-dip meter. Capacitances are in $\mu\mu f.$ except where specified otherwise; fixed resistors are ½ watt. Fixed capacitors are ceramic.

BT₁—8.4-volt mercury transistor battery (RCA No. VS312).
BT₂—1.5-volt mercury cell (RCA VS 313).
C₁—100-$\mu\mu f.$ midget variable (Hammerlund MAPC-100-B).
CR₁—1N34 or equiv.
L₁—3-5 Mc.: 72 turns No. 28 enam., ½-inch diam., 1 inch long, close-wound.
    5-10 Mc.: 43 turns*
    10-17 Mc.: 17 turns*
    17-30 Mc.: 7 turns*
    28-40 Mc.: 3 turns*
M₁—0-1 milliammeter.
Q₁—2N247.

Q₂—2N107, CK722, or 2N222.
R₁—3-5 Mc.: 39,000 ohms**.
    5-10 Mc.: 10,000 ohms**.
    10-17 Mc.: 4700 ohms**.
    17-30 Mc.: 4700 ohms**.
    28-40 Mc.: 10,000 ohms**.
R₂—0.5-megohm control.
S₁—D.p.s.t. toggle mounted on R_2.
* No. 24 wire, ½-inch diameter, 32 turns per inch (B & W 3004 Miniductor), mounted inside ¾-inch diameter polystyrene coil form (Amphenol 24-5H).
** Mounted in coil form with coil of same range.

Audio-Frequency Oscillators

Fig. 21-21—Inside the case of the transistor oscillator. All components are mounted on the flanged section of the two-piece box. The oscillator is at the right in this view, with connections anchored to tie points placed on either side of the coil socket. Q_1 is visible just below the tuning capacitor. CR_1 is mounted on the tie-point strip above the coil socket. The d.c. amplifier circuit is to the left of the mercury battery; the 1.5-volt cell is mounted beside the variable resistor, using a lug soldered to the + terminal for support.

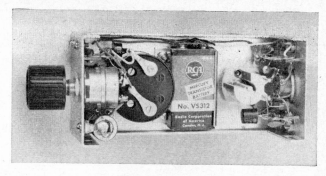

amplifiers and modulators is an audio-frequency signal generator or oscillator. Checks for distortion, gain, and the troubles that occur in such amplifiers do not require elaborate equipment; the principal requirement is a source of one or more audio tones having a good sine wave form, at a voltage level adjustable from a few volts down to a few millivolts so the oscillator can be substituted for the type of microphone to be used.

An easily constructed oscillator of this type is shown in Figs. 21-22 to 21-24, inclusive. Three audio frequencies are available, approximately 200, 900 and 2500 cycles. These three frequencies are sufficient for testing the frequency response of an amplifier over the range needed for voice communication.

The circuit uses a double triode as a cathode-coupled oscillator, the second section of the tube providing the feedback necessary for oscillation through the common cathode connection. The 3-watt lamp in this feedback loop acts as a variable resistance to control the oscillation amplitude and thus maintain the operating conditions at the point where the best wave form is generated. This operating point is set by the "oscillation control," R_1. The frequency is determined by the resistance and capacitance in

Fig. 21-22—Bottom view of the audio oscillator, showing the power-supply components and amplitude-control lamp, I_1. The lamp is mounted by wires soldered to its base. The selenium rectifier is supported by a tie-point strip. Placement of resistors, which are hidden by the other components, is not critical. The unit fits in a 4 × 5 × 6 inch box.

CR_1—20-ma. selenium rectifier.
I_1—3-watt, 115-volt lamp (G.E. 3S6).
L—8 henrys, 40 ma. (Thordarson 20C52).
R_1, R_2—Volume controls.
S_1—2-pole 5-position (3 used) rotary switch.
S_2—D.p.d.t. toggle.
S_3—S.p.s.t. toggle (mounted on R_1).
T_1—Power transformer, 150 volts, 25 ma.; 6.3 volts 0.5 amp. (Merit P-3046).

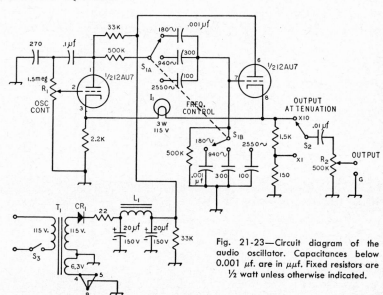

Fig. 21-23—Circuit diagram of the audio oscillator. Capacitances below 0.001 μf. are in μμf. Fixed resistors are ½ watt unless otherwise indicated.

flow through a load resistance which in general is chosen to equal the characteristic impedance of the transmission line to be connected to the receiver's input terminals. The resistance then substitutes for the line, and the amount of r.f. noise fed to the input terminals of the receiver is controlled by controlling the d.c. through the diode.

The usefulness of the noise generator in amateur work lies in the fact that it provides a means for adjusting the "front-end" circuits of a receiver for optimum signal-to-noise ratio (see sections on receiver design). Although it can be built at little expense, it is actually more effective for this purpose than costly laboratory-type signal generators. A simple circuit using a crystal diode is shown in Fig. 21-25. Fig. 21-26 illus-

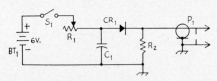

Fig. 21-25—Circuit of a simple crystal-diode noise generator.

BT_1—Dry-cell battery, any convenient type.
C_1—500-$\mu\mu$f. ceramic, disk or tubular.
CR_1—Silicon diode, 1N21 or 1N23 (do not use ordinary germanium diodes).
P_1—Coaxial fitting, cable type.
R_1—50,000-ohm control, counterclockwise logarithmic taper.
R_2—51 or 75 ohms, ½-watt composition.
S_1—S.p.s.t. toggle (may be mounted on R_1).

![Inside view of the audio oscillator]

Fig. 21-24—Inside view of the audio oscillator. The a.c. switch. S_3, is mounted on the output control at the left on the panel. The ceramic capacitors in the frequency-determining circuits are mounted on the rotary switch, S_1, at the right. S_2 is above the tube, and T_1 is on the near edge of the chassis, which is a U-shaped piece of aluminum 3½ inches deep with 1½ inch lips. R_1 is mounted on the near lip at the left.

the coupling circuit between the first-section plate and second-section grid. Various values of capacitance can be selected by means of S_1 to set the frequency. The actual frequencies measured in the unit shown in the photographs are given on the diagram. They may be either increased or decreased by using smaller or larger capacitances, respectively.

Output is taken from the cathode of the second triode section. Either the full output, 1.5 volts, or approximately one-tenth of it can be selected by S_2. On either of these two ranges smooth control of output is provided by R_2.

The built-in power supply uses a small transformer and a selenium rectifier to develop approximately 150 volts. Hum is reduced to a negligible level by the filter consisting of the 8-henry choke and 20-μf. capacitors.

An oscilloscope is useful for preliminary checking of the oscillator since it will show wave form. R_1 should be set at the point that will ensure oscillation on all three frequencies when switching from one to the other.

● NOISE GENERATORS

A noise generator is a device for creating a controllable amount of radio-frequency noise ("hiss"-type noise) evenly distributed throughout the frequency spectrum of interest. The simplest type of noise generator is a diode, either vacuum-tube or crystal, with direct current flowing through it. The current is also made to

trates the construction, the principal requirement being that R_2 should be mounted right on the terminals of the coaxial fitting and that lead lengths should be as short as possible in the circuit formed by C_1, CR_1 and R_2. If these lead lengths are negligible the instrument should give uniform performance up to at least 150 Mc. R_2 should match the particular line and input impedance for which the receiver is designed.

To use the generator, screw the coaxial fitting on the receiver's input fitting, open S_1, and measure the noise output of the receiver using an a.c. vacuum-tube voltmeter or similar a.f. voltage indicator. Make sure that the receiver's r.f. and audio gain controls are set well within the linear range, and do not use a.v.c. Then turn on the noise generator and set R_1 for an appreciable increase in output, say twice the original noise voltage, and note the dial setting. Receiver front-end adjustments may then be made with the object of attaining the same noise increase with the lowest possible direct current through the diode — that is, with the largest possible resistance at R_1.

The instrument may be used for comparing different receivers or different front-end arrangements, since this type of measurement is independent of receiver bandwidth (which has a marked effect on the actual signal-to-noise

R.F. Measurements

Fig. 21-26—Crystal-diode noise generator mounted in a 1⅝ × 2⅛ × 4-inch box. Most of the space is occupied by the miniature 6-volt dry-cell battery. The coaxial fitting (PL-259) can be mounted to the box by cutting a hole in a small square sheet-copper plate to make a snug fit over the end of the body of the connector and then soldering it in place. Holes can be drilled in the plate for mounting screws. The diode can be mounted in improvised clips, the larger being a small-size grid-grip and the smaller a miniature socket contact.

ratio). For consistent measurements the battery voltage should be checked to make sure that it does not change with the setting of R_1.

(Further information on noise generators, with additional references, may be found in *QST* for July, 1953.)

R.F. Measurements

● R.F. CURRENT

R.f. current-measuring devices use a **thermocouple** in conjunction with an ordinary d.c. instrument. The thermocouple is made of two dissimilar metals which, when heated, generate a small d.c. voltage. The thermocouple is heated by a resistance wire through which the r.f. current flows, and since the d.c. voltage developed is proportional to the heating, which in turn is proportional to the power used by the heating element, the deflections of the d.c. instrument are proportional to power rather than to current. This causes the calibrated scale to be compressed at the low-current end and spread out at the high-current end. The useful range of such an instrument is about 3 or 4 to 1; that is, an r.f. ammeter having a full-scale reading of 1 ampere can be read with satisfactory accuracy down to about 0.3 ampere, one having a full scale of 5 amperes can be read down to about 1.5 amperes, and so on. No single instrument can be made to handle a wide range of currents. Neither can the r.f. ammeter be shunted satisfactorily, as can be done with d.c. instruments, because even a very small amount of reactance in the shunt will cause the readings to be highly dependent on frequency.

Fig. 21-27 shows a convenient way of using an r.f. ammeter for measuring current in a coaxial line. The instrument is simply mounted in a metal box with a short lead from each terminal

Fig. 21-27—R.f. ammeter mounted for connecting into a coaxial line for measuring power. A "2-inch" instrument will fit into a 2 × 4 × 4 metal box.

to a coaxial fitting. The shunt capacitance of an ammeter mounted in this way has only a negligible effect on accuracy at frequencies as high as 30 Mc. if the instrument has a bakelite case. Metal-cased meters should be mounted on a bakelite panel which in turn can be mounted behind a cut-out that clears the meter case by ¼ inch or so.

● R.F. VOLTAGE

An **r.f. voltmeter** is a rectifier-type instrument in which the r.f. is converted to d.c., which is then measured with a d.c. instrument. The best type of rectifier for most applications is a crystal diode, such as the 1N34 and similar types, because its capacitance is so low as to have

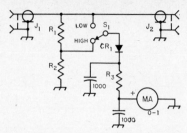

Fig. 21-29—Dual-range r.f. voltmeter circuit. Capacitances are in $\mu\mu$f.; capacitors are disk ceramic.

CR₁—1N34 or equivalent.
J₁, J₂—Coaxial connectors, chassis-mounting type.
R₁—1000 ohms, 1 watt.
R₂—3300 ohms, 2 watts.
R₃—App. 22,000 ohms (see text), ½ watt.
S₁—S.p.d.t. rotary switch (Centralab 1460).

little effect on the behavior of the r.f. circuit to which it is connected. The principal limitation of these rectifiers is their rather low value of safe inverse peak voltage. Vacuum-tube diodes are considerably better in this respect, but their size, shunt capacitance, and the fact that power is required for heating the cathode constitute serious disadvantages in many applications.

One of the principal uses for such voltmeters is as null indicators in r.f. bridges, as described later in this chapter. Another useful application is in measurement of the voltage between the conductors of a coaxial line, to show when a transmitter is adjusted for optimum output. In either case the voltmeter impedance should be high compared with that of the circuit under measurement, to avoid taking appreciable power, and the relationship between r.f. voltage and the reading of the d.c. instrument should be as linear as possible — that is, the d.c. indication should be directly proportional to the r.f. voltage at all points of the scale.

All rectifiers show a variation in resistance with applied voltage, the resistance being highest when the applied voltage is small. These variations can be fairly well "swamped out" by using a high value of resistance in the d.c. circuit of the rectifier. A resistance of at least 10,000 ohms is necessary for reasonably good linearity with a 0–1 milliammeter. High resistance in the d.c. circuit also raises the impedance of the r.f. voltmeter and reduces its power consumption.

The basic voltmeter circuit is shown in Fig. 21-28. It is simply a half-wave rectifier with a meter and a resistor, R_1, for improving the linearity. The time constant of C_1R_1 should be large compared with the period of the lowest radio frequency to be measured — a condition that can easily be met if R_1 is at least 10,000 ohms and C_1 is 0.001 μf. or more — so C_1 will stay charged near the peak value of the r.f. voltage. The radio-frequency choke may be omitted if there is a low-resistance d.c. path through the circuit being measured. C_2 provides additional r.f. filtering for the d.c. circuit.

the components in such a way as to minimize stray coupling between them and to keep them fairly well separated from metal surfaces.

For accurate calibration (the power method described below may be used) R_3 should be adjusted, by selection of resistors or using two in series to obtain the desired value, so that the meter reads full scale, with S_1 set for the low range, with 20 volts r.m.s. on the line. A frequency in the vicinity of 14 Mc. should be used. Then, with S_1 set for the high range, various resistors should be tried at R_1 or R_2 until with the same voltage the meter reads 20 per cent of full scale. The resistance variations usually will be within the range of 10 per cent tolerance resistors of the values specified. The readings at various other voltages should be observed in order to check the linearity of the scale.

Calibration

Calibration is not necessary for purely comparative measurements. A calibration in actual voltage requires a known resistive load and an r.f. ammeter. The setup is the same as for r.f. power measurement as described later, and the

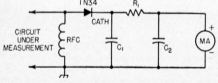

Fig. 21-28—R.f. voltmeter circuit using a crystal rectifier and d.c. microammeter or 0–1 milliammeter.

The simple circuit of Fig. 21-28 is useful for voltages up to about 20 volts, a limitation imposed by the inverse-peak voltage ratings of crystal diodes. A dual range voltmeter circuit, 0–20 and 0–100 volts, is shown in Fig. 21-29. A voltage divider, R_1R_2, is used for the higher range. An instrument using this circuit is shown in Fig. 21-30. It is designed for connection into a coaxial line. The principal constructional precautions are to keep leads short, and to mount

Fig. 21-30—Dual-range r.f. voltmeter for use in coaxial line, using a 0-1 d.c. milliammeter. The voltage-divider resistors, R_1 and R_2 (Fig. 21-29) are at the center in the lower compartment. The bypass capacitors and R_3 are mounted on a tie-point strip at the right. The unit is built in a 4 × 6 × 2 inch aluminum chassis, with an aluminum partition connecting the two sides of the box to form a shielded space. A bottom plate, not shown, is used to complete the shielding.

Measuring Inductance and Capacity

voltage calibration is obtained by calculation from the known power and known load resistance, using Ohm's Law: $E = \sqrt{PR}$. As many points as possible should be obtained, by varying the power output of the transmitter, so that the linearity of the voltmeter can be checked.

● R.F. POWER

Measurement of r.f. power requires a resistive load of known value and either an r.f. ammeter or a calibrated r.f. voltmeter. The power is then either I^2R or E^2/R, where R is the load resistance in ohms.

The simplest method of obtaining a load of known resistance is to use an antenna system with coax-coupled matching circuit of the type described in the chapter on transmission lines. When the circuit is adjusted, by means of an s.w.r. bridge, to bring the s.w.r. down to 1 to 1 the load is resistive and of the value for which the bridge was designed (52 or 75 ohms).

The r.f. ammeter should be inserted in the line in place of the s.w.r. bridge after the matching has been completed, and the transmitter then adjusted — without touching the matching circuit — for maximum current. A 0–1 ammeter is useful for measuring the approximate range 5–50 watts in 52-ohm line, or 7.5–75 watts in 75-ohm line; a 0–3 instrument can be used for 13–450 watts in 52-ohm line and 20–675 watts in 75-ohm line. The accuracy is usually greatest in the upper half of the scale.

An r.f. voltmeter of the type described in the preceding section also can be used for power measurement in a similar setup. It has the advantage that, because its scale is substantially linear, a much wider range of powers can be measured with a single instrument.

● INDUCTANCE AND CAPACITANCE

The ability to measure inductance and capacitance saves time that might otherwise be spent in cut-and-try. A convenient instrument for this purpose is the grid-dip oscillator, described earlier in this chapter.

For measuring inductance, use is made of a capacitance of known value as shown at A in Fig. 21-31. With the unknown coil connected to the standard capacitor, couple the grid-dip meter to the coil and adjust the oscillator frequency for the grid-current dip, using the loosest coupling that gives a detectable indication. The inductance is then given by the formula

$$L_{\mu h.} = \frac{25,330}{C_{\mu\mu f.} \cdot f^2_{Mc.}}$$

The reverse procedure is used for measuring capacitance — that is, a coil of known inductance is used as a standard as shown at B. The unknown capacitance is

$$C_{\mu\mu f.} = \frac{25,330}{L_{\mu h.} \cdot f^2_{Mc.}}$$

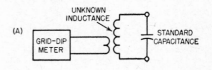

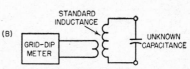

Fig. 21-31—Setups for measuring inductance and capacitance with the grid-dip meter.

The accuracy of this method depends on the accuracy of the grid-dip meter calibration and the accuracy with which the standard values of L and C are known. Postage-stamp silver-mica capacitors make satisfactory capacitance standards, since their rated tolerance is ± 5 per cent. Equally good inductance standards can be made from commercial machine-wound coil material.

A single pair of standards will serve for measuring the L and C values commonly used in amateur equipment. A good choice is 100 $\mu\mu f.$ for the capacitor and 5 $\mu h.$ for the coil. Based on these values the chart of Fig. 21-33 will give the unknown directly in terms of the resonant frequency registered by the grid-dip meter. In measuring the frequency the coupling between the grid-dip meter and resonant circuit should be kept at the smallest value that gives a definite indication.

A correction should be applied to measurements of very small values of L and C to include the effects of the shunt capacitance of the mounting for the coil, and for the inductance of the leads to the capacitor. These amount to approximately 1 $\mu\mu f.$ and 0.03 $\mu h.$, respectively, with the method of mounting shown in Fig. 21-32.

Coefficient of Coupling

The same equipment can be used for measurement of the coefficient of coupling between two

Fig. 21-32—A convenient mounting, using binding-post plates, for L and C standards made from commercially-available parts. The capacitor is a 100-$\mu\mu f.$ silver mica unit, mounted so the lead length is as nearly zero as possible. The inductance standard, 5 $\mu h.$, is 17 turns of No. 3015 B & W Miniductor, 1-inch diameter, 16 turns per inch.

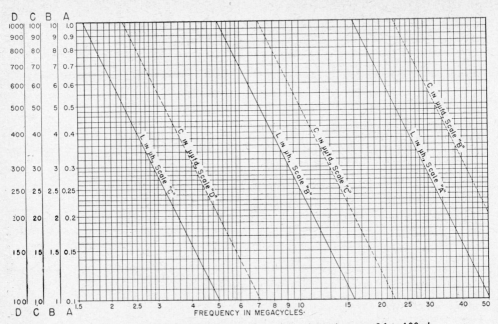

Fig. 21-33—Chart for determining unknown values of L and C in the range 0.1 to 100 μh. and 2 to 1000 $\mu\mu$f., using standards of 100 $\mu\mu$f. and 5 μh.

coils. This simply requires two measurements of inductance (of *one* of the coils) with the coupled coil first open-circuited and then short-circuited. Connect the 100-$\mu\mu$f. standard capacitor to one coil and measure the inductance with the terminals of the second coil open. Then short the terminals of the second coil and again measure the inductance of the first. The coefficient of coupling is given by

$$k = \sqrt{1 - \frac{L_2}{L_1}}$$

where k = coefficient of coupling
  L_1 = inductance of first coil with terminals of second coil open
  L_2 = inductance of first coil with terminals of second coil shorted.

● R.F. RESISTANCE

Aside from the bridge methods used in transmission-line work, described later, there is relatively little need for measurement of r.f. resistance in amateur practice. Also, measurement of resistance by fundamental methods is not practicable with simple equipment. Where such measurements are made, they are usually based on known characteristics of available resistors used as standards.

Most types of resistors have so much inherent reactance and skin effect that they do not act like "pure" resistance at radio frequencies, but instead their effective resistance and impedance vary with frequency. This is especially true of wire-wound resistors. Composition (carbon) resistors of 25 ohms or more as a rule have negligible inductance for frequencies up to 100 Mc. or so. The skin effect also is small, but the shunt capacitance cannot be neglected in the higher values of these resistors, since it reduces their impedance and makes it reactive. However, for most purposes the capacitive effects can be considered to be negligible in composition resistors of values up to 1000 ohms, for frequencies up to 50 to 100 Mc., and the r.f. resistance of such units is practically the same as their d.c. resistance. Hence they can be considered to be practically pure resistance in such applications as r.f. bridges, etc., provided they are mounted in such a way as to avoid magnetic coupling to other circuit components, and are not so close to grounded metal parts as to give an appreciable increase in shunt capacitance.

Antenna and Transmission-Line Measurements

Two principal types of measurements are made on antenna systems: (1) the standing-wave ratio on the transmission line, as a means for determining whether or not the antenna is properly matched to the line (alternatively, the input resistance of the line or antenna may be measured); (2) the comparative radiation field strength in the vicinity of the antenna, as a means for checking the directivity of a beam antenna and as an aid in adjustment of element tuning and phasing. Both types of measurements can be made with rather simple equipment.

Field Strength Meters

● FIELD-STRENGTH MEASUREMENTS

The radiation intensity from an antenna is measured with a device that is essentially a very simple receiver equipped with an indicator to give a visual representation of the comparative signal strength. Such a **field-strength meter** is used with a "pick-up antenna" which should always have the same polarization as the antenna being checked — e.g., the pick-up antenna should be horizontal if the transmitting antenna is horizontal. Care should be taken to prevent stray pickup by the field-strength meter itself or by any transmission line that may connect it to the pick-up antenna.

Field-strength measurements preferably should be made at a distance of several wavelengths from the transmitting antenna being tested. Measurements made within a wavelength of the antenna may be misleading, because of the possibility that the measuring equipment may be responding to the combined induction and radiation fields of the antenna, rather than to the radiation field alone. Also, if the pick-up antenna has dimensions comparable with those of the antenna under test it is likely that the coupling between the two antennas will be great enough to cause the pick-up antenna to tend to become part of the radiating system and thus result in misleading field-strength readings.

A desirable form of pick-up antenna is a dipole installed at the same height as the antenna being tested, with low-impedance line such as 75-ohm Twin-Lead connected at the center to transfer the r.f. signal to the field-strength meter. The length of the dipole need only be great enough to give adequate meter readings. A half-wave dipole will give high sensitivity, but such length will not be needed unless the distance is several wavelengths and a relatively insensitive meter is used.

Field-Strength Meters

The crystal-detector wavemeter described earlier in this chapter may be used as a field-strength meter. It may be coupled to the transmission line from the pick-up antenna through the coaxial-cable jack, J_1.

The indications with a crystal wavemeter connected as shown in Fig. 21-10 will tend to be "square law" — that is, the meter reading will be proportional to the square of the r.f. voltage. This exaggerates the effect of relatively small adjustments to the antenna system and gives a false impression of the improvement secured. The meter reading can be made more linear by connecting a fairly large resistance in series with the milliammeter (or microammeter). About 10,000 ohms is required for good linearity. This considerably reduces the sensitivity of the meter, but the lower sensitivity can be compensated for by making the pick-up antenna sufficiently large.

Transistorized Wavemeter and Field-Strength Meter

A sensitive field-strength meter can be made by using a transistor as a d.c. amplifier following

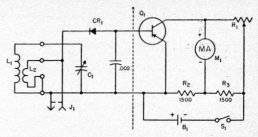

Fig. 21-34—Transistor d.c. amplifier applied to the wavemeter of Fig. 21-10 to increase sensitivity. Components not listed below are the same as in Fig. 21-10.

B_1—Small flashlight cell.
M_1—0-1 d.c. milliammeter (see text).
Q_1—2N107, CK722, etc.
R_1—10,000-ohm control.
R_2, R_3—1500 ohms, ½ watt.
S_1—S.p.s.t. toggle (on-off switch).

the crystal rectifier of a wavemeter. A circuit of this type is shown in Fig. 21-34. Depending on the characteristics of the particular transistor used, the amplification of current may be 10 or more times, so that a 0–1 milliampere d.c. instrument becomes the equivalent of a sensitive microammeter.

The circuit to the left of the dashed line in Fig. 21-34 is the same as the wavemeter circuit of Fig. 21-10, and the transistor amplifier can easily be accommodated in the case shown in Figs. 21-11 and 21-12.

The transistor is connected in the common-emitter circuit with the rectified d.c. from the crystal diode flowing in the base-emitter circuit. Since there is a small residual current in the collector circuit with no current flowing in the base-emitter circuit, the d.c. meter is connected in a bridge arrangement so the residual current can be balanced out. This is accomplished, in the absence of any signal input to the transistor base, by adjusting R_1 so that the voltage drop across it is equal to the voltage drop from collector to emitter in the transistor. R_2 and R_3, being of the same resistance, have equal voltage drops across them and so there is no difference of potential across the meter terminals until the collector current increases because of current flow in the base-emitter circuit.

The collector current in a circuit of this type is not strictly proportional to the base current, particularly for low values of base current. The meter readings are not directly proportional to the field strength, therefore, but tend toward "square law" response just as in the case of a simple diode with little or no resistance in its d.c. circuit. For this reason the d.c. meter, M_1, should not have too-high sensitivity if reasonably linear response is desired. A 0-1 milliammeter will be satisfactory.

The zero balance should be checked at intervals while the instrument is in use, since the residual current of the transistor is sensitive to temperature changes.

● **IMPEDANCE AND STANDING-WAVE RATIO**

Adjustment of antenna matching systems requires some means either of measuring the input impedance of the antenna or transmission line, or measuring the standing-wave ratio. "Bridge" methods are suitable for either measurement.

There are many varieties of bridge circuits, the two shown in Fig. 21-35 being among the most popular for amateur purposes. The simple

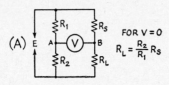

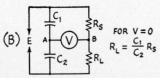

Fig. 21-35—Basic bridge circuits. (A) Resistance bridge; (B) resistance-capacitance bridge. The latter circuit is used in the "Micromatch," with R_S a very low resistance (1 ohm or less) and the ratio C_1/C_2 adjusted accordingly for a desired line impedance.

resistance bridge of Fig. 21-35A consists essentially of two voltage dividers in parallel across a source of voltage. When the voltage drop across R_1 equals that across R_S the drops across R_2 and R_L are likewise equal and there is no difference of potential between points A and B. Hence the voltmeter reading is zero and the bridge is said to be "balanced." If the drops across R_1 and R_S are not equal, points A and B are at different potentials and the voltmeter will read the difference. The operation of the circuit of Fig. 21-35B is similar, except that one of the voltage dividers is capacitive instead of resistive.

Because of the characteristics of practical components at radio frequencies, the circuit of Fig. 21-35A is best suited to applications where the ratio R_1/R_2 is fixed; this type of bridge is particularly well suited to measurement of standing-wave ratio. The circuit of Fig. 21-35B is well adapted to applications where a variable voltage divider is essential (since C_1 and C_2 may readily be made variable) as in measurement of unknown values of R_L.

S.W.R. Bridge

In the circuit of Fig. 21-35A, if R_1 and R_2 are made equal, the bridge will be balanced when $R_L = R_S$. This is true whether R_L is an actual resistor or the input resistance of a perfectly matched transmission line, provided R_S is chosen to equal the characteristic impedance of the line. Even if the line is not properly matched, the bridge will still be balanced for power traveling *outward* on the line, since outward-going power sees only the Z_0 of the line until it reaches the

load. However, power reflected back from the load does not "see" a bridge circuit and the reflected voltage registers on the voltmeter. From the known relationship between the outgoing or "forward" voltage and the reflected voltage, the s.w.r. is easily calculated:

$$S.W.R. = \frac{V_0 + V_r}{V_0 - V_r}$$

where V_0 is the forward voltage and V_r is the reflected voltage. The forward voltage is equal to $E/2$ since R_S and R_L (the Z_0 of the line) are equal. It may be measured either by disconnecting R_L or shorting it.

Measuring Voltages

For the s.w.r. formula above to apply with reasonable accuracy (particularly at high standing-wave ratios) the current taken by the voltmeter must be inappreciable compared with the currents through the bridge "arms." The voltmeter used in bridge circuits employs a crystal diode rectifier (see discussion earlier in this chapter) and in order to meet the above requirement — as well as to have linear response, which is equally necessary for calibration purposes — should use a resistance of at least 10,000 ohms in series with the milliammeter or microammeter.

Since the voltage applied to the line is measured by shorting or disconnecting R_L (that is, the line input terminals), while the reflected voltage is measured with R_L connected, the load on the source of voltage E is different in the two measurements. If the regulation of the voltage source is not perfect, the voltage E will not remain the same under these two conditions. This can lead to large errors. Such errors can be avoided by using a second voltmeter to maintain a check on the voltage applied to the bridge, readjusting the

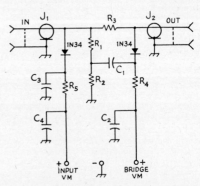

Fig. 21-36—Bridge circuit for s.w.r. measurements. This circuit is intended for use with a d.c. voltmeter, range 5 to 10 volts, having a resistance of 10,000 ohms per volt or greater.

C$_1$, C$_2$, C$_3$, C$_4$—0.005- or 0.01-µf. disk ceramic.
R$_1$, R$_2$—47-ohm composition, ½ or 1 watt.
R$_3$—52- or 75-ohm (depending on line impedance) composition, ½ or 1 watt; precision type preferred.
R$_4$, R$_5$—10,000 ohms, ½ watt.
J$_1$, J$_2$—Coaxial connectors.
Meter connects to either "input" or "bridge" position as required.

S.W.R. Bridges

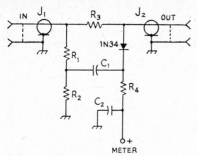

Fig. 21-37—A simple bridge circuit useful for impedance-matching in coaxial lines.

C_1, C_2—0.005- or 0.01-μf. disk ceramic.

R_1, R_2—47-ohm composition, ½ watt.

R_3—52- or 75-ohm (depending on line impedance) composition, ½ watt; precision type preferred.

R_4—1000-ohm composition, ½ watt.

J_1, J_2—Coaxial connector.

The meter may be a 0-1 milliammeter or d.c. voltmeter of any type having a sensitivity of 1000 ohm per volt or greater, and a full-scale range of 5 to 10 volts. Negative side of meter connects to ground.

coupling to the voltage source to maintain constant applied voltage during the two measurements. Since the "input" voltmeter is simply used as a reference, its linearity is not important, nor does its reading have to bear any definite relationship to that of the "bridge" voltmeter, except that its range has to be at least twice that of the latter.

A practical circuit incorporating these features is given in Fig. 21-36.

If the bridge is to be used merely for antenna adjustment, where the object is to secure the lowest possible s.w.r. rather than to measure the s.w.r. accurately, the voltmeter requirements are not stringent. In this case the object is to get as close to a "null" or balance (that is, zero reading) as possible. At or near exact balance the voltmeter impedance is not important. Neither is it necessary to maintain constant input voltage to the bridge. This simplifies the bridge circuit considerably, Fig. 21-37 being a practical example. The construction of a bridge of this type suitable for antenna and transmission line adjustments is shown in Fig. 21-38.

Bridge Construction

A principal point in the construction of an s.w.r. bridge is to avoid coupling between the resistors forming the bridge arms, and between the arms and the voltmeter circuit. This can be done by keeping the resistance arms separated and at right angles to each other, and by placing the crystal and its connecting leads so that the loop so formed is not in inductive relationship with any loops formed by the bridge arms. Shielding between the bridge arms and the crystal circuit is helpful in reducing such couplings, although it is not always necessary. The two resistors forming the "ratio arms," R_1 and R_2, should have identical relationships with metal parts, to keep the shunt capacitances

equal, and also should have the same lead lengths so the inductances will balance. Leads should be kept as short as possible.

Testing and Calibration

In a bridge intended for s.w.r. measurement (Fig. 21-36) rather than simple matching, the first check is to apply just enough r.f. voltage, at the highest frequency to be used, so that the bridge voltmeter reads full scale with the load terminals open. Observe the input voltage, then short-circuit the load terminals and readjust the input to the same voltage. The bridge voltmeter should again register full scale. If it does not, the ratio arms, R_1 and R_2, probably are not exactly equal. These two resistors should be carefully matched, although their actual value is not critical. If a similar test at a low frequency shows better balance, the probable cause is stray inductance or capacitance in one arm not balanced by equal strays in the other.

After the "short" and "open" readings have been equalized, the bridge should be checked for null balance with a "dummy" resistance, equal to the line impedance, connected to the load terminals. It is convenient to mount a half- or 1-watt resistor of the proper value in a coax connector, keeping it centered in the connector and using the minimum lead length. The bridge voltmeter should read zero at all frequencies. A reading above zero that remains constant at all frequencies indicates that the "dummy" resistor is

Fig. 21-38—An inexpensive bridge for matching adjustments using the circuit of Fig. 21-37. It is built in a 1⅝ × 2⅛ × 4-inch "Channel-lock" box. The standard resistor, R_3, bridges the two coax connectors. A pin jack is provided for connection to the d.c. meter, 0-1 ma. or 0-500 μa.; the meter negative can be connected to the case or to one of the coax fittings.

not matched to R_3, while readings that vary with frequency indicate stray reactive effects or stray coupling between parts of the bridge.

When the operation is satisfactory on the two points just described, the null should be checked with the dummy resistor connected to the bridge through several different lengths of transmission line, to ensure that R_3 actually matches the line impedance. If the null is not complete in this test both the dummy resistor and R_3 will have to be adjusted until a good match is obtained. With care, composition resistors can be filed down to raise the resistance, so it is best to start with resistors somewhat low in value. With each change in R_3, adjust the dummy resistor to give a good null when connected directly to the bridge, then try it at the end of several different lengths of line, continuing until the null is satisfactory under all conditions of line length and frequency.

With a high-impedance voltmeter, the s.w.r. readings will closely approximate the theoretical curve of Fig 21-39. The calibration can be checked by using composition resistors as loads.

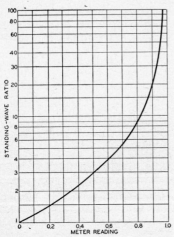

Fig. 21-39—Standing-wave ratio in terms of meter reading (relative to full scale) after setting forward voltage to full scale.

Adjust the transmitter coupling so that the bridge voltmeter reads full scale with the output terminals open, and then check the input voltage. Connect various values of resistance across the output terminals, making sure that the input voltage is readjusted to be the same in each case, and note the reading with the meter in the bridge position. This check should be made at a low frequency such as 3.5 Mc. in order to minimize the effect of reactance in the resistors. The s.w.r. is given by

$$S.W.R. = \frac{R_L}{R_0} \text{ or } \frac{R_0}{R_L}$$

where R_0 is the line impedance for which the bridge has been adjusted to null, and R_L is the resistance used as a load. Use the formula that places the larger of the two resistances in the numerator. If the readings do not correspond exactly for the same s.w.r. when appropriate resistors above and below the line impedance for which the bridge is designed are used, a possible reason is that the current taken by the voltmeter is affecting the measurements.

Using the Bridge

The operating procedure is the same whether the bridge is used for matching or for s.w.r. measurement. Apply power with the load terminals either open or shorted, and adjust the input until the bridge voltmeter reads full scale. Because the bridge operates a very low power level it may be necessary to couple it to a low-power driver stage rather than to the final amplifier. Alternatively, the plate voltage and excitation for the final amplifier may be reduced to the point where the power output is of the order of a few watts. Then connect the load and observe the voltmeter reading. For matching, adjust the matching network until the best possible null is obtained. For s.w.r. measurement, note the r.f. input voltage to the bridge after adjusting for full-scale with the load terminals open or shorted, then connect the load and readjust the transmitter for the same input voltage. The bridge voltmeter then indicates the standing-wave ratio as given by Fig. 21-39.

Antenna systems are in general resonant systems and thus exhibit a purely resistive impedance at only one frequency or over a small band of frequencies. In making bridge measurements, this will cause errors if the r.f. energy used to operate the bridge is not free from harmonics and other spurious components, such as frequencies lower than the desired operating frequency that may be fed through the final amplifier from a frequency-doubler stage. When a good null cannot be secured in, for example, the course of adjusting a matching section for 1-to-1 s.w.r., a check should be made to ensure that only the desired measurement frequency is present. An indicating-type absorption frequency meter coupled to the load usually will show whether energy on undesired frequencies is present in significant amounts. If so, additional selectivity must be used between the source of power and the measuring circuit.

Bridge for Monitoring S.W.R.

The low power level at which resistance-type bridges must operate is a disadvantage when the bridge is used as an operating adjunct — e.g., for the adjustment of matching circuits when changing bands, or for readjustment of such circuits within a band. For this purpose a bridge is needed that will carry the full power output of the transmitter without absorbing an appreciable fraction of it.

The "Monimatch" shown in Figs. 21-40 to 21-43, inclusive, is such a device. It makes use of the combined effects of inductive and capacitive coupling between the center conductor of a coaxial line and a length of wire parallel to it. When the coupled wire is properly terminated in a resistance, the voltage induced in it by power travelling along the line in one direction will be balanced out in the crystal-rectifier r.f. voltmeter

Monimatch

Fig. 21-40—Monimatch and indicator unit. The bridge is contained in the 2 × 4 × 4-inch aluminum box at the left. The indicator unit, made separate from the bridge in case the latter has to be installed in a spot where the meter would not be readily visible, is in a 3 × 4 × 5-inch box. Any convenient length of three-conductor cable (preferably shielded) can be used to connect the two.

circuit, but power travelling along the line in the opposite direction will cause a voltmeter indication. If the bridge is adjusted to match the Z_0 of the coaxial line being used, the voltmeter will respond only to the reflected voltage, just as in the case of the resistance-type bridges. The power consumed in the bridge is below one watt, even at the maximum power permitted amateur transmitters.

The circuit of Fig. 21-41 has two such bridge circuits so either the incident or reflected voltage can be measured.

The sensitivity of this type of bridge is proportional to frequency, so higher power is required for a given voltmeter deflection at low than at high frequencies. Typical values of "forward" rectified current (with R_1, Fig. 21-42, at zero resistance) are as follows, with a bridge adjusted for a characteristic impedance of 52 ohms:

Band	10 *Watts R.F.*	50 *Watts R.F.*
3.5 Mc.	70 $\mu a.$	250 $\mu a.$
7 Mc.	200 $\mu a.$	1 ma.
14 Mc.	750 $\mu a.$	Over 1 ma.
21–28 Mc.	Over 1 ma.	Over 1 ma.

A current of 1 ma. on 3.5 Mc. can be obtained

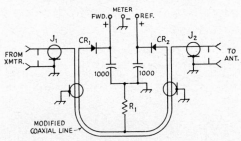

Fig. 21-41—Circuit of the Monimatch. The bridge element is a 24-inch length of coaxial cable modified as described in the text. Capacitors are disk ceramic; capacitances in $\mu\mu f.$
CR$_1$, CR$_2$—General-purpose germanium diodes (1N34A, etc.)
J$_1$, J$_2$—Coaxial fittings, chassis-mounting type.
R$_1$—Approximately 35 ohms for 52-ohm line; see text.

with a power level of somewhat over 200 watts. These currents depend somewhat on the internal resistance of the d.c. instrument.

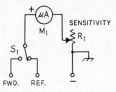

Fig. 21-42—Indicator-unit circuit. For low power and low frequencies, M$_1$ should be a 0-100 microammeter. A 0-1 milliammeter will suffice in other cases.
R$_1$—25,000-ohm control.
S$_1$—S.p.d.t. toggle.

The sensitivity also increases with an increase in cable length, but the cable should not be much longer than about 1/20 wavelength, to avoid standing-wave effects in the pick-up circuit. The length given in Fig. 21-41 is suitable for frequencies up to about 50 Mc. For higher frequencies the length should be decreased in proportion to the wavelength. This reduces the sensitivity considerably at the lower frequencies, so it is advisable to make separate units for v.h.f. and the frequencies below 30 Mc.

The additional conductor in the bridge shown in the photographs is a length of No. 30 enameled wire. To insert it under the cable shield, first loosen the braid by bunching it from the ends toward the center. Punch a small hole about ½ inch from each end of the braid and insert the end of the wire through one hole, then work it under the braid until it can be pulled out through the other hole. Next, smooth out the braid to its original length, being careful not to apply so much pressure that the enamel on the wire is scratched. Then open a small hole in the braid at the exact center of the length and fish enough of the No. 30 wire through to make the connection for R_1, again being careful about scraping the enamel off. Check with an ohmmeter to make sure the wire and braid are not short circuited. Then wrap the ends of the braid with

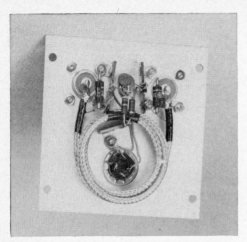

Fig. 21-43—Constructional details of the Monimatch (Fig. 21-40). This unit uses RG-58/U (52-ohm) cable, formed into several circular turns so the center where the tap for R_1 is taken off will be close to the input and output connectors. The crystal diodes are mounted on tie points alongside the coax fittings so leads are kept as short as possible. The terminating resistor R_1 consists of two resistors (47 and 150 ohms) in parallel to give a resistance of approximately 35 ohms. The socket for d.c. connections to the indicator unit is an Amphenol 71-4S (71-3S can be substituted). Outside braid of the cable is spot soldered between adjacent turns in several places for mechanical support and to ensure good grounding.

a turn or two of bare wire to prevent fraying and apply a drop or two of solder. The completed assembly may then be wound in a circle or other form that will bring the center connection near the two ends, and finally installed as shown in Fig. 21-43.

With heavier cable than the RG-58/U used in the unit shown it will probably be necessary to use a larger box. RG-58/U is rated for 430 watts of r.f. up to 30 Mc. and, RG-59/U for 680 watts. For higher powers RG-8/U or RG-11/U should be used. An example of construction using heavier cable is shown in the section on transmission lines. Aside from power, the type of cable should be chosen to match the characteristic impedance of the line with which the Monimatch is to be used.

A dummy antenna of the same resistance as the Z_0 of the line should be used to adjust R_1 (Fig. 21-41). A suitable dummy may be made by connecting four 220-ohm 1-watt composition resistors in parallel for 52-ohm line (or four 300-ohm resistors for 75-ohm line). Make the connecting leads as short as possible. The transmitter may be used as a source of power if its output can be reduced to about 4 watts, or a 40-watt lamp may be connected in series in the line from the transmitter to the bridge if the transmitter power cannot be reduced below 50 watts. With power applied (preferably at 28 Mc.) through J_1 and the dummy connected to J_2, try values for R_1 until the meter reading is zero with S_1 in the "reflected" position. It is best to start with the resistance a little high (a few trials will show

which way to go) and then try various values of resistance in parallel until a good null reading is secured. The final value should lie between the limits of 25 and 100 ohms. Finally, reverse the transmitter and load connections, when a good null should be obtained with the switch in the "forward" position. The "forward" and "reflected" readings should be substantially identical both ways if the construction is symmetrical.

With S_1 in the "forward" position the meter gives a relative indication of power output, and thus is useful for transmitter tuning. With S_1 in the "reflected" position the meter reading will be zero when the line is properly matched.

Impedance Bridge

The bridge shown in Figs. 21-44 to 21-46, inclusive, uses the basic circuit of Fig. 21-35B and incorporates a "differential" capacitor to obtain an adjustable ratio. When a resistive load of unknown value is connected in place of R_L, the C_1/C_2 ratio may be varied to attain a balance, as indicated by a null reading. The capacitor settings can be calibrated in terms of resistance at R_L, so the unknown value can be read off the calibration.

The differential capacitor consists of two identical capacitors on the same shaft, arranged so that when the shaft is rotated to increase the capacitance of one unit, the capacitance of the other decreases. The practical circuit of the bridge is given in Fig. 21-45. Satisfactory operation hinges on observing the same constructional precautions as in the case of the s.w.r. bridge. Although a high-impedance voltmeter is not

Fig. 21-44—An RC bridge for measuring unknown values of impedance. The bridge operates at an r.f. input voltage level of about 5 volts. The aluminum box is 4 by 5 by 6 inches.

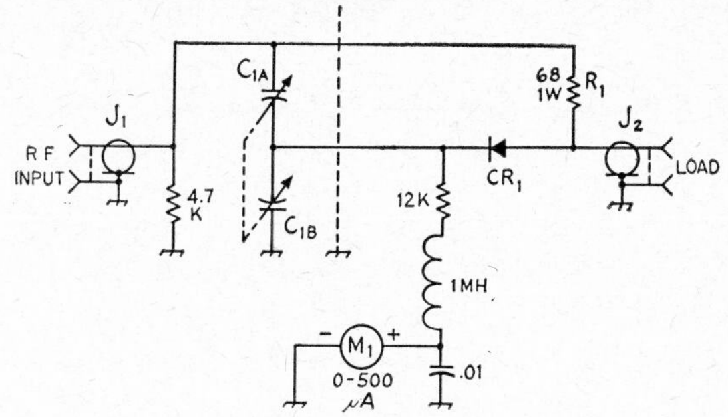

Impedance Bridge

Fig. 21-45—Circuit of the impedance bridge. Resistors are composition, ½ watt except as noted. Fixed capacitors are ceramic.

C_1—Differential capacitor, 11-161 $\mu\mu$f. per section (Millen 28801).

CR_1—Germanium diode (1N34, 1N48, etc.).

J_1, J_2—Coaxial connectors, chassis type.

M_1—0-500 microammeter.

essential, since the bridge is always adjusted for a null, the use of such a voltmeter is advisable because its better linearity makes the actual null settings more accurately observable.

With the circuit arrangement and capacitor shown, the useful range of the bridge is from about 5 ohms to 400 ohms. The calibration is such that the percentage accuracy of reading is approximately constant at all parts of the scale. The midscale value is in the range 50–75 ohms, to correspond to the Z_0 of coaxial cable. The reliable frequency range of the bridge includes all amateur bands from 3.5 to 54 Mc.

Checking and Calibration

A bridge constructed as shown in the photographs should show a complete null at all frequencies within the range mentioned above when a 50-ohm "dummy" load of the type described earlier in connection with the s.w.r. bridge is connected to the load terminals. The bridge may be calibrated by using a number of ½-watt 5% tolerance composition resistors of different values in the 5–400 ohm range as loads, in each case balancing the bridge by adjusting C_1 for a null reading on the meter. The leads between the test resistor and J_2 should be as short as possible, and the calibration preferably should be done in the 3.5-Mc. band where stray inductance and capacitance will have the least effect.

Using the Bridge

Strictly speaking, a simple bridge can measure only purely resistive impedances. When the load is a pure resistance, the bridge can be balanced to a good null (meter reading zero). If the load has a reactance component the null will not be complete; the higher the ratio of reactance to resistance in the load the poorer the null reading. The operation of the bridge is such that when an exact null cannot be secured, the readings approximate the resistive component of the load for very low values of impedance, and approximate the total impedance at very high values of impedance. In the mid-range the approximation to either is poor, for loads having considerable reactance.

In using the bridge for adjustment of matching networks C_1 is set to the desired value (usually the Z_0 of the coaxial line) and the matching network is then adjusted for the best possible null.

PARALLEL-CONDUCTOR LINES

Bridge measurements made directly on parallel-conductor lines are frequently subject to considerable error because of "antenna" currents flowing on such lines. These currents, which are either induced on the line by the field around the antenna or coupled into the line from the transmitter by stray capacitance, are in the same phase in both line wires and hence do not balance out like the true transmission-line currents. They will nevertheless actuate the bridge voltmeter, causing an indication that has no relationship to the standing-wave ratio.

S.W.R. Measurements

The effect of "antenna" currents on s.w.r.

Fig. 21-46—All components except the meter are mounted on one of the removable sides of the box. The variable capacitor is mounted on an L-shaped piece of aluminum (with half-inch lips on the inner edge for bolting to the box side) 2 inches wide, 2¼ inches high and 2¾ inches deep, to shield the capacitor from the other components. The terminals project through holes as shown, with associated components mounted directly on them and the load connector, J_2. Since the rotor of C_1 must not be grounded, the capacitor is operated by an extension shaft and insulated coupling.

The lead from J_1 to C_{1A} should go directly from the input connector to the capacitor terminal (lower right) to which the 68-ohm resistor is attached. The 4700-ohm resistor is soldered across J_1.

measurements can be largely overcome by using a coaxial bridge and coupling it to the parallel-conductor line through a properly designed impedance-matching circuit. A suitable circuit is given in Fig. 21-47. An antenna coupler can be used for the purpose. In the balanced tank circuit the "antenna" or parallel components on the line tend to balance out and so are not passed on to the s.w.r. bridge. It is essential that L_1 be coupled to a "cold" point on L_2 to minimize capacitive coupling, and also desirable that the center of L_2 be grounded to the chassis on which the circuit is mounted. Values should be such that L_2C_2 can be tuned to the operating frequency and that L_1 provides sufficient coupling, as described in the transmission-line chapter. The measurement procedure is as follows:

Connect a noninductive ($\frac{1}{2}$- or 1-watt carbon) resistor, having the same value as the characteristic impedance of the parallel-conductor line, to the "line" terminals. Apply r.f. to the bridge, adjust the taps on L_2 (keeping them equidistant

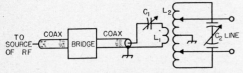

Fig. 21-47—Circuit for using coaxial s.w.r. bridge for measurements on parallel-conductor lines. Values of circuit components are identical with those used for the similar "antenna-coupler" circuit discussed in the chapter on transmission lines.

from the center), while varying the capacitance of C_1 and C_2, until the bridge shows a null. After the null is obtained, do not touch any of the circuit adjustments. Next, short-circuit the "line" terminals and adjust the r.f. input until the bridge voltmeter reads full scale. Remove the short-circuit and test resistor, and connect the regular transmission line. The bridge will then indicate the standing-wave ratio on the line.

The circuit requires rematching, with the test resistor, whenever the frequency is changed appreciably. It can, however, be used over a portion of an amateur band without readjustment, with negligible error.

Impedance Measurements

Measurements on parallel-conductor lines and other balanced loads can be made with the impedance bridge previously described by using a balun of the type shown schematically in Fig. 21-48. This is

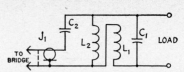

Fig. 21-48—Tuned balun for coupling between balanced and unbalanced lines. L_1 and L_2 should be built as a bifilar winding to get as tight coupling as possible between them. Typical constants are as follows:

Freq., Mc.	L_1, L_2	C_1	C_3
28	3 turns each on 2-inch form, equally spaced over $\frac{7}{16}$ inch, total.	4 $\mu\mu f.$	420 $\mu\mu f.$
14	Same as 28 Mc.	39 $\mu\mu f.$	0.0015 $\mu f.$
7	8 turns of 150-ohm Twin-Lead, no spacing between turns, on $2\frac{3}{4}$-inch dia. form.	None	0.001 $\mu f.$
3.5	Same as 7 Mc.	62 $\mu\mu f.$	0.0045 $\mu f.$

Capacitors in unit shown in Fig. 21-49 are NPO disk ceramic. Units may be paralleled to obtain proper capacitance.

an autotransformer having a 2-to-1 turns ratio and thus provides a 4-to-1 step-down in impedance from a balanced load to the output circuit of the bridge, one side of which is grounded. L_1 and L_2 must be as tightly coupled as possible, and so should be constructed as a bifilar winding. The circuit is resonated to the operating frequency by C_1, and C_2 serves to tune out any residual reactance that may be present because the coupling between the two coils is not quite perfect.

Fig. 21-49 shows one method of constructing such a balun. The two interwound coils are made as nearly identical as possible, the "finish" end of the first being connected to the "start" end of the second through a short lead running under the winding inside the form. The center of this lead is tapped to give the connection to the shell side of the coax connector. C_1 should be chosen to resonate the circuit at the center of the band for which the balun is designed with J_1 open, and C_2 should resonate the circuit to the same frequency with both J_1 and the "load" terminals shorted. The frequency checks may be made with a grid-dip meter. (For further details, see QST for August, 1955.)

Fig. 21-49—Balun construction (W2ZE). 150-ohm Twin-Lead may be used for the bifilar winding in place of the ordinary wire shown. Symmetrical construction with tight coupling between the two coils is essential to good performance.

S.W.R. Measurements

With the balun in use the bridge is operated in the same way as previously described, except that all impedance readings must be multiplied by 4. The balun also may be used for s.w.r. measurements on 300-ohm line in conjunction with a resistance bridge designed for 75-ohm coaxial line.

The "Twin-Lamp"

A simple and inexpensive standing-wave indicator for 300-ohm line is shown in Fig. 21-50. It consists only of two flashlight lamps and a short piece of 300-ohm line. When laid flat against the line to be checked, the coupling is such that outgoing power on the line causes the lamp nearest to the transmitter to light, while reflected power lights the lamp nearest the load. The power input to the line should be adjusted to make the lamp nearest the transmitter light to full brilliance. If the line is properly matched

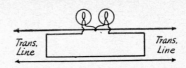

Fig. 21-51—Wiring diagram of the "twin-lamp" standing-wave indicator.

and the reflected power is very low, the lamp toward the antenna will be dark. If the s.w.r. is high, the two lamps will glow with practically equal brilliance.

The length of the piece of 300-ohm line needed in the twin-lamp will depend on the transmitter power and the operating frequency. A few inches will suffice with high power at high frequencies, while a foot or two may be needed with low power and at low frequencies.

In constructing the twin-lamp, cut one wire in the exact center of the piece and peel the ends back on either side just far enough to provide leads to the flashlight lamps. Remove about ¼ inch of insulation from one wire of the main transmission line at some convenient point. Use the lowest-current flashlight bulbs or dial lamps available. Solder the tips of the bulbs together and connect them to the bare point in the transmission line, then solder the ends of the cut portion of the short piece to the shells of the bulbs. Figs. 21-50 and -51 should make the construction clear.

The twin-lamp will respond to "antenna" currents on the transmission line in much the same way as the bridge circuits discussed earlier. There is therefore always a possibility of error in its indications, unless it has been determined by other means that "antenna" currents are inconsequential compared with the true transmission-line current.

Fig. 21-50—The "twin-lamp" standing-wave indicator mounted on 300-ohm Twin-Lead. Scotch tape is used for fastening.

The Oscilloscope

The **cathode-ray oscilloscope** gives a visual representation of signals at both audio and radio frequencies and can therefore be used for many types of measurements that are not possible with instruments of the types discussed earlier in this chapter. In amateur work, one of the principal uses of the scope is for displaying an amplitude-modulated signal so a phone transmitter can be adjusted for proper modulation and continuously monitored to keep the modulation percentage within proper limits. For this purpose a very simple circuit will suffice, and a typical circuit is described later in this section.

The versatility of the scope can be greatly increased by adding amplifiers and linear deflection circuits, but the design and adjustment of such circuits tends to be complicated if optimum performance is to be secured, and is somewhat outside the field of this section. Special components are generally required. Oscilloscope kits for home assembly are available from a number of suppliers, and since their cost compares very favorably

with that of a home-built instrument of comparable design, they are recommended for serious consideration by those who have need for or are interested in the wide range of measurements that is possible with a fully equipped scope.

● CATHODE-RAY TUBES

The heart of the oscilloscope is the **cathode-ray tube,** a vacuum tube in which the electrons emitted from a hot cathode are first accelerated to give them considerable velocity, then formed into a beam, and finally allowed to strike a special translucent screen which *fluoresces,* or gives off light at the point where the beam strikes. A beam of moving electrons can be moved laterally, or **deflected,** by electric or magnetic fields, and since its weight and inertia are negligibly small, it can be made to follow instantly the variations in periodically changing fields at both audio and radio frequencies.

The electrode arrangement that forms the electrons into a beam is called the **electron gun.**

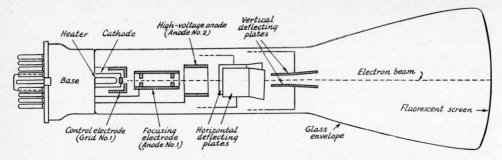

Fig. 21-52—Typical construction for a cathode-ray tube of the electrostatic-deflection type.

In the simple tube structure shown in Fig. 21-52, the gun consists of the cathode, grid, and anodes Nos. 1 and 2. The intensity of the electron beam is regulated by the grid in the same way as in an ordinary tube. Anode No. 1 is operated at a positive potential with respect to the cathode, thus accelerating the electrons that pass through the grid, and is provided with small apertures through which the electron stream passes. On emerging from the apertures the electrons are traveling in practically parallel straight-line paths. The electrostatic fields set up by the potentials on anode No. 1 and anode No. 2 form an **electron lens** system which makes the electron paths converge or focus to a point at the fluorescent screen. The potential on anode No. 2 is usually fixed, while that on anode No. 1 is varied to bring the beam into focus. Anode No. 1 is, therefore, called the **focusing electrode**.

Electrostatic deflection, the type generally used in the smaller tubes, is produced by **deflecting plates**. Two sets of plates are placed at right angles to each other, as indicated in Fig. 21-52. The fields are created by applying suitable voltages between the two plates of each pair. Usually one plate of each pair is connected to anode No. 2, to establish the polarities of the vertical and horizontal fields with respect to the beam and to each other.

Formation of Patterns

When periodically-varying voltages are applied to the two sets of deflecting plates, the path traced by the fluorescent spot forms a **pattern** that is stationary so long as the amplitude and phase relationships of the voltages remain unchanged. Fig. 21-53 shows how one such pattern is formed. The horizontal sweep voltage is assumed to have the "sawtooth" waveshape indicated. With no voltage applied to the vertical plates the trace simply sweeps from left to right across the screen along the horizontal axis $X–X'$ until the instant H is reached, when it reverses direction and snaps back to the starting point. The sine-wave voltage applied to the vertical plates similarly would trace a line along the axis $Y–Y'$ in the absence of any deflecting voltage on the horizontal plates. However, when both voltages are present the position of the spot at any instant depends upon the voltages on both sets of plates at that instant. Thus at time B the horizontal voltage has moved the spot a short distance to the right and the vertical voltage has similarly moved it upward, so that it reaches the actual position B' on the screen. The resulting trace is easily followed from the other indicated positions, which are taken at equal time intervals.

Types of Sweeps

A sawtooth sweep-voltage wave shape, such as is shown in Fig. 21-53, is called a **linear sweep**, because the deflection in the horizontal direction is directly proportional to time. If the sweep were perfect the **fly-back** time, or time taken for the spot to return from the end (H) to the beginning (I or A) of the horizontal trace, would be zero, so that the line HI would be perpendicular to the axis $Y–Y'$. Although the fly-back time cannot be made zero in practicable sweep-voltage generators it can be made quite small in comparison to the time of the desired trace AH, at least at most frequencies within the audio range. The line $H'I'$ is called the **return trace**; with a linear sweep it is less brilliant than the pattern, because the spot is moving much more rapidly during the fly-back time than during the time of the main trace.

The linear sweep shows the shape of the wave

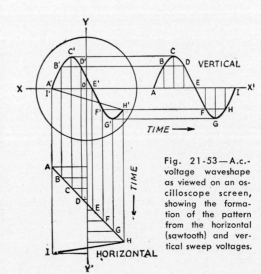

Fig. 21-53—A.c.-voltage waveshape as viewed on an oscilloscope screen, showing the formation of the pattern from the horizontal (sawtooth) and vertical sweep voltages.

Oscilloscopes

in the same way that it is usually represented graphically. If the period of the a.c. voltage applied to the vertical plates is considerably less than the time taken to sweep horizontally across the screen, several cycles of the vertical or "signal" voltage will appear in the pattern.

For many amateur purposes a satisfactory horizontal sweep is simply a 60-cycle voltage of adjustable amplitude. In modulation monitoring (described in the chapter on amplitude modulation) audio-frequency voltage can be taken from the modulator to supply the horizontal sweep. For examination of audio-frequency wave forms, the linear sweep is essential. Its frequency should be adjustable over the entire range of audio frequencies to be inspected on the oscilloscope.

Lissajous Figures

When sinusoidal a.c. voltages are applied to the two sets of deflecting plates in the oscilloscope the resultant pattern depends on the relative amplitudes, frequencies and phase of the two voltages. If the ratio between the two frequencies is constant and can be expressed in integers a stationary pattern will be produced. This makes it possible to use the oscilloscope for determining an unknown frequency, provided a variable frequency standard is available, or for determining calibration points for a variable-frequency oscillator if a few known frequencies are available for comparison.

The stationary patterns obtained in this way are called **Lissajous figures**. Examples of some of the simpler Lissajous figures are given in Fig. 21-54. The frequency ratio is found by counting the number of loops along two adjacent edges. Thus in the third figure from the top there are three loops along a horizontal edge and only one along the vertical, so the ratio of the vertical frequency to the horizontal frequency is 3 to 1. Similarly, in the fifth figure from the top there are four loops along the horizontal edge and three along the vertical edge, giving a ratio of 4 to 3. Assuming that the known frequency is applied to the horizontal plates, the unknown frequency is

$$f_2 = \frac{n_2}{n_1} f_1$$

where f_1 = known frequency applied to horizontal plates,

f_2 = unknown frequency applied to vertical plates,

n_1 = number of loops along a vertical edge, and

n_2 = number of loops along a horizontal edge.

An important application of Lissajous figures is in the calibration of audio-frequency signal generators. For very low frequencies the 60-cycle power-line frequency is held accurately enough to be used as a standard in most localities. The medium audio-frequency range can be covered by comparison with the 440- and 600-cycle modulation on the WWV transmissions. An oscilloscope having both horizontal and vertical

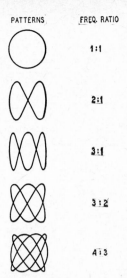

Fig. 21-54—Lissajous figures and corresponding frequency ratios for a 90-degree phase relationship between the voltages applied to the two sets of deflecting plates.

amplifiers is desirable, since it is convenient to have a means for adjusting the voltages applied to the deflection plates to secure a suitable pattern size. It is possible to calibrate over a 10-to-1 range, both upwards and downwards, from each of the latter frequencies and thus cover the audio range useful for voice communication.

Basic Oscilloscope Circuit

The essential oscilloscope circuit is shown in

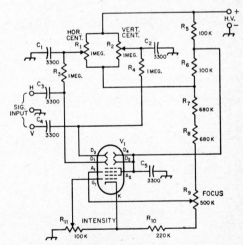

Fig. 21-55—Oscilloscope circuit for modulation monitoring. Constants are for 1500- to 2500-volt h.v. supply. For 1000-1500 volts, omit R_8 and connect the bottom end of R_7 to the top end of R_9.

C_1-C_5, inc.—3000-volt disk ceramic.
R_1, R_2, R_9, R_{11}—Volume-control type, linear taper.
R_3, R_4, R_5 R_6, R_{10}—½ watt.
R_7, R_8—1 watt.
V_1—Electrostatic-deflection cathode-ray tube, 2- to 5-inch. See tube tables for base connections and heater ratings of type chosen.

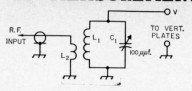

Fig. 21-55. The minimum requirements are supplying the various electrode potentials, plus controls for focusing and centering the spot on the face of the tube and adjusting the spot intensity. The circuit of Fig. 21-55 can be used with electrostatic-deflection tubes from two to five inches in face diameter, with voltages up to 2500. This includes practically all the types popular for small oscilloscopes.

The circuit has provision for introducing signal voltages to the two sets of deflecting plates. Either set of deflecting electrodes (D_1D_2, or D_3D_4) may be used for either horizontal or vertical deflection, depending on how the tube is mounted.

The high voltage may be taken from a transmitter power supply if desired. The current is only a milliampere or so. The voltage preferably should be constant, such as is obtained from a supply having a constant load — e.g., the supply for the Class C amplifier in an a.m. transmitter.

In the circuit of Fig. 21-55 the centering controls are at the full supply voltage above ground and therefore should be carefully insulated by being mounted on bakelite or similar material rather than directly on a metal panel or chassis. Insulated couplings or extension shafts should be used. The focussing control is also several hundred volts above ground and should be similarly insulated.

The tube should be protected from stray magnetic fields, either by enclosing it in an iron or steel box or by using one of the special c.r. tube shields available. If the heater transformer (or other transformer) is mounted in the same cabinet, care must be used to place it so the stray field around it does not deflect the spot. The spot cannot be focussed to a fine point when influenced by a transformer field.

Modulation Monitoring

The addition of Fig. 21-56 to the basic circuit of Fig. 21-55 provides all that is necessary for modulation checking. The r.f. from the transmitter is applied to the vertical plates through a tuned circuit L_1C_1 and link L_2. When adjusted to the transmitter operating frequency the tuned circuit furnishes ample deflection voltage even from a low-power transmitter, and C_1 can be used to control the pattern height.

Deflection voltage for the horizontal plates can be taken from the modulation transformer secondary of an a.m. transmitter, or 60-cycle deflection can be used to give a wave-envelope type pattern. In either case a maximum of about 200 volts r.m.s. will give full-width deflection. This voltage is almost independent of the size of c.r. tube used. Methods of using such a scope for modulation checking are described in the chapter on amplitude modulation.

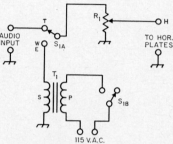

Fig. 21-56—Circuits for supplying r.f., audio, and a.c. voltages to oscilloscope deflection plates for modulation monitoring.

C_1—100-$\mu\mu$f. variable, receiving type.
L_1—1.75 Mc.: 30 enam. close-wound on 1-inch form, coil length ¾ inch.
    3.5-8 Mc.: 30 turns No. 22 enam., close-wound on 1-inch form.
    13-30 Mc.; 7 turns No. 22, spread to ¾ inch length on 1-inch form.
L_2—2 or more turns, as required for sufficient coupling, at cold end of L_1.
R_1—Volume control, 0.25 megohm or more.
S_1—D.p.d.t. switch.
T_1—Interstage audio transformer, any type. Use secondary-to-primary turns ratio of 1-to-1 to 2-to-1.

Frequency Limitations of Oscilloscopes

Most commercial or kitted oscilloscopes include vacuum-tube amplifiers between the input terminals and the deflection plates, to increase the sensitivity and usefulness of the instrument. Depending upon the construction of the amplifiers, their useful frequency range may be only as high as several hundred kc., although more expensive instruments will include amplifiers that work in the megacycle range. The operator should acquaint himself with the frequency limitations of the 'scope through study of the specifications, since attempts to pass, e.g., a 450-kc. i.f. signal through an amplifier that cuts off at 100 kc. are doomed to failure. No such frequency limits apply when the connection is made directly to the deflection plates, and consequently r.f. at 20 to 30 Mc. can be applied by the method shown in Fig. 21-56. A practical limitation will be found when r.f. from the vertical plates is (stray) capacitively coupled to the horizontal-deflection plates; this will show as a thickening of the trace. In some instances it can be reduced by r.f. bypassing of the horizontal deflection plates.

CHAPTER 22

Assembling a Station

The actual location inside the house of the "shack" — the room where the transmitter and receiver are located — depends, of course, on the free space available for amateur activities. Fortunate indeed is the amateur with a separate room that he can reserve for his hobby, or the few who can have a special small building separate from the main house. However, most amateurs must share a room with other domestic activities, and amateur stations will be found tucked away in a corner of the living room, a bedroom, a large closet, or even under the kitchen stove! A spot in the cellar or the attic can almost be classed as a separate room, although it may lack the "finish" of a normal room.

Regardless of the location of the station, however, it should be designed for maximum operating convenience and safety. It is foolish to have the station arranged so that the throwing of several switches is required to go from "receive" to "transmit," just as it is silly to have the equipment arranged so that the operator is in an uncomfortable and cramped position during his operating hours. The reason for building the station as safe as possible is obvious, if you are interested in spending a number of years with your hobby!

● CONVENIENCE

The first consideration in any amateur station is the operating position, which includes the operator's table and chair and the pieces of equipment that are in constant use (the receiver, send-receive switch, and key or microphone). The table should be as large as possible, to allow sufficient room for the receiver or receivers, frequency-measuring equipment, monitoring equipment, control switches, and keys and microphones, with enough space left over for the logbook, a pad and pencil, and perhaps a *large* ash tray. Suitable space should be included for radiogram blanks and a call book, if these accessories are in frequent use. If the table is small, or the number of pieces of equipment is large, it is often necessary to build a shelf or rack for the auxiliary equipment, or to mount it in some less convenient location in or under the table. If one has the facilities, a semicircular "console" can be built of wood, or a simpler solution is to use two small wooden cabinets to support a table top of wood or Masonite. A flush-type door will make an excellent table top. Home-built tables or consoles can be finished in any of the available oil stains, varnishes, paints or lacquers. Many operators use a large piece of plate glass over part of their table, since it furnishes a good writing surface and can cover miscellaneous charts and tables, prefix lists, operating aids, calendar, and similar accessories.

If the major interests never require frequent band changing, or frequency changing within a band, the transmitter can be located some distance from the operator, in a location where the meters can be observed from time to time (and the color of the tube plates noted!). If frequent band or frequency changes are a part

Here's one way to build a console. Use a 4-foot × 4-foot × ½-inch piece of plywood for a center section, and a couple of 3-drawer chests for the end sections. This gives plenty of operating space in a small area. (W5KSE, El Paso, Texas)

of the usual operating procedure, the transmitter should be mounted close to the operator, either along one side or above the receiver, so that the controls are easily accessible without the need for leaving the operating position.

A compromise arrangement would place the v.f.o. or crystal-switched oscillator at the operating position and the transmitter in some convenient location not adjacent to the operator. Since it is usually possible to operate over a portion of a band without retuning the transmitter stages, an operating position of this type is an advantage over one in which the operator must leave his position to make a change in frequency.

Controls

The operator has an excellent chance to exercise his ingenuity in the location of the operating controls. The most important controls in the station are the receiver tuning dial and the send-receive switch. The receiver tuning dial should be located four to eight inches above the operating table, and if this requires mounting the receiver off the table, a small shelf or bracket will do the trick. With the single exception of the amateur whose work is almost entirely in traffic or rag-chew nets, which require little or no attention to the receiver, it will be found that the operator's hand is on the receiver tuning dial most of the time. If the tuning knob is too high or too low, the hand gets cramped after an extended period of operating, hence the importance of a properly located receiver. The majority of c.w. operators tune with the left hand, preferring to leave the right hand free for copying messages and handling the key, and so the receiver should be mounted where the knob can be reached by the left hand. Phone operators aren't tied down this way, and tune the communications receiver with the hand that is more convenient.

The hand key should be fastened securely to the table, in a line just outside the right shoulder and far enough back from the front edge of the table so that the elbow can rest on the table. A good location for the semiautomatic or "bug" key is right next to the hand-key, although some operators prefer to mount the automatic key in front of them on the left, so that the right forearm rests on the table parallel to the front edge.

The best location for the microphone is directly in front of the operator, so that he doesn't have to shout across the table into it, or run up the speech-amplifier gain so high that all manner of external sounds are picked up. If the microphone is supported by a boom or by a flexible "goose neck," it can be placed in front of the operator without its base taking up valuable table space.

In any amateur station worthy of the name, it should be necessary to throw no more than one switch to go from the "receive" to the "transmit" condition. In phone stations, this switch should be located where it can be easily reached by the hand that isn't on the receiver. In the case of c.w. operation, this switch is most conveniently located to the right or left of the key, although some operators prefer to have it mounted on the left-hand side of the operating position and work it with the left hand while the right hand is on the key. Either location is satisfactory, of course, and the choice depends upon personal preference. Some operators use a foot-controlled switch, which is a convenience but doesn't allow too much freedom of position during long operating periods.

If the microphone is hand-held during phone operation, a "push-to-talk" switch on the microphone is convenient, but hand-held

Here's a console that was designed with operating convenience in mind. W7EBG built it almost entirely out of ¾" plywood, with strips of 2 × 2 along the bottom edges for caster supports. It is assembled with bolts so that it can be readily dismantled for shipping. Over-all dimensions are 48" wide, 40½" high, with the horizontal desk top 16" wide and the sloping portion 15" wide.

Controls

microphones tie up the use of one hand and are not too desirable, although they are widely used in mobile and portable work.

The location of other switches, such as those used to control power supplies, filaments, phone/c.w. change-over and the like, is of no particular importance, and they can be located on the unit with which they are associated. This is not strictly true in the case of the phone/c.w. DX man, who sometimes has need to change in a hurry from c.w. to phone. In this case, the change-over switch should be at the operating table, although the actual change-over should be done by a relay controlled by the switch.

If a rotary beam is used the control of the beam should be convenient to the operator. The direction indicator, however, can be located anywhere within sight of the operator, and does not have to be located on the operating table unless it is included with the control.

Frequency Spotting

In a station where a v.f.o. is used, or where a number of crystals are available, the operator should be able to turn on only the oscillator of his transmitter, so that he can spot accurately his location in the band with respect to other stations. This allows him to see if he has anything like a clear channel, or to see what his frequency is with respect to another station. Such a provision can be part of the "send-receive" switch. Switches are available with a center "off" position, a "hold" position on one side, for turning on the oscillator only, and a "lock" position on the other side for turning on the transmitter and antenna relays. If oscillator keying is used, the key serves the same purpose, provided a "send-receive" switch is available to turn off the high-voltage supplies and prevent a signal going out on the air during adjustment of the oscillator frequency.

For phone operation, the telegraph key or an auxiliary switch can control the transmitter oscillator, and the "send-receive" switch can then be wired into the control system so as to control the oscillator as well as the other circuits.

Comfort

Of prime importance is the comfort of the operator. If you find yourself getting tired after a short period of operating, examine your station to find what causes the fatigue. It may be that the chair is too soft or hasn't a straight back or is the wrong height for you. The key or receiver may be located so that you assume an uncomfortable position while using them. If you get sleepy fast, the ventilation may be at fault. (Or you may need sleep!)

● POWER CONNECTIONS AND CONTROL

Following a few simple rules in wiring your power supplies and control circuits will make it an easy job to change units in the station. If the station is planned in this way from the start, or if the rules are recalled when you are rebuilding, you will find it a simple matter to revise your station from time to time without a major rewiring job.

It is neater and safer to run a single pair of wires from the outlet over to the operating table or some central point, rather than to use a number of adapters at the wall outlet.

Interconnections

The wiring of any station will entail two or three common circuits, as shown in Fig. 22-3. The circuit for the receiver, monitoring equipment and the like, assuming it to be taken from a wall outlet, should be run from the wall to an inconspicuous point on the operating table, where it terminates in a multiple outlet large enough to handle the required number of plugs. A single switch between the wall outlet and the receptacle will then turn on all of this equipment at one time.

The second common circuit in the station is that supplying voltage to rectifier- and transmitter-tube filaments, bias supplies, and anything else that is not switched on and off during transmit and receive periods. The coil power for control relays should also be obtained from this circuit. The power for this circuit can come from a wall outlet or from the transmitter line, if a special one is used.

The third circuit is the one that furnishes power to the plate-supply transformers for the r.f. stages and for the modulator. (See section on Power Supplies for high-power considerations.) When it is opened, the transmitter is disabled except for the filaments, and the transmitter should be safe to work on. However, one always feels safer when working on the transmitter if he has turned off every power source.

With these three circuits established, it becomes a simple matter to arrange the station for different conditions and with new units. Anything on the operating table that runs all the time ties into the first circuit. Any new power supply or r.f. unit gets its filament power from the second circuit. Since the third circuit is controlled by the send-receive switch (or relay), any power-supply primary that is to be switched on and off for send and receive connects to circuit C.

Break-In and Push-To-Talk

In c.w. operation, "break-in" is any system that allows the transmitting operator to hear the other station's signal during the "key-up" periods between characters and letters. This allows the sending station to be "broken" by the receiving station at any time, to shorten calls, ask for "fills" in messages, and speed up operation in general. With present techniques, it requires the use of a separate receiving antenna or a "t.r. box" and, with high power, some means for protecting the receiver from the transmitter when the key is "down." Several methods, applicable to high-power stations, are described in Chapter Eight. If the transmitter is low-powered (50 watts or so), no special equipment is required except the separate receiving antenna and a receiver that "recovers" fast. Where break-in operation is used, there should be a switch on the operating table to turn off the plate supplies when adjusting the oscillator to a new frequency, although during all break-in work this switch will be closed.

"Push-to-talk" is an expression derived from the "push" switch on some microphones, and it means a phone station with a single control for all change-over functions. Strictly speaking, it should apply only to a station where this single send-receive switch must be held in place during transmission periods, but any fast-acting switch will give practically the same effect. A control switch with a center "off" position, and one "hold" and one "lock" position, will give more flexibility than a straight "push" switch. The one switch must control the transmitter power supplies, the receiver "on-off" circuit and, if one is used, the antenna change-over relay. The receiver control is necessary to disable its output during transmit periods, to avoid acoustic feedback.

Switches and Relays

It is dangerous to use an overloaded switch in the power circuits. After it has been used for some time, it may fail, leaving the power on the circuit even after the switch is thrown to the "off" position. For this reason, large switches, or relays with adequate ratings, should be used to control the plate power. Relays are rated by coil voltages (for their control circuits) and by their contact current and voltage ratings. Any switch or relay for the power-control circuits of an amateur station should be conservatively rated; overloading a switch or relay is very poor economy. Switches rated at 20 amperes at 125 volts will handle the switching of circuits at the kilowatt level, but the small toggle switches rated 3 amperes at 125 volts should be used only in circuits up to about 150 watts.

When relays are used, the send-receive switch closes the circuit to their coils, thus closing the relay contacts. The relay contacts are in the power circuit being controlled, and thus the switch handles only the relay-coil current. As a consequence, this switch can have a low current rating.

● SAFETY

Of prime importance in the layout of the station is the personal safety of the operator and of visitors, invited or otherwise, during normal operating practice. If there are small children in the house, every step must be taken to prevent their accidental contact with power leads of any voltage. A locked room is a fine idea, if it is possible, otherwise housing the transmitter and power supplies in metal cabinets is an excellent, although expensive, solution. Lacking a metal cabinet, a wooden cabinet or a wooden framework covered with wire screen is the next-best solution. Many stations have the power supplies housed in metal cabinets in the operating room or in a closet or basement, and this cabinet or entry is kept locked — with the key out of reach of everyone but the operator. The power leads are run through conduit to the transmitter, using ignition cable for the high-voltage leads. If the power supplies and transmitter are in the same cabinet, a lock-type main switch for the incoming line power is a good precaution.

A simple substitute for a lock-type main switch is an ordinary line plug with a short connecting wire between the two pins. By wiring a female receptacle in series with the main power line in the transmitter, the shorting plug will act as the main safety lock. When the plug is removed and hidden, it will be impossible to energize the transmitter, and a stranger or child isn't likely to spot or suspect the open receptacle.

An essential adjunct to any station is a **shorting stick** for discharging any high voltage to ground before any work is done in the transmitter. Even if interlocks and power-supply bleeders are used, the failure of one or more of these components may leave the transmitter in a dangerous condi-

This neat "built-in" installation features separate finals and exciters for each band, along with room for receiver, frequency meter, oscilloscope, Q multiplier and v.h.f. converter. All units are mounted on the three large panels; the panels are hinged at the bottom so that they can be lowered for service work on the individual units. A common power supply is used, and band-changing consists of turning on the filaments in the desired r.f. section. (W9OVO, Sturgeon Bay, Wisc.)

tion. The shorting stick is made by mounting a small metal hook, of wire or rod, on one end of a dry stick or bakelite rod. A piece of ignition cable or other well-insulated wire is then run from the hook on the stick to the chassis or common ground of the transmitter, and the stick is hung alongside the transmitter. Whenever the power is turned off in the transmitter to permit work on the rig, the shorting stick is first used to touch the several high-voltage leads (plate r.f. choke, filter capacitor, tube plate connection, etc.) to insure that there is no high voltage at any of these points. This simple device has saved many a life. Use it!

Fusing

A minor hazard in the amateur station is the possibility of fire through the failure of a component. If the failure is complete and the component is large, the house fuses will generally blow. However, it is unwise and inconvenient to depend upon the house fuses to protect the lines running to the radio equipment, and every power supply should have its primary circuit individually fused, at about 150 to 200 per cent of the maximum rating of the supply. Circuit breakers can be used instead of fuses if desired.

Wiring

Control-circuit wires running between the operating position and a transmitter in another part of the room should be hidden, if possible. This can be done by running the wires under the floor or behind the base molding, bringing the wires out to terminal boxes or regular wall fixtures. Such construction, however, is generally only possible in elaborate installations, and the average amateur must content himself with trying to make the wires as inconspicuous as possible. If several pairs of leads must be run from the operating table to the transmitter, as is generally the case, a single piece of rubber- or

vinyl-covered multiconductor cable will always look neater than several pieces of rubber-covered lamp cord, and it is much easier to sweep around or dust.

The antenna wires always present a problem, unless coaxial-line feed is used. Open-wire line from the point of entry of the antenna line should always be arranged neatly, and it is generally best to support it at several points. Many operators prefer to mount any antenna-tuning assemblies right at the point of entry of the feedline, together with an antenna changeover relay (if one is used), and then the link from the tuning assembly to the transmitter can be made of inconspicuous coaxial line. If the transmitter is mounted near the point of entry of the line, it simplifies the problem of "What to do with the feeders?"

Lightning Protection

The antenna system usually associated with amateur radio equipment is most vulnerable to lightning due to its height and length. To validate one's insurance, the antenna installation must comply with the National Board of Fire Underwriters Electrical Code which says:

> *Lightning Arresters — Transmitting Stations.* Except where protected by a continuous metallic shield (coax) which is permanently and effectively grounded, or the antenna is permanently and effectively grounded, each conductor of a lead-in for outdoor antenna shall be provided with a lightning arrester or other suitable means which will drain static charges from the antenna system.

If coaxial line is used, compliance with the above is readily achieved by grounding the shield of the coax at the point where it is nearest to the ground outside the house. Use a heavy wire — the aluminum wire sold for grounding TV antennas is good. If the cable can be run underground, a grounding stake should be located at the point where the cable enters the ground, at the an-

A neat operating bench can be built from wood and covered with linoleum. There is enough room on the table shown here to house the transmitter, receiver, and numerous adjuncts and accessories. Interconnecting wiring is run behind the units or underneath the table. (W3AQN, York, Pa.)

tenna end. The grounding stake, to be effective in soils of average conductivity, should be not less than 10 feet long and, if possible, plated with a metal that will not corrode in the local soil. Making connection to the outside of the outer conductor of the coaxial line will normally have no effect on the s.w.r. in the line, and consequently it can be done at any point or points.

Open-wire or Twin-Lead transmission lines can be protected by installing a spark gap such as the one sketched in Fig. 22-1. The center contact should be grounded with a No. 4 or larger wire. The gaps can be made from $\frac{1}{8} \times \frac{1}{2}$-inch flat brass rod shaped as shown, and the gaps should be set sufficiently far apart to prevent flash-over during normal operation of the transmitter. Depending upon the power of the transmitter and the s.w.r. pattern on the line, the gap may run anything from 1/32 to 3/16 inch. It may spark intermittently when a thunderstorm is building up or is in the general area.

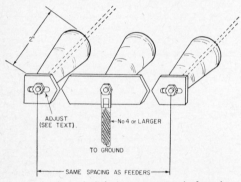

Fig. 22-1—A simple lightning arrester made from three stand-off or feed-through insulators and sections of brass or copper strap. It should be installed in the open-wire or Twin-Lead line at the point where it is nearest the ground outside the house. The heavy ground lead should be as short and direct as possible.

Rotary beams using a T or gamma match and with each element connected to the boom will usually be grounded through the supporting metal tower. If the antenna is mounted on a wooden pole or on the top of the house, a No. 4

or larger wire should be connected from the beam to the ground by the shortest and most direct route possible, using insulators where the wire comes close to the building. From a lightning-protection standpoint, it is desirable to run the coaxial and control lines from a beam down a metal tower and underground to the shack. If the tower is well grounded and the antenna is higher than any surrounding objects, the combination will serve well as a lightning rod.

The sole purpose of lightning rods or grounded roofs is to protect a building in case a lightning stroke occurs; there is no accepted evidence that any form of protection can prevent a stroke.*

Experiments have indicated that a high vertical conductor will generally divert to itself direct hits that might otherwise fall within a cone-shaped space of which the apex is the top of the conductor and the base a circle of radius approximately two times the height of the conductor. Thus a radio mast may afford some protection to low adjacent structures, but only when low-impedance grounds are provided.

Underwriters' Code

The National Electrical Safety Code, Pamphlet 70, Standard of the National Board of Fire Underwriters, deals with electric wiring and apparatus. The Code was set up to protect persons and buildings from the electrical hazards arising from the use of electricity, radio, etc. Article 810 is entitled "Radio Equipment." The scope of this article, section 8101, says, "The article applies to radio and television receiving equipment and to amateur radio transmitting equipment, but not to the equipment used in carrier-current operation."

The Board of Fire Underwriters sets up the code as a minimum standard for good practice. Most cities adopt the code, or parts of it, either entirely or with certain amendments which may apply to that particular city. It is up to the city to enforce these rules. When a violation is reported, periodic checks are made by an inspector until a correction is made and to insure

* See "Code for Protection Against Lightning," *National Bureau of Standards Handbook 46*, for sale by the Superintendent of Documents, Washington 25, D. C.

In this station arrangement, eight small panels near the front of the table carry the auxiliary gear. From left to right: (1) loud speaker with selector switch to receivers or monitor; (2) conelrad receiver and automatic transmitter disabler; (3) Monimatch; (4) antenna selector switch; (5) intercom to other rooms in house; (6) station control switch; (7) beam rotator control; (8) transmission timer and monitor. All eight accessory units are completely enclosed in perforated aluminum and are plug in. (K9HGJ, Milwaukee, Wisc.)

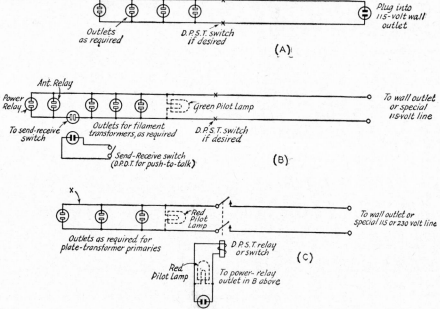

Fig. 22-2—Power circuits for a high-power station. A shows the outlets for the receiver, monitoring equipment, speech amplifier and the like. The outlets should be mounted inconspicuously on the operating table. B shows the transmitter filament circuits and control-relay circuits, if the latter are used. C shows the plate-transformer primary circuits, controlled by the power relay. Where 230- and 115-volt primaries are controlled simultaneously, point "X" should connect to the "neutral" or common. A heavy-duty switch can be used instead of the relay, in which case the antenna relay would be connected in circuit C. If 115-volt pilot lamps are used, they can be connected as shown. Lower-voltage lamps must be connected across suitable windings on transformers. With "push-to-talk" operation, the "send-receive" switch can be a d.p.d.t. affair, with the second pole controlling the "on-off" circuit of the receiver.

against future recurrence. The National Electric Code is only a minimum standard, and compliance with its rules will assure less operating failures and hazards, and greater safety.

The pamphlet is available by writing the National Board of Fire Underwriters at 85 John Street, New York 38, N. Y. Ask for No. 70.

Parts of the Underwriters' Code deal with power wiring and, in addition to the requirement of the use of Underwriters Laboratory approved materials and fittings, have the following to say of direct interest to amateurs:

"All switches shall indicate clearly whether they are open or closed.

"All (switch) handles throughout a system . . . shall have uniform open and closed positions.

". . . supply circuits shall not be designed to use the grounds normally as the sole conductor for *any part* of the circuit."

The latter means that wire conductor should be used for all parts of the power circuit. Dependence should not be placed on water pipes, etc., as one side of a circuit.

CHAPTER 23

BCI and TVI

Every amateur has the obligation to make sure that the operation of his station does not, because of any shortcomings in equipment, cause interference with other radio services. It is unfortunately true that much of the interference that amateurs cause to broadcast and television reception is directly the fault of BC and TV receiver construction. Nevertheless, the amateur can and should help to alleviate interference even though the responsibility for it does not lie with him.

Successful handling of interference cases requires winning the listener's cooperation. Here are a few pointers on how to go about it.

Clean House First

The first step obviously is to make sure that the transmitter has no radiations outside the bands assigned for amateur use. The best check on this is your own a.m. or TV receiver. It is always convincing if you can demonstrate that you do not interfere with reception in your own home.

Don't Hide Your Identity

Whenever you make equipment changes — or shift to a hitherto unused band or type of emission — that might be expected to change the interference situation, check with your neighbors. If no one is experiencing interference, so much the better; it does no harm to keep the neighborhood aware of the fact that you are operating without bothering anyone.

Should you change location, announce your presence and conduct occasional tests on the air, requesting anyone whose reception is being spoiled to let you know about it so steps may be taken to eliminate the trouble.

Act Promptly

The average person will tolerate a limited amount of interference, but the sooner you take steps to eliminate it, the more agreeable the listener will be; the longer he has to wait for you, the less willing he will be to cooperate.

Present Your Story Tactfully

When you interfere, it is natural for the complainant to assume that your transmitter is at fault. If you are certain that the trouble is not in your transmitter, explain to the listener that the reason lies in the receiver design, and that some modifications may have to be made in the receiver if he is to expect interference-free reception.

Arrange for Tests

Most listeners are not very competent observers of the various aspects of interference. If at all possible, enlist the help of another amateur and have him operate your transmitter while you see for yourself what happens at the affected receiver.

In General

In this "public relations" phase of the problem a great deal depends on your own attitude. Most people will be willing to meet you half way, particularly when the interference is not of long standing, if you as a person make a good impression. Your personal appearance is important. So is what you say about the receiver — no one takes kindly to hearing his possessions derided. If you discuss your interference problems on the air, do it in a constructive way — one calculated to increase listener cooperation, not destroy it.

Interference With Standard Broadcasting

Interference with a.m. broadcasting usually falls into one or more rather well-defined categories. An understanding of the general types of interference will avoid much cut-and-try in finding a cure.

Transmitter Defects

Out-of-band radiation is something that must be cured at the transmitter. Parasitic oscillations are a frequently unsuspected source of such radiations, and no transmitter can be considered satisfactory until it has been thoroughly checked for both low- and high-frequency parasitics. Very often parasitics show up only as transients, causing key clicks in c.w. transmitters and "splashes" or "burps" on modulation peaks in a.m. transmitters. Methods for detecting and eliminating parasitics are discussed in the transmitter chapter.

In c.w. transmitters the sharp make and break that occurs with unfiltered keying causes transients that, in theory, contain frequency components through the entire radio spectrum. Practically, they are often strong enough in the immediate vicinity of the transmitter to cause serious interference to broadcast reception. Key clicks can be eliminated by the methods detailed in the chapter on keying.

A distinction must be made between clicks generated in the transmitter itself and those set up by the mere opening and closing of the key contacts when current is flowing. The latter are of the same nature as the clicks heard in a receiver when a wall switch is thrown to turn a light on or off, and may be more troublesome nearby than the clicks that actually go out on the signal. A filter for eliminating them usually has to be installed as close as possible to the key contacts.

Overmodulation in a.m. phone transmitters generates transients similar to key clicks. It can be prevented either by using automatic systems for limiting the modulation to 100 per cent, or by continuously monitoring the modulation. Methods for both are described in the chapter on amplitude modulation.

BCI is frequently made worse by radiation from the power wiring or the r.f. transmission line. This is because the signal causing the interference, in such cases, is radiated from wiring that is nearer the broadcast receiver than the antenna itself. Much depends on the method used to couple the transmitter to the antenna, a subject that is discussed in the chapters on transmission lines and antennas. If it is at all possible the antenna itself should be placed so that it is not in close proximity to house wiring, telephone and power lines, and similar conductors.

Image and Oscillator-Harmonic Responses

Most present-day broadcast receivers use a built-in loop antenna as the grid circuit for the mixer stage. The selectivity is not especially high at the signal frequency. Furthermore, an appreciable amount of signal pick-up usually occurs on the a.c. line to which the receiver is connected, the signal so picked up being fed to the mixer grid by stray means.

As a result, strong signals from nearby transmitters, even though the transmitting frequency is far removed from the broadcast band, can force themselves to the mixer grid. They will normally be eliminated by the i.f. selectivity, except in cases where the transmitter frequency is the image of the broadcast signal to which the receiver is tuned, or when the transmitter frequency is so related to a harmonic of the broadcast receiver's local oscillator as to produce a beat at the intermediate frequency.

These image and oscillator-harmonic responses tune in and out on the broadcast receiver dial just like a broadcast signal, except that in the case of harmonic response the tuning rate is more rapid. Since most receivers use an intermediate frequency in the neighborhood of 455 kc., the interference is a true image only when the amateur transmitting frequency is in the 1800-kc. band. Oscillator-harmonic responses occur from 3.5- and 7-Mc. transmissions, and sometimes even from higher frequencies.

Since images and harmonic responses occur at definite frequencies on the receiver dial, it is possible to choose operating frequencies that will avoid putting such a response on top of the broadcast stations that are favored in the vicinity. While your signal may still be heard when the receiver is tuned off the local stations, it will at least not interfere with program reception.

There is little that can be done to most receivers to cure interference of this type except to reduce the amount of signal getting into the set through the a.c. line. A line filter such as is shown in Fig. 23-1 often will help accomplish this. The values used for the coils and capacitors are in general not critical. The effectiveness of the filter may depend considerably on the ground connection used, and it is advisable to use a short ground lead to a cold-water pipe if at all possible. The line cord from the set should be bunched up, to minimize the possibility of pick-up on the cord. It may be necessary to install the filter inside the receiver, so that the filter is connected between the line cord and the set wiring, in order to get satisfactory operation.

Cross-Modulation

With phone transmitters, there are occasionally cases where the voice is heard whenever the broadcast receiver is tuned to a BC station, but there is no interference when tuning between stations. This is cross-modulation, a result of rectification in one of the early stages of the receiver. Receivers that are susceptible to this trouble usually also get a similar type of interference from regular broadcasting if there is a strong local BC station and the receiver is tuned to some *other* station.

The remedy for cross-modulation in the receiver is the same as for images and oscillator-harmonic response—reduce the strength of the amateur signal at the receiver by means of a line filter.

The trouble is not always in the receiver, since cross modulation can occur in any nearby rectifying circuit — such as a poor contact in water or steam piping, gutter pipes, and other conductors in the strong field of the transmitting antenna — external to both receiver and transmitter. Locating the cause may be difficult, and is best attempted with a battery-operated portable broadcast receiver used as a "probe" to find the spot where the interference is most intense. When such a spot is located, inspection of the metal structures in the vicinity should indicate the cause. The remedy is to make a good electrical bond between the two conductors having the poor contact.

Audio-Circuit Rectification

The most frequent cause of interference from operation at 21 Mc. and higher frequencies is rectification of a signal that by some means gets into the audio system of the receiver. In the milder cases an amplitude-modulated signal will be heard with reasonably good quality, but is not tunable — that is, it is present no matter what the frequency to which the receiver dial is set. An unmodulated carrier may have no observable effect in such cases beyond causing a little hum. However, if the signal is very strong there will be a reduction of the audio output level of the receiver whenever the carrier is thrown on. This causes an annoying "jumping" of the program when the interfering signal is keyed. With phone transmission the change in audio level is not so objectionable because it occurs at less frequent intervals. Rectification ordinarily gives no audio output from a frequency-modulated signal, so the interference can be made almost unnoticeable if f.m. or p.m. is used instead of a.m.

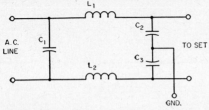

Fig. 23-1—"Brute-force" a.c. line filter for receivers. The values of C_1, C_2 and C_3 are not generally critical; capacitances from 0.001 to 0.01 μf. can be used. L_1 and L_2 can be a 2-inch winding of No. 18 enameled wire on a half-inch diameter form. In making up such a unit for use external to the receiver, make sure that there are no exposed conductors to offer a shock hazard.

Interference of this type usually results from a signal on the power line being coupled by some means into the audio circuits, although the pickup also may occur on the set wiring itself. A "brute-force" line filter as described above may or may not be completely effective, but in any event is the simplest thing to try. If it does not do the job, some modification of the receiver will be necessary. This usually takes the form of a simple filter connected in the grid circuit of the tube in which the rectification is occurring. Usually it will be the first audio amplifier, which in most receivers is a diode-triode type tube.

Filter circuits that have proved to be effective are shown in Fig. 23-2. In A, the value of the grid leak in the combined detector/first audio tube is reduced to 2 to 3 megohms and the grid is bypassed to chassis by a 250-$\mu\mu$f. mica or ceramic capacitor. A somewhat similar method that does not require changing the grid resistor is shown at B. In C, a 75,000-ohm (value not critical) resistor is connected between the grid pin on the tube socket and all other grid connections. In combination with the input capacitance of the tube this forms a low-pass filter to prevent r.f. from reaching the grid. In some cases, simply bypassing the heater of the detector/first audio tube to chassis with a 0.001-μf. or larger capacitor will suffice. In all cases, check to see that the a.c. line is bypassed to chassis; if it is not, install bypass capacitors (0.001 to 0.01 μf.).

Handling BCI Cases

Assuming that your transmitter has been checked and found to be free from spurious radiations, get another amateur to operate your station, if possible, while you make the actual check on the interference yourself. The following procedure should be used.

Tune the receiver through the broadcast band, to see whether the interference tunes like a regular BC station. If so, image or oscillator-harmonic response is the cause. If there is interference only when a BC station is tuned in, but not between stations, the cause is cross modulation. If the interference is heard at all settings of the tuning dial, the trouble is pickup in the audio circuits. In the latter case, the receiver's volume control may or may not affect the strength of the interference, depending on the means by which your signal is being rectified.

Having identified the cause, explain it to the set owner. It is a good idea to have a line filter with you, equipped with enough cord to replace the set's line cord, so it can be tried then and there. If it does not eliminate the interference, explain to the set owner that there is nothing further that can be done without modifying the receiver. Recommend that the work be done by a competent service technician, and offer to advise the service man on the cause and remedy. Don't offer to work on the set yourself, but if you are asked to do so use your own judgment about complying; set owners sometimes complain about the over-all performance of the receiver afterward, often without justification. If you work on it, take it to your station so the effect of the changes you make can be observed, and return the receiver promptly when you have finished.

● MISCELLANEOUS TYPES OF INTERFERENCE

The operation of amateur phone transmitters occasionally results in interference on telephone lines and in audio amplifiers used in public-address work and for home music reproduction. The cause is rectification of the signal in an audio circuit.

Telephone Interference

Telephone interference can be cured by connecting a bypass capacitor (about 0.001 μf.) across the microphone unit in the telephone handset. The telephone companies have capacitors for this purpose. When such a case occurs, get in touch with the repair department of the phone company, giving all the particulars. Do not attempt to work on the telephone yourself.

Hi-Fi and P. A. Systems

In interference to public-address and "hi-fi" installations the principal sources of signal pick-up are the a.c. line or a line from the power amplifier to a speaker. All amplifier units should be bonded together and connected to a good ground such as a cold-water pipe. Make sure that the a.c. line is

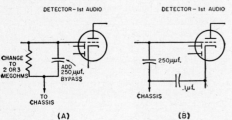

(A)　　　　(B)

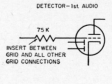

(C)

Fig. 23-2—Methods of eliminating r.f. from the grid of a combined detector/first-audio stage. At A, the value of the grid leak is reduced to 2 or 3 megohms, and a bypass capacitor is added. At B, both grid and cathode are bypassed.

V.H.F. Television

bypassed to chassis in each unit with capacitors of about 0.01 μf. at the point where the line enters the chassis. The speaker line similarly should be bypassed to the amplifier chassis with about 0.001 μf.

If these measures do not suffice, the shielding on the amplifiers may be inadequate. A shield cover and bottom pan should be installed in such cases.

The spot in the system where the rectification is occurring often can be localized by seeing if the interference is affected by the volume control setting; if not, the cause is in a stage following the volume control.

Television Interference *(See also Chap. 17)*

Interference with the reception of television signals usually presents a more difficult problem than interference with a.m. broadcasting. In BCI cases the interference almost always can be attributed to deficient selectivity or spurious responses in the BC receiver. While similar deficiencies exist in many television receivers, it is also true that amateur transmitters generate harmonics that fall inside many or all television channels. These spurious radiations cause interference that ordinarily cannot be eliminated by anything that may be done at the receiver, so must be prevented at the transmitter itself.

The over-all situation is further complicated by the fact that television broadcasting is in three distinct bands, two in the v.h.f. region and one in the u.h.f.

V.H.F. Television

For the amateur who does most of his transmitting on frequencies below 30 Mc. the TV band of principal interest is the low v.h.f. band between 54 and 88 Mc. If harmonic radiation can be reduced to the point where no interference is caused to Channels 2 to 6, inclusive, it is almost certain that any harmonic troubles with channels above 174 Mc. will disappear also.

The relationship between the v.h.f. television channels and harmonics of amateur bands from 14 through 28 Mc. is shown in Fig. 23-3. Harmonics of the 7- and 3.5-Mc. bands are not shown because they fall in every television channel. However, the harmonics above 54 Mc. from these bands are of such high order that they are usually rather low in amplitude, although they may be strong enough to interfere if the television receiver is quite close to the amateur transmitter.

Low-order harmonics — up to about the sixth — are usually the most difficult to eliminate.

Of the amateur v.h.f. bands, only 50 Mc. will have harmonics falling in a v.h.f. television channel (channels 11, 12 and 13). However, a transmitter for any amateur v.h.f. band may cause interference if it has multiplier stages either operating in or having harmonics in one or more of the v.h.f. TV channels. The r.f. energy on such frequencies can be radiated directly from the transmitting circuits or coupled by stray means to the transmitting antenna.

Frequency Effects

The degree to which transmitter harmonics or other undesired radiation actually in the TV channel must be suppressed depends principally on two factors, the strength of the TV sig-

nal on the channel or channels affected, and the relationship between the frequency of the spurious radiation and the frequencies of the TV picture and sound carriers within the channel. If the TV signal is very strong, interference can be eliminated by comparatively simple methods. However, if the TV signal is very weak, as in "fringe" areas where the received picture is visibly degraded by the appearance of set noise or "snow" on the screen, it may be necessary to go to extreme measures.

In either case the intensity of the interference depends very greatly on the exact frequency of the interfering signal. Fig. 23-4 shows the placement of the picture and sound carriers in the standard TV channel. In Channel 2, for example, the picture carrier frequency is $54 + 1.25 = 55.25$ Mc. and the sound carrier frequency is

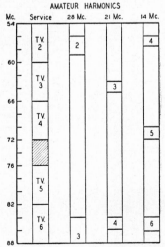

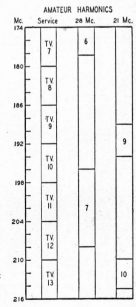

Fig. 23-3—Relationship of amateur-band harmonics to v.h.f. TV channels. Harmonic interference from transmitters operating below 30 Mc. is most likely to be serious in the low-channel group (54 to 88 Mc.).

549

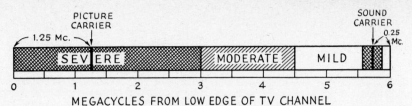

PICTURE CARRIER

SOUND CARRIER

SEVERE MODERATE MILD

MEGACYCLES FROM LOW EDGE OF TV CHANNEL

Fig. 23-4—Location of picture and sound carriers in a monochrome television channel, and relative intensity of interference as the location of the interfering signal within the channel is varied without changing its strength. The three regions are not actually sharply defined as shown in this drawing, but merge into one another gradually.

$60 - 0.25 = 59.75$ Mc. The second harmonic of 28,010 kc. (56,020 kc. or 56.02 Mc.) falls $56.02 - 54 = 2.02$ Mc. above the low edge of the channel and is in the region marked "Severe" in Fig. 23-4. On the other hand, the second harmonic of 29,500 kc. (59,000 kc. or 59 Mc.) is $59 - 54 = 5$ Mc. from the low edge of the channel and falls in the region marked "Mild." Interference at this frequency has to be about 100 times as strong as at 56,020 kc. to cause effects of equal intensity. Thus an operating frequency that puts a harmonic near the picture carrier requires about 40 db. more harmonic suppression in order to avoid interference, as compared with an operating frequency that puts the harmonic near the upper edge of the channel.

For a region of 100 kc. or so either side of the sound carrier there is another "Severe" region where a spurious radiation will interfere with reception of the sound program, and this region also should be avoided. In general, a signal of intensity equal to that of the picture carrier will not cause noticeable interference if its frequency is in the "Mild" region shown in Fig. 23-4, but the same intensity in the "Severe" region will utterly destroy the picture.

Interference Patterns

The visible effects of interference vary with the type and intensity of the interference. Complete "blackout," where the picture and sound disappear completely, leaving the screen dark, occurs only when the transmitter and receiver are quite close together. Strong interference ordinarily causes the picture to be broken up, leaving a jumble of light and dark lines, or turns the picture "negative" — the normally white parts of the picture turn black and the normally black

parts turn white. "Cross-hatching" — diagonal bars or lines in the picture — accompanies the latter, usually, and also represents the most common type of less-severe interference. The bars are the result of the beat between the harmonic frequency and the picture carrier frequency. They are broad and relatively few in number if the beat frequency is comparatively low — near the picture carrier — and are numerous and very fine if the beat frequency is very high — toward the upper end of the channel. Typical cross-hatching is shown in Fig. 23-5. If the frequency falls in the "Mild" region in Fig. 23-4 the cross-hatching may be so fine as to be visible only on close inspection of the picture, in which case it may simply cause the apparent brightness of the screen to change when the transmitter carrier is thrown on and off.

Whether or not cross-hatching is visible, an amplitude-modulated transmitter may cause

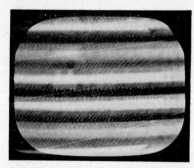

Fig. 23-6—"Sound bars" or "modulation bars" accompanying amplitude modulation of an interfering signal. In this case the interfering carrier is strong enough to destroy the picture, but in mild cases the picture is visible through the horizontal bars. Sound bars may accompany modulation even though the unmodulated carrier gives no visible cross-hatching.

"sound bars" in the picture. These look about as shown in Fig. 23-6. They result from the variations in the intensity of the interfering signal when modulated. Under most circumstances modulation bars will not occur if the amateur transmitter is frequency- or phase-modulated. With these types of modulation the cross-hatching will "wiggle" from side to side with the modulation.

Except in the more severe cases, there is seldom any effect on the sound reception when interference shows in the picture, unless the frequency is quite close to the sound carrier. In the latter

Fig. 23-5—"Cross-hatching," caused by the beat between the picture carrier and an interfering signal inside the TV channel.

Reducing Harmonic Generation

event the sound may be interfered with even though the picture is clean.

Reference to Fig. 23-3 will show whether or not harmonics of the frequency in use will fall in any television channels that can be received in the locality. It should be kept in mind that not only harmonics of the final frequency may interfere, but also harmonics of any frequencies that may be present in buffer or frequency-multiplier stages. In the case of 144-Mc. transmitters, frequency-multiplying combinations that require a doubler or tripler stage to operate on a frequency actually in a low-band v.h.f. channel in use in the locality should be avoided.

Harmonic Suppression

Effective harmonic suppression has three separate phases:

1) Reducing the amplitude of harmonics generated in the transmitter. This is a matter of circuit design and operating conditions.

2) Preventing stray radiation from the transmitter and from associated wiring. This requires adequate shielding and filtering of all circuits and leads from which radiation can take place.

3) Preventing harmonics from being fed into the antenna.

It is impossible to build a transmitter that will not generate *some* harmonics, but it is obviously advantageous to reduce their strength, by circuit design and choice of operating conditions, by as large a factor as possible before attempting to prevent them from being radiated. Harmonic radiation from the transmitter itself or from its associated wiring obviously will cause interference just as readily as radiation from the antenna, so measures taken to prevent harmonics from reaching the antenna will not reduce TVI if the transmitter itself is radiating harmonics. But once it has been found that the transmitter itself is free from harmonic radiation, devices for preventing harmonics from reaching the antenna can be expected to produce results.

● REDUCING HARMONIC GENERATION

Since reasonably efficient operation of r.f. power amplifiers always is accompanied by harmonic generation, good judgment calls for operating all frequency-multiplier stages at a very low power level — plate voltages not exceeding 250 or 300. When the final output frequency is reached, it is desirable to use as few stages as possible in building up to the final output power level, and to use tubes that require a minimum of driving power.

Circuit Design and Layout

Harmonic currents of considerable amplitude flow in both the grid and plate circuits of r.f. power amplifiers, but they will do relatively little harm if they can be effectively bypassed to the cathode of the tube. Fig. 23-7 shows the paths followed by harmonic currents in an amplifier circuit; because of the high reactance of the tank coil there is little harmonic current in it, so the harmonic currents simply flow through the tank capacitor, the plate (or grid) blocking capacitor, and the tube capacitances. The lengths of the leads forming these paths is of great importance, since the inductance in this circuit will resonate with the tube capacitance at some frequency in the v.h.f. range (the tank and blocking capacitances usually are so large compared with the tube capacitance that they have little effect on the resonant frequency). If such a resonance happens to occur at or near the same frequency as one of the transmitter harmonics, the effect is just the same as though a harmonic tank circuit had been deliberately introduced; the harmonic at that frequency will be tremendously increased in amplitude.

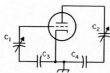

Fig. 23-7—A v.h.f. resonant circuit is formed by the tube capacitance and the leads through the tank and blocking capacitors. Regular tank coils are not shown, since they have little effect on such resonances. C_1 is the grid tuning capacitor and C_2 is the plate tuning capacitor. C_3 and C_4 are the grid and plate blocking or bypass capacitors, respectively.

Such resonances are unavoidable, but by keeping the path from plate to cathode and from grid to cathode as short as is physically possible, the resonant frequency usually can be raised above 100 Mc. in amplifiers of medium power. This puts it between the two groups of television channels.

It is easier to place grid-circuit v.h.f. resonances where they will do no harm when the amplifier is link-coupled to the driver stage, since this generally permits shorter leads and more favorable conditions for bypassing the harmonics than is the case with capacitive coupling. Link coupling also reduces the coupling between the driver and amplifier at harmonic frequencies, thus preventing driver harmonics from being amplified.

The inductance of leads from the tube to the tank capacitor can be reduced not only by shortening but by using flat strip instead of wire conductors. It is also better to use the chassis as the return from the blocking capacitor or tuned circuit to cathode, since a chassis path will have less inductance than almost any other form of connection.

The v.h.f. resonance points in amplifier tank circuits can be found by coupling a grid-dip meter covering the 50–250 Mc. range to the grid and plate leads. If a resonance is found in or near a TV channel, methods such as those described above should be used to move it well out of the TV range. The grid-dip meter also should be used to check for v.h.f. resonances in the tank coils, because coils made for 14 Mc. and below usually will show such resonances. In making the check, disconnect the coil entirely from the transmitter and move the grid-dip meter coil along it while exploring for a dip in the 54–88 Mc. band. If a resonance falls in a TV channel that is in use in the locality, changing the number of turns will move it to a less-troublesome frequency.

Operating Conditions

Grid bias and grid current have an important effect on the harmonic content of the r.f. currents in both the grid and plate circuits. In general, harmonic output increases as the grid bias and grid current are increased, but this is not necessarily true of a *particular* harmonic. The third and higher harmonics, especially, will go through fluctuations in amplitude as the grid current is increased, and sometimes a rather high value of grid current will minimize one harmonic as compared with a low value. This characteristic can be used to advantage where a particular harmonic is causing interference, remembering that the operating conditions that minimize one harmonic may greatly increase another.

For equal operating conditions, there is little or no difference between single-ended and push-pull amplifiers in respect to harmonic generation. Push-pull amplifiers are frequently trouble-makers on even harmonics because with such amplifiers the even-harmonic voltages are in phase at the ends of the tank circuit and hence appear with equal amplitude across the whole tank coil, if the center of the coil is not grounded. Under such circumstances the even harmonics can be coupled to the output circuit through stray capacitance between the tank and coupling coils. This does not occur in a single-ended amplifier having an inductively coupled tank, if the coupling coil is placed at the cold end, or with a pi-network tank.

Harmonic Traps

If a harmonic in only one TV channel is particularly bothersome — frequently the case when the transmitter operates on 28 Mc. — a trap tuned to the harmonic frequency may be installed in the plate lead as shown in Fig. 23-8. At the harmonic frequency the trap represents a very high impedance and hence reduces the amplitude of the harmonic current flowing through the tank circuit. In the push-pull circuit both traps have the same constants. The L/C ratio is not critical but a high-C circuit usually will have least effect on the performance of the plate circuit at the normal operating frequency.

Since there is a considerable harmonic voltage across the trap, radiation may occur from the trap unless the transmitter is well shielded. Traps should be placed so that there is no coupling between them and the amplifier tank circuit.

A trap is a highly selective device and so is useful only over a small range of frequencies. A second- or third-harmonic trap on a 28-Mc. tank circuit usually will not be effective over more than 50 kc. or so at the fundamental frequency, depending on how serious the interference is without the trap. Because they are critical of adjustment, it is better to prevent TVI by other means, if possible, and use traps only as a last resort.

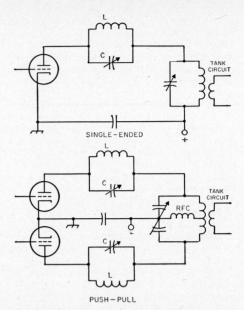

Fig. 23-8—Harmonic traps in an amplifier plate circuit. L and C should resonate at the frequency of the harmonic to be suppressed. C may be a 25- to 50-$\mu\mu$f. midget, and L usually consists of 3 to 6 turns about $\frac{1}{2}$ inch in diameter for Channels 2 through 6. The inductance should be adjusted so that the trap resonates at about half capacitance of C before being installed in the transmitter. The frequency may be checked with a grid-dip meter. When in place, the trap should be adjusted for minimum interference to the TV picture.

● PREVENTING RADIATION FROM THE TRANSMITTER

The extent to which interference will be caused by direct radiation of spurious signals depends on the operating frequency, the transmitter power level, the strength of the television signal, and the distance between the transmitter and TV receiver. Transmitter radiation can be a very serious problem if the TV signal is weak, if the TV receiver and amateur transmitter are close together, and if the transmitter is operated with high power.

Shielding

Direct radiation from the transmitter circuits and components can be prevented by proper shielding. To be effective, a shield must completely enclose the circuits and parts and must have no openings that will permit r.f. energy to escape. Unfortunately, ordinary metal boxes and cabinets do not provide good shielding, since such openings as louvers, lids, and holes for running in connections allow far too much leakage.

A primary requisite for good shielding is that all joints must make a good electrical connection along their entire length. A small slit or crack will let out a surprising amount of r.f. energy; so will ventilating louvers and large holes such as those used for mounting meters. On the other hand, small holes do not impair the shielding very greatly, and a limited number of ventilating

Preventing Radiation

holes may be used if they are small — not over ¼ inch in diameter. Also, wire screen makes quite effective shielding if the wires make good electrical connection at each crossover. Perforated aluminum such as the "do-it-yourself" sold at hardware stores also is good, although not very strong mechanically. If perforated material is used, choose the variety with the smallest openings. The leakage through large openings can be very much reduced by covering such openings with screening or perforated aluminum, well bonded to all edges of the opening.

The intensity of r.f. fields about coils, capacitors, tubes and wiring decreases very rapidly with distance, so shielding is more effective, from a practical standpoint, if the components and wiring are not too close to it. It is advisable to have a separation of several inches, if possible, between "hot" points in the circuit and the nearest shielding.

For a given thickness of metal, the greater the conductivity the better the shielding. Copper is best, with aluminum, brass and steel following in that order. However, if the thickness is adequate for structural purposes (over 0.02 inch) and the shield and a "hot" point in the circuit are not in close proximity, any of these metals will be satisfactory. Greater separation should be used with steel shielding than with the other materials not only because it is considerably poorer as a shield but also because it will cause greater losses in near-by circuits than would copper or aluminum at the same distance. Wire screen or perforated metal used as a shield should also be kept at some distance from high-voltage or high-current r.f. points, since there is considerably more leakage through the mesh than through solid metal.

Where two pieces of metal join, as in forming a corner, they should overlap at least a half inch and be fastened together firmly with screws or bolts spaced at close-enough intervals to maintain firm contact all along the joint. The contact surfaces should be clean before joining, and should be checked occasionally — especially steel, which is almost certain to rust after a period of time.

The leakage through a given size of aperture in shielding increases with frequency, so such points as good continuous contact, screening of large holes, and so on, become even more important when the radiation to be suppressed is in the high band — 174–216 Mc. Hence 50- and 144-Mc. transmitters, which in general will have frequency-multiplier harmonics of relatively high intensity in this region, require special attention in this respect if the possibility of interfering with a channel received locally exists.

Lead Treatment

Even very good shielding can be made completely useless when connections are run to external power supplies and other equipment from the circuits inside the shield. Every such conductor leaving the shielding forms a path for the escape of r.f., which is then radiated by the connecting wires. Hence a step that is essential in every case is to prevent harmonic currents from flowing on the leads leaving the shielded enclosure.

Harmonic currents always flow on the d.c. or a.c. leads connecting to the tube circuits. A very effective means of preventing such currents from being coupled into other wiring, and one that provides desirable bypassing as well, is to use shielded wire for all such leads, maintaining the shielding from the point where the lead connects to the tube or r.f. circuit right through to the point where it leaves the chassis. The shield braid should be grounded to the chassis at both ends and at frequent intervals along the path.

Good bypassing of shielded leads also is essential. Bearing in mind that the shield braid about the conductor confines the harmonic currents to the *inside* of the shielded wire, the object of bypassing is to prevent their escape. Figs. 23-9 and 23-10 show the proper way to bypass. The small-type 0.001-μf. ceramic disk capacitor, when mounted on the end of the shielded wire as shown in Fig. 23-9, actually forms a series-resonant circuit in the 54-88-Mc. range and thus represents practically a short-circuit for low-band TV harmonics. The exposed wire to the connection terminal should be kept as short as is physically possible, to prevent any possible harmonic pickup exterior to the shielded wiring. Disk capacitors of this capacitance are available in several voltage ratings up to 3000 volts. For higher voltages, the maximum capacitance available is approximately 500 μμf., which is large enough for good bypassing of harmonics. Alternatively, mica capacitors may be used as shown in Fig. 23-10, mounting the capacitor flat against the chassis and grounding the end of the shield braid directly to chassis, keeping the exposed part as short as possible. Either 0.001-μf. or 470-μμf. (500 μμf.) capacitors should be used. The larger capacitance is series-resonant in Channel 2 and the smaller in Channel 6.

Fig. 23-9—Proper method of bypassing the end of a shielded lead using disk ceramic capacitor. The 0.001-μf. size should be used for 1600 volts or less; 500 μμf. at higher voltages. The leads are wrapped around the inner and outer conductors and soldered, so that the lead length is negligible. This photograph is about four times actual size.

Fig. 23-10—Bypassing with a mica capacitor the end of a high-voltage lead. The end of the shield braid is soldered to a lug fastened to the chassis directly underneath. The other terminal of the capacitor is similarly bolted directly to the chassis. When the bypass is used at a terminal connection block the "hot" lead should be soldered directly to the terminal, if possible, but in any event connected to it by a very short lead.

These bypasses are essential at the connection-block terminals, and desirable at the tube ends of the leads also. Installed as shown with shielded wiring, they have been found to be so effective that there is usually no need for further harmonic filtering. However, if a test shows that additional filtering is required, the arrangement shown in Fig. 23-11 may be used. Such an r.f. filter should be installed at the tube end of the shielded lead, and if more than one circuit is filtered care should be taken to keep the r.f. chokes separated from each other and so oriented as to minimize coupling between them. This is necessary for preventing harmonics present in one circuit from being coupled into another.

In difficult cases involving Channels 7 to 13 — i.e., close proximity between the transmitter and receiver, and a weak TV signal — additional lead-filtering measures may be needed to prevent radiation of interfering signals by 50- and 144-Mc. transmitters. A recommended method is shown in Fig. 23-12. It uses a shielded lead bypassed with a ceramic disk as described above, with the addition of a low-inductance feed-through type capacitor and a small r.f. choke, the capacitor being used as a terminal for the external connection. For voltages above 400, a capacitor of compact construction (as indicated in the caption) should be used, mounted so that there is a very minimum of exposed lead, inside the chassis, from the capacitor to the connection terminal.

As an alternative to the series-resonant bypassing described above, feed-through type capacitors such as the Sprague "Hypass" type may

be used as terminals for external connections. The ideal method of installation is to mount them so they protrude through the chassis, with thorough bonding to the chassis all around the hole in which the capacitor is mounted. The principle is illustrated in Fig. 23-13.

Meters that are mounted in an r.f. unit should be enclosed in shielding covers, the connections being made with shielded wire with each lead bypassed as described above. The shield braid should be grounded to the panel or chassis immediately outside the meter shield, as indicated in Fig. 23-14. A bypass may also be connected across the meter terminals, principally to prevent any fundamental current that may be present from flowing through the meter itself. As an alternative to individual meter shielding the meters may be mounted entirely behind the panel, and the panel holes needed for observation may be covered with wire screen that is carefully bonded to the panel all around the hole.

Care should be used in the selection of shielded wire for transmitter use. Not only should the insulation be conservatively rated for the d.c. volt-

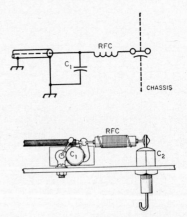

Fig. 23-12—Additional lead filtering for harmonics or other spurious frequencies in the high v.h.f. TV band (174-216 Mc.).

C_1—0.001-μf. disk ceramic.

C_2—0.001-μf. feed-through bypass (Erie Style 326). (For 500-2000-volt lead, substitute Plasticon Glass mike, LSG-251, for C_2.)

RFC—14 inches No. 26 enamel close-wound on 3/16-inch diam. form or resistor.

age in use, but the insulation should be of material that will not easily deteriorate in soldering. The r.f. characteristics of the wire are not especially important, except that the attenuation of harmonics in the wire itself will be greater if the

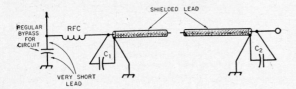

Fig. 23-11—Additional r.f. filtering of supply leads may be required in regions where the TV signal is very weak. The r.f. choke should be physically small, and may consist of a 1-inch winding of No. 26 enameled wire on a 1/4-inch form, close-wound. Manufactured single-layer chokes having an inductance of a few microhenrys also may be used.

Preventing Radiation

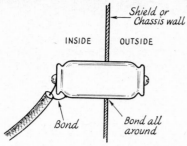

Fig. 23-13—The best method of using the "Bypass" type feed-through capacitor. Capacitances of 0.01 to 0.1 μf. are satisfactory. Capacitors of this type are useful for high-current circuits, such as filament and 115-volt leads, as a substitute for the r.f. choke shown in Fig. 23-11, in cases where additional lead filtering is needed.

insulating material has high losses at radio frequencies: in other words, wire intended for use at d.c. and low frequencies is preferable to cables designed expressly for carrying r.f. The attenuation also will increase with the length of the wire; in general, it is better to make the leads as long as circumstances permit rather than to follow the more usual practice of using no more lead than is actually necessary. Where wires cross or run parallel, the shields should be spot-soldered together and connected to the chassis. For high voltages, automobile ignition cable covered with shielding braid is recommended.

Proper shielding of the transmitter requires that the r.f. circuits be shielded entirely from the external connecting leads. A situation such as is shown in Fig. 23-15, where the leads in the r.f. chassis have been shielded and properly filtered but the chassis is mounted in a large shield, simply invites the harmonic currents to travel over the chassis and on out over the leads *outside* the chassis. The shielding about the r.f. circuits should make complete contact with the chassis

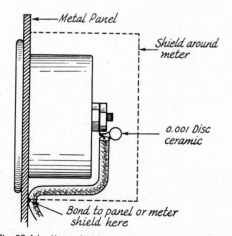

Fig. 23-14—Meter shielding and bypassing. It is essential to shield the meter mounting hole since the meter will carry r.f. through it to be radiated. Suitable shields can be made from 2½- or 3-inch diameter metal cans or small metal chassis boxes.

on which the parts are mounted.

Checking Transmitter Radiation

A check for transmitter radiation always should be made before attempting to use low-pass filters or other devices for preventing harmonics from reaching the antenna system. The only really satisfactory indicating instrument is a television receiver. In regions where the TV signal is strong an indicating wavemeter such as one having a crystal or tube detector may be useful; if it is possible to get any indication at all from harmonics either on supply leads or around the transmitter itself, the harmonics are probably strong enough to cause interference. However, the absence of any such indication does not mean that harmonic interference will not be caused. If the techniques of shielding and lead filtering described in the

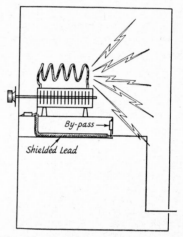

Fig. 23-15—A metal cabinet can be an adequate shield, but there will still be radiation if the leads inside can pick up r.f. from the transmitting circuits.

preceding section are followed, the harmonic intensity on any external leads should be far below what any such instruments can detect.

Radiation checks should be made with the transmitter delivering full power into a dummy antenna, such as an incandescent lamp of suitable power rating, preferably installed inside the shielded enclosure. If the dummy must be external, it is desirable to connect it through a coax-matching circuit such as is shown in Fig. 23-16. Shielding the dummy antenna circuit is also desirable, although it is not always necessary.

Make the radiation test on all frequencies that are to be used in transmitting, and note whether or not interference patterns show in the received picture. (These tests must be made while a TV signal is being received, since the beat patterns will not be formed if the TV picture carrier is not present.) If interference exists, its source can be detected by grasping the various external leads (by the insulation, not the live wire!) or bringing the hand near meter faces, louvers, and other possible points where harmonic energy might escape

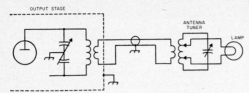

Fig. 23-16—Dummy-antenna circuit for checking harmonic radiation from the transmitter and leads. The matching circuit helps prevent harmonics in the output of the transmitter from flowing back over the transmitter itself, which may occur if the lamp load is simply connected to the output coil of the final amplifier. See transmission-line chapter for details of the matching circuit. Tuning must be adjusted by cut-and-try, as the bridge method described in the transmission-line chapter will not work with lamp loads because of the change in resistance when the lamps are hot.

from the transmitter. If any of these tests cause a *change* — not necessarily an *increase* — in the intensity of the interference, the presence of harmonics at that point is indicated. The location of such "hot" spots usually will point the way to the remedy. If the TV receiver and the transmitter can be operated side-by-side, a length of wire connected to one antenna terminal on the receiver can be used as a probe to go over the transmitter enclosure and external leads. This device will very quickly expose the spots from which serious leakage is taking place.

As a final test, connect the transmitting antenna or its transmission line terminals to the outside of the transmitter shielding. Interference created when this test is applied indicates that weak currents are on the outside of the shield and can be conducted to the antenna when the normal antenna connections are used. Currents of this nature represent interference that can be conducted *over* low-pass filters, etc., and which therefore cannot be eliminated by such filters.

● PREVENTING HARMONICS FROM REACHING THE ANTENNA

The third and last step in reducing harmonic TVI is to keep the spurious energy generated in or passed through the final stage from traveling over the transmission line to the antenna. It is seldom worthwhile even to attempt this until the radiation from the transmitter and its connecting leads has been reduced to the point where, with the transmitter delivering full power into a dummy antenna, it has been determined by actual testing with a television receiver that the radiation is below the level that can cause interference. If the dummy antenna test shows enough radiation to be seen in a TV picture, it is a practical certainty that harmonics will be coupled to the antenna system no matter what preventive measures are taken.

In inductively coupled output systems, some harmonic energy will be transferred from the final amplifier through the mutual inductance between the tank coil and the output coupling coil. Harmonics of the output frequency transferred in this way can be greatly reduced by providing

sufficient selectivity between the final tank and the transmission line. A good deal of selectivity, amounting to 20 to 30 db. reduction of the second harmonic and much higher reduction of higher-order harmonics, is furnished by a matching circuit of the type shown in Fig. 23-16 and described in the chapter on transmission lines. An "antenna coupler" is therefore a worthwhile addition to the transmitter.

In 50- and 144-Mc. transmitters, particularly, harmonics not directly associated with the output frequency — such as those generated in low-frequency early stages of the transmitter — may get coupled to the antenna by stray means. For example, a 144-Mc. transmitter might have an oscillator or frequency multiplier at 48 Mc., followed by a tripler to 144 Mc. Some of the 48-Mc. energy will appear in the plate circuit of the tripler, and if passed on to the grid of the final amplifier will appear as a 48-Mc. modulation on the 144-Mc. signal. This will cause a spurious signal at 192 Mc., which is in the high TV band, and the selectivity of the tank circuits may not be sufficient to prevent its being coupled to the antenna. Spurious signals of this type can be reduced by using link coupling between the driver stage and final amplifier (and between earlier stages as well) in addition to the suppression afforded by using an antenna coupler.

Capacitive Coupling

The upper drawing in Fig. 23-17 shows a parallel-conductor link as it might be used to couple into a parallel-conductor line through a matching circuit. Inasmuch as a coil is a sizable metallic object, there is capacitance between the final tank coil and its associated link coil, and between the matching-circuit coil and its link. Energy coupled through these capacitances travels over the link circuit and the transmission line as though these were merely single conductors. The tuned circuits simply act as masses of metal and offer no selectivity at all for capacitively-coupled energy. Although the actual capacitances are small, they offer a good coupling medium for frequencies in the v.h.f. range.

Capacitive coupling can be reduced by coupling

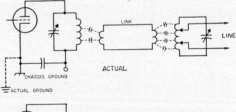

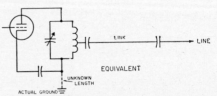

Fig. 23-17—The stray capacitive coupling between coils in the upper circuit leads to the equivalent circuit shown below, for v.h.f. harmonics.

Keeping Harmonics From the Antenna

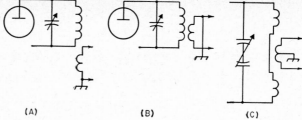

Fig. 23-18—Methods of coupling and grounding link circuits to reduce capacitive coupling between the tank and link coils. Where the link is wound over one end of the tank coil the side toward the hot end of the tank should be grounded, as shown at B.

(A)   (B)   (C)

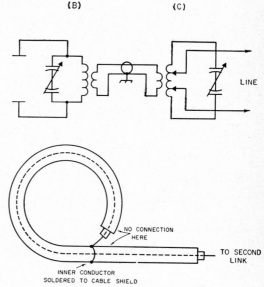

to a "cold" point on the tank coil — the end connected to ground or cathode in a single-ended stage. In push-pull circuits having a split-stator capacitor with the rotor grounded for r.f., all parts of the tank coil are "hot" at even harmonics, but the center of the coil is "cold" at the fundamental and odd harmonics. If the center of the tank coil, rather than the rotor of the tank capacitor, is grounded through a bypass capacitor the center of the coil is "cold" at all frequencies, but this arrangement is not very desirable because it causes the harmonic currents to flow through the coil rather than the tank capacitor and this increases the harmonic transfer by pure inductive coupling.

With either single-ended or balanced tank circuits the coupling coil should be grounded to the chassis by a short, direct connection as shown in Fig. 23-18. If the coil feeds a balanced line or link, it is preferable to ground its center, but if it feeds a coax line or link one side may be grounded. Coaxial output is much preferable to balanced output, because the harmonics have to stay *inside* a properly installed coax system and tend to be attenuated by the cable before reaching the antenna coupler.

At high frequencies — and possibly as low as 14 Mc. — capacitive coupling can be greatly reduced by using a shielded coupling coil as shown in Fig. 23-19. The inner conductor of a length of coaxial cable is used to form a one-turn coupling coil. The outer conductor serves as an open-circuited shield around the turn, the shield being grounded to the chassis. The shielding has no effect on the inductive coupling. Because this construction is suitable only for one turn, the coil is not well adapted for use on the lower frequencies where many turns are required for good coupling. Shielded coupling coils having a larger number of turns are available commercially. A shielded coil is particularly useful with push-pull amplifiers when the suppression of even harmonics is important.

A shielded coupling coil or coaxial output will not prevent stray capacitive coupling to the antenna if harmonic currents can flow over the *outside* of the coax line. In Fig. 23-20, the arrangement at either A or C will allow r.f. to flow over the outside of the cable to the antenna system. The proper way to use coaxial cable is to shield the transmitter completely, as shown at B, and make sure that the outer conductor of the cable is a continuation of the transmitter shielding. This prevents r.f. inside the transmitter from getting out by any path except the *inside* of the cable. Harmonics flowing *through* a coax line can be stopped from reaching the antenna system by an

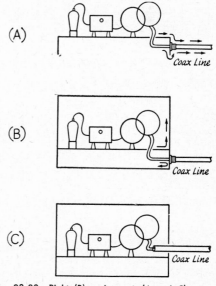

LINE

NO CONNECTION HERE

TO SECOND LINK

INNER CONDUCTOR SOLDERED TO CABLE SHIELD

Fig. 23-19—Shielded coupling coil constructed from coaxial cable. The smaller sizes of cable such as RG-59/U are most convenient when the coil diameter is 3 inches or less, because of greater flexibility. For larger coils RG-8/U or RG-11/U can be used.

(A)   Coax Line

(B)   Coax Line

(C)   Coax Line

Fig. 23-20—Right (B) and wrong (A and C) ways to connect a coaxial line to the transmitter. In A or C, harmonic energy coupled by stray capacitance to the outside of the cable will flow without hindrance to the antenna system. In B the energy cannot leave the shield and can flow out only through, not over, the cable.

antenna coupler or by a low-pass filter installed in the line.

Low-Pass Filters

A low-pass filter properly installed in a coaxial line, feeding either a matching circuit (antenna coupler) or feeding the antenna directly, will provide very great attenuation of harmonics. When the main transmission line is of the parallel-conductor type, the coax-coupled matching-circuit arrangement is highly recommended as a means for using a coax low-pass filter.

A properly designed low-pass filter will not introduce appreciable power loss at the fundamental frequency if the coaxial line in which it is inserted is terminated so that the s.w.r. is low. (The s.w.r. can easily be measured by means of a simple bridge as described in the chapters on measurements and transmission lines.) Such a filter has the property of passing without loss all frequencies below its "cut-off" frequency, but simultaneously has large attenuation for all frequencies above the cut-off frequency.

Low-pass filters of simple and inexpensive construction for use with transmitters operating below 30 Mc. are shown in Figs. 23-21 and 23-23. The former is designed to use mica capacitors of readily available capacitance values, for compactness and low cost. Both use the same circuit, Fig. 23-22, the only difference being in the L and C values. Technically, they are three-section filters having two full constant-k sections and two m-derived terminating half-sections, and their attenuation in the 54–88-Mc. range varies from over 50 to nearly 70 db., depending on the frequency and the particular set of values used. Above 174 Mc. the theoretical attenuation is better than 85 db., but will depend somewhat

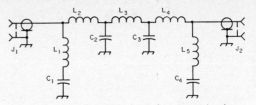

Fig. 23-22—Low-pass filter circuit for attenuating harmonics in the TV bands. J_1 and J_2 are chassis-type coaxial connectors. In the table below the letters refer to the following:

A—Using 100- and 70-$\mu\mu$f. 500-volt silver mica capacitors in parallel for C_2 and C_3.

B—Using 70- and 50-$\mu\mu$f. silver mica capacitors in parallel for C_2 and C_3.

C—Using 100- and 50-$\mu\mu$f. mica capacitors, 1200-volt (case-style CM-45) in parallel for C_2 and C_3.

D and E—Using variable air capacitors, 500- to 1000-volt rating, adjusted to values given (see measurements chapter for data on measuring capacitance).

	A	B	C	D	E	
Z_0	52	75	52	52	75	ohms
f_c	36	35.5	41	40	40	Mc.
f_∞	44.4	47	54	50	50	Mc.
f_1	25.5	25.2	29	28.3	28.3	Mc.
f_2	32.5	31.8	37.5	36.1	36.1	Mc.
C_1, C_4	50	40	50	46	32	$\mu\mu$f.
C_2, C_3	170	120	150	154	106	$\mu\mu$f.
L_1, L_5	5½	6	4	5	6½	turns*
L_2, L_4	8	11[1]	7	7	9½	turns*
L_3	9	13	8	8½	11½	turns*

*No. 12 or No. 14 wire, ½-inch inside diameter, 8 turns per inch.

[1] A 9-turn coil with closer turn spacing to give the same inductance is shown in Fig. 23-21.

on internal resonant conditions associated principally with the lead lengths to the capacitors. These leads should be kept as short as is physically possible.

The power that filters using mica capacitors can handle safely is determined by the voltage and current limitations of the capacitors. The power capacity is least at the highest frequency. The unit using postage-stamp silver mica capacitors is capable of handling approximately 50 watts in the 28-Mc. band, when working into a properly-matched line, but is good for about 150 watts at 21 Mc. and 300 watts at 14 Mc. and lower frequencies. A filter with larger mica capacitors (case type CM-45) will carry about 250 watts safely at 28 Mc., this rating increasing to 500 watts at 21 Mc. and a kilowatt at 14 Mc. and lower. If there is an appreciable mismatch between the filter and the line which it works, these ratings will be considerably decreased, so in order to avoid capacitor failure it is highly essential that the line on the output side of the filter be carefully matched by its load. This can be done with an s.w.r. bridge,

Fig. 23-21—An inexpensive low-pass filter using silver-mica postage-stamp capacitors. The box is a 2 by 4 by 6 aluminum chassis. Aluminum shields, bent and folded at the sides and bottom for fastening to the chassis, form shields between the filter sections. The diagonal arrangement of the shields provides extra room for the coils and makes it easier to fit the shields in the box, since bending to exact dimensions is not essential. The bottom plate, made from sheet aluminum, extends a half inch beyond the ends of the chassis and is provided with mounting holes in the extensions. It is held on the chassis with sheet-metal screws.

Low-Pass Filters

Fig. 23-23—Low-pass filter using variable air capacitors. The box is a 2 by 5 by 7 aluminum chassis, fitted with a bottom plate of similar construction to the one used in Fig. 23-21.

install L_2 and L_4 and adjust L_2 to make the circuit formed by L_1, L_2, C_1 and C_2 (without the short across J_1) resonate at f_2 as given in the table. Do the same with L_4 for the circuit formed by L_4, L_5, C_3 and C_4. Then replace L_3 and check with the grid-dip meter at any coil in the filter; a distinct resonance should be found at or very close to the cut-off frequency, f_c. The filter is then ready for use.

The filter constants suggested at D and E in Fig. 23-22 are based on the optimum design for good impedance characteristics — that is, with $m = 0.6$ in the end sections — and a cut-off frequency below the standard i.f. for television receivers (sound carrier at 41.25 Mc.; picture carrier at 45.75 Mc.). This is to avoid possible harmonic interference from 21 Mc. and below to the receiver's intermediate amplifier. The other designs similarly cut off at 41 Mc. or below, but m in these cases is necessarily based on the capacitances available in standard fixed capacitors.

Filters for 50- and 144-Mc. Transmitters

Since a low-pass filter must have a cut-off frequency above the frequency on which the transmitter operates, a filter for a v.h.f. transmitter cannot be designed for attenuation in all television channels. This is no handicap for v.h.f. work but means that the filter will not be effective when used with lower-frequency transmitters, unless it happens that no TV channels in use in the locality fall inside the pass band of the filter.

Fig. 23-24 shows a filter for 52-ohm coax suitable for a 50-Mc. transmitter of any power up to the authorized limit. The circuit diagram is given in Fig. 23-25. If the values of inductance and capacitance can be measured (see chapter on measurements) the components can be preset and assembled without further adjustment. Alternatively, the grid-dip meter method described earlier may be used. The resonant frequencies are:

and the matching is easy to control if the line from the filter terminates in a matching circuit of the type described in the chapter on transmission lines.

The power capacity of these filters can be increased considerably by substituting r.f. type fixed capacitors (such as the Centralab 850 series) or variable air capacitors, in which event the power capability will be such as to handle the maximum amateur power on any band. The construction can be modified to accommodate variable air capacitors as shown in Fig. 23-23.

Using fixed capacitors of standard tolerances, there should be little difficulty in getting proper filter operation. A grid-dip meter with an accurate calibration should be used for adjustment of the coils. First, wire up the filter without L_2 and L_4. Short-circuit J_1 at its inside end with a screwdriver or similar conductor, couple the grid-dip meter to L_1 and adjust the inductance of L_1, by varying the turn spacing, until the circuit resonates at f_∞ as given in the table. Do the same thing at the other end of the filter with L_5. Then couple the meter to the circuit formed by L_3, C_2 and C_3, and adjust L_3 to resonate at the frequency f_1 as given by the table. Then remove L_3.

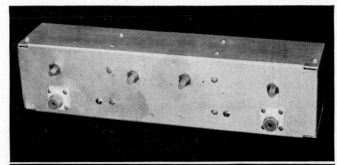

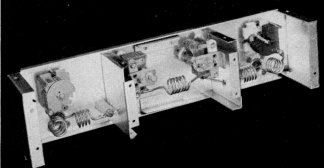

Fig. 23-24 — Low-pass filter fo use with 50-Mc. transmitters and 52-ohm line. It uses variable air capacitors adjusted to the proper capacitance values and is suited to powers up to a kilowatt.

$\left.\begin{array}{l} L_1C_1 \ (J_1 \text{ shorted, } L_3 \text{ disconnected}) \\ L_5C_4 \ (J_3 \text{ shorted, } L_4 \text{ disconnected}) \end{array}\right\}$ 81.5 Mc.

$L_3C_2C_3 \ (L_2 \text{ and } L_4 \text{ disconnected})$ 46 Mc.

$\left.\begin{array}{l} L_1L_2C_1C_2 \ (L_3 \text{ disconnected}) \\ L_4L_5C_3C_4 \ (L_3 \text{ disconnected}) \end{array}\right\}$ 58.5 Mc.

The cut-off frequency is approximately 65 Mc.

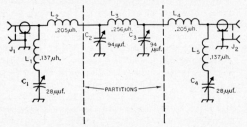

Fig. 23-25—Circuit diagram of the low-pass filters for 50- and 144-Mc. transmitters. Values on the drawing are for the 50-Mc. filter. Partitions are not used in the 144-Mc. unit.

C_1, C_4—50 Mc.; 50-$\mu\mu$f. variable, shaft-mounted, set to middle of tuning range (Johnson 50L15). 144 Mc.: 11-$\mu\mu$fd. ceramic (10-$\mu\mu$f. usable).

C_2, C_3—50 Mc.: 100-$\mu\mu$f. variable, shaft-mounted set with rotor $\frac{1}{4}$ inch out of stator (Bud MC-905). 144 Mc.: 38-$\mu\mu$f. stand-off bypass (Erie Style 721A).

50-Mc. coil data:

L_1, L_5—3$\frac{1}{2}$ turns $\frac{5}{8}$ inch long. Top leads $\frac{3}{4}$ inch, bottom leads $\frac{1}{4}$ inch long.

L_2, L_4—4$\frac{1}{2}$ turns $\frac{5}{8}$ inch long. Leads $\frac{1}{2}$ inch long each end.

L_3—5$\frac{1}{2}$ turns $\frac{7}{8}$ inch long. Leads 1 inch long each. All 50-Mc. coils No. 12 tinned, $\frac{1}{2}$-inch diam., coil length measured between right-angle bends where leads begin.

144-Mc. coil data:

L_1, L_5—3 turns $\frac{1}{4}$ inch long. Leads $\frac{1}{4}$ inch long each end.

L_2, L_4—2 turns $\frac{1}{8}$ inch long. Leads 1 inch long each end.

L_3—5 turns $\frac{3}{4}$ inch long. Leads $\frac{5}{8}$ inch long each end. All 144-Mc. coils No. 18 tinned, $\frac{1}{4}$-inch diam., lengths measured as for 50-Mc. coils.

J_1, J_2—Coaxial fitting.

The case for the 50-Mc. filter is a standard aluminum slip-cover type box measuring $3\frac{1}{8}$ by 13 by $2\frac{5}{8}$ inches. The two end capacitors, C_1 and C_4, are mounted with their two stator posts toward the ends of the filter. The two larger units are mounted in the center compartment with their rotor shafts toward the middle. The top leads from coils L_1 and L_5 are wrapped around the stator terminals of C_1 and C_4, and the bottom leads fit directly into the coaxial input and output

fittings. The outer ends of coils L_2 and L_4 are soldered to the coaxial fitting terminals, and their inner ends are soldered to lugs supported on one-inch ceramic stand-off insulators. Leads from the stand-offs go through holes in the partitions to the bottom stator lugs on C_2 and C_3. L_3 is soldered to the two upper lugs on these two capacitors, thus completing the filter circuit. Lead lengths for the coils given in the parts list are the total lengths to be left when the winding is completed, including the portions that will be used in soldering operations.

This filter will give high attenuation in Channels 4–6 and all the high-band channels, and thus will take care of most of the spurious signals generated in a 50-Mc. transmitter.

A filter for low-power 144-Mc. transmitters is shown in Fig. 23-26. It is designed for maximum attenuation in the 190–215 Mc. region to suppress the spurious radiations in that range that frequently occur with 144-Mc. transmitters, but also has good attenuation for all frequencies above 170 Mc. Optimum capacitance values are given in Fig. 23-25. If possible, several units of the nearest standard values available should be measured and those having values closest to the optimum used. The inductance values are too small to be measured with sufficient accuracy, so the filter should be adjusted as follows:

First, mount L_1 and C_1, short J_1 temporarily at its inner terminals, and adjust L_1 until the combination resonates at 200 Mc. as shown by a grid-dip meter. Next, remove the short from J_1 and connect L_2 and C_2, adjusting L_2 until the circuit formed by $L_1L_2C_1C_2$ resonates at 144 Mc. Then disconnect L_2 and mount L_3 between C_2 and C_3. Adjust L_3 until the circuit $L_3C_2C_3$ resonates at 112 Mc. Next, disconnect L_3 and follow a similar procedure starting from the other end with L_5 and C_4. Finally, reconnect all coils and a check at any point in the filter should show resonance at 160 Mc., the approximate cut-off frequency.

The case for the 144-Mc. filter is made from flashing copper and is $1\frac{1}{4}$ inches square by $7\frac{1}{8}$ inches long. The main portion of the case is cut from a single piece with the end tabs folded down and soldered to the sides. Flanges are folded over at the bottom, and a cover is made to slip over these.

Filter Installation

In order to give the harmonic attenuation of

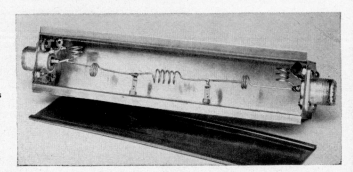

Fig. 23-26—A 52-ohm low-pass filter for 144-Mc. transmitters.

which it is capable, a low-pass filter must be installed in such a way that *all* the output of the transmitter flows through it. If harmonic currents are permitted to flow on the outside of the connecting coaxial cables, they will simply flow over the filter and on up to the antenna, and the filter does not have an opportunity to stop them. That is why it is so important to reduce the radiation from the transmitter and its leads to negligible proportions.

Fig. 23-27 shows the proper way to install a filter between a shielded transmitter and a matching circuit. Note that the coax, together with the shields about the transmitter and filter, forms a continuous shield to keep all the r.f. inside. It is thus forced to flow through the filter and the harmonics are attenuated. If there is no harmonic energy left after passing through the filter, shielding from that point on is not necessary; consequently, the matching circuit or antenna coupler does not need to be shielded. However, the antenna-coupler chassis arrangement shown in Fig. 23-27 is desirable because it will tend to prevent fundamental-frequency energy from flowing from the matching circuit back over the transmitter; this helps eliminate feed-back troubles in audio systems.

If the antenna is driven through coaxial line the matching circuit shown in Fig. 23-27 may be omitted. In that case the line goes directly from the filter to the antenna.

When a filter does not seem to give the harmonic attenuation of which it should be capable, the probable reason is that harmonics are bypassing it because of improper installation and inadequate transmitter shielding, including lead filtering. However, occasionally there are cases where the circuits formed by the cables and the apparatus to which they connect become resonant at a harmonic frequency. This greatly increases the harmonic output at that frequency. Such troubles can be completely overcome by substituting a slightly different cable length. The most critical length is that connecting the transmitter to the filter. Checking with a grid-dip meter at the final amplifier output coil usually will show whether an unfavorable resonance of this type exists.

● SUMMARY

The methods of harmonic elimination outlined in this chapter have been proved beyond doubt to be effective even under highly unfavorable conditions. It must be emphasized once more, however, that the problem must be solved one step at a time, and the procedure must be in logical order. It cannot be done properly without two items of simple equipment: a grid-dip meter and wavemeter covering the TV bands, and a dummy antenna.

The proper procedure may be summarized as follows:

1) Take a critical look at the transmitter on the basis of the design considerations outlined under "Reducing Harmonic Generation".

2) Check all circuits, particularly those connected with the final amplifier, with the grid-dip meter to determine whether there are any resonances in the TV bands. If so, rearrange the circuits so the resonances are moved out of the critical frequency region.

3) Connect the transmitter to the dummy antenna and check with the wavemeter for the presence of harmonics on leads and around the transmitter enclosure. Seal off the weak spots in the shielding and filter the leads until the wavemeter shows no indication at any harmonic frequency.

4) At this stage, check for interference with a TV receiver. If there is interference, determine the cause by the methods described previously and apply the recommended remedies until the interference disappears.

5) When the transmitter is completely clean on the dummy antenna, connect it to the regular antenna and check for interference on the TV receiver. If the interference is not bad, an antenna coupler or matching circuit installed as previously described should clear it up. Alternatively, a low-pass filter may be used. If neither the antenna coupler nor filter makes any difference in the interference, the evidence is strong that the interference, at least in part, is being caused by receiver overloading because of the strong fundamental-frequency field about the TV antenna and receiver. (See later section for identification of fundamental-frequency interference.) A coupler and/or filter, installed as described above, will invariably make a difference in the intensity of the interference if the interference is caused by transmitter harmonics alone.

6) If there is still interference after installing

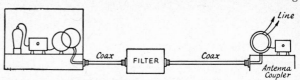

Fig. 23-27—The proper method of installing a low-pass filter between the transmitter and antenna coupler or matching circuit. If the antenna is fed through coax the matching circuit may be omitted but the same construction should be used between the transmitter and filter. The filter should be thoroughly shielded.

the coupler and/or filter, and the evidence shows that it is probably caused by a harmonic, more attenuation is needed. A more elaborate filter may be necessary. However, it is well at this stage to assume that part of the interference may be caused by receiver overloading, and take steps to alleviate such a condition before trying highly-elaborate filters, traps, etc., on the transmitter.

● HARMONICS BY RECTIFICATION

Even though the transmitter is completely free from harmonic output it is still possible for interference to occur because of harmonics generated outside the transmitter. These result from rectification of fundamental-frequency currents induced in conductors in the vicinity of the transmitting antenna. Rectification can take place at any point where two conductors are in poor electrical contact, a condition that frequently exists in plumbing, downspouting, BX cables crossing each other, and numerous other places in the ordinary residence. It also can occur in any exposed vacuum tubes in the station, in power supplies, speech equipment, etc., that may not be enclosed in the shielding about the r.f. circuits. Poor joints anywhere in the antenna system are especially bad, and rectification also may take place in the contacts of antenna change-over relays. Another common cause is overloading the front end of the communications receiver when it is used with a separate antenna (which will radiate the harmonics generated in the first tube) for break-in.

Rectification of this sort will not only cause harmonic interference but also is frequently responsible for cross-modulation effects. It can be detected in greater or less degree in most locations, but fortunately the harmonics thus generated are not usually of high amplitude. However, they can cause considerable interference in the immediate vicinity in fringe areas, especially when operation is in the 28-Mc. band. The amplitude decreases rapidly with the order of the harmonic, the second and third being the worst. It is ordinarily found that even in cases where destructive interference results from 28-Mc. operation the interference is comparatively mild from 14 Mc., and is negligible at still lower frequencies.

Nothing can be done at either the transmitter or receiver when rectification occurs. The remedy is to find the source and eliminate the poor contact either by separating the conductors or bonding them together. A crystal wavemeter (tuned to the fundamental frequency) is useful for hunting the source, by showing which conductors are carrying r.f. and, comparatively, how much.

Interference of this kind is frequently intermittent since the rectification efficiency will vary with vibration, the weather, and so on. The possibility of corroded contacts in the TV receiving antenna should not be overlooked, especially if it has been up a year or more.

● TV RECEIVER DEFICIENCIES

Front-End Overloading

When a television receiver is quite close to the transmitter, the intense r.f. signal from the transmitter's fundamental may overload one or more of the receiver circuits to produce spurious responses that cause interference.

If the overload is moderate, the interference is of the same nature as harmonic interference; it is caused by harmonics generated in the early stages of the receiver and, since it occurs only on channels harmonically related to the transmitting frequency, is difficult to distinguish from harmonics actually radiated by the transmitter. In such cases additional harmonic suppression at the transmitter will do no good, but any means taken

at the receiver to reduce the strength of the amateur signal reaching the first tube will effect an improvement. With very severe overloading, interference also will occur on channels *not* harmonically related to the transmitting frequency, so such cases are easily identified.

Cross-Modulation

Under some circumstances overloading will result in cross-modulation or mixing of the amateur signal with that from a local f.m. or TV station. For example, a 14-Mc. signal can mix with a 92-Mc. f.m. station to produce a beat at 78 Mc. and cause interference in Channel 5, or with a TV station on Channel 5 to cause interference in Channel 3. Neither of the channels interfered with is in harmonic relationship to 14 Mc. Both signals have to be on the air for the interference to occur, and eliminating either at the TV receiver will eliminate the interference.

There are many combinations of this type, depending on the band in use and the local frequency assignments to f.m. and TV stations. The interfering frequency is equal to the amateur fundamental frequency either added to or subtracted from the frequency of some local station, and when interference occurs in a TV channel that is not harmonically related to the amateur transmitting frequency the possibilities in such frequency combinations should be investigated.

I. F. Interference

Some TV receivers do not have sufficient selectivity to prevent strong signals in the intermediate-frequency range from forcing their way through the front end and getting into the i.f. amplifier. The once-standard intermediate frequency of, roughly, 21 to 27 Mc., is subject to interference from the fundamental-frequency output of transmitters operating in the 21-Mc. band. Transmitters on 28 Mc. sometimes will cause this type of interference as well.

A form of i.f. interference peculiar to 50-Mc. operation near the low edge of the band occurs with some receivers having the standard "41-Mc." i.f., which has the sound carrier at 41.25 Mc. and the picture carrier at 45.75 Mc. A 50-Mc. signal that forces its way into the i.f. system of the receiver will beat with the i.f. picture carrier to give a spurious signal on or near the i.f. sound carrier, even though the interfering signal is not actually in the nominal passband of the i.f. amplifier.

There is a type of i.f. interference unique to the 144-Mc. band in localities where certain u.h.f. TV channels are in operation, affecting only those TV receivers in which double-conversion type plug-in u.h.f. tuning strips are used. The design of these strips involves a first intermediate frequency that varies with the TV channel to be received and, depending on the particular strip design, this first i.f. may be in or close to the 144-Mc. amateur band. Since there is comparatively little selectivity in the TV signal-frequency circuits ahead of the first i.f., a signal from a 144-Mc. transmitter will "ride into" the

TV Receiver Deficiencies

i.f., even when the receiver is at a considerable distance from the transmitter. The channels that can be affected by this type of i.f. interference are:

Receivers with 21-Mc. second i.f.	Receivers with 41-Mc. second i.f.
Channels 14–18, inc.	Channels 20–25, inc.
Channels 41–48, inc.	Channels 51–58, inc.
Channels 69–77, inc.	Channels 82 and 83.

If the receiver is not close to the transmitter, a trap of the type shown in Fig. 23-30 will be effective. However, if the separation is small the 144-Mc. signal will be picked up directly on the receiver circuits and the best solution is to readjust the strip oscillator so that the first i.f. is moved to a frequency not in the vicinity of the 144-Mc. band. This has to be done by a competent technician.

I.f. interference is easily identified since it occurs on all channels — although sometimes the intensity varies from channel to channel — and the cross-hatch pattern it causes will rotate when the receiver's fine-tuning control is varied. When the interference is caused by a harmonic, overloading, or cross modulation, the structure of the interference pattern does not change (its intensity may change) as the fine-tuning control is varied.

High-Pass Filters

In all the above cases the interference can be eliminated if the fundamental signal strength can be reduced to a level that the receiver can handle. To accomplish this with signals on bands below 30 Mc., the most satisfactory device is a high-pass filter having a cut-off frequency between 30 and 54 Mc., installed at the tuner input terminals of the receiver. Circuits that have proved effective are shown in Figs. 23-28 and 23-29. Fig. 23-29 has one more section than the filters of Fig. 23-28 and as a consequence has somewhat better cut-off characteristics. All the circuits given are designed to have little or no effect on

the TV signals but will attenuate all signals lower in frequency than about 40 Mc. These filters preferably should be constructed in some sort of shielding container, although shielding is not always necessary. The dashed lines in Fig. 23-2 show how individual filter coils can be shielded from each other. The capacitors can be tubular ceramic units centered in holes in the partitions that separate the coils.

Simple high-pass filters cannot always be applied successfully in the case of 50-Mc. transmissions, because they do not have sufficiently-sharp cut-off characteristics to give both good attenuation at 50-54 Mc. and no attenuation above 54 Mc. A more elaborate design capable of giving the required sharp cut-off has been described (Ladd, "50-Mc. TVI — Its Causes and Cures," QST, June and July, 1954). This article also contains

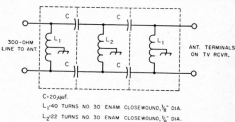

C = 20 μμf.

L₁: 40 TURNS NO. 30 ENAM. CLOSEWOUND, ⅛" DIA.

L₂: 22 TURNS NO. 30 ENAM. CLOSEWOUND, ⅛" DIA.

Fig. 23-29—Another type of high-pass filter for 300-ohm line. The coils may be wound on ⅛-inch diameter plastic plastic knitting needles. Important: Do not use a direct ground on the chassis of a transformerless receiver. Ground through a 0.001-μf. mica capacitor.

other information useful in coping with the TVI problems peculiar to 50-Mc. operation. As an alternative to such a filter, a high-Q wave trap tuned to the transmitting frequency may be used, suffering only the disadvantage that it is quite selective and therefore will protect a receiver from overloading over only a small range of transmitting frequencies in the 50-Mc. band. A trap of this type using quarter-wave sections of Twin-Lead is shown in Fig. 23-30. These "suck-out" traps, while absorbing energy at the frequency to which they are tuned, do not affect the receiver operation otherwise. The assembly should be slid along the TV antenna lead-in until the most effective position is found, and then fastened securely in place with Scotch Tape. An insulated tuning tool should be used for adjustment of the trimmer capacitor, since it is at a "hot" point and will show considerable body-capacitance effect.

High-pass filters are available commercially at moderate prices. In this connection, it should be understood by all parties concerned that while an amateur is responsible for *harmonic* radiation from his transmitter, it is no part of his responsibility to pay for or install filters, wave traps, etc. that may be required at the receiver to prevent interference caused by his *fundamental* frequency. The set owner should be advised to get in touch with the organization from which he purchased the receiver or which services it, to make arrangements for proper installation. Proper in-

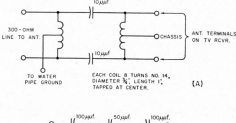

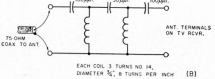

Fig. 23-28—High-pass filters for installation at the TV receiver antenna terminals. A—balanced filter for 300-ohm line, B—for 75-ohm coaxial line. Important: Do not use a direct ground on the chassis of a transformerless receiver. Ground through a 0.001-μf. mica capacitor.

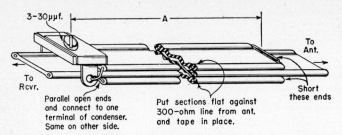

Fig. 23-30—Absorption-type wave trap using sections of 300-ohm line tuned to have an electrical length of ¼ wavelength at the transmitter frequency. Approximate physical lengths (dimension A) are 40 inches for 50 Mc. and 11 inches for 144 Mc., allowing for the loading effect of the capacitance at the open end. Two traps are used in parallel, one on each side of the line to the receiver.

stallation usually requires that the filter be installed right at the input terminals of the r.f. tuner of the TV set and not merely at the external antenna terminals, which may be at a considerable distance from the tuner. The question of cost is one to be settled between the set owner and the organization with which he deals.

Some of the larger manufacturers of TV receivers have instituted arrangements for cooperating with the set dealer in installing high-pass filters at no cost to the receiver owner. FCC-sponsored TVI Committees, now operating in many cities, have all the information necessary for effectuating such arrangements. To find out whether such a committee is functioning in your community, write to the FCC field office having jurisdiction over your location. A list of the field offices is contained in *The Radio Amateur's License Manual*, published by ARRL.

If the fundamental signal is getting into the receiver by way of the line cord a line filter such as that shown in Fig. 23-1 may help. To be most effective it should be installed inside the receiver chassis at the point where the cord enters, making the ground connections directly to chassis at this point. It may not be so helpful if placed between the line plug and the wall socket unless the r.f. is actually picked up on the house wiring rather than on the line cord itself.

Antenna Installation

Usually, the transmission line between the TV receiver and the actual TV antenna will pick up a great deal more energy from a nearby transmitter than the television receiving antenna itself. The currents induced on the TV transmission line in this case are of the "parallel" type, where the phase of the current is the same in both conductors. The line simply acts like two wires connected together to operate as one. If the receiver's antenna input circuit were perfectly balanced it would reject these "parallel" or "unbalance" signals and respond only to the true transmission-line ("push-pull") currents; that is, only signals picked up on the actual antenna would cause a receiver response. However, no receiver is perfect in this respect, and many TV receivers will respond strongly to such parallel currents. The result is that the signals from a nearby amateur transmitter are much more intense at the first stage in the TV receiver than they would be if the receiver response were confined entirely to energy picked up on the TV antenna alone. This situation can be improved by using shielded transmission line — coax or, in the balanced form, "twinax" — for the receiving installation. For best results the line should terminate in a coax fitting on the receiver chassis, but if this is not possible the shield should be grounded to the chassis right at the antenna terminals.

The use of shielded transmission line for the receiver also will be helpful in reducing response to harmonics actually being radiated from the transmitter or transmitting antenna. In most receiving installations the transmission line is very much longer than the antenna itself, and is consequently far more exposed to the harmonic fields from the transmitter. Much of the harmonic pickup, therefore, is on the receiving transmission line when the transmitter and receiver are quite close together. Shielded line, plus relocation of either the transmitting or receiving antenna to take advantage of directive effects, often will result in reducing overloading, as well as harmonic pickup, to a level that does not interfere with reception.

● U.H.F. TELEVISION

Harmonic TVI in the u.h.f. TV band is far less troublesome than in the v.h.f. band. Harmonics from transmitters operating below 30 Mc. are of such high order that they would normally be expected to be quite weak; in addition, the components, circuit conditions and construction of low-frequency transmitters are such as to tend to prevent very strong harmonics from being generated in this region. However, this is not true of amateur v.h.f. transmitters, particularly those working in the 144-Mc. and higher bands. Here the problem is quite similar to that of the low v.h.f. TV band with respect to transmitters operating below 30 Mc.

There is one highly favorable factor in u.h.f. TV that does not exist in the most of the v.h.f. TV band: If harmonics are radiated, it is possible to move the transmitter frequency sufficiently (within the amateur band being used) to avoid interfering with a channel that may be in use in the locality. By restricting operation to a portion of the amateur band that will not result in harmonic interference, it is possible to avoid the necessity for taking extraordinary precautions to prevent harmonic radiation.

The frequency assignment for u.h.f. television consists of seventy 6-megacycle channels (Nos. 14 to 83, inclusive) beginning at 470 Mc. and ending at 890 Mc. The harmonics from amateur bands above 50 Mc. span the u.h.f. channels as shown in Table 23-I. Since the assignment plan

TV Receiver Radiation

TABLE 23-I

Harmonic Relationship—Amateur V.H.F. Bands and U.H.F. TV Channels

Amateur Band	Harmonic	Fundamental Freq. Range	U.H.F. TV Channel Affected	Amateur Band	Harmonic	Fundamental Freq. Range	U.H.F. TV Channel Affected
144 Mc.	4th	144.0–144.5	31	220 Mc.	3rd	220–220.67	45
		144.5–146.0	32			220.67–222.67	46
		146.0–147.5	33			222.67–224.67	47
		147.5–148.0	34			224.67–225	48
	5th	144.0–144.4	55		4th	220–221	82
		144.4–145.6	56			221–222.5	83
		145.6–146.8	57	420 Mc	2nd	420–421	75
		146.8–148	58			421–424	76
	6th	144–144.33	79			424–427	77
		144.33–145.33	80			427–430	78
		145.33–147.33	81			430–433	79
		147.33–148	82			433–436	80
						436–439	81
						439–442	82
						442–448	83

calls for a minimum separation of six channels between any two stations in one locality, there is ample opportunity to choose a fundamental frequency that will move a harmonic out of range of a local TV frequency.

● COLOR TELEVISION

The color TV signal includes a subcarrier spaced 3.58 megacycles from the regular picture carrier (or 4.83 Mc. from the low edge of the channel) for transmitting the color information. Harmonics which fall in the color subcarrier region can be expected to cause break-up of color in the received picture. This modifies the chart of Fig. 23-3 to introduce another "severe" region centering around 4.8 Mc. measured from the low-frequency edge of the channel. Hence with color television reception there is less opportunity to avoid harmonic interference by choice of operating frequency. In other respects the problem of eliminating interference is the same as with black-and-white television.

● INTERFERENCE FROM TV RECEIVERS

The TV picture tube is swept horizontally by the electron beam 15,750 times per second, using a wave shape that has very high harmonic content. The harmonics are of appreciable amplitude even at frequencies as high as 30 Mc., and when radiated from the receiver can cause considerable interference to reception in the amateur bands. While measures to suppress radiation of this nature are required by FCC in currently manufactured receivers, many older sets have had no such treatment. The interference takes the form of rather unstable, a.c.-modulated signals spaced at intervals of 15.75 kc.

Studies have shown that the radiation takes place principally in three ways, in order of their importance: (1) from the a.c. line, through stray coupling to the sweep circuits; (2) from the antenna system, through similar coupling; (3) directly from the picture tube and sweep-circuit wiring. Line radiation often can be reduced by bypassing the a.c. line cord to the chassis at the point of entry, although this is not completely effective in all cases since the coupling may take place outside the chassis beyond the point where the by passing is done. Radiation from the antenna is usually suppressed by installing a high-pass filter on the receiver. The direct radiation requires shielding of high-potential leads and, in some receivers, additional bypassing in the sweep circuit; in severe cases, it may be necessary to line the cabinet with screening or similar shielding material.

Incidental radiation of this type from TV and broadcast receivers, when of sufficient intensity to cause serious interference to other radio services (such as amateur), is covered by Part 15 of the FCC rules. When such interference is caused, the user of the receiver is obligated to take steps to eliminate it. The owner of an offending receiver should be advised to contact the source from which the receiver was purchased for appropriate modification of the receiving installation. TV receiver dealers can obtain the necessary information from the set manufacturer.

It is usually possible to reduce interference very considerably, without modifying the TV receiver, simply by having a good amateur-band receiving installation. The principles are the same as those used in reducing "hash" and other noise — use a good antenna, such as the transmitting antenna, for reception; install it as far as possible from a.c. circuits; use a good feeder system such as a properly balanced two-wire line or coax with the outer conductor grounded; use coax input to the receiver, with a matching circuit if necessary; and check the receiver to make sure that it does not pick up signals or noise with the antenna disconnected. These measures not only reduce interference from sweep radiation and a.c. line noise, but also build up the strength of the desired signal, so that the overall improvement in signal-to-interference ratio is very much worth-while.

565

CHAPTER 24

Operating a Station

The enjoyment of our hobby comes mostly from the operation of our station once we have finished its construction. Upon the *station* and its *operation* depend the communication records that are made. The standing of individuals as amateurs and respect for the capabilities of the whole institution of amateur radio depend to a considerable extent on the practical communications established by amateurs, the aggregate of all our station efforts.

An operator with a slow, steady, clean-cut method of sending has a big advantage over the poor operator. The technique of speaking in connected thoughts and phrases is equally important for the voice operator. Good sending is partly a matter of practice but patience and judgment are just as important qualities of an operator as a good "fist."

Operating knowledge embracing standard procedures, development of skill in employing c.w. to expand the station range and operating effectiveness at minimum power levels and some net know-how are all essentials in achieving a triumphant amateur experience with top station records, personal results, and demonstrations of what our stations can do in practical communications.

● OPERATING COURTESY AND TOLERANCE

Normal operating interests in amateur radio vary considerably. Some prefer to rag-chew, others handle traffic, others work DX, others concentrate on working certain areas, countries or states and still others get on for an occasional contact only to check a new transmitter or antenna.

Interference is one of the things we amateurs have to live with. However, we can conduct our operating in a way designed to alleviate it as much as possible. *Before putting the transmitter on the air, listen on your own frequency.* If you hear stations engaged in communication on that frequency, stand by until you are sure no interference will be caused by your operations, or *shift to another frequency.* No amateur or any group of amateurs has any *exclusive* claim to any frequency in any band. We must work together, each respecting the rights of others. Remember, those other chaps can cause you as much interference as you cause them, sometimes more!

In this chapter we'll recount some fundamentals of operating success, cover major procedures for successful general work and include proper forms to use in message handling and other fields. Note also the sections on special activities, awards and organization. These permit us all to develop through our organization more success together than we could ever attain by separate uncoordinated efforts that overlook the precepts established through operating experience.

● C.W. PROCEDURE

The best operators, *both* those using voice and c.w., observe certain operating procedures regarded as "standard practice."

1) *Calls.* Calling stations may call efficiently by transmitting the call signal of the station called three times, the letters DE, followed by one's own station call sent three times. (Short calls with frequent "breaks" to listen have proved to be the best method.) Repeating the call of the station called four or five times and signing not more than two or three times has proved excellent practice, thus: W0BY W0BY W0BY W0BY W0BY DE W1AW W1AW AR.

CQ. The general-inquiry call (CQ) should be sent not more than five times without interspersing one's station identification. The length of repeated calls is carefully limited in intelligent amateur operating. (CQ is not to be used when testing or when the sender is not expecting or looking for an answer. Never send a CQ "blind." Always be sure to listen on the transmitting frequency first.)

The directional CQ: To reduce the number of useless answers and lessen QRM, every CQ call should be made informative when possible.

> *Examples:* A United States station looking for any Hawaiian amateur calls: CQ KH6 CQ KH6 CQ KH6 DE W4IA W4IA W4IA K. A Western station with traffic for the East Coast when looking for an intermediate relay station calls: CQ EAST CQ EAST CQ EAST DE W5IGW W5IGW W5IGW K. A station with messages for points in Massachusetts calls: CQ MASS CQ MASS CQ MASS DE W7CZY W7CZY W7CZY K.

Hams who do not raise stations readily may find that their sending is poor, their calls ill-timed or judgment in error. When conditions are right

"...A LONG CALL IS UNNECESSARY"

to bring in signals from the desired locality, you can call them. Reasonably short calls, with appropriate and brief breaks to listen, will raise stations with minimum time and trouble.

2) *Answering a Call:* Call three times (or less); send DE; sign three times (or less); after contact is established decrease the use of the call signals of both stations to *once or twice.* When a station receives a call but does not receive the call letters of the station calling, QRZ? may be used. It means "By whom am I being called?" QRZ should not be used in place of CQ.

3) *Ending Signals and Sign-Off:* The proper use of $\overline{AR}$, K, $\overline{KN}$, $\overline{SK}$ and CL ending signals is as follows:

$\overline{AR}$ — End of transmission. Recommended after call to a specific station before contact has been established.

> *Example:* W6ABC W6ABC W6ABC W6ABC W6ABC DE W9LMN W9LMN $\overline{AR}$. Also at the end of transmission of a radiogram, immediately following the signature, preceding identification.

K — Go ahead (any station). Recommended after CQ and at the end of each transmission during QSO when there is no objection to others breaking in.

> *Example:* CQ CQ CQ DE W1ABC W1ABC K or W9XYZ DE W1ABC K.

$\overline{KN}$ — Go ahead (specific station), all others keep out. Recommended at the end of each transmission during a QSO, or after a call, when calls from other stations are not desired and will not be answered.

> *Example:* W4FGH DE XU6GRL $\overline{KN}$.

$\overline{SK}$ — End of QSO. Recommended before signing *last* transmission at end of a QSO.

> *Example:* .... $\overline{SK}$ W8LMN DE W5BCD.

CL — I am closing station. Recommended when a station is going off the air, to indicate that it will not listen for any further calls.

> *Example:* .... $\overline{SK}$ W7HIJ DE W2JKL CL.

4) *Testing.* When it is necessary for a station to make test signals they must not continue for more than 10 seconds and must be composed of a series of VVV followed by the call sign of the station emitting the test signals. *Always listen first* to find a clear spot if possible, to avoid causing unwarranted QRM of a QSO in progress.

5) *Receipting* for conversation or traffic: Never receipt for a transmission until it has been entirely received. "R" means "transmission received as sent." Use R *only* when *all* is received correctly.

6) *Repeats.* When most of a transmission is lost, a call should be followed by correct abbreviations to ask for repeats. When a few words on the end of a transmission are lost, the *last word received correctly* is given after ?AA, meaning "all after." When a few words at the beginning of a transmission are lost, ?AB for "all before" a stated word should be used. The quickest way to ask for a fill in the middle of a transmission is to send the last word received correctly, a ques-

tion mark, then the next word received correctly. Another way is to send "?BN [word] and [word]."

Do not send words twice (QSZ) unless it is requested. Send single. Do not fall into the bad habit of sending double *without a request* from fellows you work. Don't say "QRM" or "QRN" when you mean "QRS." Don't CQ unless there is definite reason for so doing. When sending CQ, use judgment.

General Practices

When a station has receiving trouble, the operator asks the transmitting station to "QSV." The letter "R" is often used in place of a decimal point (e.g., "3R5 Mc.") or the colon in time designation (e.g., "2R30 PM"). A long dash is sometimes sent for "zero."

The law concerning superfluous signals should be noted. If you *must* test, disconnect the antenna system and use an equivalent "dummy" antenna. Send your call frequently when operating. Pick a time for adjusting the station apparatus when few stations will be bothered.

The up-to-date amateur station uses "break-in." For best results send at a medium speed. Send evenly with proper spacing. The standard-type telegraph key is best for all-round use. Regular daily practice periods, two or three periods a day, are best to acquire real familiarity and proficiency with code.

No excuse can be made for "garbled" copy. Operators should copy what is sent and refuse to acknowledge a whole transmission until every word has been received correctly. *Good operators do not guess.* "Swing" in a fist is *not* the mark of a good operator. Unusual words are sent twice, the word repeated following the transmission of "?". If not *sure,* a good operator systematically asks for a fill or repeat. Sign your call frequently, interspersed with calls, and at the end of all transmissions.

On Good Sending

Assuming that an operator has learned sending properly, and comes up with a precision "fist" — not fast, but clean, steady, making well-formed rhythmical characters and spacing beautiful to listen to — he then becomes subject to outside pressures to his own possible detriment in everyday operating. He will want to "speed it up" because the operator at the other end is going faster, and so he begins, unconsciously, to run his words together or develops a "swing."

Perhaps one of the easiest ways to get into bad habits is to do too much playing around with special keys. Too many operators spend only enough time with a straight key to acquire "passable" sending, then subject their newly-developed "fists" to the entirely different movements of bugs, side-swipers, electronic keys, or what-have-you. All too often, this results in the ruination of what may have become a very good "fist."

Think about your sending a little. Are you satisfied with it? You should not be — ever. Nobody's sending is perfect, and therefore *every* operator should continually strive for improvement. Do you ever run letters together — like Q for MA, or P for AN — especially when you are in a hurry? Practically everybody does at one time or another. Do you have a "swing"? Any recognizable "swing" is a deviation from perfection. Strive to send like tape sending; copy a W1AW Bulletin and try to send it with the same spacing using a local oscillator on a subsequent transmission.

Check your spacing in characters, between characters and between words occasionally by making a recording of your fist on an inked tape recorder. This will show up your faults as nothing else will. Practice the correction of faults.

● USING A BREAK-IN SYSTEM

Break-in avoids unnecessarily long calls, prevents QRM, gives more communication per hour of operating. Brief calls with frequent short pauses for reply can approach (but not equal) break-in efficiency.

A separate receiving antenna facilitates break-in operation. It is only necessary with break-in to pause just a moment with the key up (or to cut the carrier momentarily and pause in a phone conversation) to listen for the other station. The click when the carrier is cut off is as effective as the word "break."

C.w. telegraphy break-in is usually simple to arrange. With break-in, ideas and messages to be transmitted can be pulled right through the holes in the QRM. Snappy, efficient amateur work with break-in usually requires a separate receiving antenna and arrangement of the transmitter and receiver to eliminate the necessity for throwing switches between transmissions.

In calling, the transmitting operator sends the letters "BK" at intervals during his call so that stations hearing the call may know that break-in is in use and take advantage of the fact. *He pauses at intervals* during his call, to listen for a moment for a reply. If the station being called does not answer, the call can be continued.

With a tap of the key, the man on the receiving end can interrupt (if a word is missed). The other operator is constantly monitoring, awaiting just such directions. It is not necessary that *you* have perfect facilities to take advantage of break-in when the stations you work are break-in-equipped. After any invitation to *break* is given (and at each pause) press your key — and contact can start *immediately*.

● VOICE OPERATING

The use of proper procedure to get best results is just as important as in using code. In telegraphy words must be spelled out letter by letter. It is therefore but natural that abbreviations and shortcuts should have come into widespread use. In voice work, however, abbreviations are not necessary, and should have less importance in our operating procedure.

The letter "K" has been agreed to in telegraphic practice so that the operator will not have to pound out the separate letters that spell the words "go ahead." The voice operator can *say* the words "go ahead" or "over," or "come in please."

One laughs on c.w. by spelling out HI. On phone *use* a laugh when one is called for. Be natural as you would with your family and friends.

The matter of reporting *readability* and *strength* is as important to phone operators as to those using code. With telegraph nomenclature, it is necessary to spell out words to describe signals or use abbreviated signal reports. But on voice, we have the ability to "say it with words." "Readability four, Strength eight" is the best way to give a quantitative report. Reporting can be done so much more meaningfully with ordinary words: "You are weak but you are in the clear and I can understand you, so go ahead," or "Your signal is strong but you are buried under local interference." Why not say it with words?

Voice Equivalents to Code Procedure

Voice	Code	Meaning
Go ahead; over	K	Self-explanatory
Wait; stand by	AS	Self-explanatory
Received	R	Receipt for a correctly-transcribed message or for "solid" transmission with no missing portions

Phone-Operating Practice

Efficient voice communication, like good c.w. communication, demands good operating. Adherence to certain points "on getting results" will go a long way toward improving our phone-band operating conditions.

Use push-to-talk technique. Where possible arrange on-off switches, controls or voice-controlled break-in for fast back-and-forth exchanges that emulate the practicality of the wire telephone.

Voice Operating

This will help reduce the length of transmissions and keep brother amateurs from calling you a "monologuist" — a guy who likes to hear himself talk!

Listen with care. Keep noise and "backgrounds" out of your operating room to facilitate good listening. It is natural to answer the strongest signal, but take time to listen and give some consideration to the *best* signals, regardless of strength. Every amateur cannot run a kilowatt, but there is no reason why every amateur cannot have a signal of good quality, and utilize uniform operating practices to aid in the understandability and ease of his own communications.

Interpose your call regularly and at frequent intervals. Three short calls are better than one long one. In calling CQ, one's call should certainly appear at least once for every five or six CQs. Calls with frequent breaks to listen will save time and be most productive of results. In identifying, always transmit your *own* call last. *Don't* say "This is W1ABC standing by for W2DEF"; say "W2DEF, this is W1ABC, over." FCC regulations show the call of the transmitting station sent *last.*

Include country prefix before call. It is not correct to say "9RRX, this is 1BDI." Correct and legal use is "W9RRX, this is W1BDI." FCC regulations require proper use of calls; stations have been cited for failure to comply with this requirement.

Monitor your own frequency. This helps in timing calls and transmissions. Transmit when there is a chance of being copied successfully — not when you are merely "more QRM." Timing transmissions is an art to cultivate.

Keep modulation constant. By turning the gain "wide open" you are subjecting anyone listening to the diversion of whatever noises are present in or near your operating room, to say nothing of the possibility of feedback, echo due to poor acoustics, and modulation excesses due to sudden loud noises. Speak near the microphone, and don't let your gaze wander all over the station causing sharply-varying input to your speech amplifier; at the same time, keep far enough from the microphone so your signal is not modulated by your breathing. Change distance or gain only as necessary to insure uniform transmitter performance without overmodulation, splatter or distortion.

Make connected thoughts and phrases. Don't mix disconnected subjects. Ask questions consistently. Pause and get answers.

Have a pad of paper handy. It is convenient and desirable to jot down questions as they come in the course of discussion in order not to miss any. It will help you to make intelligent to-the-point replies.

Steer clear of inanities and soap-opera stuff. Our amateur radio and also our personal reputation as serious communications workers depend on us.

Avoid repetition. Don't repeat back what the other fellow has just said. Too often we hear a conversation like this: "Okay on your new antenna there, okay on the trouble you're having

with your receiver, okay on the company who just came in with some ice cream, okay . . . [etc.]." Just *say* you received everything O.K. Don't try to prove it.

Use phonetics only as required. When clarifying genuinely doubtful expressions and in getting your call identified positively we suggest use of the ARRL Phonetic List. Limit such use to really-necessary clarification.

The speed of radiotelephone transmission (with perfect accuracy) depends almost entirely upon the skill of the two operators involved. One must learn to speak at a rate allowing perfect understanding as well as permitting the receiving operator to copy down the message text, if that is necessary. Because of the similarity of many English speech sounds, the use of alphabetical word lists has been found necessary. All voice-operated stations should use a *standard* list as needed to identify call signals or unfamiliar expressions.

ARRL Word List for Radiotelephony

ADAM	JOHN	SUSAN
BAKER	KING	THOMAS
CHARLIE	LEWIS	UNION
DAVID	MARY	VICTOR
EDWARD	NANCY	WILLIAM
FRANK	OTTO	X-RAY
GEORGE	PETER	YOUNG
HENRY	QUEEN	ZEBRA
IDA	ROBERT	

Example: W1AW . . . W 1 ADAM WILLIAM . . . W1AW

Round Tables. The round table has many advantages if run properly. It clears frequencies of interference, especially if all stations involved are on the same frequency, while the enjoyment value remains the same, if not greater. By use of push-to-talk, the conversation can be kept lively and interesting, giving each station operator ample opportunity to participate without waiting overlong for his turn.

Round tables can become very unpopular if they are not conducted properly. The monologuist, off on a long spiel about nothing in particular, cannot be interrupted; *make your transmissions short and to the point.* "Butting in" is discourteous and unsportsmanlike; *don't enter a round table, or any contact between two other amateurs, unless you are invited.* It is bad enough trying to copy through prevailing interference without the added difficulty of poor voice quality; *check your transmitter adjustments frequently.* In general, follow the precepts as hereinbefore outlined for the most enjoyment in round tables as well as any other form of radiotelephone communication.

● WORKING DX

Most amateurs at one time or another make "working DX" a major aim. As in every other phase of amateur work, there are right and wrong ways to go about getting best results in working foreign stations, and it is the intention of this section to outline a few of them.

The ham who has trouble raising DX stations

readily may find that poor transmitter efficiency is not the reason. He may find that his sending is poor, or his calls ill-timed, or his judgment in error. When conditions are right to bring in the DX, and the receiver sensitive enough to bring in several stations from the desired locality, the way to work DX is to use the appropriate frequency and timing and *call these stations*, as against the common practice of calling "CQ DX."

The call CQ DX means slightly different things to amateurs in different bands:

a) On v.h.f., CQ DX is a general call ordinarily used only when the band is open, under favorable "skip" conditions. For v.h.f. work such a call is used for looking for new states and countries, also for distances beyond the customary "line-of-sight" range on most v.h.f. bands.

b) CQ DX on our 7-, 14-, 21- and 28-Mc. bands may be taken to mean "General call to any foreign station." The term "foreign station" usually refers to any station in a foreign continent. (*Experienced* amateurs in the U. S. A. and Canada do *not* use this call, but *answer* such calls made by foreign stations.)

c) CQ DX used on 3.5 Mc. under winter-night conditions may be used in this same manner. At other times, under average 3.5-Mc. propagation conditions, the call may be used in domestic work when looking for new states or countries in one's own continent, usually applying to stations located over 1000 miles distant from you.

The way to work DX is not to use a CQ call at *all* (in our continent). Instead, use your best tuning skill — and listen — and listen — and *listen. You have to hear them before you can work them.* Hear the desired stations first; time your calls well. Use your utmost skill. A sensitive receiver is often more important than the power input in working foreign stations. If you can hear stations in a particular country or area, chances are that you will be able to work someone there.

"---DO A LOT OF SNOOPING"

One of the most effective ways to work DX is to know the operating habits of the DX stations sought. Doing too much transmitting on the DX bands is not the way to do this. Again, *listening* is effective. Once you know the operating habits of the DX station you are after you will know when and where to call, and when to remain silent waiting your chance.

Some DX stations indicate where they will tune for replies by use of "10U" or "15D." (See point 4 of the DX Operating Code.) In voice work the overseas operator may say "listening on 14,225 kc." or "tuning upward from 28,500 kc." Many a DX station will not reply to a call on his exact frequency.

ARRL has recommended some operating procedures to DX stations aimed at controlling some of the thoughtless operating practices sometimes used by W/VE amateurs. A copy of these recommendations (Operating Aid No. 5) can be obtained free of charge from ARRL Headquarters.

In any band, particularly at line-of-sight frequencies, when directional antennas are used, the directional CQ such as CQ W5, CQ north, etc., is the preferable type of call. Mature amateurs agree that CQ DX is a wishful rather than a practical type of call for most stations in the North Americas looking for foreign contacts. Ordinarily, it is a cause of unnecessary QRM.

Conditions in the transmission medium make all field strengths from a given region more nearly equal at a distance, irrespective of power used. In general, the higher the frequency band, the less important power considerations become. This accounts in part for the relative popularity of the 14-, 21- and 28-Mc. bands among amateurs who like to work DX.

DX OPERATING CODE
(For W/VE Amateurs)

Some amateurs interested in DX work have caused considerable confusion and QRM in their efforts to work DX stations. The points below, if observed by all W/VE amateurs, will go a long way toward making DX more enjoyable for everybody.

1. Call DX only after he calls CQ, QRZ?, signs $\overline{SK}$, or phone equivalents thereof.

2. Do *not* call a DX station:
   a. On the frequency of the station he is working until you are *sure* the QSO is over. This is indicated by the ending signal $\overline{SK}$ on c.w. and any indication that the operator is listening, on phone.
   b. Because you hear someone else calling him.
   c. When he signs $\overline{KN}$, $\overline{AR}$, CL, or 'phone equivalents.
   d. Exactly on his frequency.
   e. After he calls a directional CQ, unless of course you are in the right direction or area.

3. Keep within frequency-band limits. Some DX stations operate outside. Perhaps they can get away with it, but you cannot.

4. Observe calling instructions of DX stations. "10U" means call ten kc. *up* from his frequency, "15D" means 15 kc. *down*, etc.

5. Give honest reports. Many foreign stations *depend* on W and VE reports for adjustment of station and equipment.

6. Keep your signal clean. Key clicks, chirps, hum or splatter give you a bad reputation and may get you a citation from FCC.

7. *Listen* for and *call* station you want. Calling CQ DX is not the best assurance that the *rare* DX will reply.

8. When there are several W or VE stations waiting to work a DX station, avoid asking him to "listen for a friend." Let your friend take his chances with the rest. Also avoid engaging DX stations in rag-chews against their wishes.

DATE TIME	STATION CALLED	CALLED BY	HIS FREQ. OR DIAL	HIS SIGNALS RST	MY SIGNALS RST	FREQ. MC.	EMIS- SION TYPE	POWER INPUT WATTS	TIME OF ENDING QSO	OTHER DATA
11-16-53										
6:15 PM	WØTQD	×	3.65	589	569X	3.5	A1	250	6:43	Tfc - rec'd 6, sent 10
7:20	CQ	×				7				
7:21	×	W4TWI	7.16	369	579				7:32	Vy heavy QRM on me
9:25	W8UKS	×	3.83	59	47	3.9	A3	100	10:05	Sam
11-18-53										
7:05 AM	VK4EL	×	14.03			14	A1	250		Answered a W6
7:09	ZL2ACV	×	14.07	339	559X				7:20	
7:21	×	KA2KW	14.07	469X	349				7:33	First KA
7:36	CQ	×								
7:37	×	W6TI	14.01	589	589C				8:12	

KEEP AN ACCURATE AND COMPLETE STATION LOG AT ALL TIMES! F.C.C. REQUIRES IT.

A page from the official ARRL log is shown above, answering every Government requirement in respect to station records. Bound logs made up in accord with the above form can be obtained from Headquarters for a nominal sum or you can prepare your own, in which case we offer this form as a suggestion. The ARRL log has a special wire binding and lies perfectly flat on the table.

● **KEEPING AN AMATEUR STATION LOG**

The FCC requires every amateur to keep a complete station operating record. It may also contain records of experimental tests and adjustment data. A stenographer's notebook can be ruled with vertical lines in any form to suit the user. The Federal Communications Commission requirements are that a log be maintained that shows (1) the date and time of *each* transmission, (2) *all calls* and transmissions made (whether two-way contacts resulted or not), (3) the input power to the last stage of the transmitter, (4) the frequency band used, (5) the time of *ending* each QSO and the operator's identifying signature for responsibility for each session of operating. Messages may be written in the log or separate records kept — but record must be retained for one year as required by the FCC. For the convenience of amateur station operators ARRL stocks both logbooks and message blanks, and if one uses the official log he is sure to comply fully with the Government requirements if the precautions and suggestions included in the log are followed.

Message Handling

Amateur operators in the United States and a few other countries enjoy a privilege not available to amateurs in most countries — that of handling third-party message traffic. In the early history of amateur radio in this country, some amateurs who were among the first to take advantage of this privilege formed an extensive relay organization which became known as the American Radio Relay League.

Thus, amateur message-handling has had a long and honorable history and, like most services, has gone through many periods of development and change. Those amateurs who handled traffic in 1914 would hardly recognize it the way some of us do it today, just as equipment in those days was far different from that in use now. Progress has been made and new methods have been developed in step with advancement in communication techniques of all kinds. Amateurs who handled a lot of traffic found that organized operating schedules were more effective than random relays, and as techniques advanced and messages increased in number, trunk lines were organized, spot frequencies began to be used, and there sprang into existence a number of traffic nets in which many stations operated on the same frequency to effect wider coverage in less time with fewer relays; but the old methods are still available to the amateur who handles only an occasional message.

Although message handling is as old an art as is amateur radio itself, there are many amateurs who do not know how to handle a message and have never done so. As each amateur grows older and gains experience in the amateur service, there is bound to come a time when he will be called upon to handle a written message, during a communications emergency, in casual contact with one of his many acquaintances on the air, or as a result of a request from a non-amateur friend. Regardless of the occasion, if it comes to you, you will want to rise to it! Considerable embarrassment is likely to be experienced by the amateur who finds he not only does not know the form in which the message should be prepared, but does not know what to do with the message once it has been filed or received in his station.

Traffic work need not be a complicated or time-consuming activity for the casual or occasional message-handler. Amateurs may participate in traffic work to whatever extent they wish, from an occasional message now and then to becoming a part of organized traffic systems.

This chapter explains some principles so the reader may know where to find out more about the subject and may exercise the message-handling privilege to best effect as the spirit and opportunity arise.

Responsibility

Amateurs who originate messages for transmission or who receive messages for relay or delivery should first consider that in doing so they are accepting the responsibility of clearing the message from their station on its way to its destination in the shortest possible time. Forty-eight hours after filing or receipt is the generally-accepted rule among traffic-handling amateurs, but it is obvious that if every amateur who relayed the message allowed it to remain in his station this long it might be a long time reaching its destination. Traffic should be relayed or delivered as quickly as possible.

Message Form

Once this responsibility is realized and accepted, handling the message becomes a matter of following generally-accepted standards of form and transmission. For this purpose, each message is divided into four parts: the preamble, the address, the text and the signature. Some of these parts themselves are subdivided. It is necessary in preparing the message for transmission and in actually transmitting it to know not only what each part is and what it is for, but to know in what *order* it should be transmitted, and to know the various procedure signals used with it when sent by c.w. If you are going to send a message, you may as well send it right.

Standardization is important! There is a great deal of room for expressing originality and individuality in amateur radio, but there are also times and places where such expression can only cause confusion and inefficiency. Recognizing the need for standardization in message form and message transmitting procedures, ARRL has long since recommended such standards, and most traffic-interested amateurs have followed them. In general, these recommendations, and the various changes they have undergone from year to year, have been at the request of ama-

teurs participating in this activity, and they are completely outlined and explained in *Operating an Amateur Radio Station*, a copy of which is available upon request or by use of the coupon at the end of this chapter.

Clearing a Message

Amateurs not experienced in message handling should depend on the experienced message-handler to get a message through, if it is important; but the average amateur can enjoy operating with a message to be handled either through a local traffic net or by free-lancing. The latter may be accomplished by careful listening for an amateur station at desired points. directional CQs, use of the National Calling and Emergency frequencies, or by making and keeping a schedule with another amateur for regular work between specified points. He may well aim at learning and enjoying through doing. The joy and accomplishment in thus developing one's operating skill to top perfection has a reward all its own.

The best way to clear a message is to put it into one of the many organized traffic networks, or to give it to a station who can do so. There are many amateurs who make the handling of traffic their principal operating activity, and many more still who participate in this activity to a greater or lesser extent. The result is a system of traffic nets which spreads to all corners of the United States and covers most U. S. possessions and Canada. Once a message gets into one of these nets, regardless of the net's size or coverage, it is systematically routed toward its destination in the shortest possible time.

If you decide to "take the bull by the horns" and put the message into a traffic net yourself (and more power to you if you do!), you will need to know something about how traffic nets operate, and the special Q signals and procedure they use to dispatch all traffic with a maximum of efficiency. Reference to net lists in *QST* (usually in the November and January issues) will give you the frequency and operating time of the net in your section, or of other nets into which your message can go. Listening for a few minutes at the time and frequency indicated should acquaint you with enough fundamentals to enable you to report into the net and indicate your traffic. From that time on you follow the instructions of the net control station, who will tell you when and to whom (and on what frequency, if different from the net frequency) to send your message. Since most nets use the special "QN" signals, it is usually very helpful to have a list of these before you (list available from ARRL Hq., Operating Aid No. 9).

Network Operation

About this time, you may find that you are enjoying this type of operating activity and want to know more about it and increase your proficiency. Many amateurs are happily "addicted" to traffic handling after only one or two brief exposures to it. Much traffic is at present being conducted by c.w., since this mode of com-

Here is an example of a plain-language message in correct ARRL form. The preamble is always sent as shown: number, station of origin, check, place of origin, time filed, date.

Emergency Communication

munication seems to be popular for record purposes — but this does not mean that high code speed is a necessary prerequisite to working in traffic networks. There are many nets organized specifically for the slow-speed amateur, and most of the so-called "fast" nets are usually glad to slow down to accommodate slower operators, especially those nets at state or section level.

The significant facet of net operation, however, is that code speed alone does *not* make for efficiency — sometimes quite the contrary! A high-speed operator who does not know net procedure can "foul up" a net much more completely and more quickly than can a slow operator. It is a proven fact that a bunch of high-speed operators who are not "savvy" in net operation cannot accomplish as much during a specified period as an equal number of slow operators who *know* net procedure. Don't let low code speed deter you from getting into traffic work. Given a little time, your speed will reach the point where you can compete with the best of them. Concentrate first on learning net procedure, for most traffic nowadays is handled on nets.

Much traffic is also handled on phone. This mode is exceptionally well suited to short-range traffic work and requires knowledge of phonetics and procedure peculiar to voice operation. Procedure is of paramount importance on phone, since the public may be listening. The major problem, of course, is QRM.

Teamwork is the theme of net operation. The net which functions most efficiently is the net in which all participants are thoroughly familiar with the procedure used, and in which operators refrain from transmitting except at the direction of the net control station, and do not occupy time with extraneous comments, even the exchange of pleasantries. There is a time and place for everything. When a net is in session it should concentrate on handling traffic until all traffic is cleared. Before or after the net is the time for rag-chewing and discussion. Some details of net operation are included in *Operating an Amateur Radio Station*, mentioned earlier, but the whole story cannot be told. There is no substitute for actual participation.

The National Traffic System

To facilitate and speed the movement of message traffic, there is in existence an integrated national system by means of which originated traffic will normally reach its destination area the same day the message is originated. This system uses the local section net as a basis. Each section net sends a representative to a "regional" net (normally covering a call area) and each "regional" net sends a representative to an "area" net (normally covering a time zone). After the area net has cleared all its traffic, its members then go back to their respective regional nets, where they clear traffic to the various section net representatives. By means of connecting schedules between the area nets, traffic can flow both ways so that traffic originated on the West Coast reaches the East Coast with a maximum of dispatch, and vice versa. In general local section nets function at 1900, regional nets at 1945, area nets at 2030 and the same or different regional personnel again at 2130. Some section nets conduct a late session at 2200 to effect traffic delivery the same night. Local standard time is referred to in each case.

The NTS plan somewhat spreads traffic opportunity so that casual traffic may be reported into nets for efficient handling one or two nights per week, early or late; or the ardent traffic man can operate in *both* early and late groups and in between to roll up impressive totals and speed traffic reliably to its destination. Old-time traffic men who prefer a high degree of organization and teamwork have returned to the traffic game as a result of the new system. Beginners have shown more interest in becoming part of a system nationwide in scope, in which *anyone* can participate. The National Traffic System has vast and intriguing possibilities as an amateur service. It is open to any amateur who wishes to participate.

The above is but the briefest résumé of what is of necessity a rather complicated arrangement of nets and schedules. Complete details of the System and its operation are available to anyone interested. Just drop a line to ARRL Headquarters.

Emergency Communication

One of the most important ways in which the amateur serves the public, thus making his existence a national asset, is by his preparation for and his participation in communications emergencies. Every amateur, regardless of the extent of his normal operating activities, should give some thought to the possibility of his being the only means of communication should his community be cut off from the outside world. It has happened many times, often in the most unlikely places; it has happened without warning, finding some amateurs totally unprepared; it can happen to *you*. Are you ready?

There are two principal ways in which any amateur can prepare himself for such an eventuality. One is to provide himself with equipment capable of operating on any type of emergency power (i.e., either a.c. or d.c.), and equip-

THE CROSSROADS

ment which can readily be transported to the scene of disaster. Mobile equipment is especially desirable in most emergency situations.

Such equipment, regardless of how elaborate or how modern, is of little use, however, if it is not used properly and at the right times; and so another way for an amateur to prepare himself for emergencies, by no means less important than the first, is to *learn to operate efficiently*. There are many amateurs who feel that they know how to operate efficiently but who find themselves considerably handicapped at the crucial time by not knowing proper procedure, by being unable, due to years of casual amateur operation, to adapt themselves to snappy, abbreviated transmissions, and by being unfamiliar with message form and routing procedures. It is dangerous to overrate your ability in this respect; it is far better to assume that you have much to learn.

In general it can be said that there is more emergency equipment available than there are operators who know properly how to operate during emergency conditions, for such conditions require clipped, terse procedure with complete break-in on c.w. and fast push-to-talk on phone. The casual rag-chewing aspect of amateur radio, however enjoyable and worth-while in its place, must be forgotten at such times in favor of the business at hand. There is only one way to gain experience in this type of operation, and that is by practicing it. During an emergency is no time for practice; it should be done beforehand, as often as possible, on a regular basis.

This leads up to the necessity for emergency organization and preparedness. ARRL has long recognized this necessity and has provided for it. The Section Communications Manager (whose address appears on page 6 of every issue of *QST*) is empowered to appoint certain qualified amateurs in his section for the purpose of coordinating emergency communication organization and preparedness in specified areas or communities. This appointee is known as an Emergency Coordinator for the city or town. One is specified for each community. For coordination and promotion at section level a Section Emergency Coordinator arranges for and recommends the appointments of various Emergency Coordinators at activity points throughout the section. Emergency Coordinators organize amateurs in their communities according to local needs for emergency communication facilities.

The community amateurs taking part in the local organization are members of the Amateur Radio Emergency Corps (AREC). *All* amateurs are invited to register in the AREC, whether they are able to play an active part in their local organization or only a supporting role. Application blanks are available from your EC, SEC, SCM or direct from ARRL Headquarters. In the event that inquiry reveals no Emergency Coordinator appointed for your community, your SCM would welcome a recommendation either from yourself or from a radio club of which you are a member. By holding an amateur operator license, you have the responsibility both to your community and to amateur radio to uphold the traditions of the service.

Among the League's publications is a booklet entitled *Emergency Communications*. This booklet, while small in size, contains a wealth of information on AREC organization and functions and is invaluable to any amateur participating in emergency or civil defense work. It is free to AREC members and should be in every ama-

---

Before Emergency

PREPARE yourself by providing a transmitter-receiver setup together with an emergency power source upon which you can depend.

TEST both the dependability of your emergency equipment and your own operating ability in the annual ARRL Simulated Emergency Test and the several annual on-the-air contests, especially Field Day.

REGISTER your facilities and your availability with your local ARRL Emergency Coordinator. If your community has no EC, contact your local civic and relief agencies and explain to them what the Amateur Service offers the community in time of disaster.

In Emergency

LISTEN before you transmit. Never violate this principle.

REPORT at once to your Emergency Coordinator so that he will have up-to-the-minute data on the facilities available to him. Work with local civic and relief agencies as the EC suggests, offer these agencies your services directly in the absence of an EC.

RESTRICT all on-the-air work in accordance with FCC regulations, Sec. 12.156, whenever FCC "declares" a state of communications emergency.

QRRR is the official ARRL "land SOS," a distress call for emergency only. It is for use *only* by a station seeking assistance.

RESPECT the fact that the success of the amateur effort in emergency depends largely on circuit discipline. The established Net Control Station should be the supreme authority for priority and traffic routing.

COOPERATE with those we serve. Be ready to help, but stay off the air unless there is a specific job to be done that you can handle more efficiently than any other station.

COPY all bulletins from W1AW. During time of emergency special bulletins will keep you posted on the latest developments.

After Emergency

REPORT to ARRL Headquarters as soon as possible and as fully as possible so that the Amateur Service can receive full credit. Amateur Radio has won glowing public tribute in many major disasters since 1919. Maintain this record.

ARRL Operating Organization

teur's shack. Drop a line to the ARRL Communications Department if you want a copy, or use the coupon at the end of this chapter.

The Radio Amateur Civil Emergency Service

In order to be prepared for any eventuality, FCC and the Office of Civil and Defense Mobilization (OCDM), in collaboration with ARRL, have promulgated the Radio Amateur Civil Emergency Service. RACES is a temporary amateur service, intended primarily to serve civil defense and to continue operation during any extreme national emergency, such as war. It shares certain segments of frequencies with the regular Amateur Service on a nonexclusive basis. Its regulations have been made a sub-part of the familiar amateur regulations; that is, the original regulations have become sub-part A, the RACES regulations being added as sub-part B. Copies of both parts are included in the latest edition of the ARRL *License Manual.*

If *every* amateur participated, we would still be far short of the total operating personnel required properly to implement RACES. As the service which bears the responsibility for the successful implementation of this important function, we face not only the task of installing (and in some cases building) the necessary equipment, but also of the training of thousands of additional people. This can and should be a function of the local unit of the Amateur Radio Emergency Corps under its EC and his assistants, working in close collaboration with the local civil defense organization.

The first step in organizing RACES locally is the appointment of a Radio Officer by the local civil defense director, possibly on the recommendation of his communications officer. A complete and detailed communications plan must be approved successively by local, state and OCDM regional directors, by the OCDM National office, and by FCC. Once this has been accomplished, applications for station authorizations under this plan can be submitted direct to FCC. *QST* will carry further information from time to time, and ARRL will keep its field officials fully informed by bulletins as the situation requires. A complete bibliography of *QST* articles dealing with the subject of civil defense and RACES is available upon request from the ARRL Communications Department.

In the event of war, civil defense will place great reliance on RACES for radio communications. RACES is an Amateur Service. Its implementation is logically a function of the Amateur Radio Emergency Corps — an *additional* function in peacetime, but probably an exclusive function in wartime. Therefore, your best opportunity to be of service will be to register with your local EC, and to participate *actively* in the local AREC/RACES program.

ARRL Operating Organization

Amateur operation must have point and constructive purpose to win public respect. Each individual amateur is the ambassador of the entire fraternity in his public relations and attitude toward his hobby. ARRL field organization adds point and purpose to amateur operating.

The Communications Department of the League is concerned with the practical operation of stations in all branches of amateur activity. Appointments or awards are available for rag-chewer, traffic enthusiast, phone operator, DX man and experimenter.

There are seventy-three ARRL Sections in the League's field organization, which embraces the United States, Canada and certain other territory. Operating affairs in each Section are supervised by a Section Communications Manager elected by members in that section for a two-year term of office. Organization appointments are made by the section managers, elected as provided in the Rules and Regulations of the Communications Department, which accompany the League's By-Laws and Articles of Association. Section Communications Managers' addresses for all sections are given in full in each issue of *QST*. SCMs welcome monthly activity reports from all amateur stations in their jurisdiction.

Whether your activity embraces phone or telegraphy, or both, there is a place for you in League organization.

● LEADERSHIP POSTS

To advance each type of station work and group interest in amateur radio, and to develop practical communications plans with the greatest success, appointments of leaders and organizers in particular single-interest fields are made by SCMs. Each leadership post is important. Each provides activities and assistance for appointee groups and individual members along the lines of natural interest. Some posts further the general ability of amateurs to communicate efficiently at all times, by pointing activity toward networks and round tables, others are aimed specifically at establishment of provisions for organizing the amateur service as a stand-by communications group to serve the public in disaster, civil defense need or emergency of any sort. The SCM appoints the following in accordance with section needs and individual qualifications:

PAM	Phone Activities Manager. Organizes activities for OPSs and voice operators in his section. Promotes phone nets and recruits OPSs.
RM	Route Manager. Organizes and coordinates c.w. traffic activities. Supervises and promotes nets and recruits ORSs.
SEC	Section Emergency Coordinator. Promotes and administers section emergency radio organization.
EC	Emergency Coordinator. Organizes amateurs of a community or other local area for emergency radio service; maintains liaison with officials and agencies served; also with other local communication facilities. Sponsors tests, recruits for AREC and encourages alignment with RACES.

● STATION APPOINTMENTS

ARRL's field organization has a place for every active amateur who has a station. The Communications Department organization exists to increase individual enjoyment and station effectiveness in amateur radio work, and we extend a cordial invitation to every amateur to participate fully in the activities and to apply to the SCM for one of the following station appointments. ARRL membership and the General Class license or VE equivalent is prerequisite to appointments, except OES is available to Novice/Technician grades.

OPS   Official Phone Station. Sets high voice operating standards and procedures, furthers phone nets and traffic.

ORS   Official Relay Station. Traffic service, operates c.w. nets; noted for 15 w.p.m. and procedure ability.

OBS   Official Bulletin Station. Transmits ARRL and FCC bulletin information to amateurs.

OES   Official Experimental Station. Collects and reports v.h.f.-u.h.f.-s.h.f. propagation data, may engage in facsimile, TT, TV, work on 50 Mc. and/or above. Takes part as feasible in v.h.f. traffic work, reports same, supports v.h.f. nets, observes procedure standards.

OO   Official Observer. Sends cooperative notices to amateurs to assist in frequency observance, insures high-quality signals, and prevents FCC trouble.

Emblem Colors

Members wear the ARRL emblem with black-enamel background. A red background for an emblem will indicate that the wearer is SCM. SECs, ECs, RMs, and PAMs may wear the emblem with green background. Observers and all *station* appointees are entitled to wear blue emblems.

● SECTION NETS

Amateurs can add much experience and pleasure to their own amateur lives, and substance and accomplishment to the credit of all of amateur radio, when organized into effective interconnection of cities and towns.

The successful operation of a net depends a lot on the Net Control Station. This station should be chosen carefully and be one that will not hesitate to enforce each and every net rule and set the example in his own operation.

A progressive net grows, obtaining new members both directly and through other net members. Bulletins may be issued at intervals to keep in direct contact with the members regarding general net activity, to keep tab on net procedure,

make suggestions for improvement, keep track of active members and weed out inactive ones.

A National Traffic System is sponsored by ARRL to facilitate the over-all expeditious relay and delivery of message traffic. The system recognizes the need for handling traffic beyond the section-level networks that have the popular support of both phone and c.w. groups (OPS and ORS) throughout the League's field organization. Area and regional provisions for NTS are furthered by Headquarters correspondence. The ARRL Net Directory, revised in December each year, includes the frequencies and times of operation of the hundreds of different nets operating on amateur band frequencies.

Radio Club Affiliation

ARRL is pleased to grant affiliation to any amateur society having (1) at least 51% of the voting club membership as full members of the League, and (2) at least 51% of members government-licensed radio amateurs. In high school radio clubs *bearing the school name*, the first above requirement is modified to require one full member of ARRL in the club. Where a society has common aims and wishes to add strength to that of other club groups and strengthen amateur radio by affiliation with the national amateur organization, a request addressed to the Communications Manager will bring the necessary forms and information to initiate the application for affiliation. Such clubs receive field-organization bulletins and special information at intervals for posting on club bulletin boards or for relay to their memberships. A travel plan providing communications, technical and secretarial contact from the Headquarters is worked out seasonally to give maximum benefits to as many as possible of the several hundred active *affiliated* radio clubs. Papers on club work, suggestions for organizing, for constitutions, for radio courses of study, etc., are available on request.

Club Training Aids

One section of the ARRL Communications Department handles the Training Aids Program. This program is a service to ARRL affiliated clubs. Material is aimed at education, training and entertainment of club members. Interesting quiz material is available.

Training Aids include such items as motion-picture films, film strips, slides, audio tapes and lecture outlines. Bookings are limited to ARRL-affiliated clubs, since the visual aids listings are not sufficiently extensive to permit such services to other groups.

All Training Aids materials are loaned free (except for shipping charges) to ARRL affiliated clubs. Numerous groups use this ARRL service to good advantage. If your club is affiliated but has not yet taken advantage of this service, you are missing a good chance to add the available features to your meeting programs and general club activities. Watch club bulletins and *QST* or write the ARRL Communications Department for TA-21 and TA-32.

Operating Activities and Awards

● W1AW

The Maxim Memorial Station, W1AW, is dedicated to fraternity and service. Operated by the League headquarters, W1AW is located about four miles south of the Headquarters offices on a seven-acre site. The station is on the air daily, except holidays, and available time is divided between different bands and modes.

Telegraph and phone transmitters are provided for all bands from 1.8 to 144 Mc. The normal frequencies in each band for c.w. and voice transmissions are as follows: 1820, 3555, 3945, 7080, 7255, 14,100, 14,280, 21,075, 21,330, 28,080, 29,000, 50,900 and 145,600 kc. Operating-visiting hours and the station schedule are listed every other month in *QST*.

Operation is roughly proportional to amateur interest in different bands and modes, with one kw. except on 160 and v.h.f. bands. W1AW's daily bulletins and code practice aim to give operational help to the largest number.

All amateurs are invited to visit W1AW, as well as to work the station from their own shacks. The station was established to be a living memorial to Hiram Percy Maxim and to carry on the work and traditions of amateur radio.

● OPERATING ACTIVITIES

Within the ARRL field organization there are several special activities. First week ends of each month are often occasions for ARRL officials, officers and directors to get together over the air from their own stations. This activity is known to the gang as the LO (League officials) party. For all appointees, quarterly CD parties are scheduled additionally to develop operating ability and a spirit of fraternalism.

In addition to those for appointees and officials, ARRL sponsors various other activities open to all amateurs. The DX-minded amateur may participate in the Annual ARRL International DX Competition during February and March. This popular contest may bring you the thrill of working new countries and building up your DXCC totals; certificate awards are offered to top scorers in each country and ARRL section (see page 6 of any *QST*) and to club leaders. Then there is the ever-popular Sweepstakes in November. Of domestic scope, the SS affords the opportunity to work new states for that WAS award. A Novice activity is planned annually. The interests of v.h.f. enthusiasts are also provided for in contests held in January, June and September of each year. Where enough logs (three) are received to constitute minimum "competition" a certificate in spot activities, such as the "SS" and v.h.f. party, is awarded the leading newcomer for his work considered only in competition with other newcomers.

As in all our operating, the idea of having a good time is combined in the Annual Field Day with the more serious thought of preparing ourselves to render public service in times of emergency. A premium is placed on the use of equipment without connection to commercial power sources. Clubs and individual groups always enjoy themselves in the "FD," and learn much about the requirements for operating under knockabout conditions afield.

ARRL contest activities are diversified to appeal to all operating interests, and will be found announced in detail in issues of *QST* preceding the different events.

● AWARDS

The League-sponsored operating activities heretofore mentioned have useful objectives and provide much enjoyment for members of the fraternity. Achievement in amateur radio is recognized by various certificates offered through the League and detailed below.

WAS Award

WAS means "Worked All States." This award is available regardless of affiliation or nonaffiliation with any organization. Here are the simple rules to follow in going after your WAS:

1) Two-way communication must be established on the amateur bands with each of the states; any and all amateur

bands may be used. A card from the District of Columbia may be submitted in lieu of one from Maryland.

2) Contacts with all states must be made from the same location. Within a given community one location may be defined as from places no two of which are more than 25 miles apart.

3) Contacts may be made over any period of years, provided only that all contacts are from the same location, and except that only contacts with Alaska dated January 3, 1959 or later count, and only contacts with Hawaii dated August 21, 1959 or later count.

4) QSL cards, or other written communications from stations worked confirming the necessary two-way contacts, must be submitted by the applicant to ARRL headquarters.

5) Sufficient postage must be sent with the confirmations to finance their return. No correspondence will be returned unless sufficient postage is furnished.

6) The WAS award is available to all amateurs. It is required that the confirmations submitted be placed *alphabetically in order by states*.

7) Address all applications and confirmations to the Communications Department, ARRL, 38 La Salle Road, West Hartford, Conn.

DX Century Club Award

Here are the rules under which the DX Century Club Award will be issued to amateurs who have worked and confirmed contact with 100 countries in the postwar period.

1) The DX Century Club Award Certificate for confirmed contacts with 100 or more countries is available to all amateurs everywhere in the world.

2) Confirmations must be submitted direct to ARRL headquarters for all countries claimed. Claims for a total of 100 countries must be included with first application. Confirmation from foreign contest logs may be requested in the case of the ARRL International DX Competition only, subject to the following conditions:

a) Sufficient confirmations of other types must be submitted so that these, plus the DX Contest confirmations, will total 100. In every case, Contest confirmations must not be requested for any countries from which the applicant has regular confirmations. That is, contest confirmations will be granted only in the case of countries from which applicants have no regular confirmations.

b) Look up the contest results as published in *QST* to see if your man is listed in the foreign scores. If he isn't, he did not send in a log and no confirmation is possible.

c) Give year of contest, date and time of QSO.

d) In future DX Contests do not request confirmations until after the final results have been published, usually in one of the early fall issues. Requests before this time must be ignored.

3) The ARRL Countries List, printed periodically in *QST*, will be used in determining what constitutes a "country." This chapter contains the Postwar Countries List.

4) Confirmations must be accompanied by a list of claimed countries and stations to aid in checking and for future reference.

5) Confirmations from additional countries may be submitted for credit each time ten additional confirmations are available. Endorsements for affixing to certificates and showing the new confirmed total (110, 120, 130, etc.) will be awarded as additional credits are granted. ARRL DX Competition logs from foreign stations may be utilized for these endorsements, subject to conditions stated under (2).

6) All contacts must be made with amateur stations working in the authorized amateur bands or with other stations licensed to work amateurs.

7) In cases of countries where amateurs are licensed in the normal manner, credit may be claimed only for stations using regular government-assigned call letters. No credit may be claimed for contacts with stations in any countries in which amateurs have been temporarily closed down by special government edict where amateur licenses were formerly issued in the normal manner.

8) All stations contacted must be "land stations" . . . contacts with ships, anchored or otherwise, and aircraft, cannot be counted.

9) All stations must be contacted from the same call area, where such areas exist, or from the same country in cases where there are no call areas. One exception is allowed to this rule: where a station is moved from one call area to another, or from one country to another, all contacts must be made from within a radius of 150 miles of the initial location.

10) Contacts may be made over any period of years from November 15, 1945, provided only that all contacts be made under the provisions of Rule 9, and by the same station licensee; contacts may have been made under different call letters in the same area (or country), if the licensee for all was the same.

11) Any altered or forged confirmations submitted for CC credit will result in disqualification of the applicant. The eligibility of any DXCC applicant who was ever barred from DXCC to reapply, and the conditions for such application, shall be determined by the Awards Committee. Any holder of the Century Club Award submitting forged or altered confirmations must forfeit his right to be considered for further endorsements.

12) Operating ethics: Fair play and good sportsmanship in operating are required of all amateurs working toward the DX Century Club Award. In the event of specific objections relative to continued poor operating ethics an individual may be disqualified from the DXCC by action of the ARRL Awards Committee.

13) Sufficient postage for the return of confirmations must be forwarded with the application. In order to insure the safe return of large batches of confirmations, it is suggested that enough postage be sent to make possible their return by first-class mail, registered.

14) Decisions of the ARRL Awards Committee regarding interpretation of the rules as here printed or later amended shall be final.

15) Address all applications and confirmations to the Communications Department, ARRL, 38 La Salle Road, West Hartford 7, Conn.

WAC Award

The WAC award, Worked All Continents, is issued by the International Amateur Radio Union (IARU) upon proof of contact with each of the six continents. Amateurs in the U.S.A., Possessions and Canada should apply for the award through ARRL, headquarters society of the IARU. Those elsewhere must submit direct to their own IARU member-society. Residents of countries not represented in the Union may apply directly to ARRL for the award. Two basic types of WAC certificates are issued. One contains no endorsements and is awarded for c.w., or a combination of c.w. and phone contacts; the other is awarded when all work is done on phone. There is a special endorsement to the phone WAC when all of the confirmations submitted clearly indicate that the work was done on two-way s.s.b. The *only* special band endorsements are for 3.5 and 50 Mc.

Code Proficiency Award

Many hams can follow the general idea of a contact "by ear" but when pressed to "write it down" they "muff" the copy. The Code Proficiency Award permits each amateur to prove himself as a proficient operator, and sets up a system of awards for step-by-step gains in copying proficiency. It enables every amateur to check his code proficiency, to better that proficiency, and to receive a certification of his receiving speed.

This program is a whale of a lot of fun. The League will give a certificate to any licensed radio amateur who demonstrates that he can copy perfectly, for at least one minute, plain-language Continental code at 10, 15, 20, 25, 30 or 35

words per minute, as transmitted during special monthly transmissions from W1AW and W6OWP.

As part of the ARRL Code Proficiency program W1AW transmits plain-language practice material each evening at speeds from 5 to 35 w.p.m. All amateurs are invited to use these transmissions to increase their code-copying ability. Non-amateurs are invited to utilize the lower speeds, 5, 7½ and 10 w.p.m., which are transmitted for the benefit of persons studying the code in preparation for the amateur license examination. Refer to any issue of *QST* for details of the practice schedule.

Rag Chewers Club

The Rag Chewers Club is designed to encourage friendly contacts and discourage the "hello-good-by" type of QSO. It furthers fraternalism through amateur radio. Membership certificates are awarded.

How To Get in: (1) Chew the rag with a member of the club for at least a solid half hour. This does not mean a half hour spent in trying to get a message over through bad QRM or QRN, but a solid half hour of conversation or message handling. (2) Report the conversation by card to The Rag Chewers Club, ARRL, Communications Department, West Hartford, Conn., and ask the member station you talk with to do the same. When *both reports* are received you will be sent a membership certificate entitling you to all the privileges of a Rag Chewer.

How To Stay in: (1) Be a conversationalist on the air instead of one of those tongue-tied infants who don't know any words except "cuagn" or "cul," or "QRU" or "nil." Talk to the fellows you work with and get to know them. (2) Operate your station in accordance with the radio laws and ARRL practice. (3) Observe rules of courtesy on the air. (4) Sign "RCC" after each call so that others may know you can talk as well as call.

A-1 Operator Club

The A-1 Operator Club should include in its ranks every good operator. To become a member, one must be nominated by at least two operators who already belong. General keying or voice technique, procedure, copying ability, judgment and courtesy all count in rating candidates under the club rules detailed at length in *Operating an Amateur Radio Station*. Aim to make yourself a fine operator, and one of these days you may be pleasantly surprised by an invitation to belong to the A-1 Operator Club, which carries a worth-while certificate in its own right.

Brass Pounders League

Every individual reporting more than a speci-fied minimum in official monthly traffic totals is given an honor place in the *QST* listing known as the Brass Pounders League and a certificate to recognize his performance is furnished by the SCM. In addition, a *BPL Traffic Award* (medallion) is given to individual amateurs working at their own stations after the third time they "make BPL" provided it is duly reported to the SCM and recorded in *QST*.

The value to amateurs in operator training, and the utility of amateur message handling to the members of the fraternity itself as well as to the general public, make message-handling work of prime importance to the fraternity. Fun, enjoyment, and the feeling of having done something really worth while for one's fellows is accentuated by pride in message files, records, and letters from those served.

Old Timers Club

The Old Timers Club is open to anyone who holds an amateur call at the present time, and who held an amateur license (operator or station) 20-or-more years ago. Lapses in activity during the intervening years are permitted.

If you can qualify as an "Old Timer," send an outline of your ham career. Indicate the date of your first amateur license and your present call. If eligible for the OTC, you will be added to the roster and will receive a membership certificate.

● INVITATION

Amateur radio is capable of giving enjoyment, self-training, social and organization benefits in proportion to what the individual amateur puts into his hobby. All amateurs are invited to become ARRL members, to work toward awards, and to accept the challenge and invitation offered in field-organization appointments. Drop a line to ARRL Headquarters for the booklet *Operating an Amateur Radio Station*, which has detailed information on the field-organization appointments and awards. Accept today the invitation to take full part in all League activities and organization work.

CONELRAD COMPLIANCE

The FCC rules for the Amateur Service concerned with requirements in the event of enemy attack are contained in the ARRL *License Manual* as part of the amateur regulations, Sections 12.190 through 12.196. These are the rules for *control* of *electromagnetic radiation*, conelrad, to minimize radio navigational aids to an enemy. Read and follow these rules. They concern you.

Amateurs are required to *shut down* when a Conelrad Radio Alert is indicated. FCC requires monitoring, by some means, of a broadcast station while you operate. By use of proper equipment, each amateur can make his conelrad compliance routine and almost automatic. You will find descriptions of such devices, most of them quite simple, in this *Handbook* and in *QST*.

Operating Abbreviations and Prefixes

● Q SIGNALS

Given below are a number of Q signals whose meanings most often need to be expressed with brevity and clearness in amateur work. (Q abbreviations take the form of questions only when each is sent followed by a question mark.)

QRG Will you tell me my exact frequency (or that of......)? Your exact frequency (or that of......) is......kc.

QRH Does my frequency vary? Your frequency varies.

QRI How is the tone of my transmission? The tone of your transmission is..... (1. Good; 2. Variable; 3. Bad).

QRK What is the readability of my signals (or those of......)? The readability of your signals (or those of.....) is..... (1. Unreadable; 2. Readable now and then; 3. Readable but with difficulty; 4. Readable; 5. Perfectly readable).

QRL Are you busy? I am busy (or I am busy with ......). Please do not interfere.

QRM Are you being interfered with? I am interfered with.

QRN Are you troubled by static? I am being troubled by static.

QRO Must I increase power? Increase power.

QRP Must I decrease power? Decrease power.

QRQ Shall I send faster? Send faster (......words per min.).

QRS Shall I send more slowly? Send more slowly (.... w.p.m.).

QRT Shall I stop sending? Stop sending.

QRU Have you anything for me? I have nothing for you.

QRV Are you ready? I am ready.

QRW Shall I tell.....that you are calling him on .....kc.? Please inform.....that I am calling him on.....kc.

QRX When will you call me again? I will call you again at......hours (on........kc.).

QRZ Who is calling me? You are being called by..... (on......kc.).

QSA What is the strength of my signals (or those of ......)? The strength of your signals (or those of.....) is....... (1. Scarcely perceptible; 2. Weak; 3. Fairly good; 4. Good; 5. Very good).

QSB Are my signals fading? Your signals are fading.

QSD Is my keying defective? Your keying is defective.

QSG Shall I send.....messages at a time? Send..... messages at a time.

QSL Can you acknowledge receipt? I am acknowledging receipt.

QSM Shall I repeat the last message which I sent you, or some previous message? Repeat the last message which you sent me [or message(s) number(s).....].

QSO Can you communicate with....direct or by relay? I can communicate with.....direct (or by relay through.....).

QSP Will you relay to.....? I will relay to.....

QSV Shall I send a series of Vs on this frequency (or ....kc.)? Send a series of Vs on this frequency (or.....kc.).

QSW Will you send on this frequency (or on....kc.)? I am going to send on this frequency (or on ....kc.).

QSX Will you listen to.....on.....kc.? I am listening to......on.....kc.

QSY Shall I change to transmission on another frequency? Change to transmission on another frequency (or on....kc.).

QSZ Shall I send each word or group more than once? Send each word or group twice (or....times).

QTA Shall I cancel message number....as if it had not been sent? Cancel message number.....as if it had not been sent.

QTB Do you agree with my counting of words? I do not agree with your counting of words; I will repeat the first letter or digit of each word or group.

QTC How many messages have you to send? I have.... messages for you (or for.....).

QTH What is your location? My location is.....

QTR What is the exact time? The time is......

Special abbreviations adopted by ARRL:

QST General call preceding a message addressed to all amateurs and ARRL members. This is in effect "CQ ARRL."

QRRR Official ARRL "land SOS." A distress call for emergency use only by a station in an emergency situation.

THE R-S-T SYSTEM

READABILITY

1 — Unreadable.

2 — Barely readable, occasional words distinguishable.

3 — Readable with considerable difficulty.

4 — Readable with practically no difficulty.

5 — Perfectly readable.

SIGNAL STRENGTH

1 — Faint signals, barely perceptible.

2 — Very weak signals.

3 — Weak signals.

4 — Fair signals.

5 — Fairly good signals.

6 — Good signals.

7 — Moderately strong signals.

8 — Strong signals.

9 — Extremely strong signals.

TONE

1 — Extremely rough hissing note.

2 — Very rough a.c. note, no trace of musicality.

3 — Rough low-pitched a.c. note, slightly musical.

4 — Rather rough a.c. note, moderately musical.

5 — Musically-modulated note.

6 — Modulated note, slight trace of whistle.

7 — Near d.c. note, smooth ripple.

8 — Good d.c. note, just a trace of ripple.

9 — Purest d.c. note.

If the signal has the characteristic steadiness of crystal control, add the letter X to the RST report. If there is a chirp, the letter C may be added to so indicate. Similarly for a click, add K. The above reporting system is used on both c.w. and voice, leaving out the "tone" report on voice.

A.R.R.L. COUNTRIES LIST • Official List for ARRL Postwar DXCC

Prefix	Country
AC3	Sikkim
AC4	Tibet
AC5	Bhutan
AP2	Pakistan
BV, (C3)	Formosa
BY, (C)	China
C9	Manchuria
CE	Chile
CE9, KC4, LU-Z, VKØ, VP8, ZL5, etc.	Antarctica
CE9	(See VP8)
CEØA —	Easter Island
CEØZ	Juan Fernandez Archipelago
CM, CO	Cuba
CN2	Tangier
CN8, CN9	Morocco
CP	Bolivia
CR4	Cape Verde Islands
CR5	Portuguese Guinea
CR5	Principe, Sao Thome
CR6	Angola
CR7	Mozambique
CR8	Goa (Portuguese India)
CR9	Macao
CR1Ø	Portuguese Timor
CT1	Portugal
CT2	Azores
CT3	Madeira Islands
CX	Uruguay
DJ, DL, DM	Germany
DU	Philippine Islands
EA	Spain
EA6	Balearic Islands
EA8	Canary Islands
EA9	Ifni
EA9	Rio de Oro
EA9	Spanish Morocco
EAØ	Spanish Guinea
EI	Republic of Ireland
EL	Liberia
EQ	Iran
ET2	Eritrea
ET3	Ethiopia
F	France
FA	Algeria
FB8	Amsterdam & St. Paul Islands
FB8	Comoro Islands
FB8	Kerguelen Islands
FB8	Madagascar
FB8	Tromelin Island
FC (unofficial)	Corsica
FD	Togo
FE8	French Cameroons
FF8	French West Africa
FG7	Guadeloupe
FI8	French Indo-China
FK8	New Caledonia
FL8	French Somaliland
FM7	Martinique
FN	French India
FO8	Clipperton Island
FO8	French Oceania
FP8	St. Pierre & Miquelon Islands
FQ8	French Equatorial Africa
FR7	Reunion Island
FS7	Saint Martin
FU8, YJ1	New Hebrides
FW8	Wallis & Futuna Islands
FY7	French Guiana & Inini
G	England
GC	Channel Islands
GD	Isle of Man
GI	Northern Ireland
GM	Scotland
GW	Wales
HA	Hungary
HB	Switzerland
HC	Ecuador
HC8	Galapagos Islands
HE	Liechtenstein
HH	Haiti
HI	Dominican Republic
HK	Colombia
HKØ	Archipelago of San Andres and Providencia
HL	Korea
HP	Panama
HR	Honduras
HS	Thailand
HV	Vatican City
HZ	Saudi Arabia
I1, IT1	Italy
I1	Trieste
I5	Italian Somaliland
IS1	Sardinia
JA, KA	Japan
JT1	Mongolia
JY	Jordan
JZØ	Netherlands New Guinea
K, W	United States of America
KA	(See JA)
KAØ, KG6I	Bonin & Volcano Islands
KB6	Baker, Howland & American Phoenix Islands
KC4	(See CE9)
KC4	Navassa Island
KC6	Eastern Caroline Islands
KC6	Western Caroline Islands
KG1	(See OX)
KG4	Guantanamo Bay
KG6	Mariana Islands
KG6I—	(See KAØ)
KH6	Hawaiian Islands
KJ6	Johnston Island
KL7	Alaska
KM6	Midway Islands
KP4	Puerto Rico
KP6	Palmyra Group, Jarvis Island
KR6	Ryukyu Islands
KS4B	Serrana Bank & Roncador Cay
KS4	Swan Island
KS6	American Samoa
KV4	Virgin Islands
KW6	Wake Island
KX6	Marshall Islands
KZ5	Canal Zone
LA	Jan Mayen
LA	Norway
LA	Svalbard
LU	Argentina
LU-Z	(See CE9, VP8)
LX	Luxembourg
LZ	Bulgaria
M1	San Marino
MP4	Bahrein Island
MP4	Qatar
MP4	Trucial Oman
OA	Peru
OD5	Lebanon
OE	Austria
OH	Finland
OHØ	Aland Islands
OK	Czechoslovakia
ON4	Belgium
OQ5, Ø	Belgian Congo
OX, KG1	Greenland
OY	Faeroes
OZ	Denmark
PAØ, PI1	Netherlands
PJ	Netherlands West Indies
PJ2M—	Sint Maarten
PK1, 2, 3	Java
PK4	Sumatra
PK5	Netherlands Borneo
PK6	Celebes & Molucca Islands
PX	Andorra
PY	Brazil
PYØ	Fernando de Naronha
PYØ	Trinidade & Martin Vaz Islands
PZ1	Netherlands Guiana
SL, SM	Sweden
SP	Poland
ST2	Sudan
SU	Egypt
SV	Crete
SV	Dodecanese
SV	Greece
TA	Turkey
TF	Iceland
TG	Guatemala
TI	Costa Rica
TI9	Cocos Island
UA1, 2, 3, 4, 6	European Russian Socialist Federated Soviet Republic
UA1	Franz Josef Land
UA9, Ø	Asiatic Russian S.F.S.R.
UAØ	Wrangel Island
UB5	Ukraine
UC2	White Russian S.S.R.
UD6	Azerbaijan
UF6	Georgia
UG6	Armenia
UH8	Turkoman
UI8	Uzbek
UJ8	Tadzhik
UL7	Kazakh
UM8	Kirghiz
UN1	Karelo-Finnish Republic
UO5	Moldavia
UP2	Lithuania
UQ2	Latvia
UR2	Estonia
VE, VO	Canada
VK	Australia (including Tasmania)
VK	Lord Howe Island
VK9, ZC3	Christmas Island
VK9	Cocos Islands
VK9	Nauru Island
VK9	Norfolk Island
VK9	Papua Territory
VK9	Territory of New Guinea
VKØ	(See CE9)
VKØ	Heard Island
VKØ	Macquarie Island
VO	(See VE)
VP1	British Honduras
VP2	Anguilla
VP2	Antigua, Barbuda
VP2	British Virgin Islands
VP2	Dominica
VP2	Granada & Dependencies
VP2	Montserrat
VP2	St. Kitts, Nevis
VP2	St. Lucia
VP2	St. Vincent & Dependencies
VP3	British Guiana
VP4	Trinidad & Tobago
VP5	Jamaica (including Cayman Isls.)
VP5	Turks & Caicos Islands
VP6	Barbados
VP7	Bahama Islands
VP8	(See CE9)
VP8	Falkland Islands
VP8, LU-Z	South Georgia
VP8, LU-Z	South Orkney Islands
VP8, LU-Z	South Sandwich Islands
VP, LU-Z, CE9	South Shetland Islands
VP9	Bermuda Islands
VQ1	Zanzibar
VQ2	Northern Rhodesia
VQ3	Tanganyika Territory
VQ4	Kenya
VQ5	Uganda
VQ6	British Somaliland
VQ8	Chagos Islands
VQ8	Mauritius
VQ8	Rodriguez Island
VQ9	Seychelles
VR1	British Phoenix Islands
VR1	Gilbert & Ellice Islands & Ocean Island
VR2	Fiji Islands
VR3	Fanning & Christmas Islands
VR4	Solomon Islands
VR5	Tonga Islands
VR6	Pitcairn Island
VS1	Singapore
VS2	(See 9M2)
VS4	Sarawak
VS5	Brunei
VS6	Hong Kong
VS9	Aden & Socotra
VS9	Maldive Islands
VS9	Sultanate of Oman
VU2	India
VU4	Laccadive Islands
VU5	Andaman and Nicobar Islands
W	(See K)
XE, XF	Mexico
XE4	Revilla Gigedo
XV5	(See 3W8)
XW8	Laos
XZ2	Burma
YA	Afghanistan
YI	Iraq
YJ1	(See FU8)
YK	Syria
YN, YNØ	Nicaragua
YO	Roumania
YS	Salvador
YU	Yugoslavia
YV	Venezuela
YVØ	Aves Island
ZA	Albania
ZB1	Malta
ZB2	Gibraltar
ZC3	(See VK9)
ZC4	Cyprus
ZC5	British North Borneo
ZC6, 4X4	Palestine
ZD1	Sierra Leone
ZD2	Nigeria
ZD3	Gambia
ZD4	(See 9G1)
ZD4	Gold Coast, Togoland
ZD6	Nyasaland
ZD7	St. Helena
ZD8	Ascension Island
ZD9	Tristan da Cunha & Gough Islands
ZE	Southern Rhodesia
ZK1	Cook Islands
ZK1	Manihiki Islands
ZK2	Niue
ZL	Chatham Islands
ZL	Kermadec Islands
ZL	New Zealand
ZL5	(See CE9)
ZM6	British Samoa
ZM7	Tokelau (Union) Islands
ZP	Paraguay
ZS1, 2, 4, 5, 6	Union of South Africa
ZS2	Prince Edward & Marion Islands
ZS3	Southwest Africa
ZS7	Swaziland
ZS8	Basutoland
ZS9	Bechuanaland
3A	Monaco
3V8	Tunisia
3W8, XV5	Vietnam
4S7	Ceylon
4W1	Yemen
4X4	Israel
5A	Libya
7G1 (unofficial)	Rep. of Guinea
9G1, ZD4	Ghana
9K2	Kuwait
9M2	Malaya
9N1	Nepal
9S4	Saar
	Aldabra Islands
	Cambodia

INTERNATIONAL PREFIXES

AAA-ALZ	United States of America	SSN-STZ	Sudan
AMA-AOZ	Spain	SUA-SUZ	Egypt
APA-ASZ	Pakistan	SVA-SZZ	Greece
ATA-AWZ	India	TAA-TCZ	Turkey
AXA-AXZ	Commonwealth of Australia	TDA-TDZ	Guatemala
AYA-AZZ	Argentine Republic	TEA-TEZ	Costa Rica
BAA-BZZ	China	TFA-TFZ	Iceland
CAA-CEZ	Chile	TGA-TGZ	Guatemala
CFA-CKZ	Canada	THA-THZ	France and Colonies and Protectorates
CLA-CMZ	Cuba	TIA-TIZ	Costa Rica
CNA-CNZ	Morocco	TJA-TZZ	France and Colonies and Protectorates
COA-COZ	Cuba	UAA-UQZ	Union of Soviet Socialist Republics
CPA-CPZ	Bolivia	URA-UTZ	Ukrainian Soviet Socialist Republic
CQA-CRZ	Portuguese Overseas Provinces	UUA-UZZ	Union of Soviet Socialist Republics
CSA-CUZ	Portugal	VAA-VGZ	Canada
CVA-CXZ	Uruguay	VHA-VNZ	Commonwealth of Australia
CYA-CZZ	Canada	VOA-VOZ	Canada
DAA-DMZ	Germany	VPA-VSZ	British Colonies and Protectorates
DNA-DQZ	Belgian Congo	VTA-VWZ	India
DRA-DTZ	Bielorussian Soviet Socialist Republic	VXA-VYZ	Canada
DUA-DZZ	Republic of the Philippines	VZA-VZZ	Commonwealth of Australia
EAA-EHZ	Spain	WAA-WZZ	United States of America
EIA-EJZ	Ireland	XAA-XIZ	Mexico
EKA-EKZ	Union of Soviet Socialist Republics	XJA-XOZ	Canada
ELA-ELZ	Liberia	XPA-XPZ	Denmark
EMA-EOZ	Union of Soviet Socialist Republics	XQA-XRZ	Chile
EPA-EQZ	Iran	XSA-XSZ	China
ERA-ERZ	Union of Soviet Socialist Republics	XTA-XTZ	France and Colonies and Protectorates
ESA-ESZ	Estonia	XUA-XUZ	Cambodia
ETA-ETZ	Ethiopia	XVA-XVZ	Viet-Nam
EUA-EZZ	Union of Soviet Socialist Republics	XWA-XWZ	Laos
FAA-FZZ	France and Colonies and Protectorates	XXA-XXZ	Portuguese Overseas Provinces
GAA-GZZ	Great Britain	XYA-XZZ	Burma
HAA-HAZ	Hungarian People's Republic	YAA-YAZ	Afghanistan
HBA-HBZ	Switzerland	YBA-YHZ	Republic of Indonesia
HCA-HDZ	Ecuador	YIA-YIZ	Iraq
HEA-HEZ	Switzerland	YJA-YJZ	New Hebrides
HFA-HFZ	People's Republic of Poland	YKA-YKZ	Syrian Republic
HGA-HGZ	Hungarian People's Republic	YLA-YLZ	Latvia
HHA-HHZ	Republic of Haiti	YMA-YMZ	Turkey
HIA-HIZ	Dominican Republic	YNA-YNZ	Nicaragua
HJA-HKZ	Republic of Colombia	YOA-YRZ	Roumanian People's Republic
HLA-HMZ	Korea	YSA-YSZ	Republic of El Salvador
HNA-HNZ	Iraq	YTA-YUZ	Yugoslavia
HOA-HPZ	Republic of Panama	YVA-YYZ	Venezuela
HQA-HRZ	Republic of Honduras	YZA-YZZ	Yugoslavia
HSA-HSZ	Thailand	ZAA-ZAZ	Albania
HTA-HTZ	Nicaragua	ZBA-ZJZ	British Colonies and Protectorates
HUA-HUZ	Republic of El Salvador	ZKA-ZMZ	New Zealand
HVA-HVZ	Vatican City State	ZNA-ZOZ	British Colonies and Protectorates
HWA-HYZ	France and Colonies and Protectorates	ZPA-ZPZ	Paraguay
HZA-HZZ	Saudi Arabia	ZQA-ZQZ	British Colonies and Protectorates
IAA-IZZ	Italy and Colonies	ZRA-ZUZ	Union of South Africa
JAA-JSZ	Japan	ZVA-ZZZ	Brazil
JTA-JVZ	Mongolian People's Republic	2AA-2ZZ	Great Britain
JWA-JXZ	Norway	3AA-3AZ	Monaco
JYA-JYZ	Jordan	3BA-3FZ	Canada
JZA-JZZ	Netherlands New Guinea	3GA-3GZ	Chile
KAA-KZZ	United States of America	3HA-3UZ	China
LAA-LNZ	Norway	3VA-3VZ	Tunisia
LOA-LWZ	Argentine Republic	3WA-3WZ	Viet-Nam
LXA-LXZ	Luxembourg	3YA-3YZ	Norway
LYA-LYZ	Lithuania	3ZA-3ZZ	People's Republic of Poland
LZA-LZZ	People's Republic of Bulgaria	4AA-4CZ	Mexico
MAA-MZZ	Great Britain	4DA-4IZ	Republic of the Philippines
NAA-NZZ	United States of America	4JA-4LZ	Union of Soviet Socialist Republics
OAA-OCZ	Peru	4MA-4MZ	Venezuela
ODA-ODZ	Lebanon	4NA-4OZ	Yugoslavia
OEA-OEZ	Austria	4PA-4SZ	Ceylon
OFA-OJZ	Finland	4TA-4TZ	Peru
OKA-OMZ	Czechoslovakia	4UA-4UZ	United Nations
ONA-OTZ	Belgium and Colonies	4VA-4VZ	Republic of Haiti
OUA-OZZ	Denmark	4WA-4WZ	Yemen
PAA-PIZ	Netherlands	4XA-4XZ	State of Israel
PJA-PJZ	Netherlands Antilles	4YA-4YZ	International Civil Aviation Organization
PKA-POZ	Republic of Indonesia	5AA-5AZ	Libya
PPA-PYZ	Brazil	5CA-5CZ	Morocco
PZA-PZZ	Surinam	5LA-5LZ	Liberia
QAA-QZZ	(Service abbreviations)	5PA-5QZ	Denmark
RAA-RZZ	Union of Soviet Socialist Republics	9AA-9AZ	San Marino
SAA-SMZ	Sweden	9KA-9KZ	Kuwait
SNA-SRZ	People's Republic of Poland	9NA-9NZ	Nepal
SSA-SSM	Egypt	9SA-9SZ	Saar

Abbreviations

ABBREVIATIONS FOR C.W. WORK

Abbreviations help to cut down unnecessary transmission. However, make it a rule not to abbreviate unnecessarily when working an operator of unknown experience.

AA	All after	OB	Old boy
AB	All before	OM	Old man
ABT	About	OP-OPR	Operator
ADR	Address	OSC	Oscillator
AGN	Again	OT	Old timer; old top
ANT	Antenna	PBL	Preamble
BCI	Broadcast interference	PSE-PLS	Please
BCL	Broadcast listener	PWR	Power
BK	Break; break me; break in	PX	Press
BN	All between; been	R	Received as transmitted; are
B4	Before	RAC	Rectified alternating current
C	Yes	RCD	Received
CFM	Confirm; I confirm	REF	Refer to; referring to; reference
CK	Check	RPT	Repeat; I repeat
CL	I am closing my station; call	SED	Said
CLD-CLG	Called; calling	SEZ	Says
CUD	Could	SIG	Signature; signal
CUL	See you later	SINE	Operator's personal initials or nickname
CUM	Come	SKED	Schedule
CW	Continuous wave	SRI	Sorry
DLD-DLVD	Delivered	SVC	Service; prefix to service message
DX	Distance	TFC	Traffic
ECO	Electron-coupled oscillator	TMW	Tomorrow
FB	Fine business; excellent	TNX-TKS	Thanks
GA	Go ahead (or resume sending)	TT	That
GB	Good-by	TU	Thank you
GBA	Give better address	TVI	Television interference
GE	Good evening	TVL	Television listener
GG	Going	TXT	Text
GM	Good morning	UR-URS	Your; you're; yours
GN	Good night	VFO	Variable-frequency oscillator
GND	Ground	VY	Very
GUD	Good	WA	Word after
HI	The telegraphic laugh; high	WB	Word before
HR	Here; hear	WD-WDS	Word; words
HV	Have	WKD-WKG	Worked; working
HW	How	WL	Well; will
LID	A poor operator	WUD	Would
MILS	Milliamperes	WX	Weather
MSG	Message; prefix to radiogram	XMTR	Transmitter
N	No	XTAL	Crystal
ND	Nothing doing	YF (XYL)	Wife
NIL	Nothing; I have nothing for you	YL	Young lady
NR	Number	73	Best regards
NW	Now; I resume transmission	88	Love and kisses

W/K CALL AREAS BY STATES

Alabama	4	Montana	7
Alaska	KL7	Nebraska	Ø
Arizona	7	Nevada	7
Arkansas	5	New Hampshire	1
California	6	New Jersey	2
Colorado	Ø	New Mexico	5
Connecticut	1	New York	2
Delaware	3	North Carolina	4
Florida	4	North Dakota	Ø
Georgia	4	Ohio	8
Hawaii	KH6	Oklahoma	5
Idaho	7	Oregon	7
Illinois	9	Pennsylvania	3
Indiana	9	Rhode Island	1
Iowa	Ø	South Carolina	4
Kansas	Ø	South Dakota	Ø
Kentucky	4	Tennessee	4
Louisiana	5	Texas	5
Maine	1	Utah	7
Maryland (and District of Columbia)	3	Vermont	1
Massachusetts	1	Virginia	4
Michigan	8	Washington	7
Minnesota	Ø	West Virginia	8
Mississippi	5	Wisconsin	9
Missouri	Ø	Wyoming	7

▶ *Operating an Amateur Radio Station* covers the details of practical amateur operating. In it you will find information on Operating Practices, Emergency Communication, ARRL Operating Activities and Awards, the ARRL Field Organization, Handling Messages, Network Organization, "Q" Signals and Abbreviations used in amateur operating, important extracts from the FCC Regulations, and other helpful material. It's a handy reference that will serve to answer many of the questions concerning operating that arise during your activities on the air.

▶ *Emergency Communications* is the "bible" of the Amateur Radio Emergency Corps. Within its eight pages are contained the fundamentals of emergency communication which every amateur interested in public service work should know, including a complete diagrammatical plan adaptable for use in any community, explanation of the role of the American Red Cross and FCC's regulations concerning amateur operation in emergencies. The Radio Amateur Civil Emergency Service (RACES) comes in for special consideration, including a table of RACES frequencies on the front cover.

The two publications described above may be obtained without charge by any *Handbook* reader. Either or both will be sent upon request.

Vacuum Tubes and Semiconductors

For the convenience of the designer, the receiving-type tubes listed in this chapter are grouped by filament voltages and construction types (glass, metal, miniature, etc.). For example, all miniature tubes are listed in Table I, all metal tubes are in Table II, and so on.

Transmitting tubes are divided into triodes and tetrodes-pentodes, then listed according to rated plate dissipation. This permits direct comparison of ratings of tubes in the same power classification.

For quick reference, all tubes are listed in numerical-alphabetical order in the index. Types having no table reference are either obsolete or of little use in amateur equipment. Base diagrams for these tubes are listed, however.

Tube Ratings

Vacuum tubes are designed to be operated within definite maximum (and minimum) ratings. These ratings are the maximum safe operating voltages and currents for the electrodes, based on inherent limiting factors such as permissible cathode temperature, emission, and power dissipation in electrodes.

In the transmitting-tube tables, maximum ratings for electrode voltage, current and dissipation are given separately from the typical operating conditions for the recommended classes of operation. In the receiving-tube tables, because of space limitations, ratings and operating data are combined. Where only one set of operating conditions appears, the positive electrode voltages shown (plate, screen, etc.) are, in general, also the maximum rated voltages.

For certain air-cooled transmitting tubes, there are two sets of maximum values, one designated as CCS (Continuous Commercial Service) ratings, the other ICAS (Intermittent Commercial and Amateur Service) ratings. Continuous Commercial Service is defined as that type of service in which long tube life and reliability of performance under continuous operating conditions are the prime consideration. Intermittent Commercial and Amateur Service is defined to include the many applications where the transmitter design factors of minimum size, light weight, and maximum power output are more important than long tube life. ICAS ratings are considerably higher than CCS ratings. They permit the handling of greater power, and although such use involves some sacrifice in tube life, the period over which tubes give satisfactory performance in intermittent service can be extremely long.

The plate dissipation values given for transmitting tubes should not be exceeded during normal operation. In plate modulated amplifier applications, the maximum allowable carrier-condition plate dissipation is approximately 66 percent of the value listed and will rise to the maximum value under 100-per-cent sinusoidal modulation.

Typical Operating Conditions

The typical operating conditions given for transmitting tubes represent, in general, maximum ICAS ratings where such ratings have been given by the manufacturer. They do not represent the *only* possible method of operation of a particular tube type. Other values of plate voltage, plate current, grid bias, etc., may be used so long as the maximum ratings for a particular voltage or current are not exceeded.

Equivalent Tubes

The equivalent tubes listed in Table VIII are used occasionally in amateur service. In addition to the types listed, other equivalents are available for special purposes such as series-heater string operation in TV receivers. These types require unusual values of heater voltage (3.15, 4.2, etc.), and have controlled warm-up time characteristics to minimize voltage unbalance during starting. Except for heater design, these types correspond electrically and mechanically to 6-volt prototypes.

INDEX TO TUBE TABLES

CHAPTER 25

INDEX TO VACUUM-TUBE TYPES

Base-diagram section pages V5-V14. Classified data pages V15-V32.

Type	Page	Base
00-A	—	4D
01-A	—	4D
0A2	V23	5BO
0A3	V23	4AJ
0A4G	V23	4V
0A5	V23	Fig. 19
0B2	V23	5BO
0B3	V23	4AJ
0C2	V23	5BO
0C3	V23	4AJ
0D3	V23	4AJ
0G3	—	5BO
0Y4	—	4BU
0Z4	—	4R
0Z4A	—	4R
1	—	4G
1A3	V15	5AP
1A4P	—	4M
1A4T	—	4K
1A5GT	—	6X
1A6	—	6L
1A7GT	V21	7Z
1AB5	—	5BF
1AB6	—	7DH
1AC6	—	7DH
1AE4	—	6AR
1AF4	V15	6AR
1AF5	—	6AU
1AH5	—	6AU
1AJ4	—	6AR
1AX2	—	9Y
1B3GT	—	3C
1B4	—	4M
1B5	—	6M
1B7GT	—	7Z
1B8GT	—	8AW
1C3	—	5CF
1C5GT	—	6X
1C6	—	6L
1C7G	—	7Z
1C21	—	4V
1D5GP	—	5Y
1D5GT	—	5R
1D7G	—	7Z
1D8GT	—	8AJ
1DN5	V15	6BW
1E3	—	9BG
1E4G	—	5S
1E5GP	—	5Y
1E7G	—	8C
1EP1-2-11	V30	11V
1F4	—	5K
1F5G	—	6X
1F6	—	6W
1F7G	—	7AD
1G3-GT/ 1B3-GT	V24	3C
1G4GT	—	5S
1G5G	—	6X
1G6GT	—	7AB
1H4G	—	5S
1H5GT	V21	5Z
1H6G	—	7AA
1J3	V24	3C
1K3	V21	3C
1J5G	—	6X
1J6GT	—	7AB
1L4	V15	6AR
1L6	V15	7DC
1LA4	—	5AD
1LA6	—	7AK
1LB4	—	5AD
1LB6	—	8AX
1LC5	—	7AO
1LC6	—	7AK
1LD5	—	6AX
1LE3	—	4AA
1LF3	—	4AA
1LG5	—	7AO
1LH4	V21	5AG
1LN5	V21	7AO
1N5GT	V21	5Y
1N6G	—	7AM
1P5GT	—	5Y
1Q5GT	—	6AF
1R4	—	4AH
1R5	V15	7AT
1S4	V15	7AV
1S5	V15	6AU
1SA6GT	—	6CA
1SB6GT	—	6CB
1T4	V15	6AR
1T5GT	—	6X
1U4	V15	6AR
1U5	V15	6BW
1U6	—	7DC
1-V	—	4G
1V2	V24	9U
1W4	—	5BZ
1X2	—	9Y
1X2A	—	9Y
1X2B	—	9Y
1Y2	—	4P
1Z2	—	7CB
2A3	—	4D
2A4G	—	5S
2A5	—	6B
2A6	—	6G
2A7	—	7C
2AP1A	V30	11L
2B4	—	5A
2B6	—	7J
2B7	—	7D
2B22	—	Fig. 22
2B25	V24	3T
2BP1-11	V30	12E
2C4	—	5AS
2C21	—	7BH
2C22	—	4AM
2C25	—	4D
2C26A	—	4BB
2C34	V25	Fig. 70
2C36	V25	Fig. 21
2C37	V25	Fig. 21
2C39	V26	—
2C39WA	V21	—
2C40	V25	Fig. 11
2C43	V25	Fig. 11
2C51	—	8CJ
2C52	—	8BD
2D21	V23	7BN
2E5	—	6R
2E22	V28	5J
2E24	V28	7CL
2E25	V28	5BJ
2E26	V28	7CK
2E30	V15	7CQ
2E30	V28	7CQ
2EA5	V15	7EW
2EN5	V15	7FL
2G5	—	6R
2S/4S	—	5D
2V2	—	8FV
2V3G	—	4Y
2W3	—	4X
2X2	—	4AB
2X2-A	V24	4AB
2Y2	V24	4AB
2Z2	V24	4B
3A2	—	9DT
3A3	—	8EZ
3A4	V15	7BB
3A5	V15	7BC
3A8GT	—	8AS
3ACP1-7-11	V30	14J
3AP1-4	V30	7AN
3AP1A	V30	7CE
3B4	—	7CY
3B5GT	—	7AP
3B7	—	7BE
3B24	V24	Fig. 49
3B25	—	4P
3B26	—	Fig. 18
3B27	—	4P
3B28	V24	4P
3BP1-4-11	V30	14A
3BP1A	V30	14G
3C4	—	6BX
3C5GT	—	7AQ
3C6	—	7BW
3C22	V26	Fig. 17
3C23	—	3G
3C24	V25	2D
3C28	V25	Fig. 31
3C34	V25	3G
3CP1	V30	11C
3CX100A	V26	—
3D6	—	6BB
3D23	—	Fig. 30
3D24	V28	Fig. 75
3DK6	V15	7CM
3DP1A	V30	14H
3DP7	V30	14H
3DX3	—	Fig. 24
3E5	—	6BX
3E6	—	7CJ
3E22	—	8BY
3E29	V28	7BP
3EA5	V21	7EW
3EP1	V30	11N
3FP7	V30	14B
3FP7A	V30	14J
3GP1-4-5-11	V30	11A
3GP1A	V30	11N
3GP4A	V30	11N
3JP1—12	V30	14J
3JP1A—11A	V30	14J
3KP1-4-11	V30	11M
3LE4	—	6BA
3LF4	V21	6BB
3MP1	V30	12F
3Q4	V15	7BA
3Q5GT	V21	7AP
3RP1-4	V30	12E
3RP1A	V30	12E
3S4	V15	7BA
3SP1-4-7	V30	12E
3UP1	V30	12F
3V4	V21	6BX
3WP1-2-11	V30	12T
3X100A11	V26	—
3-25A3	V25	3G
3-25D3	V25	2D
3-50A4	V25	3G
3-50D4	V25	2D
3-50G2	—	2D
3-75A2	V26	2D
3-75A3	V26	2D
3-100A2	V26	2D
3-100A4	V26	2D
3-150A2	V27	4BC
3-150A3	V26	4BC
3-200A3	V27	Fig. 28
3-250A2	V27	2N
3-250A4	V27	2N
3-300A2	V27	4BC
3-300A3	V27	4BC
4A6G	—	8L
4C32	—	2N
4C34	V27	2N
4C36	—	Fig. 31
4CX300A	V29	—
4CX1000	V29	—
4D21	V29	5BK
4D22	V28	Fig. 26
4D23	—	5BK
4D32	V29	Fig. 27
4DK6	V21	7CM
4E27	V29	7BM
4E27A	V29	7BM
4EW6	V15	7CM
4X150A	V29	Fig. 75
4X150G	V29	—
4X250B	V29	Fig. 75
4-65A	V29	Fig. 25
4-125A	V29	5BK
4-250A	V29	5BK
4-400A	V29	5BK
4-1000A	V29	—
5A6	—	9L
5ABP1-7-11	V30	14J
5ADP1-7-11	V30	14J
5AJP1	V30	Fig. 78
5AMP1	V30	14U
5AP1-4	V30	11A
5AQP1	V30	14G
5AS4A	V24	5T
5ATP1-11	V30	14V
5AU4	V24	5T
5AW4	V24	5T
5AX4GT	—	5T
5AZ4	—	5T
5BP1	V30	11A
5BP1A	V30	11N
5BP7A	V30	11N
5CP1-11	V30	14B
5CP1A	V30	14J
5CP1B-11B	V30	14J
5CP7A	V30	14J
5CP11A	V30	14J
5CP12	V30	14J
5D22	V29	5BK
5EA8	V21	9AE
5FV8	V21	9FA
5GP1	V30	11A
5HP1-4	V30	11A
5HP1A	V30	11N
5JP1A-4A	V30	11S
5LP1A-4A	V30	11T
5MP1-11	V30	7AN
5NP1-4	V30	11A
5R4GY	V24	5T
5R4GYA	V24	5T
5RP1A-4A	V30	14P
5SP1-4	V30	14K
5T4	V24	5T
5U4G	V24	5T
5U4GA-GB	V24	5T
5UP1-11	V30	12E
5V3	V24	5T
5V4G	V21	5L
5V4GA	V24	5L
5VP7	V30	11N
5W4GT	V24	5T
5X3	—	4C
5X4G	V24	5Q
5XP1	V30	14P
5XP1A-11A	V30	14P
5Y3-G-GT	V24	5T
5Y3WGT	—	5T
5Y4-G-GT	V24	5Q
5YP1	V30	14Q
5Z3	V24	4C
5Z4	V24	5L
5-125B	V29	7BM
6A3	—	4D
6A4	—	5B
6A5GT	—	6T
6A6	V21	7B
6A7	V21	7C
6A8	V19	8A
6AB4	V15	5CE
6AB5	—	6R
6AB6G	—	7AU
6AB7	V19	8N
6AB8	—	9AT
6AC5GT	V20	6Q
6AC6G	—	7AU
6AC7	V19	8N
6AD5G	—	6Q
6AD6G	—	7AG
6AD7G	V20	8AY
6AD8	V15	9T
6AE5G	—	6Q
6AE6G	—	7AH
6AE7GT	—	7AX
6AE8	V21	8DU
6AF4	—	7DK
6AF4A	V15	7DK
6AF5G	—	6Q
6AF6G	—	7AG
6AF7G	—	8AG
6AG5	V15	7BD
6AG6G	—	7S
6AG7	V19	8Y
6AH4GT	V20	8EL
6AH5G	—	6AP
6AH6	V15	7BK
6AH7GT	—	8BE
6AJ4	—	9BX
6AJ5	—	7BD
6AJ7	—	8N
6AJ8	—	9CA
6AK5	V15	7BD
6AK6	V15	7BK
6AK7	—	8Y
6AK8	—	9E
6AL5	V15	6BT
6AL6G	—	6AM
6AL7GT	V20	8CH
6AM4	V15	9BX
6AM5	—	6CH
6AM6	—	7DB
6AM8	V21	9CY
6AM8A	V15	9CY
6AN4	V15	7DK
6AN5	V15	7BD
6AN6	—	7BJ
6AN7	—	9Q
6AN8	V21	9DA
6AN8A	V15	9DA
6AQ4	—	7DT
6AQ5	V21	7BZ
6AQ5A	V15	7BZ
6AQ6	V15	7BT
6AQ7GT	V20	8CK
6AR5	V15	6CC
6AR6	V20	6BQ
6AR7GT	V20	7DE
6AR8	V15	9DP
6AS5	V15	7CV
6AS6	V15	7CM
6AS7G	V20	8BD
6AS7GA	V22	8BD
6AS8	V15	9DS
6AT6	V15	7BT
6AT8	V22	9DW
6AT8A	V15	9DW
6AU4GT	—	4CG
6AU5GT	V20	6CK
6AU6	V22	7BK
6AU6A	V15	7BK
6AU7	V22	9A
6AU8	—	9DX
6AU8A	V15	9DX
6AV4	V24	5BS
6AV5GA	V20	6CK
6AV5GT	—	6CK
6AV6	V15	7BT
6AW7GT	—	8CQ
6AW8A	V15	9DX
6AX4GT	—	4CG
6AX5GT	V24	6S
6AX6G	—	7Q
6AX7	V22	9A
6AX8	V15	9AE
6AZ8	V15	9ED
6B4G	—	5S
6B5	—	6AS
6B6G	—	7V
6B7	—	7D
6B8	V19	8E
6BA6	V15	7BK
6BA7	V15	8CT
6BA8A	V15	9DX
6BC4	V15	9DR
6BC5	V15	7BD
6BC7	V15	9AX
6BC8	V15	9AJ
6BD4	—	Fig. 80
6BD4A	—	Fig. 80
6BD5GT	V20	6CK
6BD6	V15	7BK
6BD7	—	9Z
6BE6	V16	7CH
6BE7	—	9AA
6BE8	V22	9EG
6BE8A	V16	9EG
6BF5	V16	7BZ
6BF6	V16	7BT
6BG6G	—	5BT
6BG6GA	V20	5BT
6BH5	V16	9AZ
6BH6	V16	7CM
6BH8	V16	9DX
6BJ5	—	6CH
6BJ6A	V16	7CM
6BJ7	V16	9AX
6BJ8	V16	9ER
6BK5	V16	9BQ
6BK6	V16	7BT
6BK7	—	9AJ
6BK7A	—	9AJ
6BK7B	V16	9AJ
6BL7GTA	V20	8BD
6BL8	V16	Fig. 83
6BM5	—	7BZ
6BN4	V16	7EG
6BN6	V16	7DF
6BN7	—	9AJ
6BN8	V16	9ER
6BQ5	V16	9CV
6BQ6GA	V22	6AM
6BQ6GT	—	6AM
6BQ6GTA	V22	6AM
6BQ6GTB/ 6CU6	V20	6AM
6BQ7	—	9AJ
6BQ7A	V16	9AJ
6BR7	—	9BC
6BR8	V22	9FA
6BR8A	V16	9FA
6BS5	—	9BK
6BS7	—	9BB
6BS8	V16	9AJ
6BT6	V16	7BT
6BT8	V16	9FE
6BU5	—	8FP
6BU6	V16	7BT
6BU8	V16	9FG
6BV7	—	9BU
6BV8	V16	9FJ
6BW4	V24	9DJ
6BW6	—	9AM
6BW7	—	9AQ
6BW8	V16	9HK
6BX4	V24	5BS
6BX6	—	9AQ
6BX7GT	V20	8BD
6BX8	V16	9AJ
6BY5G	V24	6CN
6BY6	V16	7CH
6BY7	—	9AQ
6BY8	V16	9FN
6BZ6	V16	7CM
6BZ7	V16	9AJ
6BZ8	V16	9AJ
6C4	V16	6BG
6C4	V25	6BG
6C5	V19	6Q
6C6	V22	6F
6C7	—	7G
6C8G	—	8G
6CA4	V24	9M
6CA5	V16	7CV
6CB5	—	8GD
6CB5A	V20	8GD
6CB6	V22	7CM
6CB6A	V16	7CM
6CD6G	V22	5BT
6CD6GA	V20	5BT
6CE5	V16	7BD
6CF6	V16	7CM
6CG6	V16	7BK
6CG7	V16	9AJ
6CG8	V22	9GF
6CG8A	V16	9GF
6CH6	—	9BA
6CH7	—	9EW
6CH8	V16	9FT
6CJ6	—	9AS
6CK4	V20	8JB
6CK6	—	9AR
6CL5	V20	8GD
6CL6	V16	9BV
6CL8	V22	9FX
6CL8A	V16	9FX
6CM6	V16	9CK
6CM7	V16	9ES
6CM8	V16	9FZ
6CN7	V16	9EN
6CQ6	—	7DB
6CQ8	V16	9GE
6CR6	V16	7EA
6CR8	V16	9GJ
6CS5	V16	9CK
6CS6	V16	7CH
6CS7	V16	9EF
6CS8	V22	9FZ
6CU5	V16	7CV
6CU6	V20	6AM
6CU8	V22	9GM
6CX7	—	9FC
6CX8	V16	9DX
6CY5	V16	7EW
6CY7	V16	9EF
6CZ5	V16	9HN
6D4	V23	5AY
6D6	—	6F
6D7	—	7H
6D8G	—	8A
6DA4	V24	4CG
6DB5	V16	9GR
6DB6	V16	7CM
6DC6	V16	7CM
6DE6	V16	7CM
6DE7	V16	9HF
6DK6	V16	7CM
6DR7	V16	9HF
6DS5	V17	7BZ
6DG6GT	V20	7S
6DN6	V20	5BT
6DN7	V20	8BD
6DQ5	V20	8JC
6DQ6B	V20	6AM
6DT5	V17	9CV
6DT6	V17	7EN
6DT8	V17	9DE
6DW5	V17	9CK
6E5	—	6R
6E6	—	7B
6E7	—	7H
6E8G	—	8O
6EA7	V20	8BD
6EA8	V17	9AE
6EB8	V17	9DX
6EF6	V20	7S
6EH5	V17	7CV
6ES8	V17	9DE
6EV5	V17	7EW
6EW6	V22	7CM
6EY6	V20	7AC
6EZ5	V20	7AC
6EZ8	V17	9KA
6F4	V21	7BR
6F4	V25	7BR
6F5	V19	5M
6F6	V19	7AC
6F7	—	7E
6F8G	—	8G
6FH6	V20	6AM
6FM8	V17	9KR
6FV6	V17	7FQ
6FV8	V17	9FA
6G5	—	6R
6G6G	V20	7S
6H4GT	—	5AF
6H5	—	6R
6H6	V19	7Q
6H8G	—	8E
6J4	V17	7BQ
6J5	V19	6Q
6J6	V22	7BF
6J6A	V17	7BF
6J6A	V25	7BF
6J7	V19	7R
6J8G	—	8H
6K5GT	—	5U
6K6GT	V20	7S

VACUUM-TUBE DATA

Type	Page	Base	Type	Page	Base	Type	Page	Base	Type	Page	Base	Type	Page	Base
3K7	V19	7R	7E7	V20	8AE	12DV7	V18	9JY	25C5	V22	7CV	89	—	6F
3K8	—	8K	7EP4	V30	11N	12DV8	—	9HR	25C6G	—	7AC	90C1	V23	5BO
3L4	V21	7BR	7EV6	V22	7AC	12DW5	V22	9CK	25C6GA	V22	7S	99	—	4D
3L5G	—	6Q	7F7	V22	8AC	12DW7	V18	9JC	25CA5	—	7CV	100TH	V26	2D
3L6	V22	7AC	7F8	V20	8BW	12DW8	—	9JC	25CD6GA	V22	5BT	100TL	V26	2D
3L6GA	V22	7S	7G7	—	8V	12DY8	V18	9JD	25CD6GB	V22	5BT	111H	—	2D
3L6GB	V19	7S	7G8	—	8BV	12DZ6	V18	7BK	25CU6	V22	6AM	112-A	—	4D
3L6GX	—	7S	7GP4	V30	14G	12E5GT	—	6Q	25D8GT	—	8AF	117L7GT	V24	8AO
3L7	V19	7T	7H7	—	8V	12EA6	V18	7BK	25DN6	V22	5BT	117M7GT	V24	8AO
3M5	—	9N	7J7	—	8BL	12EC8	V18	9FA	25DQ6	—	6AM	117N7GT	V21	8AV
3M6G	—	7S	7JP1-4-7	V30	14R	12ED5	V18	7CV	25EC6	V22	5BT	117N7GT	V24	8AV
3M7G	—	7R	7K7	V20	8BF	12EF6	V22	7S	25EH5	V22	7CV	117P7GT	V24	8AV
3M8GT	—	8AU	7L7	—	8V	12EG6	V18	7CH	25F5	V18	7CV	117Z3	V24	4CB
3N4	—	7CA	7N7	V22	8AC	12EK6	V18	7BK	25L6GT	V22	7S	117Z4GT	—	5AA
3N5	—	6R	7Q7	V22	8AL	12EL6	V18	7FB	25N6G	—	7W	117Z6GT	—	7Q
3N6G	—	7AU	7R7	—	8AE	12EM6	V18	9HV	25S	—	6M	128AS	—	5A
3N7	V19	8B	7S7	—	8BL	12EN6	V21	7S	25SA7GT	V22	8AD	150T	—	2N
3N8	V25	8B	7T7	—	8V	12EZ5GT	—	5M	25T	V25	3G	152TH	V26	4BC
3N8	—	9T	7V7	—	8V	12F5	V18	9FH	25W4GT	—	4CG	152TL	V27	4BC
3P5GT	—	6Q	7VP1	V30	14R	12FK6	V18	7BT	25W6GT	V22	7S	182-B	—	4D
3P7G	—	7U	7W7	—	8BJ	12FM6	V18	7BT	25X6GT	—	7Q	183	—	4D
3P8G	—	8K	7X6	—	7AJ	12FP7	—	14E	25Y4GT	—	5AA	203-A	—	4E
3Q4	—	9S	7X7	V22	8BZ	12FT6	V18	7BT	25Y5	—	6G	203-H	—	3N
3Q5G	—	6Q	7Y4	—	5AB	12G4	V22	6BG	25Z3	V24	4G	204-A	—	4E
3Q6G	—	6Y	7Z4	—	5AB	12G7G	—	7V	25Z4	—	5AA	205-D	—	4E
3R4	V19	9R	9BM5	—	14G	12G8	—	9CZ	25Z5	V24	6E	211	V26	4E
3R6G	—	6AW	9BM6	—	7BZ	12GP7	—	14S	25Z6	V24	7Q	212-E	—	Fig. 43
3R7	V19	7V	9BW6	—	9AM	12H4	V18	7DW	26	—	4D	217-A	—	4AT
3R8	V17	9E	9NP1	—	6BN	12H6	V22	7Q	26A6	—	7BK	217-C	—	4AT
3S4	V22	9AC	10	—	4D	12HP7	—	11J	26A7GT	—	8BU	227-A	—	Fig. 53
3S4A	V17	9AC	10EB8	V22	9DX	12J5GT	V22	6Q	26BK6	—	7BT	241-B	—	Fig. 44
3S6GT	—	5AK	10GP4	—	14G	12J7GT	V22	7R	26C6	—	7BT	242-A	—	4E
3S7	—	7R	10HP4	—	14G	12J8	V18	9GC	26CG6	—	7BK	242-B	—	4E
3S8GT	V20	8CB	10Y	V25	4D	12K5	V18	7EK	26D6	—	7CH	242-C	—	4E
3SA7GT	V19	8R	11/12	—	4F	12K7GT	V22	7R	26Z5W	—	9BS	249-B	—	Fig. 29
3SB7Y	V19	8R	12A4	V17	9AG	12K8	V22	8K	27	—	5A	250TH	V27	2N
3SC7	V19	8S	12A5	—	7F	12L6GT	V21	7S	28Z5	—	5AB	250TL	V27	2N
3SD7GT	V20	8N	12A6	V21	7S	12L8GT	—	8BU	30	—	4D	254	V26	2N
3SE7GT	—	8N	12A7	—	7K	12Q7GT	—	7V	31	—	4D	254-A	—	Fig. 57
3SF5	V19	6AB	12A8GT	V22	8A	12R5	V18	7CV	32	—	4K	254-B	—	Fig. 57
3SF7	V19	7AZ	12AB5	V17	9EU	12S8GT	V22	8CB	32ET5	V18	8Z	261-A	—	4E
3SG7	V19	8BK	12AC6	V17	7BK	12SA7	V22	8R	32L7GT	—	8Z	270-A	—	Fig. 39
3SH7	V19	8BK	12AD6	V17	7CH	12SC7	V22	8S	33	—	5K	276-A	—	4E
3SH7L	—	8BK	12AD7	V17	9A	12SF5	V22	6AB	34	—	4M	282-A	—	Fig. 57
3SJ7	V19	8N	12AE6A	V17	7BT	12SF7	V22	7AZ	35/51	—	5E	284-B	—	3N
3SJ7Y	V19	8N	12AE7	V17	9A	12SG7	V22	8BK	35A5	V21	6AA	284-D	—	4E
3SK7	V19	8N	12AF6	V17	7BK	12SH7	V22	8BK	35B5	V18	7BZ	295-A	—	4E
3SL7GT	V20	8BD	12AG6	—	7CH	12SJ7	V22	8N	35C5	V22	7CV	300T	—	2N
3SN7GT	V22	8BD	12AH7GT	V17	8BE	12SK7	V22	8N	35L6GT	V22	7S	303-A	—	4E
3SN7GTA	V22	8BD	12AH8	—	9BP	12SL7GT	V22	8BD	35T	V25	3G	304-A	—	Fig. 39
3SN7GTB	V20	8BD	12AJ6	V17	7BT	12SN7GT	V22	8BD	35TG	V25	2D	304-B	—	2D
3SQ7GT	V19	8Q	12AL5	V22	6BT	12SN7GTA	V22	8BD	35W4	V24	5BQ	304TH	V27	4BC
3SS7	V19	8Q	12AL8	V17	9GS	12SQ7	V22	8Q	35Y4	—	5AL	304TL	V27	4BC
3SS7	V19	8N	12AQ5	V17	7BZ	12SR7	V22	8Q	35Z3	—	4Z	305-A	—	Fig. 59
3ST7	—	8Q	12AT6	V22	7BT	12SW7	—	8Q	35Z4GT	V24	5AA	306-A	—	Fig. 63
3SU7GTY	V22	8BD	12AT7	V17	9A	12SX7	—	8BD	35Z5G	V24	6AD	307-A	—	Fig. 61
3SV7	—	7AZ	12AU6	V22	7BK	12SY7	V21	8R	35Z6G	—	7Q	308-B	—	Fig. 43
3SZ7	—	8Q	12AU7A	V17	9A	12U7	V18	9A	36	—	5E	310	—	4D
3T4	V17	7DK	12AV5GA	V22	6CK	12V6GT	—	7S	36AM3	V24	5BQ	311	V26	4E
3T5	—	6R	12AV6	V22	7BT	12W6GT	V22	7S	37	—	5A	311CH	—	Fig. 32
3T6GM	—	6Z	12AV7	V17	9A	12X4	V24	5BS	38	—	5F	312-A	—	Fig. 68
3T7	—	7V	12AW6	V17	7CM	12Z3	—	4G	39/44	—	5F	312-E	—	Fig. 44
3T8	V22	9E	12AW7	—	7CM	12Z5	—	7L	40	—	4D	316-A	V25	—
3T8A	V17	9E	12AX4GT	—	4CG	14A4	—	5AC	40Z5GT	—	6AD	327-A	—	Fig. 50
3U3	—	9BM	12AX4GTA	—	4CG	14A5	—	6AA	41	V22	6B	327-B	—	Fig. 50
3U4GT	V24	4CG	12AX7	V17	9A	14A7	V22	8V	42	V22	6B	342-B	—	4E
3U5	—	6R	12AY7	V17	9A	14AF7	V22	8AC	43	—	6B	356-A	—	Fig. 55
3U6GT	V20	7S	12AZ7A	V17	9A	14AP1-4	—	12A	45	—	4D	361-A	—	4E
3U7G	—	7R	12B4	V22	9AG	14B6	V22	8W	45Z3	—	5AM	376-A	—	4E
3U8	V22	9AE	12B4A	V17	9AG	14B8	—	8X	45Z5GT	—	6AD	417-A	V22	9V
3U8	V17	9AE	12B6M	—	6Y	14C5	—	6AA	46	—	5C	482-B	—	4D
3V3	—	9BD	12B7	—	8V	14C7	—	8V	47	—	5B	483	—	4D
3V3A	—	9BD	12B7ML	—	8V	14E6	—	8W	48	—	6A	485	—	5A
3V4	V24	9M	12B8GT	—	8T	14E7	—	8AE	49	—	5C	527	—	Fig. 53
3V5GT	V20	6AO	12BA6	V22	7BK	14F7	V22	8AC	50	—	4D	559	—	Fig. 10
3V6	V22	7AC	12BA7	V22	8CT	14F8	—	8BW	50A5	V22	6AA	575-A	—	4AT
3V6GTA	V19	7S	12BD6	V22	7BK	14H7	—	8V	50AX6G	—	7Q	592	V27	Fig. 28
3V7G	—	7V	12BE6	V22	7CH	14J7	—	8BL	50B5	V18	7BZ	705-A	V27	Fig. 45
3V8	V17	9AH	12BF6	V22	7BT	14N7	V22	8AC	50BK5	V22	9BQ	717-A	—	8BK
3W4GT	—	4CG	12BH7	—	9A	14Q7	V22	8AL	50C5	V22	7CV	756	—	4D
3W5G	—	6S	12BH7A	V17	9A	14R7	—	8AE	50C6G	V22	7S	800	—	2D
3W6GT	V20	7S	12BK5	V22	9BQ	14S7	—	8BL	50C6GA	V21	7S	801A/801	V25	4D
3W7G	—	7R	12BL6	V22	7BT	14V7	—	8V	50DC4	V24	5BQ	802	—	6BM
3X4/6063	V24	7CF	12BL6	V17	7BK	14W7	—	8BJ	50L6GT	V22	7S	803	V29	5J
3X5GT	V24	6S	12BN6	V22	7DF	14X7	—	8BZ	50T	—	2D	804	—	Fig. 61
3X6G	—	7AL	12BQ6GA	V22	6AM	14Y4	—	5AB	50X6	—	7AJ	805	V26	3N
3X8	—	9AK	12BQ6GT	V22	6AM	14Z3	—	4G	50Y6GT	V24	7Q	806	V27	2N
3X8A	V17	9AK	12BQ6GTB	V22	6AM	15	—	5F	50Y7GT	—	8AN	807	V28	5AW
3Y3G	—	4AC	12BR7A	V17	9CF	15A6	—	9AR	50Z6G	V24	7Q	807W	V28	5AW
3Y5	—	6J	12BT6	V22	7BT	15E	V25	Fig. 51	50Z7G	—	8AN	808	—	2D
3Y6G	V22	7S	12BU6	V22	7BT	16A5	—	9BL	51	—	5E	809	V25	3G
3Y6GA	V20	7S	12BW4	V22	9DJ	17	—	3G	52	—	5C	810	V27	2N
3Y7G	V22	7S	12BV7	V17	9BF	17Z3	—	9CB	53	—	7B	811	V26	3G
3Y7G	—	8B	12BY7A	V17	9BF	18	—	6B	53A	—	Fig. 53	811A	V26	3G
3Z3	V24	4G	12BZ6	V22	7CM	18FW6	V18	7CC	55	—	6G	812	V26	3G
3Z4	V24	5D	12BZ7	V17	9A	18FX6	V18	7CH	56	—	5A	812A	V26	3G
3Z5	—	6K	12C5	V22	7CV	18FY6	V18	7BT	56AS	—	5A	812H	—	3G
3Z7G	—	8B	12C8	V22	8E	19	—	6C	57	—	6F	813	V29	5BA
3ZY5G	—	6X	12CA5	V22	7CV	19CL8A	V22	9FX	57AS	—	6F	814	V28	Fig. 64
4A4	V22	5AS	12CM6	V22	9CK	19X3	—	9BM	58	—	6F	815	V28	8BY
4A6	—	6AA	12CN5	V17	7CV	19Y3	—	9BM	58AS	—	6F	822	V24	4P
4A6	V22	7AJ	12CR6	V22	7EA	20	—	4D	59	—	7A	822	—	3N
4A7	V20	8V	12CS5	V22	9CK	20AP1-4	—	12A	70A7GT	—	8AB	822S	—	2D
4A8	V20	8U	12CS6	V22	7CH	20J8GM	—	8H	70L7GT	—	8AA	826	V26	7BO
4B7	—	8BO	12CT8	—	9DA	21A6	—	9AS	71-A	—	4D	829	V29	5J
4AD7	—	8V	12CU5	V22	7CV	21EX6	V21	5BT	72	—	4Y	829-A	—	7BP
4AF7	—	8AC	12CU6	V22	6AM	22	—	4K	73	—	4Y	829B	V28	7BP
4AG7	—	8V	12CX6	V17	7BK	24-A	—	5E	75	V22	6G	830	—	4D
4AH7	V20	8V	12DB5	V22	9GR	24-G	V25	2D	75TH	V26	2D	830B	V26	3G
4AJ7	—	8V	12DE8	V17	Fig. 81	24XH	V30	Fig. 1	75TL	V26	2D	831	—	Fig. 40
4AK7	V20	8V	12DF5	V24	9BS	25A6	—	7S	76	—	5A	832	—	7BP
4B4	V22	5AC	12DF7	V22	9A	25A7GT	—	8F	77	—	6F	832A	V28	7BP
4B5	V22	6AE	12DK7	V17	9HZ	25AC5G	—	6Q	78	V22	6F	833	V27	Fig. 41
4B6	V22	8V	12DL8	V17	9HR	25AV5GA	—	6CK	79	—	6H	834	—	2D
4B7	V20	8V	12DQ6A	V22	6AM	25AV5GT	—	6CK	80	V24	4C	835	—	4E
4B8	V22	8X	12DQ7	V18	9BF	25AX4GT	—	4CG	81	—	4B	836	V24	4P
4C4	—	4AH	12DS7A	V18	9JU	25B5	—	6D	82	V24	4C	837	V28	6BM
4C5	V22	6AA	12DT5	V22	9HN	25B6G	—	7S	83	V24	4C	838	—	4E
4C6	—	8W	12DT7	V18	9A	25B8GT	—	8T	83-V	V24	4AD	840	—	4E
4D7	V20	8V	12DT8	V22	9BF	25BK5	—	9BQ	84/6Z4	V24	4D	841	—	4D
4E5	V21	8BN	12DU7	V18	9JX	25BQ6GA	V22	6AM	85	—	6G	841A	—	3G
4E6	—	8W				25BQ6GT	V22	6AM	85AS	—	6G	841SW	—	3G
						25BQ6GTB	V22	6AM						

Type	Page	Base
843	—	5A
844	—	5AW
849	—	Fig. 39
850	—	Fig. 47
852	—	2D
860	—	Fig. 58
861	—	Fig. 42
864	—	4D
865	—	Fig. 57
866	—	4P
866A-AX	V24	4P
866B	V24	4P
866jr	V24	4B
871	—	4P
872A/872	V24	4AT
874	—	4S
878	—	4P
879	—	4AB
884	V23	6Q
885	—	5A
902A	V30	8CD
905	V30	5BP
905A	V30	5BR
906P1-11	V30	7AN
907	V30	5BP
908A	V30	7CE
909	—	5BP
910	—	7AN
911	—	7AN
913	V30	913
914A	—	6BF
930B	V26	3G
938	—	4E
950	—	5K
951	—	4M
954	V21	5BB
955	V21	5BC
955	V25	5BC
956	V21	5BB
957	—	5BD
958	—	5BD
958A	V21	5BD
958A	V25	5BD
959	V21	5BE
967	V23	3G
975A	—	4AT
991	V23	—
1003	—	4R
1005	—	5AQ
1006	—	4C
1201	V21	8BN
1203	—	4AH
1204	—	8BO
1206	—	8BV
1221	V22	6F
1223	V22	7R
1229	—	4K
1230	—	4D
1231	—	8V
1232	—	8V
1265	V23	4AJ
1266	V23	4AJ
1267	V23	4V
1273	—	8V
1274	—	6S
1275	—	4C
1276	—	4D
1280	—	8V
1284	—	8V
1291	—	7BE
1293	—	4AA
1294	—	4AH
1299	—	6BB
1602	—	4D
1603	—	6F
1608	—	4D
1609	V21	5B
1610	—	Fig. 62
1611	—	7S
1612	V19	7T
1613	—	7S
1614	V28	7AC
1616	—	4P
1619	V28	Fig. 74
1620	V19	7R
1621	V19	7S
1622	V19	7AC
1623	V25	3G
1624	V28	Fig. 66
1625	V28	5AZ
1626	—	6Q
1627	—	2N
1628	—	Fig. 54
1629	—	6RA
1631	V22	7AC
1632	V22	7S
1633	—	8BD
1634	V22	8S
1635	V20	8B
1641	—	Fig. 52
1642	—	7BH

Type	Page	Base
1644	—	Fig. 4
1654	—	2Z
1802P1-11	V30	11A
1805P1-4	V30	11A
1806P1	V30	11N
1851	—	7R
1852	V19	8N
1853	V19	8N
2002	V30	Fig. 1
2005	V30	Fig. 1
2050	V23	8BA
2051	—	8BA
2523N/128A	—	5A
5514	V26	4BO
5516	V28	7CL
5517	—	5BU
5556	—	4D
5562	—	Fig. 30
5590	—	7BD
5591	V22	7BD
5608	—	7BD
5608A	—	7B
5610	—	6CG
5618	—	7CU
5651	V23	5BO
5654	V22	7BD
5656	—	9F
5662	V23	Fig. 79
5663	—	7CE
5670	V22	8CJ
5675	V25	Fig. 21
5679	V22	7CX
5686	V18	9G
5687	V18	9H
5690	—	Fig. 38
5691	V22	8BD
5692	V22	8BD
5693	V19	8N
5694	—	8CS
5696	V23	7BN
5722	V18	5CB
5725	V22	7CM
5726	V22	6BT
5727	V23	7BN
5731	—	5BC
5749	V22	7BK
5750	V22	7CH
5751	V22	9A
5755	—	9J
5763	V28	9K
5764	V25	Fig. 21
5765	—	Fig. 21
5766	See 2C37	
5767	See 2C37	
5768	V21	Fig. 21
5794	—	Fig. 21
5812	—	7CQ
5814	—	9A
5814A	V22	9A
5823	V23	4CK
5824	V21	7S
5825	—	4P
5839	—	6S
5842	V18	9V
5844	—	7BF
5845	—	5CA
5847	—	9X
5852	—	6S
5857	—	9AB
5866	V26	Fig. 3
5867	V27	Fig. 3
5871	V22	7AC
5876	—	Fig. 21
5879	V18	9AD
5881	V22	7AC
5890	V23	12J
5893	V25	Fig. 21
5894A	V28	Fig. 7
5910	V22	6AR
5915	V22	7CH
5920	—	7BF
5933	V28	5AZ
5961	—	8R
5962	V23	2AG
5963	V22	9A
5964	V22	7BF
5965	V22	9A
5993	—	Fig. 35
5998	V23	8BD
6005	—	7BZ
6023	—	9CD
6026	V25	Fig. 16
6028	—	7BD
6045	—	7BF
6046	V22	7AC
6057	V22	9A
6058	V22	6BT
6059	V22	9BC
6060	V22	9A
6061	V22	9AM
6062	—	9K

Type	Page	Base
6063	V24	7CF
6064	V22	7DB
6065	V22	7DB
6066	V22	7BT
6067	V23	9A
6072	—	9A
6073	V23	5BO
6074	V23	5BO
6080	V23	8BD
6082	V21	8BD
6083	—	Fig. 5
6084	—	9BJ
6085	—	9A
6086	—	9BK
6087	—	5L
6101	V23	7BF
6132	V23	9BA
6135	—	6BG
6136	V23	7BK
6137	—	8N
6140	—	9BY
6141	—	9BZ
6146	V28	7CK
6155	V29	5BK
6156	V29	5BK
6157	—	Fig. 36
6158	—	9A
6159	V28	7CK
6173	V21	Fig. 34
6197	—	9BV
6201	V23	9A
6211	—	9A
6216	—	Fig. 37
6218	—	9CG
6227	—	9BA
6252	V28	Fig. 7
6263	V25	—
6264	V25	—
6265	V23	7CM
6287	—	9CT
6299	V21	—
6308	V23	8EX
6350	V23	9CZ
6354	V23	Fig. 12
6360	V28	Fig. 13
6374	—	9BW
6386	V18	8CJ
6417	V28	9K
6443	—	9BW
6485	V23	7BK
6524	V28	Fig. 76
6660	V23	7CC
6661	V23	7CM
6662	V23	7CM
6663	V23	6BT
6669	V23	7BZ
6677	V23	9BV
6678	V23	9AE
6679	V23	9A
6680	V23	9A
6681	V23	9A
6816	V29	Fig. 77
6829	V23	9A
6850	V28	Fig. 76
6883	V28	7CK
6884	V29	Fig. 77
6887	V18	6BT
6893	V28	7CK
6897	V23	—
6907	—	Fig. 7
6939	V28	Fig. 13
6973	V18	9EU
7000	V23	7R
7025	V20	9A
7027	V20	8HY
7034	V29	Fig. 75
7035	V29	Fig. 75
7077	V21	—
7094	V29	Fig. 82
7137	V23	7BQ
7258	V18	9DA
7360	Chap. 11	9KS
7551	V28	9LK
7558	V28	9LK
7700	V23	6F
8000	V27	2N
8001	V29	7BM
8003	V26	3N
8005	V26	3G
8008	—	Fig. 8
8012	V25	Fig. 54
8013-A	—	4P
8016	—	3C
8020	—	4P
8025	V25	4AQ
9001	V18	7BD
9002	V18	7BS
9002	V25	7BS
9003	V18	7BD
9004	V21	4BJ
9005	V21	5BG

Type	Page	Base
9006	V18	6BH
AT-340	—	5BK
AX9900	V26	Fig. 3
AX9901	V27	Fig. 3
AX9903	V28	Fig. 7
AX9905	—	Fig. 20
AX9909	—	Fig. 5
AX9910	V28	Fig. 7
BA	—	4J
BH	—	4J
BR	—	4H
CE220	—	4P
CK1005	—	5AQ
CK1006	—	4C
CK1007	—	Fig. 73
DR3B27	—	4P
DR123C	—	Fig. 15
DR200	—	2N
EEC81	V23	9A
EEC82	V23	9A
EEC83	V23	9A
EF50	—	9C
F123A	—	Fig. 15
F127A	—	Fig. 15
G84	V24	4B
GL2C39A	V26	—
GL2C39B	V26	—
GL2C44	—	Fig. 9
GL5C24	V27	Fig. 15
GL146	V26	Fig. 56
GL152	V26	Fig. 56
GL159	—	Fig. 56
GL169	—	Fig. 56
GL446A	—	Fig. 11
GL446B	—	Fig. 11
GL464A	—	Fig. 9
GL559	—	Fig. 10
GL6442	V25	—
GL6463	—	9CZ
GL8012A	V25	Fig. 54
HD203A	—	3N
HF60	—	2D
HF75	—	2D
HF100	—	2D
HF120	—	4F
HF140	—	4F
HF175	—	Fig. 46
HF200	—	2N
HF201A	V27	Fig. 15
HF250	—	2N
HF300	V27	2N
HK24	V25	3G
HK54	V26	2D
HK57	—	Fig. 33
HK154	—	2D
HK158	—	2D
HK252L	—	4BC
HK253	—	4AT
HK254	—	2N
HK257	V29	7BM
HK257B	V29	7BM
HK304L	—	4BC
HK354	—	2N
HK354C	—	2N
HK354D	—	2N
HK354E	—	2N
HK354F	—	2N
HK454H	—	2N
HK454L	—	2N
HK654	—	2N
HV12	—	3N
HV18	—	2N
HV27	—	3N
HY6J5GTX	—	6Q
HY6L6GTX	—	7AC
HY24	—	4D
HY25	—	3G
HY30Z	—	4BO
HY31Z	V25	Fig. 60
HY40	—	3G
HY40Z	—	3G
HY51A	—	3G
HY51B	—	3G
HY51Z	—	4BO
HY57	—	3G
HY60	—	5AW
HY61	—	5AW
HY63	—	Fig. 72
HY65	—	Fig. 72
HY67	—	Fig. 65
HY69	—	Fig. 64
HY75	—	2T
HY75A	V25	2T
HY114B	V25	2T
HY615	V25	Fig. 71
HY801A	—	4D
HY866jr	—	4P
HY1231Z	V25	Fig. 60
HY1269	V28	Fig. 65
HYE1148	V25	Fig. 71
KT66	V23	7AC
KY21	V23	—

Type	Page	Base
NU2C35	—	Fig. 2
PE340	—	5BK
PL172	V29	—
PL6549	V29	Fig. 1
PL6569	V27	Fig. 3
PL6580	V27	5BK
RK10	—	4D
RK11	—	3G
RK12	—	3G
RK15	—	4D
RK16	—	5A
RK17	—	5F
RK18	—	3G
RK19	—	4AT
RK20	—	Fig. 6
RK20A	—	Fig. 6
RK21	—	4P
RK22	—	Fig. 5
RK23	—	6BM
RK24	—	4D
RK25	V28	6BM
RK25B	—	6BM
RK28	—	5J
RK28A	—	5J
RK30	—	2D
RK31	—	3G
RK32	—	2D
RK33	—	Fig. 6
RK34	V25	Fig. 7
RK35	—	2D
RK36	—	2D
RK37	—	2D
RK38	—	2D
RK39	—	5AW
RK41	—	5AW
RK42	—	4D
RK43	—	6C
RK44	—	6BM
RK46	—	Fig. 6
RK47	—	Fig. 6
RK48	—	Fig. 6
RK48A	—	Fig. 6
RK49	—	6A
RK51	—	3G
RK52	—	3G
RK56	—	5AW
RK57	—	3N
RK58	—	3N
RK59	—	Fig. 6
RK61	V23	—
RK62	—	4D
RK63	—	2N
RK63A	—	2N
RK64	—	5AW
RK65	—	Fig. 4
RK66	—	Fig. 6
RK75	—	Fig. 6
RK100	—	Fig. 6
RK705A	—	Fig. 4
RK866	—	4P
T20	V25	3G
T21	—	6A
T40	V25	3G
T55	V26	3G
T60	—	2D
T100	—	2D
T125	—	2N
T200	V27	2N
T300	V27	—
T814	—	3N
T822	—	3N
TB35	—	Fig. 3
TUF20	—	2T
TW75	—	2D
TW150	—	2N
TZ20	V25	3G
TZ40	V25	3G
UE100	—	2D
UE468	—	Fig.
UH35	—	3G
UH50	—	2D
UH51	—	2D
V70	—	3N
V70A	—	3N
V70B	—	3G
V70C	—	3G
V70D	V26	3G
VR75	V23	4AJ
VR90	V23	4AJ
VR105	V23	4AJ
VR150	V23	4AJ
VT52	—	4D
VT127A	V26	Fig.
VT191	V25	—
WE304A	—	2D
X6030	—	Fig.
XXB	—	Fig.
XXD	V23	8AC
XXL	—	5AC
XXFM	—	8BZ
ZB60	—	2D
ZB120	—	4E

SEMICONDUCTORS

Type	Page	Type	Page	Type	Page	Type	Page	Type	Page	Type	Page	Type	Page
1N34	V32	1N68	V32	1N118	V32	2N35	V31	2N175	V31	2N372	V31	CK768	V
1N34A	V32	1N68A	V32	1N126A	V32	2N43	V31	2N218	V31	2N374	V31	HB1	V
1N35	V32	1N69A	V32	1N127A	V32	2N44	V31	2N219	V31	2N376	V31	HB2	V
1N38	V32	1N70A	V32	1N128	V32	2N68	V31	2N233	V31	2N384	V31	HB3	V
1N38A	V32	1N77A	V32	1N151	V32	2N78	V31	2N247	V31	2N411	V31	HB4	V
1N39A	V32	1N81	V32	1N152	V32	2N94	V31	2N248	V31	2N412	V31	HB5	V
1N48	V32	1N82	V32	1N153	V32	2N94A	V31	2N255	V31	2N428	V31	HB6	V
1N52A	V32	1N82A	V32	1N158	V32	2N104	V31	2N256	V31	2N499	V31	M150	V
1N54A	V32	1N89	V32	1N191	V32	2N105	V31	2N270	V31	2N544	V31	M500	V
1N55A-B	V32	1N90	V32	1N192	V32	2N107	V31	2N274	V31	2N561	V31	OC71	V
1N56A	V32	1N91	V32	1N198A	V32	2N109	V31	2N292	V31	2N586	V31	OC72	V
1N58A	V32	1N95	V32	1N279	V32	2N123	V31	2N301	V31	2N588	V31	SB100	V
1N60	V32	1N96	V32	1N283	V32	2N131	V31	2N301A	V31	2N677	V31	V15	V
1N63	V32	1N97	V32	1N294	V32	2N132A	V31	2N306	V31	2N1014	V31	V20	V
1N64	V32	1N98	V32	1N295	V32	2N139	V31	2N307	V31	2N1102	V31	V27	V
1N65	V32	1N99	V32	1N448	V32	2N140	V31	2N331	V31	2N1266	V31	V33	V
1N66	V32	1N100	V32	1N634	V32	2N155	V31	2N351	V31	AO-1	V31	V39	V
1N67	V32	1N116	V32	1N636	V32	2N167	V31	2N370	V31	AO-1	V31	V47	V
1N67A	V32	1N117	V32	2N34	V31	2N169A	V31	2N371	V31	CK722	V31	V56	V

VACUUM-TUBE BASE DIAGRAMS

Socket connections correspond to the base designations given in the column headed "Base" in the classified tube-data tables. Bottom views are shown throughout. Terminal designations are as follows:

A	= Anode	D	= Deflecting Plate	IS	= Internal Shield	RC	= Ray-Control Electrode
B	= Beam	F	= Filament	K	= Cathode	Ref	= Reflector
BP	= Bayonet Pin	FE	= Focus Elect.	NC	= No Connection	S	= Shell
BS	= Base Sleeve	G	= Grid	P	= Plate (Anode)	TA	= Target
C	= Ext. Coating	H	= Heater	P_1	= Starter-Anode	U	= Unit
CL	= Collector	IC	= Internal Con.	P_{BF}	= Beam Plates	•	= Gas-Type Tube

Alphabetical subscripts D, P, T and HX indicate, respectively, diode unit, pentode unit, triode unit or hexode unit in multi-unit types. Subscript CT indicates filament or heater tap.

Generally when the No. 1 pin of a metal-type tube in Table II, with the exception of all triodes, is shown connected to the shell, the No. 1 pin in the glass (G or GT) equivalent is connected to an internal shield.

E.I.A. (R.E.T.M.A.) TUBE BASE DIAGRAMS

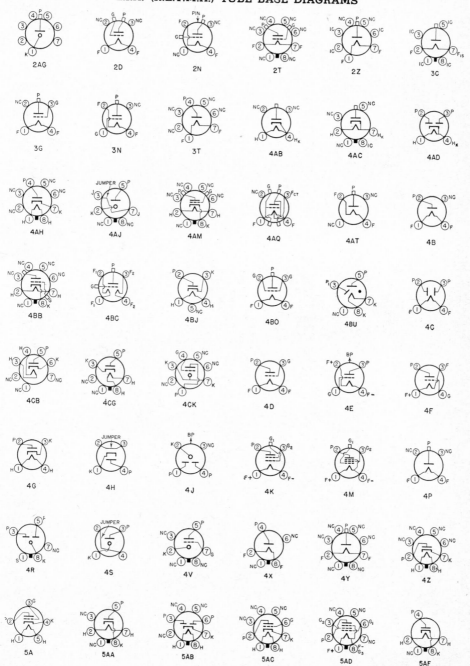

TUBE BASE DIAGRAMS

Bottom views are shown. Terminal designations on sockets are given on page V5.

TUBE BASE DIAGRAMS

Bottom views are shown. Terminal designations on sockets are given on page V5.

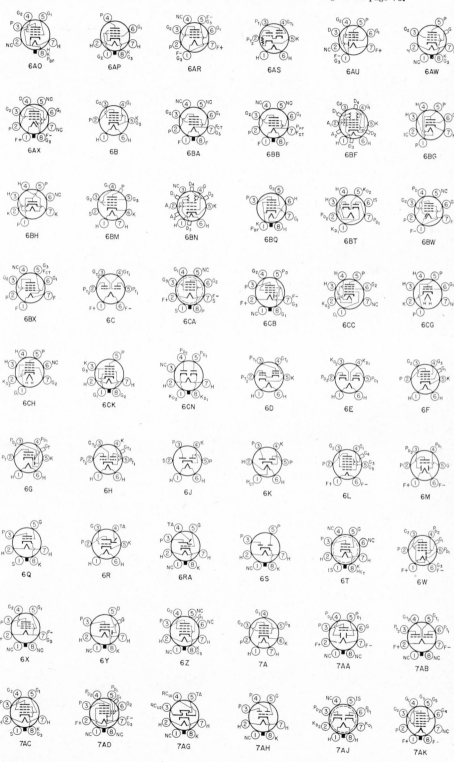

TUBE BASE DIAGRAMS

Bottom views are shown. Terminal designations on sockets are given on page V5.

TUBE BASE DIAGRAMS

Bottom views are shown. Terminal designations on sockets are given on page V5.

TUBE BASE DIAGRAMS

Bottom views are shown. Terminal designations on sockets are given on page V5.

TUBE BASE DIAGRAMS

Bottom views are shown. Terminal designations on sockets are given on page V5.

TUBE BASE DIAGRAMS

Bottom views are shown. Terminal designations on sockets are given on page V5.

TUBE BASE DIAGRAMS

Bottom views are shown. Terminal designations on sockets are given on page V5.

TUBE BASE DIAGRAMS

Bottom views are shown. Terminal designations on sockets are given on page V5.

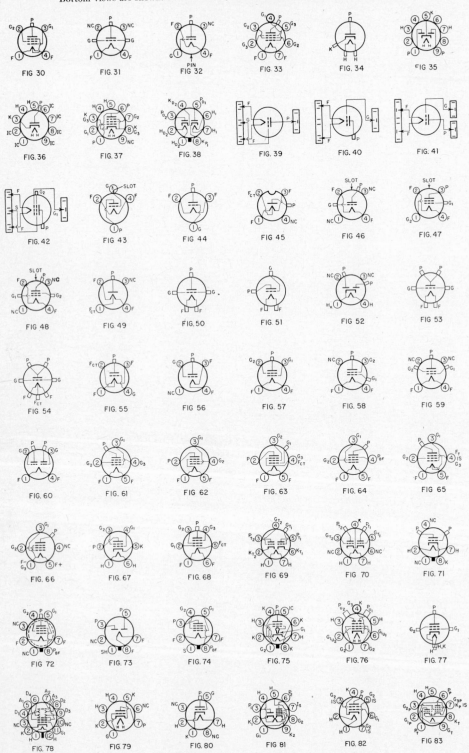

Name	Base	Fil. or Heater V.	Amp.	Cap. μμf. Cin	Cout	Cgp	Plate Supply V.	Grid Bias	Screen Volts	Screen Ma.	Plate Ma.	Plate Res. Ohms	Transconductance[11]	Amp. Factor[4]	Load Res. Ohms	Watts Output
H.f. Diode	5AP	1.4	0.15	—	—	—	Max. a.c. voltage per plate —117. Max. output current —0.5 ma.								
Sharp Cut-off Pent.	6AR	1.4	0.025	3.8	7.6	0.009	90	0	90	0.55	1.8	1.8 meg.	1050	—	—	—
Diode—Remote Cut-off Pent.	6BW	1.4	0.05	—	—	—	67.5	0	67.5	0.55	2.1	600K	630	—	—	—
Sharp Cut-off Pent.	6AR	1.4	0.05	3.6	7.5	0.008	90	0	90	2.0	4.5	350K	1025	—	—	—
Pentagrid Conv.	7DC	1.4	0.05	7.5	12	0.3	90	0	45	0.6	0.5	650K	300	—	—	—
Pentagrid Conv.	7AT	1.4	0.05	7.0	12	0.3	90	0	67.5	3.5	1.3	400K	280	Grid No. 1 100K		
Pentagrid Pwr. Amp.	7AV	1.4	0.1	—	—	—	90	−7.0	67.5	1.4	7.4	100K	1575	—	8K	0.270
Diode—Pentode A₁ Amp. R.f. Amp.	6AU	1.4	0.05	—	—	—	67.5	0	67.5	0.4	1.4	600K	625	—	—	—
							90	0	90	Screen Resistor 3 meg., grid 10 meg.				1 meg.	0.050
Variable-μ Pent.	6AR	1.4	0.05	3.6	7.5	0.01	90	0	67.5	1.4	3.5	500K	900	—	—	—
Sharp Cut-off Pent.	6AR	1.4	0.05	3.6	7.5	0.01	90	0	90	0.5	1.6	1 meg.	900	—	—	—
Diode Pentode	6BW	1.4	0.05	—	—	—	67.5	0	67.5	0.4	1.6	600K	625	—	—	—
Beam Pwr. Pent. A₁ Amp. / A₁ Amp.[3] / AB₁ Amp.[3] / AB₂ Amp.[3]	7CQ	6.0	0.65	9.5	6.6	0.2	250	450*	250	3.3/7.4	44[2]	63K	3700	40[5]	4.5K	4.5
							250	225*	250	6.6/14.8	88[2]	—	—	80[5]	9K[6]	9
							250	−25	250	3/13.5	82[2]	—	—	48[5]	8K[6]	12.5
							250	−30	250	4/20	120[2]	—	—	40[5]	3.8[6]	17
Sharp Cut-off Pent.	7EW	2.4	0.60	3.8	2.3	0.06	250	—	150	10	10	150K	8000	—	—	—
Dual Diode	7FL	2.1	0.45	—	—	—	Max. a.c. voltage per plate —200 Max. output current—5.0 ma.									
Pwr. Amp. Pent.	7BB	1.4	0.2	4.8	4.2	0.34	135	−7.5	90	2.6	14.9[2]	90K	1900	—	8K	0.6
		2.8	0.1				150	−8.4	90	2.2	14.1[2]	100K		—		0.7
H.f. Dual Triode[10]	7BC	1.4	0.22	0.9	1.0	3.2	90	−2.5	—	—	3.7	8.3K	1800	15	—	—
		2.8	0.11													
Sharp Cut-off Pent.	7CM	3.15	0.6	6.3	1.9	0.02	300	−6.5	150	3.8	12	—	9800	—	—	—
Pwr. Amp. Pent.	7BA	1.4	0.1	5.5	3.8	0.2	90	−4.5	90	2.1	9.5	100K	2150	—	10K	0.27
		2.8	0.05							1.7	7.7	120K	2000	—	10K	0.24
Pwr. Amp. Pent.	7BA	1.4	0.1	—	—	—	90	−7	67.5	1.4	7.4	100K	1575	—	8K	0.27
		2.8	0.05							1.1	6.1		1425	—		0.235
Sharp Cut-off Pent.	7CM	4.2	0.6	10	2.4	0.04	300	−3.5	180	3.2	11	—	1400	—	—	—
U.h.f. Triode	5CE	6.3	0.15	2.2	0.5	1.5	250	200*	—	—	10	10.9K	5500	60	—	—
Dual Diode—Pent.	9T	6.3	0.3	4.0	4.6	0.002	250	−2	85	2.3	6.7	1 meg.	1100	—	—	—
U.h.f.— Triode A₁ Amp. / Osc. 950 Mc.	7DK	6.3	0.225	2.2	0.45	1.9	80	150*	—	—	16	2.27K	6600	15	—	—
							100	10KΩ	—	0.4[9]	22	—	—		—	—
Sharp Cut-off Pent.	7BD	6.3	0.3	6.5	1.8	0.03	250	180*	150	2.0	6.5	800K	5000	—	—	—
							100	180*	100	1.4	4.5	600K	4550	—	—	—
Sharp Cut-off Pent. Amp. / Pent. Triode Amp.	7BK	6.3	0.45	10	2.0	0.03	300	160*	150	2.5	10	500K	9600	—	—	—
							150	160*	—	—	12.5	3.6K	11K	40	—	—
U.h.f. Triode	9BX	6.3	0.225	4.4	0.18	2.4	125	68*	—	—	16	4.2K	10K	42	—	—
Sharp Cut-off Pent.	7BD	6.3	0.175	4.0	2.8	0.02	180	200*	150	2.4	7.7	690K	5100	—	—	—
							150	330*	140	2.2	7	420K	4300	—	—	—
							120	200*	120	2.5	7.5	340K	5000	—	—	—
Pwr. Amp. Pent.	7BK	6.3	0.15	3.6	4.2	0.12	180	−9	180	2.5	15	200K	2300	—	10K	1.1
Dual Diode[10]	6BT	6.3	0.3	—	—	—	Max. r.m.s. voltage —117. Max. d.c. output current —9 ma.[1]									
U.h.f. Triode	9BX	6.3	0.225	4.4	0.16	2.4	150	100*	—	—	7.5	10K	9000	90	—	—
Diode—Sharp Cut-off Pent.	9CY	6.3	0.45	6.0	2.6	0.015	200	120*	150	2.7	11.5	600K	7000	—	—	—
U.h.f. Triode	7DK	6.3	0.225	2.8	0.28	1.7	200	100*	—	—	13	—	10K	70	—	—
Beam Pwr. Pent.	7BD	6.3	0.45	9.0	4.8	0.075	120	120*	120	12	35	12.5K	8000	—	2.5K	1.3
Medium-μ Triode	9DA	6.3	0.45	2.0	2.7	1.5	200	−6	—	—	13	5.75K	3300	—	—	—
Sharp Cut-off Pent.				7.0	2.3	0.04	200	180*	150	2.8	9.5	30K	6200	—	—	—
Beam Pwr. Pent.	7BZ	6.3	0.45	8.3	8.2	0.35	180	−8.5	180	3/4	30[2]	58K	3700	29[5]	5.5K	2.0
							250	−12.5	250	4.5/7	47[2]	52K	4100	45[5]	5K	4.5
Dual Diode—High-μ Triode	7BT	6.3	0.15	1.7	1.5	1.8	100	−1	—	—	0.8	61K	1150	70	—	—
							250	−3	—	—	1	58K	1200	70	—	—
Pwr. Amp. Pent.	6CC	6.3	0.4	—	—	—	250	−16.5	250	5.7/10	35[2]	65K	2400	34[5]	7K	3.2
							250	−18	250	5.5/10	33[2]	68K	2300	32[5]	7.6K	3.4
Sheet Beam	9DP	6.3	0.3	—	—	—	TV Color Ckts.—Synchronous Detector—Burst Gate									
Beam Pwr. Amp.	7CV	6.3	0.8	12	6.2	0.6	150	−8.5	150	2/6.5	36[2]	—	5600	35[5]	4.5K	2.2
Sharp Cut-off Pent.	7CM	6.3	0.175	4	3	0.2	120	−2	120	3.5	5.2	110K	3200	—	—	—
Diode—Sharp Cut-off Pent.	9DS	6.3	0.45	7	2.2	0.04	200	180*	150	3	9.5	300K	6200	—	—	—
Duplex Diode—High-μ Triode	7BT	6.3	0.3	2.3	1.1	2.1	250	−3	—	—	1	58K	1200	70	—	—
Medium-μ Triode	9DW	6.3	0.45	2	0.5	1.5	100	100*	—	—	8.5	6.9K	5800	40	—	—
Sharp Cut-off Pent.				4.5	0.9	0.025	250	200*	150	1.6	7.7	750K	4600	—	—	—
Sharp Cut-off Pent.	7BK	6.3	0.3	5.5	5	0.0035	250	68*	150	4.3	10.6	1 meg.	5200	—	—	—
Medium-μ Triode	9DX	6.3	0.6	2.6	0.34	2.2	150	150*	—	—	9	8.2K	4900	40	—	—
Sharp Cut-off Pent.				7.5	3.4	0.06	200	82*	125	3.4	15	150K	7000	—	—	—
Dual Diode—High-μ Triode	7BT	6.3	0.3	2.2	0.8	2.0	250	−2	—	—	1.2	62.5K	1600	100	—	—
High-μ Triode	9DX	6.3	0.6	3.2	0.32	2.2	200	−2	—	—	4	17.5K	4000	70	—	—
Sharp Cut-off Pent.				11	2.8	0.036	200	180*	150	3.5	13	400K	9000	—	—	—
Medium-μ Triode	9AE	6.3	0.45	2.5	1	1.8	150	56*	—	—	18	5K	8500	40	—	—
Sharp Cut-off Pent.				5	3.5	0.006	250	120*	110	3.5	10	400K	4800	—	—	—
Medium-μ Triode	9ED	6.3	0.45	2	1.7	1.7	200	−6	—	—	13	5.75K	3300	19	—	—
Semiremote Cut-off Pent.				6.5	2.2	0.02	200	180*	150	3	9.5	300K	6000	—	—	—
Remote Cut-off Pent.	7BK	6.3	0.3	5.5	5	0.0035	250	68*	100	4.2	11	1 meg.	4400	—	—	—
Pentagrid Conv.	8CT	6.3	0.3	Osc.	20KΩ		250	−1	100	10	3.8	1 meg.	950	—	—	—
Medium-μ Triode	9DX	6.3	0.6	2.5	0.7	2.2	200	−8	—	—	8	6.7K	2700	18	—	—
Sharp Cut-off Pent.				11	2.8	0.036	200	180*	150	3.5	13	400K	9000	—	—	—
U.h.f. Medium-μ Triode	9DR	6.3	0.225	2.9	0.26	1.6	150	100*	—	—	14.5	4.8K	10K	48	—	—
Sharp Cut-off Pent.	7BD	6.3	0.3	6.5	1.8	0.03	250	180*	150	2.1	7.5	800K	5700	—	—	—
Triple Diode	9AX	6.3	0.45	—	—	—	Max. diode current per plate = 12 Ma. Max. htr.-cath. volts = 200									
Medium-μ Dual Triode[10]	9AJ	6.3	0.4	2.5	1.3	1.4	150	220*	—	—	10	—	6200	35	—	—
Remote Cut-off Pent.	7BK	6.3	0.3	4.3	5.0	0.005	100	−1	100	5	13	150K	2550	—	—	—
							250	−3	100	3	9	800K	2000	—	—	—

Type	Name	Base	V.	Amp.	Cin	Cout	Cgp	Plate Supply V.	Grid Bias	Screen Volts	Screen Ma.	Plate Ma.	Plate Res. Ohms	Transconductance[11]	Amp. Factor[4]	Load Res. Ohms
6BE6	Pentagrid Conv.	7CH	6.3	0.3	Osc. 20KΩ			250	−1.5	100	6.8	2.9	1 meg.	475	—	—
6BE8A‡	Medium-μ Triode	9EG	6.3	0.45	2.8	1.5	1.8	150	56*	—	—	18	5K	8500	40	—
	Sharp Cut-off Pent.				4.4	2.6	0.04	250	68*	110	3.5	10	400K	5200	—	—
6BF5	Beam Pwr. Amp.	7BZ	6.3	1.2	14	6	0.65	110	−7.5	110	4/10.5	39²	12K	7500	36⁵	2.5K
6BF6	Dual Diode—Medium-μ Triode	7BT	6.3	0.3	1.8	0.8	2	250	−9	—	—	9.5	8.5K	1900	16	10K
6BH5	Remote Cut-off Pent.	9AZ	6.3	0.2	4.9	5.5	0.002	250	−2.5	100	1.7	6.0	1.1 meg.	2200	—	—
6BH6	Sharp Cut-off Pent.	7CM	6.3	0.15	5.4	4.4	0.0035	250	−1	150	2.9	7.4	1.4 meg.	4600	—	—
6BH8‡	Medium-μ Triode	9DX	6.3	0.6	2.6	0.38	2.4	150	−5	—	—	9.5	5.15K	3300	17	—
	Sharp Cut-off Pent.				7	2.4	0.046	200	82*	125	3.4	15	150K	7000	—	—
6BJ6A	Remote Cut-off Pent.	7CM	6.3	0.15	4.5	5.5	0.0035	250	−1	100	3.3	9.2	1.3 meg.	3800	—	—
6BJ7	Triple Diode	9AX	6.3	0.45	Max. peak inverse plate voltage = 330 V. Max. d.c. plate current each diode = 1.0 Ma.											
6BJ8‡	Dual Diode—Medium-μ Triode	9ER	6.3	0.6	2.8	0.38	2.6	250	−9	—	—	8	7.15K	2800	20	—
6BK5	Beam Pwr. Pent.	9BQ	6.3	1.2	13	5	0.6	250	−5	250	3.5/10	37²	100K	8500	35⁵	6.5K
6BK6	Dual Diode—High-μ Triode	7BT	6.3	0.3	—	—	—	250	−2	—	—	1.2	62.5K	1600	100	—
6BK7B	Medium-μ Dual Triode[10]	9AJ	6.3	0.4	3	1	1.8	150	56*	—	—	18	4.6K	9300	43	—
6BL8	Triode	Fig. 83	6.3	.43	2.5	1.8	1.5	250	−1.3	—	—	14	—	5000	20	—
	Pentode				5.2	3.4	.025	250	−1.3	175	2.8	10	400K	6200	47	—
6BN4	Medium-μ Triode	7EG	6.3	0.2	3.2	1.4	1.2	150	−220*	—	—	9	6.3K	6800	43	—
6BN6	Gated-Beam Pent.	7DF	6.3	0.3	4.2	3.3	0.004	80	−1.3	60	5	0.23	—	—	—	68K
6BN8‡	Dual Diode—High-μ Triode	9ER	6.3	0.6	3.6	0.25	2.5	250	−3	—	—	1.6	28K	2500	70	—
6BQ5	Pwr. Amp. Pent.	9CV	6.3	0.76	10.8	6.5	0.5	300	−7.3	200	10.8	49.5²	38K	—	—	5.2K
6BQ7A	Medium-μ Dual Triode[10]	9AJ	6.3	0.4	2.85	1.35	1.15	150	220*	—	—	9	6.1K	6400	39	—
6BR8A‡	Medium-μ Triode	9FA	6.3	0.45	2.5	0.4	1.8	150	56*	—	—	18	5K	8500	40	—
	Sharp Cut-off Pent.				5	2.6	0.015	250	68*	110	3.5	10	400K	5200	—	—
6BS8	Low-Noise Dual Triode[10]	9AJ	6.3	0.4	2.6	1.35	1.15	150	220*	—	—	10	5K	7200	36	—
6BT6	Dual Diode—High-μ Triode	7BT	6.3	0.3	—	—	—	250	−3	—	—	1	58K	1200	70	—
6BT8	Dual Diode—Pent.	9FE	6.3	0.45	7	2.3	0.04	200	180*	150	2.8	9.5	300K	6200	—	—
6BU6	Dual Diode—Low-μ Triode	7BT	6.3	0.3	—	—	—	250	−9	—	—	9.5	8.5K	1900	16	10K
6BU8	Dual Pent.[10]	9FG	6.3	0.3	6	3¹	—	100¹	—	67.5	3.3	2.2	—	—	—	—
6BV8‡	Dual Diode—Medium-μ Triode	9FJ	6.3	0.6	3.6	0.4	2	200	330*	—	—	11	5.9K	5600	33	—
6BW8	Dual Diode—Pent.	9HK	6.3	0.45	4.8	2.6	0.02	250	68*	110	3.5	10	250K	5200	—	—
6BX8	Dual Triode[10]	9AJ	6.3	0.4	—	—	1.4	65	−1	—	—	9	—	6700	25	—
6BY6	Pentagrid Amp.	7CH	6.3	0.3	5.4	7.6	0.08	250	−2.5	100	9	6.5	E_c3 = −2.5 V.	1900	—	—
6BY8‡	Diode—Sharp Cut-off Pent.	9FN	6.3	0.3	5.5	5	0.0035	250	68*	150	4.3	10.6	1 meg.	6200	—	—
6BZ6	Semiremote Cut-off Pent.	7CM	6.3	0.3	7.5	1.8	0.02	200	180*	150	2.6	11	600K	6100	—	—
6BZ7	Medium-μ Dual Triode[10]	9AJ	6.3	0.4	2.5	1.35	1.15	150	220*	—	—	10	5.6K	6800	38	—
6BZ8	Dual Triode[10]	9AJ	6.3	0.4	—	—	—	125	100*	—	—	10¹	5.6K	8000	45	—
6C4	Medium-μ Triode	6BG	6.3	0.15	1.8	1.3	1.6	250	−8.5	—	—	10.5	7.7K	2200	17	—
6CA5	Beam Pent.	7CV	6.3	1.2	15	9	0.5	125	−4.5	125	4/11	36²	15K	9200	37⁵	4.5K
6CB6A‡	Sharp Cut-off Pent.	7CM	6.3	0.3	6.5	1.9	0.02	200	180*	150	2.8	9.5	600K	6200	—	—
6CE5‡	R.f. Pent.	7BD	6.3	0.3	6.5	1.9	0.03	200	180*	150	2.8	9.5	600K	6200	—	—
6CF6	Sharp Cut-off Pent.	7CM	6.3	0.3	6.5	1.9	0.02	200	180*	150	2.8	9.5	600K	6200	—	—
6CG6	Semiremote Cut-off Pent.	7BK	6.3	0.3	5	5	0.008	200	−8	150	2.3	9	720K	2000	—	—
6CG7‡	Medium-μ Dual Triode[10]	9AJ	6.3	0.6	2.3	2.2	4	250	−8	—	—	9	7.7K	2600	20	—
6CG8A‡	Medium-μ Triode	9GF	6.3	0.45	2.6	0.05	1.5	100	100*	—	—	8.5	6.9K	5820	40	—
	Sharp Cut-off Pent.				4.8	0.9	0.03	200	200*	150	1.6	7.7	750K	4600	—	—
6CH8	Medium-μ Triode	9FT	6.3	0.45	1.9	1.6	1.6	200	−6	—	—	13	5.75K	3300	19	—
	Sharp Cut-off Pent.				7	2.25	0.025	200	180*	150	2.8	9.5	300K	6200	—	—
6CL6	Pwr. Amp. Pent.	9BV	6.3	0.65	11	5.5	0.12	250	−3	150	7/7.2	31²	150K	11K	30⁵	7500
6CL8A‡	Medium-μ Triode	9FX	6.3	.45	2.7	0.4	1.8	300	—	—	—	15	5K	8000	40	—
	Sharp Cut-off Tetrode				5	2.4	.02	300	−1	300	4	12	100K	6200	—	—
6CM6	Beam Pwr. Amp.	9CK	6.3	0.45	8	8.5	0.7	315	−13	225	2.2/6	35²	80K	3750	34⁵	8.5K
6CM7‡	Medium-μ Triode No. 1	9ES	6.3	0.6	2	0.5	3.8	200	−7	—	—	5	11K	2000	20	—
	Dual Triode Triode No. 2				3.5	0.4	3	250	−8	—	—	10	4.1K	4400	18	—
6CM8‡	High-μ Triode	9FZ	6.3	0.45	1.6	0.22	1.9	250	−2	—	—	1.8	50K	2000	100	—
	Sharp Cut-off Pent.				6	2.6	0.02	200	180*	150	2.8	9.5	300K	6200	—	—
6CN7‡	Dual Diode—High-μ Triode	9EN	6.3	0.3	1.5	0.5	1.8	100	−1	—	—	0.8	54K	1300	70	—
			3.15	0.6				250	−3	—	—	1	58K	1200	70	—
6CQ8‡	Medium-μ Triode	9GE	6.3	0.45	2.7	0.4	1.8	125	56*	—	—	15	5K	8000	40	—
	Sharp Cut-off Tetrode				5	2.5	0.019	125	−1	125	4.2	12	140K	5800	—	—
6CR6	Diode—Remote Cut-off Pent.	7EA	6.3	0.3	—	—	—	250	−2	100	3	9.5	200K	1950	—	—
6CR8‡	Triode	9GJ	6.3	0.45	2	1.4	1.6	125	−2	—	—	12	5.5K	4000	22	—
	Pentode				6	2.8	0.018	125	56*	125	3	13	300K	7700	—	—
6CS5	Beam Pwr. Pent.	9CK	6.3	1.2	15	9	0.5	200	180*	125	2.2	47²	28K	8000	—	4K
6CS6	Pentagrid Amp.	7CH	6.3	0.3	5.5	7.5	0.05	100	−1	30	1.1	0.75	1 meg.	950	E_c3 = 0 V.	—
6CS7‡	Medium-μ Triode No. 1	9EF	6.3	0.6	1.8	0.5	2.6	250	−8.5	—	—	10.5	7.7K	2200	17	—
	Dual Triode Triode No. 2				3.0	0.5	2.6	250	−10.5	—	—	19	3.45K	4500	15.5	—
6CU5	Beam Pwr. Pent.	7CV	6.3	1.2	13.2	8.6	0.7	120	−8	110	4/8.5	50²	10K	7500	—	2.5K
6CX8	Medium-μ Triode	9DX	6.3	0.75	2.2	0.38	4.4	150	150*	—	—	9.2	8.7K	4600	40	—
	Sharp Cut-off Pent.				9	4.4	0.06	200	68*	125	5.2	24	70K	10K	—	—
6CY5	Sharp Cut-off Tetrode	7EW	6.3	0.2	4.5	3	0.03	125	−7	80	1.5	10	100K	8000	—	—
6CY7	Dissimilar—Dual Triode	9EF	6.3	0.75	1.5⁷	0.3⁷	1.8⁷	250⁷	−3⁷	—	—	1.2⁷	52K⁷	1300⁷	68⁷	—
					5⁸	1⁸	4.4⁸	150⁸	620*⁸	—	—	30⁸	920⁸	5400⁸	5⁸	—
6CZ5	Beam Pwr. Amp. A₁ Amp.	9HN	6.3	0.45	8	8.5	0.7	250	−14	250	4.6/8	48²	73K	4800	46⁵	4K
	AB₁ Amp.[3]							350	−23.5	280	3/13	103²	—	—	46⁵	7.5K⁶
6DB5	Beam Pwr. Amp.	9GR	6.3	1.2	15	9	0.5	200	180*	125	2.2/8.5	46/47	28K	8000	—	4K
6DB6	Dual Diode—High-μ Triode	7CM	6.3	0.3	6	5	0.0035	150	−1	150	6.6	5.8	50K	2050	E_c3 = −3 V.	—
6DC6	Semiremote Cut-off Pent.	7CM	6.3	0.3	6.5	2	0.02	200	180*	150	3	9	500K	5500	—	—
6DE6	Sharp Cut-off Pent.	7CM	6.3	0.3	6.3	1.9	0.02	200	180*	150	2.8	9.5	600K	6200	—	—
6DE7	Dissimilar—Dual Triode	9HF	6.3	0.9	2.27	0.52⁷	4.2⁷	250⁷	−117	—	—	5.5⁷	8.75K⁷	2000⁷	17.5⁷	—
					5.5⁸	1⁸	8.5⁸	150⁸	−17.5⁸	—	—	35⁸	925⁸	6500⁸	6⁸	—
6DK6	Sharp Cut-off Pent.	7CM	6.3	0.3	6.3	1.9	.02	300	−6.5	150	3.8	12	—	9800	—	—
6DR7	Dissimilar—Dual Triode	9HF	6.3	0.9	2.2	0.34	4.5	330	−3	—	—	1.4	—	1600	68⁷	—
					5.5	1.0	8.5	275	−17.5	—	—	35	—	6500	6⁸	—

TABLE I—MINIATURE RECEIVING TUBES—Continued — V17

Type	Name	Base	V.	Amp.	C_{in}	C_{out}	C_{gp}	Plate Supply V.	Grid Bias	Screen Volts	Screen Ma.	Plate Ma.	Plate Res. Ohms	Transconductance	Amp. Factor	Load Res. Ohms	Watts Output
6DS5	Beam Pwr. Amp.	7BZ	6.3	0.8	9.5	6.3	0.19	250	-8.5	200	3/10	32[2]	28K	5800	32[5]	8K	3.8
								250	270*	200	3/9	25[2]	28K	5800	27[5]	8K	3.6
6DT5	Pwr. Amp. Pent.	9CV	6.3	0.76	10.8	6.5	0.5	300	-7.3	200	10.8	49.5[2]	28K	38K	—	5.2K	17
6DT6	Sharp Cut-off Pent.	7EN	6.3	0.3	5.8	—	0.02	150	560*	100	2.1	1.1	150K	615	—		
6DT8	High-μ Dual Triode[10]	9DE	6.3	0.3	2.7	1.6	1.6	250	200*	—	—	10	10.9K	5500	60		
6DW5	Beam Pwr. Amp.	9CK	6.3	1.2	14	9	0.5	200	-22.5	150	2	55	15K	5500	—		
6EA8	Triode	9AE	6.3	.45	3	.3	1.7	330	-12	—	—	18	5K	8500	40		
	Sharp Cut-off Pent.				5	2.6	.02	330	-9	330	4	12	80K	6400	—		
6EB8	High-μ Triode	9DX	6.3	.75	2.4	.36	4.4	330	-5	—	—	2	37K	2700	100		
	Sharp Cut-off Pent.				11	4.2	0.1	330	-9	—	7	25	75K	12.5K	—		
6EH5	Power Pentode	7CV	6.3	1.2	17	9	.65	135	0	117	14.5	42	11K	14.6K	—	3K	1.4
6ES8	Dual Triode	9DE	6.3	.365	3.4	1.7	1.9	130	-1.2	—	—	15	—	12.5K	34		
6EV5	Sharp Cut-off Tet.	7EW	6.3	0.2	4.5	2.9	0.035	250	-1	80	0.9	11.5	150K	8800	—		
6EZ8	Triple Triode No. 1	9KA	6.3	.45	2.6	1.4	1.5	330	-4	—	—	4.2	13.6K	4200	57		
	Triode No. 2 & 3					1.2											
6FM8	Duplex Diode	9KR	6.3	.45	2.4	.16	1.8	Max. a.c. voltage = 200. Max. d.c. output current = 5 ma.									
	Diode				2.2												
	Triode				1.5			330	-1	—	—	1	58K	1200	70		
6FV6	Sharp Cut-off Tetrode	7FQ	6.3	.2	4.5	3	.03	125	-1	80	1.5	10	100K	8000	—		
6FV8	Triode	9FA	6.3	.45	2.8	1.5	1.8	330	-1	—	—	14	5K	8K	40		
	Pentode				5	2	.02	330	-1	125	4	12	200K	6.5K	—		
6J4	Grounded-Grid Triode	7BQ	6.3	0.4	7.5	3.9	0.12	150	100*	—	—	15	4.5K	12K	55		
6J6A	Medium-μ A1 Amp.[10]	7BF	6.3	0.45	2.2	0.4	1.6	100	50*	—	—	8.5*	7.1K	5300	38		
	Dual Triode Mixer							150	810*	—	—	4.8	10.2K	1900	Osc. peak voltage = 3 V		
6R8	Triple Diode-Triode	9E	6.3	0.45	1.5	1.1	2.4	250	-9	—	—	9.5	8.5K	1900	16		
6S4A	Medium-μ Triode	9AC	6.3	0.6	4.2	0.9	2.6	250	-8	—	—	26	3.6K	4500	16	10K	0.3
6T4	U.h.f. Triode	7DK	6.3	0.225	2.6	0.25	1.7	80	150*	—	—	18	1.86K	7000	13		
6T8A	Triple Diode-High-μ Triode	9E	6.3	0.45	1.6	1	2.2	100	-1	—	—	0.8	54K	1300	70		
								250	-3	—	—	1	58K	1200	70		
6U8A	Medium-μ Triode	9AE	6.3	0.45	2.5	0.4	1.8	150	56*	—	—	18	5K	8500	40		
	Sharp Cut-off Pent.				5	2.6	0.01	250	68*	110	3.5	10	400K	5200	—		
6V8	Triple Diode—Triode	9AH	6.3	0.45	—	—	—	100	-1	—	—	0.8	54K	1300	70		
								250	-3	—	—	1	58K	1200	70		
6X8A	Medium-μ Triode	9AK	6.3	0.45	2.0	0.5	1.4	100	100*	—	—	8.5	6.9K	—	40		
	Sharp Cut-off Pent.				4.3	0.7	0.09	250	200*	150	1.6	7.7	750K	—			
12A4	Medium-μ Triode	9AG	12.6 / 6.3	0.3 / 0.6	4.9	0.9	5.6	250	-9	—	—	23	2.5K	8000	20		
								250	-12.5	—	—	4.4					
12AB5	Beam Pwr. Amp. A1 Amp. / AB1 Amp.[3]	9EU	12.6	0.2	8	8.5	0.7	250	-12.5	250	4.5/7	47[2]	50K	4100	45[5]	5K	4.5
								250	-15	250	5/13	79[2]	60K[1]	3750	70[5]	10K[6]	10
12AC6	Remote Cut-off Pent.	7BK	12.6	0.15	4.3	5	0.005	12.6	0	12.6	0.2	0.55	500K	730	—		
12AD6	Pentagrid Conv.	7CH	12.6	0.15	8	8	0.3	12.6	0	12.6	1.5	0.45	1 meg.	260	Grid No. 1 Res. 33K		
12AD7	Dual High-μ Triode[10]	9A	12.6 / 6.3	0.225 / 0.45	1.67 / 1.6[8]	0.57 / 0.45[8]	1.87 / 1.8[8]	250	-2	—	—	1.25	62.5K	1600	100		
12AE6A	Dual Diode—Medium-μ Triode	7BT	12.6	0.15	1.8	1.1	2	12.6	0	—	—	0.75	15K	1000	15		
12AE7	Low-μ Dissimilar Double Triode	9A	12.6	.45	4.7	.75	3.9	16	—	—	—	1.9	31.5K	4000	13		
					4.2	.85	3.4	16	—	—	—	7.5	985	6500	6.4		
12AF6	R.f. Pent.	7BK	12.6	0.15	5.5	4.8	0.006	12.6	0	12.6	0.35	0.75	300K	1150	—		
12AJ6	Dual Diode—High-μ Triode	7BT	12.6	0.15	2.2	0.8	2	12.6	0	—	—	0.75	45K	1200	55		
12AL8	Medium-μ Triode	9GS	12.6	0.45	1.5	0.3	12	12.6	-0.9	—	—	0.25	27K	550	15		
	Tetrode				8	1.1	0.7	12.6	-0.8	12.6**	50**	25	1K	8000	—		
12AQ5	Beam Pwr. Amp. A1 Amp. / AB1 Amp.[3]	7BZ	12.6	0.225	8.3	8.2	0.35	250	-12.5	250	4.5/7	47[2]	52K	4100	45[5]	5K	4.5
								250	-15	250	5/13	79[2]	60K[1]	3750[1]	70[5]	10K[6]	10
12AT7	High-μ Dual Triode[10]	9A	12.6 / 6.3	0.15 / 0.3	2.2[7] / 2.2[8]	0.57 / 0.4[8]	1.57 / 1.5[8]	100	270*	—	—	3.7	15K	4000	60		
								250	200*	—	—	10	10.9K	5000	60		
12AU7A	Medium-μ Dual Triode[10]	9A	12.6 / 6.3	0.15 / 0.3	1.67 / 1.6[8]	0.57 / 0.35[8]	1.57 / 1.5[8]	100	0	—	—	11.8	6.25K	3100	19.5		
								250	-8.5	—	—	10.5	7.7K	2200	17		
12AV7	Medium-μ Dual Triode[10]	9A	12.6 / 6.3	0.225 / 0.45	3.1[7] / 3.1[8]	0.57 / 0.4[8]	1.9[7] / 1.9[8]	100	120*	—	—	9	6.1K	6100	37		
								150	56*	—	—	18	4.8K	8500	41		
12AW6	Sharp Cut-off Pent.	7CM	12.6	0.15	6.5	1.5	0.025	250	200*	150	2	7	800K	5000	42		
12AX7	High-μ A1 Amp.[10]	9A	12.6	0.15	1.6[7]	0.46[7]	1.7[7]	250	-2	—	—	1.2	62.5K	1600	100		
	Dual Triode Class B		6.3	0.3	1.6[8]	0.34[8]	1.7[8]	300	0	—	—	40[2]	—	—	14[5]	16K[6]	7.5
12AY7	Medium-μ A1 Amp.	9A	12.6	0.15	1.3	0.6	1.3	250	-4	—	—	3	—	1750	40		
	Dual Triode[10] Low-Level Amp.		6.3	0.3				150	2700*	Plate resistor = 20K. Grid resistor = 0.1 meg. V. G. = 12.5							
12AZ7A	High-μ Dual Triode[10]	9A	12.6	0.225	3.1[7]	0.57	1.9[7]	100	270*	—	—	3.7	15K	4000	60		
			6.3	0.45	3.1[8]	0.4[8]	1.9[8]	250	200*	—	—	10	10.9K	5500	60		
12B4A	Low-μ Triode	9AG	12.6 / 6.3	0.3 / 0.6	5	1.5	4.8	150	-17.5	—	—	34	1.03K	6300	6.5		
12BH7A	Medium-μ Dual Triode[10]	9A	12.6 / 6.3	0.3 / 0.6	3.2[7] / 3.2[8]	0.57 / 0.4[8]	2.6[7] / 2.6[8]	250	-10.5	—	—	11.5	5.3K	3100	16.5		
12BL6	Sharp Cut-off Pent.	7BK	12.6	0.15	5.5	4.8	0.006	12.6	-0.65	12.6	0.0005	1.35	500K	1350	—		
12BR7A	Dual Diode—Medium-μ Triode	9CF	12.6 / 6.3	0.225 / 0.45	2.8	1	1.9	100	270*	—	—	3.7	15K	4000	60		
								250	200*	—	—	10	10.9K	5500	60		
12BV7	Sharp Cut-off Pent.	9BF	12.6 / 6.3	0.3 / 0.6	11	3	0.055	250	68*	150	6	25	90K	12K	1100		
12BY7A	Sharp Cut-off Pent.	9BF	12.6 / 6.3	0.3 / 0.6	11.1	3	0.055	250	68*	150	6	25	90K	12K	1200		
12BZ7	High-μ Dual Triode[10]	9A	12.6 / 6.3	0.3 / 0.6	6.5[7] / 6.5[8]	0.77 / 0.55[8]	2.5[7] / 2.5[8]	250	-2	—	—	2.5	31.8K	3200	100		
12CN5	Pentode	7CV	12.6	0.45	—	—	0.25	12.6	0	12.6	0.35	4.5	40K	3800	—		
12CX5	Sharp Cut-off Pent.	7CV	12.6	0.15	7.6	6.2	0.05	12.6	0	12.6	1.4	3	40K	3100	—		
12DE8	Diode—Remote Cut-off Pent.	Fig. 81	12.6	0.15	5.5	5.7	0.006	12.6	0	12.6	0.5	1.3	300K	1500	—		
12DK7	Dual Diode—Tetrode	9HZ	12.6	0.5	—	—	—	12.6	0	12.6	1	6	4K	5000	—	3.5K	0.01
12DL8	Dual Diode—Tetrode	9HR	12.6	0.55	12	1.3	—	12.6	-0.5	12.6**	75**	40	480	—	—	15K	7.2

TABLE I—MINIATURE RECEIVING TUBES—Continued

Type	Name	Base	Fil. or Heater		Capacitances μμf.			Plate Supply V.	Grid Bias	Screen Volts	Screen Ma.	Plate Ma.	Plate Res. Ohms	Transconductance[11]	Amp. Factor[4]	Load Res. Ohms	Watts Output
			V.	Amp.	C_{in}	C_{out}	C_{gp}										
DQ7	Beam Pwr. Pent.	9BF	12.6	.3	10	3.8	0.1	330	—	180	5.6	26	53K	10.5K	—	—	—
			6.3	.6													
DS7A	Dual Diode Pwr. Tetrode	9JU	12.6	.4	Max. a.c. voltage = 16. Max. d.c. output current = 5 ma.												
					—	—	—	16	—	16	75	40	480	15K	7.2	800	.04
DT7	High-μ Dual Triode	9A	12.6	.15	1.6	.46	1.7	300	−2	—	—	1.2	62.5K	1600	100	—	—
			6.3	.3	1.6	.34	1.7										
DU7	Dual Diode Tetrode	9JX	12.6	.275	Max. average diode current = 1.0 ma.												
					11	3.6	.6	16	—	16	1.5	12	6K	6200	—	2.7K	.025
DV7	Dual Diode Triode	9JY	12.6	.15	Max. average diode current = 1.0 ma.												
					1.3	.38	1.6	16	—	—	—	0.4	19K	750	14	—	—
DV8	Dual Diode—Tetrode	9HR	12.6	0.375	9.0	1.0	12	12.6	18*	—	—	6.8[2]	—	—	7.6	1250	.005
DW8	Diode Dissimiliar Dual Triode	9JC	12.6	.45	1.6[7]	.7	1.8	16	0	—	—	1.9[7]	—	2700	9.5	—	—
					4.4[8]	.7	3.2	16	0	—	—	7.5[8]	—	6500	6.4	—	—
DY8	Sharp Cut-off Triode Tetrode	9JD	12.6	.35	2	2	1.5	16	0	—	—	1.2	10K	2000	20	—	—
					11	3	.74	16	—	12.6	2	14	5K	6000	—	—	—
DZ6	Pwr. Amp. Pent.	7BK	12.6	0.175	12.5	8.5	.25	12.6	—	12.6	2.2	4.5[2]	25K	3800	—	—	—
EA6	R.F. Pent.	7BK	12.6	0.175	11	4	.04	12.6	−3.4	12.6	1.4	3.2[2]	32K	3800	—	—	—
EC8	Medium-μ Triode Pent.	9FA	12.6	0.225	2.6	0.4	1.7	16	−2.2	—	—	2.4	6K	4700	25	—	—
					4.6	2.6	.02	16	−1.6	12.6	—	.66	750K	2000	—	—	—
ED5	Pwr. Amp. Pent.	7CV	12.6	.45	14	8.5	.26	150	−4.5	150	11	36[2]	14K	8500	—	—	1.5
EG6	Dual Control Heptode	7CH	12.6	.15	—	—	—	30	—	12.6	2.4	.4	150K	800	—	—	—
EK6	R.F. Pent.	7BK	12.6	.2	10	5.5	.032	12.6	−4.0	12.6	2	4.4	40K	4200	—	—	—
EL6	Dual Diode—High-μ Triode	7FB	12.6	0.15	2.2	1	1.8	12.6	0	—	—	0.75	45K	1200	55	—	—
EM6	Diode—Tetrode	9HV	12.6	0.5	—	—	—	12.6	0	12.6	1	6	4K	5000	—	—	—
F8	Dual Diode—Remote Cut-off Pent.	9FH	12.6	0.15	4.5	3	0.06	12.6	0	12.6	0.38	1	333K	1000	—	—	—
FK6	Dual Diode—Low-μ Triode	7BT	12.6	0.15	1.8	.7	1.6	16	0	—	—	1.3	6.2K	1200	7.4	—	—
FM6	Dual Diode—Med.-μ Triode	7BT	12.6	0.15	2.7	1.7	1.7	30	0	—	—	1.8	5.6K	2400	13.5	—	—
FT6	Dual Diode—Triode	7BT	12.6	0.15	1.8	1.1	2.0	30	0	—	—	2	7.6K	1900	15	—	—
H4	General Purpose Triode	7DW	12.6	0.15	2.4	0.9	3.4	90	0	—	—	10	—	3000	20	—	—
			6.3	0.3				250	−8	—	—	9	—	2600	20	—	—
J8	Dual Diode—Tetrode	9GC	12.6	0.325	10.5	4.4	0.7	12.6	0	12.6	1.5	12[5]	6K	5500	—	2.7K	0.02
								12.6	−2	12.6**	85**	8	800	7000	5.6	800	0.035
K5	Tetrode (Pwr. Amp. Driver)	7EK	12.6	0.45	—	—	—	12.6	−2	12.6**	85**	8	800	7000	5.6	800	0.035
R5	Beam Pwr. Pent.	7CV	12.6	0.6	13	9	0.55	110	−8.5	110	3.3	40	13K	7000	—	—	—
U7	Dual Medium-μ Triode[10]	9A	12.6	0.15	1.6[7], [8]	0.47	1.5[7], [8]	12.6	0	—	—	1	12.5K	1600	20	—	—
FW6	Remote Cut-off Pent.	7CC	18	0.1	5.5	5	.0035	150	—	100	4.4	11	250K	4400	—	—	—
FX6	Dual Control Heptode	7CH	18	0.1	—	—	—	150	—	—	—	2.3	400K	—	—	—	—
FY6	High-μ Triode—Diode	7BT	18	0.1	2.4	.22	1.8	150	−1	—	—	.6	77K	1300	100	—	—
F5	Beam Pwr. Pent.	7CV	25	0.15	12	6	0.57	110	−7.5	110	3/7	36/37	16K	5800	—	2.5K	1.2
ET5	Beam Pwr. Pent.	7CV	32	0.1	12	6	.6	110	−7.5	130	—	—	21.5K	5500	—	2.8K	1.2
B5	Beam Pwr. Amp.	7BZ	35	0.15	11	6.5	0.4	110	−7.5	110	3/7	41[2]	—	5800	40[5]	2.5K	1.5
B5	Beam Pwr. Amp.	7BZ	50	0.15	13	6.5	0.5	110	−7.5	110	4/8.5	50[2]	14K	7500	49[5]	2.5K	1.9
86	Beam Pwr. Pent.	9G	6.3	0.35	6.4	8.5	0.11	250	−12.5	250	3[5]	27[5]	45K	3100	—	9K	2.7
87	Medium-μ Dual Triode[10]	9H	12.6	0.45	4[7]	0.67	4[7]	120	−2	—	—	36	1.7K	11K	18.5	—	—
			6.3	0.9	4[8]	0.5[8]	4[8]	250	−12.5	—	—	12.5	3K	5500	16.5	—	—
22	Noise Generating Diode	5CB	6.3	1.5	—	2.2	—	200	—	—	—	35	—	—	—	—	—
842/ 17A	High-μ Triode	9V	6.3	0.3	9.0	1.8	0.55	150	62*	—	—	26	1.8K	24K	43	—	—
879	Sharp Cut-off Pent.	9AD	6.3	0.15	2.7	2.4	0.15	250	−3	100	0.4	1.8	2 meg.	1000	—	—	—
386	Medium-μ Dual Triode[10]	8CJ	6.3	0.35	2	1.1	1.2	100	200*	—	—	9.6	4.25K	4000	17	—	—
887	Dual Diode	6BT	6.3	0.2	Max. peak inverse plate voltage = 360 V. Max. d.c. plate current each diode = 10 ma.												
973	Pwr. Pentode	9EU	6.3	.45	6	6	.4	440	−15	330	—	—	73K	4800	—	—	—
258	Sharp Cut-off Med.-μ Triode	9DA	12.6	.195	7	2.4	.4	330	—	125	3.8	12	170K	7800	—	—	—
					2	.26	1.5	330	−3	—	—	15	4.7K	4500	21	—	—
001	Sharp Cut-off Pent.	7BD	6.3	0.15	3.6	3	0.01	250	−3	100	0.7	2	1 meg.	1400	—	—	—
002	U.h.f. Triode	7BS	6.3	0.15	1.2	1.1	1.4	250	−7	—	—	6.3	11.4K	2200	25	—	—
003	Remote Cut-off Pent.	7BD	6.3	0.15	3.4	3	0.1	250	−3	100	0.9	6.7	700K	1800	—	—	—
006	U.h.f. Diode	6BH	6.3	0.15	Max. a.c. voltage = 270. Max. d.c. output current = 5 ma.												

‡ Controlled heater warm-up characteristic.
Ω Oscillator gridleak or screen-dropping resistor ohms.
* Cathode resistor ohms.
** Space-charge grid.

[1] Per Plate.
[2] Maximum-signal current for full-power output.
[3] Values are for two tubes in push-pull.
[4] Unless otherwise noted.

[5] No signal plate ma.
[6] Effective plate-to-plate.
[7] Triode No. 1.
[8] Triode No. 2.

[9] Oscillator grid current ma.
[10] Values for each section.
[11] Micromhos.
[12] Through 33K.

TABLE II—METAL RECEIVING TUBES

Characteristics given in this table apply to all tubes having type numbers shown, including metal tubes, glass tubes with "G" suffix, and bantam tubes with "GT" suffix.
For "G" and "GT" tubes not listed (not having metal counterparts), see Tables III, V, VI and VIII.

Type	Name	Base	Fil. or Heater V.	Amp.	C_{in}	C_{out}	C_{gp}	Plate Supply V.	Grid Bias	Screen Volts	Screen Ma.	Plate Ma.	Plate Res. Ohms	Transconductance[12]	Amp. Factor[13]	Load Res. Ohms	Watts Output
6A8	Pentagrid Conv.	8A	6.3	0.3	—	—	—	250	−3	100	2.7	3.5	360K	550	—	—	—
								E_{bb} (Osc.) 250 V. through 20K. Grid resistor (Osc.) 50K. I_b = 4 ma. I_{g1} = 0.4 ma.									
6AB7 1853	Remote Cut-off Pent.	8N	6.3	0.45	8	5	0.15	300	−3	200	3.2	12.5	700K	5000	—	—	—
								300	−3	30K[8]	3.2	12.5	700K	5000	—	—	—
6AC7 1852	Sharp Cut-off Pent.	8N	6.3	0.45	11	5	0.15	300	160*	150	2.5	10	1 meg.	9000	—	—	—
								300	160*	60K[8]	2.5	10	1 meg.	9000	—	—	—
6AG7	Pwr. Amp. Pent.	8Y	6.3	0.65	13	7.5	0.06	300	−3	150	7/9	30/31	130K	11K	—	10K	3
6B8	Dual-Diode—Pent.	8E	6.3	0.3	6	9	0.005	250	−3	125	2.3	10	600K	1325	—	—	—
6C5	Medium-μ Triode, A1 Amp., Biased Detector	6Q	6.3	0.3	3	11	2	250	−8	—	—	8	10K	2000	20	—	—
								250	−17	Plate current adjusted to 0.2 ma. with no signal.							
6F5	High-μ Triode	5M	6.3	0.3	5.5	4	2.4	250	−2	—	—	0.9	66K	1500	100	—	—
6F6	Pwr. Amp. Pent. — A1 Amp.[1,5]	7S	6.3	0.7	6.5	13	0.2	250	−20	250[10]	—	31/34	2.6K	2600	6.8	4K	0.85
	AB2 Amp.[1,6]							350	730*	132[11]	—	50/60	—	—	—	10K[7]	9
								350	−38	123[11]	—	48/92	—	—	—	6K[7]	13
	A1 Amp.[5]							250	−16.5	250	6/11	34/36	80K	2500	—	7K	3.2
								285	−20	285	7/13	38/40	78K	2500	—	7K	4.8
	AB2 Amp.[6]							375	−26	250	5/20	34/82	* —	—	—	10K[7]	18.5
								375	340*	250	8/18	54/77	—	—	—	10K[7]	19
6H6	Dual Diode	7Q	6.3	0.3	—	—	—	Max. a.c. voltage per plate = 150 r.m.s. Max. output current 8.0 ma. d.c								
6J5	Medium-μ Triode	6Q	6.3	0.3	3.4	3.6	3.4	250	−8	—	—	9	7.7K	2600	20	—	—
6J7	Sharp Cut-off Pent., A1 Amp., Biased Detector	7R	6.3	0.3	7	12	0.005	250	−3	100	0.5	2	1 meg.	1225	—	—	—
								250	10K*	100	Zero signal cathode current = 0.43 ma.		0.5 meg.			0.5 meg.	
6K7	Variable-μ Pent., R.f. Amp., Mixer	7R	6.3	0.3	7	12	0.005	250	−3	125	2.6	10.5	600K	1650	990	—	—
								250	−10	100	Osc. peak volts = 7						
6K8	Triode—Hexode, Hexode Conv.—Triode	8K	6.3	0.3	—	—	—	250	−3	100	6	2.5	600K	350	—	—	—
								100	50K[8]	—	—	3.8	I_{g1} (Osc.) = 0.15 ma.				
6L6-GB[2]	Beam Pwr. Amp. — A1 Amp.[1,5]	7AC	6.3	0.9	11.5	9.5	0.9	250	−20	250[10]	—	40/44	1.7K	4700	8	5K	1.4
	A1 Amp.[5] Self Bias							250	167*	250	5.4/7.2	75/78	—	1410	—	2.5K	6.5
								300	218*	200	3/4.6	51/55	—	12.710	—	4.5K	6.5
	A1 Amp.[5] Fixed Bias							250	−14	250	5/7.3	72/79	22.5K	6000	1410	2.5K	6.5
								350	−18	250	2.5/7	54/66	33K	5200	1810	4.2K	10.8
	A1 Amp.[6] Self Bias							250	125*	250	10/15	120/130	—	—	35.611	5K[7]	13.8
								270	125*	270	11/17	134/145	—	—	28.211	5K[7]	18.5
	A1 Amp.[6] Fixed Bias							250	−16	250	10/16	120/140	24.5[5]	55005	3211	5K[7]	14.5
								270	−17.5	270	11/17	134/155	23.5[5]	57005	3511	5K[7]	17.5
	AB1 Amp.[6] Self Bias							360	270*	270	5/17	88/100	—	—	40.611	9K[7]	24.5
	AB1 Amp.[6] Fixed Bias							360	−22.5	270	5/11	88/140	—	—	4511	3.8K[7]	18
								360	−22.5	270	5/15	88/132	—	—	4511	6.6K[7]	26.5
	AB2 Amp.[6] Fixed Bias							360	−18	225	3.5/11	78/142	—	—	5211	6K[7]	31
								360	−22.5	270	5/16	88/205	—	—	7211	3.8K[7]	47
L7	Pentagrid—Mixer Amp., A1 Amp., Mixer	7T	6.3	0.3	—	—	—	250	−3	100	6.5	5.3	600K	1100	−314	—	—
								250	−6	150	9.2	3.3	1 meg.	350	−1514	—	—
N7	Class-B Twin Triode, B Amp.[9], A Amp.[15]	8B	6.3	0.8	—	—	—	300	0	—	—	35/70	—	—	8211	8K[7]	10
								250	−5	—	—	6	11.3K	3100	—	—	—
Q7	Dual Diode—High-μ Triode	7V[2]	6.3	0.3	5	3.8	1.4	250	−3	—	—	1	58K	1200	70	—	—
R7	Dual Diode—Triode	7V[2]	6.3	0.3	4.8	3.8	2.4	250	−9	—	—	9.5	8.5K	1900	16	10K	0.28
S7	Remote Cut-off Pent.	7R[2]	6.3	0.15	6.5	10.5	0.005	250	−3	100	2	8.5	1 meg.	1750	—	—	—
SA7GT	Pentagrid Conv.	8R[2]	6.3	0.3	9.5	12	0.13	250	03	100	8	3.4	800K	Grid No. 1 resistor 20K.			
SB7Y	Pentagrid Conv.	8R	6.3	0.3	9.6	9.2	0.13	100	−1	100	10.2	3.6	50K	900	—	—	—
								250	−1	100	10	3.8	1 meg.	950	—	—	—
								250	22K[8]	12K[8]	12/13	6.8/6.5	Osc. Section in 88–108 Mc. Service.			
SC7	High-μ Dual Triode[5]	8S	6.3	0.3	2	3	2	250	−2	—	—	2	53K	1325	70	—	—
SF5	High-μ Triode	6AB[2]	6.3	0.3	4	3.6	2.4	250	−2	—	—	0.9	66K	1500	100	—	—
SF7	Diode—Variable-μ Pent.	7AZ	6.3	0.3	5.5	6	0.004	250	−1	100	3.3	12.4	700K	2050	—	—	—
SG7	H.f. Amp. Pent.	8BK	6.3	0.3	8.5	7	0.003	250	−2.5	150	3.4	9.2	1 meg.	4000	—	—	—
SH7	H.f. Amp. Pent.	8BK	6.3	0.3	8.5	7	0.003	250	−1	150	4.1	10.8	900K	4900	—	—	—
SJ7[4]	Sharp Cut-off Pent.	8N	6.3	0.3	6	7	0.005	250	−3	100	0.8	3	1 meg.	1650	—	—	—
SK7	Variable-μ Pent.	8N	6.3	0.3	6	7	0.003	250	−3	100	2.6	9.2	800K	2000	—	—	—
SQ7GT	Dual Diode—High-μ Triode	8Q	6.3	0.3	3.2	3	1.6	250	−2	—	—	0.9	91K	1100	100	—	—
SR7	Dual Diode—Triode	8Q	6.3	0.3	3.6	2.8	2.4	250	−9	—	—	9.5	8.5K	1900	16	—	—
SS7	Variable-μ Pent.	8N	6.3	0.15	5.5	7	0.004	250	−3	100	2	9	1 meg.	1850	—	—	—
76	Beam Pwr. Amp. — A1 Amp.[5]	7AC	6.3	0.45	10	11	0.3	180	−8.5	180	3/4	29/30	50K	3700	8.510	5.5K	2
								250	−12.5	250	4.5/7	45/47	50K	4100	12.510	5K	4.5
								315	−13	225	2.2/6	34/35	80K	3750	1310	8.5K	5.5
	AB1 Amp.[6]							250	−15	250	5/13	70/79	60K	3750	3011	10K[7]	10
								285	−19	285	4/13.5	70/92	70K	3600	3811	8K[7]	14
512	Pentagrid Amp.	7T	6.3	0.3	7.5	11	0.001	250	−3	100	6.5	5.3	600K	1100	−314	—	—
520	Sharp Cut-off Pent.	7R	6.3	0.3	7	12	0.005	250	−3	100	0.5	2	1 meg.	1225	—	—	—
521	Pwr. Amp. Pent. — A1 Amp.[1,6], A1 Amp.[6]	7S	6.3	0.7	7.5	11.5	0.2	330	500*	—	—	55/59	—	—	5411	5K[7]	2
								300	−30	300	6.5/13	38/69	—	—	6011	4K[7]	5
522	Beam Pwr. Amp.[6]	7AC	6.3	0.9	10	12	0.4	300	−20	250	4/10.5	86/125	—	—	4011	4K[7]	10
593	Sharp Cut-off Pent.	8N	6.3	0.3	5.3	6.2	0.005	250	−3	100	0.85	3	1 meg.	1650	—	—	—

* Cathode resistor-ohms.
1 Screen tied to plate.
2 No connection to Pin No. 1 for 6L6G, 6Q7G, 6R7GT/G, 6S7G, 6SA7GT/G and 6SF5-GT.
3 Grid bias = 2 volts if separate oscillator excitation is used.
4 Also type 6SJ7Y.
5 Values are for single tube or section.
6 Values are for two tubes in push-pull.
7 Plate-to-plate value.
8 Osc. grid leak—Scrn. res.
9 Values for two units.
10 Peak a.f. grid voltage.
11 Peak a.f. G-G voltage.
12 Micromhos.
13 Unless otherwise noted.
14 G3 voltage.
15 Units connected in parallel.

TABLE III—6.3-VOLT GLASS TUBES WITH OCTAL BASES

(For "G" and "GT"-type tubes not listed here, see equivalent type in Tables II and VIII; characteristics and connections will be similar)

Type	Name	Base	Fil. or Heater V.	Amp.	Capacitances μμf. Cin	Cout	Cgp	Plate Supply V.	Grid Bias	Screen Volts	Screen Ma.	Plate Ma.	Plate Res. Ohms	Transconductance [10]	Amp. Factor	Load Res. Ohms	Watts Output
6AC5GT	Triode Pwr. Amp. AB Amp.[4]	6Q	6.3	0.4	—	—	—	250	0	—	—	5[6]	36.7K	3400	125	10K[5]	8
6AD7G	Triode—Pwr. Amp. Pent. Triode Pent.	8AY	6.3	0.85	—	—	—	250 250	−25 −16.5	250	6.5/10.5	4 34/36	19K 80K	325 2500	6	— 7K	3.2
6AH4GT	Medium-μ Triode	8EL	6.3	0.75	7	1.7	4.4	250	−23	—	—	30	1.78K	4500	8	—	—
6AL7GT	Electron—Ray Indicator	8CH	6.3	0.15	—	—	—	Outer edge of any of the three illuminated areas displaced 1/16 in. min. outward with +5 volts to its electrode. Similar inward disp. with −5 volts. No pattern with −6 volts grid.									
6AQ7GT	Dual Diode—High-μ Triode	8CK	6.3	0.3	2.8	3.2	3	250	−2	—	—	2.3	44K	1600	70	—	—
6AR6	Beam Pent.	6BQ	6.3	1.2	11	7	0.55	250	−22.5	250	5	77	21K	5400	—	—	—
6AR7GT	Dual Diode—Remote Pent.	7DE	6.3	0.3	5.5	7.5	0.003	250	−2	100	1.8	7	1.2meg.	2500	—	—	—
6AS7G	Low-μ Twin Triode—D.C. Amp.[1]	8BD	6.3	2.5	6.5	2.2	7.5	135	250*	—	—	125	0.28K	7000	2	—	—
6AU5G	Beam Pwr. Amp.[8]	6CK	6.3	1.25	11.3	7	0.5	115	−20	175	6.8	60	6K	5600	—	—	—
6AV5GA	Beam Pwr. Amp.[8]	6CK	6.3	1.2	14	7.0	0.5	250	−22.5	150	2.1	55	20K	5500	—	—	—
6BD5GT	Beam Pwr. Amp.[8]	6CK	6.3	0.9				310	−200[7]	310		90[9]	—	—	—	—	—
6BG6GA	Beam Pwr. Amp.[8]	5BT	6.3	0.9	11	6	0.8	250	−15	250	4	75	25K	6000	—	—	—
6BL7GTA	Medium-μ Dual Triode[1]	8BD	6.3	1.5	4.4	0.9	6.0	250	−9	—	—	40	2150	7000	15	—	—
6BQ6GTB 6CU6	Beam Pwr. Amp.[8]	6AM	6.3	1.2	15	7	0.6	250	−22.5	150	2.1	57	14.5K	5900	—	—	—
6BX7GT	Dual Triode[1]	8BD	6.3	1.5	5	3.4	4.2	250	390*	—	—	42	1.3K	7600	10	—	—
6CB5A	Beam pwr. Amp.[8]	8GD	6.3	2.5	22	10	0.4	175	−30	175	6	90	5K	8800	—	—	—
6CD6GA	Beam Pwr. Amp.[8]	5BT	6.3	2.5	24	9.5	0.8	175	−30	175	5.5	75	7.2K	7700	—	—	—
6CK4	Low-μ Triode	8JB	6.3	1.25	8.0	1.8	6.5	550	−26	—	—	55	1.0K	6500	6.7	—	—
6CL5	Beam Pwr. Amp.[8]	8GD	6.3	2.5	20	11.5	0.7	175	−40	175	7	90	6K	6500	—	—	—
6CU6	Beam Pwr. Amp.[8]	6AM	6.3	1.2	15	7	0.55	250	−22.5	150	2.1	55	20K	5500	—	—	—
6DG6GT	Beam Pwr. Amp.	7S	6.3	1.2				200	180*	125	8.5[7]	47[7]	28K	8000	—	4K	3.8
6DN6	Beam Pwr. Pent.[8]	5BT	6.3	2.5	22	11.5	0.8	125	−18	125	6.3	70	4K	9000	—	—	—
6DN7	Dissimilar Dual Triode	8BD	6.3	0.9	2.2 4.6	0.7 1.0	4.0 5.5	350 550	−8 −9.5	—	—	8 68	9K 2K	2500 7700	22 15	—	—
6DQ5	Beam Pwr. Amp.[8]	8JC	6.3	2.5	23	11	0.5	175	−25	125	5	110	5.5K	10.5K	—	—	—
6DQ6B	Beam Pwr. Amp.[8]	6AM	6.3	1.2	15	7	0.55	250	−22.5	150	2.4	75	20K	6600	—	—	—
6EA7	Dissimilar— Dual Triode	8BD	6.3	1.05	2.2 6	0.6 1.3	4 8	350 550	−3 −9	—	—	1.5 95	34K 770	1900 6500	65 5	—	—
6EF6	Beam Pwr. Amp.[11]	7S	6.3	0.9	11.5	9	0.8	250	−18	250	2	50	—	5000	—	—	—
6EY6	Beam Pwr. Pent.	7AC	6.3	0.68	8.5	7	.7	350	−17.5	300	3	44	60K	4.4K	—	—	—
6EZ5	Beam Pwr. Pent.	7AC	6.3	0.8	9	7	.6	350	−20	300	3.5	43	50K	4.1K	—	—	—
6FH6	Beam Pwr. Pent.	6AM	6.3	1.2	33	8	.4	770	−22.5	220	1.7	75	12K	6K	—	—	—
6G6G	Beam Pwr. Amp. A1 Amp. A1 Amp.[2]	7S	6.3	0.15	5.5	7	0.5	180 180	−9 −12	180	2.5[6]	15[6] 11	175K 4.75K	2300 2000	— 9.5	10K 12K	1.1 0.25
6K6GT	Pwr. Amp. Pent.	7S	6.3	0.4	5.5	6	0.5	315	−21	250	4/9	25/28	13K	2100	—	9K	4.5
6S8GT	Triple-Diode—Triode	8CB	6.3	0.3	1.2	5	2	250	−2	—	—	1	91K	1100	100	—	—
6SD7GT	Semi-Remote Pent.	8N	6.3	0.3	9	7.5	0.0035	250	−2	125	3	9.5	700K	4250	—	—	—
6SL7GT	High-μ Dual Triode[1]	8BD	6.3	0.3	3.4	3.8	2.8	250	−2	—	—	2.3	44K	1600	70	—	—
6SN7GTB	Medium-μ Dual Triode[1]	8BD	6.3	0.6	3	1.2	4	250	−8	—	—	9	7.7K	2600	20	—	—
6U6GT	Beam Pwr. Amp.	7S	6.3	0.75	—	—	—	200	−14	135	3/13	55/62	20K	6200	—	3K	5.5
6W6GT	Beam Pwr. Amp.	7S	6.3	1.2	15	9	0.5	200	180*	125	2/8.5	46/47	28K	8000	—	4K	3.8
6Y6GA	Beam Pwr. Amp.	7S	6.3	1.25	15	1	0.7	200	−14	135	2.2/9	61/66	18.3K	7100	—	2.6K	6
1635	High-μ Dual Triode	8B	6.3	0.6	—	—	—	300	0	—	—	6.6/54	—	—	—	12K[5]	10.4
7027	Beam Pwr. Amp.	8HY	6.3	0.9	10	7.5	1.5	450	−30	350	19.2	194	—	6000	—	6K[5]	50

* Cathode resistor-ohms.
[1] Per section.
[2] Screen tied to plate.
[3] Values are for single tube.
[4] Values are for two tubes in push-pull.
[5] Plate-to-plate value.
[6] No signal current.
[7] Max. value.
[8] Horz. Deflection Amp.
[9] Cathode current.
[10] Micromhos.
[11] Vert. Deflection Amp.

TABLE IV—6.3-VOLT LOCK-IN-BASE TUBES

For other lock-in-base types see Tables V, VI, and VII

Type	Name	Base	Fil. or Heater V.	Amp.	Capacitances μμf. Cin	Cout	Cgp	Plate Supply V.	Grid Bias	Screen Volts	Screen Ma.	Plate Ma.	Plate Res. Ohms	Transconductance[3]	Amp. Factor	Load Res. Ohms	Watts Output
7A8	Octode Conv.	8U	6.3	0.15	7.5	9	0.15	250	−3	100	3.2	3	50K	Anode grid 250 Volts max.[1]			
7AH7	Remote Cut-off Pent.	8V	6.3	0.15	7	6.5	0.005	250	250*	250	1.9	6.8	1 meg.	3300	—	—	—
7AK7	Sharp Cut-off Pent.	8V	6.3	0.8	12	9.5	0.7	150	0	90	21	41	11.5K	5500	—	—	—
7B7	Remote Cut-off Pent.	8V	6.3	0.15	5	6	0.007	250	−3	100	1.7	8.5	750K	1750	—	—	—
7C7	Sharp Cut-off Pent.	8V	6.3	0.15	5.5	6.5	0.007	250	−3	100	0.5	2	2 meg.	1300	—	—	—
7E7	Dual Diode—Pent.	8AE	6.3	0.3	4.6	5.5	0.005	250	330*	100	1.6	7.5	700K	1300	—	—	—
7F8	Medium-μ Dual Triode[2]	8BW	6.3	0.3	2.8	1.4	1.2	250	500*	—	—	6	14.5K	3300	48	—	—
7K7	Dual Diode—High-μ Tri.	8BF	6.3	0.3	2.4	2	1.7	250	−2	—	—	2.3	44K	1600	70	—	—

* Cathode resistor-ohms. [1] Through 20K resistor. [2] Each section. [3] Micromhos.

TABLE V—1.5-VOLT FILAMENT BATTERY TUBES V21

ype	Name	Base	Fil. or Heater		Capacitances μμf.			Plate Supply V.	Grid Bias	Screen Volts	Screen Ma.	Plate Ma.	Plate Res. Ohms	Transcon- ductance[2]	Amp. Factor	Load Res. Ohms	Watts Output
			V.	Amp.	C_{in}	C_{out}	C_{gp}										
GT	Pentagrid Conv.	7Z	1.4	0.05	7	10	0.5	90	0	45	0.7	0.6	600K	E_{bb} Anode-grid = 90 Volts.			
T	Diode High-μ Triode	5Z	1.4	0.05	1.1	4.6	1	90	0	—	—	0.15	240K	275	65	—	—
	Sharp Cut-off Pent.	7AO	1.4	0.05	3	8	0.007	90	0	90	0.35	1.6	1.1 meg.	800	—	—	—
T	R.f. Pentode	5Y	1.4	0.05	3	10	0.007	90	0	90	0.3	1.2	1.5 meg.	750	—	—	—
	Sharp Cut-off Pent.	7CJ	2.8[1]	0.05	5.5	8	0.007	90	0	90	1.2	2.9	325K	1700	—	—	—

Center-tap filament permits 1.4 volt operation.　　　　[2] Micromhos.

TABLE VI—HIGH-VOLTAGE HEATER TUBES

See also Table VIII.

ype	Name	Base	Fil. or Heater		Capacitances μμf.			Plate Supply V.	Grid Bias	Screen Volts	Screen Ma.	Plate Ma.	Plate Res. Ohms	Transcon- ductance[2]	Amp. Factor	Load Res. Ohms	Watts Output
			V.	Amp.	C_{in}	C_{out}	C_{gp}										
	Beam Pwr. Amp.	7S	12.6	0.15	8	9	0.3	250	−12.5	250	3.5/5.5	30/32	70K	3000	—	7.5K	3.4
7GT	Medium-μ Dual Triode[1]	8BE	12.6	0.15	3.2	3	3	180	−6.5	—	—	7.6	8.4K	1900	16	—	—
6‡	Beam Pwr. Amp.	7S	12.6	0.6	14	8	0.65	200	−9.5	110	2.2	50	28K	8000	—	—	—
GT‡	Beam Pwr. Pent.	7S	12.6	0.6	15	10	0.6	110	−7.5	110	4/10	49/50	13K	8000	—	2K	2.1
								200	180*	125	2.2/8.5	46/47	28K	8000	—	4K	3.8
7	Heptode Conv.	8R	12.6	0.15	Osc.-Grid leak 20K.			250	−2	8.5	3.5	—	1 meg.	450	—	—	—
6	Beam Pwr. Pent.	5BT	21.5	0.6	22	8.5	1.1	—	−30	195	.3	67	8.5K	7700	—	—	—
	Beam Pwr. Amp.	6AA	35	0.15	—	—	—	110	−7.5	110	3/7	40/41	16K	5800	—	2.5K	1.5
GA	Beam Pwr. Amp.	7S	50	0.15	—	—	—	200	−14	135	2.2/9	61/66	18.3K	7100	—	2.6K	6
7GT	Rect.—Beam Pwr. Amp.	8AV	117	0.09	Rect. same as 117L7GT			100	−6	100	5	51	16K	7000	—	3K	1.2
	Beam Pwr. Pent.	7S	25	0.3	—	—	—	135	−22	135	2.5/14.5	61/69	15K	5000	—	1.7K	4.3
	Low-μ Dual Triode[1]	8BD	26.5	0.6	6	2.2	8	135	250*	—	—	125	0.28K	7000	2	—	—

* Cathode resistor-ohms.　　　　[1] Each section.　　　　[2] Micromhos.
‡ Controlled heater warm-up characteristic.

TABLE VII—SPECIAL RECEIVING TUBES

ype	Name	Base	Fil. or Heater		Capacitances μμf.			Plate Supply V.	Grid Bias	Screen Volts	Screen Ma.	Plate Ma.	Plate Res. Ohms	Transcon- ductance[2]	Amp. Factor	Load Res. Ohms	Watts Output
			V.	Amp.	C_{in}	C_{out}	C_{gp}										
GT	Beam Pwr. Amp.	7AP	2.8[1]	0.05	8	6.5	0.6	90	−4.5	90	1.3	9.5	90K	2200	—	8K	0.27
	Acorn Triode	7BR	6.3	0.225	2	0.6	1.9	80	150*	—	—	13	2.9K	5800	17	—	—
	Acorn Triode	7BR	6.3	0.225	1.8	0.5	1.6	80	150*	—	—	9.5	4.4K	6400	28	—	—
1201	H.f. Triode	8BN	6.3	0.15	3.6	2.8	1.5	180	−3	—	—	5.5	12K	3000	36	—	—
	Detector Amp.— A₁ Amp. Pentode (Acorn) Detector	5BB	6.3	0.15	3.4	3	0.007	250	−3	100	0.7	2	1 meg.	1400	—	—	—
								250	−6	100	I_b adjusted to 0.1 ma. with no signal.					250K	
	Medium-μ Triode (Acorn)	5BC	6.3	0.15	1	0.6	1.4	250	−7	—	—	6.3	11.4K	2200	25	—	—
								90	−2.5	—	—	2.5	14.7K	1700	25	—	—
	Remote Cut-off A₁ Amp. Pent. (Acorn) Mixer	5BB	6.3	0.15	3.4	3	0.007	250	−3	100	2.7	6.7	700K	1800	—	—	—
								250	−10	100	Oscillator peak volts −7 min.						
A	Medium-μ Triode (Acorn)	5BD	1.25	0.1	0.6	0.6	2.6	135	−7.5	—	—	3	10K	1200	12	—	—
	Sharp Cut-off Pent. (Acorn)	5BE	1.25	0.05	1.8	2.5	0.015	135	−3	67.5	0.4	1.7	800K	600	—	—	—
	Amplifier Pentode	5B	1.1	0.25	7	7	1	135	−1.5	67.5	0.65	2.5	400K	725	—	—	—
	U.h.f. "Pencil" Diode	Fig. 34	6.3	0.135	Plate to K = 1.1			Peak inverse—375 Volts. Peak I_p—50 Ma. Max. d.c. output—5.5 ma.									
	Ceramic U.h.f. Triode	—	6.3	0.24	1.9	0.01	1.0	250	−5	—	—	6.4	8.9K	9000	—	—	—
	U.h.f. Diode (Acorn)	4BJ	6.3	0.15	Plate to K = 1.3			Max. a.c. voltage—117. Max. d.c. output current—5 ma.									
	U.h.f. Diode (Acorn)	5BG	3.6	0.165	Plate to K = 0.8			Max. a.c. voltage—117. Max. d.c. output current—1 ma.									

* Cathode resistor-ohms.　　　　[1] Center-tap filament permits 1.4-volt operation.　　　　[2] Micromhos.

TABLE VIII—EQUIVALENT TUBES

The equivalent tubes listed in this table are, in general, designed for industrial, military and other special-purpose applications. These tubes are generally not directly interchangeable because of mechanical and/or electrical differences involving basing, heater characteristics, maximum ratings, interelectrode capacitances, etc.

Type	Equivalent and Table		Base	E_f[1]	I_f[2]	Type	Equivalent and Table		Base	E_f[1]	I_f[2]
	1J3	X	3C	1.25	0.2	5FV8	6FV8	I	9FA	4.7	0.6
	1H5GT	V	5AG	1.4	0.05	5V4G	5V4GA	X	5L	5.0	3.0
WA	2C39	XI	—	5.8	1.03	6A6	6N7	II	7B	6.3	0.8
5	2EA5	I	7EW	2.9	0.45	6A7	6A8	II	7C	6.3	0.3
3	3Q5GT	VII	6BB	2.8	0.05	6AE8	6K8	II	8DU	6.3	0.3
	3Q4	I	6BX	2.8	0.05	6AM8	6AM8A‡	I	9CY	6.3	0.45
6	3DK6	I	7CM	4.2	0.45	6AN8	6AN8A‡	I	9DA	6.3	0.45
8	6EA8	I	9AE	4.7	0.6	6AQ5	6AQ5A‡	I	7BZ	6.3	0.45

Type	Equivalent and Table		Base	E_f[1]	I_f[2]	Type	Equivalent and Table		Base	E_f[1]	I_f[2]
6AS7GA	6AS7G	III	8BD	6.3	2.5	12K8	6K8	II	8K	12.6	0.15
6AT8	6AT8A‡	I	9DW	6.3	1.8	12S8GT	6S8GT	III	8CB	12.6	0.15
6AU6	6AU6A‡	I	7BK	6.3	0.3	12SA7	6SA7	II	8R	12.6	0.15
6AU7‡	12AU7A	I	9A	3.15	0.6	12SC7	6SC7	II	8S	12.6	0.15
6AX7‡3	12AX7	I	9A	6.3	0.3	12SF5	6SF5	II	6AB	12.6	0.15
6BE8	6BE8A‡	I	9EG	6.3	0.45	12SF7	6SF7	II	7AZ	12.6	0.15
6BQ6GA/GTA	6BQ6GTB	III	6AM	6.3	1.2	12SG7	6SG7	II	8BK	12.6	0.15
6BR8	6BR8A‡	I	9FA	6.3	0.45	12SH7	6SH7	II	8BK	12.6	0.15
6C6	6J7		6F	6.3	0.3	12SJ7	6SJ7	II	8N	12.6	0.15
6CB6	6CB6A‡	I	7CM	6.3	0.3	12SK7	6SK7	II	8N	12.6	0.15
6CD6G	6CD6GA	III	5BT	6.3	2.5	12SL7GT	6SL7GT	III	8BD	12.6	0.15
6CG8	6CG8A‡	I	9GF	6.3	0.45	12SN7GT	6SN7GTB	III	8BD	12.6	0.3
6CL8	6CL8A‡	I	9FX	6.3	0.45	12SN7GTA	6SN7GTB	III	8BD	12.6	0.3
6CS8‡	6CR8		9FZ	6.3	0.45	12SQ7	6SQ7	II	8Q	12.6	0.15
6CU8	6AN8	I	9GM	6.3	0.45	12SR7	6SR7	II	8Q	12.6	0.15
6EW6	4EW6	I	7CM	6.3	0.4	12W6GT‡	6W6GT	III	7S	12.6	0.6
6J6	6J6A‡	I	7BF	6.3	0.45	14A7	6SK7	II	8V	12.6	0.15
6L6GA	6L6GB	I	7S	6.3	0.9	14AF7	7AF7	IV	8AC	12.6	0.15
6S4	6S4A	I	9AC	6.3	0.6	14B6	6SQ7	II	8W	12.6	0.15
6SN7GTA	6SN7GTB	III	8BD	6.3	0.6	14F7	6SL7GT	III	8AC	12.6	0.15
6SU7GTY	6SL7GT	III	8BD	6.3	0.3	14N7	6SN7GTB	III	8AC	12.6	0.6
6T8	6T8A‡	I	9E	6.3	0.45	14Q7	6SA7	II	8AL	12.6	0.15
6U8	6U8A‡	I	9AE	6.3	0.45	19CL8A	6CL8A	I	9FX	18.9	0.15
6V6	6V6GTA	I	7S	6.3	0.45	25BQ6GA	6BQ6GTB	III	6AM	25	0.3
6Y6G	6Y6GA	III	7S	6.3	1.25	25BQ6GT	6BQ6GTB	III	6AM	25	0.3
6Y6GT	6Y6GA	III	7S	6.3	1.25	25BQ6GTB‡	6BQ6GTB	III	6AM	25	0.3
7A4	6J5	II	5AS	6.3	0.3	25C5	50C5	VIII	7CV	25	0.3
7A6	6H6	II	7AJ	6.3	0.15	25C6GA	50C6GA	VIII	7S	25	0.3
7A7	6SK7	II	8V	6.3	0.3	25CA5	6CA5	I	7CV	25	0.3
7B4	6SF5	II	5AC	6.3	0.3	25CD6G	6CD6GA	III	5BT	25	0.6
7B5	6K6GT	III	6AE	6.3	0.4	25CD6GA‡	6CD6GA	III	5BT	25	0.6
7B6	6SQ7	II	8W	6.3	0.3	25CD6GB‡	6CD6GA	III	5BT	25	0.6
7B8	6V6	II	8X	6.3	0.3	25CU6	6CU6	III	6AM	25	0.3
7C5	6V6	II	6AA	6.3	0.45	25DN6‡	6DN6	III	5BT	25	0.6
7EY6‡	6EY6	III	7AC	7.2	0.6	25EC6‡	25CD6GB	VIII	5BT	25	0.6
7F7	6SL7GT	II	8AC	6.3	0.3	25EH5	6EH5	I	7CV	25	0.3
7H7	6SG7	II	8V	6.3	0.3	25L6GT	12L6GT	VI	7S	25	0.3
7N7	6SN7GT	III	8AC	6.3	0.6	25SA7GT	6SA7GT	II	8AD	—	—
7Q7	6SA7	II	8AL	6.3	0.3	25W6GT	6W6GT	III	7S	25	0.3
10EB8‡	6EB8	I	9DX	10.5	0.45	35C5	35B5	I	7CV	35	0.15
12A8GT	6A8	II	8A	12.6	0.15	35L6GT	35B5	I	7S	35	0.15
12AL5	6AL5	I	6BT	12.6	0.15	41	6K6GT	III	6B	6.3	0.4
12AT6	6AT6	I	7BT	12.6	0.15	42	6F6	II	6B	6.3	0.7
12AU6	6AU6A	I	7BK	12.6	0.15	50A5	12L6GT	VI	6AA	50	0.15
12AV5GA‡	6AV5GT	III	6CK	12.6	0.6	50BK5	6BK5	I	9BQ	50	0.15
12AV6	6AV6	I	7BT	12.6	0.15	50C5	50B5	I	7CV	50	0.15
12B4	12B4A‡3	I	9AG	12.6	0.3	50C6GA	50C6G	VI	7S	50	0.15
12BA6	6BA6	I	7BK	12.6	0.15	50L6GT	12L6GT	VI	7AC	50	0.15
12BA7	6BA7	I	8CT	12.6	0.15	75	6SQ7	II	6G	6.3	0.3
12BD6	6BD6	I	7BK	12.6	0.15	78	6K7	II	6F	6.3	0.3
12BE6	6BE6	I	7CH	12.6	0.15	417A	5842	I	9V	6.3	0.3
12BF6	6BF6	I	7BT	12.6	0.15	1221	6J7	II	6F	6.3	0.3
12BK5‡	6BK5	I	9BQ	12.6	0.6	1223	6J7	II	7R	6.3	0.3
12BK6	6BK6	I	7BT	12.6	0.15	1631	6L6GB	II	7AC	12.6	0.45
12BN6	6BN6	I	7DE	12.6	0.15	1632	12L6GT	VI	7S	12.6	0.6
12BQ6GA‡	6BQ6GTB	III	6AM	12.6	0.6	1634	6SC7	II	8S	12.6	0.15
12BQ6GT‡	6BQ6GTB	III	6AM	12.6	0.6	5591	6AK5	I	7BD	6.3	0.15
12BQ6GTB‡	6BQ6GTB	III	6AM	12.6	0.6	5654	6AK5	I	7BD	6.3	0.175
12BT6	6BT6	I	7BT	12.6	0.15	5670	2C51	I	8CJ	6.3	0.35
12BU6	6BU6	I	7BT	12.6	0.15	5679	6H6	II	7CX	6.3	0.3
12BW4	6BW4	X	9DJ	12.6	0.45	5691	6SL7GT	III	8BD	6.3	0.6
12BY7	12BY7A‡3	I	9BF	12.6	0.3	5692	6SN7GT	III	8BD	6.3	0.6
12BZ6‡	6BZ6	I	7CM	12.6	0.15	5725	6AS6	I	7CM	6.3	0.175
12C5‡	50B5	I	7CV	12.6	0.6	5726	6AL5	I	6BT	6.3	0.3
12C8	6B8	II	8E	12.6	0.15	5749	6BA6	I	7BK	6.3	0.3
12CA5‡	6CA5	I	7CV	12.6	0.6	5750	6BE6	I	7CH	6.3	0.3
12CM6	6CM6	I	9CK	12.6	0.225	5751 3	12AX7	I	9A	12.6	0.175
12CR6	6CR6	I	7EA	12.6	0.15	5814A 3	12SN7GT	VIII	9A	12.6	0.175
12CS5‡	6CS5	I	9CK	12.6	0.6	5871	6V6GTA	II	7AC	6.3	0.9
12CS6	6CS6	I	7CH	12.6	0.15	5881	6L6GB	II	7AC	6.3	0.9
12CU5‡	6CU5	I	7CV	12.6	0.6	5910	1U4	I	6AR	1.4	0.05
12CU6	6CU6	III	6AM	12.6	0.6	5915	6BY6	I	7CH	6.3	0.3
12DB5‡	6DB5	I	9GR	12.6	0.6	5963 3	12AU7A	I	9A	12.6	0.15
12DF7 3	12AX7	I	9A	12.6	0.15	5964	6J6A	I	7BF	6.3	0.45
12DQ6A‡	6DQ6B	III	6AM	12.6	0.6	5965 3	12AV7	I	9A	12.6	0.225
12DT5	6DT5	I	9HN	12.6	0.6	6046	12L6GT	VI	7AC	25	0.3
12DT8	6DT8	I	9DE	12.6	0.15	6057 3	12AX7	I	9A	12.6	0.15
12DW5‡	6DW5	I	9CK	12.6	0.6	6058	6AL5	I	6BT	6.3	0.3
12EF6‡	6EF6	III	7S	12.6	0.45	6059	6J7	II	9BC	6.3	0.15
12G4	6J5	II	6BG	12.6	0.15	6060 3	12AT7	I	9A	12.6	0.15
12H6	6H6	II	7Q	12.6	0.15	6061	6V6GTA	II	9AM	6.3	0.3
12J5GT	6J5	II	6Q	12.6	0.15	6064	6AM6	I	7DB	6.3	0.3
12J7GT	6J7	II	7R	12.6	0.15	6065	6BH6	I	7DB	6.3	0.2
12K7GT	6K7	II	7R	12.6	0.15	6066	6AT6	I	7BT	6.3	0.3

TABLE VIII—EQUIVALENT TUBES—Continued

Type	Equivalent and Table		Base	Ef[1]	If[2]	Type	Equivalent and Table		Base	Ef[1]	If[2]
67[3]	12AU7A	I	9A	12.6	0.15	6678	6U8A‡	I	9AE	6.3	0.45
80	6AS7G	III	8BD	6.3	2.5	6679[3]	12AT7	I	9A	12.6	0.15
01	6J6A	I	7BF	6.3	0.45	6680[3]	12AU7A	I	9A	12.6	0.15
32	6CH6	I	9BA	6.3	0.75	6681[3]	12AX7	I	9A	12.6	0.15
36	6AU6A	I	7BK	6.3	0.3	6829[3]	5965	VIII	9A	12.6	0.225
01[3]	12AT7	I	9A	12.6	0.15	6897	2C39	XI	—	6.3	1.05
65	6BH6	I	7CM	6.3	0.175	7000	6J7	II	7R	6.3	0.3
50[3]	12BH7A	I	9CZ	12.6	0.3	7025[3]	12AX7	VII	9A	12.6	0.15
85	6AH6	I	7BK	6.3	0.45	7137	6J4	I	7BQ	6.3	0.4
60	6BA6	I	7CC	6.3	0.3	7700	6J7	II	6F	6.3	0.3
61	6BH6	I	7CM	6.3	0.15	EEC81[3]	12AT7	I	9A	12.6	0.15
62	6BJ6A	I	7CM	6.3	0.15	EEC82[3]	12AU7A	I	9A	12.6	0.15
63	6AL5	I	6BT	6.3	0.3	EEC83[3]	12AX7	I	9A	12.6	0.15
69	6AQ5A	I	7BZ	6.3	0.45	KT-66[4]	6L6GB	II	7AC	6.3	1.27
77	6CL6	I	9BV	6.3	0.65	XXD	7AF7	IV	8AC	12.6	0.15

‡ Controlled heater warm-up characteristics.
[1] Filament or heater voltage.
[2] Filament or heater current.
[3] Heater center-tapped for operation at half voltage shown.
[4] British version of 6L6.

TABLE IX—CONTROL AND REGULATOR TUBES

Type	Name	Base	Cathode	Fil. or Heater Volts	Fil. or Heater Amp.	Peak Anode Voltage	Max. Anode Ma.	Minimum Supply Voltage	Operating Voltage	Operating Ma.	Grid Resistor	Tube Voltage Drop
2 / 3	Voltage Regulator	5BO	Cold	—	—	—	—	185	150	5-30	—	—
3/VR75	Voltage Regulator	4AJ	Cold					105	75	5-40	—	—
4G	Gas Triode	4V				With 105-120-volt a.c. anode supply, peak starter-anode a.c. voltage is 70 peak r.f. voltage 55. Peak d.c. ma = 100. Average d.c. ma = 25.						
7	Starter-Anode Type	4V	Cold									
5	Gas Pentode	Fig. 19	Cold			Plate −750 V., Screen −90 V., Grid +3 V., Pulse −85 V.						
4	Voltage Regulator	5BO	Cold	—	—	—	—	133	108	5-30	—	—
/VR90	Voltage Regulator	4AJ	Cold					125	90	5-40	—	—
	Voltage Regulator	5BO	Cold					105	75	5-30	—	—
/VR105	Voltage Regulator	4AJ	Cold					135	105	5-40	—	—
/VR150	Voltage Regulator	4AJ	Cold					185	150	5-40	—	—
1	Grid-Controlled Rectifier Relay Tube	7BN	Htr.	6.3	0.6	650 / 400	500	—	650	100	0.1-10[4] / 1.0[4]	8
	Control Tube	5AY	Htr.	6.3	0.25	$E_p=350$; Grid volts $= -50$; Avg. Ma.$=25$; Peak Ma.$=100$; Voltage drop$=16$.						
1	Voltage Regulator	5BO	Cold	—	—	—	—	125	90	1-40	—	—
	Gas Triode Grid Type	6Q	Htr.	6.3	0.6	300 / 350	300 / 300			2 / 75	25000 / 25000	—
	Grid-Controlled Rectifier	3G	Fil.	2.5	5.0	2500	500	−5[2]	—			10-24
	Voltage Regulator	—						87	55-60	2.0		
	Voltage Regulator	4AJ	Cold					130	90	5-30		
	Voltage Regulator	4AJ	Cold					70		5-40		
	Relay Tube	4V	Cold	Characteristics same as OA4G								
	Grid-Controlled Rectifier	8BA	Htr.	6.3	0.6	650	500		650		0.1-10[4]	8
	Voltage Regulator	5BO	Cold					115	87	1.5-3.5		
	Thyratron—Fuse	Fig. 79	Htr.	6.3	1.5	200[3]	I_k to fuse—150 Amp., 60 cycle, half-wave					50 V.
	Relay Service	7BN	Htr.	6.3	0.15	500[3]	100 ma. peak current; 25-ma. average.					
	Gas Thyratron	7BN	Htr.	6.3	0.6	650						
	Relay or Trigger	4CK	Cold	Max. peak inv. volts=200; Peak Ma.=100; Avg. Ma.=25.								
	Shunt Regulator	12J	Htr.	6.3	0.6	$E_{G1}= -60$ volts; $E_{G2}=200$ volts; $E_{G3}=5500$ volts. $E_P=30000$ volts; $I_{G2}=0$ Ma.; I_P Max.$=0.5$ Ma.						
	Voltage Regulator	2AG	Cold					730	700	5/55[5]		
	Series Regulator	8BD	Htr.	6.3	2.4	250	125		110	100	350[6]	—
	Voltage Regulator	8EX	Cold				3.5	115	87			
	Voltage Regulator	Fig. 12	Cold					180	150	5-15		
	Grid-Controlled Rectifier	—	Fil.	2.5	10.0				3000	500		
	Radio-Controlled Relay	—[1]	Fil.	1.4	0.05	45	1.5	30		0.5-1.5	3[4]	30

No base. Tinned wire leads.
At 1000 anode volts.
[3] Peak inverse voltage.
[4] Megohms.
[5] Values in μ amperes.
[6] Cathode resistor-ohms.

TABLE X—RECTIFIERS—RECEIVING AND TRANSMITTING
See Also Table IX—Control and Regulator Tubes

Type	Name	Base	Cathode	Fil. or Heater		Max. A.C. Voltage Per Plate	D.C. Output Current Ma.	Max. Inverse Peak Voltage	Peak Plate Current Ma.	Type
				Volts	Amp.					
1G3-GT/1B3-GT	Half-Wave Rectifier	3C	Fil.	1.25	0.2	——	1.0	33000	30	HV
1K3/1J3	Half-Wave Rectifier	3C	Fil.	1.25	0.2	——	0.5	26000	50	HV
1V2	Half-Wave Rectifier	9U	Fil.	0.625	0.3	——	0.5	7500	10	HV
2B25	Half-Wave Rectifier	3T	Fil.	1.4	0.11	1000	1.5	——	9	HV
2X2-A	Half-Wave Rectifier	4AB	Htr.	2.5	1.75	4500	7.5	——	——	HV
2Y2	Half-Wave Rectifier	4AB	Fil.	2.5	1.75	4400	5.0	——	——	HV
2Z2/G84	Half-Wave Rectifier	4B	Fil.	2.5	1.5	350	50	——	——	HV
3B24	Half-Wave Rectifier	Fig. 49	Fil.	5.0 2.5[5]	3.0 3.0	——	60 30	20000 20000	300 150	HV
3B28	Half-Wave Rectifier	4P	Fil.	2.5	5.0	——	250	10000	1000	HV
5AU4	Full-Wave Rectifier	5T	Fil.	5.0	4.5	300[3] 400[3] 500[4]	350[3] 325[3] 325[4]	1400	1075	HV
5AW4	Full-Wave Rectifier	5T	Fil.	5.0	4.0	450[3] 550[4]	250[3] 250[4]	1550	750	HV
5R4GY/5R4GYA	Full-Wave Rectifier	5T	Fil.	5.0	2.0	900[3] 950[4]	150[3] 175[4]	2800	650	HV
5T4	Full-Wave Rectifier	5T	Fil.	5.0	2.0	450	250	1250	800	HV
5U4G	Full-Wave Rectifier	5T	Fil.	5.0	3.0	Same as Type 5Z3				HV
5U4GA	Full-Wave Rectifier	5T	Fil.	5.0	3.0	300[3] 450[3] 550[4]	275[3] 250[3] 250[4]	1550	900	HV
5U4GB/5AS4A	Full-Wave Rectifier	5T	Fil.	5.0	3.0	300[3] 450[3] 550[4]	300[3] 275[3] 275[4]	1550	1000	HV
5V3	Full-Wave Rectifier	5T	Htr.	5.0	3.8	425[3] 500[4]	350	1400	1200	HV
5V4GA	Full-Wave Rectifier	5L	Htr.	5.0	2.0	375[3]	175	1400	525	HV
5W4GT	Full-Wave Rectifier	5T	Fil.	5.0	1.5	350	110	1000	——	HV
5X4G	Full-Wave Rectifier	5Q	Fil.	5.0	3.0	Same as Type 5Z3				HV
5Y3-G-GT	Full-Wave Rectifier	5T	Fil.	5.0	2.0	Same as Type 80				HV
5Y4-G-GT	Full-Wave Rectifier	5Q	Fil.	5.0	2.0	Same as Type 80				HV
5Z3	Full-Wave Rectifier	4C	Fil.	5.0	3.0	500	250	1400	——	HV
5Z4	Full-Wave Rectifier	5L	Htr.	5.0	2.0	400[4]	125	1100	——	HV
6AV4	Full-Wave Rectifier	5BS	Htr.	6.3	0.95	——	90	1250	250	HV
6AX5GT	Full-Wave Rectifier	6S	Htr.	6.3	1.2	450	125	1250	375	HV
6BW4	Full-Wave Rectifier	9DJ	Htr.	6.3	0.9	450	100	1275	350	HV
6BX4	Full-Wave Rectifier	5BS	Htr.	6.3	0.6	——	90	1350	270	HV
6BY5G	Full-Wave Rectifier	6CN	Htr.	6.3	1.6	375[3]	175	1400	525	HV
6CA4	Full-Wave Rectifier	9M	Htr.	6.3	1.0	350[3]	150	1000	450	HV
6DA4	Half-Wave Diode	4CG	Htr.	6.3	1.2	——	155	4400	900	HV
6U4GT	Half-Wave Rectifier	4CG	Htr.	6.3	1.2	——	138	1375	660	HV
6V4	Full-Wave Rectifier	9M	Htr.	6.3	0.6	350	90	——	——	HV
6X4/6063, 6X5GT	Full-Wave Rectifier	7CF, 6S	Htr.	6.3	0.6	325[3] 450[4]	70	1250	210	HV
6Z3	Half-Wave Rectifier	4G	Fil.	6.3	0.3	350	50	——	——	HV
12DF5	Full-Wave Rectifier	9BS	Htr.	6.3 12.6	0.9 0.45	450	100	1275	350	HV
12X4	Full-Wave Rectifier	5BS	Htr.	12.6	0.3	650[3] 900[4]	70 70	1250 1250	210 210	HV
25Z3	Half-Wave Rectifier	4G	Htr.	25	0.3	250	50	——	——	HV
25Z5	Rectifier-Doubler	6E	Htr.	25	0.3	125	100	——	500	HV
25Z6	Rectifier-Doubler	7Q	Htr.	25	0.3	125	100	——	500	HV
35W4	Half-Wave Rectifier	5BQ	Htr.	35[1]	0.15	125	60	330	600	HV
35Z4GT	Half-Wave Rectifier	5AA	Htr.	35	0.15	250	100	700	600	HV
35Z5G	Half-Wave Rectifier	6AD	Htr.	35[1]	0.15	125	60	——	——	HV
36AM3	Half-Wave Rectifier	5BQ	Htr.	36	0.1	117	75	365	530	HV
50DC4	Half-Wave Rectifier	5BQ	Htr.	50	0.15	117	100	330	720	HV
50Y6GT	Full-Wave Rectifier	7Q	Htr.	50	0.15	125	85	——	——	HV
50Z6G	Voltage Doubler	7Q	Htr.	50	0.3	125	150	——	——	HV
80	Full-Wave Rectifier	4C	Fil.	5.0	2.0	350[3] 500[4]	125 125	1400	375	HV
83	Full-Wave Rectifier	4C	Fil.	5.0	3.0	500	250	1400	800	MV
83-V	Full-Wave Rectifier	4AD	Htr.	5.0	2.0	400	200	1100	——	HV
84/6Z4	Full-Wave Rectifier	5D	Htr.	6.3	0.5	350	60	1000	——	HV
117L7GT/6, 117M7GT	Rectifier-Tetrode	8AO	Htr.	117	0.09	117	75	——	——	HV
117N7GT	Rectifier-Tetrode	8AV	Htr.	117	0.09	117	75	350	450	HV
117P7GT6	Rectifier-Tetrode	8AV	Htr.	117	0.09	117	75	350	450	HV
117Z3	Half-Wave Rectifier	4CB	Htr.	117	0.04	117	90	330	——	HV
816	Half-Wave Rectifier	4P	Fil.	2.5	2.0	2200	125	7500	500	MV
836	Half-Wave Rectifier	4P	Htr.	2.5	5.0	——	——	5000	1000	HV
866-A-AX	Half-Wave Rectifier	4P	Fil.	2.5	5.0	3500	250	10000	1000	MV
866B	Half-Wave Rectifier	4P	Fil.	5.0	5.0	——	——	8500	1000	MV
866 Jr.	Half-Wave Rectifier	4B	Fil.	2.5	2.5	1250	250[2]	——	——	MV
872A/872	Half-Wave Rectifier	4AT	Fil.	5.0	7.5	——	1250	10000	5000	MV

1 Tapped for pilot lamps.
2 Per pair with choke input.
3 Capacitor input.
4 Choke input.
5 Using only one-half of filament
6 Obsolete.

TABLE XI—TRIODE TRANSMITTING TUBES V25

Type	Plate Dissipation Watts	Plate Voltage	Plate Current Ma.	D.C. Grid Current Ma.	Freq. Mc. Full Ratings	Amplification Factor	Cathode Volts	Cathode Amperes	C_{in} μμf.	C_{gp} μμf.	C_{out} μμf.	Base	Class of Service[1]	Plate Voltage	Grid Voltage	Plate Current Ma.	D.C. Grid Current Ma.	Approx. Driving Power Watts	P-to-P Load Ohms	Approx. Output Power Watts
	0.6	135	7	1.0	500	12	1.25	0.1	0.6	2.6	0.8	5BD	C·T·O	135	−20	7		0.035	—	0.6
	1.5	300	30	16	250	32	6.3	0.45	2.2	1.6	0.4	7BF	C·T	150	−10	30	16		—	3.5
	1.6	250	8	2.0	250	25	6.3	0.15	1.2	1.4	1.1	7BS	C·T·O	180	−35	7	1.5		—	0.5
	1.6	180	8	2.0	250	25	6.3	0.15	1.0	1.4	0.6	5BC	C·T·O	180	−35	7	1.5		—	0.5
8	1.8	180	12	3.0	300	13	1.4	0.155	1.0	1.3	1.0	2T	C·T·O	180	−30	12	2.0	0.2	—	1.4[3]
													C·P	180	−35	12	2.5	0.3	—	1.4[3]
	2.0	150	20	8.0	500	17	6.3	0.225	2.0	1.9	0.6	7BR	C·T·O	150	−15 550* 2000[4]	20	7.5	0.2	—	1.8
A[2]	2.75[6]	350	12[6]	3.5[6]	54	18	6.3	0.3	1.5	1.5	0.5	9A	C·T·O	350	−100	24	7		—	6.0
	3.0	150	30	10	400	24	6.3	0.2	2.2	1.3	0.38	Fig. 16	C·T·O	135	1300[4]	20	9.5		—	1.25
48	3.5	300	20	4.0	300	20	6.3	0.175	1.4	1.6	1.2	Fig. 71	C·T·O	300	−35	20	2.0	0.4	—	4.0[3]
													C·P	300	−35	20	3.0	0.8	—	3.5[3]
	5.0	350	25	8.0	54	18	6.3	0.15	1.8	1.6	1.3	6BG	C·T·O	300	−27	25	7.0	0.35	—	5.5
	5	1500[5]	—	—	1200	25	6.3	0.4	1.4	2.4	0.36	Fig. 21	C·T·O[10]	1000[5]	0	900[5]	—	—	—	200[5]
	5	350	—	—	3300	25	6.3	0.4	1.4	1.85	0.02	Fig. 21	C·T·O[12]	150	3000[4]	15	3.6	—	—	0.5
	5	1500[5]	11.5	—	3300	25	6.3	0.4	1.4	1.85	0.02	Fig. 21	C·T·O[16]	1000[5]	0	1300[5]	—	—	—	200[5]
	5	165	30	8	3000	20	6.3	0.135	2.3	1.3	0.09	Fig. 21	G·G·O	120	−8	25	4		—	0.05
	5.5[6]	350	30[6]	5.0[6]	10	35	6.3	0.8	—	—	—	8B	C·T·O[11]	350	−100	60	10		—	14.5
	6.5	500	25	—	500	36	6.3	0.75	2.1	1.3	0.05	Fig. 11	C·T·O	250	−5	20	0.3		—	0.075
	8.0	400	40	13	1000	27	6.0	0.33	2.5	1.75	0.07	Fig. 21	C·T	350	−33	35	13	2.4	—	6.5
													C·P	300	−45	30	12	2.0	—	6.5
42	8.0	350	35	15	2500	47	6.3	0.9	5.0	2.3	0.03	—	C·T	350	−50	35	15		—	—
													C·P	275	−50	35	15		—	—
	10	300	80	20	250	13	6.3	0.8	3.4	2.4	0.5	Fig. 70	C·T·O	300	−36	80	20	1.8	—	16
	12	500	40	—	1250	48	6.3	0.9	2.9	1.7	0.05	Fig. 11	C·T·O	470	—	38[7]			—	9[7]
	13	400	55	25	500	27	6.3	0.28	2.9	1.7	0.08	—	C·T	350	−58	40	15	3	—	10
													C·P	320	−52	35	12	2.4	—	8
	13	400	50	25	500	40	6.3	0.28	2.95	1.75	0.07	—	C·T	350	−45	40	15	3	—	8
	15	450	65	15	8	8.0	7.5	1.25	4.1	7.0	3.0	4D	C·T·O	450	−100	65	15	3.2	—	19
													C·T·O	350	−100	50	12	2.2	—	12
	15	450	90	25	175	9.6	6.3	2.6	1.8	2.6	1.0	2T	C·T	450	−140	90	20	5.2	—	26
													C·P	400	−140	90	20	5.2	—	21
/801	20	600	70	15	60	8.0	7.5	1.25	4.5	6.0	1.5	4D	C·T	600	−150	65	15	4.0	—	25
													C·P	500	−190	55	15	4.5	—	18
													B[7]	600	−75	130	320[9]	3.0[8]	10K	45
	20	750	85	25	60	20	7.5	1.75	4.9	5.1	0.7	3G	C·T	750	−85	85	18	3.6	—	44
													C·P	750	−140	70	15	3.6	—	38
	20	750	85	30	60	62	7.5	1.75	5.3	5.0	0.6	3G	C·T	750	−40	85	28	3.75	—	44
													C·P	750	−100	70	23	4.8	—	38
													B[7]	800	0	40/136	160[9]	1.8[8]	12K	70
	20	—	—	—	600	25	5.5	4.2	1.4	1.15		Fig. 51	C·T·O	2000	−130	63	18	4.0	—	100
3	25	2000	75	25	60	24	6.3	3.0	2.7	1.5	0.3	3G	C·T·O	1500	−95	67	13	2.2	—	75
													C·T·O	1000	−70	72	9	1.3	—	47
													B[7]	2000	−80	16/80	270[9]	0.78	55.5K	110
	25	2000	75	25	100 / 60 / 150	23	6.3	3.0	2.1 / 2.5 / 2.0 / 1.7	1.8 / 1.7 / 1.6 / 1.5	0.1 / 0.4 / 0.2 / 0.3	Fig. 31 / 3G / 2D	C·T·O	2000	−170	63	17	4.5	—	100
													C·T·O	1500	−110	67	15	3.1	—	75
													C·T·O	1000	−80	72	15	2.6	—	47
													B[7]	2000	−85	16/80	290[9]	1.1[8]	55.5K	110
	25 / 17 / 25	2000 / 1600 / 2000	75 / 60 / 75	7[13]	60	24	6.3	3.0	1.7	1.6	0.2	2D	C·T	2000	−130	63	18	4	—	100
													C·P	1600	−170	53	11	3.1	—	68
													AB₂[7]	1250	−42	24/130	270[9]	3.4[8]	21.4K	112
	25	2000	75	30	60	25	6.3	3.0	2.5	1.7	0.4	3G	C·T	2000	−140	56	18	4.0	—	90
													C·P	1500	−145	50	25	5.5	—	60
	30 / 20 / 30	1000	65 / 65 / 80	20 / 20	500	18	6.3	1.92	2.7	2.8	0.35	4AQ	G·M·A	1000	−135	50	4	3.5	—	20
													C·T	800	−105	40	10.5	1.4	—	22
													C·T	1000	−90	50	14	1.6	—	35
1Z[2]	30	500	150	30	60	45	6.3 / 12.6	3.5 / 1.7	5.0	5.5	1.9	Fig. 60	C·T	500	−45	150	25	2.5	—	56
													C·P	400	−100	150	30	3.5	—	45
	30	450	80	12	500	6.5	2.0	3.65	1.2	1.6	0.8	—	C·T	450	—	80	12		—	7.5
													C·P	400	—	80	12		—	6.5
	30	1000	125	—	60	50	6.3	2.5	5.7	6.7	0.9	3G	C·T	1000	−75	100	25	3.8	—	75
													C·P	750	−60	100	32	4.3	—	55
													B[7]	1000	−9	40/200	155[9]	2.78	11.6K	145
	30	1000	100	25	60	20	6.3	2.5	5.7	6.7	0.9	3G	C·T·O	1000	−90	100	20	3.1	—	75
													C·P	750	−125	100	20	4.0	—	55
													B[7]	1000	−40	30/200	230[9]	4.2[8]	12K	145
2-A	40	1000	80	20	500	18	6.3	2.0	2.7 / 2.7	2.8 / 2.5	0.35 / 0.4	Fig. 54	C·T·O	1000	−90	50	14	1.6	—	35
													C·P	800	−105	40	10.5	1.4	—	22
													G·M·A	1000	−135	50	4.0	3.5	—	20
	40	1500	150	40	60	25	7.5	2.5	4.5	4.8	0.8	3G	C·T·O	1500	−140	150	28	9.0	—	158
													C·P	1250	−115	115	20	5.25	—	104
	40	1500	150	45	60	62	7.5	2.5	4.8	5.0	0.8	3G	C·T·O	1500	−90	150	38	10	—	165
													C·P	1250	−100	125	30	7.5	—	116
													B[7]	1500	−9	250[8]	285[9]	6.0[8]	12K	250
4	50	2000	150	50	100	39	4.1 / 5.0 / 2.5	4.0 / 1.8	4.1 / 2.5	1.8	0.3 / 0.4	3G / 2D	C·T	2000	−135	125	45	13	—	200
													C·P	1500	−150	90	40	11	—	105
													B[7]	2000	−40	4/167	255[9]	4.0[8]	27.5K	235

See page V27 for Key to Class-of-Service abbreviations.

TABLE XI—TRIODE TRANSMITTING TUBES—Continued

Type	Plate Dissipation Watts	Plate Voltage	Plate Current Ma.	D.C. Grid Current Ma.	Freq. Mc. Full Ratings	Amplification Factor	Volts	Amperes	Cin μμf.	Cgp μμf.	Cout μμf.	Base	Class of Service	Plate Voltage	Grid Voltage	Plate Current Ma.	D.C. Grid Current Ma.	Approx. Driving Power Watts	P-to-P Load Ohms	Approx. Output
HK54	50	3000	150	30	100	27	5.0	5.0	1.9	1.9	0.2	2D	C-T	3000	-290	100	25	10	—	250
													C-P	2500	-250	100	20	8.0	—	230
													B[7]	2500	-85	20/150	360[9]	5.0	40K	275
T55	55	1500	150	40	60	20	7.5	3.0	5.0	3.9	1.2	3G	C-T	1500	-170	150	18	6.0	—	170
													C-P	1500	-195	125	15	5.0	—	145
811	55	1500	150	50	60	160	6.3	4.0	5.5	5.5	0.6	3G	C-T	1500	-113	150	35	8.0	—	170
													C-P	1250	-125	125	50	11	—	120
													B[7]	1500	-9	20/200	150[9]	3.0[8]	17.6K	220
812	55	1500	150	35	60	29	6.3	4.0	5.3	5.3	0.8	3G	C-T	1500	-175	150	25	6.5	—	170
													C-P	1250	-125	125	25	6.0	—	120
													B[7]	1500	-45	50/200	232[9]	4.7[8]	18K	220
826	55	1000	140	40	250	31	7.5	4.0	3.0	2.9	1.1	7BO	C-T-O	1000	-70	130	35	5.8	—	90
													C-P	1000	-160	95	40[8]	11.5	—	70
													G-M-A	1000	-125	65	9.5	8.2	—	25
830B 930B	60	1000	150	30	15	25	10	2.0	5.0	11	1.8	3G	C-T-O	1000	-110	140	30	7.0	—	90
													C-P	800	-150	95	20	5.0	—	50
													B[7]	1000	-35	20/280	270[9]	6.0[8]	7.6K	175
811-A[19]	65	1500	175	50	60	160	6.3	4.0	5.9	5.6	0.7	3G	C-T	1500	-70	173	40	7.1	—	200
													C-P	1250	-120	140	45	10.0	—	135
													B[7]	1500	-4.5	32/313	170[9]	4.4[8]	12.4K	340
812-A	65	1500	175	35	60	29	6.3	4.0	5.4	5.5	0.77	3G	C-T	1500	-120	173	30	6.5	—	190
													C-P	1250	-115	140	35	7.6	—	130
													B[7]	1500	-48	28/310	270[9]	5.0	13.2K	340
5514	65	1500	175	60	60	145	7.5	3.0	7.8	7.9	1.0	4BO	C-T	1500	-106	175	60	12	—	200
													C-P	1250	-84	142	60	10	—	135
													B[7]	1500	-4.5	350[8]	88[8]	6.5[8]	10.5K	400
3-75A3 75TH	75	3000	225	40	40	20	5.0	6.25	2.7	2.3	0.3	2D	C-T	2000	-200	150	32	10	—	225
													C-P	2000	-300	110	15	6	—	170
													B[7]	2000	-90	50/225	350[9]	3[8]	19.3K	400
3-75A2 75TL	75	3000	225	35	40	12	5.0	6.25	2.6	2.4	0.4	2D	C-T	2000	-300	150	21	8	—	225
													C-P	2000	-500	130	20	14	—	210
													AB_2[27]	2000	-190	50/250	600[9]	5[8]	18K	350
8005	85	1500	200	45	60	20	10	3.25	6.4		1.0	3G	C-T	1500	-130	200	32	7.5	—	220
													C-P	1250	-195	190	28	9.0	—	170
													B[7]	1500	-70	40/310	310[9]	4.0	10K	300
V-70-D	85	1750	200	45	30	—	7.5	3.25	4.5	4.5	1.7	3G	C-T	1750	-100	170	19	3.9	—	225
													C-T	1500	-90	165	19	3.9	—	195
													C-P	1500	-90	165	19	3.7	—	185
													C-P	1250	-72	127	16	2.6	—	122
3-100A4 100TH	100	3000	225	60	40	40	5.0	6.3	2.9	2.0	0.4	2D	C-T	3000	-200	165	51	18	—	400
													C-P	3000	-200	165	51	18	—	400
													B[7]	3000	-65	40/215	335[9]	5.0[8]	31K	650
3-100A2 100TL	100	3000	225	50	40	14	5.0	6.3	2.3	2.0	0.4	2D	C-T	3000	-400	165	30	20	—	400
													C-P	3000	-400	165	30	20	—	400
													G-M-A	3000	-560	60	2.0	7.0	—	90
													B[7]	3000	-185	40/215	640[9]	6.0[8]	30K	450
VT127A	100	3000	—	—	150	15.5	5.0	10.4	2.7	2.3	0.35	Fig. 53	C-T	2000	-340	210	67	25	—	315
													B[7]	1500	-125	242	44	7.3	3K	200
211 311	100	1250	175	50	15	12	10	3.25	6.0 / 6.0	14.5 / 9.25	5.5 / 5.0	4E	C-T	1250	-225	150	18	7.0	—	130
													C-P	1000	-260	150	35	14	—	100
													B[7]	1250	-100	20/320	410[9]	8.0[8]	9K	260
254	100	4000	225	60	—	25	5.0	7.5	2.5	2.7	0.4	2N	C-T	3000	-245	165	40	18	—	400
													C-P	2500	-360	160	40	23	—	315
													B[7]	2500	-80	40/240	460[9]	25	25.2K	420
8003	100	1500	250	50	30	12	10	3.25	5.8	11.7	3.4	3N	C-T-O	1350	-180	245	35	11	—	250
													C-P	1100	-260	200	40	15	—	167
													B[7]	1350	-100	40/490	480[9]	10.5[8]	6K	460
3CX100A5[15]	100 / 70	1000 / 600	125[14] / 100[14]	50	2500	100	6.0	1.05	7.0	2.15	0.035	—	G-G-A	800	-20	80	30	6	—	27
													C-P	600	-15	75	40	6	—	18
3X100A1[1] 2C39	100	1000	60	40	500	100	6.3	1.1	6.5	1.95	0.03	—	G-I-C	600	-35	60	40	5.0	—	20
GL2C39A[15] GL2C39B[15]	100 70	1000	125[14]	50	500	100	6.3	1.0	6.5 / 7.0	1.9 / 1.9	0.035 / 0.035	—	C-T-O	900	-40	90	30	—	—	40
													C-P	600	-150	100[14]	50	—	—	
3C22	125	1000	150	70	500	40	6.3	2.0	4.9	2.4	0.05	Fig. 17	C-T-O	1000	-200	150	70	—	—	65
GL146	125	1500	200	60	15	75	10	3.25	7.2	9.2	3.9	Fig. 56	C-T-O	1250	-150	180	30	—	—	150
													C-P	1000	-200	160	40	—	—	100
													B[7]	1250	0	34/320	—	—	8.4K	250
GL152	125	1500	200	60	15	25	10	3.25	7.0	8.8	4.0	Fig. 56	C-T-O	1250	-150	180	30	—	—	150
													C-P	1000	-200	160	30	—	—	100
													B[7]	1250	-40	16/320	—	—	8.4K	250
805	125	1500	210	70	30	40/60	10	3.25	8.5	6.5	10.5	3N	C-T	1500	-105	200	40	8.5	—	215
													C-P	1250	-160	160	60	16	—	140
													B[7]	1500	-16	84/400	280[9]	7.0[8]	8.2K	370
AX9900/ 5866[15]	135	2500	200	40	150	25	6.3	5.4	5.8	5.5	0.1	Fig. 3	C-T	2500	-200	200	40	16	—	390
													C-P	2000	-225	127	40	16	—	204
													B[7]	2500	-90	80/330	350[9]	14[8]	15.68K	560
3-150A3 152TH	150	3000	450	85	40	20	5.0 / 10	12.5 / 6.25	5.7	4.8	0.4	4BC	C-T	3000	-300	250	70	27	—	600
													C-P	2500	-350	200	30	15	—	490
													B[7]	2500	-125	40/340	390[9]	16[8]	17K	600

[1] See page V27 for Key to Class-of-Service abbreviations.

TABLE XI—TRIODE TRANSMITTING TUBES—*Continued*   **V27**

Type	Plate Dissipation Watts	Plate Voltage	Plate Current Ma.	D.C. Grid Current Ma.	Freq. Mc. Full Ratings	Amplification Factor	Volts	Amperes	Cin μμf.	Cgp μμf.	Cout μμf.	Base	Class of Service[1]	Plate Voltage	Grid Voltage	Plate Current Ma.	D.C. Grid Current Ma.	Approx. Driving Power Watts	P-to-P Load Ohms	Approx. Output Power Watts
A2	150	3000	450	75	40	12	5	12.5	4.5	4.4	0.7	4BC	C·T	3000	−400	250	40	20	—	600
							10	6.25					B[7]	3000	−260	65/335	675[9]	3[8]	20.4K	700
A	150	2500	200	50	30	18	10−11	4.0	8.8	7.0	1.2	Fig. 15	C·T	2500	−300	200	18	8	—	380
													C·P	2000	−350	160	20	9	—	250
													B[7]	2500	−130	60/360	460[9]	8[8]	16K	600
24	160	1750	107	—	—	8	10	5.2	5.6	8.8	3.3	Fig. 15	A[1]	1500	−155	107	—	—	8.2K[5]	55
													AB[1]	1750	−200	320[8]	390[9]	—	8K	240
	175	2500	300	75	30	36	10	4.5	8.7	4.8	12	2N	C·T	2500	−180	300	60	19	—	575
													C·P	2000	−350	250	70	35	—	380
													G·M·A	2250	−140	100	2.0	4	—	75
													B[7]	2250	−60	70/450	380[9]	13[8]	11.6K	725
	175	2500	300	45	30	16.5	10	4.5	5.0	6.4	3.3	2N	C·T·O	2500	−240	300	40	18	—	575
													C·P	2000	−370	250	37	20	—	380
													G·M·A	2250	−265	100	0	2.5	—	75
													B[7]	2250	−130	65/450	560[9]	7.9[8]	12K	725
	200	2500	350	80	30	16	10	5.75	9.5	7.9	1.6	2N	C·T	2500	−280	350	54	25	—	685
													C·P	2000	−260	350	54	23	—	460
A3	200	3500	250	25[13]									C·T	3500	−270	228	30	15	—	600
	130	2600	200	25[13]	150	25	10	5.0	3.6	3.3	0.29	Fig. 28	C·P	2500	−300	200	35	19	—	375
	200	3500	250	25[13]									B[7]	2000	−50	120/500	520[9]	20[8]	8.5K	600
	200	3000	275	60	60 / 20	23	11−12	4.0	6.0	6.5	1.4	2N	C·T	3000	−400	250	28	16	—	600
													C·P	2000	−300	250	36	17	—	385
													B[7]	3000	−115	60/360	450[9]	13[8]	20K	780
	200	3000	300	—	—	23	11	6.0	6.0	7.0	1.4	—	C·T	3000	−400	250	28	16	—	600
													C·P	2000	−300	250	36	17	—	385
													B[7]	2500	−100	60/450		7.5[8]	—	750
	225	3300	300	50	30	12.6	5.0	10	6.1	4.2	1.1	2N	C·T	3300	−600	300	40	34	—	780
													C·P	3000	−670	195	27	24	—	460
													B[7]	3300	−240	80/475	930[9]	35[8]	16K	1120
A4	250	4000	350	40[13]	40	37	5.0	10.5	4.6	2.9	0.5	2N	C·T·O	2000	−100	357	94	29	—	464
													C·T·O	3000	−150	333	90	32	—	750
													C·P	2000	−160	250	60	22	—	335
													C·P	2500	−180	225	45	17	—	400
													C·P		−200	200	38	14	—	435
													AB[2][7]	1500	0	220/700	460[9]	46[8]	4.2K	630
A2	250	4000	350	35[13]	40	14	5.0	10.5	3.7	3.0	0.7	2N	C·T·O	2000	−200	350	45	24	—	455
													C·T·O	3000	−350	335	45	29	—	750
													C·P	2000	−520	250	29	24	—	335
													C·P	2500	−520	225	20	16	—	400
													C·P		−520	200	14	11	—	435
													AB[2][7]	1500	−40	200/700	780[9]	38[8]	3.8K	580
901	250	3000	400	80	100	25	5.0	14.1	7.7	5.9	0.18	Fig. 3	C·T	3000	−250	363	69	27	—	840
													C·P	2500	−300	250	70	28	—	482
													B[7]	3000	−110	570[9]	465[9]	32	14.2K	1280
69[19]	250	4000	300	120	30	45	5.0	14.5	7.6	3.7	0.1	Fig. 3	G·G·A	2500	−70	300	85	75[20]	—	555
														2500	−95	300	100	85[20]	—	710
														3500	−110	285	90	85[20]	—	805
														4000	−120	250	50	70[20]	—	820
A3 H	300	3000	900	60[13]	40	20	5.0	25	13.5	10.2	0.7	4BC	C·T·O	1500	−125	665	115	25	—	700
														2000	−200	600	125	39	—	900
								10	12.5					C·P	1500	−200	420	55	18	—	500
														2000	−300	440	60	26	—	680
														2500	−350	400	60	29	—	800
													AB[2][7]	1500	−65	1065[8]	330[9]	25[8]	2.84K	1000
A2 19	300	3000	900	50[13]	40	12	5.0	25	12.1	8.6	0.8	4BC	C·T·O	1500	−250	665	90	33	—	700
														2000	−300	600	85	36	—	900
													C·P	2000	−500	250	30	18	—	410
														2000	−500	500	75	52	—	810
								10	12.5						2500	−525	200	18	11	—	425
														2500	−550	400	50	36	—	830
													AB[1][7]	1500	−118	270/572	236[9]	0	2.54K	256
													AB[1][7]	2500	−230	160/483	460[9]	0	8.5K	610
													AB[2][7]	1500	−118	1140[8]	490[9]	39[8]	2.75K	1100
	350	3300			30								C·T·O	2250	−125	445	85	23	—	780
			500	100		35	10	10	12.3	6.3	8.5	Fig. 41		3000	−160	335	70	20	—	800
	450[15]	4000[15]			20[15]								C·P	2500	−300	335	75	30	—	635
														3000	−240	335	70	26	—	800
													B[7]	3000	−70	100/750	400[9]	20[8]	9.5K	1650
80[19]	400	4000[15]	350	120	—	45	5.0	14.5	7.6	3.9	0.1	5BK	G·G·A	4000	−110	350	92	105[20]	—	1080
														2500	−70	350	95	85	—	660

hode resistor in ohms.

KEY TO CLASS-OF-SERVICE ABBREVIATIONS

= Class-A[1] a.f. modulator.
= Class-AB[1] push-pull a.f. modulator.
= Class-AB[2] push-pull a.f. modulator.
= Class-B push-pull a.f. modulator.
M = Frequency multiplier.
P = Class-C plate-modulated telephone.
= Class-C telegraph.
·O = Class-C amplifier-osc.
G·A = Grounded-grid class-C amp.
G·O = Grounded-grid osc.

G·I·C = Grid-isolation circuit.
G·M·A = Grid-modulated amp.
[2] Twin triode. Values, except interelectrode capacitances, are for both sections in push-pull.
[3] Output at 112 Mc.
[4] Grid leak resistor in ohms.
[5] Peak valves.
[6] Per section.
[7] Values are for two tubes in push-pull.
[8] Max. signal value.
[9] Peak a.f. grid-to-grid volts.
[10] Plate-pulsed 1000-Mc. osc.

[11] Class-B data in Table II.
[12] 1000-Mc. c.w. osc.
[13] Max. grid dissipation in watts.
[14] Max. cathode current in ma.
[15] Forced-air cooling required.
[16] Plate-pulsed 3300-Mc. osc.
[17] 1900-Mc. c.w. osc.
[18] No Class-B data available.
[19] Linear-amplifier tube-operation data for single sideband in Table 11-1.
[20] Includes bias loss, grid dissipation, and feed-through power.

TABLE XII—TETRODE AND PENTODE TRANSMITTING TUBES

Type	Plate Diss. W	Plate V	Screen Diss. W	Screen V	Freq. Mc. Full	Cath. V	Cath. A	Cin μμf	Cgp μμf	Cout μμf	Base	Class of Service[14]	Plate V	Screen V	Supp. V	Grid V	Plate mA	Screen mA	Grid mA	Approx. Driving W	P-to-P Load Ω	Approx. Output
6939[3]	7.5	275	3	200	500	6.3 / 12.6	0.75 / 0.375	6.6	0.15	1.55	Fig. 13	C·T	200	200	—	-20	60	13	2	1.0	—	
												C·P	180	180	—	-20	55	11.5	1.7	1.0	—	
												C·M	200	190	—	68K[1]	46	10	2.2	0.9	—	
RK25	10	500	8	250	—	2.5 / 6.3	2 / 0.9	10	0.2	10	6BM	C·T	500	200	45	-90	55	38	4	0.5	—	2
												C·P	400	150	0	-90	43	30	6	0.8	—	1
2E30	10	250	2.5	250	160	6	0.7	10	0.5	4.5	7CQ	C·T	250	200	—	-50	50	10	2.5	0.2	—	
												AB2[6]	250	250	—	-30	40/120	4/20	2.3[7]	0.2	3.8K	
837	12	500	8	300	20	12.6	0.7	16	0.2	10	6BM	C·T	500	200	40	-70	80	15	4	0.4	—	28
												C·P	400	140	40	-40	45	20	5	0.3	—	1
7551 7558	12	300	2	250	175	12.6 / 6.3	0.38 / 0.8	10	0.15	5.5	9LK	C·P	300	250	—	-55	80	5.1	1.6	1.5	—	10
												C·P	250	250	—	-75	70	3.0	2.3	1.0	—	
5763 6417	13.5	350	2	250	50	6.0 / 12.6	0.75 / 0.375	9.5	0.3	4.5	9K	C.T.	350	250	—	-28.5	48.5	6.2	1.6	0.1	—	1
												C·P	300	250	—	-42.5	50	6	2.4	0.15	—	10
												C·M	300	250	—	-75	40	4	1	0.6	—	
												C·M[4]	300	235	—	-100	35	5	1	0.6	—	
2E24	13.5	600	2.5	200	125	6.3[5]	0.65	8.5	0.11	6.5	7CL	C·P	500	180	—	-45	54	8	2.5	0.16	—	18
												C·T	600	195	—	-50	66	10	3	0.21	—	27
2E26[13] 6893	13.5	600	2.5	200	125	6.3 / 12.6	0.8 / 0.4	12.5	0.2	7	7CK	C·T	600	185	—	-45	66	10	3	0.17	—	27
												C·P	500	180	—	-50	54	9	2.5	0.15	—	18
												AB2[6]	500	125	—	-15	22/150	32[7]	—	0.36[7]	8K	54
6360[3]	14	300	2	200	200	6.3 / 12.6	0.82 / 0.41	6.2	0.1	2.6	Fig. 13	C·T	300	200	—	-45	100	3	3	0.2	—	1
												C·P	200	100	—	15K[1]	86	3.1	3.3	0.2	—	9
												C·M[11]	300	150	—	-100	65	3.5	3.8	0.45	—	4
												AB2	300	200	—	-21.5	30/100	1/11.4	64[8]	0.04	6.5K	
2E25	15	450	4	250	125	6	0.8	8.5	0.15	6.7	5BJ	C·T·O	450	250	—	-45	75	15	4	0.4	—	24
												C·P	400	200	—	-45	60	12	3	0.4	—	16
												AB2[6]	450	250	—	-30	44/150	10/40	3	0.9[7]	6K	40
832A[3]	15	750	5	250	200	6.3 / 12.6	1.6 / 0.8	8	0.07	3.8	7BP	C·T	750	200	—	-65	48	15	2.8	0.19	—	26
												C·P	600	200	—	-65	36	16	2.6	0.16	—	17
1619	15	400	3.5	300	45	2.5	2	10.5	0.35	12.5	Fig. 74	C·T	400	300	—	-55	75	10.5	5	0.36	—	19
												C·P	325	285	—	-50	62	7.5	2.8	0.18	—	13
												AB2[6]	400	300	0	-16.5	75/150	6.5/11.5	—	0.47	6K	36
5516	15	600	5	250	80	6	0.7	8.5	0.12	6.5	7CL	C·T	600	250	—	-60	75	15	5	0.5	—	32
												C·P	475	250	—	-90	63	10	4	0.5	—	22
												AB2[6]	600	250	—	-25	36/140	1/24	47	0.16	10.5K	67
6252/ AX9910[3]	20	750	4	300	300	6.3 / 12.6	1.3 / 0.65	6.5	—	2.5	Fig. 7	C·T	600	250	—	-60	140	14	4	2.0	—	23
												C·P	500	250	—	-80	100	12	3	4.0	—	—
												B	500	250	—	-26	25/73	0.7/16	52[8]	—	20K	23
1614	25	450	3.5	300	80	6.3	0.9	10	0.4	12.5	7AC	C·T	450	250	—	-45	100	8	2	0.15	—	31
												C·P	375	250	—	-50	93	7	2	0.15	—	24
												AB1[6]	530	340	—	-36	60/160	20[7]	—	—	7.2K	50
815[3]	25	500	4	200	125	6.3 / 12.6	1.6 / 0.8	13.3	0.2	8.5	8BY	C·T·O	500	200	—	-45	150	17	2.5	0.13	—	56
												C·P	400	175	—	-45	150	15	3	0.16	—	45
												AB2	500	125	—	-15	22/150	32[7]	—	0.36[7]	8K	42
1624	25	600	3.5	300	60	2.5	2	11	0.25	7.5	Fig. 66	C·T	600	300	—	-60	90	10	5	0.43	—	35
												C·P	500	275	—	-50	75	9	3.3	0.25	—	24
												AB2[6]	600	300	—	-25	42/180	5/15	106[8]	1.2[7]	7.5K	72
6146[13]						6.3	1.25					C·T	500	170	—	-66	135	9	2.5	0.2	—	48
												C·T	750	160	—	-62	120	11	3.1	0.2	—	70
6883	25	750	3	250	60	12.6	0.625	13.5	0.22	8.5	7CK	C·T[12]	400	190	—	-54	150	10.4	2.2	3.0	—	35
												C·P	400	150	—	-87	112	7.8	3.4	0.4	—	32
												C·P	600	150	—	-87	112	7.8	3.4	0.4	—	52
6159						26.5	0.3					AB2[6]	600	190	—	-48	28/270	1.2/20	27	0.03	5K	113
												AB2[6]	750	165	—	-46	22/240	0.3/20	2.6[7]	0.04	7.4K	131
												AB1[6]	750	195	—	-50	22/205	1/26	100[8]	—	8K	120
6524[3] 6850	25	600	—	300	100	6.3 / 12.6	1.25 / 0.625	7	0.11	3.4	Fig. 76	C·T	600	200	—	-44	120	8	3.7	0.2	—	56
												C·P	500	200	—	-61	100	7	2.5	0.2	—	40
												AB2	500	200	—	-26	20/116	0.1/10	2.6	0.1	11.1K	40
807[13] 807W 5933 1625[13]	30	750	3.5	300	60	6.3 / 12.6	0.9 / 0.45	12	0.2	7	5AW / 5AZ	C·T	750	250	—	-45	100	6	3.5	0.22	—	50
												C·P	600	275	—	-90	100	4	4	0.4	—	42.
												AB2[6]	750	300	—	-32	60/240	5/10	92[8]	0.2[7]	6.95K	120
												B[10]	750	—	—	0	15/240	—	555[8]	5.3[7]	6.65K	120
2E22	30	750	10	250	—	6.3	1.5	13	0.2	8	5J	C·T·O	750	250	22.5	-60	100	16	6	0.55	—	53
AX-9903[3] 5894	40	600	7	250	250	6.3 / 12.6	1.8 / 0.9	6.7	0.08	2.1	Fig. 7	C·T	600	250	—	-80	200	16	2	0.2	—	80
												C·P	600	250	—	-100	200	24	8	1.2	—	85
829B[3] 3E29[3]	40	750	7	240	200	6.3 / 12.6	2.25 / 1.125	14.5	0.12	7	7BP	C·T	500	200	—	-45	240	32	12	0.7	—	83
												C·P	425	200	—	-60	212	35	11	0.8	—	63
												B	500	200	—	-18	27/230	—	56[8]	0.39	4.8K	76
HY1269	40	750	5	300	6	6.3 / 12.6	3.5 / 1.75	16	0.25	7.5	Fig. 65	C·T·O	750	300	—	-70	120	15	4	0.25	—	63
												C·P	600	250	—	-70	100	12.5	5	0.5	—	42
												AB2[6]	600	300	—	-35	200[7]	—	—	0.3	—	80
3D24	45	2000	10	400	125	6.3	3	6.5	0.2	2.4	Fig. 75	C·T·O	2000	375	—	-300	90	20	10	4.0	—	140
													1500	375	—	-300	90	22	10	4.0	—	105
4D22	50	750	14	350	60	12.6 / 25.2	1.6 / 0.8	28	0.27	13	Fig. 26	C·T	750	300	—	-100	240	26	12	1.5	—	135
													600	300	—	-100	215	30	10	1.25	—	100
4D32						6.3	3.75				Fig. 27	C·P	600	—	—	-100	220	28	10	1.25	—	100
													550	—	—	-100	175	17	6	0.6	—	70
												AB2[6]	600	250	—	-25	100/365	26[7]	70[8]	0.45[7]	3K	125
814	65	1500	10	300	30	10	3.25	13.5	0.1	13.5	Fig. 64	C·T	1500	300	—	-90	150	24	10	1.5	—	160
												C·P	1250	300	—	-150	145	20	10	3.2	—	130

14 See page V29 for Key to Class-of-Service abbreviations.

TABLE XII—TETRODE AND PENTODE TRANSMITTING TUBES—Continued V29

Type	Plate Dissipation Watts	Plate Voltage	Screen Dissipation Watts	Screen Voltage	Freq. Mc. Full Ratings	Cathode Volts	Cathode Amperes	C_{in} μμf.	C_{gp} μμf.	C_{out} μμf.	Base	Class of Service[14]	Plate Voltage	Screen Voltage	Suppressor Voltage	Grid Voltage	Plate Current Ma.	Screen Current Ma.	Grid Current Ma.	Approx. Driving Power Watts	P-to-P Load Ohms	Approx. Output Power Watts
4-65A[13]	65	3000	10	600	150	6	3.5	8	0.08	2.1	Fig. 25	C·T·O	1500	250	—	−85	150	40	18	3.2	—	165
													3000	250	—	−100	115	22	10	1.7	—	280
												C·P	1500	250	—	−125	120	40	16	3.5	—	140
													2500	250	—	−135	110	25	12	2.6	—	230
												AB2[6]	1800	250	—	−50	50/250	307	180[8]	2.67	20K	270
4E27/8001	75	4000	30	750	75	5	7.5	12	0.06	6.5	7BM	C·T	2000	500	60	−200	150	11	6	1.4	—	230
												C·P	1800	400	60	−130	135	11	8	1.7	—	178
HK257 HK257B	75	4000	25	750	75[16]	5	7.5	13.8	0.04	6.7	7BM	C·T	2000	500	60	−200	150	11	6	1.4	—	230
												C·P	1800	400	60	−130	135	11	8	1.7	—	178
PL-6549	75	2000	10	600	175	6	3.5	7.5	0.09	3.4	Fig. 14	C·T	2000	400	70	−125	150	12	5	0.8	—	270
												C·P	2000	400	70	−140	125	15	4	0.7	—	200
												AB2[6]	2000	400	70	−85	30/225	0.1/10	180[8]	0.057	19K	325
828	80	2000	23	750	30	10	3.25	13.5	0.05	14.5	5J	C·T	1500	400	75	−100	180	28	12	2.2	—	200
												C·P	1250	400	75	−140	160	28	12	2.7	—	150
												AB1[6]	2000	750	60	−120	50/270	2/60	240	0	18.5K	385
6816[9] 6884	115	1000	4.5	300	400	6.3 / 26.5	2.1 / 0.52	14	0.085	0.015	Fig. 77	C·T·O	900	300	—	−30	170	1	10	3	—	80
												C·P	700	250	—	−50	130	10	10	3	—	50
												AB1[6]	850	300	—	−15	80/200	0/20	30[8]	0	7K	80
												AB2[6]	850	300	—	−15	80/355	0/25	46[8]	0.3	3.96K	140
813[13]	125	2500	20	800	30	10	5	16.3	0.25	14	5BA	C·T·O	1250	300	0	−75	180	35	12	1.7	—	170
													2250	400	0	−155	220	40	15	4	—	375
												C·P	1250	300	0	−160	150	35	13	2.9	—	140
													2000	350	0	−175	200	40	16	4.3	—	300
												AB2[6]	2000	750	0	−90	40/315	1.5/58	230[8]	0.17	16K	455
													2500	750	0	−95	35/360	1.2/65	235[8]	0.35[7]	17K	650
4-125A[13] 4D21 6155	125	3000	20	600	120	5	6.5	10.8	0.07	3.1	5BK	C·T·O	2000	350	—	−100	200	50	12	2.8	—	275
													3000	350	—	−150	167	30	9	2.5	—	375
												C·P	2000	350	—	−220	150	33	10	3.8	—	225
													2500	350	—	−210	152	30	9	3.3	—	300
												AB2[6]	2500	350	—	−43	93/260	0/6	178[8]	1.07	22K	400
												AB1[6]	2500	600	—	−96	50/232	0.3/8.5	192[8]	0	20.3K	510
4E27A/ 5-125B	125	4000	20	750	75	5	7.5	10.5	0.08	4.7	7BM	C·T	3000	500	60	−200	167	5	6	1.6	—	375
													1000	750	0	−170	160	21	3	0.6	—	115
803	125	2000	30	600	20	10	5	17.5	0.15	29	5J	C·T	2000	500	40	−90	160	45	12	2	—	210
												C·P	1600	400	100	−80	150	45	25	5	—	155
7094	125	2000	20	400	60	6.3	3.2	9.0	0.5	1.8	Fig. 82	C·T	1500	400	—	−100	330	20	5	4	—	340
												C·P	1200	400	—	−130	275	20	5	5	—	240
												AB1	2000	400	—	−65	60/400	—	120[8]	0	12K	560
4X150A 4X150G[15]	150[9]	1250	12	400	500	6 / 2.5	2.6 / 6.25	15.5 / 27	0.03 / 0.035	4.5 / 4.5	Fig. 75 / —	C·T·O	1250	250	—	−90	200	20	10	0.8	—	195
												C·P	1000	250	—	−105	200	20	15	2	—	140
												AB2[6]	1250	300	—	−44	475[7]	0/65	100[8]	0.157	5.6K	425
4-250A[13] 5D22 6156	250[9]	4000	35	600	110	5	14.5	12.7	0.12	4.5	5BK	C·T·O	2500	500	—	−150	300	60	9	1.7	—	575
													3000	500	—	−180	345	60	10	2.6	—	800
												C·P	2500	400	—	−200	300	30	9	2.2	—	375
													2500	400	—	−310	225	30	9	3.2	—	510
												AB2[6]	2000	300	—	−48	510[7]	0/26	198[8]	5.57	8K	650
												AB1[6]	2500	600	—	−110	430[7]	0.3/13	180[8]	0	11.4K	625
4X250B	250[9]	2000	12	400	175	6	2.1	18.5	0.04	4.7	Fig. 75	C·T·O	2000	250	—	−90	250	25	27	2.8	—	410
												C·P	1500	250	—	−100	200	25	17	2.1	—	250
												AB1[6]	2000	350	—	−50	500[7]	30[7]	100[8]	0	8.26K	650
7034/[9] 4X150A 7035[13] 4X150D	250 250	2000 2000	12 12	300 400	150	6 / 26.5	2.6 / 0.58	16		4.4	Fig. 75	C·T·O	2000	250	—	−88	250	24	8	2.5	—	370
												C·P	1600	250	—	−118	200	23	5	3	—	290
												AB2[6]	2000	300	—	−50	100/500	0/36	106[8]	0.2	8.1K	630
												AB1[6]	2000	300	—	−50	100/420	0/36	106[8]	0	8.76K	580
4CX-300A	300[9]	2000	12	400	500	6	2.75	29.5	0.04	4.8	—	C·T	2000	250	—	−90	250	25	27	2.8	—	410
												C·P	1500	250	—	−100	200	25	17	2.1	—	250
												AB1[6]	2000	350	—	−50	500[7]	30[7]	100[8]	0	8.26K	650
4-400A	400[9]	4000	35	600	110	5	14.5	12.5	0.12	4.7	5BK	C·T·C·P	4000	300	—	−170	270	22.5	10	10	—	720
4-1000A	1000	6000	75	1000	—	7.5	21	27.2	.24	7.6	—	C·T	3000	500	—	−150	700	146	38	11	—	1430
												C·P	3000	500	—	−200	600	145	36	12	—	1390
												AB2	4000	500	—	−60	300/1200	0/95	—	11	7K	3000
4CX1000A	1000	3000	12	350	—	6	12.5	35	.005	12	—	AB1	2000	325	—	−55	500/2000	−4/60	—	—	2.8K	2160
													2500	325	—	−55	500/2000	−4/60	—	—	3.1K	2920
													3000	325	—	−55	500/1800	−4/60	—	—	3.85K	3360
PL-172	1000	3000	3.5	600	—	6	7.8	38	.09	18	—	C·T	2000	400	75	−150	725	44	22	4.1	—	1110
													2500	500	75	−175	960	64	31	6.8	—	1870
													3000	500	75	−175	900	56	24	4.8	—	2170
												AB1	2000	500	75	−110	400/1600	20/90	210[8]	—	2.65K	1820
													2500	500	75	−110	440/1600	20/85	210[8]	—	3.5K	310
													3000	500	75	−115	440/1500	10/75	200[8]	—	4.6K	2680

[1] Grid-resistor.
[2] Doubler to 175 Mc.
[3] Dual tube. Values for both sections, in push-pull. Interelectrode capacitances, however, are for each section.
[4] Tripler to 175 Mc.
[5] Filament limited to intermittent operation.
[6] Values are for two tubes in push-pull.
[7] Max.-signal value.
[8] Peak grid-to-grid a.f. volts.
[9] Forced-air cooling required.
[10] Two tubes triode connected, G_2 to G_1 through 20K Ω. Input to G_2.
[11] Tripler to 200 Mc.
[12] Typical Operation at 175 Mc.
[13] Linear-amplifier tube-operation data for single-sideband in Chap. 11.
[14] KEY TO CLASS-OF-SERVICE ABBREVIATIONS
AB_1 = Class-AB_1 push-pull a.f. modulator.
AB_2 = AB_2 push-pull a.f. modulator.
B = Class-B push-pull a.f. modulator.
C·M = Frequency multiplier.
C·P = Class-C plate-modulated telephone.
C·T = Class-C telegraph.
C·T·O = Class-C amplifier-osc.
[15] No Class B data available.
[16] HK257B 120 Mc. full rating.

TABLE XIII—ELECTROSTATIC CATHODE-RAY TUBES

Type[6]	Heater Volts	Amp.	Base	Anode No. 2 Voltage	Anode No. 1 Voltage[1]	Anode No. 3 Voltage	Cut-off Grid Voltage[2]	Deflection Avg. Volts DC/Inch D1 D2	D3 D4
P1-2-11	6.3	0.6	11V	1000	100/300	—	—14/—42	210/310	240/350
P1A	6.3	0.6	11L	1000	250	—	—30/—90	230	196
P1-11	6.3	0.6	12E	2000	300/560	—	—135	270	174
CP1-7-11	6.3	0.6	14J	2000	545	4000	—45/—75	180/220	133/163
P1-4—906-P1-4-5-11 / P1A	2.5	2.1	7AN / 7CE	1500	430	—	—25/—75	114	109
P1-4-11 / P1A	6.3	0.6	14A / 14G	2000	575	—	—30/—90	200	148
P1	6.3	0.6	11C	2000	575	—	—30/—90	124	165
P1A—3DP7	6.3	0.6	14H	2000	575	—	—30/—90	220	148
P1—1806-P1	6.3	0.6	11N	2000	575	—	—30/—90	221	165
P7 / P7A	6.3	0.6	14B / 14J	2000	575	4000	—30/—90	250	180
6P1-4-5-11	6.3	0.6	11A	1500	350	—	—25/—75	120	105
6P1A—3GP4A	6.3	0.6	11N	1500	245/437	—	—25/—75	96/144	84/126
P1-2-4-7-11-12	6.3	0.6	14J	2000	400/690	4000	—30/—90	170/230	125/270
P1A-7A-11A	6.3	0.6	14J	2000	400/690	4000	—45/—75	180/220	133/163
CP1-4-11	6.3	0.6	11M	2000	320/600	—	—0/—90	100/136	76/104
MP1[3]	6.3	0.6	12F	2000	400/700	—	—126	230/290	220/280
P1—4-3RP1A	6.3	0.6	12E	2000	330/620	—	—135	146/198	104/140
P1-4-7	6.3	0.6	12E	2000	330/620	—	—28/—135	146/198	104/140
P1	6.3	0.6	12F	2000	320/620	—	—126	240/310	232/296
VP1-2-11	6.3	0.6	12T	2000	330/620	—	—60/—100	83/101	57/70
ABP1-7-11	6.3	0.6	14J	2000	400/690	4000	—52/—87	26/34	18/24
ADP1-7-11	6.3	0.6	14J	1500	300/515	3000	—34/—56	40/50	30.5/37.5
AJP1	6.3	0.6	Fig. 78	500	400/900	6000	—30/—60	230	230
AMP1	6.3	0.6	14U	2500	0/300	—	—34/—56	40/50	20/25
AP1—1805-P1	6.3	0.6	11A	1500	430	—	—31/—57	93	90
AP4—1805-P4	6.3	0.6	11A	1500	430	—	—17.5/—57	93	90
AQP1	6.3	0.6	14G	2500	0/300	—	—34/—56	40/50	31.5/38.5
ATP1-2-7-11	6.3	0.6	14V	6000	0/700	—	—34/—56	94/116	34/42
6P1—1802-P1-2-4-5-11	6.3	0.6	11A	2000	425	—	—20/—60	84	76
6P1A	6.3	0.6	11N	2000	450	—	—20/—60	84	76
6P7A	6.3	0.6	11N	2000	375/560	—	—20/—60	70/98	63/89
CP1-2-4-5-7-11 / CP1A	6.3	0.6	14B / 14J	2000	575	4000	—30/—90	92	78
CP1B-2B-7B-11B	6.3	0.6	14J	2000	400/690	4000	—45/—75	83/101	70/86
CP7A—11A-12	6.3	0.6	14J	2000	575	4000	—30/—90	92	74
GP1	6.3	0.6	11A	2000	425	—	—24/—56	36	72
HP1-4	6.3	0.6	11A	2000	425	—	—20/—60	84.8	77
HP1A	6.3	0.6	11N	2000	450	—	—20/—60	84	76
HP1A—4A	6.3	0.6	11S	2000	333/630	4000	—45/—105	77/115	77/115
HP1A—4A	6.3	0.6	11T	2000	376/633	4000	—30/—90	83/124	72/108
MP1-4-5-11	2.5	2.1	7AN	1500	375	—	—15/—45	66	60
NP1-4	6.3	0.6	11A	2000	450	—	—20/—60	84	76
RP1A—4A	6.3	0.6	14P	2000	362/695	20000	—30/—90	140/210	131/197
SP1-4	6.3	0.6	14K	2000	363/695	4000	—30/—90	74/110	62/94
JP1-7-11	6.3	0.6	12E	2000	340/360	—	—90	56/77	46/62
VP7	6.3	0.6	11N	2000	315/562	—	—20/—60	70/98	63/89
XP1	6.3	0.6	14P	2000	362/695	20000	—30/—90	140/210	46/68
XP1A-2A-11A	6.3	0.6	14P	2000	362/695	12000	—45/—75	130/159	42/52
YP1	6.3	0.6	14Q	2000	541/1040	6000	—45/—135	108/162	36/54
EP4	6.3	0.6	11N	3000	546/858	—	—43/—100	106/158	91/137
GP4[3]	6.3	0.6	14G	3000	810/1200	—	—36/—84	93/123	75/102
JP1-P4-P7	6.3	0.6	14R	6000	1620/2400	—	—72/—168	186/246	150/204
VP1	6.3	0.6	14R	3000	800/1200	—	—84	93/123	75/102
4XH	6.3	0.6	Fig. 1	600	120	—	—60	0.14[5]	0.16[5]
02-A	6.3	0.6	8CD	600	150	—	—30/—90	139	117
05 / 05-A / 07	2.5	2.1	5BP / 5BR / 5BP	2000	450	—	—17.5/—52.5	115	97
08-A	2.5	2.1	7CE	1500	430	—	—25/—75	114	109
13	6.3	0.6	913	500	1000	—	—20/—60	299	221
002	6.3	0.6	Fig. 1	600	120	—	—	0.16[5]	0.17[5]
005	2.5	0.6	Fig. 1[4]	2000	1000	200	—35	0.5[5]	0.56[5]

[1] Bogey value for focus. Voltage should be adjustable about value shown.

[2] Bias for visual extinction of undeflected spot. Voltage should be adjustable from 0 to the higher value shown.

[3] Discontinued.

[4] Cathode connected to Pin 7.

[5] In mm. /volt d.c.

[6] Phosphor characteristics (see next column).

Designation	Color and persistance	Application
P1	Green medium	Oscilloscope.
P2	Blue-green medium	Special oscilloscopes and radar.
P4	White medium	Television.
P5	Blue very short	Photographic recording of high speed traces.
P7	Blue-white short Yellow long.	Radar indicators.
P11	Blue short	Oscilloscope.
P12	Orange long	Radar indicators.

TABLE XIV—TRANSISTORS V31

No.	Type	Maximum Ratings				Characteristics			Typical Operation Common Emitter Circuit					
		Collector			Emitter	Noise Figure Db.	Input Res. Ohms[1]	Freq. Cutoff Mc.	Use	Collector		Power Gain Db.	Output Load R. Ohms	Power Output Mw.
		Diss. Mw.	Ma.	Volts	Ma.					Ma.	Volts			
2N34	PNP	50	50	—25	10	18	1000	0.6	Audio[2]	—1.0	—6	40	30K	125
2N35	NPN	50	100	25	—10	16	1000	0.8	Audio[2]	1.0	6	40	30K	125
2N43	PNP	155	—50	—45	50	6	—	1.3	Audio	—1.0	—5	39	—	—
2N44	PNP	155	—50	—45	50	6	—	1.0	Audio	—1.0	—5	43	—	—
2N68	PNP	2500	—1500	—25	1500	—	—	0.4	Audio	—150.0	—12	23	100	600
2N78	NPN	75	20	15	—20	12	—	6.0	I.F.-R.F.	—	—	30	—	—
2N94	NPN	50	50	20	—	—	—	2.0	I.F.	0.5	6	24	100K	—
2N94A	NPN	50	50	20	—	15	—	5.0	I.F.-R.F.	0.5	6		100K	—
2N104	PNP	—	—50	—30	50	12	—	0.7	Audio	—1.0	—15	32	—	—
2N105	PNP	35	—15	—25	15	4.5	2300	0.014	Audio	—0.7	—4	42	20K	—
2N107	PNP	50	—10	—12	10	22	700	0.6	—	—1.0	—5	38	30K	—
2N109	PNP	50	—35	—12	35	—	750	—	Audio[2]	—35.0	—4.5	30	200	75
2N123	PNP	100	—150	—20	150	—	—	7.5	Switching	—5.0	—15	—	—	—
2N131A	PNP	100	—100	—30	—	22	—	0.8	Audio	—1.0	—6	—	—	—
2N132A	PNP	130	—10	—12	—	20	1000	1.2	Audio	—1.0	—6	42	30K	—
2N139	PNP	35	—15	—16	15	4.5	500	—	I.F.	—1.0	—9	30	30K	—
2N140	PNP	35	—15	—16	15	—	700	7.0	I.F.-R.F.	—0.4	—9	27	75K	—
2N155	PNP	8500	—3000	—30	—	—	20	0.3	Audio[2]	—360.0	—14	30		9[3]
2N167	NPN	65	75	30	—	—	—	8.0	I.F.-R.F.	—	—	—	—	—
2N169A	NPN	55	20	25	—20	—	500	5.0	I.F.-R.F.	1.0	5	27	15K	—
2N175	PNP	20	—2	—10	2	6	3570	—	Audio	—0.5	—4	43	—	—
2N218	PNP	35	—15	—16	15	4.5	500	—	I.F.	—1.0	—9	30	30K	—
2N219	PNP	35	—15	—16	15	—	700	7.0	I.F.-R.F.	—0.4	—9	27	75K	—
2N233	NPN	50	100	10	—	—	—	2.0	I.F.	—	—	21	—	—
2N247	PNP	35	—10	—35	10	8	—	30.0	R.F.	—1.0	—9	24	—	—
2N248	PNP	30	—	—25	—	—	—	50	R.F.	—	—	—	—	—
2N255	PNP	1500	—3000	—15	—	—	—	0.2	Audio[2]	—500.0	—6	27	—	5[3]
2N256	PNP	1500	—3000	—30	—	—	—	0.2	Audio[2]	—500.0	—12	27	—	10[3]
2N270	PNP	150	—75	—12	—75	—	—	—	Audio[2]	—	—12	32	—	500
2N274	PNP	35	—10	—35	10	8	—	30.0	R.F.	—1.0	—9	45	—	—
2N292	NPN	65	20	15	—	—	—	6.0	I.F.-R.F.	—	—	25	—	—
2N301	PNP	7500	—1000	—20	1000	—	—	—	Audio[2]	—	—14.4	30	—	12[3]
2N301A	PNP	7500	—1000	—30	1000	—	—	—	Audio[2]	—	—14.4	30	—	12[3]
2N306	NPN	50	—	20	—	—	—	0.6	Audio	—	—	—	—	—
2N307	PNP	10000	—1000	—35	—	—	—	0.3	Audio	—	—	30	—	—
2N331	PNP	200	—200	—30	200	9	—	1.0	Audio	—1.0	—6	44	—	—
2N351	PNP	10000	—3000	—40	3000	—	—	—	Audio[2]	—3000	—40	—	—	—
2N370	PNP	80	—10	—20	10	—	1750	30.0	R.F.	—1.0	—12	12.5	—	—
2N371	PNP	80	—10	—20	10	—	—	30.0	R.F.	—1.0	—12	—	—	—
2N372	PNP	80	—10	—20	10	—	100	30.0	Mixer	—1.0	—12	17	11K	—
2N374	PNP	80	—10	—25	10	—	2600	30.0	Conv.	—1.0	—12	40	—	—
2N376	PNP	10000	—3000	—30	3000	—	—	—	Audio[2]	—3000	—40	—	—	—
2N384	PNP	120	—10	—30	10	—	30	100.0	R.F.	—1.5	—20	15	—	—
2N411	PNP	80	—15	—13	15	—	700	10.0	I.F.-R.F.	—0.6	—9	32	—	—
2N412	PNP	80	—15	—13	15	—	700	10.0	I.F.-R.F.	—0.6	—9	32	—	—
2N428	PNP	150	—400	—30	400	—	—	17.0	R.F.	—	—	—	—	—
2N499	PNP	75	—50	—30	50	—	—	250.0	R.F.	—	—	—	—	—
2N544	PNP	80	—10	—18	10	—	2100	30.0	R.F.	1.0	—12	30	—	—
2N554	PNP	—	—3000	—30	3000	—	—	—	Audio	—	—	—	—	—
2N561	PNP	50000	—10000	—80	10000	—	—	—	Audio[2]	500	—28	35	150	10[3]
2N586	PNP	250	—250	—45	250	—	—	—	Switching	—	—	—	—	—
2N588	PNP	80	—50	—18	50	—	—	200.0	R.F.	—	—	—	—	—
2N677	PNP	50000	—15000	—50	—	—	—	—	Switching	—	—	60	—	—
2N1014	PNP	50000	—10000	—100	10000	—	—	—	Audio	—	—	—	—	—
2N1102	NPN	180	100	40	—100	—	500	—	Audio	—	—	—	—	—
2N1266	PNP	80	—	—10	—	—	—	—	I.F.	—	—	22	—	—
3N25	TET	25	—2	—15	2	—	—	200.0	R.F.	—	—	—	—	—
3N36	TET	30	30	7	—	—	—	50.0	R.F.	—	—	—	—	—
3N37	TET	30	20	7	—	—	—	90.0	R.F.	—	—	—	—	—
AO-1	SB	10	—5	—4.5	—	—	—	30.0	R.F.	—	—	—	—	—
CK722	PNP	180	—10	—22	10	25	800	—	—	—1.0	—6	39	20K	—
CK768	PNP	—	—5	—10	—	—	—	3.5	I.F.-R.F.	—1.0	—6	—	—	—
OC71	PNP	125	—10	—15	—	—	—	0.3	Audio	—	—	40	—	—
OC72	PNP	167	—125	—16	—	—	—	0.35	Audio	—	—	34	—	—
SB100	SB	10	—5	—4.5	—	—	—	30.0	R.F.	—0.5	—3	—	25K	—

[1] Common emitter circuit
[2] Two transistors in Class B
[3] Power output watts

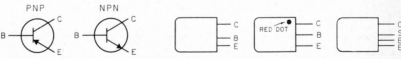

PNP   NPN

Code for identifying typical junction transistors. The leads are marked C-collector, B-base, E-emitter and S-interlead shield and metal case.

Type	Use	Max. Inverse Volts	Max. Average Ma.	Min. Forward Ma.[1]	Max. Reverse μ-Amp.
1N34	General Purpose	60	50	5.0	800 @ −50 V.
1N34A	General Purpose	75	50	5.0	500 @ −50 V.
1N35	General Purpose	50	22.5	7.5	100 @ −10 V.
1N38	General Purpose	100	50	3.0	625 @ −100 V.
1N38A	General Purpose	100	50	4.0	500 @ −100 V.
1N39A	General Purpose	225	40	4.0	600 @ −200 V.
1N48	General Purpose	85	50	4.0	833 @ −50 V.
1N52A	General Purpose	85	50	5.0	100 @ −50 V.
1N54A	Hi-Back Resistance	75	50	5.0	100 @ −50 V.
1N55A	General Purpose	170	50	4.0	500 @ −150 V.
1N56A	Hi-Conduction	50	60	15.0	300 @ −30 V.
1N58A	General Purpose	115	50	4.0	600 @ −100 V.
1N60	Vid. Detector	25	50	5.0	40 @ −20 V.
1N63	Hi-Back Resistance	125	50	4.0	50 @ −50 V.
1N64	Vid. Detector	20	50	0.1	25 @ −1.3 V.
1N65	General Purpose	85	50	2.5	200 @ −50 V.
1N66	General Purpose	60	50	5.0	800 @ −50 V.
1N67	Hi-Back Resistance	80	35	4.0	50 @ −50 V.
1N67A	Hi-Back Resistance	100	50	4.0	50 @ −50 V.
1N68	Hi-Back Resistance	100	35	3.0	625 @ −100 V.
1N68A	General Purpose	100	50	3.0	625 @ −100 V.
1N69A	General Purpose	75	40	5.0	500 @ −50 V.
1N70A	General Purpose	125	30	3.0	300 @ −50 V.
1N77A	Photo Diode	50 V., 20 MW			
1N81	General Purpose	50	30	3.0	10 @ −10 V.
1N82	Mixer	Max. Freq.—1000 Mc.	16 db. Noise Factor		
1N82A	Mixer	Max. Freq.—1000 Mc.	14 db. Noise Factor		
1N89	Restorer	80	30	3.5	100 @ −50 V.
1N90	General Purpose	75	30	5.0	750 @ −50 V.
1N91	Pwr. Rectifier	100	150	470 @ 0.5 V.	2700 @ −100 V.
1N95	General Purpose	60	250	10.0	500 @ −50 V.
1N96	General Purpose	60	250	20.0	500 @ −50 V.
1N97	General Purpose	80	250	10.0	100 @ −50 V.
1N98	Hi-Back Resistance	100	250	20.0	100 @ −50 V.
1N99	General Purpose	80	300	10.0	50 @ −50 V.
1N100	General Purpose	80	300	20.0	50 @ −50 V.
1N116	General Purpose	60	30	5.0	100 @ −50 V.
1N117	General Purpose	60	30	10.0	100 @ −50 V.
1N118	General Purpose	60	30	20.0	100 @ −50 V.
1N126A	General Purpose	75	30	5.0	850 @ −50 V.
1N127A	General Purpose	125	30	3.0	300 @ −50 V.
1N128	General Purpose	50	30	3.0	10 @ −10 V.
1N151	General Purpose	100	500	1570 @ 0.7 V.	2400 @ −100 V.
1N152	General Purpose	200	500	1570 @ 0.7 V.	1900 @ −200 V.
1N153	General Purpose	300	500	1570 @ 0.7 V.	1200 @ −300 V.
1N158	Pwr. Rectifier	380	500	—	
1N191	Computer	90	30	5.0	25 @ −10 V.
1N192	Computer	70	30	5.0	50 @ −10 V.
1N198A	Hi-Temperature	100	30	4.0	250 @ −50 V. (75°C)
1N279	Hi-Conduction	35	—	100.0	200 @ −20 V.
1N283	Hi-Conduction	25	—	200.0	80 @ −10 V.
1N294	Switching	70	60	5.0	800 @ −50 V.
1N295	Vid. Detector	40	—	—	—
1N448	100-Volt Computer	120	—	25.0	100 @ −100 V.
1N634	60-Volt Very Low Z	120	—	50.0	115 @ −100 V.
1N636	General Purpose	75	—	2.5	20 @ −20 V.
HB1	Zener Diode	Zener Volts = 7.5			
HB2	Zener Diode	Zener Volts = 20			
HB3	Zener Diode	Zener Volts = 40			
HB4	Zener Diode	Zener Volts = 75			
HB5	Zener Diode	Zener Volts = 170			
HB6	Zener Diode	Zener Volts = 300			
M150	Silicon Power Rectifier	Max. Rms. Input: 130 V., Peak Inverse: 400 V., D.C. Current: 150 Ma.			
M500	Silicon Power Rectifier	Max. Rms. Input: 130 V., Peak Inverse: 400 V., D.C. Current: 500 Ma.			
V15	Capacitor Diode	Max. Oper. Voltage −25, Range: 6.5–39 μμf.		Q At 50 Mc. −18	
V20	Capacitor Diode	Max. Oper. Voltage −20, Range: 10–50 μμf.		Q At 50 Mc. −18.7	
V27	Capacitor Diode	Max. Oper. Voltage −20, Range: 14–70 μμf.		Q At 50 Mc. −15.7	
V33	Capacitor Diode	Max. Oper. Voltage −20, Range: 17–85 μμf.		Q At 50 Mc. −14.6	
V39	Capacitor Diode	Max. Oper. Voltage −20, Range: 20–100 μμf.		Q At 50 Mc. −15.1	
V47	Capacitor Diode	Max. Oper. Voltage −20, Range: 24–120 μμf.		Q At 50 Mc. −15.4	
V56	Capacitor Diode	Max. Oper. Voltage −50, Range: 32–145 μμf.		Q At 50 Mc. −13.5	

[1] At +1 Volt

The
Catalog Section

In the following pages is a catalog file of products of the principal manufacturers and the principal distributors who serve the radio field: industrial, commercial, amateur. All firms whose advertising has been accepted for this section have met The American Radio Relay League's rigid standards for established integrity; their products and engineering methods have received the League's approval.

37th EDITION 1960

INDEX OF ADVERTISERS

★ CATALOG SECTION ★

The Radio Amateur's Handbook

The new ideas
in communications are born at...

hallicrafters

CHICAGO 24, ILLINOIS

**Export Sales: International Division,
Raytheon Mfg. Co., Waltham, Mass.
Canada: Gould Sales Co., Montreal, P. Q.**

HT-33A
Linear Amplifier

SX-101A Receiver

Heavyweight champion in stability, performance!

SX101A is setting new standards for dependability and ruggedness throughout the amateur world. It's *all* amateur; provides complete coverage, and every technical feature desired for years to come.

FREQUENCY COVERAGE: Band 1—30.5-34.5 Mc. Band 2—3.48-4.02 Mc. Band 3—6.99-7.31 Mc. Band 4—13.98-14.415 Mc. Band 5—20.99-21.52 Mc. Band 6—26.9-29.8 Mc. Band 7—10 Mc. WWV.

FEATURES: Complete coverage of five ham bands plus a 2 and 6 meter conv. band—80, 40, 20, 15, 10 meters. Large slide rule dial. Band-in-use scales individually illuminated. Illuminated S-

HT-32A
Transmitter

The new ideas in communications are born at . . .

4

effortless performance!

Beautifully engineered with extra-heavy-duty components, the HT-33A is *conservatively rated* at the maximum legal limit. You are guaranteed one of the big signals on the band, plus the effortless performance that means so much to efficiency and long life. (Conforms to F.C.D.A. specifications.)

FREQUENCY COVERAGE: Complete coverage of amateur bands; 80, 40, 20, 15, 10 meters.

FEATURES: Rated *conservatively* at the maximum legal input. Third and fifth order distortion products down in excess of 30 db. Built-in r.f. output meter greatly simplifies tune-up. All important circuits metered. Maximum harmonic suppression obtained through pi-network. Variable output loading. Protection of power supply assured by circuit breaker. HT-33A is a perfect match to Hallicrafters' famous HT-32 in size, appearance and drive requirements.

CIRCUIT DETAILS: This power amplifier utilizes a PL-172 high efficiency pentode operating in class AB1 or AB2. The tube is grid-driven across a non-inductive resistor, thus assuring the maximum stability under all possible conditions. Band switching is accomplished by one knob which selects the proper inductance value for each band. The output circuit is a pi-network with an adjustable output capacitor, so loads from 40 to 80 ohms may be accommodated. A d.c. milliameter may be switched to various circuits to measure the following: Cathode current, grid current, screen current, plate voltage, and r.f. voltage across the output line for tune-up.

TUBES: (1) PL-172 high power pentode; (2) 3B28 rectifiers; (4) OA2 screen regulators.

FRONT PANEL CONTROLS: Meter selector; Filament switch; High Voltage switch; Bias adjustment; Band switch; Plate tuning; Plate loading.

PHYSICAL DATA: Gray and black steel cabinet (matches HT-32) with brushed chrome knob trim. Size: 8¾" x 19" (relay rack panel). Shipping wt. approx. 130 lbs.

REAR CHASSIS: Co-ax input; co-ax output; filament and bias fuse; cutoff bias relay terminals; screen fuse; ground terminal.

---

meter. Dual scale S-meter. S-meter zero point independent of sensitivity control. S-meter functions with AVC off. Special 10 Mc. position for WWV. Dual conversion. Exclusive Hallicrafters' upper-lower sideband selection. Second conversion oscillators quartz crystal controlled. Tee-notch filter. Full gear drive from tuning knob to gang condensers—absolute reliability. 40:1 tuning knob ratio. Built-in precision 100 kc. evacuated marker crystal. Vernier pointer adjustment. Five steps of selectivity from 500 cycles to 5000 cycles. Precision temperature compensation plus Hallicrafters' exclusive production heat cycling for lowest drift. Direct coupled series noise limiter for improved noise reduction. Sensitivity—one microvolt or less on all amateur bands. 52 ohm antenna input. Antenna trimmer. Relay rack panel. Heaviest chassis in the industry—.089 cold rolled steel. Double spaced gang condenser. 13 tubes plus voltage regulator and rectifier. Powerline fuse.

FRONT PANEL CONTROLS: Main tuning knob with 0-100 logging dial. Pointer reset, antenna trimmer, tee-notch frequency, tee-notch depth, sensitivity, band selector, volume, selectivity, pitch (BFO), response — (upper-lower-sideband AM-CW). AVC on/off, AVC fast/slow, ANL on/off, Cal. on/off, Rec./standby.

TUBES AND FUNCTIONS: 6DC6, R.F. amplifier—6BY6, 1st converter—12 BY7A, high frequency oscillator—6BA6, 1650 kc. i.f. amplifier—12AT7, dual crystal controlled 2nd conversion oscillator—6BA6, 2nd converter—6DC6 51 kc. i.f. amplifier—6BJ7, AM detector, A.N.L., A.V.C.—6BY6 SSBCW detector—6SC7 1st audio amplifier & B.F.O.—6K6, audio power output — 6BA6, S-meter amplifier — 6AU6, 100 kc. crystal oscillator—OA2, voltage regulator—5Y3, rectifier.

PHYSICAL DATA: 20" wide, 10½" high and 16" deep—Panel size 8¾" x 19"—weight approximately 74 lbs. (Conforms to F.C.D.A. specifications.)

Acclaimed by
the most critical!

Now proven superior — vastly superior — is Hallicrafters' exclusive 5.0 mc. quartz crystal filter system. First practical *high frequency* filter, provides unprecedented rejection of unwanted sideband—50 db. or more—and *world's cleanest signal*.

Another major advance: Bridged-Tee Modulator, temperature stabilized and compensated.

FEATURES: 5.0 mc. quartz crystal filter—rejection 50 db. or more. Bridged-tee modulator. C.T.O. direct reading in kilocycles to less than 300 cycles from reference point. 144 watts plate input (P.E.P. two-tone). Five band output (80, 40, 20, 15, 10 meters). All modes of transmission — CW, AM, S.S.B. Unwanted sideband down 50 db. or more. Distortion products down 30 db. or more. Carrier suppression down 50 db. or more. Both sidebands transmitted on A.M. Precision gear driven C.T.O. Exclusive Hallicrafters patented sideband selection. Logarithmic meter for accurately tuning and carrier level adjustment. Ideal CW keying and break-in operation, Push To Talk and full voice control system built in. Phone patch input provided. Keying circuit brought out for teletype keyer.

FRONT PANEL CONTROLS, FUNCTIONS AND CONNECTIONS: Operation—power off, standby, Mox., Cal., Vox.—P.T.T. Audio level 0-10 R.F. level 0-10. Final tuning 80, 40, 20, 15, 10 meters. Function—Upper sideband, lower sideband, DSB, CW. Meter compression. Calibration level 0-10. Driver tuning 0-5. Band selector—80, 40, 20, 15, 10 meters. High stability, gear driven V.F.O. with dial drag. Microphone con. Key jack. Headphone monitor jack.

TUBES AND FUNCTIONS: 2-6146 Power output amplifier. 6CB6 Variable frequency oscillator. 12BY7 R. F. driver. 6AH6 2nd Mixer. 6AH6 3rd Mixer. 6AB4 Crystal oscillator. 12AX7 Voice control. 12AT7 Voice control. 6AL5 Voice control. 12AX7 Audio Amp. 12AU7 Audio amp. and carrier Oscillator. 12AU7 Diode Modulator. 12AT7 Sideband selecting oscillator. 6AH6 1st Mixer. 6AH6 4.95 Mc. Amp. 6AU6 9.00 Mc. Amp. 5R4GY HV Rectifier. 5V4G LV Rectifier. OA2 Voltage Regulator.

REAR CHASSIS: Co-ax antenna connector. FSK jack A.C. accessory outlet. Line fuse. Control connector. AC power line cord. Cabinet 20" wide, 10½" high, and 17" deep. Approximate shipping weight 86 lbs. (Conforms to F.C.D.A. specifications.)

hallicrafters

The engineering team that developed the incomparable SX-101 and HT-32

now offers a precision rig that puts single sideband within reach of all

HT-37 Transmitter

The heart of the now-famous HT-32—*the needed, basic performance charactertistics*—is yours in this precision-engineered new AM/CW/SSB transmitter—and at a price we did not believe possible when we began designing it! Same power. Same rugged VFO construction, and identical VOX. You'll be amazed at the smooth, distinctive speech quality that's yours for the first time at moderate cost.

FEATURES: 144 watts plate input (P.E.P. two-tone); five band output (80, 40, 20, 15, 10 meters); all modes of transmission—CW, AM, S.S.B.; unwanted sideband down 40 db. at 1KC; distortion products down 30 db. or more; carrier suppression down 50 db.; modern styling; instant CW Cal. from any mode; both sidebands transmitted on AM; precision V.F.O.; rugged heavy duty deluxe chassis; 52 ohm pi network output for harmonic suppression; dual range meter for accurate tuning and carrier level adjustment; ideal CW keying; full voice control system built in.

FRONT PANEL CONTROLS, FUNCTIONS, CON-

NECTIONS: Operation—(power off, standby, mox, cal, vox); Audio gain; R.F. level; Final tuning; Function—(upper sideband, lower sideband, DSB, CW); carrier balance; Calibration level; Driver tuning; Band selector V.F.O.; Microphone connector; Key jack.

TUBES AND FUNCTIONS: (2)-6146 Power output amplifiers; 6CB6 Variable frequency oscillator; 12BY7 R.F. driver; 6AH6 1st Mixer; 6AH6 2nd Mixer; 6AB4 Crystal oscillator; 12AX7 Voice control; 12AT7 Voice control; 6AL5 Voice control; 12AX7 Audio Amplifier; 12AT7 Audio amp and carrier Oscillator; 12AT7 Audio Modulator; (2)-12AT7 Balanced Modulators; 5R4GY HV Rectifier; 5V4G LV Rectifier; OA2 Voltage Regulator.

REAR CHASSIS: Co-ax antenna connector; Line fuse; Control connector; AC power line cord.

PHYSICAL DATA: Matching unit for SX-111; cabinet is gray steel with brushed chrome trim and knobs. Size: 9″ high x 19¼″ wide x 15½″ deep. Shipping weight: approximately 80 lbs.

The new ideas in communications are born at . . .

![h] hallicrafters

f SSB equipment

SX-110

SX-111 Receiver

Here's the receiver you've been waiting for—a real thoroughbred that retains *the essential performance characteristics* of the renowned SX-101, but at a price that can put it in your shack tomorrow! Rugged . . . dependable . . . beautifully styled, the new SX-111 is outstanding evidence that Hallicrafters aim is always to bring you the finest equipment at the lowest possible price.

FREQUENCY COVERAGE: Complete coverage of 80, 40, 20, 15 and 10 meters in five separate bands. Sixth band is tunable to 10 Mc. for crystal calibrator calibration with WWV.

FEATURES: AM/CW/SSB reception. Dual conversion, Hallicrafter's exclusive selectable sideband operation. Crystal-controlled 2nd converter. Tee-notch filter. Calibrated S-meter. Vernier dial-pointer adjustment. Series noise limiter. Built-in crystal calibrator. Exceptional electrical and mechanical stability. Large slide-rule dial.

SENSITIVITY: One microvolt on all bands, with 5 steps of selectivity from 500 to 5,000 c.p.s.

TUNING MECHANISM: New friction-and-gear type with 48:1 tuning ration. Virtually eliminates backlash.

CONTROLS: Tuning; Pointer Reset; Antenna Trimmer; T-notch Frequency; RF Gain; Audio Gain; Band Selector; Function (off/on, standby, upper or lower sideband, calibrate); AVC off/on; BFO off/on; ANL off/on; Selectivity.

TUBES: 10 tubes plus voltage regulator and rectifier. 6DC6 RF Amplifier; 6BY6 1st converter; 6C4 Oscillator; 6BA6 2nd converter; 12AT7 Dual crystal second converters; 6CB6 1650 kc. i.f. amplifier; 6DC6 i.f. amplifier (50 kc.); 6BJ7 AVC-noise limiter-detector; 12AX7 1st audio and BFO; 6AQ5 Power output; 5Y3 rectifier; AO2 Voltage regulator.

POWER SUPPLY: 105-125 volts, 50-60 cycle AC.

PHYSICAL DATA: Size: 18¾″ wide x 10¼″ deep x 8¾″ high. Attractive gray steel cabinet with brushed chrome trim. Shipping wt. approximately 40 lbs.

The last word in features and design!

SX-110 Receiver

Never before have so many outstanding, wanted features been incorporated in an all-purpose receiver—features developed originally for the highest-priced sets.

FREQUENCY COVERAGE: Broadcast Band 540-1680 kc plus three short wave bands covers 1680 kc–34 mc.

FEATURES: Slide rule bandspread dial calibrated for 80, 40, 20, 15 and 10 meter amateur bands and 11 meter citizens' band. Separate bandspread tuning condenser, crystal filter, antenna trimmer, "S" Meter, one r-f, two i-f stages.

INTERMEDIATE FREQUENCY: 455 kc.

TUNING ASSEMBLY AND DIAL DRIVE MECHANISM: Ganged, 3 section tuning capacitor assembly with electrical bandspread. Circular main tuning dial is calibrated in megacycles and has 0-100 logging scale.

AUDIO OUTPUT IMPEDANCE: 3.2 and 500 ohms.

TUBE COMPLEMENT: Seven tubes plus one rectifier: 6SG7, r-f amplifier — 6SA7, converter — 6SG7, 1st i-f amplifier—6SK7, 2nd i-f amplifier—6SC7, BFO and audio amplifier—6K6GT, Audio output—6H6, ANL-AVC-detector—6Y3GT, rectifier.

AUDIO POWER OUTPUT: 2 watts.

POWER SUPPLY: 105/125 V., 50/60 cycle AC.

PHYSICAL DATA: Gray steel cabinet with brushed chrome trim. Size 18¾″ wide x 8″ high x 10¼″ deep. Shipping weight approximately 32 lbs.

S-108 Receiver

Same basic performance as SX-110 (above) less S-Meter, antenna trimmer and crystal filter, but includes a built-in speaker.

Two outstanding speaker values

R-47 SPEAKER

Specially designed for voice and SSB. Flat response from 300 to 2850 c.p.s. Input impedance: 3.2 ohms. Size: 5½″ x 5¼″ x 3½″. Wt. 2½ lb.

R-48 SPEAKER (See photo with HT-37 and SX-111). Latest design, eliptical assembly. 3.16 oz. Alnico V magnet. Fidelity switch for music or voice. 3.2 ohm input impedance. 6½″ x 13¼″ x 8¼″.

SX-100 Most versatile receiver of all!

FREQUENCY COVERAGE: 540 kc—34 Mc. Band 1: 538 kc-1580 kc—Band 2: 1720 kc-4.9 Mc—Band 3: 4.6 Mc-13 Mc—Band 4: 12 Mc-34 Mc. Bandspread dial is calibrated for the 80, 40, 20, 15 and 10 meter amateur bands.

TYPE OF SIGNALS: AM—CW—SSB.

FEATURES: Selectable side band operation. "Tee-Notch" Filter—provides a stable non-regenerative system for the rejection of unwanted heterodyne. Also produces an effective steepening of the already excellent 500 Cycles i-f pass band and further increases the effectiveness of the advanced exalted carrier type reception. Notch depth control for maximum null adjustment. Antenna trimmer. Plug-in laboratory type evacuated 100 kc quartz crystal calibrator—included in price. Logging dials for both tuning controls. Full precision gear drive dial system. Second conversion oscillator crystal controlled—provides greater stability and additional temperature compensation of high frequency oscillator circuits. Phono jack. Socket for D.C. and remote control.

CONTROLS: Pitch control, reception, stand-by, phone jack, response control (upper and lower side band selector), antenna trimmer, notch depth, calibrator on/off, sensitivity, band selector, volume, tuning, AVC on/off noise limiter on/off, bandspread, selectivity.

INTERMEDIATE FREQUENCY: 1650 kc and 51 kc.

AUDIO OUTPUT IMPEDANCE: 3.2/500 ohms: **AUDIO POWER OUTPUT:** 1.5 watts with 10% or less distortion. **POWER SUPPLY:** 105/125 V., 50/60 cycle AC.

TUBE COMPLEMENT: 6CB6 R.F. amplifier; 6BY6, 1stconvertor;6AH6,H.F.oscillator; 6BA6, 2nd converter; 12AT7, Dual crystal second converters; (2) 6BA6, 51 kc and 1650 kc i-f amplifiers; 6BJ7, AVC-noise limiter; 6SC7, 1st audio and BFO; 6K6, Power output; 5Y3, Rectifier; OA2, Voltage regulator; 6C4, i-f amplifier—(51 kc); 6AU6, 100 kc XTAL marker.

PHYSICAL DATA: Gray black steel cabinet with brushed chrome knob trim, patterned silver back plate and red pointers. Piano hinge top. Size 18⅜" wide x 8½" high x 10⅝" deep. Shipping weight approximately 42 lbs. (*U.L. approved*)

Complete VHF Station

SR-34 Transmitter/Receiver

GENERAL DESCRIPTION: The SR-34 is designed for either AM or CW and combines complete functions of a two *and* six meter radio station. 115-V. A.C., 6-V. D.C., or 12V. D.C. Transistorized power supply. Meets F.C.D.A. matching-fund specifications.

The transmitter is crystal-controlled; up to four crystals may be switch-selected. A fifth position on this switch permits external V.F.O. operation.

The receiver is a double conversion superheterodyne with a quartz crystal controlled second oscillator. Separate oscillator and R.F. sections for each band.

All receiver functions provided—S-meter, B.F.O., ANL, etc. Sensitivities average 1 microvolt on both bands.

FRONT PANEL CONTROLS: *Receiver:* Band Selector (48.9-54.1 mc., 143.9 to 148.1 mc.): Main Tuning; Sensitivity; Audio Volume; B.F.O. Pitch; Squelch Level; Headphone Jack; AVC On/Off; ANL On/Off; B.F.O. On/Off. *Transmitter:* Function Switch (P.A., Rec., Cal., AM, CW); Power On/Off; Band Switch; Crystal Selector and V.F.O.; Oscillator Tuning; Doubler Tuning; Tripler Tuning; Final Tuning; Final Loading; Meter Switch.

POWER OUTPUT: 5 to 8 watts AM or CW, 100% mod. negative peak clipping. *Rear Apron:* Speech input level control; key jack; P.A. speaker terminals; mic. selector (high Z or carbon); mic. input; A.C. and D.C. fuses; power plug.

Also available in A.C. only model.

SX-100

SR-34

hallicrafters

S-38E

S-107

World's most popular short wave receiver!

MODEL S-38E

Latest model of Hallicrafters' most popular of all short wave receivers! Beautiful new, modern cabinet styling, improved circuitry for superior performance and utmost dependability.

FREQUENCY COVERAGE: Standard broadcast from 540-1650 kc., plus three short wave bands from 1650 kc. through 32 mc. Intermediate freq.: 455 kc.

FEATURES: Two-section tuning gang with electrical bandspread; easy-to-read, slide-rule overseas dial; oscillator for code reception; built-in 5″ speaker, universal output for headset; rear switch for speaker or headset selection. (U.L. approved)

CONTROLS: Tuning dial. Separate electrical bandspread dial with 0-100 scale. Receive/standby switch. On/off/volume. AM, CW switch. Band selector.

POWER SUPPLY: 1 watt audio power output. 105/125 volts. 50-60 cycle AC/DC. Line cord (S7D 1566) for 220 volt AC/DC available.

TUBE COMPLEMENT. Four tubes plus one rectifier: 35W4 rectifier; 50C5 audio output; 12AU6 amplifier; 12BA6 IF amplifier and B.F.O.; 12BE6 converter.

AUDIO OUTPUT: Five inch PM speaker and universal output for headset.

EXTERNAL CONNECTIONS: Phone tip jacks and terminals for single wire or doublet antenna, switch for speaker or headphones on rear. External antenna provided.

PHYSICAL DATA: Available in gray steel cabinet with silver trim, or blond or mahogany finish with gold trim. Size 12⅞″ wide x 7″ high x 9¼″ deep. Shipping weight approximately 14 lbs.

New beauty . . . new standards of performance!

MODEL S-107

COVERAGE: Standard Broadcast from 540-1630 kc plus four short wave bands over 2.5-31 and 48-54.5 mc. Intermediate frequency; 455 kc. **CONTROLS:** Main tuning in mc. Separate electrical bandspread with 0-100 logging scale plus calibration for 48-54.5 mc band, receive/standby switch, band selector 540-1630 kc, 2.5-6.3 mc, 6.3-16 mc, 14-31 mc, and 48-54.5 mc, AM/CW switch, sensitivity/phono control, noise limiter switch, on/off/volume, two-position tone switch. **BAND CHANGE MECHANISM:** Five position rotary wafer switch. **TUNING ASSEMBLY AND DIAL DRIVE MECHANISM:** Separate 2-section tuning capacitor assemblies for main tuning and band spread tuning. Slide rule dial. Phonograph jack, headphone tip jacks. Bandspread tuning calibrated for 48-54.5 mc. **ANTENNA INPUT IMPEDANCE:** Balanced/unbalanced. 50-300 ohms. **HEADPHONE OUTPUT IMPEDANCE:** Universal impedance. **AUDIO OUTPUT:** Five inch PM speaker and universal impedance output for headset. **TUBE COMPLEMENT:** Seven tubes plus one rectifier: 6C4, Osc.—6BA6, Mixer—(2) 6BA6, i-f amplifier—6H6, Det., AVC and ANL—6SC7, BFO and AF amp.—6K6GT, Output—5Y3GT, rectifier. **EXTERNAL CONNECTIONS:** speaker/phones switch and terminals for doublet or single wire antenna on rear. **AUDIO POWER OUTPUT:** One watt. **POWER SUPPLY:** 105/125 V., 50/60 cycle. AC. **PHYSICAL DATA:** Sturdy gray hammertone steel cabinet with brushed chrome trim. Size 13⅜″ wide x 7″ high x 8⅞″ deep. Shipping weight approximately 18½ lbs. (U.L. approved)

9

90901

ONE INCH INSTRUMENTATION OSCILLOSCOPE

Miniaturized, packaged panel mounting cathode ray oscilloscope designed for use in instrumentation in place of the conventional "pointer type" moving coil meters uses the 1" tube. Panel bezel matches in size and type the standard 2" square meters. Magnitude, phase displacement, wave shape, etc. are constantly visible on scope

No. 90901, 1CP1, less tube.............
No. 90911, 1EP1, less tube.............

POWER SUPPLY FOR OSCILLOSCOPE

750 volts d.c. at 3 ma. and 6.3 volts a.c. at 600 ma. 117 volts 50—60 cycle input. Designed especially for use with No. 90901 and No. 90911 one inch instrumentation oscilloscopes. 4⅝ in. high x 1⅞ x 2⅛. Octal plug for input and output. Entire assembly including rectifier is encapsulated.

No. 90202 Power Supply (complete)......

GRID DIP METER

The No. 90651 MILLEN GRID DIP METER is compact and completely self contained. The AC power supply is of the "transformer" type. The drum dial has seven calibrated uniform length scales from 1.7 MC to 300 MC with generous over laps plus an arbitrary scale for use with special application inductors. Internal terminal strip permits battery operation for antenna measurement.

No. 90651, with tube.................

Additional Inductors for Lower Frequencies
No. 46702—925 to 2000 KC..........
No. 46703—500 to 1050 KC..........
No. 46704—325 to 600 KC..........
No. 46705—220 to 350 KC..........

TONE MODULATOR

The No. 90751 Tone Modulator is a small package, containing a transistor audio oscillator and its mercury battery, which plugs into the 'phone jack of a Grid Dip Meter to modulate the signal at approximately 800 cycles for applications requiring a modulated signal.
Dimensions: only 2¾ x 1⁹⁄₁₆ x 1⁹⁄₁₆ in.
No. 90751, less battery..............

COMPACT OSCILLOSCOPES

The No. 90923 Oscilloscope is an extremely compact (3½ inch high) rack panel type, general purpose oscilloscope, utilizing the type 3XP1, 3XP2, 3XP7, or 3XP11, 3 inch by 1½ inch rectangular face cathode ray tube.
No. 90923, with tubes.................

The No. 90902, No. 90903 and No. 90905 Rack Panel Oscilloscopes, for two, three and five inch tubes, respectively, are inexpensive *basic units* comprising power supply, brilliancy and centering controls, safety features, magnetic shielding, switches, etc. As a transmitter monitor, no additional equipment or accessories are required. The well-known trapezoidal monitoring patterns are secured by feeding modulated carrier voltage from a pickup loop directly to vertical plates of the cathode ray tube and audio modulating voltage to horizontal plates. By the addition of such units as sweeps, pulse generators, amplifiers, servo sweeps, etc., all of which can be conveniently and neatly constructed on companion rack panels, the original basic 'scope unit may be expanded to serve any conceivable industrial or laboratory application.

No. 90902, less tubes................
No. 90903, less tubes................
No. 90905, less tubes................

'SCOPE AMPLIFIER—SWEEP UNIT

Vertical and horizontal amplifiers along with hard-tube, saw tooth sweep generator. Complete with power supply mounted on a standard 5¼" rack panel.
No. 90921, with tubes................

FLAT FACE OSCILLOSCOPE

90905-B 5-inch Rack Mounting Basic Oscilloscope features include: balanced deflection, front panel input terminals, rear panel input terminals, astigmatism control, blanking input terminals, flat face precision tolerance Dumont 5ADP1 tube, 1800 or 2500 volts accelerating, good sensitivity, sharp focus, horizontal selector switch, 60 cycle sine wave sweep available, power supply available to operate external equipment, minimum control interaction, rugged construction, light filter. 7 x 19 in. panel.
No. 90905-B Oscilloscope, less tubes.....

90202

907

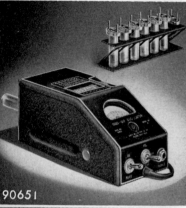

90651

90902

90903

90905

9C

9C

90921

90905-B

0672

46672 –
10
15
20
40
80

0711

811

ANTENNA BRIDGE

The Millen 90672 Antenna Bridge is an accurate and sensitive bridge for measuring impedances in the range of 5 to 500 ohms (or 20 to 2000 ohms with balun) at radio frequencies up to 200 mc. The variable element is an especially designed differential variable capacitor capable of high accuracy and permanency of calibration. Readily driven by No. 90651 Grid Dipper.

No. 90672.....................

AUDIO CLIPPER

The No. 75016 Audio Clipper is a small plug-in symmetrical type clipper with self-contained mercury batteries. It may be used to clip noise for C-W reception as well as for A-M or SSB, or it may be used to clip a sine wave input to form a square wave output.

Dimensions: only 2¾ x 1⁵⁄₁₆ x 1⁵⁄₁₆ in.

No. 75016, less batteries..............

BALUNS

The No. 46672 (1 for each amateur band) wound Balun is an accurate 2 to 1 turns ratio, high Q auto transformer with the residual reactances tuned out and with very tight coupling between the two halves of the total winding. The points of series and parallel resonance are selected so that each Balun provides an accurate 4 to 1 impedance ratio over the entire band of frequencies for which it was designed. Suitable for use with the No. 90672 Antenna Bridge or medium power transmitters.

No.46672–80/40/20/15/10.........

50 WATT EXCITER-TRANSMITTER

Modern design includes features and shielding for TVI reduction, bandswitching for 4–7–14–21–28 megacycle bands, circuit metering. Conservatively rated for use either as a transmitter or exciter for high power PA stages. 5763 oscillator-buffer-multiplier and 6146 power amplifier. Rack mounted.

No. 90801, less tubes............

VARIABLE FREQUENCY OSCILLATOR

The No. 90711 is a complete transmitter control unit with 6SK7 temperature-compensated, electron coupled oscillator of exceptional stability and low drift, a 6SK7 broad-band buffer or frequency doubler, a 6AG7 tuned amplifier which tracks with the oscillator tuning, and a regulated power supply. Output sufficient to drive a 6146 is available on 160, 80 and 40 meters and reduced output is available on 20 meters. Since the output is isolated from the oscillator by two stages, zero frequency shift occurs when the output load is varied from open circuit to short circuit. The entire unit is unusually solidly built so that no frequency shift occurs due to vibration. The keying is clean and free from annoying chirp, quick drift, jump, and similar difficulties often encountered in keying variable frequency oscillators.

No. 90711, with tubes............

HIGH VOLTAGE POWER SUPPLY

The No. 90281 high voltage power supply has a d.c. output of 700 volts, with maximum current of 235 ma. In addition, a.c. filament power of 6.3 volts at 4 amperes is also available so that this power supply is an ideal unit for use with transmitters, such as the Millen No. 90801, as well as general laboratory purposes. The power supply uses two No. 816 rectifiers The panel is standard 8¾'' x 19'' rack mounting.

No.90281, less tubes............

HIGH FREQUENCY RF AMPLIFIER

A physically small unit capable of a power output of 70 to 85 watts on 'Phone or 87 to 110 watts on C-W on 20, 15, 11, 10, 6 or 2 meter amateur bands Provision is made for quick band shift by means of the No. 48000 series VHF plug-in coils The No. 90811 unit uses either an 829-B or 3E29.

No. 90811 with 10 meter band coils, less tube........................

RF POWER AMPLIFIER

This 500 watt amplifier may be used as the basis of a high power amateur transmitter. The No. 90881 RF power amplifier is wired for use with the popular "812A" type tubes. Other popular tubes may be used. The amplifier is of unusually sturdy mechanical construction, on a 10½'' relay rack panel. Plug-in inductors are furnished for operation on 10, 20, 40 or 80 meter amateur bands. The standard Millen No. 90801 exciter unit is an ideal driver for the No. 90881 RF power amplifier.

No. 90881, with one set of coils, but less tubes.....................

75016

90801

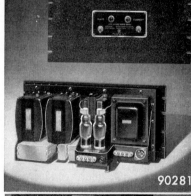

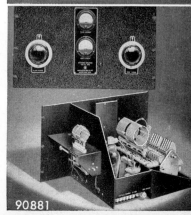

90281

90881

90201

75012

80805-M
80802-E
80802-C
80803-J
80802-B2
80801-B

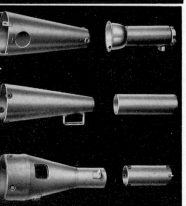

REGULATED POWER SUPPLY

A compact, uncased, regulated power supply, either for table use in the laboratory or for incorporation as an integral part of larger equipment. 250 v.d.c. unregulated at 115 ma. 105 v.d.c. regulated at 35 ma. Minus 105 v.d.c. regulated bias at 4 ma. 6.3 v. a.c. at 4.2 amps.
No. 90201, with tubes.................

INSTRUMENT DIAL

The No. 10030 is an extremely sturdy instrument type indicator. Control shaft has 1 to 1 ratio. Veeder type counter is direct reading in 99 revolutions and vernier scale permits readings to 1 part in 100 of a single revolution. Has built-in dial lock and ¼'' drive shaft coupling. May be used with multi-revolution transmitter controls, etc., or through gear reduction mechanism for control of fractional revolution capacitors, etc., in receivers or laboratory instruments.
No. 10030......................

PHASE-SHIFT NETWORK

A complete and laboratory aligned pair of phase-shift networks in a single compact 2'' x 1⁷⁄₁₆'' x 4'' case with characteristics so as to provide a phase shift between the two networks of 90° ± 1.3° over a frequency range of 225 cycles to 2750 cycles. Well adapted for use in either single sideband transmitter or receiver. Possible to obtain a 40 db suppression of the unwanted sideband. The No. 75012 precision adjusted phase-shift network eliminates the necessity of complicated laboratory equipment for network adjustment
No. 75012......................

DELAY LINES

No. 34751—Sealed flexible distributed constants line. Excellent rise time. 1350 ohms, 22 inches per microsecond or 550 ohms, 50 inches per mu.-sec. Delay cut to specifications.
No. 34700—Hermetically sealed encased line. Good rise time. 0–0.45 mu.-sec. 1350 ohm line or 0.22 mu.-sec. 500 ohm line in 1'' x 1'' x 5½'' in case. Also larger standard cases and cases made to order. Special impedances 400 to 2200 ohms.
No. 34600—Lumped delay line built to specifications. Delays 0.05 mu.-sec. to 250 mu.-sec. Impedance 50 ohms to 2000 ohms.

PHOTO MULTIPLIER SHIELDS
MU-METAL

The photo multiplier tube operates most effectively when perfectly shielded. Careful study has proven that mu-metal provides superior shielding. Millen Mu-Metal shields are available from stock for the most popular tubes.
No. 80801B for the 1P21, 1P22, 1P28, 931A
No. 80802B for the 5819, 6217, 6292, 6342.
No. 80802C for the 6199, 6291, 6467.....
No. 80802E for the 6810A, 6903..........
No. 80802F for the 6372.................
No. 80803J for the 6363, K1197..........
No. 80805M for the 6364.................

BEZELS FOR
CATHODE RAY TUBES

Standard types are of satin finish black plastic. 5'' size has neoprene support cushion and green lucite filter. 3'' and 2'' sizes have integral cushioning.
No. 80075—5''......................
No. 80073—3''......................
No. 80072—2''......................
No. 80071—1''......................

CATHODE RAY
TUBE SHIELDS

For many years we have specialized in the design and manufacture of magnetic metal shields of nicoloi and mumetal for cathode ray tubes in our own complete equipment, as well as for applications of all other principal complete equipment manufacturers. Stock types as well as special designs to customers' specifications promptly available.
No. 80045—Nicoloi for 5BP1..........
No. 80055—Nicoloi for 5CP1..........
No. 80043—Nicoloi for 3'' tube.......
No. 80042—Nicoloi for 2'' tube.......

SHIELD CASES
ALUMINUM

Effective RF shielding for coils and transformers can be provided by Millen Aluminum cans. Available in several sizes from stock.
No. 80003—1⅜'' x 1⅜'' x 4''.........
No. 80004—1⅜'' x 1⁷⁄₁₆'' x 4½''......
No. 80005—2'' x 2'' x 4⅞''..........
No. 80006—2⅛'' round x 4''..........
No. 80007—2¼'' round x 2⅜'' open ends

1003

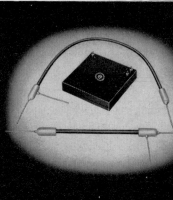

80070-SERIES

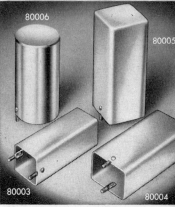

80006
80005
80003
80004

10035

0039

PANEL DIALS

The No. 10035 illuminated panel dial has 12 to 1 ratio; size, 8½" x 6½". Small No. 10039 has 8 to 1 ratio; size, 4" x 3¼". Both are of compact mechanical design, easy to mount and have totally self-contained mechanism, thus eliminating back of panel interference. Provision for mounting and marking auxiliary controls, such as switches, potentiometers, etc., provided on the No. 10035. Standard finish, either size, flat black art metal.

No. 10039 . . . .
No. 10035 . . . .

WORM DRIVE UNIT

Cast aluminum frame may be panel or base mounted. Spring loaded split gears to minimize back lash.
Standard ratio 16/1. Also in 48/1 on request
No. 10000—(state ratio) . . . .

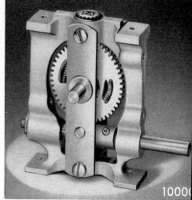

10000

DIALS AND KNOBS

Just a few of the many stock types of small dials and knobs are illustrated herewith. 10007 is 1⅝" diameter, 10009 is 2¾" and 10008 is 3½"

No. 10002 . . . .
No. 10007 . . . .
No. 10008 . . . .
No. 10009 . . . .
No. 10015 . . . .
No. 10018 . . . .
No. 10021 . . . .
No. 10065 . . . .

10009   10007

0021

10065   10008

10012

RIGHT ANGLE DRIVE

Extremely compact, with provisions for many methods of mounting. Ideal for operating potentiometers, switches, etc., that must be located, for short leads, in remote parts of chassis.
No. 10012 . . . .

HIGH VOLTAGE INSULATED SHAFT EXTENSION

No. 10061 shaft locks and the No. 39023 insulated high voltage potentiometer extension mountings are available as a single integrated unit—the No. 39024. The proper shaft length is independent of the panel thickness. The standard shaft has provision for screw driver adjustment. Special shaft arrangements are available for industrial applications. Extension shaft and insulated coupling are molded as a single unit to provide accuracy of alignment and ease of installation.
No. 39023, non locking type . . . .
No. 39024, locking type . . . .

9024   10061

39023

10060

10062

10061   10063

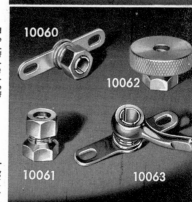

SHAFT LOCKS

In addition to the original No. 10060 and No. 10061 "DESIGNED FOR APPLICATION" shaft locks, we can also furnish such variations as the No. 10062 and No. 10063 for easy thumb operation as illustrated above. The No. 10061 instantly converts any plain "¼ shaft" volume control, condenser, etc. from "plain" to "shaft locked" type. Easy to mount in place of regular mounting nut.

No. 10060 . . . .
No. 10061 . . . .
No. 10062 . . . .
No. 10063 . . . .

TRANSMISSION LINE PLUG

An inexpensive, compact, and efficient polystyrene unit for use with the 300 ohm ribbon type polyethylene transmission lines. Fits into standard Millen No. 33102 (crystal) socket. Pin spacing ½", diameter .095".

No. 37412 . . . .

37412

33102   FULL SIZE

B

C

FULL SIZE

DIAL LOCK

Compact, easy to mount, positive in action, does not alter dial setting in operation! Rotation of knob "A" depresses finger "B" and "C" without imparting any rotary motion to Dial. Single hole mounted.
No. 10050 . . . .

JAMES ⚙ MILLEN
MALDEN · MASSACHUSETTS

TUBE SOCKETS
DESIGNED FOR APPLICATION

MODERN SOCKETS for MODERN TUBES! Long Flashover path to chassis permits use with transmitting tubes, 866 rectifiers, etc. Long leakage path between contacts. Contacts are type proven by hundreds of millions already in government, commercial and broadcast service, to be extremely dependable. Sockets may be mounted either with or without metal flange. Mounts in standard size chassis hole. All types have barrier between contacts and chassis. All but octal and crystal sockets also have barriers between individual contacts in addition.

The No. 33888 shield is for use with the 33008 octal socket. By its use, the electrostatic isolation of the grid and plate circuits of single-ended metal tubes can be increased to secure greater stability and gain.

The 33087 tube clamp is easy to use, easy to install, effective in function. Available in special sizes for all types of tubes. Single hole mounting. Spring steel, cadmium plated.

Cavity Socket Contact Discs, 33446 are for use with the "Lighthouse" ultra high frequency tube. This set consists of three different size unhardened beryllium copper multifinger contact discs. Heat treating instructions forwarded with each kit for hardening after spinning or forming to frequency requirements.

Voltage regulator dual contact bayonet socket, 33991 black phenolic insulation and 33992 with low loss mica filled phenolic insulation.

No. 33004—4 Pin Tube Socket . . . .
No. 33005—5 Pin Tube Socket . . . .
No. 33006—6 Pin Tube Socket . . . .
No. 33008—8 Pin Tube Socket . . . .
No. 33888—Shield for 33008 . . . .
No. 33087—Tube Clamp . . . .
No. 33002—Crystal Socket ¾" x .125" . .
No. 33102—Crystal Socket .487" x .095"
No. 33202—Crystal Socket ½" x .125" . .
No. 33302—Crystal Socket .487" x .050"
No. 33446—Contact Discs . . . .
No. 33991—Socket for 991 . . . .
No. 33992—Socket for 991 . . . .
No. 33207—829 Socket . . . .
No. 33305—Acorn Socket . . . .
No. 33307—Miniature Socket and Shield, ceramic . . . .
No. 33309—Noval Socket and Shield, ceramic . . . .
No. 33405—5 Pin Socket Eimac . . . .
No. 33407—Miniature Socket only, ceramic
No. 33409—Noval Socket only, ceramic . .

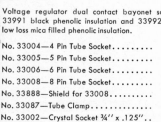

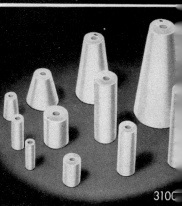

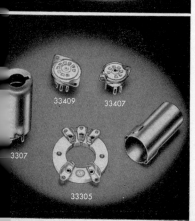

33409   33407

3307

33305

STAND-OFF INSULATORS

Steatite insulators are available in a variety of sizes—Listed below are some of the most popular.

No. 31001—Stand-off ½" x 1" . . . .
No. 31002—Stand-off ½" x 2½" . . . . . .
No. 31003—Stand-off ¾" x 2" . . . .
No. 31004—Stand-off ¾" x 3½" . . . .
No. 31006—Stand-off 5⁄32" x ⅞" . . . .
No. 31007—Stand-off ⅜" x 1" . . . .
No. 31011—Cone ¾" x ½" (box of 5) . .
No. 31012—Cone 1" x 1" . . . .
No. 31013—Cone 1½" x 1" . . . .
No. 31014—Cone 2" x 1" . . . .
No. 31015—Cone 3" x 1½" . . . .

33991

3100

04000 and 11000 SERIES
TRANSMITTING CONDENSERS

Another member of the "Designed for Application" series of transmitting variable air capacitors is the 04000 series with peak voltage ratings of 3000, 6000, and 9000 volts. Right angle drive, 1–1 ratio. Adjustable drive shaft angle for either vertical or sloping panels. Sturdy construction, thick, round-edged, polished aluminum plates with 1¾" radius. Constant impedance, heavy current, multiple finger rotor contactor of new design. Available in all normal capacities.

The 11000 series has 16/1 ratio center drive and fixed angle drive shaft.

12000 and 16000 SERIES
TRANSMITTING CONDENSERS

Rigid heavy channeled aluminum end plates. Isolantite insulation, polished or plain edges. One piece rotor contact spring and connection lug. Compact, easy to mount with connector lugs in convenient locations. Same plate sizes as 11000 series above.

The 16000 series has same plate sizes as 04000 series. Also has constant impedance, heavy current, multiple finger rotor contactor of new design. Both 12000 and 16000 series available in single and double sections and many capacities and plate spacing

THE 28000–29000 SERIES
VARIABLE AIR CAPACITORS

"Designed for Application," double bearings, steatite end plates, cadmium or silver plated brass plates. Single or double section .022" or .066" air gap. End plate size: 19/16" x 11/16". Rotor plate radius: ¾". Shaft lock, rear shaft extension, special mounting brackets, etc., to meet your requirements. The 28000 series has semi-circular rotor plate shape. The 29000 series has approximately straight frequency line rotor plate shape. Prices quoted on request. Many stock sizes.

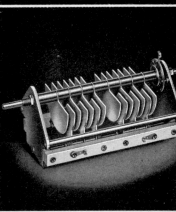

NEUTRALIZING CAPACITOR

Designed originally for use in our own No. 90881 Power Amplifier, the No. 15011 disc neutralizing capacitor has such unique features as rigid channel frame, horizontal or vertical mounting, fine thread over-size lead screw with stop to prevent shorting and rotor lock. Heavy rounded-edged polished aluminum plates are 2" diameter. Glazed Steatite insulation.

No. 15011 . . . .

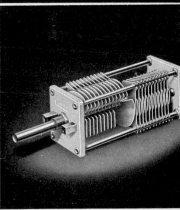

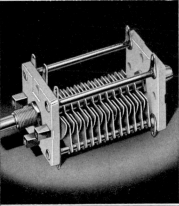

PERMEABILITY TUNED CERAMIC
FORMS

In addition to the popular shielded plug-in permeability tuned forms, 74000 series, the 69040 series of ceramic permeability tuned unshielded forms are available as standard stock items. Winding diameters available from ³⁄₁₆" to ½" and winding space from 1½" to 1½".

No. 69041—(Copper Slug). . . . .
No. 69042—(Iron Core). . . . .
No. 69043—(Copper Slug). . . . .
No. 69044—(!Iron Core). . . . .
No. 69045—(Copper Slug). . . . .
No. 69046—(Iron Core). . . . .
No. 69047—(Copper Slug). . . . .
No. 69048—(Iron Core). . . . .
No. 69051—(Copper Slug). . . . .
No. 69052—(Iron Core). . . . .
No. 69054—(Copper Slug). . . . .
No. 69055—(Copper Slug). . . . .
No. 69056—(Iron Core). . . . .
No. 69057—Copper Slug). . . . .
No. 69058—(Iron Core). . . . .
No. 69061—(Copper Slug). . . . .
No. 69062—(Iron Core). . . . .

15011

69057
69058
6905
6905

69045
69046

69043

69041
69042

TRANSMITTING TANK COILS

A full line—all popular wattages for all bands. Send for special catalog sheet.

TUNABLE COIL FORM

Standard octal base of low loss mica-filled bakelite, polystyrene ½'' diameter coil form, heavy aluminum shield, iron tuning slug of high frequency type, suitable for use up to 35 mc. Adjusting screw protrudes through center hole of standard octal socket.

No. 74001, with iron core..............
No. 74002, less iron core..............

RF CHOKES

Many have copied, few have equalled, and none have surpassed the genuine original design Millen Designed for Application series of midget RF Chokes. The more popular styles now in constant production are illustrated herewith. Special styles and variations to meet unusual requirements quickly furnished.

Figures 1 and 4 illustrate special types of RF chokes available on order. The popular 34300 and 34200 series are shown in figures 2 and 3 respectively.

General Specifications: 2.5 mh, 250 ma for types 34100, 34101, 34102, 34103, 34104 and 1 mh, 300 ma for types 34105, 34106, 34107, 34108, 34109.

No. 34100........................
No. 34101........................
No. 34102........................
No. 34103........................
No. 34104........................

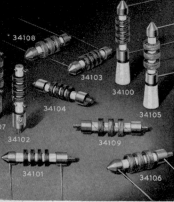

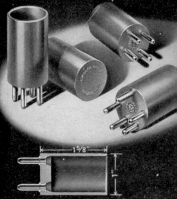

MIDGET COIL FORMS

Made of low loss mica filled brown bakelite. Guide funnel makes for easy threading of leads through pins.

No. 45000........................
No. 45004........................
No. 45005........................

OCTAL BASE AND SHIELD

Low loss phenolic base with octal socket plug and aluminum shield can 1⅞₆ x 1⅞ x 3¹⅝₆.

No. 74400........................

MINIATURE POWDERED IRON CORE RF INDUCTANCES

The No. J300—Miniature powdered iron core inductances. 0.107 in. dia. x ⅜ in. long. Inductances from 3.3 microhenries to 2.5 millihenries ± 5%. EIA standard values plus 25, 50, 150, 250, 350, 500, and 2500 microhenries. Three layer solenoids from 39 to 350 microhenries. ¼ in. wide single pi from 360 to 2500 microhenries. Special coils on order.

PHENOLIC FORM RF INDUCTANCES

The No. 34300 Inductances—Phenolic coil form with axial leads. Inductances from 1 microhenry to 2.5. millihenries ± 5%. RETMA standard values plus 25, 50, 150, 250, 350, 500, and 2500 microhenries. Solenoids from 1 to 16 microhenries. Single pi from 18 to 300 microhenries. Multiple pi for higher inductances. Forms ⁷⁄₃₂'' dia. x ⁷⁄₁₆ in. long, ³⁄₁₆'' x ⅝'', ¼'' x ¾'', and ¼'' x 1''. Special coils on order.

74400

MINIATURE IF TRANSFORMERS

Extremely high Q—approximately 200—Variable Coupling—(under, critical, and over) with all adjustments on top. Small size 1¹⁄₁₆'' x 1⁹⁄₁₆'' x 1⅞'' Molded terminal base. Air capacitor tuned. Coils completely enclosed in cup cores. T pped primary and secondary. Rugged construction. High electrical stability.

No. 61455, 455 kc. Universal Trans......
No. 61453, 455 kc. BFO..............
No. 61160, 1600 kc. Universal Trans.....
No. 61163, 1600 kc. BFO............

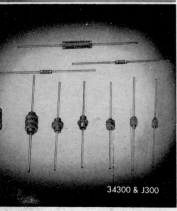

34300 & J300

61455

JAMES ⚙ MILLEN
MALDEN · MASSACHUSETTS

39005 39003

39001

39002 39006

FLEXIBLE COUPLINGS

The No. 39000 series of Millen "Designed for Application" flexible coupling units include, in addition to improved versions of the conventional types, also such exclusive original designs as the No. 39001 insulated universal joint and the No. 39006 "slide-action" coupling (in both steatite and bakelite insulation).

The No. 39006 "slide-action" coupling permits longitudinal shaft motion, eccentric shaft motion and out-of-line operation, as well as angular drive without backlash.

The No. 39005 and 39005-B (high torque) are similar to the No. 39001, but are not insulated. The steatite insulated No. 39001 has a special anti-backlash pivot and socket grip feature. All of the above illustrated units are for ¼" shaft and are standard production type units. The No. 39016 incorporates features which have long been desired in a flexible coupling. No Back Lash—Higher Flexibility—Higher Breakdown Voltage—Smaller Diameter—Shorter Length—Higher Alignment Accuracy—Higher Resistance to Mechanical Shock—Solid Insulating Barrier Diaphragm—Molded as a Single Unit.

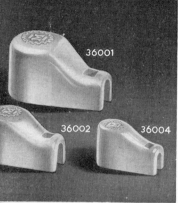

36001

36002   36004

39016

CERAMIC PLATE OR GRID CAPS

Soldering lug and contact one-piece. Lug ears annealed and solder dipped to facilitate each combination "mechanical plus soldered" connection of cable.

No. 36001—⁵⁄₁₆"......................
No. 36002—⅜"......................
No. 36004—¼"......................

SNAP LOCK PLATE CAP

For Mobile, Industrial and other applications where tighter than normal grip with multiple finger 360° low resistance contact is required. Contact self-locking when cap is pressed into position. Insulated snap button at top releases contact grip for easy removal without damage to tube.

No. 36011—⁵⁄₁₆"......................
No. 36012—⅜"......................

SAFETY TERMINAL

Combination high voltage terminal and thru-bushing Tapered contact pin fits firmly into conical socket providing large area, low resistance connection. Pin is swivel mounted in cap to prevent twisting of lead wire.

No. 37001, Black or Red.............
No. 37501, Low loss................

THRU-BUSHING

Efficient, compact, easy to use and neat appearing. Fits ¼" hole in chassis. Held in place with a drop of solder or a "nick" from a crimping tool.

No. 32150......................

3/4 SIZE

POSTS, PLATES, AND PLUGS

The No. 37200 series, including both insulated and non-insulated binding posts with associated plates and plugs, provide various combinations to meet most requirements. The posts have captive heads and keyed mounting.

The No. 37291 and No. 37223 are standard in black or red with other colors on special order. No. 37201, No. 37202, and No. 37204 and No. 37222 are available in black, red, or low loss. The No. 37202 is also available in steatite.

No. 37201—Single plates, pr...........
No. 37291—Single plates (tapered), pr...
No. 37202—Dual plates, pr............
No. 37204—Double dual plates, pr......
No. 37212—Dual plug...............
No. 37222—Non-insulated binding post, ea.
No. 37223—Insulated binding posts, ea...

37201

37223

37291   37222

37202

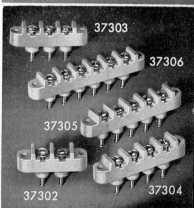

37303

37306

37305

37302   37304

STEATITE TERMINAL STRIPS

Terminal and lug are one piece. Lugs are turret type and are free floating so as not to strain L4 ceramic on wide temperature variations. Easy to mount with series of round holes. 1400 volt and 3500 volt series.

2

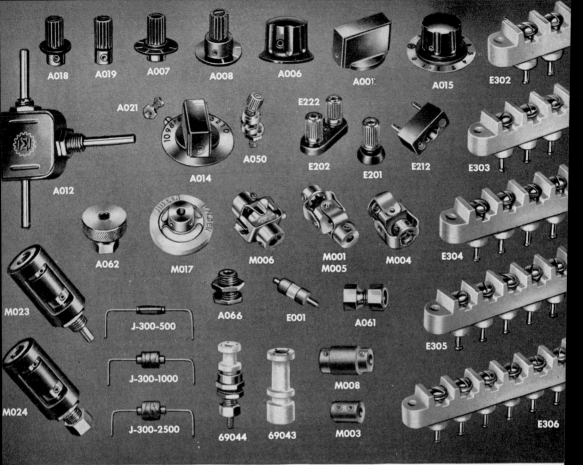

MINIATURIZED COMPONENTS

DESIGNED for **APPLICATION** miniaturized components developed for use in our own equipment such as the 90901 Oscilloscope, are now available for separate sale. Many of these parts are similar, in most details except size, to their equivalents in our standard component parts group. In certain devices where complete miniaturization is not paramount, a combination of standard and miniature components may possibly be used to advantage. For convenience, we have also listed on this page the extremely small sized coil forms from our standard catalog.

CODE	DESCRIPTION
A001	Bar knob for 1/8″ shaft. 1/2″ high by 3/4″ long.
A006	Fluted black plastic knob with brass insert for 1/8″ shaft. 1/2″ high by 3/4″ diameter.
A007	1/4″ black plastic dial knob with brass insert for 1/8″ shaft. 5/8″ diameter dial. 9/16″ high.
A008	1/4″ black plastic knob. Same as no. A007 except for style.
A012	Right angle drive for 1/8″ shafts. Single hole mounting.
A014	1″ bar dial for 1/8″ shaft. 1/2″ high. 180° or 280° dials for clockwise or counter-clockwise rotation.
A015	1″ fluted knob dial for 1/8″ shaft. 1/2″ high. Same dial plates as no. A014.
A017	1 1/8″ diameter fluted black plastic knob for 1/8″ shaft.
A018	Knob, same as no. A007 except with 3/8″ diameter skirt.
A019	Knob, same as no. A007, but without dial.
A021	Miniature metal index for miniature dials.
A050	Miniature dial lock.
A061	Shaft lock for 1/8″ diameter shaft. 1/4″-32 bushing. Nickel plated brass.
A062	Shaft lock with knurled locking nut.
A066	Shaft bearing for 1/8″ diameter shafts. Nickel plated brass Fits 17/64″ diameter hole.

CODE	DESCRIPTION
E001	Steatite ceramic standoff or tie-point. Integral mounti eyelet. 0.205″ overall diameter.
E201	Black or red plastic binding post plates for No. E222.
E202	Black or red plastic plates for two binding posts spaced 1/2
E212	Black or red plastic plug for two binding posts spaced 1/2
E222	Metal binding post with jack top.
E302A	to E306A Steatite ceramic terminal strips. 5/16″ wide. T minals spaced 3/8″ on centers. Screw type or solder ty thru-terminals.
J300–3.3	to J300–2500 Complete line of miniature inductanc 3.3 to 2500 microhenries. 3/8″ long. Diameter 0.115″ 0.297″.
M001	Insulated universal joint style flexible coupling for 1/8″ d shafts.
M003	Solid coupling for 1/8″ dia. shafts. Nickel plated brass.
M004	Universal joint style flexible coupling for 1/8″ diameter sha Inverted hubs for short length. Not insulated.
M005	Universal joint style flexible coupling for 1/8″ diameter sha External hub for maximum flexibility. Not insulated.
M006	Universal joint style flexible coupling for 1/8″ diameter sha Spring finger. Steatite ceramic insulation.
M008	Plastic insulated coupling with nickel plated brass inserts 1/8″ diameter shafts.
M017	Plastic insulated flexible coupling for 1/8″ diameter sha 17/32″ long by 15/16″ diameter. Bronze yoke.
M023	Insulated shaft extension for 1/4″-32 bushing and 1/8″ sh For mounting sub-miniature potentiometer.
M024	Locking insulated shaft extension similar to no. M023.
69043	Steatite ceramic coil form. Adjustable core. Winding sp 1/4″ diameter by 13/32″ long. Mounting 4-40 hole.
69044	Steatite ceramic coil form. Adjustable core. Winding sp 0.187″ diameter by 3/16″ long. No. 10-32 mounting.

JAMES MILLEN MFG. CO., INC

MAIN OFFICE AND FACTORY

MALDEN, MASSACHUSETTS, U.S.A.

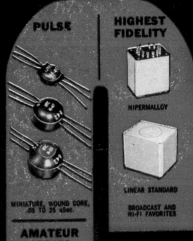

Johnson Amateur Equipment
...For Full Communication POWER!

VIKING "ADVENTURER" 50 WATT TRANSMITTER—Used to earn first Novice WA (Worked All Continents.) Self-contained, effectively TVI suppressed, instant bandswit ing 80, 40, 20, 15, and 10 meters. Operates by crystal or external VFO. An oc power receptacle located on the rear apron provides full 450 VDC at 150 ma. and 6 VAC at 2 amp. output of supply to power auxiliary equipment such as a VFO, sig monitor, or modulator for phone operation. This receptacle also permits using the output of the supply to power other equipment when the transmitter is not operating. Wi range pi-network output handles virtually any antenna without separate antenna tun Break-in keying is clean and crisp. Designed for easy assembly. With tubes, less cryst and key. Dimensions: 10⅜" x 8⅛" x 7⅜". Shipping Weight: 19 lbs.

Cat. No. 240-181-1...Kit............................Amateur Net $54.

SPEECH AMPLIFIER/SCREEN MODULATOR—Designed to provide phone operati for the "Adventurer". High gain—use with either crystal or dynamic microphones. Simp installation—only minor wiring changes necessary in "Adventurer". With tubes.

Cat. No. 250-40..Kit................................Amateur Net $12.

VIKING "NAVIGATOR" TRANSMITTER/EXCITER—This compact, flexible CW tra mitter has enough RF power to excite most high powered final amplifiers on CW and A 40 watts—bandswitching 160 through 10 meters. Highly stable, built-in VFO is temper ture compensated and voltage regulated—may also be operated crystal control. Tim sequence keying—effectively TVI suppressed. Pi-network antenna load matching fre 40 to 600 ohms. With tubes, less crystals and key. Dimensions: 13¼" x 9⅛" x 10½ Shipping Weight: 27 lbs.

Cat. No. 240-126-1...Kit............................Amateur Net $149.
Cat. No. 240-126-2...Wired and tested................Amateur Net $199.

VIKING "CHALLENGER" TRANSMITTER—Ideal for fixed station, emergency, portab or field day use, the "Challenger" is a full size transmitter with three RF stages—designe for fast, easy tuning, excellent stability and plenty of reserve drive. 70 watts phone inp 80 through 6 meters, 120 watts CW input 80 through 10 meters ... 85 watts CW inp on 6 meters! A single 6DQ6A buffer drives two husky 6DQ6A bridge neutralize tetrodes in the final amplifier. Hi "Q" wide range pi-network output—effectively T suppressed and filtered. For crystal or external VFO control. Excellent keying syste With tubes and built-in power supply.

Cat. No. 240-182-1...Kit............................Amateur Net $114.7
Cat. No. 240-182-2...Wired and tested................Amateur Net $154.7

VIKING "RANGER" TRANSMITTER—This outstanding amateur transmitter will als serve as an RF and audio exciter for high power equipment. As an exciter, it will drive a of the popular kilowatt level tubes. No internal changes necessary to switch from tran mitter to exciter operation. Self-contained, 75 watts CW or 65 watts phone inp ... instant bandswitching 160, 80, 40, 20, 15, and 10 meters. Extremely stable, built VFO or crystal control—effectively TVI suppressed—high gain audio—timed sequen (break-in) keying—adjustable wave shaping. Pi-network antenna load matching from 5 to 500 ohms. Easily assembled—with tubes, less crystals, key and microphone. 15½" 9⅝" x 14". Shipping Weight: 54 lbs.

Cat. No. 240-161-1...Kit............................Amateur Net $229.5
Cat. No. 240-161-2...Wired and tested................Amateur Net $329.5

VIKING "VALIANT" TRANSMITTER—Designed for outstanding flexibility and pe formance. 275 watts input on CW and SSB (P.E.P. with auxiliary SSB exciter), 200 wat AM. Instant bandswitching 160 through 10 meters—operates by built-in VFO or cryst control. Pi-network tank circuit will match antenna loads from 50 to 600 ohms—fine tank coil is silver-plated. Other features: TVI suppressed—timed sequence (break-in) keying—high gain push-to-talk audio system—low level audio clipping—built-in lo pass audio filter—self-contained power supplies. With tubes, less crystals, key, and micr phone. Dimensions: 21" x 11⅝" x 16¼". Shipping Weight: 83 lbs.

VIKING "FIVE HUNDRED" TRANSMITTER—Rated a full 600 watts CW . . . 500 watts phone and SSB. (P.E.P. with auxiliary SSB exciter.) All exciter stages ganged to VFO tuning. Two compact units: RF unit small enough to place on your operating desk beside receiver—power supply/modulator unit may be placed in any convenient location. Crystal or built-in VFO control—instant bandswitching 80 through 10 meters—TVI suppressed—high gain push-to-talk audio system—low level audio clipping. Pi-network output circuit with silver-plated final tank coil will load virtually any antenna system. With tubes, less crystals, key, and microphone. Dimensions: RF Unit—21" x 11⅝" x 16½". Power Supply—20⅜" x 15¾" x 10⅞". Total Shipping Weight: 200 lbs.

Cat. No. 240-500-1 . . Kit. . . . . Amateur Net $749.50
Cat. No. 240-500-2 . . Wired and tested. . . . . Amateur Net $949.50

VIKING "THUNDERBOLT" AMPLIFIER—The hottest linear amplifier on the market—handles over 2000 watts P.E.P.* input SSB; 1000 watts CW; 800 watts AM linear; **in a** completely self-contained desk-top package. Continuous coverage 3.5 to 30 mcs.—instant bandswitching. May be driven by the Viking "Navigator", "Ranger", "Pacemaker", or other unit of comparable output. Drive requirements: approximately 10 watts in Class AB_2 linear, 20 watts Class C continuous wave. With tubes and built-in power supply. Dimensions: 21" x 11⅝" x 16⁷⁄₁₆". Shipping Weight: 140 lbs.

Cat. No. 240-353-1 . . Kit. . . . . Amateur Net $524.50
Cat. No. 240-353-2 . . Wired and tested. . . . . Amateur Net $589.50

VIKING "COURIER" AMPLIFIER—Rated a solid one-half kilowatt P.E.P. input with auxiliary SSB exciter as a Class B linear amplifier; one-half kilowatt input CW or 200 watts in AM linear mode. Completely self-contained desk-top package—may be driven by the Viking "Navigator," "Ranger," "Pacemaker," or other unit of comparable output. Continuous coverage 3.5 to 30 mcs. Drive requirements: 5 to 35 watts depending upon mode and frequency desired. Pi-network output designed to match 40 to 600 ohm antenna loads. Fully TVI suppressed. Complete with tubes and built-in power supply. Dimensions: 15½" x 9⅝" x 14". Shipping Weight: 68 lbs.

Cat. No. 240-352-1 . . Kit. . . . . Amateur Net $244.50
Cat. No. 240-352-2 . . Wired and tested. . . . . Amateur Net $289.50

VIKING "6N2" TRANSMITTER—Instant bandswitching on 6 and 2 meters, this compact VHF transmitter is rated at 150 watts CW and 100 watts AM phone. Completely shielded and TVI suppressed, the "6N2" may be used with the Viking "Ranger," "Viking I," "Viking II," or similar power supply/modulator combinations capable of at least 6.3 VAC at 3.5 amp., 300 VDC at 70 ma., 300 to 750 VDC at 200 ma. and 30 or more watts audio. May be operated by built-in crystal control or external VFO with 8-9 mc. output. With tubes, less crystals, key, and microphone. Dimensions: 13⅛" x 8⅜" x 8½". Shipping Weight: 14 lbs.

Cat. No. 240-201-1 . . Kit. . . . . Amateur Net $129.50
Cat. No. 240-201-2 . . Wired and tested. . . . . Amateur Net $169.50

VIKING "6N2" THUNDERBOLT AMPLIFIER—Brand new . . . continuous bandswitched coverage on 6 and 2 meters. Rated at 1200 watts P.E.P.* input SSB and DSB, Class AB_1; 1000 watts CW input Class C; and 700 watts input AM linear, Class AB_1. Drive requirement approximately 5 watts in Class AB_1 linear or 6 watts Class C continuous wave. Effectively TVI suppressed and filtered—wide range pi network output. Outstanding efficiency—losses on 2 meters held to approximately 5%, instead of common 25% losses experienced in some other 2 meter circuitry, due to unique silver-plated anode and other external metal portions of the 7034 tubes; silver-plated inductors, capacitors, and switch. With tubes. Dimensions: 21" x 11⅝" x 16⁷⁄₁₆".
Shipping Weight: 140 lbs.

Cat. No. 240-362-1 . . Kit. . . . . Amateur Net $524.50
Cat. No. 240-362-2 . . Wired and tested. . . . . Amateur Net $589.50

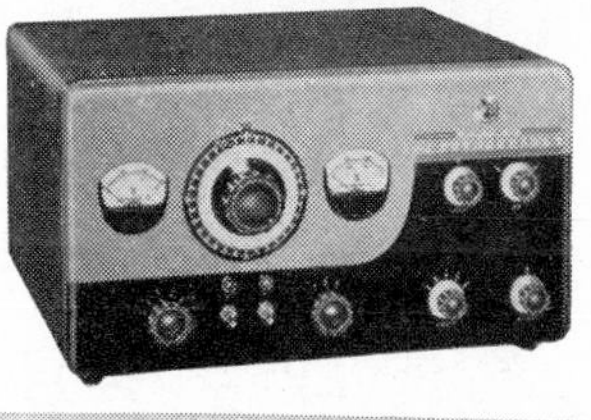

VIKING "KILOWATT" AMPLIFIER—Brilliantly designed and engineered, the Viking "Kilowatt" is the only power amplifier available which will handle full 2000 watts SSB* input and 1000 watts CW and plate-modulated AM! Class "C" final amplifier operation provides plate circuit efficiencies in excess of 70%. Final amplifier utilizes two 4-400A tetrodes in parallel, bridge neutralized. Continuous coverage 3.5 to 30 mc. Excitation requirements: 30 watts RF and 10 watts audio for AM; 10 watts peak for SSB.

Cat. No. 240-1000. Wired and tested. . . . . Amateur Net $1595.00
Cat. No. 251-101-1 . . Matching accessory desk top, back and three drawer pedestal. . . . . FOB Corry, Pa. $132.00

**The FCC permits a maximum of one kilowatt average power input for the amateur service. In SSB operation under normal conditions this results in peak envelope power inputs of 2000 watts or more depending upon individual voice characteristics.*

The E. F. Johnson Company reserves the right to change prices and specifications without notice and without incurring obligation.

E. F. Johnson Company
120 SECOND AVENUE S. W. • WASECA, MINNESOTA

Your best buy!

Johnson Station Accessories
...For Outstanding PERFORMANCE!

VIKING AUDIO AMPLIFIER—A self-contained 10-watt speech amplifier complete with power supply. Speech clipping and filtering designed to raise average modulated carrier level...improves the performance and effectiveness of your AM transmitter. Inputs provided for microphone, or line. Complete with tubes. Dimensions: 13⅞" x 8" 5⅝". Shipping Weight: 22 lbs.

Cat. No. 250-33-1..Kit........................Amateur Net $73.50
Cat. No. 250-33-2..Wired and tested..........Amateur Net $99.50

POWER REDUCER—Provides up to 20 watts continuous dissipation for 100-150 watt transmitters such as Johnson Viking, Collins 32V, or others, permitting them to serve as exciters for the Viking "Kilowatt". Completely shielded—equipped with SO-239 coaxial connectors. Dimensions: 3½" long x 2¼" diameter.

Cat. No. 250-29...........................Amateur Net $13.95

POWER DIVIDER—Provides up to 35 watts continuous dissipation. Designed to provide the proper output loading of the "Pacemaker" SSB Transmitter when used to drive the Viking Kilowatt Amplifier.

Cat. No. 250-34...........................Amateur Net $25.50

VIKING "6N2" VFO—Exceptionally stable and compact—designed to replace 8 to 9 mc. crystals in frequency multiplying 6 and 2 meter transmitters, including types using overtone oscillators. Temperature compensated and voltage regulated for minimum drift and high stability. Plexiglas dial calibrated from 144 to 148 mc., 50 to 51.5 mc. 51.5 to 53 mc. 10 to 1 vernier tuning. Complete with tubes and calibrated dial. Dimensions: 4" x 4½" x 5".

Cat. No. 240-133-1..Kit..................Amateur Net $34.95
Cat. No. 240-133-2..Wired and tested.....Amateur Net $54.95

VIKING "6N2" CONVERTER—This compact "6N2" Converter provides instant front panel switching from normal receiver operation to either 6 or 2 meters. Maximum sensitivity and low noise figure—excellent image and I. F. rejection due to double-tuned overcoupled, interstage circuits on both 6 and 2 meters. With tubes. Dimensions: 2¾" 5" x 12". Shipping Weight: 5 lbs. Available kit or wired in either 26 to 30 mcs., 28 to 3 mcs., 14 to 18 mcs., or 30.5 to 24.5 mcs. ranges. Specify range desired.

Kits.....................................Amateur Net $59.9
Wired Models............................Amateur Net $89.9

MOBILE VFO—Diminutive variable frequency oscillator designed specifically for mobil use. Rugged construction minimizes frequency shift due to road shock and vibration.. small size permits steering post mounting. Temperature compensated and voltage regulated. Calibrated 75 through 10 meters...3.75 to 4 mc. output for 75 meters and 7.0 to 7.45 for 40 to 10 meters. 10.5 mc. output also available for doubling to 15 meter With tubes. Dimensions: 4" x 4¼" x 5".

Cat. No. 240-152-1..Kit..................Amateur Net $33.9
Cat. No. 240-152-2..Wired and tested.....Amateur Net $52.5

"WHIPLOAD-6"—Provides high efficiency base loading for mobile whips with instar bandswitch selection of 75, 40, 20, 15, 11, and 10 meters. On 75 meters a specie capacitor with dial scale permits tuning entire band. Covers other bands without tuning Air-wound coil provides extremely high "Q." Fibre-glass housing protects assembly Mounts on standard mobile whip.

Cat. No. 250-26..Wired and tested........Amateur Net $16.9

VIKING "MATCHBOXES" Provides completely integrated antenna matching and switching systems for kilowatt or 275-watt transmitters. Units complete with built-in directiona coupler and indicator. Bandswitching 80, 40, 20, 15, and 10 meters. Quickly and easil match transmitter to balanced or unbalanced lines over a wide range of antenna im pedances will tune out large amounts of capacitive or inductive reactance. No "plug-in coils or "load-tapping" necessary.

275 WATT "MATCHBOX"

Cat. No.	Amateur N
250-23-3..With built-in Directional Coupler & Indicator	$86.5
250-23..Less built-in Directional Coupler & Indicator	$54.9

KILOWATT "MATCHBOX"

Cat. No.	Amateur N
250-30-3..With built-in Directional Coupler & Indicator	$149.5
250-30..Less built-in Directional Coupler & Indicator	$124.5

SWR BRIDGE—Measures standing wave ratios for effective use of a low pass filter an antenna coupler. 52 ohms impedance can be changed to 70 ohms or other value. SO-23 connectors and polarized meter jacks. Dimensions: 4¹⁄₃₂" long x 2⁵⁄₁₆" diameter.

Cat. No. 250-24..Wired and tested........Amateur Net $9.7

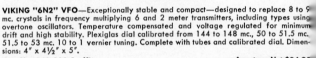

"SIGNAL SENTRY"—Monitors CW or phone signals on all frequencies to 50 mc. without tuning. Energized by transmitter RF. Mutes receiver audio for break-in. May be used as code practice oscillator with simple circuit modification. Requires 250 VDC at 5 ma.; and 6.3 VAC at .6 amp. from receiver or other source. With tubes. Dimensions: 3⅝" x 3⅞" x 3¾". Shipping Weight: 3 lbs.

Cat. No. 250-25..Wired and tested ....Amateur Net **$22.00**

CRYSTAL CALIBRATOR—Provides accurate 100 kc. check points to 55 mc. Requires 6.3 volts at .15 amps. and 150-300 volts at 2 ma. With tube, military-type crystal, power cable and extension leads. Dimensions: 1⅝" x 2½" x 1½". (Over-all height to top of tube is 3⅜".)

Cat. No. 250-28..Wired and tested.................Amateur Net **$17.95**

LOW PASS FILTER—Handles more than 1000 watts RF—provides 75 db or more attenuation above 54 mc. Insertion loss less than .25 db. Replaceable Teflon insulated fixed capacitors. SO-239 coaxial connectors. Wired and pre-tuned. Dimensions: 9" long x 2⁵⁄₁₆" diameter.

Cat. No. 250-20..Wired and pre-tuned 52 ohms.........Amateur Net **$14.95**
Cat. No. 250-35..Wired and pre-tuned 72 ohms.........Amateur Net **$14.95**

ATTENUATORS—These T-pad attenuators provide 6 db of attenuation with required power dissipation to enable various units to serve as exciters for the Viking "Thunderbolt" linear amplifier. Dial instantly cuts attenuator in or out of circuit. Dimensions: 4½" x 3⅛" x 9⅛". Shipping Weight: 2 lbs.

For use with Viking "Ranger" of similar unit. Provision for 75 watt incandescent bulb so unit may be used with Viking II or similar transmitter/exciter.

Cat. No. 250-42-1.............................Amateur Net **$21.50**
Cat. No. 250-42-3 For use with HT-32, or similar unit.........Amateur Net **$21.50**

RE-TUNED BEAMS—Rugged, semi-wide spaced pre-tuned beams with balun matching sections. For 20, 15 and 10 meters. Approximately 9.0 db gain over tuned dipole—greater than 27 db front-to-back ratio with low SWR. Pattern is uni-directional, beam width is 55°. No adjustments required. Boom assemblies are of 2" galvanized steel tubing, elements are aluminum alloy tubing. No loading devices needed for flutter dampening or corona discharge.

Cat. No. (With 3 elements, beam and balun)		Amateur Net
38-420-3	20 Meter Beam—20' Boom. 84 lbs. Net Weight	$139.50
38-415-3	15 Meter Beam—13'7" Boom. 53 lbs. Net Weight	110.00
38-410-3	10 Meter Beam—10' Boom. 42 lbs. Net Weight	79.50

ROTOMATIC ROTATOR—Safely supports multiple arrays weighing up to several hundred pounds, even under heavy icing conditions or high wind loading. Rotates 1 RPM—over-all gear reduction 12,000 to 1. Rotator housing is cast aluminum, with 5/16" steel rotating table. Includes desk top control box for automatic and accurate antenna azimuth bearing.

Cat. No.		Amateur Net
38-116..	With limit switches for 370° rotation—coaxial line	$354.00
38-108..	Beam switching relay	$ 22.00
44-16...	8 Conductor cable for rotator, per ft	$ .26

"MATCHSTICK"—Fully automatic, pre-tuned multi-band vertical antenna system. Band-switching 80 through 10 meters. Remotely motor driven from operating position. Easily mounts on roof top or in limited space location. Low SWR (less than 2 to 1) all bands. Impedance: 52 ohms. Complete with 35' mast, base, tuning network, relays, control box and 6 nylon guy ropes. Shipping Weight: 38 lbs.

Cat. No. 137-102..Pre-tuned.....................Amateur Net **$129.50**

T-R SWITCH—Provides instantaneous high-efficiency electronic antenna switching. Excellent receiver isolation. Gain: 0 db at 30 mcs.; 6 db at 3.5 mcs. Rated at 4000 watts peak power. Instantaneous break-in on SSB, DSB, CW or AM. Will not affect transmission line SWR—provides an effective impedance match to most receivers through 3 to 30 mc. range. With tube, power supply, and provision for RF probe, etc. Dimensions: 4³⁄₁₆" x 4⅜" x 5⁵⁄₁₆". Shipping Weight: 5 lbs.

Cat. No. 250-39..Wired and tested...................Amateur Net **$27.75**

DIRECTIONAL COUPLER AND INDICATOR—Provides continuous reading of SWR and relative power in transmission line. Coupler may be permanently installed in 52 ohm coaxial line—handles maximum legal power as specified by FCC. Standard tip jacks permit use of commercial multimeter as indicating instrument—reference sheets showing curves supplied for popular multimeter basic ranges. Indicator is a 0-100 micro-ammeter calibrated in SWR and relative power. Monitors incident or reflected power quickly with flip of a switch. Coupler dimensions: 6¼" long x 2⁵⁄₁₆" diameter. Shipping Weight: 2 lbs. Indicator dimensions: 4" x 4⅜" x 4¼". Shipping Weight: 4 lbs.

Cat. No. 250-37..Coupler, Wired and tested...........Amateur Net **$11.75**
Cat. No. 250-38 Indicator, Wired and tested...........Amateur Net **$25.00**

KEYS AND PRACTICE SETS—Johnson also manufactures a complete line of semi-automatic, high speed, standard, heavy duty and practice keys; code practice sets and buzzers. See your distributor for complete information.

The E. F. Johnson Company reserves the right to change prices and specifications without notice and without incurring obligation.

E. F. Johnson Company

120 SECOND AVENUE S. W. • WASECA, MINNESOTA

Your best buy!

Johnson Components
...Tops for QUALITY!

The E. F. Johnson Company also manufactures a complete line of electronic components for those of you who prefer to design and build your own transmitting equipment and accessories. The complete line is covered in Catalog 978 ... write for your free copy today!

KNOBS AND DIALS—Includes a new group of molded ny collet knobs available in 13 bright colors; and a distinctive line matching knobs and dials suitable for use on the finest electro and electrical equipment. Available with phenolic skirts, etched a anodized aluminum skirts with markings, or flat dial scores engrav and filled. Collet knobs are constructed of tough, shock-proof ny —designed for use with ⅛" shafts; standard phenolic knobs me MIL-P-14 specifications, and are furnished with heavy brass inse for ¼" shafts.

INSULATORS—High quality steatite and porcelain insulato Heavily glazed surfaces and heavy nickel-plated brass hardwa suitable for exposed application. May be supplied with scre and nuts or with jacks to accommodate standard banana plug Through-panel and stand-off types. Also antenna insulators, bus ings, and feeder insulators.

PILOT LIGHTS—A complete selection of standardized pi lights. Faceted jewel or wide-angle lucite lens types; enclosed open body styles; standard bayonet, candelabra, or miniatu screw types, and a wide variety of mounting brackets and asse blies. Jewels available in clear, red, green, amber, blue, and op All Johnson pilot lights are described in detail in Pilot Light Catal 750a—send for your copy!

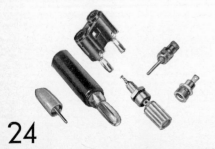

CONNECTORS—A complete line of new nylon connectors available in addition to standard banana jacks and plugs. Nyl components include insulated solderless tip and banana plugs, ti and banana jacks, tip jack and sleeve assemblies, metal-clad ti jacks, and a 6-way binding post. In thirteen bright colors—nyl components are designed to operate through an extremely wid temperature range and high relative humidity conditions. (Voltag breakdown up to 11,000 volts.) Solderless nylon plugs are easy assemble—both plugs and jacks require a minimum amount o mounting space.

VARIABLE CAPACITORS

PE "M"—These diminutive capacitors provide the perfect answer to oblems encountered in the design of compact radio frequency equipment. dge-type stator terminal provides extremely low inductance path to both tor supports. Soldered bearing and heavily anchored stator supports ure extreme rigidity.

PE "S"—Midway between types "M" and "K" in size, design is compact d construction rugged. Equipped with DC-200 treated steatite end frame d nickel-plated brass plates—an excellent choice where higher capacity lues than provided in "M" types is required in small space.

PES "C" AND "D"—Functional favorites built to exacting standards for dium power RF equipment. Dual types have centered rotor connection for lance. End frames tapped for panel mounting. Brackets furnished for chassis unting.

PES "E" AND "F"—Rugged units provide a large amount of pacity per cubic inch and extremely low capacity to the chassis. Panel or assis mounting.

PE "G"—Neutralizing capacitors for medium and low-powered stages nstructed on the rotor-stator principle. Panel or chassis mounting.

PE "J"—Heavy-duty miniature type has wider spacing than most small variables, yet occupies little more space. Useful for small space plate tank cuits and low power stages where standard miniatures have insufficient ate spacing.

PE "K"—Widely used for military and many commercial applications, e Johnson type "K" features DC-200 impregnated steatite end frames, tted stator contacts, and extra-rigid soldered plate construction.

PE "L"—A superior quality general purpose capacitor embodying im-rtant advances in design and construction. The rotor bearing and stator pport rods are actually soldered directly to the ceramic (steatite) end frames, aking the capacitor virtually vibration-proof.

PE "N"—Extremely high voltage rating in proportion to size requiring a all mounting area. Constant voltage rating throughout full capacity range. ese are of the aluminum cup and cylinder type of construction and are pported by a steatite frame with cast aluminum mounting bracket.

YPE "R"—The rugged Johnson version of a popular standardized capa-or. Featuring extra heavy steatite stator support insulators and soldered 23" thick brass plates; all metal parts heavily nickel-plated for corrosion-sistance.

TYPE "U"—New design—rotor and stator are precision machined from one piece of solid brass, offering excellent uniformity and outstanding mechanical stability. Low cost due to automatic production techniques. High torque-to-mass ratio. Excellent, low temperature coefficient.

TYPE "T"—Tiny new sub-miniature air variable built to comply with MIL-C-92 specifications. Excellent mechanical stability, "Q" greater than 3000 at 1 Mc., and high torque-to-mass ratio. Available only in production quantities for commercial applications.

TYPE "U"

TYPE "T"

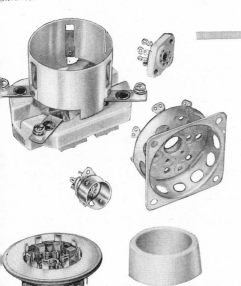

TUBE SOCKETS

Johnson steatite and porcelain tube sockets are available in three grades: Standard, Industrial, and Military. All are manufactured to rigidly controlled specifications, and all are made of only the highest quality materials.

Bayonet Types—include Medium, Jumbo, and Super Jumbo 4 pin models.

Steatite Wafer Types—available in 4, 5, 6, 7, and 8 pin standard sockets as well as Super Jumbo 4 pin, Giant 5 and 7 pin models and VHF transmitting Septar base types.

Miniature Types—are steatite insulated and available in Miniature 7 and 9 pin models. Matching miniature shields also available.

Special Purpose Types—include sockets for tubes such as the 204A and 849, the 833A, 304TL, 5D21, 705A, and other special types.

For High Power Transmitting Tubes—such as the 4X150A, 4X150D, 4X250B, 4CX250B, 4X250F, 7034, 7035. Available in several designs—with or without screen grid by-pass capacitor. Basic socket molded of low-dielectric loss-factor Kel-F plastic. Contacts are low-resistance silver-plated beryllium copper.

E. F. Johnson Company

120 SECOND AVENUE S.W. · WASECA, MINNESOTA

Typical RCA Beam Power Tubes for amateur service

RCA Transmitting Tube Manual TT-4 ...256 fact-filled pages covering 108 RCA power tube types and 13 RCA high-voltage rectifier types. Available at your RCA Industrial Tube Distributor. Or send $1.00 to RCA Commercial Eng., Sec. A-11-M, Harrison, N. J.

RCA HAM TIPS...Written by hams for hams. A regular publication carrying up-to-the-minute articles, and latest "tips" for the shack. Free from your RCA Industrial Tube Distributor.

AN RCA POWER TUBE FOR EVERY POWER LEVEL

Popular RCA "High-Perveance" Power Tubes for Transmitter Application
(listed according to power-input ratings)

RCA Type	Beam Power or Triode	Class of Service	Max. Plate Input Watts	Max. DC Plate Volts	Max. freq. For full Input (Mc)	Heater (H) or Filament (F) Volts
5763	Beam Power	CW	17	350	50	6.0 (H)
		AM	15	300		
6417	Beam Power	Same as RCA-5763, except for heater voltage				12.6 (H)
2E26	Beam Power	CW	40	600	125	6.3 (H)
		SSB	37.5	500		
		AM	27	500		
2E24	Beam Power	Same as RCA-2E26, but has quick-heating filament				6.3 (F)
6893	Beam Power	Same as RCA-2E26, except for heater voltage				12.6 (H)
832-A*	Beam Power	CW	50**	750	200	6.3▲ (H)
		AM	36**	600		12.6● (H)
807	Beam Power	CW	75	750	60	6.3 (H)
		SSB	90	750		
		AM	60	600		
1625	Beam Power	Same as RCA-807, except for heater voltage and use of medium-7-pin base				12.6 (H)
6524*	Beam Power	CW	85**	600	100	6.3 (H)
		SSB	85**	600		
		AM	55**	500		
6850*	Beam Power	Same as RCA-6524, except for heater voltage				12.6 (H)
6146	Beam Power	CW	90	750	60	6.3 (H)
		SSB	85	750		
		AM	67.5	600		
6883	Beam Power	Same as RCA-6146, except for heater voltage				12.6 (H)
829-B*	Beam Power	CW	120**	750	200	6.3▲ (H)
		SSB	120**	750		12.6● (H)
		AM	90**	600		
7270	Beam Power	CW	315	1350	60	6.3 (H)
		SSB	250	1350		
		AM	210	1100		
811-A	Triode	CW	260	1500	30	6.3 (F)
		SSB	235	1500		
		AM	175	1250		
812-A	Triode	CW	260	1500	30	6.3 (F)
		AM	175	1250		
8005	Triode	CW	300	1500	60	10 (F)
		AM	240	1250		
7034/ 4X150A	Beam Power	CW	500	2000	150	6.0 (H)
		SSB	630	2250		
		AM	320	1600		
7094	Beam Power	CW	500	1500	60	6.3 (H)
		SSB	400	2000		
		AM	335	1200		
813	Beam Power	CW	500	2250	30	10 (F)
		SSB	450	2500		
		AM	400	2000		
8000	Triode	CW	750	2500	30	10 (F)
		SSB	510	2750		
		AM	500	2000		
833-A	Triode	CW	1000, plus	3300	30	10 (F)
		SSB	1000, plus	3300		
		AM	1000	3000		

*Twin-Type   **Total for both units   ▲For parallel-heater connection   ●For series-heater connection

Available in a choice of input power ratings *up to the legal limit*, RCA power tubes are the Amateur's answer for power reliability in virtually every rf and af power application you can name. And remember this: Many RCA power tubes for amateurs do not require expensive air-system sockets.

The quick-reference chart shown here will help you pick the popular RCA types you need—from more than 90 types of beam power tubes and triodes available for amateur transmitter application. Note that every type listed on this chart has "high-perveance" design...a development that enables you to get *the power you want at relatively low plate voltage.* And note this, too: Every type is conservatively rated to assure long hours of "solid" QSO's.

Whether you are planning high power or low power, CW or 'phone, AM or SSB—you'll get more watts for your "transmitter dollar" when you design, or when you "retube", with "RCA's".

That's why RCA Power Tubes continue to be top choice among the leading transmitter designers. Your RCA Industrial Tube Distributor handles the complete line.

RADIO CORPORATION OF AMERICA
Electron Tube Division   Harrison, N. J.   27

BUILD YOUR OWN HEATHKIT® HAM GEAR

HEATHKIT HAM EQUIPMENT IS DESIGNED BY HAMS WHO KNOW YOUR PROBLEMS AND NEEDS.

PROVEN, "ON THE AIR" PERFORMANCE

"SENECA" VHF HAM TRANSMITTER KIT

Beautifully styled and a top performer of highest quality throughout. The "Seneca" is a completely self-contained 6 and 2 meter transmitter featuring a built-in VFO for both 6 and 2 meters, and 4 switch-selected crystal positions, 2 power supplies, 5 radio frequency stages, and 2 dual-triode audio stages. Panel controls allow VFO or crystal control, phone or CW operation on both amateur bands. An auxiliary socket provides for receiver muting, remote operation of antenna relay and remote control of the transmitter such as with the Heathkit VX-1 Voice Control. Features up to 120 watts input on phone and 140 watts on CW in the 6 meter band. Ratings slightly reduced in the 2 meter band. Ideal for ham operators wishing to extend transmission into the VHF region. Shpg. Wt. 56 lbs.

HEATHKIT VHF-1 $159⁹⁵

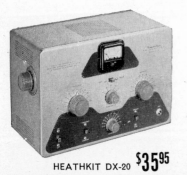

HEATHKIT DX-20 $35⁹⁵

DX-20 CW TRANSMITTER KIT

Designed exclusively for CW work, the DX-20 provides the novice as well as the advanced-class CW operator with a low cost transmitter featuring high operating efficiency. Single-knob bandswitching covers 80, 40, 20, 15 and 10 meters using crystals or an external VFO. Pi network output circuit matches antenna impedances between 50 and 1,000 ohms. Employs a single 6DQ6A tube in the final amplifier stage for plate power input of 50 watts. A 6CL6 serves as the crystal oscillator. The husky power supply uses a heavy duty 5U4GB rectifier and top-quality "potted" transformer for long service life. Easy-to-read panel meter indicates final grid or plate current selected by the panel switch. Complete RF shielding to minimize TVI interference. Easy-to-build with complete instructions provided. Shpg. Wt. 19 lbs.

HEATH COMPANY Benton Harbor, Michigan a subsidiary of Daystrom, Inc.

28

Mobile Gear...for the Ham on the Go!

"CHEYENNE" MOBILE HAM TRANSMITTER KIT

All the fun and excitement . . . plus the convenience of mobile operation are yours in the all-new Heathkit "Cheyenne" transmitter. The neat, compact, and efficient circuitry provides you with high power capability in mobile operation, with low battery drain using carrier controlled modulation. All necessary power is supplied by the model MP-1 described below. Covers 80, 40, 20, 15 and 10 meters with up to 90 watts input on phone. Features built-in VFO, modulator, 4 RF stages, with a 6146 final amplifier and pi network (coaxial) output coupling. High quality components are used for long service life and reliable operation, along with rugged chassis construction to withstand mobile vibrations and shock. Thoughtful circuit layout provides for ease of assembly with complete instructions and detailed pictorial diagrams to insure success. A spotting switch is also provided. A specially designed ceramic microphone is included to insure effective modulation with plenty of "punch". Plan now to enjoy the fun of mobile operation by building this superb transmitter. Shpg. Wt. 19 lbs.

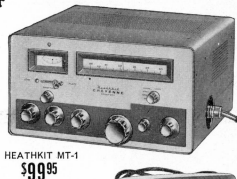

HEATHKIT MT-1
$99⁹⁵

"COMANCHE" MOBILE HAM RECEIVER KIT

Everything you could ask for in modern design mobile gear is provided in the "Comanche" . . . handsome styling, rugged construction, top quality components . . . and, best of all, a price you can afford. The "Comanche" is an 8-tube superheterodyne ham band receiver operating AM, CW and SSB on the 80, 40, 20, 15 and 10 meter amateur bands. A 3 mc crystal lattice-type IF filter permits the receiver to use single conversion without image interference, and at the same time creates a steep sided 3 kc flat top IF bandpass characteristic comparable to mechanical type filters. The neat, compact and easy-to-assemble circuitry features outstanding sensitivity, stability and selectivity on all bands. Circuit includes an RF stage, converter, 2 IF stages, 2 detectors, noise limiter, 2 audio stages and a voltage regulator. Sensitivity is better than 1 microvolt on all bands and signal-to-noise ratio is better than 10 db down at 1 microvolt input. One of the finest investments you can make in mobile gear. Shpg. Wt. 19 lbs.

HEATHKIT MR-1
$119⁹⁵

MOBILE SPEAKER KIT

A matching companion speaker for the "Comanche" mobile receiver. Housed in a rugged steel case with brackets provided for easy installation on fire wall or under dashboard, etc. Uses 5 PM speaker with 8 ohm voice coil. Measures 5" H. x 5" W. x 2½" D. Shpg. Wt. 4 lbs.

HEATHKIT AK-7
$5⁹⁵

HEATHKIT AK-6
$4⁹⁵

HEATHKIT MP-1
$44⁹⁵

MOBILE POWER SUPPLY KIT

This heavy duty transistor power supply furnishes all the power required to operate both the MT-1 Transmitter and MR-1 Receiver. It features two 2N442 transistors in a 400 cycle switching circuit, supplying a full 120 watts of DC power. Under intermittent operation it will deliver up to 150 watts. Kit contains everything required for complete installation, including 12' of heavy battery cable, tap-in studs for battery posts, power plug and 15' of connecting cable. Chassis size is 9¹⁄₁₆" L. x 4¾" W. x 2" H. Operates from 12-14 volt battery source. Circuit convenience provided by self-contained relay which allows push-to-talk mobile operation. Shpg. Wt. 8 lbs.

MOBILE BASE MOUNT KIT

The AK-6 Base Mount is designed to hold both transmitter and receiver conveniently at driver's side. Universal mounting bracket has adjustable legs to fit most automobiles. Shpg. Wt. 5 lbs.

POWER METER KIT

This handy unit picks up energy from your mobile antenna and indicates when your transmitter is tuned for maximum output. A variable sensitivity control is provided. Features a strong magnet on a swivel-mount for holding it on a car dashboard or other suitable spot. Has its own antenna or may be connected to existing antenna. Sensitive 200 ua meter. Shpg. Wt. 2 lbs.

HEATHKIT PM-2
$12⁹⁵

29

COMPANION UNITS

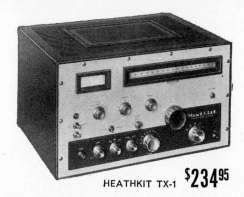

HEATHKIT TX-1 $234.95

"APACHE" HAM TRANSMITTER KIT

The many features and modern styling of the "Apache" will provide you with just about everything you could ask for in transmitting facilities. Emphasizing high quality the "Apache" operates with a 150 watt phone input and 180 watt CW input. In addition to CW and phone operation, built-in switch selected circuitry provides for single-sideband transmission using the SB-10 External adapter. The newly designed, compact and stable VFO provides low drift frequency control necessary for SSB transmission. A slide rule type illuminated rotating VFO dial with full gear drive vernier tuning provides ample bandspread and precise frequency settings. The bandswitch allows quick selection of the amateur bands on 80, 40, 20, 15 and 10 meters. This unit also has adjustable low-level speech clipping and a low distortion modulator stage employing two of the new 6CA7/EL34 tubes in push-pull class AB operation. Time sequence keying is provided for "chirpless" break-in CW operation. The final amplifier is completely shielded for TVI protection and neutralized for greater stability. A cooling fan is also provided. The formed one-piece cabinet with convenient access hatch provides accessibility to tubes and crystal sockets. Die-cast aluminum knobs and control panel escutcheons add to the attractive styling of the transmitter. Pi network output coupling matches antenna impedances between 50 and 72 ohms. A "spotting" push button enables the operator to "zero beat" an incoming frequency without putting the transmitter on the air. Equip your ham shack now for top transmitting enjoyment with this outstanding unit. Shpg. Wt. 110 lbs. Shipped motor freight unless otherwise specified.

HEATHKIT SB-10

$89.95

SINGLE SIDEBAND ADAPTER KIT

Designed as a compatible plug-in adapter unit for the TX-1 "Apache" transmitter, this unit lets you operate on SSB at a minimum of cost, yet does not affect the normal AM and CW functions of the transmitter. By making a few simple circuit modifications, the DX-100 and DX-100-B transmitters can be used, utilizing all existing RF circuitry. Extremely easy to operate and tune, the adapter employs the phasing method for generating a single-sideband signal, thus allowing operation entirely on fundamental frequencies. The critical audio phase shift network is supplied completely preassembled and wired in a sealed plug-in unit. Produces either a USB, LSB or DSB signal, with or without carrier insertion. Covers 80, 40, 20, 15 and 10 meter bands. An easy-to-read panel meter indicates power output to aid in tuning. A built-in electronic voice control with anti-trip circuit is also provided. 10 watts PEP output. Unwanted sideband suppression is in excess of 30 db and carrier suppression is in excess of 40 db. An EL84/6BQ5 tube is used for linear RF output. Shpg. Wt. 12 lbs.

MODIFICATION KIT: Modifies DX-100 and DX-100-B for use with the SB-10 Adapter. Model MK-1. Shpg. Wt. 1 lb. $8.95.

HEATHKIT AR-3
$29.95
(less cabinet)

HEATHKIT QF-1
$9.95

ALL-BAND RECEIVER KIT

A fine receiver for the beginning ham or short wave listener, designed for high circuit efficiency and easy construction. Covers 550 kc to 30 mc in four bands clearly marked on a slide-rule dial. Transformer operated power supply. Features include: bandswitch, bandspread tuning, phone-standby-CW switch, phone jack, antenna trimmer, noise eliminator, RF gain control and AF control. Shpg. Wt. 12 lbs.

CABINET: Opt. extra. No. 91-15A. Shpg. Wt. 5 lbs. $4.95.

"Q" MULTIPLIER KIT

Useful on crowded phone and CW bands, this kit adds selectivity and signal rejection to your receiver. Use it with any AM receiver having an IF frequency between 450 and 460 kc that is not AC-DC type. Provides an effective "Q" of approximately 4,000 for extremely sharp "peak" or "null". The QF-1 is powered from the receiver with which it is used. Shpg. Wt. 3 lbs.

30

OF DISTINCTIVE QUALITY

ACCESSORY SPEAKER KIT

Handsomely designed and color styled to match the "Mohawk" receiver this heavy duty 8" speaker with 4.7 ounce magnet provides excellent tone quality. Housed in attractive ⅜" plywood cabinet with perforated metal grille. Speaker impedance is 8 ohms. Shpg. Wt. 7 lbs.

HEATHKIT AK-5
$9⁹⁵

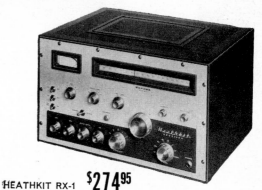

HEATHKIT RX-1 **$274⁹⁵**

"MOHAWK" HAM RECEIVER KIT

Styled to match the "Apache" transmitter the "Mohawk" ham band receiver provides all the functions required for clear, rock-steady reception. Designed especially for ham band operation this 15-tube receiver features double conversion with IF's at 1682 kc and 50 kc and covers all the amateur frequencies from 160 through 10 meters on 7 bands with an extra band calibrated to cover 6 and 2 meters using a converter. Specially designed for single sideband reception with crystal controlled oscillators for upper and lower sideband selection. A completely preassembled wired and aligned front end coil bandswitch assembly assures ease of construction and top performance of the finished unit. Other features include 5 selectivity positions from 5 kc to 500 CPS, bridge T-notch filter for excellent heterodyne rejection, and a built-in 100 kc crystal calibrator. The set provides a 10 db signal-to-noise ratio at less than 1 microvolt input. Each ham band is separately calibrated on a rotating slide rule dial to provide clear frequency settings with more than ample bandspread. Front panel features S-meter, separate RF, IF and AF gain controls, T-notch tuning, T-notch depth, ANL, AVC, BFO, Bandswitch tuning, antenna trimmer, calibrate set, calibrate on, CW-SSB-AM, receive-standby, upper-lower sideband, selectivity, phone jack and illuminated gear driven vernier slide rule tuning dial. Attractively styled with die-cast aluminum control knobs and escutcheons. No external alignment equipment is required for precise calibration of the "Mohawk". All adjustments are easily accomplished using the unique method described in the manual. An outstanding buy in a communications receiver. Shpg. Wt. 66 lbs. Shipped motor freight unless otherwise specified.

HEATHKIT AM-2
$15⁹⁵

REFLECTED POWER METER KIT

The AM-2 measures forward and reflected power or standing wave ratio. Handles a peak power of well over 1 kilowatt of energy and covers 160 through 6 meters. Input and output impedance provided for 50 or 75 ohm lines. No external power required for operation. Use it also to match impedances between exciters or RF sources and grounded grid amplifiers. Shpg. Wt. 3 lbs.

BALUN COIL KIT

Match unbalanced coaxial lines, found on most modern transmitters, to balanced lines of either 75 or 300 ohms impedance with this handy transmitter accessory. Capable of handling power input up to 200 watts, the B-1 may be used with transmitters and receivers covering 80 through 10 meters. No adjustment required. Shpg. Wt. 4 lbs.

HEATHKIT B-1
$8⁹⁵

HEATHKIT VX-1
$23⁹⁵

ELECTRONIC VOICE CONTROL KIT

Eliminate hand switching with this convenient kit. Switch from receiver to transmitter by merely talking into your microphone. Sensitivity controls allow adjustment to all conditions. Power supply is built in and terminal strip on the rear of the chassis accommodates receiver and speaker connections and also a 117 volt antenna relay. Shpg. Wt. 5 lbs.

HEATHKIT VF-1
$19⁵⁰

VFO KIT

Far below the cost of crystals to obtain the same frequency coverage this variable frequency oscillator covers 160, 80, 40, 20, 15 and 10 meters with three basic oscillator frequencies. Providing better than 10 volt average RF output on fundamentals, the VF-1 is capable of driving the most modern transmitters. Requires only 250 volts DC at 15 to 20 ma, and 6.3 VAC at 0.45 a. Illuminated dial reads direct. Shpg. Wt. 7 lbs.

31

Save 1/2 or more...with Heathkits

HEATHKIT DX-100-B **$189⁵⁰**

HEATHKIT DX-40 **$64⁹⁵**

DX-100-B PHONE AND CW TRANSMITTER KIT

A long standing favorite in the Heathkit line, the DX-100-B combines modern styling and circuit ingenuity to bring you an exceptionally fine transmitter at an economical price. Panel controls allow VFO or crystal control, phone or CW operation on all amateur bands up to 30 mc. The rugged one-piece formed cabinet features a convenient top-access hatch for changing crystals and making other adjustments. The chassis is punched to accept sideband adapter modifications. Featured are a built-in VFO, modulator, and power supply, complete shielding to minimize TVI, and a pi network output coupling to match impedances from 50 to 72 ohms. RF output is in excess of 100 watts on phone and 120 watts on CW. Band coverage is from 160 through 10 meters. For operating convenience single-knob bandswitching and illuminated VFO dial on meter face are provided. A pair of 6146 tubes in parallel are employed in the output stage modulated by a pair of 1625's. Shpg. Wt. 107 lbs. Shipped motor freight unless otherwise specified.

DX-40 PHONE AND CW TRANSMITTER KIT

An outstanding buy in its power class the DX-40 provides both phone and CW operation on 80, 40, 20, 15 and 10 meters. A single 6146 tube is used in the final amplifier stage to provide full 75 watt plate power input on CW or controlled carrier modulation peaks up to 60 watts for phone operation. Modulator and power supplies are built in and single-knob band-switching is combined with the pi network output circuit for complete operating convenience. Features a D'Arsonval movement panel meter. A line filter and liberal shielding provides for high stability and minimum TVI. Provision is made for three crystals easily accessible through a "trap door" in the back of the cabinet. A 4-position switch selects any of the three crystals or jack for external VFO. Power for the VFO is available on the rear apron of the chassis. Easy-to-follow step-by-step instructions let assembly proceed smoothly from start to finish even for an individual who has never built electronic equipment before. Shpg. Wt. 25 lbs.

Free Send now for latest Heathkit Catalog describing in detail over 100 easy-to-assemble kits for the Hi-Fi fan, radio ham, boat owner and technician.

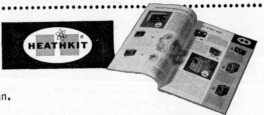

Turn your skills into profit installing and maintaining G-E Two-Way Mobile Radio

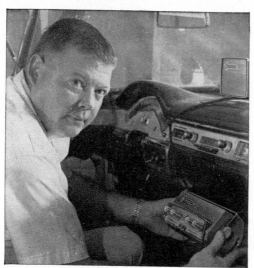

Dan Trueblood, W4ESB, of Goldsboro, N.C. is shown installing a customer's new General Electric Transistorized Progress Line mobile unit. A ham since 1935, Dan has been an authorized General Electric Service technician for two-way radio for five years. He currently operates single side band with a full kilowatt, when he's not busy selling, installing and maintaining G-E two-way radio.

Thousands of new mobile radio systems are being installed every year—for delivery services, salesmen, taxis, gas and electric utilities, industrial and construction vehicles, and many other uses. All these systems require *service* — service your unique background and knowledge can be easily adapted to provide.

Servicing two-way radio can be a full-time vocation, or a profitable sideline. Many highly successful General Electric mobile radio service stations were founded by licensed radio amateurs, and many now utilize the skills of hams such as yourself on a part-time basis as well as full-time. Working in an authorized G-E Service Station is also an ideal way in which to prepare for the second or first class Commercial Radio Operator's license, required for commercial mobile radio servicing.

G-E two-way radio equipment is designed and built with the serviceman in mind. General Electric's famous Progress Line, for example, features interchangeable rack-mounted transmitter, receiver and power supply for fast servicing. G.E.'s new line of transistorized portable and mobile equipment offers even greater service advantages.

Find out how you can become an authorized G-E serviceman. Write National Service Manager, General Electric Company, Communication Products Dept., Section 30, Mountain View Road, Lynchburg, Virginia.

Progress Is Our Most Important Product

GENERAL ⊛ ELECTRIC

MS/AN CONNECTORS

Relied upon since 1939. Latest design advancement is new "Stub E" construction—shortest lightest "E."

MINNI**E** CONNECTORS

Complete new family of miniature "E's"—altitude-moisture resistant. Sizes 12 to 22—3 to 48 contacts.

RF CONNECTORS

All RF series available, including remarkable Subminax. New Quick-Crimp BNC's cut assembly time in half.

PRIN-CIR CONNECTORS

Receptacles, plugs and adapters with super-reliable gold-plated contacts. From 6 to 22 contacts.

RACK & PANEL CONNECTORS

Seven families available for every R & P application. Patented crimp Poke-Home contacts in 93 & 94 series.

COAXIAL CABLE

Most complete line anywhere of RG-/U polyethylene and Teflon coaxial cables. Miniatures also.

ALL STANDARD AMPHENOL COMPONENTS STOCKED IN DEPTH BY YOUR AUTHORIZED AMPHENOL DISTRIBUTOR...

◄ ASK FOR YOUR COPY OF CATALOG IEC!

AMPHENOL DISTRIBUTOR DIVISION
BROADVIEW, ILLINOIS

Amphenol-Borg Electronics Corporation

Collins mobile transceiver

KWM-2

Another Collins creative design – the advanced amateur's 80-10 meter transceiver – system engineered for mobile and home operation.

Superior single sideband performance in a variety of installations is assured by the Collins KWM-2 Mobile Transceiver. Engineered for the amateur who desires an 80 through 10 meter mobile transceiver, the KWM-2 design incorporates time-proven and advanced communication concepts.

The Mobile Transceiver provides outstanding frequency stability on fourteen 200 kc bands from 3.4 mc to 30.0 mc. With 175 watts PEP input on SSB, or 160 watts on CW, the KWM-2 provides ample power for dependable amateur communication. Filter type SSB generation, Collins permeability-tuned variable oscillator, crystal-controlled HF double conversion oscillator, VOX and anti-trip circuits, and exclusive ALC and RF inverse feedback are among the features of the KWM-2. The Collins Mechanical Filter, RF amplifier, all tuned circuits, and several tubes perform the dual role of transmitting and receiving. CW break-in and monitoring sidetone circuits are built-in, and all four plugs in the mobile mount connect the KWM-2 automatically. A connector on the rear provides for antenna selection or loading coil selection for mobile operation.

The Collins KWM-2 Mobile Transceiver weighs 18 lbs. 3 oz. and measures 7¾″ H (including legs), 14¾″ W, and 13¼″ D. Mounts, accessories, and power supplies are available for 12 v dc, and 115 v ac operation.

See the KWM-2 now on display at your Collins Distributor. Ask for the colorful KWM-2 brochure with complete specifications.

Collins

superiority in single sideband systems

S/LINE

The S/Line is a complete station for the advanced amateur. The 32S-1 Transmitter and 75S-1 Receiver may be operated separately or as a transceiver in which the receiver controls the transmitter frequency. The 312B-4 Speaker Console integrates the two units further with over-all station control, and control of a directional wattmeter for maximum output efficiency. For the amateur desiring the strongest signal, the 30S-1 Linear Amplifier provides maximum legal output with greatly simplified operation.

32S-1 Transmitter

The 32S-1 is an SSB or CW transmitter with a nominal output of 100 watts on all amateur bands between 3.5 and 29.7 mc. Input power is 175 watts PEP on SSB or 160 watts on CW.

The transmitter covers 3.5 to 30 mc except for the 5.0-6.5 mc range. Crystal sockets, crystals and bandswitch position are provided for ten 200 kc bands, with the standard amateur configuration equipped as follows: 3.4-3.6, 3.6-3.8, 3.8-4.0; 7.0-7.2, 7.2-7.4; 14.0-14.2, 14.2-14.4; 21.0-21.2, 21.2-21.4, 21.4-21.6. Crystal sockets and bandswitch positions also are provided for three 200 kc bands between 28 and 29.7 mc. One of these sockets is equipped with a crystal for 28.5 to 28.7 mc. A fourteenth position, corresponding to the WWV position on the receiver, can be used for an additional 200 kc band in the 9.5-15.0 mc range, if desired.

Features which have made Collins amateur SSB equipment famous are incorporated into the 32S-1, including Mechanical Filter-type sideband generation; stable, permeability-tuned VFO; crystal-controlled HF oscillator; RF inverse feedback for better linearity; automatic load control for higher average talk power and protection against flattopping.

For ac operation, the 516F-2 Power Supply is used with the 32S-1; for 12 v dc operation, the 516E-1 used with the KWM-1 and KWM-2 may be used with minor modification.

Specifications

EMISSION: SSB — upper or lower sideband. CW— keyed tone.

POWER INPUT: 175 watts PEP on SSB. 160 watts on CW.

POWER OUTPUT: 100 watts PEP nominal (slightly lower on 10 meters) into 50 ohms.

OUTPUT IMPEDENCE: 50 ohms nominal with not more than approximately 2 to 1 SWR. Impedance match variable 25-100 ohms.

FREQUENCY STABILITY: After warm-up, over-all stability due to temperature, humidity, pressure and voltage variation is 100 cps. Calibration accuracy: 1 kc.

VISUAL DIAL ACCURACY: 200 cps on all bands.

ELECTRICAL DIAL ACCURACY: After calibration: 300 cps on all bands.

HARMONIC AND OTHER SPURIOUS RADIATION: Carrier suppression −40 db. Unwanted sideband −50 db. Oscillator feed-through and/or mixer products −50 db. Second harmonic −50 db. 3rd order distortion −30 db.

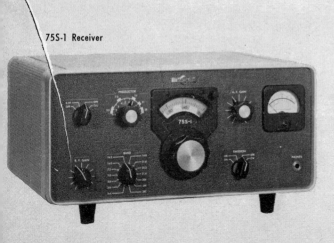

75S-1 Receiver

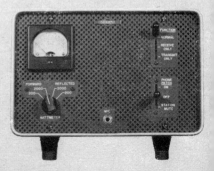

312B-4 Speaker Console

312B-4 Speaker Console

The 312B-4 (pictured between 75S-1 and 32S-1 below) houses a speaker, and RF directional watt-meter with 200 and 2000 watt scales, and switches for various station control functions.

75S-1 Receiver

The 75S-1 provides SSB, CW and AM reception on all amateur bands between 3.5 and 29.7 mc. It is capable of coverage of the entire HF spectrum between 3.5 and 30 mc by selection of the appropriate HF heterodyning crystals.

The standard amateur configuration includes crystal sockets, crystals and bandswitch positions for: 3.4-3.6, 3.6-3.8, 3.8-4.0; 7.0-7.2, 7.2-7.4; 14.0-14.2, 14.2-14.4; 21.0-21.2, 21.2-21.4, 21.4-21.6. Crystal sockets and bandswitch positions are also provided for three 200 kc bands between 28 and 29.7 mc, with one of the sockets equipped with a crystal for 28.5 to 28.7 mc. A crystal and bandswitch position is also provided for 14.8-15.0 mc for reception of WWV and WWVH for time and frequency calibration data.

The same standard of excellence and many of the design features of the 75A-4 are incorporated in the 75S-1. These include dual conversion with a crystal-controlled first heterodyning oscillator; bandpass first IF; stable, permeability-tuned VFO; RF amplifier designed to minimize cross modulation products; Mechanical Filter; excellent AVC characteristics; and both product and diode detector.

New features include the use of only 150 volts on vacuum tube plates, use of silicon diodes in lieu of conventional high vacuum rectifier; and choice of three degrees of selectivity (with optional CW filter).

A power connector at the rear of the 75S-1 chassis provides for disabling the internal ac power supply so that the 12 v dc power supply for the KWM-2 may power the receiver as well as the transmitter.

Specifications

VISUAL DIAL ACCURACY: 200 cps on all bands.
ELECTRICAL DIAL ACCURACY: (after calibration) 300 cps on all bands.

SENSITIVITY: The CW sensitivity is better than 1 microvolt (with a 50-ohm dummy antenna) for a 15 db signal-plus-noise-to-noise ratio.
SELECTIVITY: 2.1 kc Mechanical Filter for SSB; 0.5 kc Mechanical Filter (not supplied) for CW; 4.0 kc IF transformer passband for AM.
SPURIOUS RESPONSE: Image rejection is more than 50 db. Internal spurious signals below 1 microvolt equivalent antenna input.

30S-1 Linear Amplifier

The 30S-1 is a completely self-contained, single tube, grounded grid linear amplifier. Requiring 70 to 100 watts driving power (from the 32S-1 or KWM-2, for example), it provides the full legal power input for SSB (1 kw average) or 1 kw input for CW. The tube used is the Eimac 4CX1000A. The 30S-1 may be used on any frequency between 3.4 and 30 mc.

The 30S-1 may be loaded into an antenna without exceeding the legal dc input of 1 kw during tune-up. Front panel switching makes two different power levels immediately available for SSB operation: 100 watts from the exciter alone or the full 1 kw meter average input for SSB. The air blower for the 4CX1000A operates quietly — barely audible in a quiet room. The power supply for the 30S-1, which is housed in the lower portion of the cabinet, provides cathode bias voltage, screen voltage and 3000 volts for the 4CX1000A plate. Space is provided in this compartment for the 516F-2 Power Supply.

Extended Frequency Versions of the S/Line

The 32S-1 and 75S-1 are available in extended frequency versions, designated the 75S-2 and 32S-2. The two differ from the original only in that an additional crystal board has been added beneath the chassis. In this board is placed the standard complement of ham band crystals normally received with the equipment. The upper board is left empty so that the amateur may place whatever additional crystals he may desire up to a total of 14. A front panel switch is added to allow switching between the two crystal boards.

32S-1 Transmitter

30S-1 Linear Amplifier

Collins accessories
S/LINE
and KWM-2

302C-3 Directional Wattmeter– Measures forward and reflected power on 200 and 2000 watt scales. Coupler unit mounts separate from indicator-control box. Power loss and mismatch introduced by the instrument are negligible.

B312-1 Directional Coupler – The coupler unit from the 302C-3 for amateurs who desire to utilize an optional meter and switch for a customized fixed installation or for a mobile installation.

351E Table Mounts – For mounting the S/Line and KWM-2 on planes, boats, etc. May be fastened to any flat surface. Front clamps attach to the feet of the units for secure hold-down. 351E-1 for 32S-1, 75S-1; 351E-2 for 312B-4, 516F-2; 351E-3 for 312B-3, 351E-4 for KWM-2.

351D-2 Mobile Mount – Provides secure mounting for KWM-2 in most automobiles. Cantilever arms fold out of the way when KWM-2 is removed.

Mating plugs connect power, receive-transmit antenna, noise blanker, antenna and antenna control as KWM-2 slides into place. Cables included.

312B-5 Speaker Console and External PTO– Used with KWM-2 in fixed station operation to provide separate receiving and transmitting control, and directional wattmeter.

399C-1 Speaker and External PTO–Contains speaker and external PTO for separate receiver and transmitter control of KWM-2.

136 Series Noise Blankers – Provide effective reduction of impulse-type noise, particularly ignition noise. 136A-1 for 75S-1; 136B-1 for KWM-1; 136B-2 for KWM-2; 136C-1 for 75A-4.

312B-3 Speaker – Contains a 5" x 7" speaker and connecting cable. Attractively styled to match receiver and transmitter.

516F-2 AC Power Supply– Operates from 115 v ac, 50-60 cps. Provides all voltages for the 32S-1.

516E-1 Power Supply – Operates from 12 v dc. Provides all required voltages for the KWM-2 or 32S-1 and 75S-1 for mobile or portable operation. Transistorized for maximum efficiency and minimum maintenance. The 516E-2, a 28 v dc supply may also be used.

For addresses of Collins dealers or further information and complete specifications on the entire Collins S/Line and accessories, write to: Amateur Sales, Collins Radio Company, Cedar Rapids, Iowa.

COLLINS

COLLINS RADIO COMPANY • CEDAR RAPIDS, IOWA • DALLAS, TEXAS • BURBANK, CALIFORNIA

302C-3

351E-1

312B-5

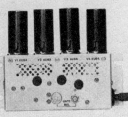

136B-2

516F-2

516E-1

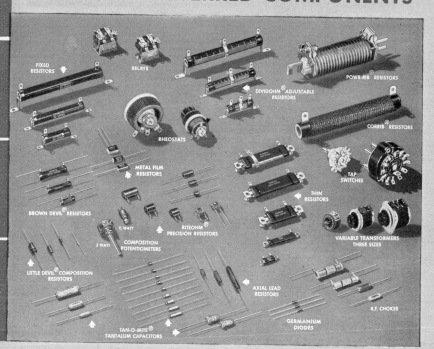

If it weren't for Amateur Radio 25 years ago, there'd be no Eimac tubes today...

Twenty-five years ago W6UF and W6CHE were unhappy with the way final amplifier tubes were performing. They decided to do something about it. They founded a company, called their products Eimac tubes and ran their first ad in QST, November, 1934.

What has happened since is reviewed in part on these pages. At Eimac W6UF and W6CHE, and 120 other amateur radio operators are on-the-air getting just as much of a thrill out of their hobby today as they did then and enjoying it much more.

150T "The only tube the low power man can buy, yet still use effectively at higher power" was the case for the first Eimac tube, the 150T triode, in 1934. It was designed primarily for the amateur and established Eimac tube characteristics for the future—clean, hard vacuums, simplified design, lower driving power, high mutual conductance and superior overload capability.

450T Only two years later in 1936, the statement could proudly be made that "practically every major airline uses Eimac tubes." The 450T triode had captured the imagination and fulfilled the critical desires of aviation and was first choice in ground-to-air communications. It featured a new type thoriated tungsten filament by Eimac ending premature emission failures and guaranteed never to fail because of gas released internally. Later, in 1938, Eimac tubes went into TV service at Station KTSL.

3X2500A3 FM and Eimac tubes were together from the start. By the time Major Armstrong had convinced the world that FM was a great advancement in broadcasting, Eimac tubes were in nearly every experimental FM broadcast station in the nation. The first tubes used were the internal anode triodes. In 1945 the external anode triode 3X2500A3 was introduced and subsequently used in the world's most powerful FM transmitter —50,000 watts.

304T In 1940 the Eimac multi-unit triodes made their debut to provide a high power, low voltage tube with uncommonly low internal resistance which would operate efficiently up to 200mc. In actual service the tubes operated with as much as 20,000 volts on the plate—10 times the rated voltage. The 304T, four triodes in one, was then and is now acclaimed as a top linear amplifier tube.

VT 127 The Navy held its first sea radar tests in 1939. Generating the power were Eimac 100T triodes. Two years later when World War II started, this equipment was the prototype of the first radar to see action in the Pacific. Airborne radar with its demands for smaller antenna meant higher frequency operation. The Eimac 15E met all requirements and made possible 26,000 radar sets used universally by the Navy. Said the Navy, "No other single type of airborne electronic equipment contributed as much." Many of the renowned VT series radar tubes were another Eimac contribution.

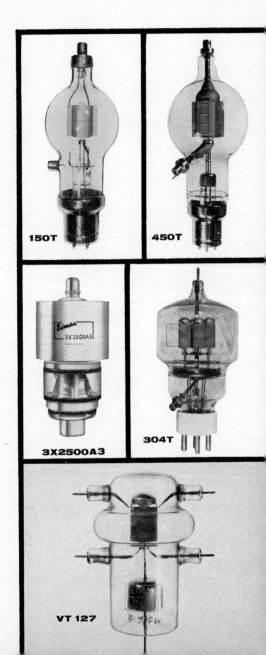

150T 450T

3X2500A3 304T

VT 127

4-125A FAMILY

4X150A

4-125A FAMILY (5 TUBES) In 1945 Eimac led in power tetrode development with the introduction of the 4-125A as the first of its radial-beam family. These tubes set the standard for the tetrode art and are known for their low driving power requirements, low grid emission, low grid-plate capacitances, minimized neutralization requirements and dependable VHF performance.

4X150A Radial-beam power tetrode advantages in the rugged, compact external anode package was introduced by Eimac in 1946 with the 4X500A followed closely by the incomparable 4X150A. This unique approach enabled smaller, high power, high frequency equipment and coaxial cavity circuits. The Eimac 4X150A has since become the most copied of transmitting tubes and father of the modern 4CX250B and 4CX300A.

AMPLIFIER KLYSTRON Despite its reputation in leading tetrode development and manufacture, Eimac saw the shortcomings of grid tubes for UHF, in 1948, and started a development program in amplifier klystrons. The result — Eimac external-cavity ceramic klystrons — the most extensively used tubes in tropospheric communications. From the initial Pole Vault system to White Alice and NATO, these klystrons are unrivaled.

4CX300A, 4CX250B, 4CX1000A, 4CX5000A Ceramic is replacing glass in the Eimac tube line-up. Over 50 tube types now have the advantages of the ceramic enve-lope. Its ability to withstand thermal and physical shock has application benefits. Other extras are also built in, such as smaller size without power sacrifice, high temperature and precise tolerance processing.

X626 Super power, 1.25 megawatts of long-pulse power, at UHF is now available with the Eimac X626. In Ballistic Missile detection and tracking, or interplanetary DX, (this tube holds the record to Venus and back — 56,000,000 miles), the X626 is now an important part of our space age.

TWT Now, microwave in the form of ceramic traveling wave tubes and reflex klystrons. Eimac is engaged in the development and manufacture of new electron devices to propagate the uncrowded spectrum at Super High Frequencies and above.

X626

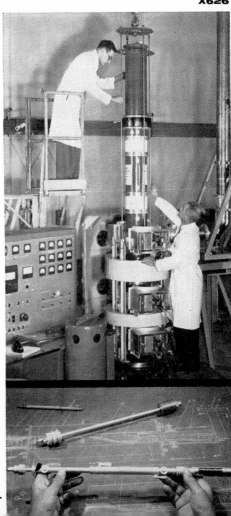

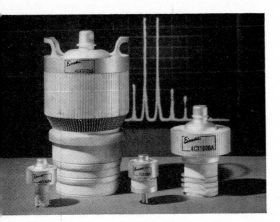

The dependable tubes of yesteryear have not been forgotten. They are constantly improved. Most of the oldtimers on review here are still available and many are replacements for originals that have finally given in after years and years of service.

EITEL-McCULLOUGH, INC.
San Carlos, California

TWT

BURTON BROWNE/New York

Send for this FREE National Catalog for up-to-date information on America's finest receivers!

Gives Complete Specifications, Full List of Accessories, Latest Prices on these Famous NATIONAL RECEIVERS.

HRO-60
Features widest frequency coverage of any receiver available, 50 kc to 54 mc . . . the world's most famous receiver.

NC-400
National's newest general coverage receiver. Covers 540 kc to 31 mc in 7 bands. 18 tubes (including rectifier) AM-CW-SSB. May be used in fixed channel or diversity operation.

NC-303
National's newest "ham band only" receiver. 10 separate dial scales cover 160 to 1¼ meters. Dual conversion. New 5-position "IF SHIFT" provides optimum selectivity for a CW-PHONE-PHONE NET-VHF-Selectable SSB.

NC-109
One of America's lowest price SSB receivers! Covers 540 kc to 40 mc. National's exclusive "MICROTOME" filter provides 5 degrees of sharp selectivity for all modes of operation. VOICE—CW—SSB.

NC-188
Low-priced general coverage receiver. Covers 540 kc to 40 mc, and is directly calibrated for the 4 general coverage ranges and five bandspread ranges for 80-10 meter amateur bands.

NC-66
AC/DC-Battery Portable. Covers 150 kc to 23 mc in 5 bands. Exclusive RDF-66 Direction Finder Accessory provides accurate navigation for small boats.

NC-60
Special "A"
. . . First all-new, low-priced shortwave/standard broadcast receiver in over 10 years! Covers 540 kc to 31 mc in 4 bands. 110 volt AC/DC. Built-in speaker.

NATIONAL RECEIVERS AND ACCESSORIES ARE SOLD ONLY BY FRANCHISED DISTRIBUTORS. MOST OF THESE DISTRIBUTORS OFFER TRADE-IN ALLOWANCES AND LIBERAL BUDGET TERMS.

National RADIO CO., INC.
MELROSE 76, MASS.
A wholly owned subsidiary of National Co., Inc.
Export: AD AURIEMA, INC. 85 Broad St., New York, N.Y., U.S.A.
In Canada: CANADIAN MARCONI CO., 830 Bayview Ave., Toronto, Ont.
Specifications subject to change without notice.

Send for this FREE National Catalog to meet your Component Requirements

GENERAL CATALOG

In addition to the components mentioned below, National Radio Co. also manufactures complete lines of capacitors, tanks, grid and plate caps, IF transformers, ceramic insulators, bushings, spreaders, couplings, terminal assemblies, and other electronic and electro-mechanical components. Write for components catalog covering your specific applications.

MIL-SPEC KNOBS

Type KMS. Complete line of standard plastic control knobs made in conformance with MS-91528. Four basic types (with or without skirts), three shaft sizes, gloss or matte finishes, or to your color specifications . . . in all Mil-Spec sizes.

UNIVERSAL CERAMIC COIL FORMS

For military and commercial applications. Available in five standard sizes with or without terminal collars. Terminal collars accept up to four terminals per collar. All materials are in accordance with applicable MIL-SPECS. Pre-assembled forms to your prints quoted upon request.

CHOKES

R-45 SERIES: Ferrite bead chokes for frequencies from 5 to 200 mc. R-40 SERIES: Ferrite-core chokes, extremely high Q for small size. Fungus-proof varnish impregnation per MIL-V137A. R-25 SERIES: MIL-inductance chokes for high frequency circuits. Inductance per MIL-C15305A, coil forms per MIL-P-14, impregnation per MIL-V-173A. R-33, R-50, R-60 SERIES: RF coils molded on phenolic forms per MIL-P-14.

HR KNOBS

TYPE HRS: Molded Tenite knobs, grey, black or to specifications. TYPE HRT: Large deLuxe knobs designed for National's receivers, now available by popular request. TYPE HRB: Band switching knob or other applications where switch is turned to several index positions. TYPE HRM: Small brass knurled knobs. TYPE HRK: Fluted, large black Bakelite knobs. TYPE HRP: Chip resistant black Bakelite knob without pointer. TYPE HRP-P: Same as HRP but with pointer.

"FLUSH MOUNT" CAPTIVE NUTS

National Exclusive! Flush fit on _both_ sides of aluminum sheet provides permanent tapped holes. Stainless steel 303 as per MIL-S-853A, passivated finish as per MIL-P12011. Additional types to meet MIL SPECS P-11268, E-5400, and E-16400. Captive studs also available.

SOCKETS, CAPS, TERMINALS

TYPE CIR: Tube sockets of grade L-4 ceramic materials (JAN-1-10 spec.) in four models. TYPE CS: Crystal mounting sockets for crystal holders (JAN-1-10 spec.). TYPES XM-10, XM-50: Heavy-duty, metal shell sockets for four-pin tubes. TYPES XLA-7: Low-loss socket for 6F4 and 950 series acorn tubes. TYPES SPP-3, SPP-9: Plate caps of grade L-4 steatite (JAN-1-10 spec.) with silver or tin plated beryllium copper grips. TYPES GG-8, 12, 24: Grid grips made in two types, three sizes, variety of materials . . . clip grip, or loop grip . . . other specifications also.
TERMINAL/ASSEMBLIES: TYPE FWC: Insulators molded of mica-filled Bakelite. TYPE FWE: Nickel plated brass jacks. TYPE FWA: Nickel plated brass binding posts. TYPE FWT: Plugs for stacking. TYPES FWH, FWJ: Terminal assemblies.

PRECISION RIGHT ANGLE, VERNIER DRIVES

TYPE PRAD: Right angle drive remote operation of low torque units. TYPE RAD: Right angle drive for ganging capacitors, potentiometers or other parts in inaccessible locations. TYPE AN: Vernier mechanism for use with any 3/16" National knobs and others. TYPE AVD: Vernier mechanism similar to type AN except that the output shaft is non-insulated.

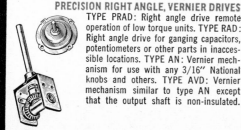

Specifications subject to change without notice.

PRESENTS 1960's TOP PRODUCTS IN QUALITY AND PERFORMANCE

LPA-1

LPS-1

Grounded Grid Linear Amplifier

New! Advanced design amplifier incorporating every element needed for fool-proof, reliable operation. This smartly-styled *full kilowatt* package of power takes up no more table space than a receiver. Can be driven by commercial and home-built exciters in the 100-watt output class. Includes R.F. section complete with tubes, blower, filament and bias supply and optional input matching unit. Pi-network output circuit for precise tuning and loading on 80-40-20-15-10 meters.

POWER SUPPLY UNIT LPS-1 — Designed as companion to the LPA-1 for side-by-side installation or remote location. Switching panel removable for remote control. Full wave single-phase bridge rectifier with four Type 816 mercury vapor tubes included. R.F. filtering. Heavy-duty transformer core stacks and superior high-voltage insulation for reliable, continuous operation at 1 KW.

MATCHING UNITS MODEL LPA-MU & MODEL LPA-MU-2 — Compact, pretuned bandswitching assembly for matching fixed-output type exciters to B&W amplifier, insures maximum input drive on all bands. Model LPA-MU is designed for the LPA-1 and is installed so that input matching to the final is accomplished automatically when amplifier is bandswitched. Model LPA-MU-2 is similar, but is designed for previous B&W amplifiers Models L-1000-A and L-1001-A. Assembled, ready for installation with instructions and fittings.

5100-B

Medium Powered Transmitter 5100-B

Completely self-contained including power supply and VFO. Bandswitching on the 80-40-20-15-10 meter bands. Peak envelope power 180 watts CW-SSB; 145 watts AM. Excellent SSB when used with the 51SB-B described below. Stable VFO accurately calibrated for all amateur bands including 10 meters. Bias system provides complete cutoff under key-up conditions. Excellent TVI suppression. Pi-network output. The 5100-B makes a superlatively well regulated driver for a grounded grid class "B" linear, with output to spare.

51SB

Single Sideband Generator 51SB

Excellent SSB with your present transmitter. Provides push-to-talk, speaker deactivating circuit, TVI suppression. Complete bandswitching on 80-40-20-15-10 meters. Utilizes frequency control method of your present rig. R-F portion has 90° phase shift network, double balanced modulator, and two class "A" R.F. voltage amplifiers. All operating controls on the front panel. Input impedance 50 ohms resistive; input voltage 1.5–2.0 RMS on all bands.

MODEL 51SB-B — For use with B&W 5100-B from which it derives all operating power.

BARKER & WILLIAMSON, INC.
Bristol, Pennsylvania

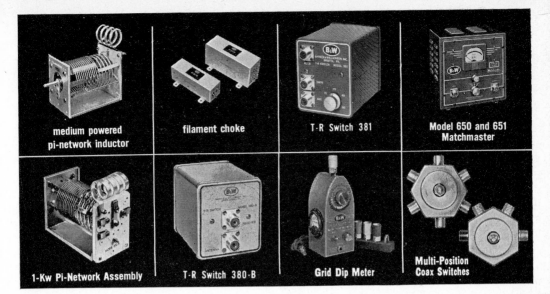

| medium powered pi-network inductor | filament choke | T-R Switch 381 | Model 650 and 651 Matchmaster |
| 1-Kw Pi-Network Assembly | T-R Switch 380-B | Grid Dip Meter | Multi-Position Coax Switches |

Pi-Network Inductor Assemblies

Integral bandswitched Pi-network inductors for single or parallel tube operation 80 through 10 meters. Give top efficiency in Class "C" or linear operation using triodes or tetrodes in conventional and grounded grid circuits. Ample current-carrying capacity and optimum "Q" over entire operating range. *Model 850A* — Conservatively rated at 1 KW on CW-SSB and AM with 100% modulation. Max. voltage: 4000 VDC on CW-SSB; 2500–3000 on AM with 100% modulation. *Model 851* — Medium powered with rating of 250 watts on AM phone and 500 watts on CW-SSB. Max. voltage: 2000 VDC on CW-SSB; 1250 VDC on AM phone.

Grid Dip Meter

A highly accurate, sensitive instrument. May be used as a grid-dip oscillator, signal generator, or absorption wavemeter. Five color-coded plug-in coils cover 1.75 to 260 mc. Color-coded dial easily read. Operates from 110 VAC. Easy to use in hard-to-get-at places. Model 600.

T-R Switches

Fully automatic electronic antenna switching from transmitter to receiver and vice versa. Ideal for fast break-in operation on SSB-AM-CW-DSB. Fail-safe design eliminates risk of transmitter damage if switch is not energized. Match 52-75 ohm coax lines. *Model 381* handles full legal power with wide safety margin. Selectable bandswitching, 80 through 10 meters, for high signal-to-noise ratio and minimum intermodulation effect from local broadcast and TVI. For commercial applications, Model 381 handles up to 5 KW SSB and CW under SWR conditions not exceeding 1.5 to 1 using 72 ohm coax

line, and higher power with 52 ohm line. *Model 380-B* is designed for medium power applications. Has broadband circuitry which eliminates tuning and adjustment.

Multi-Position Coax Switches

For 75 or 52 ohm line. Instantly switches coax lines . . . no screwing or unscrewing coax connectors. Handles up to 1 KW modulated power. Max. cross-talk —45db at 30 mc. Model 550A 5-position switch. Model 551A 2-pole, 2-position switch.

Low Pass Filter

For Transmitters to 1KW. Minimum 85 db attenuation throughout TV bands. Uses exclusive B&W patented wave-guide design in novel multi-sectional construction giving greater attenuation in less space at lower cost. Model 425 for 52 ohms impedance. Model 426 for 75 ohms.

Matchmaster

Self-contained in 6" x 8" x 8" steel cabinet. Serves as dummy load for transmitter tests. SWR measurements throughout range of 500 kc to 30 mc. Direct-reading R.F. watt meter up to 125 watts, higher powers by sampling. Integral SWR bridge for matching antennas and other loads to transmitter. Model 650 for 52 ohm line, Model 651 for 75 ohms.

R. F. Filament Chokes

Used with standard filament transformers in grounded grid amplifier circuitry. Broadband design requires no tuning 80 through 10 meters. Packaged in steel case with mounting brackets. *Model FC-15* — For one or two tubes requiring not more than 15 amps fil. current. *Model FC-30* — For one or two tubes of up to 30 amps fil. current.

45

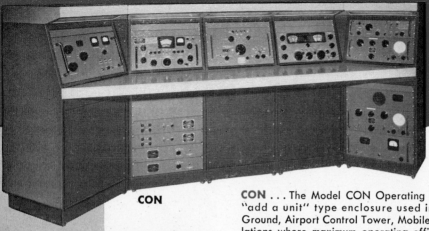

CON

GPR-90

GPR-90RX

CON ... The Model CON Operating Console is an unusual "add a unit" type enclosure used in Point to Point, Air-Ground, Airport Control Tower, Mobile and Shipboard installations where maximum operating efficiency and equipment flexibility is required. The units are made up of standard 19" assemblies which can be used to form straight line, "L", "U" and many other arrangements.........................**Bulletin 211**

GPR-90 (R-825/URR)...a general purpose communications receiver of the double conversion superheterodyne type covering the frequency range of .51 to 31 mcs. Stable—selective—accurate—built-in crystal calibrator......**Bulletin 179**

GPR-90RX (R-840/URR) ... Provides the same high quality characteristics of the GPR-90 but also permits the use of 10 precisely adjustable crystal positions available from the front panel plus a rear deck input for an external high stability control oscillator or synthesizer........................**Bulletin 205**

GSB ... Single Sideband Adapter of the filter slicer type permitting accurate and simple tuning of SSB, AM, CW and MCW. Filter provides additional selectivity and pass-band tuning. Upper and lower sidebands are selected by a flip of a switch..**Bulletin 194**

SBT-1K ( ) ... Single Sideband Transmitter is a conservatively rated general purpose transmitter providing at least 1 KW PEP from 2—32 mcs.—SSB—ISB—DSB—CW—MCW—FS. Rugged, compact, serviceable, completely bandswitched—ideally suited for mobile, marine, fixed station operations. Four models available......................................**Bulletin 237**

GPT-750 ( ) 2 (AN/URT-17A)...is a fully bandswitched, continuously tunable (2-32MC) radio transmitter. The building block concept makes this transmitter versatile, easy to install, operate and maintain. Four models available. SSB, ISB, DSB, AM, CW, MCW, FAX, FS. The GPT-750 ( )2 is ideally suited for fixed station, mobile and shipboard operation.

Bulletin 227

GSB

SBT-1KA

GPT-750D

HF/LF communications
it's TMC

• ISB • CW • MCW • AM • FS

VOX (0-330/FR)...a direct reading, high stability, Variable Frequency Oscillator providing continuously variable output over the frequency range of 2—64 mcs.
Bulletin 134A

XFL-2 ...The TMC Frequency Shift Exciter System, Model XFL-2 is combined low and high frequency shift system. The system combines the TMC Low Frequency Adapter, Model LFA with TMC Frequency Shift Exciter, Model XFK to provide versatile operation over a wide range of frequencies—1 to 6.9 mcs. and 50 to 500 Kcs....................................**Bulletin 154**

SBT-350 (   ) ... Compact, rugged Radio Transmitter capable of at least 350 watts PEP from 2—32 mcs. SSB—ISB—DSB CW—MCW—FS low level AM—completely bandswitched—five models available...**Bulletin 220**

PTE-1 ... Single Sideband Analyzer designed for the specific purpose of tuning and aligning single sideband exciters and transmitters permitting a visual analysis of intermodulation distortion products, hum and noise The PTE-1 consists of 3 basic TMC units: Spectrum Analyzer Model FSA (AN/URM-116); A VFO TMC Model VOX (0-330/FR) and a Two-tone Generator TMC Model TTG (C-579/URT)..........**Bulletin 231**

GPT-10K (AN/FRT-39) . . . is a conservatively rated general purpose radio transmitter capable of at least 10 KW PEP output from 4-28 mcs. All power amplifier stages are linear and the final incorporates a ceramic tube for greater efficiency and reliability. All components housed within a single attractive enclosure including sideband exciter—VFO, spectrum analyzer, F.S. Exciter and complete "on the air'" testing circuitry. ....**Bulletin 207B**

The TECHNICAL MATERIEL CORP.

MAMARONECK, NEW YORK

VOX

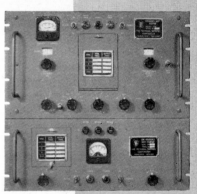

XFL-2

SBT-350 B

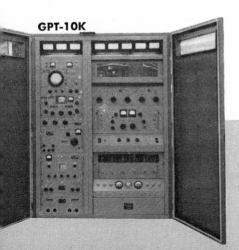

GPT-10K

PTE-1

electron tubes

HELPFUL CHARTS & LITERATURE FREE: Write for CONDENSED TUBE CATALOG, information at a glance, rapid tube data reference tables, 26 pages of condensed information arranged for quick reference. Address your distributor or Amperex direct.

COMMUNICATION

INDUSTRIAL

RECTIFICATION

SPECIAL PURPOSE

RADIATION DETECTION

AMATEUR

ELECTRO-MEDICAL

SEMICONDUCTORS

A FULL RANGE OF TRANSISTORS A
SEMICONDUCTOR DIODES AVAILA

Detailed Data Sheets on any of t
tubes, and applications enginee
service are yours for the asking.

§The AMPEREX types 6268 and 6
are not only improved versions
completely interchangeable
every respect with the Types 4
and 5C22 respectively. They hav
minimum guaranteed life of 1
hours due to the self-contain
self-regulating sources of hydro;

‡Includes sensing plate. For ther
static control, ordered separa
either:

(a) "Water Saver" Thermostat
sembly, Cat. No. S-17024, P
$5.25.

(b) "Overload Protection" Ther
stat Assembly, Cat. No. S-17
$5.25.

**Price on request.

#Price for this tube includes 1
Federal Excise Tax.

Prices subject to change with
notice.

RADIATOR CREDIT FOR FORCED AIR-COOLED TUBES

Tube Type	Users Allowa
889RA	$20
891R, 892R	30
5604	75
5667	20
6445	30
6447	30
6757	75
6801	75

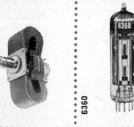
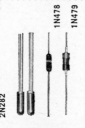

5868/AX9902 · DX151 · 6961 · 6757
5551A · 2N282 · 1N478 · 1N479 · 5894 · 7377
5780 & DX125 · 6360 · 6939 · 18517 · 18515
6977 · 6688 · 6BQ5/EL84 · 7459

Amperex®

ELECTRONIC CORP.
HICKSVILLE, L. I., N. Y.
IN CANADA: ROGERS ELECTRONIC
TUBES & COMPONENTS, 116 VAN-
DERHOOF AVE., TORONTO 17, ONT.

BEAM POWER TUBES

Type No.	Price
807	$2.90
6146	5.00
6159	5.00
PE06/40N	5.95

DIODE, CLIPPER

Type No.	Price
6339	$44.50

COUNTERS, GEIGER

Type No.	Price
75N	$16.50
75NB3	16.50
80N	45.00
85NB3	22.70
90CB	27.00
90NB	27.00
90NB4	27.00
100C	54.00
100CB	58.00
100HB	54.00
100N	43.50
100NB	45.50
120C	90.00
120CB	95.00
120N	90.00
120NB	95.00
150N	61.00
150NB	66.00
153C	91.00
160G	66.00
170G	110.00
180G	50.00
200C	67.00
200CB	71.00
200HB	67.00
200N	56.00
200NB	58.50
230C	43.00
230N	41.00
240C	43.00
240N	41.00
912NB	53.00
18503	28.00
18508	127.00
18509-01	22.40
18510	127.00
18515	186.50
18516	206.25
18517	373.00
18518	412.50

CONDENSERS, VACUUM

Type No.	Price
VC25/20	$22.00
VC25/32	25.25
VC50/20	26.25
VC50/32	29.50
VC100/20	32.00
VC100/32	35.00
VC250/32	75.00

COUNTER, DECADE

Type No.	Price
6370/EIT	$16.50

DIODE, DAMPER

Type No.	Price
#6R3/EY81	$2.80

TWIN DIODE, "PREMIUM QUALITY"

Type No.	Price
#5726/E91AA	$2.10

DIODE, VTVM

Type No.	Price
6923/EA52	$13.00

IGNITRONS

Type No.	Price
‡5551A/652	$65.00
‡5552A/651	99.00
‡5553B/655	245.00
5555/653B	316.00
‡5822A	116.00

TUNING INDICATORS

Type No.	Price
#1M3/DM70	$1.95
#6BR5/EM80	2.45
#6CD7/EM34	3.65
#6DA5/EM81	2.45
#6FG6/EM84	2.95
#DM71	2.00

KLYSTRONS

Type No.	Price
DX122	**
DX123	**
DX124	**
DX151	**

KLYSTRON, REFLEX

Type No.	Price
2K25	$39.50

MAGNETRONS

Type No.	Price
2J42	$160.00
2J48	250.00
4J47	500.00
4J57	270.00
4J58	270.00
4J59	270.00
5586	417.00
5657	417.00
5780A	**
6589	**
6972	325.00

PENTODES

Type No.	Price
#6AU6	$2.10
828	27.50
6083/AX9909	14.25
EFP60	8.75

PENTODE, DUO-DIODE

Type No.	Price
#6DC8/EBF89	$3.25

PENTODE, FRAME GRID

Type No.	Price
5847	$18.21

PENTODES, HI-FI

Type No.	Price
#6BQ5/EL84	$2.35
#6CA7/EL34	6.20
#6CW5/EL86	3.50
#8BQ5/XL84	2.60
#6267/EF86	2.75
#7189	3.60

TRIODE-PENTODES, HI-FI

Type No.	Price
#6BM8/ECL82	$3.00
#50BM8/UCL82	3.00

PENTODES, "PREMIUM QUALITY"

Type No.	Price
5654/E95F	$3.20
6084/E80F	3.75
6227/E80L	3.75
6686/E81F	5.00
6688/E180F	8.00
6689/E83F	4.50
E90F	**
E99F	**

TRIODE-PENTODES

Type No.	Price
#6U8	$3.30
#6BL8/ECF80	3.80

TRIODE-PENTODE "PREMIUM QUALITY"

Type No.	Price
E80CF	**

PENTODES, SUBMINIATURE

Type No.	Price
6007/5913	$1.50
6008/5911	1.50

RECTIFIERS

Type No.	Price
#1S2A/DY87	$2.75
#5AR4/GZ34	4.20
#5R4G-Y	1.90
#6CA4/EZ81	2.10
#6V4/EZ80	1.50
575A	22.15
673	22.15
8020AX	15.00

RECTIFIERS, MERCURY

Type No.	Price
857B	$235.00
866AX	2.65
869B	150.00
869BL	150.00
872AX	9.90
6508	80.00
6693	25.00
7136	25.00
8008AX	9.90

RECTIFIERS, XENON

Type No.	Price
3B28	$7.60
4B32	13.50

VOLTAGE REFERENCE TUBES

Type No.	Price
OE3/85A1	$2.50
OG3/85A2	2.50

VOLTAGE REFERENCE TUBE "PREMIUM QUALITY"

Type No.	Price
5651	$2.50

VOLTAGE REGULATORS

Type No.	Price
OA2	$1.75
OB2	1.90
90C1	2.50
6354/150B2	3.00

TETRODES

Type No.	Price
4-125A	$36.00
4-250A	46.50
4-400A	55.00
4CX250B	45.00
4X150A	38.95
4X150D	38.95
4X250B	42.50
4X250F	42.50
4X500A	121.00
6075/AX9907	250.00
6076/AX9907R	305.00
6079/AX9908	60.00
6155	36.00
6156	46.50
6979	42.50
7527	55.00

TETRODES, BEAM

Type No.	Price
813	$22.65
7378	**

TWIN TETRODES

Type No.	Price
829B	$18.90
832A	15.85
5894/AX9903	25.00
6252/AX9910	25.00
6907	25.00
6939	14.00
7377	**

THYRATRONS

Type No.	Price
2D21	$2.05
3C23	11.98
5560/FG95	33.00
5632/C3J	15.50
5684/C3JA	19.80
5685/C6JA	29.30
5727/E91N	2.70
5949/1907	**
AX260	150.00

THYRATRONS, HYDROGEN

Type No.	Price
§6268/AX9911	$32.50
§6279/AX9912	45.00

THYRATRONS, MERCURY

Type No.	Price
5557/FG17/967/1701	$9.50
5559	22.00
5869/AGR9950	25.00
5870/AGR9951	100.00
6786	200.00
AX105/FG105	53.33

THYRATRONS, XENON

Type No.	Price
2050	$1.85
5544	38.41
5545	29.30

TRIODES

Type No.	Price
#6Q4/EC80	$6.00
#6R4/EC81	2.50
450TH	77.00
450TL	77.00
501R/5759	225.00
502/5760	210.00
502R/5761	235.00
504R	245.00
805	20.00
810	25.55
811A	6.50
812A	6.50
833A	47.90
834	19.30
838	20.00
845	20.85
849	185.00
849A	185.00
880	565.00
889A	221.00
889RA	347.00
891	275.00
891R	430.00
892	270.00
892R	425.00
5604	570.00
5619	423.00
5658	565.00
5666	280.00
5667	370.00

TRIODES (Con't)

Type No.	Price
5771/356	$600.00
5866/AX9900	20.00
5867/AX9901	30.00
5868/AX9902	55.00
5923/AX9904	165.00
5924/AX9904R	231.00
5924A	275.00
6077/AX9906	1675.00
6078/AX9906R	1900.00
6333	**
6445	420.00
6446	305.00
6447	465.00
6756	388.00
6757	535.00
6758	173.00
6759	206.00
6800	350.00
6801	505.00
6960	150.00
6961	210.00
7092	125.00
7459	230.00
DX144/EC56	**
DX145/EC57	**
HF200	49.50
HF201A/468	34.50
HF300	40.50
ZB3200	390.00

TRIODES, FRAME GRID

Type No.	Price
#2ER5	$2.90
#3ER5	2.90
#4ER5	2.90
#6ER5/EC95	2.90
5842	18.21

TRIODE, INDICATOR "PREMIUM QUALITY"

Type No.	Price
6977/DM160	$3.50

TWIN TRIODES

Type No.	Price
#4ES8/XCC189	$4.55
#6AQ8/ECC85	2.60
#6DJ8/ECC88	4.55
#6ES8/ECC189	4.55
#6J6/ECC91	2.80
#9AQ8/PCC85	3.10
#12AT7/ECC81	3.05
#12AU7/ECC82	2.45
#12AX7/ECC83	2.50
#17EW8/HCC85	2.60
5920/E9OCC PQ	2.40
6085/E8OCC PQ	3.75
6201 PQ	3.25
6211 PQ	2.40
6360	**
6463 PQ	2.95
6922/E88CC PQ	4.75
7062/E180CC PQ	2.40
7119/E182CC PQ	4.15
7316	2.00
E92CC	2.40

TRIODE, GLOW DISCHARGE

Type No.	Price
5823/Z900T	$2.50

TRIGGER TUBES, COLD CATHODE

Type No.	Price
Z50T	$2.20
Z70U	1.95
Z300T	4.95
Z804U	4.30

HEPTODE, DUAL CONTROL, "PREMIUM QUALITY"

Type No.	Price
6687/E91H	$1.45

BEAM DEFLECTION TUBE "PREMIUM QUALITY"

Type No.	Price
6218/E80T	$15.00

THE STANDARD OF QUALITY

BG7 SERIES   **BH9** SERIES   **BX** SERIES   **BG9** SERIES

QUARTZ CRYSTALS

BTC-2 SERIES   **TCO-11** SERIES   **TCO-141** SERIES   **BCO-10** SERIES

OVENS

BFN-28A   **BFN-5**

CRYSTAL FILTERS

CCO-7 SERIES

PACKAGED OSCILLATORS

DOUBLE ENDED RINGING LINE

SET OF
THREE MATCHED
DELAY LINES

ULTRASONIC DELAY LINES

BLILEY ELECTRIC CO. UNION STATION BUILDING **ERIE, PENNSYLVANIA**

50

GONSET
MSB-1

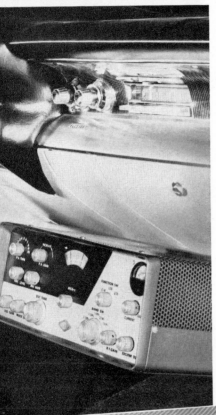
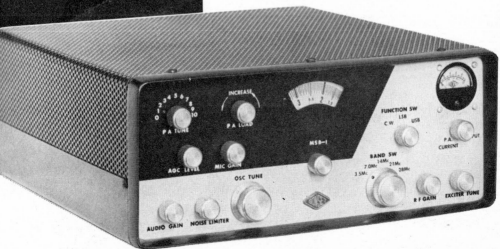

Belden Radio and Electronic

Service Rated—Quality Controlled
in Easy-to-Use Packages!

Ham Transmission Lines—
RG/U Type

8241 Type RG-59/U

8238 Type RG-11/U

Belden 72-ohm RG/U Cables are designed for lowest losses, longer service life, and maximum dependability. Cables are essentially flat with no peaks in attenuation to reduce signal on either high or low frequencies.

Ham Transmission Lines—
Parallel Type

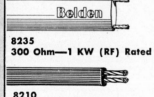

8235
300 Ohm—1 KW (RF) Rated

8210
72 Ohm—1 KW (RF) Rated

Belden transmission line cables are made with brown virgin polyethylene for best weather resistance and lowest losses. Uniform quality control prevents standing waves and mismatches.

Power Supply Cables

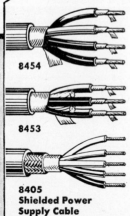

8454

8453

8405
Shielded Power
Supply Cable

Provide dependable service as power supply cords, interconnecting cables on electronic equipment, remote control circuits, special press-to-talk microphone circuits, and other ham applications. Designed for long service life with excellent mechanical and electrical characteristics, and uniform quality. Special jacket offers maximum resistance to abrasion and ozone.

One Wire Source for Everything
Electronic and Electrical

Wire for Every Ham Application

High Voltage Lead

8868

New, improved lead offers smaller diameter and greater flexibility and voltage .150" OD, 25,000 V working voltage and 50,000 V breakdown.

Antenna Rotor Cables

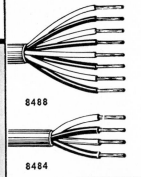

8488

8484

Sturdy, flexible, plastic insulated cable for all Ham antenna rotor applications. Cables are color coded for easier hook-up. Chrome, vinyl plastic jacket resists sun and aging.

Workbench Hook-Up Wire Dispenser Kits

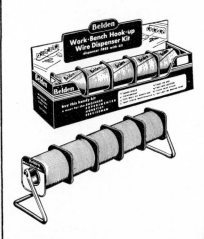

Solve the problems of waste and inconvenience for all users of Hook-Up Wire. Available in 14 most popular assortments of Vinyl, Vinyl-Nylon, Textile, and Teflon* insulated wire. Rack conveniently mounts on workbench or wall at user's finger tips.

*DuPont Trademark.

Belden
WIREMAKER FOR INDUSTRY
SINCE 1902
CHICAGO

Magnet Wire • Lead Wire • Power Supply Cords • Cord Sets and Portable Cord • Aircraft Wires • Electrical Household Cords • Electronic Wires • Welding Cable • Automotive Wire and Cable

IT'S HAMMARLUND...
for SSB *at its very best!*

the
ALL-NEW HQ-180
for general coverage

the
PROVED CHAMPION
of amateur band receivers—HQ-170

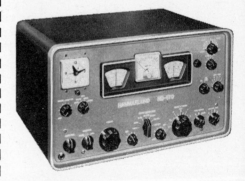

An advanced design 18-tube superheterodyne receiver with full dial coverage from 540 KCS to 30.0 MCS. Bandspread on all amateur bands within frequency range of receiver.

$429.00 (Optional clock-timer, $10.00)

No amateur receiver has ever gained as fine a reputation as the HQ-170. A 17-tube superheterodyne receiver tuning the 6, 10, 15, 20, 40, 80 and 160 meter amateur bands.

$359.00 (Optional clock-timer, $10.00)

Hammarlund shows the way to new standards of performance in SSB with the HQ-170 and HQ-180 receivers. These receivers incorporate the Hammarlund slot filter that allows attenuation up to 60 db for razor-sharp tuning, selectable sideband, selectable IF amplifier tuning, separate product detector, BFO control, crystal calibrator, selectable rates of AVC and other advanced features. Pick the one that suits you best. You can't buy better, or be more satisfied than with a Hammarlund SSB receiver...they're tops!

HAMMARLUND
MANUFACTURING COMPANY, INC.
Established 1910
460 West 34th Street, New York 1, N.Y.

50th Anniversary · A HALF CENTURY OF QUALITY PRODUCTS

In Canada: White Radio, Ltd., 41 West Ave., N. Hamilton, Ont.

54

ARRL

PUBLICATIONS

**Storehouses
of
Information
for:**

Novices

Old Timers

Students

Engineers

**Supplies
for the
Active Amateur**

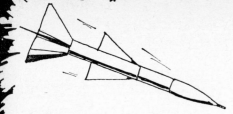

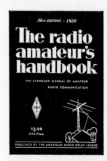

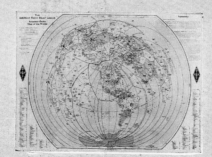

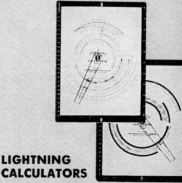

★ **QST** Although primarily a ham magazine, QST is found on the desks of engineers, technicians and just about everyone in the electronics field. There is something for everyone in QST, from the Novice to the Old Timer. QST and ARRL membership $5.00 in U.S.A., $5.25 in Canada, $6.00 elsewhere.

★ **THE RADIO AMATEUR'S HANDBOOK** Internationally recognized, universally consulted. Packed with information essential to the amateur and professional alike. Hundreds of photos, diagrams, charts and tables. $3.50 U.S.A., $4.00 U.S. Poss. and Canada, $4.50 elsewhere; Buckram Edition, $6.00 everywhere.

★ **A COURSE IN RADIO FUNDAMENTALS** A complete course of study for use with the Radio Amateur's Handbook. Applicable to individual home study or class use. $1 U.S.A. proper, $1.25 elsewhere.

★ **HOW TO BECOME A RADIO AMATEUR** Tells what amateur radio is and how to get started in this fascinating hobby. Emphasis is given to the needs of the Novice licensee, with three complete simple amateur stations featured. 50¢.

★ **THE RADIO AMATEUR'S LICENSE MANUAL** Complete with typical questions and answers to all of the FCC amateur exams—Novice, Technician, General and Extra Class. Continually kept up to date. 50¢.

★ **LEARNING THE RADIOTELEGRAPH CODE** For those who find it difficult to master the code. Designed to help the beginner. Contains practice material for home study and classroom use. 50¢.

★ **THE ARRL ANTENNA BOOK** Profusely illustrated, the Antenna Book includes information on theory and operation of antennas for all amateur bands; simple doublets, multi-element arrays, rotaries, long wires, rhombics, mobile whips, etc. $2.00 U.S.A. proper, $2.25 elsewhere.

★ **SINGLE SIDEBAND FOR THE RADIO AMATEUR** A digest of the best SSB articles from QST. Includes discussions of theory and practical "how-to-build-it" descriptions of equipment. $1.50 U.S.A. proper, $1.75 elsewhere.

★ **THE MOBILE MANUAL FOR RADIO AMATEURS** It's a collection of articles on tried and tested equipment that have appeared in QST. A "must" for the bookshelf of anyone interested in the installation, maintenance and operation of mobile stations. $2.50 U.S.A. proper, $3.00 elsewhere.

★ **HINTS AND KINKS** If you build equipment and operate an amateur radio station, you'll find this a mighty valuable book in your shack and workshop. More than 300 practical ideas. $1 U.S.A. proper, $1.25 elsewhere.

QST BINDERS

No need to let your copies of QST rest in a disordered pile. A QST binder will keep them neat and orderly. Each holds a one-year file. $3.00 (available in U.S. and Possessions only).

SUPPLIES

Active amateurs need these supplies: ARRL Logbook, 50¢ U.S.A., 60¢ elsewhere. Minilog, 30¢ U.S.A., 35¢ elsewhere. Radiogram blanks, 35¢ per pad postpaid. Message delivery cards, 5¢ each stamped, 2¢ each unstamped. Members' stationery, 100 sheets $1.00; 250 sheets $2.00; 500 sheets $3.00.

AMERICAN RADIO RELAY LEAGUE

Administrative Headquarters: West Hartford, Connecticut, U. S. A.

..................19....

AMERICAN RADIO RELAY LEAGUE,
West Hartford 7, Conn., U. S. A.

Being genuinely interested in Amateur Radio, I hereby apply for membership in the American Radio Relay League, and enclose $5.00* in payment of one year's dues, $2.50 of which is for a subscription to *QST* for the same period. [Subscription to *QST* alone cannot be entered for one year for $2.50, since membership and subscription are inseparable.] Please begin my subscription with the ....issue.

The call of my station is.........................

The class of my operator's license is...............

I belong to the following radio societies............

....

Send my Certificate of Membership ☐ or Membership Card ☐ (Indicate which) to the address below:

Name..

....

....

A bona fide interest in amateur radio is the only essential requirement, but full voting membership is granted only to licensed radio amateurs of the United States and Canada. Therefore, if you have a license, please be sure to indicate it above.

*$5.00 in the United States and Possessions.
$5.25, U. S. funds, in Canada.
$6.00, U. S. funds, in all other countries.

ALLIED RADIO EVERYTHING IN **ELECTRONICS**
CATALOG 190
1960
INDEX: PAGE 437

OUR 39th YEAR

100 N. WESTERN AVENUE • CHICAGO 80, ILLINOIS
TELEPHONE: HAymarket 1-6800

the most widely used
Amateur Supply Guide
KEEP IT HANDY...

get *everything* from our largest stocks of station gear and electronic supplies— immediate delivery at lowest prices...

ALLIED
gives you <u>every</u> buying advantage

HIGHEST TRADES: Get the absolute most for your old equipment. Tell us what you've got and what you want—we'll come up fast with the best deal anywhere.

RECONDITIONED GEAR: Large selection, new set guarantee. Ask for latest list of top reconditioned equipment at lowest prices.

EASIEST TERMS: Available on all orders over $20; only $2 down up to $50; $5 down from $51-200; only $10 down from $201 up; up to 24 months to pay. Extra: 15-day trial on all ham gear.

HAM-TO-HAM HELP

Our staff of over **30** Amateurs goes all-out to give you all the help you want. You'll like the kind of personal attention Amateurs have enjoyed at Allied for so many years. Get to know:

W8CZE
Jack Schneider
(Allied's "Mr. Ham")

W9WHF
Jim Sommerville
(write to him for that best deal)

W9BHD
Joe Huffman
(in the Ham Shack)

W9HLA
Joe Gizzi
(in the Ham Shack)

ALLIED RADIO
100 N. WESTERN AVE., CHICAGO 80, ILL.

Serving the Amateur for 39 Years

60

THE NEW RME 6900

HAM BAND RECEIVER
Model 6900

Amateur Net
$349.00

RME 6900

The design and production of communications receivers today is considerably different than in past years for two principal reasons. Costs have risen precipitously; to manufacture a receiver in the face of this and keep the price reasonable requires good tooling, long runs, and little allowance for error. Secondly, there are greater demands placed on receiver operation than ever before, versatility . . . handling ease . . . yes, amateurs have come to ask for parameters of performance almost unheard of in past years.

RME in announcing the new 6900 states without equivocation that this receiver performance is unmatched by anything near its price class. The 6900 is engineered to give optimum service for all modes of amateur communications — not merely one. Engineered under the supervision of Russ Planck, W9RGH, the 6900 has as many advanced pioneering features as its extraordinary namesake, the world famous RME69, which was the first band-switching communications receiver ever produced — over 20 years ago and still widely used today.

What makes the 6900 so Hot? First, meticulous attention to details so that every circuit is performing in an optimum manner. Second, an ingenious function selector, the Modemaster. Every circuit in the 6900 is designed to provide high selectivity; frequency stability, sensitivity and low internal noise. Finally, inclusion of *all* function controls necessary for a modern communications receiver . . . vernier control knob with overide clutch for fast tuning; RF gain; AF gain; antenna trimmer; band selector, stand-by/receive/calibrate/transmit; ANL; T-notch filter; calibrate adjustment; band selector.

Whether you operate CW; SSB; or AM, you will have the almost uncanny feeling the 6900 was designed solely for you — this is the test of a modern communications receiver that we believe only ours can meet on the operating desk.

- **CONTROLS:** 11½" Single Slide Rule Tuning Dial; Logging Scale.
- **COVERAGE:** 80, 40, 20, 15 and 10 on 5 bands plus 10 to 11 mc for WWV or WWVH.
- **Peak Selectivity plus tunable "T" Notch.**
- **Internal 100 kc Hermetically Sealed Crystal Calibrator.**
- **500-ohm Output.**
- **Noise Limiter for SSB and CW, AM.**
- **Separate Detector for Single Sideband.**
- **S Meter Calibrated in 6 db Steps Above S9 for Better Reading.**

- **Improved Fast Attack AVC Circuit.**
- **Selectable Sideband.**
- **Panel of Attractive Grey "Clad-Rex" Vinyl Bonded to Aluminum with Charcoal Trim.**
- **Front Panel Controls Re-Grouped for Ultimate Operating Ease and Convenience.**
- **SENSITIVITY:** 1 mv. 30% Modulation for 100 mw output.
- **S-N-R:** 10 db at 1 mv Input.
- **SELECTIVITY:** 500 cps, 6 db down, in CW mode.

offers optimum performance on SSB, AM or CW with no compromises

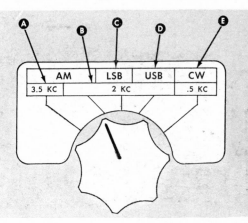

NEW...VERSATILE

Model 6900

MODEMASTER SWITCH

Gives One Hand Knob Control of 5 Distinct Functions

(A) When in the indicated AM position, a *full-wave* diode detector is used. The IF frequency response curve is 3.5 kc wide at 6 db down and, the AVC system is switched for fast attack/fast decay operation. The AM band width for this area is 3.5 kc.

(B) In this AM position all of the conditions described for function A above remain the same except that the IF response curve is narrowed to 2 kc to reject nearby signals on crowded bands.

(C) In the LSB (Lower Side Band of SSB carrier) position a series of steps occur.

    (1) The AVC system is switched to a fast attack/slow decay performance.

    (2) The Beat Frequency Oscillator is turned on and positioned for desired sideband reception.

    (3) The second conversion oscillator frequency also shifts for reception of desired sideband while the IF response curve remains the same.

    (4) An advanced Product Detector switches in to replace the Diode Detector in all SSB and CW positions.

(D) In the USB (Upper Side Band) the changes cited in function C above also occur but are designed to accommodate the Upper Side Band.

(E) When switched to the CW position:

    (1) The band pass of the IF System is reduced to 500 cycles (.5kc)

    (2) The BFO Injection Control and BFO Pitch Control becomes operational.

    (3) The AVC system is changed for optimum when operating under CW conditions.

    (4) The second conversion oscillator is positioned for reception of the upper sideband beat note.

See your RME distributor or write to

Dept. HB-60, BUCHANAN, MICH.

63

EXPERIENCED HAMS SAY
"MAKE MINE MOSLEY"
FOR BEST-EVER ANTENNA PERFORMANCE!

TRAPMASTER 10-15-20 METER ROTARY AND VERTICAL ANTENNAS

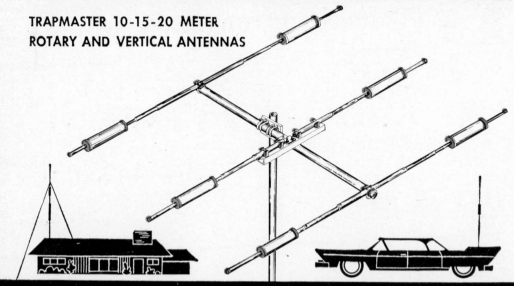

100% RUST-PROOF! STABLE ALL-WEATHER PERFORMANCE! GUARANTEED!

MODEL TA-33 — Three-element beam rated to full KW. 8 db. forward gain; 25 db. front-to-back. 1.1/1 SWR. Max. element length 28'. Boom length 14'. Turning radius 15½'. Shipping weight 53 lbs.

Net Each **$99.75**

MODEL TA-32 — Two-element beam rated to full KW. 5.5 db. forward gain; 20 db. front-to-back. 1.1/1 SWR. Max. element length 28'. Boom length 7'. Turning radius 14'5". Shipping weight 32 lbs.

Net Each **$69.50**

MODEL TA-33 Jr.—Three-element beam rated to 300W. 8 db. forward gain; 25 db. front-to-back. 1.5/1 SWR. Max. element length 26'8". Boom length 12'. Turning radius 14'9". Shipping weight 28 lbs.

Net Each **$69.50**

MODEL TA-32 Jr.—Two-element beam rated to 300W. 5.5 db. forward gain; 20 db. front-to-back. 1.5/1 SWR. Max. element length 26'8". Boom length 6'. Turning radius 13'9". Shipping weight 22 lbs.

Net Each **$49.50**

MODEL V-3—10-15-20M Vertical rated to full KW. Electrical quarter wave on each band. Requires only short radials. 11'6" from base to tip. Complete with baseplate, guy line, necessary hardware. Shipping weight 8 lbs.

Net Each **$22.95**

MODEL V-3 Jr.— Same as V-3 but rated only to 300W. Overall height 11'9". Shipping weight 6 lbs.

Net Each **$17.95**

MODEL V-4-6 — Broad-band Vertical with automatic band-switching 10 to 40M. Rated to full KW. Maintains electrical quarter wave on each band. Complete with baseplate, base insulator, guy rope, hardware. Max. height 20'. Shipping weight 12 lbs.

Net Each **$27.95**

MODEL D-4BC BASE LOADING COIL — for 75 and 80M operation of V-4-6 Antenna. Mounts easily on base section. Shipping weight 3 lbs.

Net Each **$14.95**

POWERMASTER SINGLE-BAND ROTARY ANTENNAS

Full-sized 3-element arrays 100% rust-proof! Each designed for a single band—10, 15 or 20M. Aluminum elements and boom, stainless steel hardware. 8.9 db. gain on all bands. 1.1/1 SWR.

MODEL A-310 — For 10M. 28 db. front-to-back. Max. element length 15'3". Boom length 12'. Turning radius 11'1". Shipping weight 33 lbs.

Net Each **$37.50**

MODEL A-315 — For 15M. 28 db. front-to-back. Max. element length 17'8". Boom length 12'. Turning radius 13'2". Shipping weight 34 lbs.

Net Each **$42.50**

MODEL A-320 — For 20M. 25 db. front-to-back. Max. element length 35'4". Boom length 14'. Turning radius 18'9". Shipping weight 40 lbs.

Net Each **$77.25**

TRAPMOBILE 10-15-20M MOBILE ANTENNA

MODEL MA-3 — 10, 15, 20 meter Mobile version of the famed TRAPMASTER. Stainless steel whip sections. Fits standard mounts. Length 7'8". Shipping weight 8 lbs.

Net Each **$19.95**

MOSLEY ELECTRONICS, INC., 8622 St. Charles Rock Rd., Saint Louis 14, Missouri

If It's Shown
In This Handbook

Henry Has It!

HENRY gets the new equipment First
YOU get the world's best Terms!

Low Terms

You get the best terms anywhere because Henry finances all the terms with his easy time payment plan. 10% down (or your trade-in accepted as down payment), 20 months to pay.

Long Trades

Henry *wants* to trade and he trades *big*. YOU get truly liberal allowances on your equipment. Tell us what you want to trade. We also pay cash for used equipment.

Complete Stocks

Henry has *everything* in the amateur equipment field, new or used . . . transmitters or receivers, and Henry has the NEW equipment FIRST.

Low Prices

Henry's large purchasing power means low prices to you. You just can't beat our wholesale prices.

100% Satisfaction

Henry gives you a guarantee of *"100% satisfaction"* or your *money back at the end of a 10 day trial.*

Write, wire, phone or visit either store today.

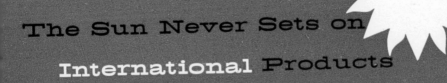

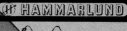

Look for HENRY

Whenever there's outstanding new amateur equipment...
priced to represent full and honest value...you'll find
a HENRY...Ted or Bob...right in the middle!

To prove the point: Here's Ted in the middle of four of Gonset's newest and finest...

The exclusive, new mobile sideband transceiver, MSB-1. And G-63, the biggest amateur communications receiver value in the 200 dollar price bracket. At Ted's elbow is the fine-performing, in-big-demand SSB transmitter/exciter, GSB-100 and Gonset's "more watts per dollar" GSB-100 linear amplifier.

● Place your order with HENRY...
for these new Gonset items...or *any* items in the big Gonset line. You'll find everything in the tremendous Henry stocks... for immediate, over-the-counter delivery or same-day shipment on mail orders. If you can't drop in, just write, wire or phone.

● Compare Henry's easiest terms...
only 6c per 1.00 per year...20 months or longer to pay...Only 10% down (or your trade-in as down payment)...No finance charges if paid within 90 days...More flexible financing because the Henrys handle their own financing.

● Henry gives you bigger trade-ins...
Henry...Ted and Bob...*want to trade*...will make you truly liberal allowances on your old equipment. Tell them what you want to trade.

Butler 1, Missouri
ORchard 9-3127

Henry Radio Stores

11240 West Olympic Blvd.
Los Angeles 64, Calif.
Ph: GRanite 7-6701

BIG TRADE-INS

"World's Largest Distributors of Short Wave Receivers"

Megacycle Meter

0.1 Mc to 940.0 Mc

Compact, lightweight and completely portable, these advanced grid-dip meters are extremely useful in determining resonant frequency of tuned circuits, antennas, transmission lines, by-pass condensers and chokes. Measure inductance and capacitance and can also be used as signal generators, wave meters, frequency meters and in many other applications. Available in the frequency ranges indicated. Special protective carrying case can be supplied for easy handling of partial or complete set of Megacycle Meters.

MODEL 59
(Power Supply)

Power supply unit consists of full-wave rectifier with voltage regulator tube and meter indicating grid current. Designed for use with Oscillators shown below. Dimensions: 5-⅛" x 6-⅛" x 7-½".

MODEL 59 OSCILLATOR
(Specifications)

Frequency Range: 2.2 Mc to 420 Mc with 7 plug-in coils
Frequency Accuracy: ±2% (individually calibrated)
Output: CW or 120-cycle modulation. Provision for external modulation.
Power Source: 117 V, 50-60 cycles, 20 watts (when used with Model 59 Power Supply)
Dimensions: 3-3/4" dia. x 2" deep

MODEL 59-LF OSCILLATOR
(Specifications)

Frequency Range: 100 Kc to 4.5Kc with 4 plug-in coils
Frequency Accuracy: ±2% (individually calibrated)
Output: CW or 120 cycle modulation. Provision for external modulation
Power Source: 117 V, 50-60 cycles, 30 watts (when used with Model 59 Power Supply)
Dimensions: 3-5/8" x 4-5/8" x 4-5/8"

MODEL 59-UHF OSCILLATOR
(Specifications)

Frequency Range: 420 Mc to 940 Mc in one range
Frequency Accuracy: ±2% (individually calibrated)
Output: CW or 120 cycle modulation. Provision for external modulation.
Power Source: 117 V, 50-60 cycles, 30 watts (when used with Model 59 Power Supply)
Dimensions: 3-5/8" x 4-5/8" x 4-5/8"

Vacuum Tube Voltmeter

(Model 162-R)

An extremely accurate instrument for providing reliable voltage and resistance measurements in laboratories, production lines and service shops. Advanced design permits the instruments use in either a horizontal or vertical position while push buttons provide direct RANDOM ACCESS to all functions and ranges to reduce operator error and fatigue. Highly developed, balanced degenerative amplifier provides stable zero and good overload protection. Single zero control for all ranges. Fully insulated A-C probe prevents short circuits and compartment provides lead and probe storage. Large, illuminated meters permit direct, easy readings.

SPECIFICATIONS

AC Voltage Range: Six ranges; 1, 3, 10, 30, 100 and 300 rms volts full-scale. Diode probe is peak reading. AC scales are calibrated to indicate rms value of a sine wave, or 70.7% of peak value.
DC Voltage Range: 1, 3, 10, 30, 100, 300 and 1000 positive and negative volts full-scale.
Ohms Range: 0.2 ohms to 500 megohms in 7 decades with 10, 100, 1,000, 10,000, 100,000 ohms, 1 megohm and 10 megohms mid-scale reading.
Voltage Accuracy: Better than ±3% of full scale.
Frequency Response: Down less than 1 db at 20 cps. Resonant frequency of probe with input terminals shorted is 350 Mc.
Input Impedance: (a) AC—Input capacitance is approximately 5 uuf; input resistance is approximately 3 megohms at low frequencies. (b) DC—Input resistance is 100 megohms for all ranges.
Power Supply: 117 volts, 50-60 cycles, 15 watts.
Dimensions: Case 10" high x 6" wide x 6" deep.
Weight: Approximately 8 pounds.

Write for free, illustrated catalog

Laboratory Standards

MEASUREMENTS
A McGraw-Edison Division
BOONTON, NEW JERSEY

HARVEY

 RCA

AUTHORIZED DISTRIBUTORS

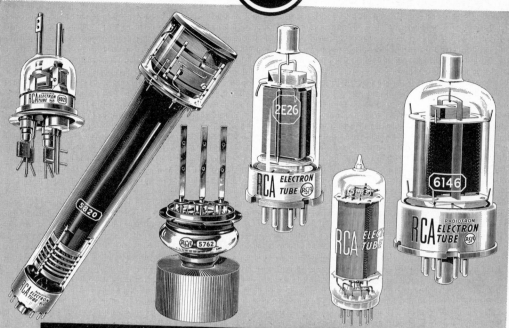

RCA Tubes and Harvey Service...
For Double Dependability!

HARVEY's line of RCA tubes is so complete, that HARVEY can fill virtually any requirement . . . right from stock . . . and *deliver at almost a moment's notice.*

This is particularly important to AM, FM, and TV Broadcasters, Industrial and Commercial users, Amateurs, and Service-Technicians, all of whom depend on tubes for sustained operation of important electronic equipment.

Write, Wire or Phone for
PROMPT HARVEY SERVICE

Visit Harvey's New Ham Radio Center. The latest and best in ham gear is always on display.

Telephone **hrc** JUdson 2-1500

HARVEY
RADIO COMPANY, INC.
103 West 43rd St., New York 36, N. Y.

72

RADIO SHACK DELIVERS

...*fast*... to Boston, Boise or Bombay ... from one of America's newest, most modern warehouses! Orders received, processed, packed, checked and delivered to shipping department in *20 minutes average time!* All orders shipped same day.

UP TO $500 IN HAM GEAR

Hallicrafters, National, Gonset, Collins, Hammarlund or any of the dozens of other names you know and respect as the finest in the field!

AMATEUR NET	MINIMUM DOWN PAYMENT
$20 to $50	Only $2 down
$50 to $200	Only $5 down
$200 to $500	Only $10 down
Over $500 — Write for terms	
UP TO 24 MONTHS TO PAY	

FOR $10 DOWN

via a fabulous new Radio Shack Time Payment Plan that lets you buy the ham gear (or any other type of electronic equipment) you've always wanted for *as little as $2 down —*

P.S. TOP TRADES, TOO!

Fill out the coupon now. We'll quote you the kind of jumbo trade-in allowance we're known for throughout the ham world!

FREE BARGAIN CATALOGS

12-month subscription yours FREE. Page after page, month after month, famous Radio Shack Bargain Catalogs give you first crack at exclusive scoops in ham gear, hi-fi equipment, optical goods, etc. Check coupon now.

GIANT 1960 ELECTRONIC GUIDE

Over 40,000 items, plus articles, etc., in the biggest, most costly handbook we've ever produced! 312 book-size 8½ x 11 pages crammed with illustrations, engineering data, charts, complete product specifications. Practically an electronics education! Only 35¢.

73

Test Site where TACO antennas are developed and 'performance tested.'

TACO
Means Antennas

...for here is an organization of engineers, technicians and skilled craftsmen devoted to the single purpose of conceiving, developing and manufacturing fine antennas and antenna systems for every military, industrial and home entertainment need.

The Doploc antenna system for tracking orbital bodies. Designed, produced and installed by TACO.

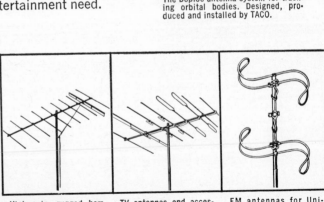

TACO telemetering antennas for all commercial and military needs.

High-gain, rugged ham beams for the 6 meter, 2 meter and 1¼ meter bands.

TV antennas and accessories available in a variety of models.

FM antennas for Unidirectional and Omnidirectional reception.

WRITE FOR COMPLETE DETAILS, STATING ANTENNAS OF INTEREST.

TECHNICAL APPLIANCE CORPORATION Sherburne, New York

HAMMARLUND HAS IT!
And ARROW Has Hammarlund!

Hammarlund Model HQ-145

The HQ-145 is feature-full and works like a charm. Covers .54-30 mc, double conversion from 10-30mc. Has crystal filter and the well-known Hammarlund 60 db slot filter. Electrical bandspread is provided with calibrated markings on the 80, 40, 20, 15 and 10 meter bands. Extremely stable, incorporating voltage regulation and temperature compensation.

Amateur Net $269.00
Amateur Net (With Clock) $279.00

Hammarlund Model HQ-170

All the best features of the finest SSB converters, plus the best features of the finest amateur receivers wrapped up in a single, outstanding receiver. Covers the 6, 10, 15, 20, 40, 80 and 160 meter amateur bands. Separate vernier tuning. Dual and triple conversion 17-tube superheterodyne. Adjustable 60 db notch filter. IF passband tuning. Adjustable AVC.

Amateur Net $359.00
Amateur Net (With Clock) $369.00

Hammarlund Model HQ-180

SSB, full coverage—.54 to 30 MCS. Band spread cal. for 80, 40, 20, 15 and 10 meter bands. Triple conversion 18-tube superhet. with ANL and AVC adjustable 60db notch filter. Separate linear detector. Tuned IF amp. with 7 selectivity positions. Selectable upper, lower or both side-bands. ± 2 KCS BFO control. Built-in 100 KCS xtal cal. Dial scale reset.

Amateur Net $429.00
Amateur Net (With Clock) $439.00

Hammarlund Model HQ-110

Dual conversion, 12 tube superheterodyne. Full coverage of 6, 10, 15, 20, 40, 80 and 160 meter amateur bands. Built-in crystal calibrator. Q-multiplier. Separate linear detector for SSB and CW. Separate stabilized BFO.

Amateur Net $249.00
Amateur Net (With Clock) $259.00

Hammarlund Model HQ-100

The hottest, fastest selling general coverage receiver on the market! Continuous tuning from 540 KCS to 30 MCS. Electrical bandspread tuning. Q multiplier for continuously variable selectivity, 10-tube superheterodyne with automatic noise limiter.

Amateur Net $189.00
Amateur Net (With Clock) $199.00

AUTHORIZED DISTRIBUTORS OF ELECTRONIC PARTS & EQUIPMENT
Arrow's Export Dept. Ships To All Parts Of The World

ARROW ▲ ELECTRONICS, INC.

65 Cortlandt Street, New York 7, N. Y. • DIgby 9-4730
525 Jericho Turnpike, Mineola, N. Y. • PIoneer 6-8686

FREE Send your QSL for FREE HAM BAND CHART

Trade-ins Welcomed
Your old equipment is worth money at Arrow. Get Arrow's deal before you buy.

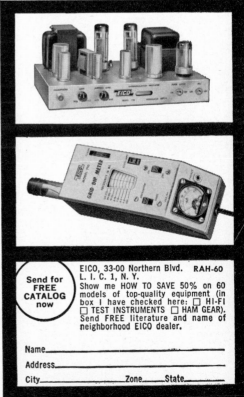

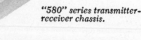

IF GONSET MAKES IT . . . ELMAR STOCKS IT!

In Northern California...in the Bay Area...long-experienced and newcoming amateurs alike have come to recognize Elmar Electronics as their best source for Gonset products.

As one of the very largest electronic suppliers to amateur, industrial, O.E.M. and R&D, Elmar stocks the Gonset line *in depth*—just as they stock over 200 other nationally known lines.

Elmar is one *big* store where you can expect-- and receive—courteous, friendly service...here *every purchaser*...even the smallest, is ten feet tall!

GET YOUR GONSET MSB-1 MOBILE SSB TRANSCEIVER AT ELMAR

Features: 125 watts P.E.P. input . . . upper and lower sideband and CW . . . all band operation . . . 10 through 80 meters . . . high stability VFO . . . VOX . . . push-to-talk provisions . . . receiver sensitivity better than 1 microvolt . . . 9 mc band-pass crystal filter for excellent transmitting and receiving selectivity . . . 100 kc crystal calibrator available as accessory . . . 12V DC power supply is transistorized . . . AC power supply is also available. MSB-1 is only 5″ High, 12″ Wide and 12″ Deep, weighs but 15 pounds less power supply . . . fits conveniently under dash of car . . . also makes a fine showing on any well-appointed operating desk. *Get your MSB-1 at Elmar.*

Order by mail too...a complete, well staffed department gives prompt, efficient attention to your mail orders.

Serving the 11 Western States...
Alaska...the Pacific Area.

Phone Elmar...

TEmplebar 4-3311

ELMAR electronics

140 - 11th Street at Madison, Oakland 7, California

TWX-OA73   W. U. FAX

PENTA POWER TUBES

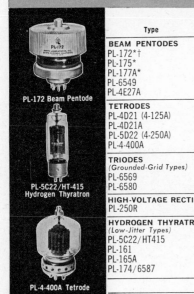

PL-172 Beam Pentode

PL-5C22/HT-415
Hydrogen Thyratron

PL-4-400A Tetrode

PL-4E27A Beam Pentode

PL-6549 Beam Pentode

PL-184 Complete
Socket for PL-172

Type	Fil. Volts	Fil. Current Amps.	Plate Diss. Max. W.	Plate Volt Max.	Plate Current Ma., Max.	Screen Voltage Max.	Price
BEAM PENTODES							
PL-172*†	6.0	8.2	1000	3,000	1000	600	$135.00
PL-175*	5.0	14.5	400	4,000	350	800	50.00
PL-177A*	6.0	3.3	75	2,000	175	600	25.00
PL-6549	6.0	3.3	75	2,000	175	600	25.00
PL-4E27A	5.0	7.5	125	4,000	200	750	40.00
TETRODES							
PL-4D21 (4-125A)	5.0	6.5	125	3,000	225	600	36.00
PL-4D21A	5.0	6.5	175	3,000	225	600	37.50
PL-5D22 (4-250A)	5.0	14.5	250	4,000	350	800	46.50
PL-4-400A	5.0	14.5	400	4,000	350	800	48.00
TRIODES (Grounded-Grid Types)							
PL-6569	5.0	14.5	250	4,000	300	μ=45	37.50
PL-6580	5.0	14.5	400	4,000	350	μ=45	45.00
HIGH-VOLTAGE RECTIFIER							
PL-250R	5.0	10.5	...	60,000**	250	...	30.50
HYDROGEN THYRATRONS (Low-Jitter Types)							
PL-5C22/HT415	6.3	10.5	...	16,000	325 amp	...	36.00
PL-161	6.3	10.5	...	16,000	325 amp	...	48.00
PL-165A	6.3	7.8	...	12,000	225 amp	...	48.00
PL-174/6587	6.3	10.5	...	16,000	325 amp	...	48.00

*Zero-suppressor Voltage Type **Peak Inverse Voltage Rating †External Anode Type

INSIST ON PENTA TUBES FOR LONG LIFE, HIGH QUALITY

The reputation of Penta power tubes for uniformly high quality, adherence to specifications, and exceptionally long life is the reason major electronic equipment manufacturers, amateurs and broadcast engineers insist upon them. Exacting quality control and life testing under conditions simulating actual use assure you of maximum performance and durability. Whether your requirements are for the new beam pentodes—for applications where superior linearity and low distortion at high efficiency are critical requirements—the new miniaturized hydrogen thyratrons—or the older conventional types—Penta is your logical source.

ACCESSORIES

Type	Description	Price
PL-C1	Glass Chimney for PL-4-400A and PL-175	$ 6.00
PL-184	Socket for PL-172, including chimney, built-in screen-grid and suppressor-grid by-pass capacitors	38.75
PL-184A	Socket for PL-172, including chimney and built-in screen-grid by-pass capacitors. Suppressor-grid grounded.	38.75
PL-C184	Plastic chimney, only, for PL-172	3.00

PENTA LABORATORIES, INC.

312 North Nopal Street, Santa Barbara, California

Sales Representatives in Principal Cities

82

Learn Code the EASY Way

Beginners, Amateurs and Experts alike recommend the **INSTRUCTOGRAPH,** *to learn code and increase speed.*

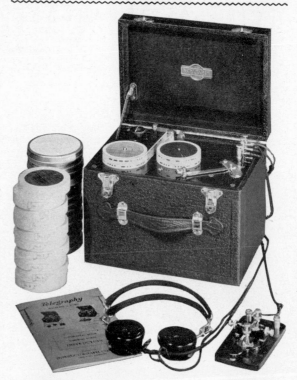
Learning the INSTRUCTOGRAPH way will give you a decided advantage in qualifying for Amateur or Commercial examinations, and to increase your words per minute to the standard of an expert. The Government uses a machine in giving examinations.

Motor with adjustable speed and spacing of characters on tapes permit a speed range of from 3 to 40 words per minute. A large variety of tapes are available — elementary, words, messages, plain language and coded groups. Also an "Airways" series for those interested in Aviation.

MAY BE PURCHASED OR RENTED

The INSTRUCTOGRAPH is made in several models to suit your purse and all may be purchased on convenient monthly payments if desired. These machines may also be rented on very reasonable terms and if when renting you should decide to buy the equipment the first three months rental may be applied in full on the purchase price.

ACQUIRING THE CODE

It is a well-known fact that practice and practice alone constitutes ninety per cent of the entire effort necessary to "Acquire the Code," or, in other words, learn telegraphy either wire or wireless. The Instructograph supplies this ninety per cent. It takes the place of an expert operator in teaching the student. It will send slowly at first, and gradually faster and faster, until one is just naturally copying the fastest sending without conscious effort.

BOOK OF INSTRUCTIONS

Other than the practice afforded by the Instructograph, all that is required is well directed practice instruction, and that is just what the Instructograph's "Book of Instructions" does. It supplies the remaining ten per cent necessary to acquire the code. It directs one how to practice to the best advantage, and how to take advantage of the few "short cuts" known to experienced operators, that so materially assists in acquiring the code in the quickest possible time. Therefore, the Instructograph, the tapes, and the book of instructions is everything needed to acquire the code as well as it is possible to acquire it.

The Instructograph

ACCOMPLISHES THESE PURPOSES:

FIRST: *It teaches you to receive telegraph symbols, words and messages.*

SECOND: *It teaches you to send perfectly.*

THIRD: *It increases your speed of sending and receiving after you have learned the code.*

With the Instructograph it is not necessary to impose on your friends. It is always ready and waiting for you. You are also free from Q.R.M. experienced in listening through your receiver. This machine is just as valuable to the licensed amateur for increasing his speed as to the beginner who wishes to obtain his amateur license.

Postal Card **WILL BRING FULL PARTICULARS IMMEDIATELY**

THE INSTRUCTOGRAPH CO.

4707 SHERIDAN ROAD
357 WEST MANCHESTER AVE.

CHICAGO 40, ILLINOIS
LOS ANGELES 3, CALIFORNIA

FORT ORANGE
Radio Distributing Co. INC.
904 BROADWAY ALBANY 4 N Y U S A
AMATEUR HEADQUARTERS

CALL ALBANY HE 6-8411 **Cable Address "Uncledave"** **NITES 77-5891**

BEFORE OR AFTER YOU EARN YOUR TICKET, REMEMBER: COME TO UNCLEDAVE FOR ADVICE—COME TO UNCLEDAVE FOR BEST PRICES ON TOP LINES!

HALLICRAFTER MODEL SX-110

FREQUENCY COVERAGE: Broadcast Band 538-1600 kc plus three short-wave bands covers 1550 kc-34 mc.

FEATURES: Slide rule bandspread dial calibrated for 80, 40, 20, 15 and 10 meter amateur bands and 11 meter citizens' band. Separate bandspread tuning condenser, crystal filter, antenna trimmer, "S" Meter, one r-f, two i-f stages. **$159.50**

HALLICRAFTER MODEL HT-32-A

FEATURES: 5.0 mc. quartz crystal filter — rejection 50 db. or more. Bridged-tee sideband modulator. C.T.O. direct reading in kilocycles to less than 300 cycles from reference point. 144 watts plate input (P.E.P. two-tone). Five band output (80, 40, 20, 15, 10 meters). All modes of transmission — CW, AM, S.S.B. Unwanted sideband down 50 db. or more. Distortion products down 30 db. or more. Carrier suppression down 50 db. or more. Both sidebands transmitted on AM. Precision gear driven C.T.O. Exclusive Hallicrafters patented sideband selection. Logarithmic meter for accuracy tuning and carrier level adjustment. Ideal CW keying and break-in operation. Full voice control system built in. **$695.00**

HALLICRAFTER MODEL SX-101-A

FEATURES: Complete coverage of six ham bands — 160, 80, 40, 20, 15, 10 meters. Large slide rule dial. Band-in-use scales individually illuminated. Illuminated S-meter. Dual scale S-meter. S-meter zero point independent of sensitivity control. S-meter functions with AVC off. Special 10 Mc position for WWV. Dual conversion. Exclusive Hallicrafters upper-lower side band selection. Second conversion oscillators quartz crystal controlled. Tee-notch filter. Full gear drive from tuning knob to gang condensers — absolute reliability. 40:1 tuning knob ratio. Built-in precision 100 kc evacuated marker crystal. Vernier pointer adjustment. Five steps of selectivity from 500 cycles to 5000 cycles. Precision temperature compensation plus Hallicrafters exclusive production heat cycling for lowest drift. Direct coupled series noise limiter for improved noise reduction. **$399.50**

HALLICRAFTER MODEL S-107

COVERAGE: Standard Broadcast from 540-1630 kc plus four short wave bands over 2.5-31 and 48-54.5 mc. Intermediate frequency; 455 kc. **$94.95**

HALLICRAFTER SPEAKER

MODEL R-48. Latest design uses new 5½" x 7½" eliptical assembly. Alnico V 3.16 oz. magnet has fully saturated air gap for exceptional damping, distortion-free response. Switch at rear for selection of music or voice response. Use with SX-101A, SX-100, SX-110, SX-62A, or any receiver with 3.2 ohm output. Gray steel 6⅝" high x 13¼" wide x 8¼" deep cabinet. Shipping weight approximately 9 lbs. **$19.95**

MODEL S-108

FREQUENCY COVERAGE: Broadcast band 538-1600 kc plus three S/W bands 1550 kc-34 mc.

FEATURES: Slide rule bandspread dial calibrated for 80, 40, 20, 15 and 10 meter amateur bands and 11 meter citizens' band. One r-f, two i-f and separate bandspread tuning condenser. Temperature compensated oscillator and built-in speaker. **$129.50**

Write Uncledave W2APF with your needs and problems.

FREE!
- NET CONTROL
- LOG SHEETS
- MESSAGE PADS

WE SPECIALIZE IN FOREIGN TRADE

TIME PAYMENTS 18 Months to pay life insurance at no extra cost

24 HR. SERVICE on stock items

85

SAVE TIME

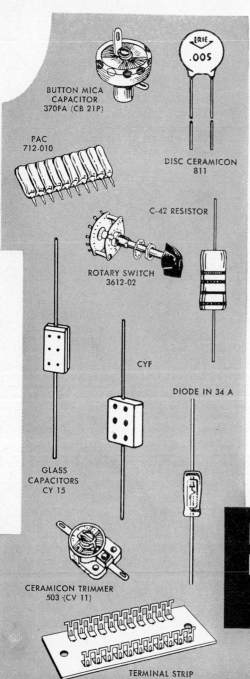

BUTTON MICA CAPACITOR 370FA (CB 21P)

PAC 712-010

DISC CERAMICON 811

C-42 RESISTOR

ROTARY SWITCH 3612-02

CYF

DIODE IN 34 A

GLASS CAPACITORS CY 15

CERAMICON TRIMMER 503 (CV 11)

TERMINAL STRIP

WITH ONE-SOURCE PICKUP AT YOUR ERIE DISTRIBUTOR

For radio work or radio fun, the one place to go for a complete selection of electronic components is your Erie distributor.

The man behind the counter can recommend just the right parts from his complete stocks of all Erie Resistor products as well as complete lines of Corning and Grigsby components. These include:

Erie diodes, ceramic and silver mica capacitors, disc ceramicons, feed-thru ceramicons, PAC's, tubular trimmers, ceramicon trimmers and terminal strips.

Corning fixed glass capacitors, glass trimmer capacitors, and glass resistors.

Grigsby rotary and lever switches.

If you do not know your local Erie distributor, write to us direct.

**Electronics Distributor Division
ERIE RESISTOR CORPORATION**
Erie, Pennsylvania
ERIE

86

about Ham Equipment

... and when you talk with us, in person or by mail, you will discover we have a genuine interest in hams and ham radio. (As a matter of fact, you'll find us steeped in ham radio right up to our earphones.) Whether you're a novice or an oldtimer, you'll enjoy talking with the many hams on our staff—W2FZ, W2AQA, W2BUS, W2JBA, W2MKH, K2VVV, K2VBD, to name a few. They'll show you the top ham equipment values...all name brands in stock, ready for immediate off-shelf delivery to save you time and money:

RCA · Hammarlund · National · Hallicrafters · Gonset · UTC · Johnson · Millen · Triad · Ohmite · Eimac · Shure · Advance · Bud · Stancor · Thordarson · Triplett · Mallory · Astatic · Simpson · Barker & Williamson · and hundreds of others.

Talk to Terminal
About Everything in Electronics ...

Ham equipment, industrial equipment, high fidelity ... Terminal has the fullest selection of name brand products that you'll ever want to see ... Talk to us first—find out about the dollar-saving advantage of Terminal's "Off-Shelf Delivery" on ham and industrial materials ... ask about our famous "P.D.Q." (Package Deal Quotes) on hi-fi equipment ... and when you do talk to us you'll find friendly, informed men who speak your language. One phone call, one order, one source for all your electronic procurements ... You can always depend on Terminal for your best deal.

Talk to Terminal Today ...

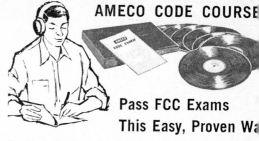

AMECO CODE COURSE

Pass FCC Exams
This Easy, Proven Wa

For Ham Radio...for your career in communicatio ...pass FCC commercial and amateur code exar and amateur theory exams. Learn code and theo this fast, easy, inexpensive way...study at hor with unbreakable phonograph records.

No. 1 — Novice Code Course. You get and keep a bum of 10 recordings (through 8 w.p.m.), sample FC type code exams, instruction book, charts to che your receiving accuracy. All for only: 45 rpm **$5.9** 33⅓ rpm **$4.95**, 78 rpm **$6.95**.

No. 2 — Senior Code Course. Everything in the Novi Course — plus. 22 recordings (through 18 w.p.m.) a typical FCC type code exams for both General ar 2nd class commercial telegraph licenses. 45 rp **$10.50**, 33⅓ rpm **$9.50**, 78 rpm **$11.50**.

No. 3 — Advanced Course. Prepares Novice operato for Amateur General class and Second class cor mercial licenses, 12 recordings (8 through 18 w.p.m plus the complete code book, typical FCC code exam 45 rpm **$4.95**, 33⅓ rpm **$4.95**, 78 rpm **$5.95**.

No. 4 — Complete Radio Theory Course. Covering th Novice, Technician, Conditional and General classe — all under one cover — with nearly 400 typical FC type questions. Simple ... no technical backgroun required. Also, free, a guide to setting up your ha station. For the amazingly low price of **$3.95**.

No. 5 — Radio Amateur Questions & Answers Licens Guide. A "must" if preparing for Novice, Technicia or General class exams. Approx. 200 questions & a swers (mostly multiple choice) similar to ones on FC exams, plus 2 sample FCC type exams. Other ques tions arranged by subject for easy study. **Only 50**

DELUXE CODE PRACTICE OSCILLATOR

In Kit Form or Wired

Produces a pure, steady tone wit no clicks or chirps. Built-in 4 inc speaker. Takes several headphone or keys. After code has bee learned, the oscillator is easily cor verted to a fine cw monitor. Ha variable tone control & volum control. Sturdy, grey hammer-ton cabinet.

Kit, with instructions, less tube (Model CPS-KL) **$11.9**
Kit, complete with tubes (Mode CPS-KT) **$13.7**
Completely wired & tested, les tubes (Model CPS-WL) **$13.1**
Completely wired & tested, with tubes (Model CPS-WT)........... **$14.9**

International Rectifiers
SELENIUM · GERMANIUM · SILICON

SELENIUM TV AND RADIO RECTIFIERS

Ratings: 25 to 156 volts AC, 50 to 1,200 ma. DC
The widest range in the industry! Designed for Radio, Television, TV booster, UHF converter and experimental applications. Input ratings from 25 to 156 volts AC and up. DC output current 50 to 1,200 MA. Write for application information. **Bulletin ER-178-A.**

SD 500 KIT, TV REPLACEMENT

All-purpose silicon replacement kit offers radio-TV men simple means of replacing all existing silicon rectifier types. Hermetically sealed diode can be wired in or plugged into fuse-clip. To 100 C; needs no heat sink. **Bulletin JB 505.**

UNISTAC SILICON TV RECTIFIER

A direct and universal replacement for all existing selenium stacks up to 500 ma. Eyelet construction. No "special socket," conversion kit or drilling required. Especially suited to the elevated operating temperatures inherent in most TV sets. **Bulletin TV-500.**

HIGH Q VOLTAGE VARIABLE CAPACITOR

Ratings: Q of 1000, 200 PIV DC
Semicap's small size, light weight, high reliability and low power requirements make it ideal for automatic frequency control, frequency modulation oscillators and filter networks. All-welded hermetically sealed, shock-proof housing. Request **Bulletin SR-205.**

SILICON RECTIFIER TUBE EQUIVALENTS

Ratings: 85 to 600 ma • 1500 to 6000 PIV.
Highly reliable series of tube replacement rectifiers rated from 1500 to 6400 PIV; 85 to 600 ma (including the ST-7 replacement for the 866 Tube) offer the superior characteristics of silicon on a wide range of high voltage applications. Complete data: **Bulletin SR-209.**

SELENIUM RECTIFIER STACKS

Ratings: From 100 ma. to 50 Amps.
Low forward voltage drop and low leakage characteristics make this series ideal for a wide variety of power applications. For details request **Bulletin C-439,** (26 volt cells); **Bulletin SR-160,** (45 to 52 volts per cell) and **Bulletin SR-152,** on high current density cells.

SUB-MINIATURE SELENIUM DIODES

Ratings: 20 to 160 volts • 100μa to 11 ma.
Ideal components for bias supplies, sensitive relays, computers etc. High resistance, (10 megohms and higher at –10 volts). Excellent linear forward characteristics. Extremely small, low in cost. Encapsulated to resist adverse environmental extremes. Specify **Bulletin SD-1B.**

SILICON VOLTAGE REGULATOR ZENER DIODES

Ratings: From 600 milliwatts to 10 watts
A complete series in 6 types. Miniature single junction types, multiple junction types and double anode units. 750 milliwatt and 1 watt types: **Bulletin SR-251,** 3.5 and 10 watt types: **Bulletin SR-252,** Multiple junction 5 watt types: SR-253, Double anode types: SR-254

PHOTOELECTRIC CELLS AND SUN BATTERIES

(Wide range of silicon and selenium types.)
Self-generating cells available in standard and custom sizes, mounted or unmounted. For details on wide selection of selenium types, request Bulletin PC-649A. Silicon solar cells with efficiencies as high as 10%. Designed to rugged military specifications. **Bulletin SR-275A.**

Never tires the arm . . . never upsets the nerves
SENDING MADE EASIER FOR EVERYBODY

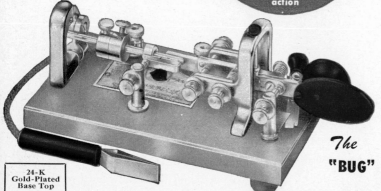

World's No. 1 Key

VIBROPLEX

Semi-automatic action

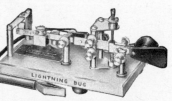

Its semi-automatic action actually performs the work for you.

Vibroplex is a pleasing key. Suits any hand or style of sending. Its easy, natural response helps develop speed fast.

You take it easy, while Vibroplex performs the arm-tiring work for you. Send the way you like best, knowing your signals are clean and easy to read.

It's the signal that counts. Vibroplex signals are uniformly good at whatever speed it is being operated.

Vibroplex never tires the arm, never upsets the nerves, as use of the old keys often does.

Precision machined, rugged. Vibroplex stands rough usage. Trouble-proof and adjustable to any desired speed. Dependable as the day is long.

Vibroplex then is the perfect key for you. Try it and see for yourself. At dealers or direct.

The "BUG"

24-K Gold-Plated Base Top

Vibroplex Super DeLuxe

Fast operation and easy action make this newest Vibroplex a popular choice among the elite. Equipped with the world's easiest sending features, in addition to all former Vibroplex features, it has a super deluxe speed control mainspring that provides greater speed range and slowest sending without extra weights. Precision machined, trouble-proof and adjustable to any desired speed. A beautiful key, built to give a lifetime of sending enjoyment. Everybody wants one. With circuit closer. DeLuxe, only **$29.95.***

Vibroplex Original

Here's a key you can buy with confidence. In daily use for over 40 years has pleased thousands with its ease of operation, strong, clean signal and all-around sending excellence. "Sure easy on the arm." Trouble-proof, adjustable to any speed. Many of these keys still in service after 30 years' use. With circuit closer, Standard **$19.95**; DeLuxe, **$23.95.***

Vibroplex Blue Racer

Small, compact, rugged built extra sturdy like the Original, but only half the size. 2 lbs. 8 oz. Occupies small space. Precision machined, adjustable to any desired speed. Has the same features as the Original and very popular with thousands of users for a fine sending performance with the least labor. With circuit closer. Standard, **$19.95**; DeLuxe, **$23.95.***

Vibroplex Carrying Case

Black simulated morocco. Cloth-lined. Reinforced corners. Flexible leather handle. Keeps key free of dirt, dust and moisture, and insures safe-keeping when not in use. With lock and key, **$6.75.**

Avoid imitations!
The "BUG" Trade Mark identifies the Genuine Vibroplex. Accept no substitute

Standard Models have: Gray base, chrome top parts. DeLuxe Models have: Polished chromium base and top parts, red trim and jewel movement. All Vibroplex models available for left hand operation. All Vibroplex keys equipped with 3/16" contacts.

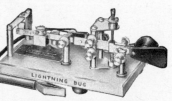

Vibroplex Lightning Bug

Beautifully styled, precision machined, rugged with an improved frame, a flat pendulum bar with slotted weights that can't work loose; a bridged damper frame prevents damage to key, an instantly adjustable dot contact spring that may be removed without disturbing the speed weights. A great buy at this low, low price. With circuit closer. Standard, **$18.95**; DeLuxe, **$22.95.***

"VIBRO-KEYER"

The Vibro-Keyer supplies the answer to the demand for Vibroplex parts for the construction of electronic transmitting units. Its beautiful beige colored base is 3½" by 4½" and weight is 2¾ pounds. It uses the DeLuxe Vibroplex contacts, main frame and super finished parts. Colorful red finger and thumb pieces. Has the same smooth and easy operating Vibroplex trunion lever, adjustable to your own taste. Priced at **$15.95.**

* Cord and wedge, $1.75 additional

You must be tired of the old-fashioned keys and their annoyances; or maybe your bug is old and not perking as you'd like, then why not hitch up to a new Vibroplex and enjoy your operating as never before. Choose yours from those illustrated here. You can be sure if it's a Vibroplex.

Prices subject to change without notice

THE VIBROPLEX CO., INC., 833 Broadway, New York 3, N. Y.

W. W. ALBRIGHT, *President*

IF YOU SEND YOU SHOULD USE THE VIBROPLEX

Buy Vibroplex for the easiest sending of your life

the "Hams" at HUDSON want to help you...

START RIGHT!

Joe Prestia, K2GZX

the famous
**BOB GUNDERSON
W2JIO**

invites you to write or come in for a chat.

You'll see the latest Ham Gear first at Hudson —one of the world's largest Electronic parts distributors, and New York's component High Fidelity center.

JUST BEGINNING? Then you need friendly, competent help to get you started right. The Old-Timers at HUDSON were all beginners once, themselves—they know YOUR problems!

Talk to one of our Amateurs, at any of the three HUDSON Stores listed below. He'll be glad to help you start right, on your "adventure into space."

TECHNICAL INFO?
We're willing and able to help you with any problem that may be puzzling you.

EQUIPMENT?
HUDSON is famous as one of the largest Distributors of Electronic Equipment in the country. We've got Complete Stocks of All Standard Brands, all FULLY GUARANTEED.

SERVICE?
Whether you shop over the counter at any of our stores, or whether you order by mail, you can depend on our speedy, efficient service—mail orders shipped same day received from our HUGE STOCKS.

PRICES?
Everybody in the Amateur Game knows, by now, that you can "do better" at HUDSON! Our nationally famous LOW PRICES make your hard-earned buck go further—much further!

TRADE-INS?
Sure, we'll give you TOP allowance on your old equipment —nobody, simply NOBODY beats our "deal."

TIME PAYMENTS?
Glad to accommodate you. Buy the gear you need, NOW, enjoy it NOW—take as long as one and a half years to pay for it.

HUDSON FREE NOVICE CLASSES held regularly at our Newark Store. Learn 5 WPM Code, and all the Theory you'll need, to pass your exam. Write Manager Joe Prestia at our Newark Store, for latest schedule.

Some of the Standard **HAM BRANDS** we carry!

RCA
RME
BUD
MILLEN
GONSET
MORROW
COLLINS*
NATIONAL
MULTI-ELMAC
HARVEY-WELLS
HAMMARLUND
E. F. JOHNSON
HALLICRAFTER
MASTER MOBILE
BARKER &
WILLIAMSON
ELECTRONICS
DOW-KEY
ILLUMITRONICS
CUSHCRAFT
NORTH HILLS

*NEWARK store only

AUTHORIZED FACTORY DISTRIBUTORS

Hudson
RADIO & TELEVISION CORP.
ELECTRONIC & SOUND EQUIPMENT

48 West 48th St., N. Y. 36, N. Y.,
TRafalgar 3-2900

212 Fulton St., N. Y. 7, N. J.,
TRafalgar 3-2900

35 William St., Newark 2, N. J.,
MArket 4-5154

92

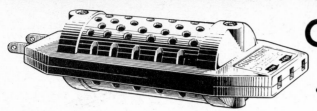

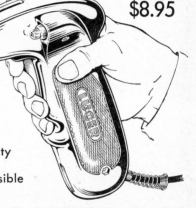
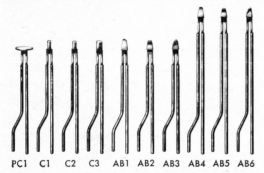

To Manufacturers and Distributors of Products Used in Short-Wave Radio Communication

THE RADIO AMATEUR'S HANDBOOK is the standard reference on the technique of high-frequency readio communication. Now in its thirty-seventh annual edition, it is used universally by radio engineers and technicians as well as by thousands of amateurs and experimenters. Year after year it has sold more widely, and now the Handbook has an annual distribution greater than any other technical handbook in any field of human activity. To manufacturers whose integrity is established and whose products meet the approval of the American Radio Relay League technical staff, and to distributors who sell these products, we offer use of space in the Handbook's Catalog Advertising Section. This section is the standard guide for amateur, commercial and government buyers of short-wave radio equipment. Particularly valuable as a medium through which complete data on products can be made easily available to the whole radio engineering and experimenting field, it offers an inexpensive method of producing and distributing a catalog impossible to attain by any other means. We solicit inquiries from qualified manufacturers and distributors.

ADVERTISING DEPARTMENT . . .

American Radio Relay League

WEST HARTFORD 7, CONNECTICUT

ILLINOIS CAPACITORS

KNOWN THE WORLD OVER

for

Time Tested Quality

For more than a quarter of a century ILLINOIS CONDENSER COMPANY has been foremost in the development of ever greater dependability and longer life in all types of capacitors. Listed below are only a few of the more popular — and most recently developed ILLINOIS capacitor types.

Sub-Miniature Electrolytic Capacitors

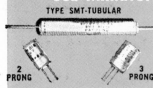

TYPE SMT-TUBULAR

2 PRONG   **3 PRONG**

A complete line for low voltage D.C. circuits. Have many advantages including hermetically-sealed Aluminum Cases with patented construction; immersion-proof; excellent life characteristics; low leakage currents; shock and vibration-resistant; ideal for applications requiring minimum size, weight and reliability.

UMP Twist prong types

PE Octal plug-in types

IHC Popular replacement types

LN Flexible lead types, screw neck mounting

UMS Molded terminal

UMT Clamp mount types

IHT Tubular pigtail types

UMC Energy storage and photo flash types

ITM and ITC Metal and Ceramic Cased Paper

MS Motor starting

BT Electrolytic and paper

ILLINI "300" BANTAM

TYPE UMP Standardized twist-prong type. Patented molded terminal construction for efficient, stable operation under extreme temperature ranges. Capacity ranges from 10 to 3,000 MFD and from 6 to 525 WVDC.

TYPE PE Hermetically sealed plug-in octal base type. Especially useful in fixed or mobile communications equipment. Operating temperature range −40°C to +85°C. Available in wide ranges of capacities and voltages.

TYPE IHC Popular multiple section types with flexible leads, insulating sleeves and mounting straps. Equally adaptable for original equipment or replacement purposes. Available in capacities from 10 to 250 MFD at 25 to 500 WVDC.

TYPE LN Extruded aluminum can type with screw neck mounting and flexible leads. Capacity ranges from 8 to 80 MFD and from 450 to 600 WVDC.

TYPE UMS Hermetically sealed inverted can type with screw neck mounting and molded-in terminals. Wide ranges of capacities and voltage ratings. Meets all government specs.

TYPE UMT Inverted can type with clamp mounting. Hermetically sealed, shock resistant with new molded terminal construction. Ideal for use in highest quality equipment. Meets all government specs. Wide capacity and voltage ranges.

TYPE IHT Popular tubular aluminum can, pigtail type electrolytic. Internal riveted construction. In capacity ranges of 1 to 2000 MFD and from 6 to 600 WVDC. Also available with solder lug terminals. Supplied with insulating sleeves.

TYPE UMC Low leakage-high capacity electrolytic for power filter packs voltage stabilization, energy storage and photo flash. Capacity ranges up to 50,000 MFD to 50 V. and 1000 MFD at 450 V.

TYPES SMT and SMTU "Miniature" and sub-miniature electrolytics with patented hermetic seals. Especially designed for printed circuits, portable equipment, transistor equipment, and any application where size and weight must be kept at an absolute minimum. Capacity ranges from 5 to 2000 MFD and from 3 to 250 WVDC available. Aluminum case types. Temperature ranges −40°C to +65°, −30°C to +85°, −30°C to +100°C.

TYPE MS Motor starting capacitors available in bakelite and aluminum cases. Long wire leads with terminals. Capacities to 5,000 MFD at 115, 220 and 320 VAC.

TYPE BT Hermetically sealed bathtub type especially designed to withstand vibration and shock. Available in electrolytic and paper capacitor types for government and commercial use.

ILLINI 300 ELECTRONIC FLASH KIT "BANTAM" A new high intensity, low voltage electronic photoflash kit featuring latest advances in tube, capacitor and reflector design. 100 watt second output. Uses standard type batteries. Easily assembled, rugged, reliable and economical to operate. AC Power Pack also available.

Technical literature and catalogs available upon request.

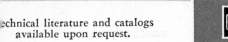

Index

INDEX

INDEX

Text

A

INDEX

INDEX

INDEX

INDEX

INDEX

INDEX

INDEX

INDEX

INDEX

INDEX

INDEX